Biochemistry

First Edition

JOHN T. TANSEY
Otterbein University
Westerville, OH

Vice President and Director, Editorial	Laurie Rosatone
Director, Science	Jessica Fiorillo
Executive Editor	Sladjana Bruno
Director, Content Enablement/ Operations	Geraldine Osnato
Marketing Manager	Michael Olsen
Product Designer/Development Editor	Joan Kalkut
Art Development Editor	Kathy Naylor
Editorial Assistant	Chris Gaudio
Marketing Assistant	Anna Pham
Senior Content Manager	Lana Barskaya
Production Editor/Media Specialist	Patricia Gutierrez
Senior Photo Editor	Simon Eckley
Art Director/Cover Designer	Wendy Lai
Cover Image ©	Courtesy of John T. Tansey

PDB ID: 3DZY
Chandra, V., Huang, P., Hamuro, Y., Raghuram, S., Wang, Y., Burris, T.P., Rastinejad, F. (2008) Structure of the intact PPAR-gamma-RXR- nuclear receptor complex on DNA. Nature 456: 350-356 DOI: 10.1038/nature07413
The image was generated using NGL:
Rose AS, Hildebrand PW (2015) NGL Viewer: a web application for molecular visualization. Nucleic Acids Res. 43:W576-579) and the RCSB PDB (HYPERLINK "http://www.rcsb.org" www.rcsb.org).

This book was set in 10/12 STIX by Aptara Corporation and printed and bound by by Quad/Graphics. The cover was printed by Quad/Graphics.

This book is printed on acid free paper.

Founded in 1807, John Wiley & Sons, Inc. has been a valued source of knowledge and understanding for more than 200 years, helping people around the world meet their needs and fulfill their aspirations. Our company is built on a foundation of principles that include responsibility to the communities we serve and where we live and work. In 2008, we launched a Corporate Citizenship Initiative, a global effort to address the environmental, social, economic, and ethical challenges we face in our business. Among the issues we are addressing are carbon impact, paper specifications and procurement, ethical conduct within our business and among our vendors, and community and charitable support. For more information, please visit our Web site: www.wiley.com/go/citizenship.

Library of Congress Cataloging-in-Publication Data

Names: Tansey, John T., 1969- author.
Title: Biochemistry / John T. Tansey.
Description: First edition. | Hoboken, NJ : John Wiley & Sons, [2020] |

Includes bibliographical references and index. |
Identifiers: LCCN 2018039788 (print) | LCCN 2018041068 (ebook) | ISBN 9781119402633 (Adobe PDF) | ISBN 9781119321507 (ePub) | ISBN 9781119402565 (pbk. : alk. paper)
Subjects: | MESH: Biochemical Phenomena
Classification: LCC RB112.5 (ebook) | LCC RB112.5 (print) | NLM QU 34 | DDC 612.015--dc23
LC record available at https://lccn.loc.gov/2018039788

The inside back cover will contain printing identification and country of origin if omitted from this page. In addition, if the ISBN on the back cover differs from the ISBN on this page, the one on the back cover is correct.

Printed in the United States of America

V10008644_030819

Dedication

To Emily, Aidan, and Eli for their love, support, and encouragement.
We did it!

To my professors and teachers for all they have taught me. I owe you so much.
I can never thank you enough. I hope I've made you proud.

To my students for their curiosity. You continue to inspire me. I hope this work
helps future generations of scientists and clinicians.

Brief Contents

Contents

10 Lipids II: Metabolism and Transport of Complex Lipids   351

11 Amino Acid and Amine Metabolism   397

Medical Applications

Courtesy of Edward Syguda, Otterbein University

JOHN T. TANSEY John Tansey received his B.S. in Biochemistry and Molecular Biology from the University of Massachusetts, Amherst, and his Ph.D. in Biochemistry from Wake Forest University. Following his graduate degree, John undertook a postdoctoral fellowship at the National Institutes of Health in the lab of Dr. Constantine Londos where he led the team that generated and characterized the perilipin 1 knockout mouse. John's scientific interests are a natural extension of his postdoctoral studies and focus on the structure and function of the perilipins, a class of lipid droplet proteins that regulate neutral lipid storage and breakdown. John has been teaching for the past seventeen years in the Chemistry department and Biochemistry and Molecular Biology program at Otterbein University, a primarily undergraduate institution outside Columbus, Ohio. He has also taught at the community college and graduate level. John was awarded both the Best New Teacher and Master Teacher awards from his university. He is an education fellow of the American Society for Biochemistry and Molecular Biology (ASBMB) and is a member of the editorial board of Biochemistry and Molecular Biology Education (BAMBEd). In addition to his basic science interests, he has studied the use of science fiction or other readings to promote engagement and discussion in science classes, integration of codes of conduct and basic ethics in science courses, and development of curricula and tools for programmatic assessment. When he isn't teaching or in the lab, John enjoys cooking, the outdoors, games, and a good laugh.

Preface

Over time, few fields have changed as much as biochemistry. During the past 50 years, advances in computing, technology, and molecular biology have radically changed how we approach biochemical questions. The laboratory tools available to biochemists continue to improve and change. Obviously, what was current in 1959, 1979, or even 1999 will not suffice now. Arguably, the current rate of change in biochemistry is greater than in many other fields of science and mathematics, and the materials faculty choose to use in their courses should reflect those changes. Biochemistry is a living, breathing science.

Perhaps in light of how biochemistry is changing as a science, biochemistry is also changing as an undergraduate course of study. A very different pool of students now takes undergraduate biochemistry courses compared to even a few years ago. These students include biology majors pursuing advanced life science degrees, an expanded pool of pre-professional and pre-med students, and ACS-certified chemistry majors. These changes have arisen partially due to student perceptions of the value of biochemistry as well as changes from both professional societies and revisions to the MCAT.

We would be remiss if we did not mention the students themselves. As students with more diverse scientific backgrounds are enrolling in biochemistry, biochemistry courses must adapt to help these students optimize their strengths and maximize their learning. Students have significant distractions and demands on their time. This often increases demand on both students and faculty. Clearly, there must be new solutions and pedagogies to help meet these emerging challenges.

Biochemistry by John Tansey caters to a variety of majors and backgrounds with relevant, engaging examples while still preserving balance between the classical and modern and between chemistry and biology. Further, *Biochemistry,* delivered in the next generation of WileyPLUS, provides opportunities for the development and integration of digital tools that take advantage of changes in student attitudes, student familiarity with technology, and different approaches to teaching and learning.

Approach

Biochemistry uses a thematic approach to present concepts with a chemical perspective in a biological context, and highlights four important themes:

- **Evolution.** Biomolecules, like all life, have changed over time through the mutation of genes, selection of properties and traits, and transmission of the genes that yield the most favorable traits.

- **Structure and Function.** Basic units of structure define the function of biomolecules and all living things.

- **Information Flow, Exchange, and Storage.** All levels of biomolecular organization depend on molecular interactions and information transfer.

- **Pathways and Transformations of Matter and Energy.** Biomolecules, and all biological systems, change through organic reaction pathways governed by the laws of thermodynamics and kinetics.

Biochemistry emphasizes the core competencies advocated by several professional and governmental agencies. Higher level thinking skills such as data interpretation and experimental design are then developed from these core competencies.

The text presents material recommended by the American Society for Biochemistry and Molecular Biology in a way that is suitable for a variety of course structures. Material is organized so that the first half is suitable for the one-semester biochemistry course, including descriptive biochemistry, metabolism, elementary enzyme kinetics and mechanisms, allosteric regulation, DNA/RNA structure/function, signal transduction, and supramolecular assemblies. Second semester coverage focuses on specific topics at greater levels of detail. By placing structure and function of biomolecules often in the same chapter as their metabolism, biochemistry is presented as a more integrated subject. The modular nature of the chapters means that instructors can easily customize content and change the order in which topics are covered to suit their classes' needs without a disruption or disconnect in the flow of material.

While organic chemistry remains as an assumed prerequisite for the course, the text will also draw from physical chemical principles (such as thermodynamics and kinetics) approached from a general chemistry perspective. Presenting the material this way facilitates division of material for those students only taking a single biochemistry course and allows for differentiated learning at higher levels (for example, signal transduction is introduced in the first semester but revisited at a greater level of detail in the second).

Biochemistry provides more continuity with other science courses and texts by emphasizing worked problems throughout and expanded end-of-chapter problems with a wide range of subject matter and difficulty. The worked problems are both qualitative (conceptual) and quantitative to model for students the biochemical reasoning they need to succeed in the course. Students will often be asked to analyze data and make critical assessments of experiments.

To help students understand biochemistry at a deeper level than rote memorization, topics are integrated and cross-referenced to enhance pattern recognition. By pointing out similarities and differences in major types of biochemical reactions, mechanisms, enzyme controls, metabolic pathways, and signal transduction, students can more easily build conceptual frameworks.

Given the role of biochemistry in modern medicine and the advances that have been made in science over the past few decades, it makes sense to emphasize these topics and use complex examples from animals in teaching biochemistry. While this may make the material more complex in some instances than simply studying analogous systems in *E.coli*, it provides an important frame of reference for students who are interested in biomedical applications.

Visual literacy is the ability to recognize and understand ideas conveyed through visible actions or images, such as illustrations. In our digital age, the ability of scientists or medical professionals to interpret data, complex illustrations, and images is critical. In developing the illustrations for *Biochemistry*, clean, crisp images and micrographs that use common themes, structures, and color palettes are used throughout. This consistent approach gives the illustrations a common feel and creates familiarity for the student, such that they immediately understand the type of figure being displayed, its relative importance, and how to put the figure into a broader context.

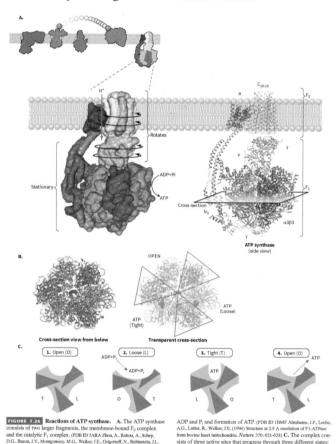

FIGURE 7.26 **Reactions of ATP synthase.** **A.** The ATP synthase consists of two larger fragments, the membrane-bound F_0 complex and the catalytic F_1 complex. (PDB ID 5ARA Zhou, A., Rohou, A., Schep, D.G., Bason, J.V., Montgomery, M.G., Walker, J.E., Grigorieff, N., Rubinstein, J.L. (2015) Structure and conformational states of the bovine mitochondrial ATP synthase by cryo-EM. *Elife* 4: e10180-e10180) **B.** As the F_1 complex rotates past the b subunits, the conformation of a and b change, resulting in binding of ADP and P_i and formation of ATP. (PDB ID 1BMF Abrahams, J.P., Leslie, A.G., Lutter, R., Walker, J.E. (1994) Structure at 2.8 A resolution of F1-ATPase from bovine heart mitochondria. *Nature* 370: 621-628) **C.** The complex consists of three active sites that progress through three different states: open, where nothing is bound; loose, where ADP and P_i bind; and tight, where the change in conformation generates ATP.

Finally, the project emphasizes that biochemistry is an interdisciplinary and collaborative science conducted in a societal context. Each chapter has specific current topics or topics for ethical discussion that ask students to engage with these concepts in a meaningful and fact-based way. There may not be clear answers to some of these questions, but they are clearly important topics worthy of discussion.

Organization

In many texts, students' initial steps into biochemistry are divided into a discussion of the molecules found in biochemical systems and the metabolism of these molecules. This creates two problems. First, students taking a two-semester biochemistry sequence must retain and apply the descriptive biochemistry they learned several months earlier when discussing the metabolism of these molecules. It also often creates situations where material can be encapsulated and segregated in some aspect of a chapter. For example, if enzyme kinetics and mechanisms are only emphasized in a single chapter, students may be under the impression that they exist as one-off topics not pertinent to other discussions instead of part of an integrated whole.

One-Semester Course

Because of its organization and integration, *Biochemistry* can be used for either a one- or a two-semester sequence. The first 12 chapters, suitable for a one-semester course, begin with a review of chemical principles germane to biochemistry. These include free energy, thermodynamics, weak forces, organic functional groups, solubility, and the properties of water. This is followed by a review of the structure and function of nucleic acids and central dogma of biology. This material is presented so that all students have foundational concepts and tools in both chemistry and biology prior to discussion of biochemical systems. The remainder of the introductory chapters covers the basics of amino acid chemistry and protein structure in chapter 3, enzyme kinetics and mechanisms in chapter 4, and the structure of the cell and signal transduction in chapter 5. These chapters build on one another but are modular so that material is easily customized. The first five chapters provide a solid basis for the discussions of metabolism that occur in chapters 6–12. Chapter 6 begins with a discussion of carbohydrates followed by glycolysis, gluconeogenesis, and the fates of pyruvate. Chapter 7 explores the citric acid cycle and electron transport and builds from chapter 6. Chapter 8 returns to carbohydrate metabolism to discuss the structure, function, and metabolism of glycogen, but it also discusses the pentose phosphate pathway and several other roles of complex carbohydrates, including glycoproteins and the extracellular matrix. Chapter 9 introduces and describes the numerous classes of lipids, and chapter 10 covers lipoprotein and membrane lipid biosynthesis, cholesterol metabolism, and neutral lipid metabolism. These two chapters parallel the format of chapters 6 and 8 and describe lipids and their metabolism. Chapter 11 discusses amino acid metabolism, the urea cycle, and scavenging of amino acid skeletons. Kidney function and metabolism of xenobiotics are also discussed in chapter 11. Neither of these topics are commonly covered in biochemistry texts but help complete the story of metabolism and the excretion of waste products. Chapter 11 also reiterates aspects of ion transport, protein structure, and regulation of metabolism that have been encountered and built on throughout the text. Finally, chapter 12 integrates all of metabolism and ties fundamental pathways into metabolic disease, including the hormonal integration of pathways and organ systems that help regulate metabolism. Discussion of a variety of metabolic diseases (for example, diabetes or starvation) helps clarify and define metabolic states for the student. This approach differs from other works in that it builds from aspects of biochemistry discussed in the previous 11 chapters and integrates it with modern diseases and human health.

Two-Semester Course

Chapter 13, nucleotide metabolism can be covered as part of either central metabolism or nucleic acid metabolism, allowing instructors to easily place it in either arrangement. Chapters 14, 15, 16, and 17 cover DNA replication, transcription, translation, and the regulation of translation, respectively. These chapters again approach the central dogma from a modern biochemical approach. The most recently solved structures and regulatory mechanisms such as RNAi and riboswitches are discussed alongside discussions of more classical structures such as operons. The final portion of the text revisits key concepts covered in the first 12 chapters in greater detail. Chapter 18 examines protein structure/function and discusses how structures of proteins are determined using EM, NMR, and X-ray diffraction as well as databases of these structures such as the Protein Data Bank. Chapter 19 revisits allosterism in detail and discusses protein-ligand interactions and the ways that proteins are regulated. Chapter 20 discusses protein engineering in greater detail, including techniques ranging from the more biological (epitope tagging and site-directed mutagenesis) to the more biophysical (solid phase peptide synthesis and codon hijacking). Chapter 21 presents both classical and modern techniques to purify these molecules. Chapter 22 discusses -omics and mass spectrometry and how these data-driven approaches are more and more commonly found in the laboratory and clinic. Signal transduction is reexamined in chapter 23 with an emphasis on some of the signaling pathways that are not commonly encountered in introductory biochemistry but are clearly relevant and applicable. These include the Toll-like receptors, MAP kinase, and PKB/Akt. This chapter builds from what was first learned in chapter 5, reemphasized throughout intermediary metabolism and added to in the transitional chapters on gene regulation. Chapter 24 covers macromolecular processes including secretory pathways, protein trafficking, molecular motors, and biochemical aspects of neuroscience and development. This chapter again builds from what has been seen in previous chapters on protein structure-function but applies the concepts to these more complex aspects of cellular or organismal biology. The final chapter of the text (Chapter 25) unites topics and concepts throughout to discuss plant and agricultural biochemistry. Chapter 25 is as much a review of all the basic concepts found in the book as it is a discussion of photosynthesis and how plants function on the biochemical level.

WileyPLUS

The next generation of WileyPLUS is designed to make learning and teaching easier. The customization features, quality question banks, interactive eTextbook and analytical tools allow you to quickly create a customized course that tracks student learning trends. Your students also have intuitive tools to stay engaged and on-track such as syncing calendar and student mobile app.

Features

- *Context/Bigger Picture:* Chapters begin and end with a short analogy and discussion that puts the content of the chapter into the broader context of biochemistry.

- *Common Themes:* Examples of the four guiding themes encountered in the chapter provide students with pertinent examples that ground the concepts in the chapter with the broader themes used throughout the book.

- *Dynamic Figures:* This interactivity summarizes and illustrates key points of the chapter and provides tools such as quizzes to help students learn key pathways and access to each protein or enzyme in the chapter through the NGL viewer. Students can manipulate enzymes and proteins to reinforce key features described in the text. In addition, the examples are linked to the Protein Data Bank (PDB) so that students can quickly access the actual structure and publication.

DYNAMIC FIGURE 6.1
Carbohydrates can be simply classified as monosaccharides (single building blocks) or polysaccharides (polymers of monosaccharides). Polysaccharides can serve structural roles or can serve as a stored form of energy. Monosaccharides can be catabolized into pyruvate. Likewise, pyruvate can be used to synthesize new glucose through gluconeogenesis.

COMMON THEMES

Evolution's outcomes are conserved.	• Many of the pathways we will see in this chapter are conserved throughout evolution.
	• In contrast to genes discussed in other chapters, such as the genes involved in eicosanoids and steroid metabolism, the genes coding for enzymes involved in glycolysis are found throughout biology and are therefore more ancient in origin.
	• Because glycolysis is so basic to the existence of an organism, mutations that disrupt this pathway are often lethal or put organisms at such an evolutionary disadvantage that they generally fail to pass on these genes.
Structure determines function.	• Monosaccharides are a family of molecules that are largely related through stereochemistry.
	• Monosaccharides are frequently depicted in Fischer projections to highlight their stereochemical differences. However, in solution, these molecules adopt a cyclic hemiacetal or hemiketal structure; this structure is best seen in a Haworth projection.
	• In the broadest sense, polysaccharides can be functionally characterized as being energy stores or as providing structure to the organism.
	• Energy-storing polysaccharides can either be linear like amylose or highly branched like amylopectin or glycogen. The branched forms enable the mobilization of monosaccharides at a higher rate, because release can happen simultaneously from several sites.
	• Structural polysaccharides are generally linear molecules, with multiple places where the strands can interact with one another through weak forces (typically hydrogen bonding, dipole–dipole, and electrostatic interactions).
	• The structure of many enzymes is conserved throughout biology, and many of the same chemical reactions are employed in the breakdown and biosynthesis of carbohydrates in divergent species.
Biochemical information is transferred, exchanged, and stored.	• Carbohydrate metabolism is regulated by several allosteric regulators and kinases that inhibit or activate key enzymes in the glycolytic pathway.
Biomolecules are altered through pathways involving transformations of energy and matter.	• In this as in other chapters, we will see that energetically unfavorable reactions become favorable when coupled to reactions with very negative ΔG° values. Although we typically think of this in terms of ATP hydrolysis, reactions of other groups such as phosphoesters or thioesters are common in biochemistry. Likewise, reactions that have ΔG° values close to zero can be tipped to move in either direction by changing the concentrations of substrates or products.
	• The synthesis of glucose and the degradation of monosaccharides use similar reactions but different pathways. Key steps are different, and compartmentalization is important. A similar theme is seen in fatty acid metabolism.

- *Worked Problems:* Each section of the text contains qualitative and quantitative worked problems. These problems help students engage with the material and think like a biochemist.

- *Worked Problem Videos:* Solved-problem videos by the author are included for many of the Worked Problems. These videos allow students to work through the problems with an expert, giving the student insight into the thought process used to solve biochemistry problems.

WORKED PROBLEM 7.2 | Anaplerotic reactions

Acetyl-CoA contributes directly to the formation of citrate, but acetate is not considered an anaplerotic intermediate. Explain why this is the case.

Strategy Review the reactions of the citric acid cycle. What does "anaplerosis" mean?

Solution Anaplerotic reactions "build up" levels of citric acid cycle intermediates, replenishing them. The intermediates most often discussed include α-ketoglutarate, succinyl-CoA, and oxaloacetate. The reactions of the citric acid cycle themselves are not thought of as anaplerotic because they do not lead to an increase in

the concentration of that intermediate; the product of the reaction is immediately used by the next step. Because the formation of citrate from acetyl-CoA and oxaloacetate is part of the citric acid cycle, this step does not really elevate to the concentrations of intermediates and it is not anaplerotic.

Follow-up question In several neurodegenerative processes, fluctuations of glutamate and glutamine levels lead to low energy levels in the cell by slowing down the citric acid cycle. Suggest how depletion of cellular glutamate could reduce flux through the citric acid cycle.

- *End-of-Chapter Problems:* Each chapter includes nearly 50 problems written by the author. These problems use research and biomedical examples to reinforce key concepts in the chapter. In addition to problems that address content, each chapter includes three additional problem sets—Data Interpretation, Experimental Design, and Ethics and Social Responsibility—requiring students to think at a higher level and defend and support their views. Detailed worked solutions written by the author preserve a consistent problem-solving pedagogy throughout.

- *Relevance, Explorations, and Applications:* Each chapter contains three types of boxed features focusing on current issues germane to the topics found in each chapter:

  - *Medical Biochemistry* illustrates how biochemistry has advanced and informed medicine, offers hope for cures, and indicates where more research is necessary.

- *Biochemistry* ties key concepts covered in general or organic chemistry to biochemistry and uses biochemical examples to illustrate these points.

- *Societal and Ethical Biochemistry* examines societal and ethical questions that are currently faced by investigators and members of society. These range from genetically modified organisms to the use of cultured cells in the laboratory.

- *Bioinformatics Exercises:* Written by Rakesh Mogul, *California State Polytechnic University–Pomona*, these activities are a combination of tutorials and questions that ask students to use digital tools such as PDB, GenBank, BLAST, the KEGG database, and other resources to become familiar with these modern research tools.

Instructor Supplements

- Instructor's Solutions by John Tansey. Detailed explanations to each worked example and end-of-chapter problem by the author provide consistent problem-solving pedagogy throughout the text. Students are provided with the answers to odd-numbered problems only.

- Test Bank by Anne Grippo, *Arkansas State University,* contains multiple-choice, text entry, molecular drawing, and short answer questions.

- PowerPoint Lecture Slides by Tanea Reed, *Eastern Kentucky University*, highlight topics to help reinforce students' grasp of essential concepts.

- PowerPoint Art Slides and jpegs. All of the art and tables are available as both slides and jpeg files.

- Personal Response System ("Clicker") Questions are written by Michael Chen, *California State University–Los Angeles.*

Acknowledgments

This book may have only one author, but it has been far from a solo project. I have been so fortunate to have a great team of people that I have worked with over the years. This began with John Stout, my Wiley textbook representative who asked me back in 2009 what I liked or disliked about current texts and set me on this journey. From there I was introduced to Joan Kalkut. Joan has served in many roles on this project including project manager, editor, and product designer. Her sustained energy and optimism has been nothing short of amazing. More than anyone, her drive has helped this project along, offering both deadlines and words of encouragement, and many, many edits. Thank you, Joan, for believing in this project; it wouldn't have happened without you. For several years Clifford Mills played the role of project manager and fellow New England sports fan. Cliff was patient and encouraging and kept the project rolling through the first draft of the manuscript. Sadly, Cliff passed on before this project came

to fruition. He is still sorely missed. As we completed the first draft of the manuscript, art editor Kathy Naylor joined the team. Kathy's experience in developing art to describe complex scientific principles has been invaluable. Her attention to detail and organizational skills have been incredible and have also helped make this such a better project than it would have been otherwise. Finally, at Wiley, I need to thank Sladjana Bruno, Executive Editor; Patricia Gutierrez, Production Editor and Media Specialist; Geraldine Osnato, Director of Content Enablement and Operations; and Michael Olsen, Marketing Manager.

Other people I need to single out and thank include my accuracy checkers Joseph Provost, Tanea Reed, Leanna Patton, and Hannah Bailey. Despite their best efforts and the work of hundreds of people I'm sure there are mistakes that have crept through. Any errors are mine, but please gently remind me of them to help make future editions of this a better work. I also need to thank Laura Lynn Gonzalez and her team at Dynamoid as well as Laura Zapanta, Spencer Jordan, Rebekah Dalton, and Erin Hughes for their work on the Dynamic Figures. I would be remiss if I didn't thank the members of my advisory panel (Laura Zapanta, Paul Craig, Emily Westover, Kerry Smith, Cheryl Ingram-Smith, and Ron Gary). These reviewers gave multiple rounds of detailed feedback. Their expertise in teaching and in different aspects of biochemistry helped shape this book in its early stages and throughout its development.

Finally, I would also like to thank all of the faculty members who helped review this work as it was being developed. This project would not be possible without their hard work, input, and suggestions.

Reviewers

Alabama
Jong Kim, Alabama A&M University

Arkansas
Anne Grippo, Arkansas State University
Denise Greathouse, University of Arkansas, Fayetteville

Arizona
Scott Lefler, Arizona State University

California
Jinah Choi, UC-Merced
Douglas McAbee, California State University Long Beach
Elizabeth Komives, UC San Diego
Rakesh Mogul, California State Polytechnic University, Pomona
Joseph Provost, University of San Diego
Brian Sato, University of California, Irvine
Jay Brewster, Pepperdine University
Ellis Bell, University of San Diego
Pavan Kadandale, University of California, Irvine
Elaine Carter, Los Angeles City College

Florida
Frank Mari, Florida Atlantic University
David Brown, Florida Gulf Coast University
Alberto Haces, Florida Atlantic University
Sulekha Coticone, Florida Gulf Coast University

Georgia
Mary Peek, Georgia Institute of Technology

Iowa
Charles Brenner, University of Iowa

Illinois
Paul Strieleman, University of Chicago
Keith Gagnon, Southern Illinois University

Indiana
Andrew Kusmierczyk, Indiana University-Purdue University Indianapolis
Ann Kirchmaier, Purdue University
Ann Taylor, Wabash College

Kentucky
Tanea Reed, Eastern Kentucky University
Kevin Williams, Western Kentucky University

Louisiana
Patricia Moroney, Louisiana State University
Lucy Robinson, LSU Health Sciences Center-Shreveport

Massachusetts
Emily Westover, Bandeis University
Adele Wolfson, Wellesley College

Maryland
Allison Tracy, University of Maryland, Baltimore County

Michigan
Robert Stach, University of Michigan-Flint
Michael Pikaart, Hope College
Deborah Heyl-Clegg, Eastern Michigan University
Stephen Juris, Central Michigan University

Minnesota
David Mitchell, College of Saint Benedicts, Saint John's University
Henry Jakubowski, College of Saint Benedicts, Saint John's University
Debra Martin, Saint Mary's University of Minnesota

Missouri
Peter Tipton, University of Missouri-Columbia
Ruth Birch, Fontbonne University
Brent Znosko, Saint Louis University
Blythe Janowiak, Saint Louis University

North Carolina
Brooke Christian, Appalachian State University
Megen Culpepper Appalachian State University
Brian Coggins, Duke University

North Dakota
Daniel Barr, University of Mary

Nebraska
Robert Mackin, Creighton University
Madhavan Soundararajan, University of Nebraska-Lincoln
Rich Lomneth, University of Nebraska-Omaha
Jodi Kreiling, University of Nebraska-Omaha

New Mexico
David Bear, University of New Mexico School of Medicine
Martina Rosenberg, University of New Mexico

Nevada
Ronald Gary, University of Nevada, Las Vegas

New York
Paul Craig, Rochester Institute of Technology
Scott Bello, Rensselaer Polytechnic Institute
Christopher Stoj, Niagara University
Carla Theimer, University at Albany, SUNY

Ohio
Michael Lieberman, University of Cincinnati College of Medicine
Tim Mueser, University of Toledo
Amy Stockert, Ohio Northern University, Raabe College of Pharmacy
John Cogan, The Ohio State University
Stephen Mills, Xavier University

Oklahoma
Donald Ruhl, Oklahoma State University

Pennsylvania
Laura Zapanta, University of Pittsburgh
Daniel Dries, Juniata College
Felicia Barbieri, Gwynedd Mercy University

South Carolina
Kerry Smith, Clemson University
Cheryl Ingram-Smith, Clemson University
Srikripa Chandrasekaran, Clemson University

Texas
Kayunta Johnson-Winters, University of Texas at Arlington
Mian Jiang, University of Houston Downtown

Utah
Bethany Buck-Koehntop, University of Utah

Virginia
Deborah Polayes, George Mason University
Pinky McCoy, Old Dominion University

Washington
Jeff Watson, Gonzaga University
Jeffery Corkill, Eastern Washington University

Wisconsin
Kevin Siebenlist, Marquette University, College of Health Sciences
Jim Lawrence, University of Wisconsin, Stevens Point

West Virginia
Michael Gunther, West Virginia University School of Medicine

Canada
Isabelle Barretee-Ng, University of Calgary
Adrienne Wright, University of Alberta
Odette Laneuville, University of Ottawa
Daman Bawa, University of Toronto Scarborough

United Kingdom
Kevin Gaston, University of Bristol

Biochemistry

CHAPTER 1

The Chemical Foundations of Biochemistry

gap/Shutterstock

While the study of biochemistry may seem daunting or foreign, it has its basis in many things that should be familiar to you.

Chemistry in Context

An archeologist who has discovered a lost civilization would be confronted with numerous questions. How did that civilization function? How did it store food and confront challenges to survive? How did it archive and pass information from one generation to the next? If there were some way to translate the writings found into something understandable, we would stand a better chance of discovering what went on in that civilization.

This story is an analogy for where we begin with biochemistry, the study of life at the molecular level. In this analogy, the civilization is any system we choose to study, from the bacterium *Escherichia coli* to humans. From the perspective of the biochemist, the language that unites these systems and explains how and why things occur is chemistry.

This chapter focuses on several topics that will be helpful in defining and explaining biochemical reactions throughout the rest of the text. These topics include thermodynamics, equilibrium, organic reaction mechanisms, and some of the basics of structure and function. The chapter then goes on to discuss water, the properties of acids and bases, and buffers (systems resistant to changes in pH). It is intended to be a review of specific topics pertinent to biochemistry.

The dialect of chemistry that we speak in biochemistry is specialized. Biochemistry deals in aqueous systems; in small, multifunctional organics; and in large polymers. The systems have been optimized by eons of natural selection and will continue to be altered throughout time as conditions and selective pressures change. However, the foundational laws that all systems must abide by are chemical in nature.

COMMON THEMES

Evolution's outcomes are conserved.	• Evolution takes advantage of the basic laws of chemistry, and it must abide by those laws as systems change.
Structure determines function.	• The rules that dictate the behavior of small chemical structures also apply to macromolecules. • The properties and reactivity of organic functional groups also apply to biochemical systems.
Biochemical Information is transferred, exchanged, and stored.	• Information is stored in polymers of organic compounds. • Flow, exchange, and storage of information all follow the basic laws of chemistry.
Biomolecules are altered through pathways involving transformations of energy and matter.	• The basic laws of chemistry and thermodynamics apply to biochemical systems as they do to classical chemical systems.

1.1 General Chemical Principles

Chemistry is the study of matter. We observe molecules and how they behave, we create new ways to synthesize molecules, we characterize molecules using light or other wavelengths of the electromagnetic spectrum, and we determine how molecules form and break down. General chemistry, the introductory subject taught in high school and the first year of college, is a combination of several different subdisciplines of chemistry, including:

- *organic* chemistry—the study of carbon-containing molecules
- *inorganic* chemistry—the study of compounds comprised of elements other than carbon
- *analytical* chemistry—the identification, quantitation, and precise analysis of compounds
- *physical* chemistry—the study of the interactions of matter with energy

General chemistry covers several topics that are highly pertinent to biochemistry and is a good place to begin a review of chemical principles. Most of the topics covered in general chemistry are important to biochemistry and can help to explain many important biological principles, but they are not often discussed in a biochemical context in a general chemistry course. Few, if any, biochemical examples are used, and students are sometimes left with the impression that the material lacks relevance. Nothing could be further from the truth. Biochemical examples can be used to illustrate any chemical principle. Freed from this bias, you can begin to think of biological questions as having answers written in the language of chemistry.

1.1.1 The basic principles of thermodynamics describe all systems

Thermodynamics is the study of energy, and it is an important concept in biochemistry. Studying the thermodynamics of a reaction or system gives us valuable information about how and why a reaction can occur. In some cases, it can also provide information about the conditions required for a reaction to occur: for example, whether energy is required, if the reaction sits on the knife edge of an equilibrium constant, or if the loss of a group such as carbon dioxide (CO_2) helps to drive the reaction forward. Most important, it can tell us whether a reaction will proceed in the forward direction. Thus, understanding the basics of thermodynamics helps to paint a rich chemical picture of what is happening in a biological process.

Fundamental laws describe energy in thermodynamics This section briefly reviews the three fundamental laws of thermodynamics in the context of biochemical systems.

The first law of thermodynamics states that all energy is conserved. That is, energy cannot be created or destroyed but only converted from one form to another. This law of thermodynamics is one of the easiest for people to understand, yet it can be one of the most complex when dissected. When we discuss the conservation of energy in a strictly physical sense, we often think of potential and kinetic energy; this can be illustrated by the example of a roller coaster. At the top of a hill, the roller coaster has potential energy, but as it moves down the hill, some of that potential energy is converted to kinetic energy (the speed of the roller coaster). For biological systems, we often think of potential energy in terms of the energy trapped in the chemical bonds of food or other energy-storage molecules such as adenosine triphosphate (ATP) (Figure 1.1). The kinetic energy of a biological system could be the locomotion of that organism or the movement of fluids or gases in chambers of the organism, but there are many other ways in which energy can be used. For example, energy in biological systems can be used to generate electrochemical potentials by pumping ions across an otherwise impermeable barrier, heat energy can be released in biological systems to increase the temperature of the organism or the immediate surroundings, and chemical energy can be converted into a photon of light by bioluminescent organisms. There is no shortage of ways that energy can be used, but all of the ways obey the first law of thermodynamics.

FIGURE 1.1 **Structure of ATP.** Adenosine triphosphate contains three phosphate groups linked via a phosphoanhydride or phosphoester bond to adenosine. (Wessner, *Microbiology*, 1e, copyright 2013, John Wiley & Sons. This material is reproduced with permission of John Wiley & Sons, Inc.)

When we discuss the energetics of any reaction, we can describe the energy as being exchanged in terms of heat or in terms of work. Heat is the amount of thermal energy that is dissipated or absorbed by a system, whereas work is generally defined as a force applied over a distance or as a change in pressure or volume. Because most biochemical systems operate under constant pressure, the heat of a reaction is a close approximation of the energy of that system. We define this energy as the **enthalpy**, *H*.

*The second law of thermodynamics states that the **entropy, S**, of the universe is always increasing and that the entropy of any system tends toward increasing randomness and disorder.* This definition should be familiar to us on a macroscopic scale. If we consider gas molecules distributed throughout a flask, these molecules are randomly distributed. Similarly, the air we breathe has a statistically random sample of gas molecules. It would be unthinkable to walk down the street and encounter a pocket of carbon dioxide molecules that had randomly and spontaneously assembled out of the mixture. A better definition is the number of potential ways we could arrange those molecules or, to put it more scientifically, "the number of microstates a system can achieve." This definition is somewhat more detailed than disorder, and it can be used to explain a greater variety of phenomena. Imagine a system containing two objects, one of which is cool, the other warm. The atoms that make up the warmer object have more kinetic energy, more molecular motion, and more microstates, while the cooler atoms have less motion and therefore fewer microstates. According to the second law, it is impossible to trap and segregate the thermal energy from the cool object and use it to further heat the warm object. Therefore, it is not possible to use an ice cream cone to cook a hot dog, and a metal bar will not spontaneously segregate energy from one end of the bar to the other, cooling one end while warming the other.

The third law of thermodynamics states that the entropy of a perfect crystalline system at 0 Kelvin is 0. Consider an absolutely pure and perfect crystal of a monomolecular solid. As the crystal cooled to lower and lower temperatures, it would have less and less vibration. As the crystal approached 0 K, the molecular motion would decrease and the number of possible microstates would also approach zero. Of the three laws of thermodynamics, this one seemingly has the least impact on biochemistry because living systems never operate at such low temperatures. However, this definition of the third law allows us to define entropy (0 K = no entropy) and therefore merits mention here.

Free energy relates both enthalpy and entropy in a single useful term

Building from the three laws of thermodynamics, there are two key parameters to discuss: enthalpy and entropy. Although enthalpy is useful in predicting the direction of a reaction, not all of the energy released can be used as enthalpy because some of it is consumed in the generation of entropy. Likewise, while entropy is important, the amounts of entropy are typically much smaller than enthalpy for a given reaction. While neither term alone can accurately describe the energetics of a reaction, the **Gibbs free energy** or simply **free energy** relates these two parameters in a simple expression:

$$G = H - TS$$

Often, free energies are compared to one another. Due to experimental constraints, these are expressed not as ultimate values (G) but rather as the change in the value (ΔG). The Gibbs free energy expression thus becomes:

$$\Delta G = \Delta H - T\Delta S$$

where the change in the free energy is related to the change in the enthalpy of the reaction, minus the change in the entropy multiplied by the temperature, measured in Kelvin (Table 1.1).

The equilibrium constant of a reaction can also be expressed in terms of ΔG. Although a negative value of ΔG is often thought of as meaning that a reaction is favorable, it really means that it is favorable in the forward direction. Hence, a ΔG value of zero indicates that a system is at equilibrium, a negative value indicates that the reaction proceeds in the forward direction, and a positive value indicates that the reaction is favorable in the reverse direction.

Although ΔG can predict the net direction of a reaction, it does not affect $\Delta G^{\ddagger}$, **the free energy of the transition state** or the free energy of activation. In other words, ΔG gives the energy difference between the reactants and products, but not the energetic "hill" that has to be climbed to go from one to the other. Thus, ΔG does not predict reaction rate. Reactions with ΔG values of -30, -0.3, $+0.3$, or $+30$ kJ/mol may all proceed at the same rate.

The Gibbs free energy describes the amount of energy available to do work at constant temperature and pressure, or the amount of energy that is unavailable because it is lost to increasing entropy. Because biochemical systems are defined as operating under constant pressure rather than constant volume, the Gibbs free energy is used in most biochemical applications.

The standard state in biochemical systems

In all chemical systems, including biochemistry, scientists define reference states or standard states. The **standard state** is defined by a temperature at 25°C (298 K), a pressure of 1 atmosphere, and solutes with an activity of 1 (roughly corresponding to their molar concentration). These criteria are used to define the

TABLE 1.1 Common Reactions with a Strongly Negative $\Delta G^{\circ\prime}$ Found in Biochemistry

Compound and Hydrolysis Reaction	$\Delta G^{\circ\prime}$ (kJ/mol)
Phosphoenolpyruvate $\rightarrow$ Pyruvate + P_i	−62.2
1,3-bisphosphoglycerate $\rightarrow$ 3-phosphoglycerate + P_i	−49.6
Creatine phosphate $\rightarrow$ Creatine + P_i	−43.3
Acetyl phosphate $\rightarrow$ Acetate + P_i	−43.3
Adenosine-5′-triphosphate $\rightarrow$ ADP + P_i	−35.7
Adenosine-5′-triphosphate $\rightarrow$ ADP + P_i (with excess Mg^{2+})	−30.5
Adenosine-5′-diphosphate $\rightarrow$ AMP + P_i	−35.7
Pyrophosphate $\rightarrow$ P_i + P_i (in 5 mM Mg^{2+})	−33.6
Adenosine-5′-triphosphate $\rightarrow$ AMP + PP_i (excess Mg^{2+})	−32.3
Uridine diphosphoglucose $\rightarrow$ UDP + glucose	−31.9
Acetyl-coenzyme A $\rightarrow$ Acetate + CoA	−31.5
S-Adenosylmethionine $\rightarrow$ Methionine + adenosine	−25.6
Glucose-1-phosphate $\rightarrow$ Glucose + P_i	−21.0
Glycerol-3-phosphate $\rightarrow$ Glycerol + P_i	−9.2
Adenosine-5′-monophosphate $\rightarrow$ Adenosine + P_i	−9.2

free energy of the standard state, $\Delta G°$. The biochemical standard state is $\Delta G°'$. This includes the activity of water (the value used in free energy calculations) as 1 and the pH as 7.0.

The free energy of the standard state is important to know because it can provide important information regarding the favorability of a reaction, that is, whether or not it will proceed in the forward direction under standard conditions. However, by itself the free energy is not enough to predict the favorability of a reaction. To do so requires that the standard free energy change be related to the conditions in the reaction. Specifically, for any reaction where:

$$a\,A + b\,B \rightarrow c\,C + d\,D$$

$$\Delta G = \Delta G° + RT \ln([C]^c[D]^d/[A]^a[B]^b)$$

For any reaction, the direction of the reaction (the free energy) is a function of the free energy of the standard state, the temperature, T, the ideal gas constant, R, and the natural log of the ratio of the products to reactants in the reaction. While this final term may look similar to an equilibrium constant, recall that these concentrations are the ones found in the cell and are not at equilibrium. The final term is the reaction quotient, sometimes denoted as Q.

Some important biological molecules have a large negative free energy of hydrolysis

Some molecules have groups that will hydrolyze, cleaving the bond through the addition of water, with large, negative free energy values. This happens because these molecules have certain properties such as charge–charge repulsion, bond enthalpy, and differences in hydration. Adenosine triphosphate (ATP) is the best known of these molecules (**Figure 1.2**), but there are others. Any of the nucleoside triphosphates (the other building blocks of ribonucleic acid, RNA) can and do serve as molecules that donate energy to reactions. Cleavage of the phosphoanhydride bond also increases the number of available resonance states and results in an overall increase in entropy. When these molecules are hydrolyzed, typically one or two phosphate groups are cleaved away from the nucleoside phosphate. The energy of this reaction is used to drive reactions that would otherwise be energetically unfavorable in the forward direction.

Many other phosphorylated groups, for example, phosphoenolates, also serve as a temporary repository of energy (**Figure 1.3**). The energy liberated in these reactions is also used to drive reactions. Recall that enols are tautomeric forms of a ketone. Phosphoenolates can be generated by phosphorylating a hydroxyl group, followed by generation of a double bond via dehydration of a neighboring hydroxyl group. This phosphate has a much more negative free energy of hydrolysis and therefore a much higher transfer potential. These groups are used by the cell as one means of synthesis of ATP. The free energy of transfer from the enol to ADP is negative. Once the phosphate is lost, the enol tautomerizes into its keto form.

Knowing that these molecules hydrolyze spontaneously and have large negative ΔG values provides no information about rate. In the absence of a **catalyst** to accelerate the rate of breakdown, ATP can be isolated and stored indefinitely. In the instance of ATP, there is a relatively large activation energy barrier ($\Delta G^{\ddagger}$) that must be overcome for these molecules to react.

FIGURE 1.2 Hydrolysis of ATP. ATP can either lose one phosphate (P_i) or two phosphates together (termed pyrophosphate, PP_i, not shown). The hydrolysis of these phosphates is highly exergonic with a large negative ΔG value (a thermodynamically favorable reaction). (Karp, *Cell and Molecular Biology: Concepts and Experiments*, 7e, copyright 2013, John Wiley & Sons. This material is reproduced with permission of John Wiley & Sons, Inc.)

FIGURE 1.3 **Phosphoenolates.** **A.** Ketones can tautomerize into an enol. **B.** Addition of the phosphate can trap the enol in a phosphoenolate, such as phosphoenol pyruvate (PEP). Hydrolysis of these molecules has very large negative ΔG values and can drive many reactions in the cell, including the formation of ATP.

Unfavorable reactions can be made energetically possible by coupling them to favorable ones

On their own, many biochemical reactions are thermodynamically unfavorable in the forward direction ($\Delta G > 0$). For example, forming an ester between a phosphate group and a hydroxyl group generally has a positive free energy of reaction. In biochemistry, these reactions can still proceed in the forward direction by being coupled to thermodynamically favorable reactions (**Figure 1.4**). A common thermodynamically favorable reaction is the hydrolysis of ATP to ADP and P_i (inorganic phosphate), which has a $\Delta G^{\circ\prime}$ of −30.5 kJ/mol (**Table 1.2**). Instead of being hydrolyzed, the phosphate of ATP could be transferred to the hydroxyl group of another molecule. From a thermodynamic perspective, we could separate this reaction into two separate reactions: the hydrolysis of ATP to ATP and inorganic phosphate (P_i), and the esterification of phosphate to the hydroxyl of the new molecule. The energies of the two reactions are added together to find the net ΔG for the entire reaction.

ATP is used to drive many reactions, but in theory, any molecule with a favorable free energy of hydrolysis ($\Delta G < 0$) can be used.

Reaction 1	Glucose + P_i ⟶	Glucose-6-phosphate	+18.0 kJ/mol	(unfavorable)
Reaction 2	ATP + H_2O ⟶	ADP + P_i	−30.5 kJ/mol	(favorable)
Overall reaction:	**Glucose + ATP ⟶**	**Glucose-6-phosphate + ADP**	**−12.5 kJ/mol**	**(overall favorable)**

FIGURE 1.4 **Coupling favorable and unfavorable reactions.** The formation of glucose-6-phosphate in the cell is energetically unfavorable ($\Delta G^{\circ\prime} = 18$ kJ/mol). The hydrolysis of ATP, reaction 2, is large and negative ($\Delta G^{\circ\prime} = -30.5$ kJ/mol). When these two reactions are coupled together and the phosphate from ATP is used to form glucose-6-phosphate, the energies of the individual reactions are additive, resulting in an overall favorable reaction ($\Delta G^{\circ\prime} = -12.5$ kJ/mol).

TABLE 1.2   Common Organic Functional Groups Found in Biochemistry

Functional Group	Structure	Notes
Oxygen-containing groups		
Hydroxyl	R—O—H	Hydroxyl groups are common to all classes of biological molecules. The participate in numerous reactions including esterifications, dehydrations, and oxidations.
Carbonyl (aldehydes and ketones)	$R-\overset{\displaystyle \|}{\underset{\displaystyle O}{C}}-H$	The polar carbonyl group participates in numerous biochemical reactions. Frequently carbonyl carbons are subjected to nucleophilic attack by hydroxy or amino groups.
Carboxyl	$R-\overset{\displaystyle \|}{\underset{\displaystyle O}{C}}-O^-$	Carboxyl groups are weak acids. They are common functional groups and participate in the formation of several other groups, including esters and amides.
Ester	$R^1-\overset{\displaystyle \|}{\underset{\displaystyle O}{C}}-O-R^2$	Esters are the result of a hydroxyl and carboxylic acid reacting with one another. Esters are commonly found in many lipids.
Sulfur analogs		
Thiol	R—S—H	Thiol groups can be thought of as hydroxyl analogs. They are found in the amino acid cysteine.
Disulfide	R—S—S—R′	Disulfides result from the reaction of two thiol groups together. Disulfide reducing agents cleave the disulfide and restore the two thiols.
Thioester	$R^1-\overset{\displaystyle \|}{\underset{\displaystyle O}{C}}-S-R^2$	Thioesters have a large negative free energy of hydroylsis.
Nitrogen analogs		
Amino	$R-\overset{\displaystyle H}{\underset{\displaystyle H}{\overset{\displaystyle \|}{\underset{\displaystyle \|}{N^+}}}}-H$	Amino groups are common to all classes of biological molecules. The lone pair of electrons on the amino group can acquire a proton resulting in a positively charged amino group.
Amide	$R-\overset{\displaystyle \|}{\underset{\displaystyle O}{C}}-\overset{\displaystyle R}{\underset{\displaystyle H}{N}}$	Amides are formed through the reaction of an amine and a carboxylic acid. Peptides are the amide linkages found in proteins, but other amide bonds are found throughout biochemistry.
Phosphorous-containing groups		
Phosphates	$O^--\overset{\displaystyle O^-}{\underset{\displaystyle O}{\overset{\displaystyle \|}{\underset{\displaystyle \|}{P}}}}-OH$	Phosphate, also known as inorganic phosphate, P_i, is commonly found in all biological systems.
Phosphoesters	$R-O-\overset{\displaystyle O}{\underset{\displaystyle OH}{\overset{\displaystyle \|}{\underset{\displaystyle \|}{P}}}}-OH$	Phosphoesters are the result of the addition of a phosphate group to a hydroxyl group.
Phosphanhydrides	$R^1-O-\overset{\displaystyle O^-}{\underset{\displaystyle O}{\overset{\displaystyle \|}{\underset{\displaystyle \|}{P}}}}-O-\overset{\displaystyle O^-}{\underset{\displaystyle O}{\overset{\displaystyle \|}{\underset{\displaystyle \|}{P}}}}-O^-$	Phosphanhydrides are commonly found in nucleoside triphosphates like ATP and have a large negative free energy of hydrolysis.
Other groups		
Enol	$R-\overset{\displaystyle OH}{\underset{}{\overset{\displaystyle \|}{C}}}=C\overset{\displaystyle H}{\underset{\displaystyle H}{}}$	Enols are tautomers of carbonyl groups. In biochemistry they are often trapped as phosphoenolates.

1.1.2 | Equilibrium describes a specific thermodynamic state

Equilibrium refers to the chemical state when the rates of the forward and reverse state of a reaction are equal. The rates can be fast or slow, provided the net rate of product formed or reactant used is zero. Likewise, the concentrations of reactant and product do not need to be the same (and often are not). While it may seem confusing at first that a system can still be at equilibrium when the ratio of products to reactants is 1×10^9 or 1×10^{-9}, values commonly span this range.

We define the **equilibrium constant, K_{eq}**, as the ratio of products to reactants at equilibrium. For the given reaction at equilibrium:

$$a \, A + b \, B \rightleftharpoons c \, C + d \, D$$
$$K_{eq} = [C]^c \, [D]^d / [A]^a \, [B]^b$$

Combining this equation with our previous definition of the free energy of the reaction,

$$\Delta G = \Delta G^\circ + RT \ln([C]^c [D]^d / [A]^a [B]^b)$$

we obtain an expression that defines the free energy of any reaction as the sum of the standard free energy and the temperature and gas law constant, multiplied by the natural log of the ratio of concentrations in the reaction.

Because equilibrium is defined here as the point at which there is no net reaction, ΔG at equilibrium is zero. As a result, ΔG° becomes:

$$\Delta G^\circ = -RT \ln K_{eq}$$

Rearranging this equation describes the equilibrium constant in terms of the other parameters:

$$K_{eq} = e^{-\Delta G^\circ / RT}$$

Effectively, this means that the free energy of a reaction can be used in the standard state to describe the equilibrium constant, or vice versa. The free energy is therefore simply another way to describe the equilibrium constant.

All systems tend toward equilibrium, despite the ratio of reactants to products. If reactants are mixed in a beaker in the absence of product, they will begin to react to form product. Likewise, if the products of this same reaction are mixed together in a beaker and allowed to react, reactants will eventually appear. If a system at equilibrium is in some way perturbed, it will react to return to equilibrium. This observation is known as **Le Châtelier's principle** and is a feature of all systems, including biochemical systems. If the concentrations of reactants are increased above the equilibrium concentration, the reaction will proceed in the forward direction to compensate by making more products. Likewise, if the concentration of product is increased, the reaction will proceed in the reverse direction to generate more reactant. A biochemical example of this occurs in erythrocytes (red blood cells). In tissues, erythrocytes acquire carbon dioxide from muscle and quickly convert it into carbonic acid (H_2CO_3) via the enzyme carbonic anhydrase. In the lung, carbon dioxide concentrations are low and the process moves in the reverse direction, generating carbon dioxide from carbonic acid.

Enzymes, or any catalyst for that matter, will not perturb or in any way alter equilibrium concentrations; they will only help a reaction to reach equilibrium more quickly.

Although often used interchangeably in the popular literature, equilibrium should not be confused with **homeostasis**, the ability of an organism to live within its energetic and chemical means. An organism living in homeostasis is not consuming more energy than it is using or using its energy stores; however, it is not at chemical equilibrium with its environment. An organism that has reached equilibrium with its environment is, in all biochemical ways of thinking, dead.

1.1.3 | Kinetics describes the rate of chemical reactions

Kinetics is the field of study that analyzes the rates of chemical reactions. Some reactions involve a single reactant being transformed to a single product, while others involve multiple reactants leading to multiple products. The rate of a reaction depends on general factors including the concentration of products and reactants, temperature, and factors specific to that individual reaction. The rate of any chemical reaction can be described using a mathematical expression termed a rate law. These laws link the rate, the change in concentration over time, to the concentration of the starting materials multiplied by a constant, k, the rate constant. The rate constant takes into account the temperature and factors such as how often a collision between reactants leads to products.

$$A + B \rightarrow C$$

$$\text{Rate} = d[C]/dt = k[A][B]$$

In the simple example shown above, two molecules, A and B, react to form the molecule C. Based on the rate law given above, the rate of this reaction is linearly dependent on the concentration of both A and B; thus, doubling the concentration of A doubles the rate, and the same is true for B. The rate needs to be experimentally determined: the rate law for that reaction is then derived from experimental data; however, once a rate law has been determined, it is possible to calculate reaction rates from given concentrations, or concentrations from observed rates.

1.1.4 Thermodynamics, equilibrium, and kinetics are used together to describe biochemical reactions and systems

The direction of any reaction depends on the initial and final energies of the starting materials and products (ΔG), and the concentrations of the reactants. The rate of a reaction is related to the activation energy ($\Delta G^{\ddagger}$), not to the initial or final states. When a catalyst acts on a reaction, it lowers the activation energy, affecting the rate constant k. The catalyst does not affect ΔG, nor does it affect the equilibrium concentrations of reactants and products, which are also ΔG dependent. The lowering of the energetic barrier between products and reactants is the same if the reaction is going in the forward or reverse direction; therefore, the rates of *both* reactions are increased. Hence, a catalyst can help a system to reach equilibrium more quickly, but it cannot change equilibrium concentrations.

When considering biochemical systems, the same rules apply, but nearly all biochemical reactions are catalyzed by specific protein catalysts termed **enzymes**. Enzymes lower activation energy by forming more stable states and facilitating collisions between reactants (**Figure 1.5**). It may be hard to conceptualize how "lower activation energy" translates to actual chemistry. Imagine two molecules such as ATP and glucose that may react together to form a glucose phosphate and ADP. Although these molecules could react with each other in

---

WORKED PROBLEM 1.1 | Using thermodynamics to examine reactions

Examine the following two reactions.

ATP + H_2O → ADP + P_i $\qquad\qquad$ $\Delta G^{\circ\prime} = -30.5\,\text{kJ/mol}$

Glucose + P_i → Glucose-6-phosphate + H_2O $\quad$ $\Delta G^{\circ\prime} = +18.0\,\text{kJ/mol}$

What is the standard free energy change for the formation of glucose-6-phosphate from glucose and ATP? That is, what is the standard free energy change for the reaction:

ATP + glucose → Glucose-6-phosphate + ADP

Strategy The energies of thermodynamic properties, such as free energy, are additive. Combine the energies to find the overall energy of the reaction.

Solution Adding the free energies of the first two reactions, we see that the overall free energy for the two reactions combined ($-30.5\,\text{kJ/mol} + 18.0\,\text{kJ/mol}$) is negative and exergonic ($-12.5\,\text{kJ/mol}$). Therefore, the reaction will proceed in the forward direction.

The formation of glucose-6-phosphate from glucose and phosphate is energetically unfavorable in the forward direction. Rather, it is endergonic with a positive $\Delta G^{\circ\prime}$ value. Nevertheless, glucose-6-phosphate is found in the cell because of the presence of ATP. The large negative $\Delta G^{\circ\prime}$ of hydrolysis of ATP allows it to act as a phosphate donor. More important, it provides the energy needed for this reaction to happen.

Follow-up question The ΔG values used in the previous problem were in the standard state ($\Delta G^{\circ\prime}$). What factors will modify ΔG in the cell? How could ΔG be made more negative, and would this affect how quickly the reaction proceeds?

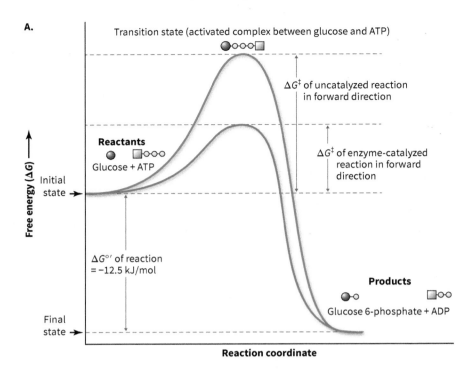

FIGURE 1.5 **Reaction coordinates and catalysis.** **A.** Enzymes do not alter the initial or final states but rather lower the activation energy by stabilizing the transition state ($\Delta G^{\ddagger}$), to increase rate. (Karp, *Cell and Molecular Biology: Concepts and Experiments,* 7e, copyright 2013, John Wiley & Sons. This material is reproduced with permission of John Wiley & Sons, Inc.) **B.** and **C.** This is done in part by constraining the reactants in the active site of the enzyme.

the absence of a catalyst, simple random collisions between the molecules will rarely have the proper direction of collision and enough energy for the reaction to occur. Now imagine these two molecules held in an enzyme in the correct orientation to react with one another, or brought together so that a reaction is more favorable; this gives a picture of what the lowering of the transition-state energy looks like on a physical level.

1.1 Summary

- There are three fundamental laws of thermodynamics:
  - Energy is conserved. In general, the energy of a biochemical system can be defined as its enthalpy.
  - The entropy of a spontaneous reaction is always increasing.
  - $S = 0$ at 0 Kelvin.
- Both enthalpy and entropy contribute to biochemical processes. We can aggregate these terms into one expression: the Gibbs free energy, ΔG.
- The free energy of a reaction describes the equilibrium state ($\Delta G = 0$) and whether a reaction will move in the forward ($\Delta G < 0$) or reverse direction ($\Delta G > 0$).
- The equilibrium state is one in which the rates of the forward and reverse reactions are equal; hence, there is no net production or loss of product or starting material. It can be expressed in terms of the equilibrium constant, K_{eq} (a ratio of the equilibrium concentrations) or in terms of free energy.
- Le Châtelier's principle states that all reactions seek to move toward equilibrium from other states.
- Kinetics is the study of chemical rates. Most biochemical reactions employ protein catalysts called enzymes to lower activation energies and increase reaction rates.

1.1 Concept Check

- Describe the basic concepts of thermodynamics, equilibrium, and kinetics in your own words.
- Use these concepts to describe a basic biochemical problem.

1.2 Fundamental Concepts of Organic Chemistry

Biochemistry draws from all fields of chemistry to help answer questions, but organic chemistry has been the classical gateway into this field. This happens largely because most biological molecules contain carbon. This section focuses on four aspects of organic chemistry to prepare for the study of biochemistry: functional groups, solubility and polarity, mechanism, and polymer chemistry.

1.2.1 Chemical properties and reactions can be sorted by functional groups

Functional groups are fragments of a molecule, such as a hydroxyl or carbonyl group. Understanding how each group reacts, as well as its properties, makes it possible to apply that information to other molecules. Likewise, if a functional group does not behave as expected, the hypothesis needs to be re-examined, and theories or understanding of the system may need to change.

Many of the common functional groups found in biochemistry will be familiar (Table 1.2). They include hydroxyl groups, carbonyl groups, amines, and carboxylic acids. Others, such as thiols and phosphates may be less familiar. These groups combine to generate more complex molecules such as amides and disulfides.

Many of the molecules studied in biochemistry were identified before systematic methods of nomenclature were adopted, and therefore they have common names. Other molecules use the older Greek lettering system instead of numbering to identify the location of functional groups in a molecule (**Figure 1.6**). Although this is not the International Union of Pure and Applied Chemistry (IUPAC) nomenclature system that is used in organic chemistry, dissecting the name of a molecule can still help provide clues to its structure and function. For example, as the name implies, α-ketoglutarate contains a carbonyl group (keto) α to a carboxylate (ending in the suffix "-ate"). Without knowing other information, such as the structure of

α-ketoglutarate

Fatty acid

FIGURE 1.6 **Organic nomenclature using the Greek lettering system.** In α-ketoglutarate the carbonyl (keto) group is α to the higher priority carboxyl group. Fatty acids are broken down through a process termed β-oxidation. The oxidation occurs on the β-carbon.

glutarate, it is not possible to draw out the full structure, but the name still provides a guide. Likewise, fatty acids are broken down through a process termed β-oxidation. In this example, the oxidation occurs at the β-carbon.

1.2.2 The solubility and polarity of a molecule can be determined from its structure

All biochemistry occurs in aqueous systems. Water is the common denominator, and it is required in some way and at some level for all life to occur. When the National Aeronautics and Space Administration (NASA) searches for life on other planets, the first molecule they often look for is water. Water is the most common solvent used in biochemistry; hence, most biological molecules need to be soluble in water. Molecules can be made more water soluble by incorporating more polar groups, like hydroxyl groups and thiols, or charged groups, such as amine and carboxylate salts; phosphates; and, in some instances, sulfates.

Although all living systems require water, not all biochemical reactions occur in water. There are microenvironments in the cell or within individual macromolecules that exclude water. These systems are hydrophobic and nonpolar. Reactions that might not occur in an aqueous system can occur within a hydrophobic microenvironment in an enzyme. Likewise, although a cell is largely a watery place, hydrophobic groups on an otherwise water-soluble molecule can tether or anchor that molecule in a hydrophobic location; for example, a water soluble protein can be anchored within a hydrophobic layer of a cell membrane.

In addition to the structure and polarity of a molecule, stereochemistry also plays a key role in biochemical systems. This is discussed in **Societal and Ethical Biochemistry: The relevance of stereochemistry**.

Societal and Ethical Biochemistry

The relevance of stereochemistry

Stereochemistry plays a critical but subtle role in biochemistry. Due to the nature of biological molecules—mostly organic, often with multiple functional groups—many of them are chiral. As we build larger molecules from smaller chiral building blocks, these macromolecules are also chiral. Being chiral themselves, enzymes often catalyze chiral or stereospecific reactions. Overall, most of biochemistry is chiral or contains molecules that are chiral in at least one carbon center. We may refer to these pairs of isomers using the R and S system, in which stereoisomers are assigned by priority of functional groups, or the D and L system, in which chiral molecules rotate plane polarized light.

Fortunately, through evolution, nature uses a conserved set of molecules; with few exceptions, these have the same stereochemistry. Therefore, humans can obtain the amino acids they need to build new proteins from their diet (from animal, plant, or even microbial sources) and not worry about the chirality of those amino acids. The same is not true, however, for molecules made in the laboratory.

It can be difficult and expensive to produce stereochemically pure substances. Instead, when creating molecules where chirality may be important, the effort is spent on removing chiral centers or preventing their formation in the first place. A good illustration of this is in pharmaceutical development. Many pharmaceuticals bind to, and thus block or activate, either enzymes or receptors, leading to downstream biological effects. Although many pharmaceuticals have been designed to avoid chiral centers as far as possible, a lot of drugs still have them.

Having different stereoisomers of a drug can have a variety of effects. For example, the over-the-counter pain reliever ibuprofen has a single chiral center; this drug is supplied as a racemic mixture or mixture of the two stereoisomers, but only the S isomer is biologically active. The R isomer has no known effect. Conversely, for the drug naproxyn, the S enantiomer is the over-the-counter pain reliever, whereas the R enantiomer causes liver toxicity or hepatotoxicity. Therefore, naproxyn is synthesized and sold as the stereochemically pure S enantiomer. Similarly, dextromethorphan is a common over-the-counter cough suppressant, or antitussive, whereas levomethorphan, its enantiomer, is a powerful narcotic opioid analgesic.

_R_-Naproxen   **_S_-Naproxen**

Dextromethorphan   **Levomethorphan**

Pharmaceutical companies are now aware that racemic drugs are likely to have an active and an inactive component, or one isomer that is causing the desired effect and one that is causing other effects or no effect. Advances in synthetic chemistry have made it possible to produce and test enantiomerically pure compounds, that is, only the *R* or *S* isomers. Often, when the pure drug is tested, it is found that a lower dosage of the drug can be used, and adverse effects, due to the other isomer or to metabolites of the drug, can be avoided. For example, citalopram (Celexa) is a selective serotonin reuptake inhibitor (SSRI), an antidepressant supplied as a racemic mixture. Although the adverse effects of this drug are relatively mild, there are common effects of SSRIs, such as weight gain and decreased libido. The stereochemically pure L isomer (escitalopram, Lexapro) minimizes these adverse effects. This raises some interesting scientific questions, such as whether the D isomer is responsible for the adverse effects, and if so, why and how? A smaller amount of the pure drug (the L isomer) is needed, which provides more options for delivery systems, and this puts less of a metabolic burden on the liver to detoxify other stereoisomers.

There are other advantages for pharmaceutical companies in pursuing stereochemically pure compounds. Because the effectiveness and safety of the parent compound has already been demonstrated, it is often easier and quicker to bring these drugs to market. Also, drugs that are stereochemically pure are considered new in terms of patent protection. Thus a drug company can theoretically extend patent protection on a drug, up to another 17 years (the length of a patent on a pharmaceutical compound).

1.2.3 Reaction mechanisms attempt to explain how a reaction occurs

An organic reaction mechanism is an evidence-based explanation of how a reaction occurs. In a mechanism, we follow the flow of electrons from electron-rich nucleophiles to electron-poor nuclei. In reaction mechanisms, the direction of the arrow indicates the direction of electron flow. The headedness of the arrow indicates the number of electrons. A double-headed arrow ($\rightarrow$) means two electrons are flowing, whereas a single-headed arrow ($\rightharpoonup$) indicates one electron, or radical transfer.

The reaction mechanisms covered in organic chemistry are generally relatively simple in comparison to the enzymatically catalyzed reaction mechanisms in biochemistry. Biochemical

WORKED PROBLEM 1.2 | Properties of a biological molecule

Shown below is the structure of sphingomyelin, a molecule that is involved in cell-to-cell communication and has a structural role in the cell membrane. Which functional groups can you identify in sphingomyelin? Would you anticipate that this molecule would be soluble in water or in a nonpolar solvent? Which functional groups in this molecule would interact with water molecules and how?

Strategy Compare the figure of sphingomyelin to Table 1.2. Which functional groups can you identify? Are those groups polar or nonpolar?

Solution There are multiple functional groups in sphingomyelin: a quaternary amine, a phosphate in a phosphodiester, an amide, a hydroxyl, and an alkene. The charged moieties (the phosphate and amine) and the hydroxyl will help make that end of the molecule water soluble. The amide has lone pairs of electrons on both the oxygen and nitrogen; these can participate in hydrogen bonding as hydrogen-bond acceptors but not as hydrogen-bond donors. The hydrocarbon tails, on the other hand, are not going to be water soluble, making the entire molecule **amphipathic**—literally, a molecule with affinities for both water and oil.

Follow-up question What would be the products if the amide bond of the molecule were hydrolyzed?

A. Reaction

$$CH_3Cl + OH^- \longrightarrow CH_3OH + Cl^-$$

B. Organic reaction mechanism

| **Nucleophile attacks alkyl halide** | **Transition state** | **Substitution product** |

C. Enzyme reaction mechanism

FIGURE 1.7 **Reaction mechanisms.** **A.** A typical substitution reaction studied in organic chemistry. **B.** The mechanism of the example shown in A (an S_N1 substitution reaction). **C.** A biochemical reaction mechanism, while more complicated, illustrates the underlying principles, such as electron flow, intermediates, and nucleophilic attack, are the same.

reaction mechanisms can be quite complex, employing multiple steps, such as the mechanism of triose phosphate isomerase (**Figure 1.7**). In either instance, the same basic rules apply. A reaction mechanism explains the making and breaking of bonds at the molecular level. Arrows indicate the number of electrons and direction of electron flow, and electrons flow from regions of high electron density to regions of low electron density. Frequently in biochemistry these mechanisms employ nucleophiles and electrophiles similar or identical to ones that you have seen in organic chemistry.

1.2.4 Many biochemical molecules are polymers

Many of the molecules discussed so far are small, with molecular weights below 500 g/mol. However, many if not all of these small molecules have functional groups such as alcohols, amines, and carboxylic acids that facilitate the formation of **polymers**. Polymers are macromolecular assemblies of smaller building blocks termed **monomers**, and they may be connected in a linear fashion, like the cars of a train, or in a branched fashion, like the branches of a tree.

| Monomer 1 | Monomer 2 | Growing polymer |

WORKED PROBLEM 1.3 | Creating a polymer

The ethylene glycol ester of *N*-Formylglycine reacts with tris(hydroxymethyl)aminomethane (referred to as TRIS) to form an amide bond. The reaction is shown below:

Formylglycine glycol ester   **TRIS**

Formylglycyl-TRIS

Propose a possible mechanism for this reaction. Can these compounds polymerize?

Strategy Examine the given reaction. What are the reactants and products? How might these starting materials react together to yield the final product?

Solution The mechanism of amide bond formation in the ribosome, the protein assembly complex in the cell, involves an amino acyl ester as the donor group for adding amino acids to the growing protein. Ester aminolysis is also a common organic synthetic technique.

These compounds cannot polymerize. To simplify and facilitate study of this reaction, a formyl protecting group (CHO) is coupled to the amino group of the glycine glycol ester. The formyl group ensures that only one reaction can occur—the reaction between the formylglycine glycol ester and the amino group of TRIS. If that formyl group was missing, the glycine groups could probably polymerize.

Follow-up question   Would you anticipate that this reaction would proceed more favorably at an acidic pH or a basic pH?

While biochemistry is often thought of as the study of small organic molecules, it is equally a study in polymer chemistry and macromolecules. DNA, RNA, proteins, and enzymes are polymers, as are molecules such as glycogen, starch, and cellulose. Other molecules, for instance, some lipids, are not polymers, but they are assembled in a modular fashion, similar to polymers. Common themes are found throughout the biosynthesis and degradation of these molecules.

Polymers in biochemistry can be broadly categorized as those that have been coded for by some sort of template, for example DNA, RNA, and proteins, and those that have their structures determined by other means, such as carbohydrates. In both instances, the bonds that hold the polymer together generating amides, phosphodiesters, or acetals have a higher energy than the starting materials. That is, formation of a polymer requires an input of chemical energy. Polymers are formed using activated intermediates, that is, compounds that can "donate" a monomer to the growing polypeptide chain. Whereas the synthesis of a polymer requires the input of energy, the net reactions of the breakdown of a polymer releases energy. This release of energy comes not from breaking chemical bonds but in the formation of new, more stable products. Therefore, polymers can be used to store energy and drive otherwise unfavorable reactions.

1.2 Summary

- In organic chemistry molecules are categorized by functional groups. Many of the same functional groups are used in biochemistry.
- All biological systems are aqueous, and water is the solvent most commonly associated with biochemistry; however, certain microenvironments in a cell or macromolecule may exclude water. Polar or charged functional groups make organic molecules more soluble in water and less soluble in a hydrophobic environment.
- An organic chemical reaction can be partially explained using an organic reaction mechanism. The reaction mechanism shows how electrons flow, to explain the chemistry observed. Such diagrams are useful in dissecting how complex molecules such as enzymes function.
- Many biological molecules are polymers of simpler building blocks. Proteins are made from amino acids, nucleic acids from nucleotides, and complex carbohydrates from simple sugars. Other molecules including some lipids are not polymers but are made in a similar modular fashion.

1.2 Concept Check

- Identify which functional groups are polar and which are nonpolar.
- Identify which functional groups make a molecule more soluble in water, and which make it more soluble in a nonpolar environment, such as hexane or olive oil.
- Illustrate a simple reaction mechanism.
- Describe the basic guidelines for any organic reaction mechanism.

1.3 The Chemistry of Water

Life is amazingly diverse and robust. It can exist without oxygen, at extreme temperatures, and in environments ranging from dilute to nearly saturated with salts and dissolved inorganic molecules. However, one common denominator to all of life is the need for water.

A.

Positive side

Hydrogen   Hydrogen

104.5°

Oxygen

$\delta+$

$\delta-$

Negative side

B.

1.3.1 The structure of water provides clues about its properties

Water is so common on Earth that it is easy to forget that it is unique among solvents (**Figure 1.8**). Water has two lone pairs of electrons on the oxygen atom and two polar H—O bonds. The polarity in the oxygen–hydrogen bond comes from the unequal sharing of electrons between the weakly electronegative hydrogen and the highly electronegative oxygen atom. The lone pairs of electrons give water a bent shape, with a nearly tetrahedral bond angle (104.5° in water compared to 109.5° in a truly tetrahedral center). Water's bent shape allows its polar H—O bonds to contribute to an overall dipole moment which runs through the entirety of the water molecule.

The polarity of water influences the strength of ionic interactions Chemists categorize the polarity of a solvent using a constant known as the **dielectric constant**, the ability of an insulating liquid to carry current, measured in Debye units, D. Vacuum and air both have dielectric constants close to 1 D. Typical nonpolar solvents used in organic chemistry (hexane, benzene, or oils) have dielectric constants of 2 to 4 D (**Figure 1.9**). Ethanol and acetone have dielectric constants in the low 20s. Water, on the other hand, has a dielectric constant of 80 D, one of the highest values known.

The dielectric constant comes into play in coulombic interactions, defined by an equation that describes the interactions between charged species. Coulomb's law is:

$$F = kQ_1Q_2/r^2D$$

where F is the force between the two charges, k is the Coulomb's law constant, Q_1 and Q_2 are the charges, r^2 is the square of the distance between the forces, and D is the dielectric constant of the medium containing the charges.

FIGURE 1.8 **Structure of water.** **A.** A single molecule of water has a 104.5° bond angle and a dipole moment running through its center. It has a bent geometry due to lone pairs of electrons on oxygen. (Trefil; Hazen, *The Sciences: An Integrated Approach,* 7e, copyright 2013, John Wiley & Sons. This material is reproduced with permission of John Wiley & Sons, Inc.) **B.** In ice, water forms a tetrahedral lattice with each water molecule forming four hydrogen bonds with other molecules.

A.

NaCl crystal

B. Dielectric Constants of Common Laboratory Liquids

Solvent	Dielectric Constant (D)
Water	78.5
Ethyl alcohol	24.3
Acetone	20.7
Acetic acid	6.2
Benzene	2.3
Hexane	1.9

FIGURE 1.9 **Coulombic interactions.** Coulombic interactions describe the forces that hold ions together. **A.** Sodium and chloride ions in a crystal are disrupted and dissolved by water molecules. The water molecules form hydration shells around each of the ions. (Karp, *Cell and Molecular Biology: Concepts and Experiments,* 7e, copyright 2013, John Wiley & Sons. This material is reproduced with permission of John Wiley & Sons, Inc.) **B.** The dielectric constant of some common solvents. Water has one of the highest dielectric constants known.

Coulomb's law states that the strength of an ionic interaction is the product of the charge of the two charges and a constant, divided by the square of the distance between those ions and the dielectric constant. This means that the force holding the two ions together decreases as the distance between the ions increases, or as the strength of the dielectric constant increases.

The high dielectric constant of water means that it can readily solubilize many ionic solids and significantly decrease ionic interactions. As a simple example, table salt can dissolve in water but not in vegetable oil. The interactions of water molecules with the sodium and chloride ions contribute more than the interactions of those ions with one another. Vegetable oil, with a far lower dielectric constant, is unable to overcome the interactions of the ions in the crystal and, as a result, the salt will not dissolve.

Although water can decrease the strength of ionic interactions, this observation should be used cautiously. Biochemistry is rich with microenvironments that may exclude water and strengthen ionic interactions.

1.3.2 Hydrogen bonding among water molecules is one of the most important weak forces in biochemistry

Hydrogen bonds are a weak force resulting from a strongly electronegative atom (typically oxygen, nitrogen, or fluorine) bound to a hydrogen atom (**Figure 1.10**). The polarity of the bond between these atoms results in a partial positive charge on the hydrogen. The hydrogen bond is the weak interaction between one of these hydrogen atoms and the lone pair of electrons on another electronegative atom. The presence of a hydrogen atom in a molecule is not sufficient for formation of a hydrogen bond; for example, methane (CH_4) does not exhibit hydrogen bonding.

Water has two hydrogen atoms bound to oxygen and two lone pairs of electrons; thus, it can form up to four hydrogen bonds at any one time. Water is unique in this regard, having equal numbers of hydrogen bond donors (hydrogen atoms bound to oxygen) and hydrogen bond acceptors (lone pairs). In liquid water, it has been calculated that any individual water molecule is involved in 3.7 hydrogen bonds at any one time.

The properties of hydrogen bonds   Hydrogen bonds are considered a weak force (10 to 40 kJ/mol in biological systems) when compared to a covalent bond (200 to 600 kJ/mol). The strength of a hydrogen bond is based partially on the angle between the electronegative hydrogen and the lone pair. A linear (180°) alignment produces the strongest bond. As with other bonds, hydrogen bonds have an optimal bond distance. For a hydrogen bond between a hydroxyl proton and the lone pair of electrons on another oxygen atom, the optimal length is 2.0 Å, but this can vary from 1.5 to 2.2 Å. The distance between the two non-hydrogen atoms is 2.5 to 3.2 Å.

Hydrogen bonds are not as strong as covalent bonds, but there are many hydrogen bonds within biological macromolecules. Water molecules and many biological molecules contain functional groups such as hydroxyl, amine, carbonyl, and carboxyl groups that can participate in hydrogen bonding, with tens to billions of hydrogen bonds occurring at all times in biological molecules. For example, hydrogen bonds lend strength to the cellulose in wood and plant fibers and proteins in wool and silk. Hydrogen bonds are also necessary to form the double helix of DNA.

Hydrogen bonds influence the properties of bulk water

Hydrogen bonds influence the properties of water in other ways. Water exhibits a property known as surface tension. The surface tension of water, which is illustrated by its ability to bead on a hydrophobic surface and resist an opposing force, is in part a product of the high degree of hydrogen bonding at the air–water interface. Biological systems take advantage of surface tension, but they also produce molecules to eliminate the tension. For example, water striders use surface tension to skim the surface of water, whereas in the lung, detergent-like molecules disrupt the surface tension making it easier for our lungs to expand, allowing us to breathe.

Water also has a high heat capacity, which is defined as the amount of energy needed to raise 1 gram of material by 1°C. At 4.18 J/g · K, water has a much higher heat capacity than most compounds. This is in part due

FIGURE 1.10 **Hydrogen bonding.** **A.** Hydrogen bonding is common between water molecules or between water and other molecules found in biological systems. **B.** While fluorine is not commonly found in biochemistry, it is an important element in numerous drugs, including the antidepressant Prozac.

to the energy needed to disrupt the hydrogen-bonding network of water to generate molecular motion—in other words, to raise the water's temperature. The heat capacity of water means that, in nature, water is relatively slow to heat up or cool down, and water is therefore liquid over a relatively broad temperature range. In effect, the heat capacity of water serves as a natural thermal buffer, helping to regulate the temperature of biochemical systems.

1.3.3 Water can ionize to acids and bases in biochemical systems

Acids, bases, and buffer systems are also important in biochemistry. There are several ways to describe acids and bases. Using the Arrhenius definition, acids are H^+ donors and bases generate an increased concentration of OH^-. Although limited, this definition works well in many cases, especially when examining strong acids or bases. For compounds containing ammonia or an amine, the Arrhenius definition fails to explain the molecule's behavior. The **Brønsted-Lowry** definition of acids and bases categorizes acids as proton donors and bases as proton acceptors. Using this latter definition, we see that ammonia and most other amines accept a proton from water, making the solution more basic.

When examining biochemical systems, it is important to consider the protonation state of an acid or base in biochemical systems. A protonated amine is not a base; rather, it is an acid because it can act as a proton donor but not an acceptor.

The acid ionization constant and pK_a describe the strength of an acid

The acidity of a proton can be measured using its acid ionization constant, K_a:

$$K_a = [H^+][A^-]/[HA]$$

where H^+ is the proton concentration, A^- is the conjugate base of the acid, and [HA] is the concentration of the acid at equilibrium, expressed in units of molarity.

Strong acids are almost 100% ionized in solution and hence have high K_a values. Conversely, weak acids are poorly ionized, often 1 molecule in 100 to 1 in 10 million, leading to small K_a values. These values are difficult to conceptualize, but taking the negative logarithm gives a whole number, the **pK_a** value, which is about 2.0 to 7.0 for weak acids (**Table 1.3**). The

TABLE 1.3 K_a and pK_a Values for Weak Acids Used in Biochemistry

Acid	K_a	pK_a
H_3PO_4	7.08×10^{-3}	2.15 (pK_1)
Succinic acid	6.17×10^{-5}	4.21 (pK_1)
Oxalate$^-$	5.37×10^{-5}	4.27 (pK_2)
Acetic acid	1.74×10^{-5}	4.76
Succinate$^-$	2.29×10^{-6}	5.64 (pK_2)
H_2CO_3	4.47×10^{-7}	6.35 (pK_1)
$H_2PO_4^-$	1.51×10^{-7}	6.82 (pK_2)
3-(N-Morpholino)propanesulfonic acid (MOPS)	7.08×10^{-8}	7.15
N-2-hydroxyethylpiperazine-N'-2-ethanesulfonic acid (HEPES)	3.39×10^{-8}	7.47
Tris(hydroxymethyl)aminomethane (TRIS)	8.32×10^{-9}	8.08
Boric acid	5.75×10^{-10}	9.24
NH_4^+	5.62×10^{-10}	9.25
Glycine (amino group)	1.66×10^{-10}	9.78
HCO_3^-	4.68×10^{-11}	10.33 (pK_2)
HPO_4^{2-}	4.17×10^{-13}	12.38 (pK_3)

Source: Dawson, R.M.C., Elliott, D.C., Elliott, W.H., and Jones, K.M., *Data for Biochemical Research* (3rd ed.), pp. 424–425, Oxford Science Publications (1986); *and* Good, N.E., Winget, G.D., Winter, W., Connolly, T.N., Izawa, S., and Singh, R.M.M., *Biochemistry* **5**, 467 (1966).

higher the pK_a is, the less acidic is the proton. Although in general chemistry we often think of the acidic proton in a weak acid as coming from a carboxylic acid, it is possible to determine a pK_a value for any proton. Hydroxyl protons have pK_a values of 14.0 to 16.0, whereas alkane protons may have values in the mid- to upper 30s, which is far beyond the values found in biochemistry. The pK_a value is a logarithmic rather than a linear value, so a change of three pK_a units is actually a 1,000-fold change in value. In addition, pK_a values can be modified significantly by neighboring atoms within a molecule. Introduction of electron withdrawing groups, or resonance states within the same molecule, or alterations to the local environment around a molecule of interest can change a pK_a value radically. For example, molecules that would normally not deprotonate in aqueous solution often do so readily when bound to an enzyme.

The pH scale is used to measure hydrogen ion concentration
The hydrogen ion concentration of a system can range from 1 to 1×10^{-14} M. The pH scale transforms these concentrations into values that are easier to comprehend. Again, because these values are small, taking the logarithm of the value helps to generate numbers that are easier to work with. The **pH** is the negative logarithm of the hydrogen ion concentration, providing a scale that runs from 0 to 14.

In biochemistry, the pH of a reaction is critical; many important macromolecular interactions in biochemistry are dictated by weak forces that may be sensitive to changes in pH. Likewise, many catalytic mechanisms employ simple acid–base chemistry that fail to react outside a narrow pH range.

FIGURE 1.11 **Buffers.** Weak acids and bases will either ionize to release a proton or absorb one. Solutions buffer best over a range of ±1 pH unit around the pK_a value (the pH at which there are equal concentrations of conjugate acid and conjugate base).

Biochemical systems are buffered from changes in pH
Buffers are chemical systems that are resistant to changes in pH. They are mixtures of weak acids, and their conjugate base (**Figure 1.11**). The mixture buffers the pH by acting like a proton sponge, releasing or absorbing protons to resist changes in pH. Buffers made with weak acids work best at pH values nearest the pK_a value of the weak acid in the system. The expression that is used to calculate the pH of a buffer system is the **Henderson–Hasselbalch** equation:

$$pH = pK_a + \log[A^-]/[HA]$$

where pH is the pH in question, the pK_a is the pK_a of the weak acid, $[A^-]$ is the molar concentration of the conjugate base of the weak acid, and [HA] is the concentration of the un-ionized weak acid, also expressed in units of molarity, M. The Henderson–Hasselbalch equation illustrates why buffers are only effective at pH values near the pK_a of the acid or base. If the pH is more than 1 pH unit from these values, the logarithmic term begins to dominate the equation, and the ratio of acid to conjugate base in the buffer fails to regulate pH. However, at pH values near the pK_a value, up to a 10-fold change in acid or base concentration will be blunted by the effect of the buffer.

It is often useful to see how an equation is derived. The derivation of the Henderson–Hasselbalch equation is shown in **Biochemistry: The derivation of the Henderson–Hasselbalch equation.**

The pH at which a weak acid or conjugate base system will buffer is a function of its pK_a, but the total amount of acid or base that can be consumed is a function of the concentration.

Biochemistry

The derivation of the Henderson–Hasselbalch equation

The Henderson–Hasselbalch equation is a valuable expression in biochemistry. It relates the pH of a solution to the pK_a value of the weak acid in question, and the ratio of the concentration of weak acid to that of the conjugate base of the weak acid. The equation is useful for performing calculations with buffer solutions and pH; it is also relatively easy to derive. Although it is probably easier to simply know or look up the Henderson–Hasselbalch equation, deriving it illustrates several other important pieces of acid–base chemistry and how the equations are put together, a useful tool when examining or deriving other equations.

A weak acid (HA) will partially ionize in aqueous solution to give a proton (H⁺) and the conjugate base of the weak acid (A⁻).

Expressing these as molar quantities at equilibrium allows us to write an acid ionization constant, K_a:

$$K_a = \frac{[H^+][A^-]}{[HA]}$$

Taking the base-10 logarithm of both sides gives:

$$\log_{10} K_a = \log_{10}\left(\frac{[H^+][A^-]}{[HA]}\right)$$

The right-hand side of the equation can be rearranged to isolate the log of the hydrogen ion concentration. Adding logarithms is the equivalent of multiplying integer values:

$$\log_{10} K_a = \log_{10}[H^+] + \log_{10}\left(\frac{[A^-]}{[HA]}\right)$$

Next, we can simplify the equation. The abbreviation used when taking the negative log of a term, is p (as in pH and pK_a). The above cases use the log (not the negative log), so the equation can be simplified to:

$$-pK_a = -pH + \log_{10}\left(\frac{[A^-]}{[HA]}\right)$$

Rearranging the pK_a and pH terms gives the familiar form of the Henderson–Hasselbalch equation:

$$pH = pK_a + \log_{10}\left(\frac{[A^-]}{[HA]}\right)$$

Thus, if two potassium phosphate buffers have been prepared in the laboratory, both at pH 7.3, and one buffer is 10 mM and the other 100 mM, the latter will have the ability to consume more acid or base. This is termed the **buffer capacity** of a system.

Biochemical systems are buffered by several different combinations of weak acids and their conjugate bases or weak bases and their conjugate acids. The most common buffering system in the blood is the bicarbonate/carbonate buffer. Cells use a combination of bicarbonate and phosphate to buffer against pH changes. Common biological buffers used in the laboratory include bicarbonate, phosphate, and acetate. Both carbonate and phosphate are polyprotic acids, acids that can donate more than one proton. Generally, only one of these ionizations plays a role in buffering of biochemical systems. In the laboratory, small organic molecules are often chosen to buffer near a specific pH; these include TRIS, MOPS, and HEPES.

TRIS
tris(hydroxymethyl)aminomethane

MOPS
3-(N-Morpholino)propanesulfonic acid

HEPES
4-(2-hydroxyethyl)-1-piperazineethanesulfonic acid

In an experiment, if there is no means of buffering, it is easy for the pH to change rapidly. In the early days of experimental biochemistry, the lack of control of factors such as buffering and pH made it difficult to obtain consistent results from repeated experiments, and this generated spurious and false results (referred to as artifacts). Buffers help regulate and control biochemical experiments, and standardize results. Biochemical systems are buffered for similar reasons; the inability to regulate pH can result in wide fluctuations, many of which could be harmful to the organism. Altering the pH of a system can have implications on the molecular level such as the ability of a protein to bind to a small molecule. This can have significant effects on the organism, for example, on the ability to carry oxygen to tissues that need it.

The buffering capacity of the blood is discussed in **Medical Biochemistry: Buffers in blood**.

Medical Biochemistry

Buffers in blood

Buffers play a central role in biochemistry. In the laboratory, students are advised to always use a buffered solution for a biochemical experiment. Naturally occurring bodies of water, including streams, lakes, and even oceans, have low millimolar levels of dissolved compounds such as carbon dioxide and phosphate, which provide minor amounts of buffering. The dissolved compounds are also partially responsible for the observed pH. However, the necessity and effect of buffering are most evident inside an organism. In the blood, the bicarbonate ion (HCO_3^-, pK_a 6.3) is the primary molecule responsible for buffering and maintaining a tight pH range around 7.35 (± 0.1 pH units). Other ions, such as phosphate, ammonia, or organic ions, play minor roles in blood buffering but are found at a much lower concentration than bicarbonate (17 to 24 mM in healthy humans), or have pK_a values too far from 7.35 to be effective. At physiological pH we are outside the pH range at which bicarbonate would buffer a solution: ±1 pH unit around the pK_a value or, for bicarbonate, 5.3 to 7.3. At pH 7.35 the ratio of bicarbonate to carbonic acid is over 10:1.

Several factors account for the observed pH. First, the organism can regulate pH through the release or reabsorption of CO_2 either in the lung or kidney. Second, while less important than bicarbonate, other molecules, such as phosphate and proteins, can also participate in buffering. It may seem paradoxical that the organism operates outside the optimal buffering range; however, the bicarbonate buffering system has several advantages. Tissues produce acidic waste products, and this system provides a means by which the organism can rapidly respond to increased acid levels. Carbon dioxide is generated when carbon-containing molecules are oxidized for energy, and this CO_2 must be eliminated from the body. Carbon dioxide typically diffuses out of cells and into the bloodstream. There, dissolved carbon dioxide enters red blood cells or erythrocytes, where it is acted on by the enzyme carbonic anhydrase, catalyzing the formation of carbonic acid (H_2CO_3) from carbon dioxide and water. The carbonic acid generated is mildly acidic ($pK_{a1} = 6.35$), and it rapidly ionizes to form a bicarbonate anion and a hydronium ion. The second pK_a (pK_{a2}) is 10.33 and is not typically encountered in biological systems. The bicarbonate that is generated in this reaction accumulates in the erythrocyte. These reactions would rapidly reach equilibrium were it not for the chloride–bicarbonate exchange protein, which is found in the membrane of the erythrocyte and exchanges a bicarbonate ion for a chloride ion. This process ensures that there is no significant accumulation of bicarbonate in the erythrocyte, and keeps the reaction moving in the forward direction in carbon dioxide generating tissues.

In the lung, there is a low concentration or partial pressure of carbon dioxide. Thus, as blood passes through the lung, the described reactions occur in reverse: chloride rushes out of the erythrocyte and bicarbonate rushes in. The latter protonates and is rapidly degraded to carbon dioxide, which is free to diffuse out of the erythrocyte and blood, and is exhaled and eliminated by the lung. The erythrocyte demonstrates several chemical principles including equilibrium, Le Châtelier's principle, solubility, permeability, and catalysis. In addition, the bicarbonate generated serves as a buffer for the blood, bathing tissues in a constant pH close to 7.35.

In times of excessive acid production, such as during anaerobic muscle exertion or in several disease states, more acid is produced than the buffer system can compensate for, and blood pH levels drop below pH 7.2. This condition, known as acidosis, can have serious consequences. At pH 6.8, the level of acidity is such that it becomes difficult for the blood to deliver oxygen to tissues that need it. Damage can quickly result to tissues, cells, and the molecules that make up those cells. In the clinic, sodium bicarbonate is used to raise the pH of the blood until the underlying cause of the acidosis can be determined.

In other conditions, the blood may become dangerously alkaline (above pH 7.45). This may happen, for example, when a person hyperventilates, in which case too much carbon dioxide is exhaled, depleting the body of its buffering capacity. In this instance, carbon dioxide can be recovered by having a patient breathe an environment enriched in carbon dioxide, such as a paper bag, to increase the amount of carbon dioxide and bicarbonate dissolved in blood.

WORKED PROBLEM 1.4 | Working with buffers

You have been asked to prepare 1 liter of a 50 mM buffer (pH 5.2) for an experiment. In the laboratory are the following buffers: TRIS, MOPS, phosphate, and acetate.

Which buffer will you choose to make, and how will you make it?

Strategy Examine the pK_a values for each buffer in Table 1.3. How does that information help in choosing which buffer to use?

Solution Buffers only work over a range of ±1 pH unit around the pK_a of the acid or base in the buffer. Of the four buffers available, only one, acetate, has a pK_a near 5.2 (4.7). To make the buffer, you would measure out enough acetate to make 1 liter of final solution but dilute it into less than the final volume. You would then adjust the pH of this solution with a solution of base like NaOH to the desired pH (5.2). Finally, you would then dilute the buffer to the final volume (1 liter).

Follow-up question If you have a solution of 50 mM acetic acid and 50 mM sodium acetate, how much of each would you need to make 1 liter of pH 5.5 buffer?

1.3 Summary

- Water is:
  - necessary for life
  - the central solvent in biochemistry
  - highly polar
  - particularly effective at making hydrogen bonds—bonds between a hydrogen attached to an electronegative atom and another electronegative atom.
- All biological systems require water, and it is the solvent most commonly associated with biochemistry; however, microenvironments in a cell or macromolecule may exclude water. Polar or charged functional groups make organic molecules more soluble in water and less soluble in a hydrophobic environment.
- Water has the ability to ionize, forming H^+ and OH^-, affecting pH.

- Buffers are pairs of weak acids and their conjugate base (or weak bases and their conjugate acid).
- Buffers act to resist changes in pH. The compositions of a buffer and the pH can be calculated using the Henderson–Hasselbalch equation.

1.3 Concept Check

- Describe water and its interactions on the molecular level.
- Describe hydrogen bonding and how it imparts to water many of the properties it exhibits.
- Perform calculations with both strong and weak acids and bases, including pH calculations.
- Perform calculations using buffers and the Henderson–Hasselbalch equation.

The Bigger Picture

General chemical principles form a critical part of the foundation of biochemistry. The laws and principles seen in chemistry are also at work in biological systems. This is truly enlightening. Instead of memorizing random chemicals and isolated principles, the overarching rules of chemistry mean that there is an order and structure to the reactions and principles of biochemistry. There are reasons for molecules reacting or not reacting in particular ways, reasons why molecules are found in particular locations in the cell, and reasons why molecules assemble in particular ways. These reasons are grounded in chemistry and are the basic chemical principles that form the foundation of life.

Bioinformatics Exercises

Exercise 1 The Periodic Table of the Elements and Domains of Life

Exercise 2 Organic Functional Groups and the Three-Dimensional Structure of Vitamin C

Exercise 3 Structure and Solubility

Exercise 4 Amino acids, Ionization, and pK values

Problems

1.1 General Chemical Principles

1. In your own words, explain the three laws of thermodynamics and the terms "system," "surroundings," and "free energy."

2. What is the difference between ΔG, $\Delta G°$, $\Delta G°'$ and $\Delta G^{\ddagger}$? Can any of these be used interchangeably, and if so, when?

3. All biochemical macromolecules are folded into complex shapes held together in part by weak forces. Discuss the thermodynamics of these processes. Are they favorable or unfavorable? Which thermodynamic terms (ΔG, ΔH, ΔS, and others) are important in folding into a stable conformation? What other phenomena (bond breaking or forming, changes in entropy, and so on) contribute to the larger thermodynamic parameters?

4. In glycolysis, glucose is broken down to yield energy. If the equilibrium constant of the isomerization of glucose-6-phosphate to fructose-6-phosphate is 0.5, would this reaction proceed in the forward or reverse direction? What is the free energy of the reaction? Using standard conditions (1 M) as an initial state, what are the equilibrium boncentrations?

5. If we consider the polymerization of a water soluble monomer into a polymer, is this process entropically positive or negative? What types of interactions need to be considered?

6. The ketone body β-hydroxybutyrate is a small molecule found in some metabolic states. In organisms, β-hydroxybutyrate will spontaneously decarboxylate into acetone and carbon dioxide. Write a rate law for this reaction. What factors will contribute to this rate?

1.2 Organic Chemistry Review

7. Examine these amino acids. Which functional groups can you identify? What types of bonds can these groups form?

8. Functional groups can often be transformed from one type of group to another. Examine the common functional groups in Table 1.2.

Based on your knowledge of organic chemistry, how would you synthesize these functional groups? What would you need for starting materials? What could you do with these groups? What other molecules could you make and how?

9. Amino acids are the building blocks of proteins. Can you put these amino acids into order of increasing solubility in water?

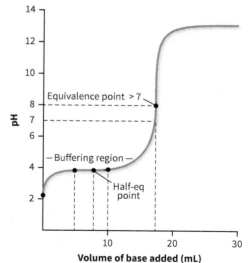

10. Which of these molecules would you anticipate has the highest solubility in water? Which would be most soluble in hexane?

11. Examine the structures given in problem 10. If each were dissolved in water, how would the water molecules surround these solutes? What sorts of interactions would occur and where?

12. Based on your knowledge of organic chemistry, propose a mechanism for the hydration of an alkene.

13. Propose a mechanism for the base-catalyzed cleavage of an ester.

14. If a polymer is 1,000 monomers long and includes four different types of monomers, how many different combinations of the monomers are possible?

15. Examine the structure of the polymer shown. What are the monomeric units of that polymer?

16. The structure of polymers is dictated by the monomers that make up the polymer. Examine the list of functional groups in Table 1.2. What types of bonds and forces could these groups use to interact with one another?

1.3 The Chemistry of Water

17. Examine the functional groups in Table 1.2. Which of these can hydrogen bond with water? How and where will these bonds form?

18. Which of these bonds would be the shortest H bond, and why? OH–O, OH–N, OH–F

19. A molecule of water is said to participate in 3.7 hydrogen bonds at any one time. How could you calculate this number? How could you measure it?

20. What is the pH value of each of these solutions?

   a. 0.1 M HCl

   b. 3 M H_2SO_4

   c. 50 mM HNO_3

   d. 12 mM HCl

21. What is the pH value of each of these solutions?

   a. 0.2 M NaOH   **c.** 100 mM $Ca(OH)_2$

   b. 2 M KOH   **d.** 10 mM KOH

22. What is the pH value of each of these solutions?

   a. 0.3 M acetic acid   **c.** 100 mM phosphoric acid

   b. 3 M acetic acid   **d.** 43 mM H_2CO_3

23. What is the pH value of each of these solutions?

   a. 25 mM ammonia   **c.** 80 mM TRIS base

   b. 140 mM $NaHCO_3$ **d.** 0.5 M KH_2PO_4

24. What percentage of a solution of acetic acid is ionized at pH 5.6? What percentage of a solution of HCl is ionized at the same pH?

25. What is the final pH if you have a 1 micromolar solution of HCl and dilute it 1,000 fold?

26. What is the final pH if you have 700 mL of a sodium acetate buffer (50 mM, pH 5.0) and you add 10 mL of 1 M NaOH?

27. How much 6 M HCl do you need to add if you have 800 mL of 100 mM TRIS, pH 10.2 and you wish to lower the pH to 7.0?

28. Normal blood pH is approximately 7.35 and the concentration of carbonate and bicarbonate ions (total) is approximately 20 mM. What is the ratio of carbonate to bicarbonate ions in the blood under these conditions?

29. Buffering capacity is the property of a buffer to resist changes in pH. Which has more buffering capacity: a liter of 50 mM MOPS, pH 6.9 or 100 mL of 1 M MOPS at the same pH?

Data Interpretation

30. In the titration curve of a weak acid with a strong base, where is the equivalence point? What is the pK_a of this acid? Over what pH range would this solution act as a buffer?

Experimental Design

31. Based on your knowledge of organic chemistry, how could you increase the solubility of an amine or a carboxylic acid in an aqueous solution?

32. Tryptophan is an amino acid, one of the building blocks of proteins. It has a hydrophobic side chain. Design an experiment to test the solubility of tryptophan in 150 mM NaCl.

33. Based on your experiences in organic chemistry, how would you identify an unknown molecule? What organic techniques would you use? What are the limitations of those techniques? Based on your current knowledge of biochemistry, what are the strengths and drawbacks of employing organic techniques to identify biological molecules?

34. If you were asked to make 1 liter of 140 mM KCl, how would you do it? Give a detailed description, including the steps in the process and the pieces of glassware you would use.

35. How would you go about making 500 milliliters of 100 mM TRIS buffer, pH 7.4? Describe the steps involved, including which apparatus and glassware you would use and when.

Ethics and Social Responsibility

36. As you begin your studies in biochemistry, what do you think are the important ethical and social questions in this field?

37. All professional organizations have codes of conduct. These include the codes of conduct for the American Society for Biochemistry and Molecular Biology, the International Union for Biochemistry and Molecular Biology, the American Chemical Society, the American Medical Association, and others. Using the Internet, examine one of these organization's codes of conduct. Is there anything that you find surprising?

38. Various governmental agencies regulate the sale of certain biomolecules, ranging from drugs to foods to fuels. Is this regulation justified, and if so, why?

39. If you were to examine the effect that table sugar has on the body, you could find many ways in which it elicits physiological and metabolic changes. Why is sugar not considered a drug? Find a reliable resource that defines drugs and pharmaceuticals. What differentiates drugs from other molecules?

40. How are ethics violations or issues of impropriety handled at your institution or company?

41. Drug companies have patent protection for drugs that they have developed and are on the market. If an enantiomerically pure drug can be developed from a racemate, the company is given a new patent on the stereochemically pure compound. Do you feel this situation is justified?

Suggested Readings

1.1 General Chemical Principles

Alberty, R. A. *Thermodynamics of Biochemical Reactions.* New York, NY: John Wiley and Sons, 2003.

Jesperson, N. D., J. E. Brady, and A. Hyslop. *Chemistry: The Molecular Nature of Matter.* 6th ed. New York, NY: John Wiley and Sons, 2012.

Pauling, L., *The Nature of the Chemical Bond and the Structure of Molecules and Crystals.* Ithaca, NY: Cornell University Press, 1960.

Tinoco, I., K. Sauer, J. C. Wang, J. D. Puglisi, G. Harbison, and D. Rovnyak. *Physical Chemistry: Principles and Applications in Biological Sciences.* 5th ed. Englewood Cliffs, NJ: Prentice Hall, 2013.

Van Holde, K. E. *Physical Biochemistry.* 2nd ed. Englewood Cliffs, NJ: Prentice Hall, 1985.

Van Holde, K. E., W. C. Johnson, and P. S. Ho. *Principles of Physical Biochemistry.* 2nd ed. Englewood Cliffs, NJ: Prentice Hall, 2006.

1.2 Fundamental Concepts of Organic Chemistry

Cahn, R. S, C. K. Ingold, and V. Prelog. "Specification of Molecular Chirality." *Angewandte Chemie International Edition* 5, no. 4 (1966): 385–415.

Carey, F. A., and R. J. Sundberg. *Advanced Organic Chemistry, Part A, Structure and Mechanisms.* 5th ed. New York, NY: Springer 2007

Grossman, R. B. *The Art of Writing Reasonable Organic Reaction Mechanisms.* 2nd ed. New York, NY: Springer, 2002.

Klein, D. *Organic Chemistry.* New York, NY: Wiley and Sons, 2012.

Smith, M. B., and J. March. *March's Advanced Organic Chemistry.* 5th ed. New York, NY: Wiley and Sons, 2001.

1.3 The Chemistry of Water

Beynon, R. J., and J. S. Easterby. *Buffer Solutions: The Basics*, New York, NY: IRL Press, 1996.

Halperin, M. L., and M. B. Goldstein. *Fluid, Electrolyte, and Acid-Base Physiology: A Problem-Based Approach.* 3rd ed. Philadelphia, PA: W.B. Saunders, 1999.

Jeffrey, G. A., and W. Saenger. *Hydrogen Bonding in Biological Structures.* New York, NY: Springer, 1994.

Pauling, L., *The Nature of the Chemical Bond and the Structure of Molecules and Crystals.* Ithaca, NY: Cornell University Press, 1960.

Segel, I. H., *Biochemical Calculations.* 2nd ed. New York, NY: Wiley and Sons, 1976.

The Chemical Foundations of Biochemistry

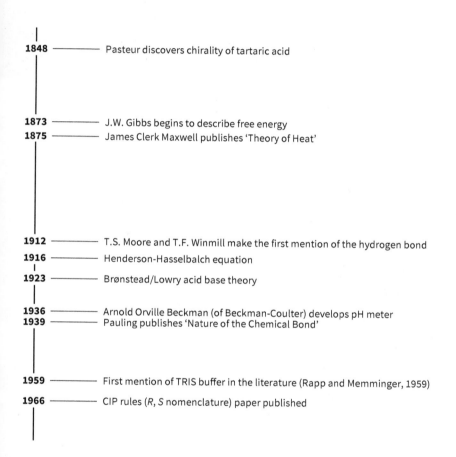

1848 — Pasteur discovers chirality of tartaric acid

1873 — J.W. Gibbs begins to describe free energy
1875 — James Clerk Maxwell publishes 'Theory of Heat'

1912 — T.S. Moore and T.F. Winmill make the first mention of the hydrogen bond
1916 — Henderson-Hasselbalch equation
1923 — Brønstead/Lowry acid base theory

1936 — Arnold Orville Beckman (of Beckman-Coulter) develops pH meter
1939 — Pauling publishes 'Nature of the Chemical Bond'

1959 — First mention of TRIS buffer in the literature (Rapp and Memminger, 1959)
1966 — CIP rules (*R, S* nomenclature) paper published

Nucleic Acids

Codes are languages that we have yet to elucidate.

Nucleic Acids in Context

It is easy to imagine how even a small amount of information, such as a credit card or social security number, could be misused if it were to get into the wrong hands. In many cases data is often encrypted to keep it safe. We could also imagine how, if there were an error in the code on a credit card number, an e-mail address, or mailing address, it could result in a problem with an online order. It would be easy to charge items to the wrong account or the items may be sent to the wrong place. Depending on where these errors occurred, it may be more difficult to rectify the situation.

Life, too, uses a code; unlike online data, life's code is written in nucleic acids. This code can be duplicated, transcribed into RNA, and finally translated into protein; these processes are referred to as replication, transcription and translation, respectively. Each of these processes occurs in all living creatures, all of which use the same genetic code. Hence, a piece of DNA coding for a human protein can be inserted into other organisms to produce those proteins for research or therapeutic use.

This chapter describes the physical and chemical properties of nucleic acids; reviews the basics of the central dogma, that is, how information in DNA is transcribed into RNA and then translated into protein; and describes how nucleic acids can be manipulated to alter mRNA and protein levels in the organism. An overview of this process is seen in **Dynamic Figure 2.1.**

CHAPTER OUTLINE

2.1 Nucleic Acids Have Distinct Structures

2.2 Nucleic Acids Have Many Cellular Functions

2.3 The Manipulation of Nucleic Acids Has Transformed Biochemistry

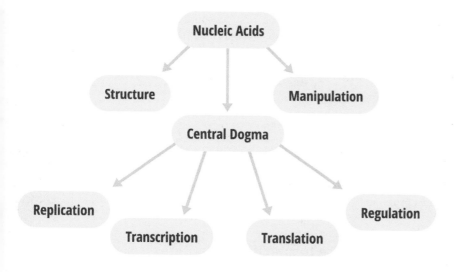

DYNAMIC FIGURE 2.1
DNA is the genetic material for nearly all organisms. It can be copied and passed from one generation of cells to the next, can be transcribed into RNA, and that code can be translated into protein. Techniques have been developed to analyze DNA sequences. Because the DNA code is conserved throughout biology, science has been able to use genes and enzymes from one organism to alter a DNA sequence and therefore alter the protein product.

COMMON THEMES

Evolution's outcomes are conserved.	• The classic observations and deductions made by Charles Darwin when he formulated the theory of evolution are equally relevant when we examine the molecular aspects of gene transmission.
	• Genetic traits, coded for by deoxyribonucleic acid (DNA) or ribonucleic acid (RNA), are conserved throughout evolution. Small, gradual changes in these coding sequences can be tracked through history to generate an evolutionary family tree.
Structure determines function.	• DNA molecules are made up of base pairs and have information coded within those base pairs.
	• The structure of DNA helps to explain how complex phenomena such as DNA replication occur, and how proteins interact with DNA (either specifically or nonspecifically) to organize DNA and regulate function.
	• RNA molecules can have complex structures that can encode information, regulate gene expression, or act catalytically.
Biochemical information is transferred, exchanged, and stored.	• Both DNA and RNA can serve as repositories of information that can be stored, translated into another type of molecule (RNA or protein), and transmitted to future generations.
Biomolecules are altered through pathways involving transformations of energy and matter.	• The nucleotide building blocks of RNA are used by the organism as a source of energy in numerous other chemical reactions.

2.1 Nucleic Acids Have Distinct Structures

The **nucleic acids** deoxyribonucleic acid (DNA) and ribonucleic acid (RNA) are among the most highly recognized molecules. In many ways, these molecules are biochemistry in a microcosm. While they may be familiar to you, your earlier studies of these may not have included a chemical focus. This section first presents the basic chemical composition of DNA and RNA, and the building blocks used to construct these molecules. It then discusses how weak forces give rise to the complex structures that these molecules adopt.

2.1.1 Nucleic acids can be understood at the chemical level

DNA and RNA are anionic polymers that were originally identified in the nucleus, hence the name "nucleic acid," and are constructed from nucleotide monomers.

A **nucleotide** consists of three parts—a nitrogenous base, a carbohydrate, and a phosphate. Each figures prominently in the chemistry of the molecule. This section considers each of these parts.

Nitrogenous bases give rise to specific nucleotides

Nitrogenous bases are heterocyclic structures that contain either one or two rings (**Figure 2.2**). The structures containing a single ring are the **pyrimidines** (named for their structural similarity to pyrimidine), and those containing two rings are **purines** (named for their structural similarity to purine). A simple way to recall and relate these two types of molecule is that the shorter name goes with the larger molecule, for example, purines are bicyclic. Each of these basic structures is modified to contain additional keto, amine, and methyl groups, which can participate in hydrogen bonding. Some of the nitrogens in the ring systems bear hydrogens and are also capable of hydrogen bonding. Although these molecules are referred to as bases and contain several amines within the ring systems, the pK_a values of the nitrogens are outside the physiological range; that is, they are never found in an ionized state.

The common purines are **adenine** (A) and **guanine** (G). These bicyclic bases are found in both RNA and DNA, and they appear in nucleotides that serve other functions in the cell, such as adenosine triphosphate, ATP. Cells also contain purines that are not found in nucleic acids; these include caffeine, theobromine, uric acid, and xanthine. Some of these molecules are involved in the metabolism of nitrogenous bases or nitrogenous waste, whereas others are potent signaling molecules.

The monocyclic pyrimidines that are commonly found are **cytosine** (C), **thymine** (T), and **uracil** (U). Here we see a difference between DNA and RNA. DNA contains the bases C and T, while RNA contains C and U. As is true for the purines, these bases and nucleotides also serve other roles in biochemistry in addition to being found in DNA and RNA.

Both purines and pyrimidines are aromatic structures. The aromatic ring imparts extra stability through resonance stabilization. It also means that nucleotides, and the nucleic acids made from them, will absorb in the ultraviolet (UV) region of the electromagnetic spectrum. This property is commonly used to measure concentrations of nucleic acids.

The aromatic properties and resonance states of purines and pyrimidines also facilitate several instances of tautomerization (**Figure 2.3**). In these forms, migration of protons can result in molecules with the properties of a carbonyl group (the keto form) or a hydroxyl group (the enol form). This could also result in an amino group changing to an imino group. In most instances in nature, the keto or amino form of any molecule will predominate, and nitrogenous bases are no exception. However, there are several instances, usually pH dependent, where enols can also be observed.

The tautomeric switch from keto to enol form is important on several fronts. First, the presence of a ketone versus a hydroxyl will change the hydrogen bonding properties of the molecule. As outlined in the next section, this ability to precisely hydrogen bond is of central importance in nucleic acid chemistry. Second, hydroxyl groups are important as catalytic centers in some nucleic acids, and this property may also be affected by tautomerism.

FIGURE 2.2 Nitrogenous bases. The nitrogenous bases that make up DNA are the purines adenine and guanine and the pyrimidines cytosine and thymine. In RNA uracil takes the place of thymine.

Addition of a carbohydrate to a nitrogenous base produces a nucleoside

Nitrogenous bases are coupled to a carbohydrate structure through a glycosidic bond, that is, a bond to a carbohydrate, to form a **nucleoside** (**Figure 2.4**). The different carbohydrates used in DNA and RNA give rise to the names of these two molecules. RNA uses the carbohydrate **ribose**. In a ribonucleoside, the base is attached to the 1′ carbon of the five-membered ribose ring; the atoms of the carbohydrate ring are given the designation "′" or "prime" to distinguish them from the atoms of the base. The carbohydrate rings in nucleosides are numbered from the 1′ position around the carbohydrate ring to the 5′ position. Ribose has two characteristic hydroxyl groups on the 2′ and 3′ carbons found on the bottom face of the ring. In contrast, the 5′ carbon is found on the upper face of the ring.

DNA and other deoxyribonucleosides contain **2′-deoxyribose,** often referred to simply as deoxyribose, a ribose molecule that lacks the hydroxyl group on the 2′ position.

Addition of phosphate groups produces a nucleotide

A nucleotide is formed by the addition of a phosphate to a nucleoside. This occurs via a phosphoester linkage to the hydroxyl group on the 5′ carbon of the ribose or 2′-deoxyribose ring. When added to ribose-containing nucleosides, this produces adenosine monophosphate (AMP), guanosine monophosphate (GMP), cytosine monophosphate (CMP), or uracil monophosphate (UMP). Correspondingly, the addition of phosphates to 2′-deoxyribonucleosides results in 2′-deoxyadenosine monophosphate (dAMP) and the other 2′-deoxy analogs: dGMP, dCTP, and dTTP.

Additional phosphate groups can be added through phosphoanhydride linkages. This results in the diphosphate and triphosphate forms of the aforementioned nucleotide monophosphates, that is, ADP and ATP or their deoxy analogs, dADP and dATP, and so on, as noted in Figure 2.4.

The phosphate groups added to these nucleosides and deoxynucleosides produce negatively charged molecules at neutral pH. ATP, for example, has three phosphate groups linked together through phosphoanhydride bonds, giving it a charge of -4 at pH 7.2. Therefore, these molecules are polyprotic acids; that is, they can donate more than one proton. Because of the negative charge on these phosphates, nucleotide triphosphates and deoxynucleotide triphosphates often form complexes with divalent metal ions (metal ions with a 2+ charge), most notably magnesium ions (Mg^{2+}). In these instances, the phosphates wrap around and cradle the metal ion. Often in biochemistry divalent metal ions are required for reactions involving nucleotide triphosphates and deoxynucleotide triphosphates.

The phosphates found on nucleotides and deoxynucleotides will hydrolyze with large, negative ΔG values. This energy can be used to drive reactions in the cell by coupling an otherwise energetically unfavorable reaction, such as the addition of a phosphate group to a hydroxyl, to a favorable one, such as the hydrolysis of ATP. Although ATP is the best known molecule that can be used to drive reactions, all of the nucleotide triphosphates are involved in providing energy to help drive specific reactions in the cell.

Finally, many nucleotide metabolites also play roles in cellular signaling. Compounds such as cyclic AMP (cAMP) that have a 5′ to 3′ phosphodiester linkage are found in signaling pathways ranging from the bacterium *E. coli* to humans.

Nucleic acids are polymers of nucleotides

Because nucleotides contain both free hydroxyl groups and phosphates, they are capable of forming diester linkages between

Common   **Rare**

Keto form   **Thymine**   **Enol form**

Amino form   **Cytosine**   **Imino form**

Amino form   **Adenine**   **Imino form**

Keto form   **Guanine**   **Enol form**

Keto form   **Uracil**   **Enol form**

FIGURE 2.3 **Tautomeric forms of bases.** The bases of DNA can undergo keto-enol tautomerism. While not usually apparent, these forms can lead to mismatches or changes to the DNA sequence if improperly paired. (Snustad; Simmons, *Principles of Genetics*, 6e, copyright 2012, John Wiley & Sons. This material is reproduced with permission of John Wiley & Sons, Inc.)

FIGURE 2.4 **Nucleosides, ribose, and deoxyribose.**
A. Nucleosides are comprised of a nitrogenous base
and a ribose sugar. Nucleotides are comprised of the
base, sugar, and a phosphate esterified to the 5′ carbon.
Nucleotides can have one (AMP), two (ADP), or three
(ATP) phosphates (Black, *Microbiology: Principles and
Explorations,* 8e, copyright 2012, John Wiley & Sons. This
material is reproduced with permission of John Wiley & Sons,
Inc.) **B.** Deoxyribonucleotides use deoxyribose, which is
missing an oxygen on the 2′ position of the ribose ring.
(Alters, *Biology: Understanding Life,* 1e, copyright 2006, John
Wiley & Sons. This material is reproduced with permission of
John Wiley & Sons, Inc.)

two or more molecules (**Figure 2.5**). This occurs most commonly between the hydroxyl group
on the 3′ carbon of one nucleotide and the phosphate connected to the 5′ carbon of another.
Ribonucleotides polymerize to form RNA, and 2-deoxyribonucleotides polymerize to form
DNA. DNA is typically comprised of two strands running in opposite directions (termed an
antiparallel configuration).

Polymers formed of a small number of nucleotides can be referred to by number, for
example, a *di*nucleotide or *tri*nucleotide. However, larger polymers, including five to ten or
more nucleotides, are often referred to as oligomers (or oligos for short). Nucleic acids can be
lengthy, stretching for hundreds of millions of monomers.

Perhaps one of the most fascinating aspects of biochemistry is that these polymers are
copied from a template, resulting in an almost perfect copy each time. The information stored
in this sequence of bases is the code of life, and is usually represented as a sequence of single
letters resulting from the bases A, C, G, and T (or U in the case of RNA). The information
coded within these bases provides the cell with the directions for *how* to make protein, *where*
or in *which* cells to synthesize these proteins, and to some extent *when* and under which conditions to do so.

2.1.2 The complex shapes of nucleic acids are the result of numerous weak forces

Nucleic acids differ with regard to their structure. RNA consists of a single strand, often several thousand bases or more in length, folded back on itself in a complex configuration that
is unique for each molecule. DNA differs from this in that it is typically comprised of two
strands which then twist around each other, resulting in the characteristic double helix that is
so familiar. This section discusses the various aspects and forces involved in forming nucleic

Sugar phosphate backbone   **Antiparallel DNA strands**   **Hydrogen bonding in A-T and G-C base pairs**

FIGURE 2.5 **Nucleic acids are polymers.** Nucleic acids are generally macromolecules, long strings of nucleotides or deoxynucleotides. Nucleotides in each strand are joined via phosphate esters between the 5′ carbon, the phosphate, and the 3′ carbon of the next nucleotide. RNA is single stranded while DNA is double stranded with the strands running in opposite directions. The bases of DNA hydrogen bond with one another forming base pairs. (Snustad; Simmons, *Principles of Genetics,* 6e, copyright 2012, John Wiley & Sons. This material is reproduced with permission of John Wiley & Sons, Inc.)

acid structures. Although discussed here in relation to nucleic acids, these same forces shape all other biological molecules as well.

The structure of DNA is a double helix
DNA consists of two antiparallel strands, each of which is a polymer of deoxyribonucleotides. These strands align like a ladder: the bases of DNA pair up (A binding to T, and G binding to C) to form the rungs of the ladder, and the phosphates and deoxyribose (the sugar-phosphate backbone) form the sides of the ladder. Finally, the entire structure twists upon itself to generate the double helix (**Figure 2.6**).

As the DNA helix forms, several details become clear. The bases of DNA stack up on one another. This generates a hydrophobic core to DNA, and helps to stabilize the structure. The helix of DNA has about 10.3 bases per turn; with about 0.34 Å per base pair (bp), the entire length of one turn of DNA is about 3.4 Å. Although short structures of DNA are often depicted as a roughly cylindrical shape, DNA is fairly flexible throughout its length, and can be looped around organizing proteins or regulatory proteins.

DNA is a double helix. Each of the two strands is helical and the strands are slightly offset from one another. Thus, a section of DNA contains two grooves that run the length of the molecule: the larger major groove and the smaller minor groove. The diameter of these grooves, in particular the major groove, makes it easier for proteins to interact with and thus regulate DNA.

There are three known forms of DNA: A DNA, B DNA, and Z DNA. Of these, B DNA was the first type to be characterized and is the type of DNA most commonly found in cells. In contrast, A DNA is thought to be more common under laboratory conditions, for instance, in the absence of water. Both A and B forms of DNA are right-handed helices, but the B DNA helix forms a slightly tighter structure than the A DNA helix. Therefore, B DNA has a wider major groove and a narrower minor groove than A DNA. In contrast, Z DNA is a left-handed

A.

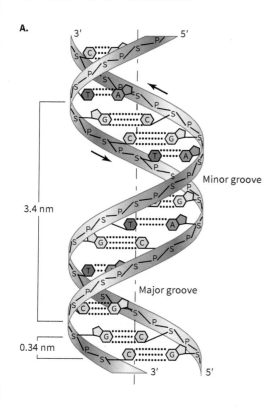

3' 5'

Minor groove

3.4 nm

Major groove

0.34 nm

3' 5'

B.

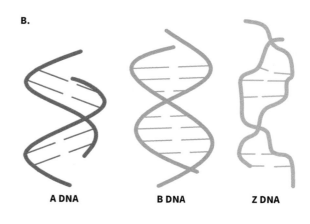

A DNA **B DNA** **Z DNA**

FIGURE 2.6 **Structure of DNA.** **A.**"B" DNA has a pitch of roughly 3.4 Å (approximately 10.4 bases) per turn of the helix. Twisting results in the double helix and the major and minor grooves through which proteins interact with the DNA. (Snustad; Simmons, *Principles of Genetics,* 6e, copyright 2012, John Wiley & Sons. This material is reproduced with permission of John Wiley & Sons, Inc.) **B.** "A" and "Z" DNA have different twists resulting in a different structure.

helix with a much wider diameter and is thought to form in some DNA-protein complexes. The roles of these different DNA structures in biology is not clear, but it may be that they play roles in the interaction of DNA with proteins.

DNA molecules can be relatively short in the laboratory, but those that are used to transmit genetic information in nature are much larger. For example, the complete collection of DNA, or genome in an average bacterium, contains about 10 million base pairs, whereas the human genome contains 3.3 billion base pairs. The largest single piece of DNA in the human genome is 249 million base pairs.

Elucidation of the structure of DNA was a watershed moment in biochemistry
Often, when some facet of nature reveals itself to science through experimentation, we struggle for a time to understand it well enough to put the observations into context and learn from what we have found. However, the discovery of the structure of DNA immediately tied together numerous observations, such as the ratios between A and T and between G and C, and laid the groundwork for others, including the elucidation of the replication of DNA. As with most great discoveries in science, answering this key question opened the door to many new questions.

Numerous weak forces are at work in the formation of the double helix
This section examines the forces involved in the formation and stabilization of the double helix. Looking first at a single strand of DNA, the strand has a hydrophilic sugar-phosphate backbone and a less hydrophilic nucleotide base. At this point, an easy assumption would be that hydrogen bonding holds DNA together. Hydrogen bonds between A and T or G and C form the basis of the genetic code, and are how recognition of sequences happens. This scenario is true in that base pairing in DNA involves hydrogen bonding; however, those bonds are slightly skewed, resulting in a weaker bond. Likewise, if the issue were merely hydrogen bonding, why would the bases not form hydrogen bonds with water? After all, there is far more water available than other nucleotides. The secret of helix formation lies in a phenomenon known as the **hydrophobic effect**, whereby hydrophobic molecules, including the bases of DNA, aggregate and group together in an oily pocket within a molecule.

The hydrophobic effect is not due to the strength of the hydrophobic interaction of molecules with one another. The **van der Waals** and **London-dispersion** forces that are found between two hydrophobic molecules are weak, being 10 to 1,000-fold weaker than any single hydrogen bond. The hydrophobic effect occurs because it takes fewer water molecules to surround and cage a larger group than single molecules. Hydrophobic molecules do not actively form groups; instead, they are pushed by water molecules interacting with each other. Freeing water from the need to cage hydrophobic molecules provides the increased energy to drive hydrophobic molecules together, creating the hydrophobic effect. Thus, helix formation can be attributed to hydrogen bonding, and hydrogen bonding between base pairs clearly drives the specificity of the assembly, but what drives the formation of the DNA duplex is not hydrogen bonds between bases, but the bulk hydrogen bonding of water.

Hydrogen bonding and the hydrophobic effect are not the only forces involved in the stabilization of DNA. In addition to these two, the charged phosphate groups on the backbone repel one another and therefore act to pull the helix apart (**Figure 2.7**). In strictly aqueous conditions, these forces are diminished by the strength and polarity of water; however, in DNA, the hydrophobic base pairs fail to decrease these forces to the same extent. Instead, the charges on the phosphate are partially balanced out by cations, most notably, divalent cations such as Mg^{2+}, and positively charged proteins.

The other forces involved in helix formation are often grouped into a single phenomenon known as **base stacking**. Base stacking involves numerous interactions: the hydrophobic effect, London-dispersion, van der Waals, dipole–dipole, and $\pi - \pi$ stacking. Collectively, these interactions stabilize the helix.

DNA can be melted or denatured, either chemically or by heating. As we might predict from the number of hydrogen bonds between the bases, DNA with a high GC content has a higher melting point than DNA with a high AT content. Buffer components such as salt or divalent metal ions also affect the melting point of DNA. Finally, chaotropes, molecules such as urea or guanidinium hydrochloride that disrupt the hydrogen bonding network of water, can denature DNA. Although these compounds have different structures, they all denature DNA by disrupting the forces that stabilize the helix. Simple means of calculating

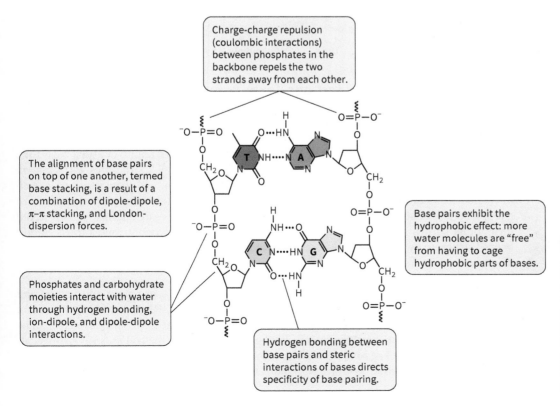

Charge-charge repulsion (coulombic interactions) between phosphates in the backbone repels the two strands away from each other.

The alignment of base pairs on top of one another, termed base stacking, is a result of a combination of dipole-dipole, $\pi-\pi$ stacking, and London-dispersion forces.

Base pairs exhibit the hydrophobic effect: more water molecules are "free" from having to cage hydrophobic parts of bases.

Phosphates and carbohydrate moieties interact with water through hydrogen bonding, ion-dipole, and dipole-dipole interactions.

Hydrogen bonding between base pairs and steric interactions of bases directs specificity of base pairing.

FIGURE 2.7
Analysis of weak forces involved in DNA stabilization. Numerous weak forces are involved in the stabilization of the DNA helix, including hydrogen bonding, coulombic interactions, hydrophobic interactions of base pairs, and the hydrophobic effect.

Biochemistry

Thermodynamics and DNA annealing

When double-stranded DNA is heated, it loses its secondary structure and denatures or melts, ultimately resulting in two single-stranded pieces of DNA. In the laboratory, the DNA sample is generally heated to above 97°C. When the temperature cools, the DNA will refold and, if this is done slowly enough, the base pairs will realign with one another, reforming double-stranded DNA.

In some of the techniques discussed in this chapter, shorter strands of DNA need to anneal to one another. The same forces apply, but for these experiments to work, the melting point of the short stretch of DNA needs to be calculated.

The simplest approximations for melting temperatures are based on the number of G:C pairs versus the number of A:T pairs in the sequence.

$$T_m = 64.9 + 41.0 \times \left(\frac{yG + zC - 16.4}{wA + xT + yG + zC} \right)$$

In this equation, w, x, y, and z are the number of bases of the respective nucleotides in the sequence, and the values calculated are in degrees Celsius. Because of the higher number of hydrogen bonds in G:C, it would be expected to have a higher melting point; however, other factors such as divalent metal ions or ionic strength also contribute to destabilization of the helix. Taking those parameters into consideration yields the following equation:

$$T_m = 100.5 + 41.0 \times \left(\frac{yG + zC - 16.4}{wA + xT + yG + zC} \right) - \left(\frac{820.0}{wA + xT + yG + zC} \right) + 16.6 \log([Na^+])$$

where again the values w, x, y, and z are the corresponding number of bases of each nucleotide.

Another factor to consider is the order of the nucleotides in the sequence. If there is a stretch rich in G:C base pairs, this region would have a higher melting temperature than would be the case if the G:C pairs were distributed throughout the sequence. This is termed the "nearest neighbor model" and is preferable to the other methods, although it is a slightly more involved calculation that takes into account the thermodynamic parameters involved in DNA–DNA interactions. Using a computer for these calculations greatly streamlines the process.

There are other models of DNA melting that use statistical mechanics to take into account the degrees of freedom of the molecules and other forces such as base stacking.

Having the correct melting temperature of small oligonucleotides can mean the difference between success and failure in many experiments. Thankfully, the algorithms discussed in this feature have been adapted for online use. Web sites quickly calculate melting temperatures using all three methods to provide a better estimate of the actual value.

the melting point of short stretches of DNA can be found in **Biochemistry: Thermodynamics and DNA annealing**.

Urea   **Guanidinium hydrochloride**

RNA is single stranded but can form complex structures

RNA molecules can form many different complex structures, each of which is unique for that particular molecule. Although RNA can form base pairs, in general RNA molecules are single stranded rather than double stranded. Often in RNA, the strand doubles back upon itself, forming double-stranded sections of about 3 to 12 nucleotides in length (**Figure 2.8**). Like DNA molecules, these structures are double helical. Other RNA structures form a stem loop structure comprising a short stretch of nucleotides, a turn, and then a second stretch of nucleotides complementary to the first. The stem part of the stem loop structure can adopt a helical conformation. RNA can also form triplexed structures, loops, and clustered formations known as pseudoknots. Each of these elements then contributes to the larger overall structure by folding into a complex three-dimensional shape. The same weak forces discussed earlier for DNA structure are also at work in RNA, helping to fold the molecule and stabilize its conformation.

In terms of function, RNA is more diverse than DNA. RNA can store information and transmit it in much the same way that DNA stores information. RNA provides information for protein synthesis in all organisms; it also forms the genome of some viruses. RNA can be catalytic (e.g., ribozymes) and the protein synthesis machinery of the cell uses RNA as its catalytic machinery. RNA can bind to small molecules either through a covalent bond by binding to an amino acid in transfer RNA (tRNA) molecules or through noncovalent interactions such as in a riboswitch.

A.

B.

FIGURE 2.8 **Complex RNA structures.** RNA molecules form complex structures. **A.** In these tRNA structures we can still observe base pairing. (Allison, *Fundamental Molecular Biology,* 2e, copyright 2012, John Wiley & Sons. This material is reproduced with permission of John Wiley & Sons, Inc) **B.** Short helical segments and complex tertiary structures also form. Modified bases are denoted using Greek letters (such as Ψ). (Allison, *Fundamental Molecular Biology,* 2e, copyright 2012, John Wiley & Sons. This material is reproduced with permission of John Wiley & Sons, Inc)

RNA is not as stable as DNA. It breaks down into nucleotides at a greater rate. RNA is also susceptible to hydrolysis under basic conditions, and even weakly alkaline solutions of pH 8 or 9 can rapidly accelerate the degradation of RNA. The reduced stability is due to the ribose ring. The 2′ hydroxyl is capable of attack on the phosphodiester bond of the backbone, resulting in cleavage (**Figure 2.9**). Hence, RNA must be treated and stored somewhat differently than DNA. While not recommended, DNA can be dissolved in water and left on the laboratory bench with few ill effects, while RNA is typically stored at −80°C in various buffers chosen to stabilize the molecule.

Frequently, fluorescent dyes are used to visualize, measure, and monitor DNA and RNA (**Figure 2.10**). Various factors affect fluorescence, but in the case of DNA and RNA the most important is whether the environment is aqueous or hydrophobic. In a more hydrophobic environment, the intensity of the fluorescence emitted by these molecules increases and the wavelength (color) of the emitted light is shifted further to the red side of the spectrum. Thus, a fluorescent dye can be used as a sensitive probe for hydrophobic environments. Fluorescent dyes, such as ethidium bromide, bind to nucleic acids and intercalate between the stacked base pairs of DNA. In this hydrophobic environment they fluoresce more brightly and at a longer wavelength than dye molecules in solution. Because DNA and RNA differ in the amount and type of base stacking that occurs, they bind to dyes with different affinity; hence, different dyes can be used to differentiate these molecules.

> Nucleophilic attack on the sugar phosphate backbone.

RNA polymer

Cyclic 2′3′ phosphodiester

Cleaved ends

FIGURE 2.9 **RNA cleavage.** The 2′ hydroxyl group on ribose is in position to undergo nucleophilic attack on the phosphate attached to the 3′ hydroxyl. Basic conditions accelerate this reaction by deprotonating the hydroxyl.

A.

Ethidium bromide

Ethidium bromide is added to DNA.

DNA

Molecules of ethidium bromide are intercalated between base pairs.

B.

Excitation

Emission

Intensity

Wavelength (nm)

250 300 350 400 450 500 550 600 650 700 750

C.

Klaus Guldbrandsen/Science Source

FIGURE 2.10 **Fluorescent dyes and DNA.** **A.** Fluorescent dyes, such as ethidium bromide, bind DNA by intercalating in between the base pairs of DNA. **B.** When bound in this hydrophobic environment the spectral properties of the dye change, increasing the amount of light emitted for every photon absorbed and undergoing a shift toward the red end of the spectrum. **C.** Dyes such as these can be used to visualize DNA in a gel.

WORKED PROBLEM 2.1 | Structure of a nucleic acid

The tRNAs are a family of short nucleic acids that play critical roles in protein synthesis. The structure of the nucleotide sequence of a tRNA is shown in figure 2.8, along with a schematic of the structures it forms and a three-dimensional representation of the final structure. What forces are involved in the folding and stabilization of this molecule?

> 5'–GCGGAUUUAGCUCAGDDGGGAGAGC-
> CCAGACUGAAYACUGGAGUCCUGUGTC-
> GAUCCACAGAAUUCGCACCA–3'

Strategy Based on our knowledge of nucleotides and nucleic acid structures, we should be able to analyze the sequence and describe the interactions that are going on in the folded molecule. What types of forces are involved in nucleic acid folding?

Solution The forces at work in the folding and stabilization of this molecule are the same as those in DNA or in other RNA

molecules. There is electrostatic repulsion of the phosphates in the backbone, hydrogen bonding of the ribose rings and bases with one another or with water, dipole–dipole interactions of various polar parts of the molecule with one another, and London-dispersion forces causing weak interactions throughout the entire molecule. However, the driving force that guides folding of this molecule is the hydrophobic effect.

Although we can explain the forces at work in the folded tRNA molecule or in short stretches of RNA, we cannot yet *predict* the folded structure of macromolecules from the sequence of its building blocks.

Follow-up question What techniques could you use to probe the structure of tRNA? What information would they provide?

2.1 Summary

- Nucleotides are the building blocks of nucleic acids.
- Nucleotides have three parts: a nitrogenous base (A, C, G, T, or U), a carbohydrate (ribose or 2'-deoxyribose) and a phosphate group.

- The nitrogenous bases of nucleotides can be categorized as purines or pyrimidines.
- The purines (A and G) are bicyclic structures.
- The pyrimidines (C, T, and U) are monocyclic.
- A, C, G, and T are the bases found in DNA, whereas A, C, G, and U are found in RNA.
- In addition to forming nucleic acids, nucleotides also play important roles in metabolism and signal transduction due to their ability to transfer phosphate groups to other molecules.
- Numerous weak forces contribute to the double-helical structure of DNA and the more complex forms of RNA, including the hydrophobic effect, hydrogen bonding, coulombic repulsion and base stacking effects.
- Nucleic acids can lose their secondary structure if heated or treated with chemical compounds that will disrupt these weak forces.
- Due to the hydroxyl group on the 2′ carbon of ribose, RNA molecules can be readily degraded under basic conditions.
- Because of their structure, nucleic acids can absorb UV light and bind fluorescent dyes.

2.1 Concept Check

- Draw the structures of the nucleotides.
- Explain how the chemical structures of nucleotides give rise to the properties of these molecules, for example, UV absorbance and hydrogen bonding.
- Explain which forces are important in the formation of a double helix or the folding of a complex RNA molecule, and how alterations to the nucleotide sequence might influence this folding.

2.2 Nucleic Acids Have Many Cellular Functions

The list of known functions of nucleic acids in biochemistry grows as research continues, but perhaps the most important function of these molecules is to code and store the information needed to produce many of the molecules necessary for life. Nucleic acids also provide a means of copying and sharing that information when the organism replicates, and of translating that code into other types of biological molecules. Nucleic acids are even involved in the regulating when these processes happen. Because it is useful to have an understanding of these processes before discussing other aspects of biochemistry, this section gives a brief overview of the **replication** of DNA, **transcription** of DNA into RNA, **translation** of RNA into protein, and regulation of these steps. It also briefly discusses how viruses and retroviruses exploit a cell's own processes to infect the cell and reproduce.

2.2.1 Replication is the process by which cells copy DNA

The genetic material of the cell is DNA, which is organized in chromosomes. Coded in the sequence of bases of DNA is the information that tells the cell how to make proteins, which proteins to make, and even when to make them. Every time a cell divides, this information must be passed on, as accurately as possible. If an organism has 1 billion base pairs of DNA in its genome and copies it with an error rate of 1 error in a million, this will result in 1,000 errors every time a cell divides. In addition, even slight errors in the DNA sequence, termed **mutations**, can disrupt the message encoded in that piece of DNA.

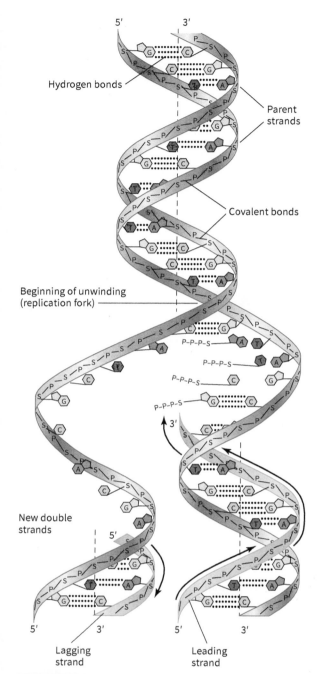

Labels in figure: 5′, 3′, Hydrogen bonds, Parent strands, Covalent bonds, Beginning of unwinding (replication fork), P-P-P-S, 3′, New double strands, 5′, 5′, 3′, 5′, 3′, Lagging strand, Leading strand

FIGURE 2.11 **Semiconservative replication.** Shown is a replication fork. In this view, DNA is being replicated moving from top to bottom. The right strand is the leading strand. As the fork unwinds (moving upward) the hydrogen bonds holding the two strands together are broken. The new strand is being synthesized moving into the divide. The left strand (the lagging strand) must be copied in the other direction in short segments measuring several hundred nucleotides in length. (Snustad; Simmons, *Principles of Genetics*, 6e, copyright 2012, John Wiley & Sons. This material is reproduced with permission of John Wiley & Sons, Inc.)

If a mutation has a negative effect, the organism may be unable to survive or propagate and thus will be unable to pass on its DNA. If, however, a mutation gives an organism some form of advantage in survival or propagation, it is more likely that this mutation will be passed on to the offspring of the organism. This is the central theme of evolution, and it is as true for bacteria living in thermal vents as it is for humans and redwood trees. All living organisms need to be able to replicate their DNA with a low error rate.

DNA replication is semiconservative

As described above, the DNA double helix is comprised of two strands of nucleotides, each of which is held together by phosphodiester bonds between 2-deoxyribose sugars (the sugar-phosphate backbone). These strands run in opposite directions. In both strands, the linkage runs between the 5′ carbon of one deoxyribose, through a phosphate, and then to the 3′ carbon of the next deoxyribose; however, the two strands are aligned so that this bonding runs in opposite directions, as shown in Figure 2.6.

DNA replication must have a low error rate, but how is it possible to copy billions of bases billions of times yet still minimize errors? The answer partially comes from the structure of DNA itself. Because of its double-stranded structure, when DNA is denatured or unraveled, each strand can serve as a template. This makes the job of copying the sequence much easier; it also provides a way to proofread the sequence. Hence, when a cell divides, each daughter cell receives a copy of DNA that contains one strand from the parent and a second strand that has recently been synthesized. This mechanism of replication whereby each of the progeny cells receives a full set of DNA comprising one strand from the parent and one copy is referred to as **semiconservative replication** (Figure 2.11). The process has interesting ramifications because, theoretically, each person has two cells within the body that contain copies of the original DNA inherited when that person was conceived.

DNA replication is bidirectional and occurs in many places at once

The antiparallel structure of DNA presents an interesting dilemma when it comes to replication. DNA polymerases (the enzymatic complexes that replicate DNA) only replicate DNA along a strand in a single direction, from 5′ to 3′. However, a double helix has two strands, each running in opposite directions. How is it possible to replicate both sides in a concerted fashion? The answer is that replication does occur on both strands and the copying is concerted, but not in unison.

As the cell begins to copy its DNA, a bubble is formed where two strands of DNA are unwound, exposing single-stranded DNA to be copied (Figure 2.12). This replication bubble results in two replication forks—regions where the bubble and single strands meet. Replication occurs and spreads outward from these forks.

A replication fork contains a large complex of enzymes and proteins, which bind and coordinate the copying of DNA. Along the **leading strand**, new nucleotides are put into position and esterified by the polymerase in the 5′ to 3′ direction. On the **lagging strand**, a region of several hundred nucleotides is looped out from the polymerase complex. Once a large enough loop has been exposed, this loop is fed through a second unit of polymerase in the opposite direction, again synthesizing the DNA 5′ to 3′. Therefore, on the

A. Prokaryotic cell

Origin

Replication fork

B. Eukaryotic cell

Replication bubble   Replication bubble

Replication
fork

FIGURE 2.12 **Replication bubbles.**   **A.** In prokaryotic cells there are relatively few origins of replication, distinct sequences where replication bubbles initiate. (Snustad; Simmons, *Principles of Genetics,* 6e, copyright 2012, John Wiley & Sons. This material is reproduced with permission of John Wiley & Sons, Inc.) **B.** In eukaryotic cells numerous replication bubbles form in each chromosome in response to cell cycle dependent kinases. (Alters, *Biology: Understanding Life,* 1e, copyright 2006, John Wiley & Sons. This material is reproduced with permission of John Wiley & Sons, Inc)

leading strand, the DNA is continually synthesized as the polymerase complex dives into the replication fork, whereas on the lagging strand, a short (200 bp) stretch of nucleotides is exposed and then filled in. Other enzymes on the lagging strand fill in gaps and join, or ligate, the strand fragments together.

DNA replication is highly regulated and coordinated   In bacteria and other prokaryotes, DNA replication is signaled by the ratios of ATP:ADP or the amount of energy available to the cell and the presence of DnaA, an ATP binding protein. DnaA is one of the proteins found in the replication fork that is involved in the unwinding of DNA. When ATP levels are high, DnaA binds to ATP and a specific sequence in the bacterial genome, known as the DNA box. Binding of the DnaA-ATP complex to the DNA box promotes replication of DNA.

In eukaryotes, DNA replication is coordinated with the cell cycle. It is more complicated than in prokaryotes, and it involves a complex signaling cascade. The key members of this cascade are the cyclins and the cyclin dependent kinases (CDKs)—enzymes that phosphorylate proteins involved in chromosomal organization and replication. Bacteria and yeast contain specific sequences where replication begins, but no such sequences are thought to exist in higher eukaryotes. Instead, the action of several kinases results in the formation of numerous pre-replication complexes, in a process known as **replication licensing**. This process can only occur in the phase of the cell cycle prior to replication; thus, DNA replication is blocked in the other phases.

DNA replication can be rapid but is nevertheless the rate-determining step in cell division. In prokaryotes, DNA polymerases can copy upwards of 1,000 nucleotides per second, moving at a speed that has been said to approach that of a jet engine. This enables a bacterium, such as *Pseudomonas aeruginosa,* to divide every 20 minutes. Eukaryotes, however, have about 1,000-fold more DNA to replicate, and eukaryotic polymerases move 10-fold slower. Replication under these conditions is too much for a single enzyme or complex to accomplish. Instead, replication forks form in thousands of places in a eukaryotic genome. Although replication is slower in eukaryotes than in prokaryotes, eukaryotic cells have astounding propensities for division; for example, some cancer cells or cultured cells in the laboratory can divide every 16 to 20 hours.

2.2.2 Transcription is the copying of DNA into an RNA message

Coded within DNA is the information necessary to synthesize proteins, the diverse molecules that carry out most of the functions of the cell. However, proteins are not made directly from the DNA code. Instead, DNA is first transcribed into RNA, in a process known as transcription. This occurs differently in prokaryotes than it does in eukaryotes (**Figure 2.13**).

A. Prokaryotic cell

B. Eukaryotic cell

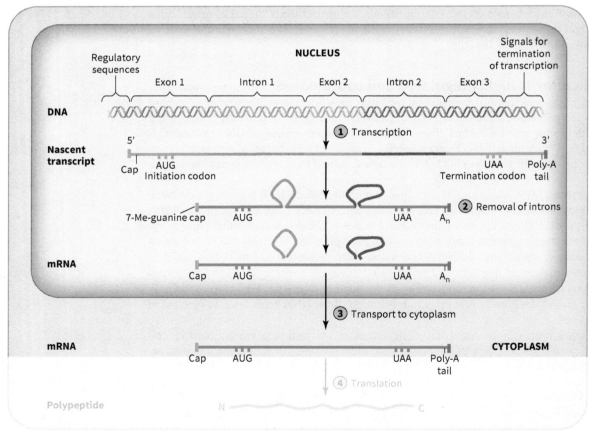

FIGURE 2.13 **Transcription.** **A.** Prokaryotic genes are transcribed into mRNA. (Snustad; Simmons, *Principles of Genetics,* 6e, copyright 2012, John Wiley & Sons. This material is reproduced with permission of John Wiley & Sons, Inc.) **B.** In eukaryotes, nascent RNA must be spliced and processed to generate a mature mRNA. The translation steps shown shaded are illustrated in Figure 2.14. (Snustad; Simmons, *Principles of Genetics,* 6e, copyright 2012, John Wiley & Sons. This material is reproduced with permission of John Wiley & Sons, Inc.)

Not all DNA contains information that codes for protein, but those regions that do code are known as **genes**. In prokaryotes, genes may be organized into **operons**, regions of a chromosome that code for multiple proteins with related purposes.

In prokaryotes, genes comprise a single message that has no gaps or breaks in it. At the front, or the 5′ end, of the gene there are stretches of DNA known as promoter regions. These regulatory sequences can bind to specific proteins known as transcription factors that will regulate the copying of the gene into a messenger RNA (mRNA) by RNA polymerase.

In eukaryotes, the process is somewhat more complicated. Eukaryotic genes are interrupted and divided into regions that code, known as **exons**, and regions that do not code, known as **introns**. As with prokaryotes, transcription factors bind to DNA in the promoter region 5′ of the coding sequence. This elicits binding of an RNA polymerase and copying of a nascent transcript—essentially an mRNA copy of the gene. The nascent message must then be processed, edited to remove the introns, and modified to lend some stability to this molecule. Introns are spliced out of the gene, resulting in a single, uninterrupted message. The 5′ end of the message is modified with a 7-methyl-guanine cap, which is thought to prevent premature degradation of the message. Other modifications are made to the opposite end of the message, with a poly-adenosine (poly-A) tail being enzymatically added to the 3′ end of most messages. This tail is not coded for in the DNA sequence, but its addition is signaled by a specific poly-A sequence at the end of the message. Like the 7-methyl guanine cap, the poly-A tail is thought to stabilize the message.

In the strictest and most classical sense, each gene codes for a single protein. However, in reality, genes in eukaryotes can be differentially spliced, or proteins can be modified after synthesis, resulting in several highly related proteins that can be made from each gene. While we tend to focus on the big picture—DNA to RNA to protein—gene expression is regulated at multiple levels: DNA itself can be modified, and there are many RNAs that regulate the function of genes and other RNAs. There are also organisms, such as retroviruses, that do not follow the central dogma.

The nearly universal nature of the central dogma means that a piece of human DNA or a human gene can be inserted into another organism for study. Species may differ in how they transcribe genes or splice or modify RNAs, but the ability to study a gene or protein by expressing it in a different organism is one of the more powerful tools of biochemistry.

2.2.3 Translation is the synthesis of proteins by ribosomes using an mRNA code

In translation, proteins are synthesized using the code found in an mRNA (**Figure 2.14**). Two other types of RNA figure prominently in this process: tRNA and ribosomal RNA (rRNA). The tRNA are small RNA molecules (approximately 180 nucleotides) that act as adapters. Each amino acid has its own type of tRNA. At the other end of the tRNA is a loop that can "read" the code of the mRNA. These tRNAs transfer a specific amino acid to a growing protein, depending on which amino acid is called for by the code in the mRNA. The macromolecular complex that brings together the mRNA and the tRNA is the **ribosome**, the protein synthesis factory of the cell. Ribosomes themselves are predominantly made of several RNA molecules termed rRNA or ribosomal RNA. These RNA molecules catalyze the addition of new amino acids to the growing amino acid chain of the new protein.

All of biology, from *E.coli* to elephants uses the same code to make proteins. Hence, it is possible to use bacteria to make human proteins from human genes, although in a bacterium, the final product may not be processed in exactly the same way as it would be in a human. In addition, it is possible to put proteins into particular cells to study their function or to better understand disease states and other problems. When studying a protein or gene using these techniques, it is important to keep in mind that the system being studied is not identical to the original, but it may be sufficiently similar to provide meaningful data.

FIGURE 2.14 **Protein synthesis (translation).** Ribosomes, mRNA, and amino acyl tRNAs act in concert to synthesize proteins. The directions of how to formulate the protein are provided by the mRNA. The tRNA molecules act as adapters and help match the amino acid with the proper code on the mRNA. Ribosomes are assemblies of RNA and protein that catalyze the reaction. The transcription steps shown shaded are illustrated in Figure 2.13. (Top: Snustad; Simmons, *Principles of Genetics,* 6e, copyright 2012, John Wiley & Sons. This material is reproduced with permission of John Wiley & Sons, Inc. Bottom: Wessner, DuPont, Charles, Neufeld, *Microbiology,* 2e, copyright 2017, John Wiley & Sons. This material is reproduced with permission of John Wiley & Sons, Inc.)

2.2.4 Regulation of replication, transcription, and translation is critical to an organism's survival and propagation

As we go through the course of a day, our needs will change. For example, we may need to consume food for energy, move from one place to another, or respond to environmental challenges. Likewise, as we grow and mature throughout development, we express different genes or alter the levels of gene expression. To be evolutionarily successful, an organism must be able to respond to its environment, grow and develop, and ultimately reproduce and transmit its genes to the next generation.

FIGURE 2.15 **Riboswitches are one mechanism to regulate gene expression.** A riboswitch consists of a complex structure formed by the 5′ end of the mRNA. This structure can bind to a small molecule, resulting in a structural change that alters transcription. (Wessner, DuPont, Charles, Neufeld, *Microbiology,* 2e, copyright 2017, John Wiley & Sons. This material is reproduced with permission of John Wiley & Sons, Inc.)

The sections above discussed how DNA is replicated and noted that different proteins known as transcription factors bind to promoter sequences in DNA, either upregulating or downregulating gene expression or the production of mRNA. However, there are several other ways in which genes may be regulated (**Figure 2.15**).

Some genes use a riboswitch. There are several different types of riboswitch, but each involves a segment of the mRNA folding into a complex shape that will bind to a small molecule, affecting the ability of the mRNA to be translated. Through this mechanism, some genes can be regulated after an mRNA is synthesized.

Other genes may be regulated by short RNA molecules that complement the mRNA, forming a double-stranded mRNA structure. These RNAs interfere with transcription or lead to message degradation, in a process known as RNA interference (RNAi). This process lends itself to several laboratory applications, and because of its ease of use and relatively low cost, it is rapidly changing how biochemical experiments are being conducted.

It used to be thought that once a gene was activated, a protein product would result. Now, it is clear that genes can be regulated in several different ways. It is also clear that proteins vary in their stability, with some having lifetimes on the order of the life of the organism and others lasting only a few seconds before being degraded. Additionally, some proteins are synthesized in a futile cycle; that is, they are synthesized and then rapidly degraded unless stabilized by the presence of some other molecule.

2.2.5 | Viruses and retroviruses use the cell's own machinery to reproduce

Viruses are small pathogenic assemblies of nucleic acids, proteins, and occasionally lipids that require a cellular host for replication. Those that contain DNA or RNA as their genetic material are typically categorized as **viruses**, whereas those that employ RNA as their genetic material but go through a DNA intermediate at some point in their life cycle are categorized as **retroviruses**. Viruses invade a cell through one of several different mechanisms; once inside a cell, the virus integrates its genetic material with that of the host. The virus then uses the host's own replication, transcription, and translation machinery to produce copies of viral nucleic acids and viral proteins. These assemble into mature virions, which are released from the cell and can then infect other cells in the organism, or other organisms.

WORKED PROBLEM 2.2 | How do mutations affect the central dogma?

DNA can be chemically damaged by exposure to UV light. As illustrated below, adjacent molecules of thymine in one strand can become cross-linked to one another, forming a cyclobutane ring.

How might this type of mutation affect replication, transcription, and translation?

Strategy Examine the structure shown. Think about what happens during replication, transcription, and translation. How would these processes be affected?

Solution Thymine dimers are a common DNA lesion. The formation of the cyclobutane ring induces strain in the DNA backbone, resulting in a bulge. In theory, the covalent linkage between the thymines could affect replication, in that a polymerase may not be able to read the thymine dimer as well as it could single thymines. Depending on where the mutation occurs in the DNA, it could affect transcription. Again, an RNA polymerase may have difficulty reading through the thymine dimer. Because translation takes place after gene transcription, it is unlikely that the mutation will affect translation.

Follow-up question Some other mutations generate oxidatively damaged or alkylated bases. How might modification to the amine or carbonyl groups of the base give rise to problems in replication, transcription, and translation?

2.2 Summary

- The double helix of DNA contains two strands that run in opposite directions. In replication, each of these strands serves as a template for a new daughter strand.
- DNA replication is semiconservative, with each progeny cell receiving one strand of new DNA and one strand of parental DNA.
- DNA replication occurs at replication forks, that is, regions where DNA has been unraveled.
- In a replication fork, the leading strand is copied as the fork unwinds. On the opposite lagging strand, DNA synthesis occurs in short fragments as the DNA is exposed. These are subsequently linked together to form one long strand.
- Transcription is the synthesis of RNA molecules from DNA. Transcription factors indicate to an RNA polymerase where to bind and start synthesizing an mRNA copy of the gene.
- In eukaryotes, mRNA molecules are modified and edited before they are translated into protein. Modifications include the splicing out of introns and the addition of a 7-methyl guanosine cap or poly-A tail.
- Translation refers to the process by which the information encoded in the mRNA molecule is translated into protein. Ribosomes, large, catalytic complexes of RNA, and tRNA, adapter molecules that insert the proper amino acid, are also important in this process.
- Viruses and retroviruses use the cell's own machinery to replicate and reproduce. This often means integration of the viral genome into the host.

2.2 Concept Check

- Describe in basic terms how replication, transcription, and translation occur.
- Explain how organisms regulate replication, transcription, and translation.

2.3 The Manipulation of Nucleic Acids Has Transformed Biochemistry

The commonality of the central dogma and the universal nature of the genetic code have had powerful implications for biochemistry and medicine. It has been said that in the first half of the twentieth century, science belonged to physics, but in the second half, the crown was abruptly passed to other fields such as biochemistry. Part of this succession is due to a biochemist's ability to manipulate the environment of the cell, and even multicellular organisms, with molecular precision. This section describes several techniques that can be used to manipulate or alter DNA, RNA, or proteins in the organism. These techniques are the basis of modern biochemistry.

2.3.1 DNA can be easily manipulated and analyzed *in vitro*

DNA is vital to life because it codes for the proteins that comprise the cell. DNA passes from generation to generation and is synonymous with many things we may consider deeply personal. Nevertheless, DNA is in fact just another chemical and, as such, can be manipulated in the laboratory. Advances in organic synthesis, molecular biology, protein expression, and enzymology have taken DNA manipulations from the advanced research laboratory to DNA instruction at the elementary school level in less than a generation. This section discusses how we can manipulate and analyze DNA.

Short DNA fragments can be synthesized chemically   Short pieces of DNA (up to approximately 70 nucleotides long) can be synthesized chemically in a technique known as solid phase oligonucleotide synthesis (**Figure 2.16**). In this technique a nucleotide is bound to a resin or bead that is trapped in a reactor. A second nucleotide is added and reacts with the first nucleotide. Further reactions with the second nucleotide are stopped by a protecting group. Unreacted materials are washed away, and the dinucleotide bound to the column is left behind in the reactor. The protecting group is removed from the dinucleotide, and the reaction is repeated with a new nucleotide. In this way, the oligonucleotide is built up one nucleotide at a time. Initially, this process was undertaken in the laboratory by hand; today, however, robotic devices can perform all of the necessary steps, making it possible to generate these molecules literally at the push of a few buttons.

The oligonucleotides generated through solid phase synthesis have multiple applications in the laboratory.

DNA can be amplified using the polymerase chain reaction   The **polymerase chain reaction** (PCR) is one of the most powerful tools developed for the manipulation of DNA fragments (**Figure 2.17**). PCR makes it possible to simply amplify or create millions of copies of DNA in a short period of time.

FIGURE 2.16 Solid phase nucleotide synthesis.   Solid phase nucleotide synthesis proceeds through the addition of protected bases to a nucleotide affixed to a solid support (a bead). The newly added group is deprotected with mild acid, and the process is repeated with a new nucleotide.

FIGURE 2.17 **Polymerase chain reaction.** Template DNA, primers, polymerase, and deoxyribonucleotides are mixed together and placed in a thermocycler, which cycles the temperatures and times precisely as needed. As the reactions proceed, the DNA is denatured, primers anneal, and polymerase extends. After 25 to 30 cycles this can result in a million-fold amplification of a single DNA sequence. (Snustad; Simmons, *Principles of Genetics,* 6e, copyright 2012, John Wiley & Sons. This material is reproduced with permission of John Wiley & Sons, Inc.)

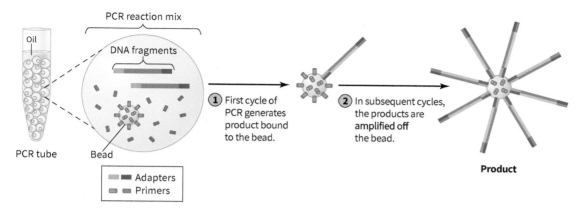

FIGURE 2.18 **Emulsion PCR.** Fragments of DNA are ligated to adapters. The fragments are emulsified with beads coated with one of the primers and PCR reagents in such a way to ensure there is only a single copy of DNA per emulsion droplet. The fragments melt and then anneal to the bead through a primer that recognizes the adapter. The PCR reaction copies the strand, and the reaction is repeated, each time generating a copy of the fragment bound to the bead.

Included in the reaction mix for PCR are:

- *template DNA*—the DNA that is going to be copied
- *primers*—short oligonucleotide sequences that flank the region to be copied
- *a polymerase*—the enzyme that replicates the DNA
- *deoxynucleotides*—the building blocks of DNA

The polymerase used in PCR has been isolated from thermophilic organisms that live in hot springs or near volcanic vents at the bottom of the ocean. In contrast to most enzymes, these polymerases will not lose activity when heated, an essential property for this reaction.

The final piece of the PCR reaction is the instrument needed to carry out the experiment. A thermocycler heats and cools the sample to facilitate DNA amplification.

First, DNA is heated to denature it, melting the double helix into two single strands. Next, the sample is cooled to allow the primers to anneal (bind) to the template strand. Then, the sample is warmed again slightly to activate the polymerase, which extends from the primers to generate a copy of the parent DNA. This cycle is repeated 25 to 30 times, resulting in over a million-fold amplification of the original molecule.

A variant of PCR is emulsion PCR (Figure 2.18). In this technique, the primers for the reaction are coupled to a microscopic agarose bead. The beads, PCR reaction mix, and DNA are emulsified in oil so that each individual bead will generate a specific PCR product. These reactions are often used to amplify genomic DNA in modern genomic DNA sequencing.

PCR is such a versatile technique that it is commonly coupled with or used as the basis of many other techniques, including DNA sequencing, genotyping, disease identification, and forensic science.

First-generation DNA sequencing technologies employed chain termination

Sequencing of a polymer such as a protein or nucleic acid is the determination of the order of the monomers that make up that polymer. One of the earliest successful systems for DNA sequencing was the Sanger method or dideoxy system (Figure 2.19). It is comprised of a sequencing mixture containing a DNA polymerase, a template to be sequenced, an oligonucleotide or sequencing primer from which the polymerase can extend, and radiolabeled deoxynucleotide triphosphates. Sequencing primers bind specifically to one region of DNA, ensuring that the region downstream will be the one that is sequenced. This mixture is divided into four reactions, and a small amount of a different 2′3′-dideoxynucleotide triphosphate is added to each. Because these nucleotides lack a hydroxyl group on the 3′ carbon of the deoxyribose ring, the polymerase is unable to extend from one of these nucleotides, which effectively

FIGURE 2.19 **First-generation DNA sequencing using the Sanger dideoxy method.** **A.** Sanger sequencing employs dideoxy nucleotides that lack hydroxyl groups on both the 2′ and 3′ carbons, blocking elongation once one of them has been incorporated. (Wessner, DuPont, Charles, Neufeld, *Microbiology,* 2e, copyright 2017, John Wiley & Sons. This material is reproduced with permission of John Wiley & Sons, Inc.) **B.** Sequencing using this method employs four different reactions, each of which contains a strand to be synthesized, a sequencing primer from which the DNA strand can be synthesized, a polymerase to make the new strand, and the four different deoxynucleotides. Each reaction also contains small amounts of a single dideoxynucleotide. The four different reactions are separated on a gel. Each band terminates with a known nucleotide (one of the dideoxynucleotides from the reaction), enabling the reading of the DNA sequence. (Wessner, DuPont, Charles, Neufeld, *Microbiology,* 2e, copyright 2017, John Wiley & Sons. This material is reproduced with permission of John Wiley & Sons, Inc.)

becomes a chain terminator, blocking further elongation from that chain. Because we know which dideoxynucleotide is in the reaction, we know which base is found at the end of that chain. The products of the four reactions are separated, based on size, on a polyacrylamide electrophoresis gel. Gel electrophoresis is a technique in which molecules are separated in a gel using an electric current. A film exposed to this gel contains bands that show the order of the bases, one at a time. In the mid-1990s, an accomplished investigator could obtain about 200 to 300 bases per set of reactions.

Fluorescent DNA sequencing permitted automation and facilitated modern genomic studies

The next evolution of DNA sequencing technology employed fluorescently tagged dye terminator nucleotides (**Figure 2.20**). Because four different fluorophores could be used, only one reaction mix was needed. In addition, the strands were separated with a capillary column rather than a gel. The entire system could now be automated, initially running as many as 384 samples at once. Thanks to technical advances, by the early 2000s this method generated 500 to 600 bases per reaction, and, by the end of the decade, the number of bases increased to almost 1,000. This technology greatly advanced sequencing, and it enabled the completion of the human genome project in 2003, two years ahead of schedule.

FIGURE 2.20 **Fluorescent PCR-based sequencing.**
A. Fluorescent sequencing is similar to dideoxy sequencing but employs nucleotides that terminate in a nucleotide coupled to a fluorescent dye. There are four dyes used, one for each different nucleotide. (Wessner, DuPont, Charles, Neufeld, *Microbiology,* 2e, copyright 2017, John Wiley & Sons. This material is reproduced with

permission of John Wiley & Sons, Inc.) **B.** The products of the reaction are separated based on size and the results automatically detected and presented as a chromatogram corresponding to the nucleotide sequence. (Wessner, DuPont, Charles, Neufeld, *Microbiology,* 2e, copyright 2017, John Wiley & Sons. This material is reproduced with permission of John Wiley & Sons, Inc.)

① DNA is fragmented and ligated to adapters.

Adapters

Fragmented genomic DNA

② Primers are bound to the plate. DNA adapters anneal to the primers.

Adapters

Single DNA strand

Primers

Plate

③ Bridge PCR extends from a primer on the plate.

anneal → extend → denature → repeat 25× → denature

PCR

④ Repeating PCR generates clusters of amplified products.

Cluster of DNA strands

⑤ Sequencing primers are annealed to the free ends of the amplified DNA. Protected fluorescent nucleotides are incorporated and read one at a time.

Fluorescent nucleotides
A
C
G
T

Plate viewed from the top

First reaction

⑥ Removal of first fluorescent signal and protecting group.

Second reaction

⑦ Removal of second fluorescent signal and protecting group.

Third reaction

The sequence of this cluster is A, G, T.

FIGURE 2.21 **Illumina sequencing.** Genomic DNA is fragmented and ligated to a linker. The other end of the linker has a different primer and both are bound to the surface of a microscope slide. Next, "bridge" PCR is used to amplify single spots on the slide between the two adapters. Sequencing is done using fluorescent dyes, and the results are read optically. Individual spots will light up in different colors on the slide, corresponding to the four different nucleotides.

Modern parallel sequencing technologies sequence millions of samples at once
Modern sequencing technologies enable the sequencing of an entire genome within days or weeks. These technologies employ from hundreds of thousands to billions of parallel reactions, which are then read optically from a microscope slide. The sequence data generated are found in short stretches, which are then assembled into a complete genome using advanced computer algorithms. This section discusses two of these technologies: Illumina sequencing, and SOLiD or two-base encoding.

In Illumina sequencing, genomic DNA is fragmented and ligated to adapters (**Figure 2.21**). These double-stranded fragments are denatured and annealed to the surface of a plate that is densely coated with both adapters. Bridge PCR, or amplification that bridges the two adapters on the surface, is carried out to amplify single copies into small spots termed "clusters." The DNA content of the cluster is identified by sequencing all of the amplified clusters at once, but one nucleotide at a time. Modified versions of fluorescent deoxynucleotides are added; each of the four different types of deoxynucleotides has a different fluorophore attached, plus a protecting group on the 3′ hydroxyl. After the sequencing reaction has been performed, the plate is read optically to determine which color (i.e., nucleotide) is present on each spot. The fluorescent dye together with the protecting group is then removed. Sequencing using Illumina technology can take upwards of ten days to complete, but an enormous amount of data is generated. Between 25 and 250 bases can be read per spot, and upwards of 3 billion samples can be analyzed in a single experiment.

SOLiD or two-base encoding is a ligase-based sequencing technology (**Figure 2.22**). SOLiD begins with DNA fragmentation and an emulsion PCR step. The beads are deposited on a slide, and a primer is added. The first set of primers shares the adapter sequence flanking the region to be sequenced; the second is eight bases in length and has a fluorescent

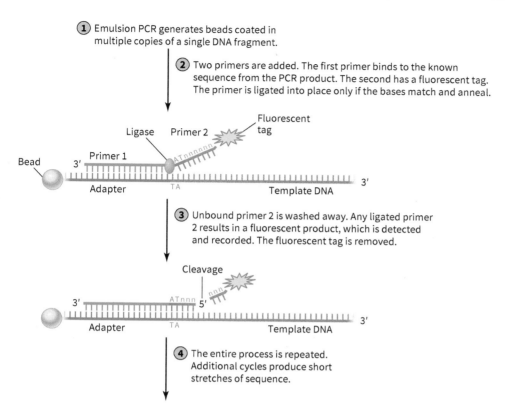

① Emulsion PCR generates beads coated in multiple copies of a single DNA fragment.

② Two primers are added. The first primer binds to the known sequence from the PCR product. The second has a fluorescent tag. The primer is ligated into place only if the bases match and anneal.

③ Unbound primer 2 is washed away. Any ligated primer 2 results in a fluorescent product, which is detected and recorded. The fluorescent tag is removed.

④ The entire process is repeated. Additional cycles produce short stretches of sequence.

FIGURE 2.22 SOLiD sequencing. SOLiD sequencing first employs emulsion PCR to generate beads from which to sequence. Two primers are added. The first is complementary to the template, while the second consists of eight nucleotides and a fluorescent tag. Ligase is added. Should the second primer bind and be ligated, the sequence will now fluoresce with the color of that tag. The samples are deprotected, and the next primer is added. Through successive cycles it becomes possible to sequence short sequences and ultimately sequence the entire genome. (Oelkerding, K.V., Dames, S.A., Durtschi, J.Y., Next-Generation Sequencing: From Basic Research to Diagnostics, *Clinical Chemistry* Apr 2009, 55 (4) 641–658; DOI: 10.1373/clinchem.2008.112789. Reproduced with permission from the American Association for Clinical Chemistry.)

group attached to it. If the two nucleotides at the 3′ end are complementary to the DNA template being sequenced, they will anneal. Ligase is added, and if the second primer anneals, it will be ligated with the first. The remaining primers are washed away. Next, fluorescence is detected wherever annealing and ligation has occurred. The fluorescent tags are removed using a nuclease and the cycle is repeated, building up short stretches of sequence, two bases at a time. Use of different primer combinations enables completion of the sequence. Typically, each spot can have somewhere around 50 bases sequenced using this technique, and upwards of 1.5 million spots can be analyzed. Run times are one to two weeks for an entire genome.

Each of these technologies has its strengths and weaknesses. Because of two-base recognition, SOLiD is better than other techniques at detecting single nucleotide polymorphisms and is less expensive per base, but it is slower than comparable techniques. All of these technologies take advantage of computer analysis of data for quality control and analysis, and all use computers to assemble the final genome from the sequences acquired.

High throughput sequencing is already being used in the clinic, as is discussed in **Medical Biochemistry: Diagnosing neonatal diseases with DNA**.

Medical Biochemistry

Diagnosing neonatal diseases with DNA

One in 20 children born in the United States has some form of inherited disease. Many diseases in children or adults have a progression to them, but in newborns, an inherited disease often presents suddenly and early, sometimes within hours of birth. Newborns are unable to verbally communicate what is wrong, and their tiny size and fragile nature make invasive procedures undesirable. Classical diagnosis of these diseases, when possible, can often take weeks to months, and requires the patient be seen by multiple specialists who deal in identifying specific classes of illnesses.

Several studies have now used next-generation DNA sequencing to diagnose these patients. In this technique, a small sample of the patient's blood is used to obtain a DNA sample. The DNA is sequenced and a set of specific genes, either mitochondrial genes or those related to inherited disease, are analyzed. This approach has several benefits. First, it simplifies the DNA analysis. Instead of having to reconstruct an entire genome, researchers can focus on the parts more likely to be affected. Second, it avoids the ethical pitfalls of obtaining the entire DNA sequence, because genes linked with other diseases such as cancer will not be analyzed. Finally, and most important, it streamlines the diagnosis. Instead of focusing on every gene, researchers narrow in on those likely to be causal. Using this technology, it is currently possible to sequence and analyze a group of 3,500 genes in a little more than a day.

More than 7,500 inherited diseases are known and, although treatments are still unavailable for most of them, knowing the prognosis offers comfort to some families. DNA sequencing studies are useful in genetic counseling, because they can help in identifying recessive disorders the parent may be carrying or diseases that were previously unknown. Perhaps the greatest benefit of such studies is that they indicate a future direction of medicine, in which personal and individual diagnoses become possible

DNA fragments can be cut and ligated using a wide array of enzymes

Knowledge of DNA sequences is most valuable when it can be used in the laboratory. DNA can be manipulated using a series of enzymes (**Figure 2.23**) that were originally identified in nature. These enzymes assist in DNA replication or serve as part of a primitive immune system for bacteria, but they are now commercially available. In many ways, this is similar to scrapbooking. In a craft or hobby store there are aisles which have numerous different patterns of scissors or paper cutters and different types of glue or adhesive, all dedicated to scrapbooking. This is analogous to what can be achieved in the laboratory as fragments of DNA are cut up and joined together (**Table 2.1**).

The enzymes that cut DNA are called **restriction enzymes**. They were originally identified as components of bacteria that enabled growth in the presence of some bacteriophages, restricting the impact of the virus. Restriction enzymes are endonucleases; that is, they cut inside a strand of nucleotides. Palindromes, such as RACECAR, are words or phrases that read the same forward as they do backward. Restriction enzymes typically recognize a palindromic sequence 4 to 8 nucleotides long and cleave the sugar-phosphate backbone on both strands, leaving either a blunt end or an overhang, referred to as the sticky end.

DNA ligases are enzymes that seal breaks in the sugar-phosphate backbone. They do not fill in missing bases but can join two blunt or complementary sticky ends together.

Copying DNA in a living organism is termed **cloning**. Subcloning involves copying only a piece of the whole, for example, a fragment of a gene. The term "cloning" is also used to mean creation of a copy of a single cell, such as a bacterial or cultured mammalian cell, or creation of a copy of an organism, such as a sheep from the DNA of a single parent cell. Copying DNA in an organism differs from amplifying a piece of DNA in a PCR reaction. Inside the organism, it is possible to copy DNA with much higher fidelity, that is, with fewer errors, and

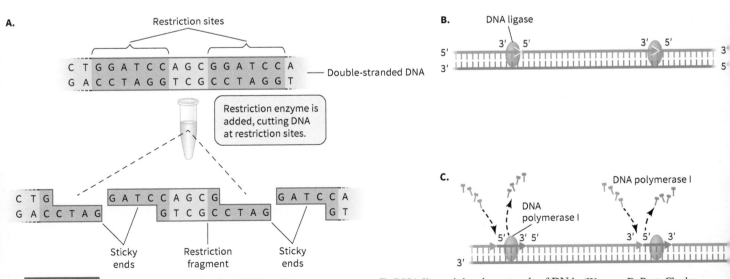

FIGURE 2.23 **Enzymes that manipulate DNA.** Numerous enzymes are commercially available to manipulate and synthesize DNA. **A.** Restriction enzymes recognize a four to eight base DNA sequence and cleave both strands of the phosphodiester backbone. (Alters, *Biology: Understanding Life*, 1e, copyright 2006, John Wiley & Sons. This material is reproduced with permission of John Wiley & Sons, Inc)

B. DNA ligase joins the cut ends of DNA. (Wessner, DuPont, Charles, Neufeld, *Microbiology*, 2e, copyright 2017, John Wiley & Sons. This material is reproduced with permission of John Wiley & Sons, Inc.) **C.** DNA polymerase synthesizes a new strand of DNA. (Wessner, DuPont, Charles, Neufeld, *Microbiology*, 2e, copyright 2017, John Wiley & Sons. This material is reproduced with permission of John Wiley & Sons, Inc.)

TABLE 2.1   Enzymes Commonly Used in Molecular Biology to Manipulate Nucleic Acids

Enzyme	Purpose/Function
Restriction enzymes	Cuts specific DNA sequences
Ligase	Joins two DNA fragments together
Polymerase (Klenow fragment)	Generates a copy of one strand of DNA from a primer and a template
Thermophilic polymerases	Polymerizes enzyme in polymerase chain reaction (PCR)
Topoisomerase	Unwinds DNA in the cell; used to partially join DNA fragments; used in place of ligase in some cloning applications
Reverse transcriptase	Converts RNA into DNA; used in producing cDNA libraries and reverse transcriptase PCR

to copy much larger pieces than is currently possible in a test tube. Bacteria are often used as part of the process of manipulating DNA.

Cutting and piecing DNA together would be easier if we had some means of holding onto the pieces like a sort of cover to the scrapbook. Nature has provided this as well. Plasmids are short (2 to 5 kb) loops of bacterial DNA that bacteria use to exchange genes with one another (**Figure 2.24**). In the laboratory, plasmids such as pBluescript II have been intentionally rearranged and mutated to provide a handy tool for DNA manipulation. These plasmids contain:

- an origin of replication sequence, called an *ori* sequence, which enables the plasmid to be replicated in bacteria
- a selectable marker, that is, a gene that provides a trait to the bacteria so that only the bacteria containing the plasmid will grow and reproduce
- a cloning site, that is, an engineered series of restriction sites that facilitate the insertion of the DNA fragment of interest

Plasmids may also have other features, depending on the research in which they are employed. For example, some plasmids have been optimized for cloning DNA, whereas others contain sequences that drive high levels of expression of mRNA, and subsequently of protein.

Plasmids are one method that can be used to clone DNA. Other methods that offer options for cloning larger fragments of DNA referred to as vectors include bacterial artificial chromosomes (BACs), yeast artificial chromosomes (YACs), and cosmids (a fusion of a plasmid with the *cos* sequences of a bacteriophage).

2.3.2 | DNA can be used to drive protein expression

This section explains how the information coded within DNA fragments can be used to alter the biochemistry of a cell or organism. For example, a cell or organism can be manipulated to produce proteins it usually lacks, or the information can be altered and tests undertaken to see how the alterations affect the proteins coded for by the gene.

Genes can be expressed or overexpressed in cultured cells   All organisms use basically the same genetic code. Because of this, it is possible to use the pieces of DNA produced in the laboratory to make RNA or protein for subsequent study. The first step is to get the pieces of DNA into the cells, a process known in bacteria as **transformation** and in eukaryotic cells as **transfection**. In several instances, the same technique can be used on either bacterial or eukaryotic cells.

FIGURE 2.24   Plasmid DNA.   Plasmids are short (less than 10 kb) circular pieces of DNA. Shown is pBluescript II, a common plasmid used in cloning. Plasmids all contain an *ori* sequence (an origin of replication) necessary for propagation in bacteria, and at least one selectable marker. Most other plasmids also contain a multiple cloning site (MCS), an engineered stretch of DNA consisting of multiple restriction sites adjacent to one another.

A.

Electroporation

1. Mix the plasmid with bacteria in the electroporation cuvette.

Cuvette

2. Select the transformed bacteria.

Colonies of bacteria

Chemical transformation

"Hybrid" plasmid

Human DNA containing gene of interest

1. Mix the plasmid with bacteria; some bacteria take up the plasmid.

Bacteria and plasmids in growth media

2. Select the transformed bacteria.

Colonies of bacteria

B.
Microinjection

Recombinant viral-mediated gene delivery

Cytoplasm

Nucleus

Electroporation

Plasma membrane

Lipofection

FIGURE 2.25 **Transformation, transfection, and infection.** **A.** Bacterial cells can be transformed either by electroporation or using chemical means. (Alters, *Biology: Understanding Life,* 1e, copyright 2006, John Wiley & Sons. This material is reproduced with permission of John Wiley & Sons, Inc) **B.** Eukaryotic cells can be infected with a virus or transfected using electroporation, cationic lipids, or microinjection. (Wessner, DuPont, Charles, Neufeld, *Microbiology,* 2e, copyright 2017, John Wiley & Sons. This material is reproduced with permission of John Wiley & Sons, Inc.)

DNA can be introduced into cells through electrical, chemical, or physical methods, or by using an engineered virus (**Figure 2.25**).

In **electroporation**, cells are suspended in a weak buffer in a cuvette with the DNA to be electroporated. A special power supply known as the electroporator sends short, strong pulses of electricity through the cuvette. These pulses are often several hundred volts and are on the order of milliseconds long. In theory, these pulses temporarily blow holes into the plasma membrane of cells and allow the cells to acquire DNA or RNA. Other molecules, such as drugs and dyes, have also been electroporated. Electroporation can be used with bacteria as well as eukaryotic cells.

In addition to electroporation, bacteria can be treated to make them chemically competent to absorb DNA. This involves treating the bacteria with different salt solutions at low temperature. Transformation efficiencies using this method are typically 10-fold lower than electroporation, but the technique is simple and effective, and does not require additional equipment.

There are several means to transform eukaryotic cells chemically. The earliest used diethylaminoethyl (DEAE) dextran or calcium phosphate. In the DEAE technique, DNA was complexed to microscopic particles of dextran, a high molecular weight carbohydrate coated with DEAE groups. The positively charged groups in DEAE attracted the negatively charged DNA and the molecules formed a complex, which was then applied to cells. These complexes were taken up by cells through endocytosis.

A second early technique that is still commonly used is calcium phosphate precipitation. DNA is mixed with a calcium-containing buffer to form DNA–calcium complexes. Following incubation, a phosphate-containing buffer is added. The calcium and phosphate ions react to form a precipitate of microscopic crystals containing the DNA. As with DEAE-dextran transfection, these crystals are thought to be absorbed by the cell through endocytosis.

The main obstacle to transfection is the insertion of DNA into the cell, that is, getting past the plasma membrane. A more recent innovation uses DNA complexed to cationic lipids to smuggle the DNA into the cell. The plasma membrane of the cell is largely composed of phospholipids. These phospholipids form a hydrophobic layer through which anything entering the cell must pass. Cationic lipids have a positively charged end that binds to the sugar-phosphate backbone of DNA, generating a liposome, or a vesicle of lipid, surrounding the DNA. The liposomes can fuse to the plasma membrane and result in high transfection efficiencies (the percentage of cells that take up the DNA molecule). This technique is sometimes referred to as lipofection.

A third means of introducing DNA is to coat it onto microscopic particles of gold or tungsten and physically blast these particles into the cell using a pulse of helium gas. This technique is referred to as biolistics (from "biological" and "ballistics"). This is often effective on cells that can be otherwise hard to transfect. A handheld version of this device called the Gene Gun is commercially available.

One final method that is commonly used to introduce DNA is to alter the genetic sequence of a virus and use that altered virus to deliver genes; this technique is known as recombinant viral-mediated gene delivery. Several viruses, including lentivirus and adenovirus, are commonly used for this procedure. The technique involves modifying the viral genome so that the DNA lacks the genes coding for proteins the virus would use to replicate, and instead inserting a gene coding for the protein of interest. This new piece of viral DNA is transfected into a packaging cell line (a cell line that has been modified to produce the viral proteins but lacks the viral DNA). When the two come together, the packaging cell can now produce a virus, but the virus lacks the proteins needed for replication and instead produces the protein of interest.

Modified viruses are currently the gold standard in gene delivery. They often have high transfection efficiencies and can transfect cells that are otherwise difficult to work with. However, some of these viruses are human pathogens and could, without proper precautions, contaminate and infect people exposed to the virus.

Once a plasmid of DNA with the proper sequence has been put into a cell, that cell's native polymerases and ribosomes will use the instructions coded within it to produce protein. However, with this modification alone, the effect will be short lived. Unless there is selective pressure on the cell, most cells will stop producing protein from a plasmid relatively quickly. Therefore, the plasmid is constructed to contain a selectable marker, a

FIGURE 2.26 **Antibiotics used in selecting cells.** Ampicillin, kanamycin, puromycin, and geneticin are all antibiotics that are used to select transformed cells. Ampicillin and kanamycin are used on prokaryotes, while puromycin and geneticin are used to treat eukaryotic cells.

gene which codes for a protein that enables cells to survive in an environment where others cannot. This gene is often an antibiotic resistance marker but can also be an enzyme that plays an important role in metabolism, such as in the production of an amino acid (**Figure 2.26**). Cells that lose this piece of DNA or stop producing the proteins coded for by the plasmid will not survive.

In addition to selection, expression in some cell types (typically eukaryotic cells) can be divided broadly into two categories: transient and stable. All transfections begin as transient transfections. In the first 24 to 48 hours following transfection, the transfection rate is highest and the proteins will be strongly expressed. However, as time goes on, the rate of transfection drops, as does the expression rate. To keep expression at a high level, cells are selected using an antibiotic appropriate for the resistance gene. In eukaryotic cells, this is often puromycin or geneticin. After treatment with the antibiotic for several rounds of cell division, the plasmid of interest is presumed to have integrated into the host chromosome and to have passed from one generation to the next. This is referred to as stable transfection.

Entire organisms can be manipulated to express genes of interest

So far, this chapter has focused on bacterial and eukaryotic cells, but technology exists to express genes in more complex organisms. In many animals, zygotes are large enough that DNA can be injected into them (**Figure 2.27**). As with transfections of other cell types, if the piece of DNA in question is able to integrate into the host genome, it will be passed from cell to cell as the organism grows and develops, resulting in an organism that contains this DNA in every cell of its body. Again, depending on the promoter sequence used to drive expression, this can mean expression in all cells or in only a select organ or tissue. This sort of experiment results in a **transgenic organism**.

Transgenic plants can be made using a somewhat different technique, also shown in Figure 2.27. For example, the bacterial plant pathogen *Agrobacter tumefaciens* has sequences that can recombine with the plant's genome. It is possible to generate a plasmid containing these sequences, modify the plasmid, and transform *Agrobacter* using the techniques previously discussed. Cultures of *Agrobacter* are then incubated with cultured plant cells. The bacteria infect some of the plant cells, and the new piece of DNA is incorporated into the plant genome. Using this technology, genes have been incorporated that can slow the ripening process, increase yield, increase resistance to plant diseases, and increase the nutrition found in plants. Currently, over 16% of all crops in the United States are genetically modified in some way. There is continuing debate and controversy at the ethical, scientific, legal, and political levels as to whether this is a good idea. A discussion of some of the ramifications of genetically modified organisms can be found in **Societal and Ethical Biochemistry: Genetically modified organisms**.

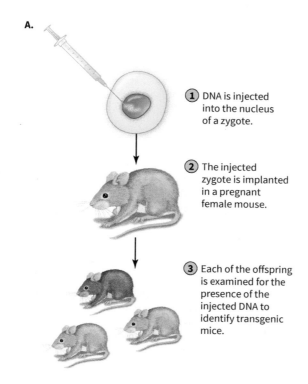

A.

1. DNA is injected into the nucleus of a zygote.

2. The injected zygote is implanted in a pregnant female mouse.

3. Each of the offspring is examined for the presence of the injected DNA to identify transgenic mice.

B.

Agrobacterium tumefaciens

Plant cell

Bacterial plasmid DNA

Plant cell DNA

3. *Agrobacterium* transfers DNA to plant cell.

1. Remove discs from plant leaf.

2. Incubate leaf disks with genetically engineered *Agrobacterium*.

4. Select for plants that have acquired genes from *Agrobacterium* and grow into mature plants.

Transgenic plant

FIGURE 2.27 Transgenic organisms. Transgenic organisms can be made by different methods depending on the organism. **A.** Transgenic mice can be made by injecting DNA into a fertilized mouse egg prior to cell division. (Snustad; Simmons, *Principles of Genetics,* 6e, copyright 2012, John Wiley & Sons. This material is reproduced with permission of John Wiley & Sons, Inc.) **B.** Transgenic plants are often made using engineered *Agrobacter* lines. The modification is made to plasmid DNA, the DNA is introduced to *Agrobacter,* and then the bacteria infect and incorporate the DNA into the plant genome. (Allison, *Fundamental Molecular Biology,* 2e, copyright 2012, John Wiley & Sons. This material is reproduced with permission of John Wiley & Sons, Inc)

Societal and Ethical Biochemistry

Genetically modified organisms

Often, science becomes popularized. This probably occurs for a variety of reasons including nationalism, power, or some great success like landing on the Moon. Other times there are causes that we embrace because we feel they personally impact us or impact others. Examples of these causes include things that affect our health or impact the environment. One of the most controversial science issues of the past decade has been genetically modified organisms (GMOs).

dscz/Getty Images

GMOs are organisms that have had their genomes manipulated in the laboratory, usually through the introduction of genes from other organisms or the manipulation of genes to alter expression levels. Since the beginning of agriculture, humanity has been breeding and crossbreeding food crops and livestock to bring out favorable characteristics. Traditionally, this has been done through selective breeding. Although few people look at golden retrievers or tulips as genetic manipulations, they are the result of tens of generations of selective breeding and inbreeding.

Scientists have now identified genes that impart desirable traits and, using the tools of molecular biology, are able to introduce the desired genes into host organisms. This type of genetic engineering has been used to create crops that are resistant to particular diseases or herbicides (Roundup Ready corn or soybeans) or produce their own pesticides (Bt Cotton). Genetic engineering also been used to create animals that have a high growth rate (AquAdvantage salmon) or produce less waste (EnviroPig).

In many ways this sounds ideal. We can grow foods using less energy and chemicals, and feed more people on an increasingly crowded planet. However, the situation is more complex. In theory at least, genes inserted into GMO could be passed on to other related species, for example from corn to grasses, resulting in other species carrying the modified trait, such as resistance to herbicides. In the case of GMO salmon, the concern is that the modified organism could escape from aquaculture and damage the native population.

Another concern is that the organism produced is the property of a company. Farmers who grow a GMO crop must buy new seeds every year from the manufacturer. Currently, it is illegal to take seeds from last year's crops and plant them. This law was enacted to protect companies producing GMO seeds and some view it as controversial.

Generation of resistant pests is another criticism of the GMO industry. This argument is most commonly made with Bt crops, crops expressing an insecticidal protein from the bacterium *Bacillus thuringiensis*, such as Bt cotton. Many are concerned that like any pesticide an overuse will lead to resistant strains of insects. Cultures of *B. thuringiensis* are a standard treatment used by many organic farmers and loss of this would make organic insect control even more difficult.

Finally, there are concerns that the driving force behind production of GMO organisms may be commercial gain rather than public good and that the benefits do not make it worth taking the risk.

Although many people may not have considered how they feel about GMOs, they are likely to have been consuming genetically modified products. In 2015, over 175 million acres of land in the United States was planted with GMO crops, including 94% of soybeans, 96% of cotton, and 93% of corn. The odds are that you have already consumed products made with GMO.

Gene sequences can be altered before expression to facilitate the study of protein function or disease states The combination of solid-phase nucleotide synthesis and PCR make it simple to alter DNA sequences through site-directed mutagenesis (a specific mutation generated at a specific site in the sequence) (**Figure 2.28**). The first step is to design and synthesize a primer that contains the mutation of interest. This primer will have a mismatch with the template DNA at the mutation, but it needs to have enough homology to be able to anneal and allow the polymerase to extend. When this primer is used in PCR, the mutation will be incorporated into the PCR product. Typically, the product created in these reactions is not a full-length copy of the coding region of the gene, known as a cDNA. Instead, a fragment containing the mutated sequence can be cut on the ends with restriction enzymes and cloned in place in the cDNA. This technique is called cassette mutagenesis. Using this approach, numerous mutations can be generated in a single sequence and swapped in or out as desired.

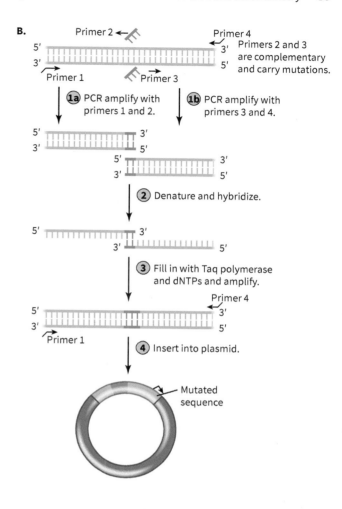

FIGURE 2.28 **Two methods of generating site-directed mutants.** **A.** In single-step mutagenesis, two primers each containing the mutation are used. These face away from each other and are used to amplify the entire plasmid. The parent plasmid is of bacterial origin and can be degraded by the restriction enzyme DpnI while the mutant PCR products are not cleaved by Dpn I. (Wessner, DuPont, Charles, Neufeld, *Microbiology,* 2e, copyright 2017, John Wiley & Sons. This material is reproduced with permission of John Wiley & Sons, Inc.) **B.** In classical PCR-based site-directed mutagenesis PCR is used to generate two separate products, each containing the mutation and a short region that overlaps the mutation site. A second round of PCR is used with flanking primers to generate a fragment that can be cloned into a plasmid. (Allison, *Fundamental Molecular Biology,* 2e, copyright 2012, John Wiley & Sons. This material is reproduced with permission of John Wiley & Sons, Inc)

2.3.3 │ Techniques can be used to silence genes in organisms

Although molecular biology techniques to produce a protein in a cell or organism are useful, there are times when it would be helpful to know what would happen if a protein were absent. Two techniques are commonly used for this type of experiment: a **knockout** organism or **gene silencing** using siRNA. A relatively new method is **CRISPR**. All three techniques are explained below.

Knockout technology effectively deletes a gene from the organism

A knockout organism takes advantage of homologous recombination to delete a gene (**Figure 2.29**). The first step is to map the gene of interest to identify intron and exon boundaries. A region of the gene to be deleted is then identified. This region often includes the start codon or results in a frameshift mutation, to ensure that any protein that is accidently produced is nonfunctional. Segments of DNA flanking the region to be deleted are selected and cloned into a knockout vector, which contains sequences to facilitate its manipulation in bacteria, and selectable markers for screening its insertion into the host organism's genome.

*neo*ʳ

Gene of interest

① Insert *neo* resistance gene into gene of interest.

Split segments of gene

*neo*ʳ

② Electroporate DNA into mouse embryonic stem cells.

③ Grow cells in selective media. Screen for proper insertion.

④ Inject transfected ES cells into blastocyst.

⑤ Implant chimeric blastocyst with both cell types into surrogate mother mouse.

⑥ Chimeric mice have cells derived from both blastocyst (black) and ES cells (white).

⑦ Breed chimeric mice with one another to generate knockout offspring.

Once generated, the knockout construct is electroporated into embryonic stem (ES) cells. The cells are cultured, and the selectable marker is used to identify cells in which the construct has integrated into the genome. In 3%–10% of these integrations, the construct will have homologously recombined with the host genome, resulting in the deletion of one of the cell's two copies of that gene. Cells must be genotyped using PCR or other techniques.

The ES cells are injected into a growing mouse embryo, termed a blastocyst, and implanted into a surrogate mother. When born, the offspring, termed **chimeras**, will have some cells derived from the original embryo and some from the ES cells. If the ES cells have contributed to the gametes of the chimera, these organisms can be interbred to produce a knockout organism.

At one level the ramifications of knocking out a gene are clear, but the broader impacts may not be. If the process is successful, the organism will lack functional copies of the deleted gene and be completely unable to produce the protein coded for by that gene. The inability to produce a particular protein can manifest in three ways. First, the deletion may have no obvious effect, either because other genes help to compensate for the missing gene or because the changes only become evident when specific assays are performed. Second, the gene may be essential for life, so its deletion causes an embryonic lethal mutation, meaning the organism dies early in development or *in utero*. Although this situation provides important data, it makes it difficult to study the system. The third option, which is perhaps the most useful, is the situation in which the knockout organism has an interesting phenotype but is still capable of reproducing and is therefore easy to study.

One final drawback of this type of experiment is the time and cost involved. The process is complex, requiring a team of experts with a range of specialized skills, and takes as long as 18 months.

RNAi offers the ability to quickly and affordably knockdown gene expression

In the late 1990s, it was discovered that eukaryotes have the ability to regulate gene expression after transcription, that is, after mRNA synthesis (**Figure 2.30**). The cell can do this by synthesizing short stretches of mRNA that are the reverse complement of the message. These strands can bind to mRNA and either trigger its destruction or block translation. Soon after the initial discovery, it was found that results could be obtained by introducing artificial

FIGURE 2.29 **Production of knockout mice.** The production of a knockout mouse begins with the generation of a knockout construct, a piece of DNA in which a central region of the gene of interest has been replaced by the *neo* selectable marker. The construct is electroporated into mouse embryonic stem cells and selected with geneticin. Surviving cells are screened to ensure that the DNA has integrated properly into the chromosome. These mutant ES cells are injected into blastocysts that are implanted into pregnant female mice. The cells develop into chimeric mice containing some cells derived from the blastocyst and some derived from the ES cells. These heterozygous mice are crossed with one another to generate knockout animals. (Steps 1-2: Snustad; Simmons, *Principles of Genetics,* 6e, copyright 2012, John Wiley & Sons. This material is reproduced with permission of John Wiley & Sons, Inc. Steps 3-7: Karp, *Cell and Molecular Biology: Concepts and Experiments*, 7e, copyright 2013, John Wiley & Sons. This material is reproduced with permission of John Wiley & Sons, Inc.)

(1) An RNAi construct is produced. This piece of DNA has a fragment of the gene that is being silenced and a reverse complement of that sequence separated by several nucleotides.

Copy 1   Copy 2

Transcription

5'   3' RNA

(2) The construct is translated into an mRNA. The complementary sequences base pair with each other and form a hairpin structure.

dsRNA
5'
3'

mRNA
5'   3'

(3) Translation of the mRNA is blocked or the mRNA is degraded by the RNA induced silencing complex (RISC).

mRNA
5'   3'

or

P   P

RNA   Translational
cleavage   repression

FIGURE 2.30 **RNAi regulating gene expression.**   RNAi is a technique for regulating gene expression post transcriptionally. Short RNAs that are complimentary to the gene being regulated are transcribed and processed in the nucleus. These form part of the gene silencing complex. (Snustad; Simmons, *Principles of Genetics,* 6e, copyright 2012, John Wiley & Sons. This material is reproduced with permission of John Wiley & Sons, Inc.)

complementary mRNA or DNA constructs into the cell. This technique has several variations but is generically known as **RNA interference** (RNAi).

A short RNA molecule can be used to interfere, but use of these molecules is typically limited because they cannot be copied and passed from one cell to the next as the cells divide. Instead, a common approach is to construct a fragment of DNA coding for a short (approximately 20 nucleotide) stretch of the coding sequence, a short loop and a reverse complement of the first sequence. When translated, this forms a short hairpin structure that uses the cells' natural RNA processing mechanisms to produce fragments that will knock down or silence the gene of interest.

There are several key differences between a knockout organism and cells treated with RNAi. Construction of a knockout mouse can take years and cost hundreds of thousands of dollars, whereas RNAi can be done in an afternoon for less than one hundred dollars. Because of the lower cost and simplicity of the technique, hundreds of genes can be knocked down at once. Unfortunately, RNAi is not completely predictable or absolute because some RNAi constructs will silence a gene but others may not. The reasons for this difference are unclear. Hence, RNAi may produce variable phenotypes in which the expression of a gene has been blunted but not shut off. Finally, because knockout organisms do not have a functional copy of the gene, they never produce functional protein, whereas RNAi works from the point at which the gene becomes expressed. This can be valuable if an RNAi can be triggered at a specific time in development or an experiment, but this also assumes that the protein will appear or disappear at a rate that can be effective in the experiment. If a gene is silenced using RNAi, we assume that the protein product of that gene is not produced, and this leads to a phenotype or effect. However, if the half-life of any pre-existing protein is long and lingers after the gene has been silenced, silencing the gene may have little effect.

Target DNA sequence

Cas9 nuclease

Guide RNA

FIGURE 2.31 CRISPR gene editing. The CRISPR system consists of a nuclease, in this case the Cas9 nuclease, and a guide RNA. The guide RNA has one end that binds to the nuclease and one that binds to the DNA sequence, guiding the nuclease to the site of cleavage. (PDB ID: 5B2R, Hirano, S., Nishimasu, H., Ishitani, R., Nureki, O. (2016) Structural Basis for the Altered PAM Specificities of Engineered CRISPR-Cas9 *Mol. Cell* 61: 886–894.)

CRISPR/Cas9 is a flexible system used for genomic engineering.

CRISPR stands for *Clus*tered *R*egularly *I*nterspaced *S*hort *P*alindromic *R*epeats. These are DNA sequences used by prokaryotes in association with a nuclease, often the CRISPR associated nuclease 9 or Cas9, to form part of the prokaryotic immune response to viruses. In this system, RNA guides Cas9 to a specific location where the enzyme binds and cuts the foreign DNA (Figure 2.31).

In the laboratory, the CRISPR/Cas9 system consists of a plasmid of DNA encoding the Cas9 nuclease and a single guide RNA. The single guide RNA consists of two parts: a gene specific sequence and a Cas9 specific sequence. The gene specific RNA guides Cas9 to the specific sequence in the genome to be edited while the other sequence binds to Cas9. Once bound at the specific site, Cas9 cuts both strands of DNA leaving exposed ends. The cell's endogenous DNA repair mechanisms rejoin these ends but often add or delete bases, resulting in the loss of gene function if the addition or deletion occurs in a coding sequence. Variations of the CRISPR system allow deletions of large sequences of DNA, permit generation of point mutations, and facilitate insertion of specific new sequences. CRISPR therefore is not simply a tool to delete or silence genes, but rather a system through which entire genomes can be edited. Furthermore, because the flexibility of the CRISPR system lies within the guide RNA sequence, changes to the system are relatively simple to make; investigators only need to change the DNA that encodes the RNA. Thousands of CRISPR experiments have been performed in just the few years since this technique was developed.

While CRISPR has made it easy to edit organisms in the laboratory, it is evident that this technique can be used to edit any genome, including the human genome. Among many ethicists this has raised concern that this technique will be used not to prevent disease but to make "improvements" to people, such as increasing intelligence or athletic performance. While these alterations still remain in the realm of science fiction, they may not be far off.

WORKED PROBLEM 2.3 | Genetic engineering

Your research advisor has heard about using a fluorescent protein from coral called mCherry to help identify the lab's protein of interest. She has a sample of the cDNA for mCherry, and you already have a cDNA for your protein. Your professor would like you to express the two joined together as one protein. How would you fuse your protein and the fluorescent protein? What steps would be involved?

Strategy Break the process down into smaller parts. What are the individual steps that need to be taken into consideration to achieve the ultimate goal, that is, expression of the protein in cells?

Solution To make a fusion of your protein with mCherry, you should first consider which type of cells will be used to produce the protein. If a large quantity is needed, then bacterial expression is often the best technique to use; however, if the protein has some sort of modification or processing that is specific to eukaryotes, another

system, for instance, cultured cells, may be more appropriate. The next step is to develop a plan for creating a DNA construct that contains cDNAs coding for both the desired protein and mCherry. These must be joined together in frame—that is, ligated in such a way as to generate a single mRNA when transcribed. This may be as simple as cutting both pieces with a restriction enzyme that leaves ends that can join to each other, or it may require the engineering of restriction sites onto each cDNA using PCR. The newly joined piece of cDNA coding for the fusion protein will need to be cloned into an expression vector, a piece of DNA that can be replicated inside the cell and has promoter sequences that will drive high levels of protein expression. Finally, a method is needed to put this piece of DNA into the bacteria. This is commonly accomplished with chemical transformation or electroporation.

Follow-up question How would this process be different if the aim were to express the protein in mammalian cells?

2.3 Summary

- Oligonucleotides up to 70 nucleotides long can be chemically synthesized in the laboratory.
- PCR can be used to amplify fragments of DNA.
- DNA can be cut and ligated, using a variety of commercially available enzymes.
- Vectors are pieces of DNA that can be inserted into different organisms such as bacteria, yeast, or other eukaryotic cells to aid in the study of their function.
- Pieces of DNA can be used to drive protein production in individual cells, or even in whole organisms, to test for function.
- Genes can be removed using homologous recombination, generating a knockout organism.
- CRISPR and RNAi are means of silencing gene expression.

2.3 Concept Check

- Describe the various techniques used in this section.
- Explain which of these techniques can be used to construct pieces of DNA to learn more about a biochemical system.
- Show how multiple techniques could be used to answer a particular question about a biochemical system in different ways or approach a problem from different directions.

The Bigger Picture

DNA is perhaps the most iconic molecule in all of science. DNA and RNA comprise the nucleic acids—molecules that store and pass on the genetic code and translate the code into proteins. This chapter describes the structures of nucleic acids at the chemical level, and the forces involved in folding of these molecules; it also reviews the basics of how DNA is duplicated in the cell (replication), how DNA is transcribed into RNA (transcription), and how RNA is translated into proteins (translation). Finally, it describes different ways in which nucleic acids can be analyzed and manipulated to assist in the study of proteins and their functions in the cell or organism.

Bioinformatics Exercises

Exercise 1 Taxonomic Trees
Exercise 2 Drawing and Visualizing Nucleotides
Exercise 3 The DNA Double Helix

Exercise 4 Analysis of Genomic DNA
Exercise 5 Restriction Enzyme Mapping

Problems

2.1 Nucleic Acids Have Distinct Structures

1. Draw the five bases that are used in DNA and RNA.

2. Each of the five bases contains nitrogen. Why are these amines not drawn in the ionized state?

3. Based on the structures of the bases, would you anticipate that they would be water soluble?

4. Examine the structure of the carbohydrate moiety in a ribonucleotide or deoxyribonucleotide. What shape is it? Where are the hydroxyl groups found relative to the rest of the molecule?

5. Several bases can tautomerize. Draw the enol form of each base. How would this affect hydrogen bonding and reactivity?

6. Nucleotides and deoxynucleotides form nucleic acids. What are some of their other roles in biochemistry?

7. Review the forces involved in the folding of DNA and RNA. Would these molecules fold differently in a nonpolar solvent such as hexane?

8. Examine the structure of a nucleotide. What weak forces are involved in interactions with other nucleotides or other molecules we have discussed? What are the relative strengths of these interactions?

9. Would the DNA helix be more or less stable in the absence of Mg^{2+}? Explain your response.

10. DNA can lose a purine base in strong acid. Propose a mechanism for the acid-catalyzed depurination of DNA.

11. A riboswitch is a posttranscriptional regulatory mechanism. In a riboswitch, one region of the mRNA can fold into a complex shape that will block translation. Binding of a small ligand stabilizes this structure. Draw a model for how this occurs. Write an equilibrium expression for the riboswitch in the presence and absence of a ligand.

12. Examine the structure of DNA. What weak forces are involved in interactions with other molecules? What are the relative strengths of these interactions?

2.2 Nucleic Acids Have Many Cellular Functions

13. What does "semiconservative replication" mean?

14. Describe the sequence of events at a replication fork as DNA is being copied.

15. Mutations are changes to DNA sequences or chemical modifications of those sequences. If DNA were methylated on a select guanine residue, how might this change the DNA sequence?

6-O-Methylguanine

16. DNA can be damaged by UV light. One sort of damage that can be caused is the formation of thiamine dimers, as shown below. How might this be harmful to the cell?

17. Describe the structure of DNA, discussing the DNA helix and the base pairs of DNA, the overall structure of a chromosome, the structure of a gene, an mRNA, a ribosome, and a protein. What are the relative sizes of each of these?

18. Some toxins block the synthesis of mRNA or proteins. Why would this effect be toxic, and how could it be used in the laboratory?

19. Consider the thermodynamics of DNA replication. What are the different thermodynamic parameters (enthalpy, entropy) that need to be considered? Why is this process favorable overall?

20. Retroviruses have an RNA genome instead of a DNA genome, and the RNA must be copied into the host's DNA. How does this process differ from other reactions in biochemistry? What additional steps must happen for the virus to infect a cell?

21. If human proteins can be made in bacteria, why are so many other techniques used for studying biochemistry and conducting biomedical research?

22. List the places where the expression of a gene and, therefore, the production of a protein can be regulated. Which are exclusively eukaryotic, which are exclusively prokaryotic, and which are both?

2.3 The Manipulation of Nucleic Acids Has Transformed Biochemistry

23. Why do restriction enzymes recognize a four to eight base-pair sequence? Why are many of these sequences palindromic? An examination of the structure of DNA may help you think about this problem.

24. How frequently would a six-base cutter cut a random sequence of DNA that is 10,000 base pairs long?

25. Sal I and EcoRI are restriction enzymes that both recognize a six-base sequence, but Sal I cuts only once in a million bases whereas EcoRI cuts every 2,800 or so. What does this say about the evolution of both the sequence and the enzymes?

26. In a cloning experiment a fragment of DNA is ligated with a vector such as a plasmid. Following the initial ligation of the sample into a vector, the new DNA construct is used to transform bacteria. Why is this step needed?

27. UV light is frequently used to monitor DNA in molecular biology experiments. Some investigators attempt to minimize exposure of their experiments to UV light. What would be the reason for this?

28. How would you generate insertions or deletions in a DNA sequence using PCR?

29. Several different types of polymerase are commercially available for PCR. Find a catalog for a company that sells molecular biology reagents. Compare the different thermophilic polymerases it offers. How do these enzymes vary?

30. What was the mythical beast known as a chimera, and why is the first organism generated in the production of a knockout mouse termed a chimera?

31. How could you engineer a restriction enzyme site into a piece of DNA?

32. What are the strengths and weaknesses of using high throughput sequencing compared to more classical methods, such as fluorescent dye terminator sequencing?

33. If PCR were performed on eukaryotic template DNA from genomic DNA, reverse transcribed RNA, and a cDNA library (a copy of the mRNA of the cell), the result would be different in each case. How would you explain those results?

34. If PCR were performed on a highly conserved gene from two species, one prokaryotic and one eukaryotic, would you anticipate different results or the same result? Why?

Data Interpretation

Questions 35–39 pertain to the following figure.

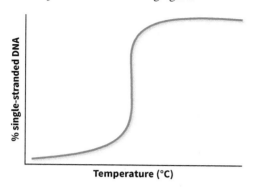

35. What does the shape of this curve tell us about the transition from double-stranded to single-stranded DNA?

36. What is the melting temperature of this piece of DNA?

37. What effect would the addition of acid have on the melting point, and what would be the reason for the effect? Draw a curve illustrating melting in the presence of acid.

38. What is the effect of the chaotrope urea on the DNA melting temperature? Draw a curve illustrating the melting point in the presence of urea.

39. What effect does EDTA (ethylenediaminetetraacetic acid) have, and why would it influence the melting temperature?

Experimental Design

40. Using PCR, describe how you could determine if a strain of corn had a mutation resulting in the partial deletion of a gene.

41. Describe three different ways that could be used to make a cultured eukaryotic cell line produce a recombinant protein.

42. Virtual PCR uses a pair of primers to search through a genomic DNA sequence for amplified fragments. Explain how this technique may be useful in the laboratory.

43. You are investigating a protein that you believe binds to DNA. You hypothesize that binding of this protein increases the melting point of DNA. Design an experiment to test your hypothesis.

44. You are studying a protein that is phosphorylated on a specific amino acid. How could you mutate the gene that codes for this protein to another amino acid?

45. Describe how you might clone a gene from a novel bacteria.

Ethics and Social Responsibility

46. Are you in favor of or against using recombinant DNA technologies to create GMOs? Are there some instances where use of genetic engineering is acceptable and others when it is not?

47. Why do most people find cloning of bacteria or cells acceptable, cloning of larger organisms such as mice or sheep questionable, and cloning of humans unethical?

48. Each of us harbors traits that are beneficial and those we might wish were different. If you could make changes to your genome to give you traits that you find favorable, would you do so? If you could increase your chances that your children would have these favorable traits, would you do so?

49. Eugenics is the process of trying to improve a population through genetics, specifically in a human population. It had a large popular following in the United States in the late 1800s to mid-1900s, but evidence of eugenic practices in the United States can be found dating to as recently as the mid-1980s. Find a book or article on eugenics. What are the ethical questions involved in using genetics to improve a population? Can you give examples from the past of how people with seemingly good intentions have committed acts we now consider atrocities?

50. Your personal DNA sequence may reveal that you are harboring mutations or alleles of genes that could put you at risk for future diseases. Would you like to know or have access to your genomic DNA sequence?

Suggested Readings

2.1 Nucleic Acids Have Distinct Structures

Branden, C., and J. Tooze. *Introduction to Protein Structure*. New York, NY: Garland Science, 1999.

Egil, M., and W. Saenger. *Principles of Nucleic Acid Structure*. Berlin, Germany: Springer Verlag, 1988.

Neidle, S. *Principles of Nucleic Acid Structure*. Cambridge, MA: Academic Press, 2007.

Sinden, R. R. *DNA Structure and Function*. Cambridge, MA: Academic Press, 1994.

2.2 Nucleic Acids Have Many Cellular Functions

Bloomfield, V. A., D. M. Crothers, and I. Tinoco, Jr. *Nucleic Acids: Structures, Properties, and Functions*. Herndon, VA: University Science Books, 2000.

Watson, J. D., T. A. Baker, S. P. Bell, A. Gann, M. Levine, and R. Losick. *Molecular Biology of the Gene*. 7th ed. San Francisco, CA: Benjamin Cummings, 2013.

2.3 The Manipulation of Nucleic Acids Has Transformed Biochemistry

Brown, T. A. *Gene Cloning and DNA Analysis: An Introduction*. Hoboken, NJ: Wiley-Blackwell, 2016.

Buckingham, L. *Molecular Diagnostics: Fundamentals, Methods, and Clinical Applications*. 2nd ed. Philadelphia, PA: F. A. Davis Co., 2011.

Dale, J. W., and M. von Schantz. *From Genes to Genomes: Concepts and Applications of DNA Technology*. Hoboken, NJ: Wiley, 2011.

Green, M. R., and J. Sambrook. *Molecular Cloning, A Laboratory Manual*. 4th ed. Oxford, England: Cold Spring Harbor Laboratory Press, 2012.

Lesk, A. M. *Introduction to Genomics*. 2nd ed. Oxford, England: Oxford Press, 2012.

McPherson, M. J., and S. G. Moller. *PCR, The Basics*. 2nd ed. New York, NY: Garland Science, 2006.

Nucleic Acids

1856 ——————— Gregor Mendel begins work cultivating peas

1859 ——————— Darwin publishes *On the Origin of Species*

1869 ——————— Miescher isolates nuclein (DNA)

1910 ——————— Thomas Hunt Morgan discovers genes are on chromosomes

1953 ——————— Watson and Crick publish double helical structure of DNA

1958 ——————— Meselson and Stahl discover DNA replication is semiconservative

1962 ——————— Nobel Prize for Watson, Crick, and Wilkins

1977 ——————— First genome sequenced (phage phiX174, 5386 bp)

1980 ——————— Sanger, Berg, and Gilbert win Nobel Prize for DNA sequencing

1982 ——————— Humulin, first recombinant human protein approved

1989 ——————— RNA is catalytic (Cech and Altman win Nobel Prize)
Capecchi, Smithies, and Evans are the first to use homologous recombination to make a knockout mouse

1993 ——————— Mullis and Smith win Nobel Prize for the polymerase chain reaction

1996 ——————— Dolly the sheep is cloned

1998 ——————— Mello and Fire discover RNAi in *C.elegans*

2003 ——————— Human genome is completed

2006 ——————— Mello and Fire win Nobel Prize for RNAi

2007 ——————— Capecchi, Smithies, and Evans win the Nobel Prize

2012 ——————— Charpentier and Doudna develop the CRISPR Cas9 system

CHAPTER 3

Proteins I

An Introduction to Protein Structure and Function

nanantachoke/ShutterStock

Just as these building materials are used in constructing office buildings, amino acids are the building blocks of proteins.

Proteins in Context

Throughout history advances in materials have changed tools and how we make them. Ancient civilizations may have used clay pots or made weapons of bronze or iron. In modern times refined alloys of aluminum have been used in applications ranging from cans to aircraft. Perhaps people in the future will mark our current era by the use of plastics or silicon microchips.

In biochemistry, we consider proteins to be a wonder material used in thousands of applications. Proteins are polymers of amino acids which have evolved to have numerous distinct functions: they can be structural or catalytic, transmit information, help protect an organism by binding to foreign molecules, provide motility, store amino acids, or transport molecules within the cell or the organism.

This chapter begins by discussing amino acids, the building blocks of proteins, then moves on to the basics of protein structure and a brief description of how these macromolecules fold into their specific conformations. The chapter ends by examining several different examples of different proteins. These aspects of protein chemistry are discussed in **Dynamic Figure 3.1**.

CHAPTER OUTLINE

3.1 Amino Acid Chemistry

3.2 Proteins Are Polymers of Amino Acids

3.3 Proteins Are Molecules of Defined Shape and Structure

3.4 Examples of Protein Structures and Functions

DYNAMIC FIGURE 3.1 Amino acids are metabolites with multiple functions in the cell. They can be polymerized into peptides and proteins, complex macromolecules with diverse functions ranging from structure to catalysis.

COMMON THEMES

Evolution's outcomes are conserved.	• Mutations to DNA sequences may result in alterations to a protein's amino acid sequence. The new protein may function normally, have a new and slightly altered function, or be completely nonfunctional.
	• The amino acid sequence of proteins can help establish the evolutionary relationship between organisms.
	• Protein structures and the amino acids they are made from have undergone billions of years of natural selection and random change (genetic drift).
Structure determines function.	• The structures of the 20 amino acids commonly found in proteins partially describe the function of these molecules. The backbone and side chains of these amino acids act in concert to give the structure of the protein.
	• An alteration to the structure of a protein changes the function of that protein.
Biochemical information is transferred, exchanged, and stored.	• The information encoded in deoxyribonucleic acid (DNA) and transcribed into messenger ribonucleic acid (mRNA) is ultimately translated into proteins.
	• Many proteins are involved in cell-to-cell communication, either between organisms or within the same organism. In such cases the proteins may be the signal, the receptor of the signal, or elements of the signaling cascade that translate the signal into an effect.
Biomolecules are altered through pathways involving transformations of energy and matter.	• Proteins are made from a common set of amino acid building blocks. Specific modifications are sometimes made to particular amino acids within a protein.
	• The synthesis of the covalent chemical bonds in a protein costs energy. In addition, the assembly of hundreds of amino acids into a single protein has a highly negative entropy. Therefore, the free energy (ΔG) of protein formation from isolated amino acids in a test tube is quite positive. In the cell, the overall reaction becomes favorable ($\Delta G < 0$) by coupling these reactions to the hydrolysis of ATP and GTP.
	• Unlike the synthesis of the peptide bonds in a protein, the folding of a protein into its final conformation is largely governed by numerous weak forces. Here, increases in entropy provided by liberation of water molecules drive $\Delta G < 0$ and lead to formation of the final structure.

3.1 | Amino Acid Chemistry

Amino acids are the building blocks of proteins, and they play critical roles in many metabolic pathways. Because of these diverse roles, amino acids are a good place to start a discussion of protein chemistry.

3.1.1 | The structure of amino acids dictates their chemical properties

As their name suggests, amino acids have a single unifying property—they have both an amine and a carboxylic acid moiety (**Figure 3.2**). Amino acids found in proteins are all α-amino acids; that is, they contain an amino group, a central α-carbon, and a carboxyl group. In 19 of the 20 common amino acids found in proteins, the amine is a primary amine bound only to the α-carbon. The remaining amino acid, proline, is technically an imino acid, containing a secondary amine with the side chain joining the backbone amine, forming a ring.

All but one of the 20 common amino acids have four different substituents: an amino group, a carboxyl group, a hydrogen, and a side chain bound to the central carbon. The side chain is referred to as "R" because it can be one of 20 different groups. These amino acids lack a plane of symmetry and are **chiral** (**Figure 3.3**). The remaining amino acid, glycine, has a hydrogen atom as a side chain; because of the plane of symmetry created by the hydrogen atom, glycine is **achiral**. As with other molecules, the three-dimensional shape of an amino acid dictates its reactivity and ability to bind to other molecules. Additionally, nature almost exclusively uses the L-enantiomer of amino acids. Unless otherwise noted, all amino acids discussed here can be assumed to be the L-enantiomer.

Both the amino and the carboxyl group of amino acids are charged in aqueous solution near neutral pH. Molecules possessing both a positive and negative charge are **zwitterions**. In some depictions of amino acids, the amino group is shown as deprotonated (NH_2) and the carboxyl as protonated (COOH). A quick check of the pK_a of these groups indicates that this cannot be the case. The pK_a of the amino group in glycine is 9.6, whereas that of the carboxyl is 2.3. Hence, at any pH between these pK_a values, both groups will be found in the ionized state (**Figure 3.4**). The pK_a values of the carboxyl and amino group may be slightly different from the values expected for a carboxylic acid or primary amine, because the proximity of the two groups to one another can influence the pK_a (causing shifts of almost 2.5 units), as can the side chain of the amino acid or the immediate environment. The change of the pK_a value of a functional group due to its immediate environment is a recurring theme in biochemistry.

FIGURE 3.2 **Structure of an amino acid.** **A.** The general structure of an α-amino acid is shown. The primary amino group, carboxyl group, and side chain are all bound to the α-carbon. (Snustad; Simmons, *Principles of Genetics*, 6e, copyright 2012, John Wiley & Sons. This material is reproduced with permission of John Wiley & Sons, Inc.) **B.** Proline is the only amino acid with a secondary amine.

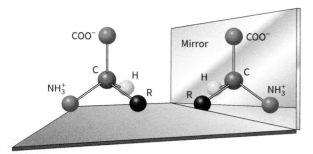

FIGURE 3.3 **Chirality of amino acids.** All amino acids, with the exception of glycine, have four different substituents on the α carbon and are therefore chiral. Glycine has an H for a side chain and therefore is achiral. Naturally occurring amino acids found in proteins are in the L configuration. (Karp, *Cell and Molecular Biology: Concepts and Experiments*, 7e, copyright 2013, John Wiley & Sons. This material is reproduced with permission of John Wiley & Sons, Inc.)

Ionized at low pH   **Zwitterionic at neutral pH**   **Ionized at high pH**

FIGURE 3.4 **Zwitterionic nature of amino acids.** Despite how structures may be depicted on paper, amino acids exist as zwitterions in neutral solutions. Changing the pH may alter the protonation of the carboxyl group or amino group.

It is possible to encounter pH values that would permit the protonation of only one state of zwitterion, such as stomach acid at pH 1, but these situations are the exception in biochemistry.

Amino acids are versatile but relatively simple molecules. The common skeleton provides a central core from which to build an amazingly diverse array of molecules.

3.1.2 The side chains of amino acids impart unique properties

Amino acids are differentiated by their **side chain or residue**, a short extension from the common backbone. The side chains can be as small as a hydrogen atom or as large as the bicyclic ring of the amino acid tryptophan. Collectively, however, amino acids are considered small molecules.

Amino acids can be organized based on the properties of their side chains (**Figure 3.5**). There are various ways to do this. The organization used here is based on the chemical properties of the side chains. This section discusses the properties of the side chain rather than the entire molecule. Keep in mind, in solution all amino acids are zwitterions and are soluble in water.

Nonpolar side chains   Amino acids with a nonpolar (hydrophobic) side chain include glycine, alanine, leucine, isoleucine, valine, proline, methionine, phenylalanine, and tryptophan. Glycine is the simplest amino acid, with a single hydrogen atom as a side chain. Alanine, the next simplest, has a methyl group as a side chain. Valine, leucine, and isoleucine have isopropyl, *sec*-butyl, and *iso*-butyl groups, respectively, as side chains and are collectively known as the branched chain amino acids (BCAAs). Proline has a side chain that connects back to the backbone nitrogen, resulting in a five-membered ring that has constrained geometry. Methionine has an ethyl methyl thioester as a side chain. Phenylalanine is simply alanine with a phenyl group added. Finally, tryptophan, the largest of the amino acids, has an aromatic, heterocyclic indole ring system comprised of both a five-membered and a six-membered ring.

Polar side chains   Amino acids with polar side groups are serine, threonine, tyrosine, cysteine, asparagine, and glutamine. Each of these side chains contains groups that are polar and can form hydrogen bonds, but are not sufficiently polar to ionize at typical physiological pH.

Three of these amino acids are alcohols. Serine is a primary alcohol, while threonine is a secondary alcohol. Tyrosine contains a phenol group with a pK_a of approximately 10. While this side chain is not typically ionized under physiological pH, the acidity of this group means that it is more reactive than other hydroxyl groups.

Cysteine can be thought of as a thiol analog of serine. The thiol in these residues is redox active—two cysteine residues can cross-link to form a disulfide bond, either within a protein or between two proteins. Cysteine can also ionize with a pK_a of 8.

Asparagine and glutamine both contain carboxamides, $CONH_2$ groups, but differ by a methylene group. The amine moiety in the carboxamide side chain is *not* ionized. If enough acid were added to protonate the amine of this group, the group would hydrolyze, resulting in a carboxylic acid and ammonia, something that does not generally occur under biological conditions.

Negatively charged side chains   Aspartate and glutamate are the only two amino acids typically categorized as having negatively charged side chains. Both contain carboxylic acids and are therefore weak acids. The pK_a of these side chains ranges from 2 to 5 and is comparable to that of other carboxylic acids. Hence, at neutral pH, most of these side chains are ionized; however, this may not be the case when these amino acids have been incorporated into proteins and their local environment has changed. Aspartate and glutamate are the ionized forms of aspartic and glutamic acid, respectively. Like asparagine and glutamine, aspartate and glutamate differ by a methylene unit.

Positively charged side chains   Lysine, arginine, and histidine are designated as having positively charged side chains. As with their negatively charged counterparts, they are

Nonpolar side chains

Alanine	**Valine**	**Leucine**	**Isoleucine**	**Methionine**	**Phenylalanine**	**Tryptophan**
(Ala or A)	(Val or V)	(Leu or L)	(Ile or I)	(Met or M)	(Phe or F)	(Trp or W)

Properties of side chains
Hydrophobic side chains are nonpolar and incapable of hydrogen bonding. These side chains may be aliphatic or aromatic.

Polar: negatively charged side chains

Polar: positively charged side chains

Aspartate	**Glutamate**		**Lysine**	**Arginine**	**Histidine**
(Asp or D)	(Glu or E)		(Lys or K)	(Arg or R)	(His or H)

Properties of side chains
Negatively charged amino acids contain a carboxyl group and are commonly deprotonated at physiological pH.

Properties of side chains
Positively charged amino acids include lysine, arginine, and histidine. These residues contain amino groups. Lysine and arginine have pK_a values of 10.5 and 12.5 and are protonated and positively charged at physiological pH. The side chain of histidine has a pK_a of 6.0 and is partially protonated at physiological pH.

Polar: uncharged side chains

Serine	**Threonine**	**Glutamine**	**Asparagine**	**Tyrosine**
(Ser or S)	(Thr or T)	(Glu or Q)	(Asn or N)	(Tyr or Y)

Properties of side chains
Polar side chains are hydrophilic but are not usually ionized at physiological pH.

Side chains with unique properties

Glycine	**Cysteine**	**Proline**
(Gly or G)	(Cys or C)	(Pro or P)

This side chain consists only of a hydrogen atom and can fit into either a hydrophilic or hydrophobic environment. Glycine often resides at sites where two polypeptides come into close contact.

Though this side chain has polar, uncharged character, it has the unique property of forming a covalent bond with another cysteine to form a disulfide link.

Though this side chain has hydrophobic character, it has the unique property of creating kinks in polypeptide chains and disrupting ordered secondary structure.

FIGURE 3.5 Amino acids.   The 20 amino acids are grouped by hydrophobic, polar, positively charged, and negatively charged side chains. Their names are shown in one- and three-letter abbreviations. (Karp, *Cell and Molecular Biology: Concepts and Experiments*, 7e, copyright 2013, John Wiley & Sons. This material is reproduced with permission of John Wiley & Sons, Inc.)

TABLE 3.1 The pKa of Amino Acid Side Chains

Amino acid	Three-letter abbreviation	One-letter abbreviation	pKa
Amino			9.30
Arginine	Arg	R	12.48
Lysine	Lys	K	10.53
Tyrosine	Tyr	Y	10.07
Cysteine	Cys	C	8.18
Histidine	His	H	6.00
Glutamate	Glu	E	4.25
Aspartate	Asp	D	3.65
Carboxyl			2.10

ionized or partially ionized at physiological pH. Lysine's side chain is a primary amine at the end of a 4-carbon long chain. Arginine has a guanidinium group ($NHC(NH_2)_2^+$) and uses resonance to distribute the positive charge across this system. Histidine has a heterocyclic imidazole group as a side chain. This group can become protonated and deprotonated with a pK_a near 6.0, making it the only amino acid with a pK_a in the physiological range.

Amino acids are known by either one-letter or three-letter abbreviations

All amino acids have both a one-letter and a three-letter abbreviation. These are shown in Figure 3.5, with the structure of the amino acid side chains. Although most of these abbreviations are self-explanatory, it is worth highlighting some of them. The three-letter abbreviation for isoleucine is Ile rather than Iso (because "iso" is used to describe the chemistry of other groups like *iso*-butyl). Asparagine and glutamine are abbreviated to Asn and Gln, and aspartate and glutamate to Asp and Glu, respectively. If it is unclear whether the side chain is an aspartate or asparagine, the abbreviation Asx is given; similarly, Gsx is used to denote a glutamine or glutamate.

The system for deriving the one-letter abbreviations for amino acids is also relatively simple. In most instances, the first letter of the amino acid is the abbreviation (A for alanine, S for serine, etc.); however, some amino acids share a common first letter and thus have to be differentiated. The amino acids that do not use their first letter include glutamine (Q, which can be remembered as Q-tamine), asparagine (N, remembered as asparagiNne), arginine (R, remembered as Arrrgh!-anine), and tryptophan (W, if stared at long enough, readers may start to see the W in the structure of tryptophan). The other amino acids that have single letter abbreviations that do not match their first letter are aspartate (D) and glutamate (E), which at least fall in alphabetical order. Finally, lysine is K, and there is no easy way to remember that one.

The ionization of amino acid side chains

The side chains of amino acids are partially responsible for the way in which a protein folds and mainly responsible for the chemistry the protein can conduct. The functional groups of the 20 amino acids commonly found in proteins have pK_a values throughout the pH range encountered by living systems (Table 3.1). Most of these values are as expected, with carboxylic acids typically in the range of 2 to 5, and amines at the other end of the spectrum in the range of 10 to 12. Others that are worthy of mention include histidine with a pK_a near 6, cysteine with a pK_a near 8 (due to its thiol side chain) and tyrosine with a pK_a near 10 (due to its phenolic group). However, these are the pK_a values of the protons on free amino acids in solution; folded into a protein or in the active site of an enzyme, these values may be changed radically by the local environment in the protein.

FIGURE 3.6 Amino acids not commonly found in proteins. Other amino acids play different roles in biochemistry. Some of these molecules are found in proteins (4-hydroxyproline, for example) while others are neurotransmitters (GABA) or play roles in metabolism (ornithine and citrulline are components of the urea cycle).

3.1.3 Amino acids have various roles in biochemistry

This chapter focuses on amino acids as the building blocks of proteins, but the 20 common amino acids also serve other roles in biochemistry. Several of these molecules are important in detoxifying ammonia and shuttling amino groups throughout the organism. Almost half of the 20 common amino acids are used as neurotransmitters, and many other neurotransmitters arise from decarboxylated amino acids.

In addition, there are other amino acids not commonly found in proteins but are involved, for example, in lipid metabolism, such as carnitine and taurine, or amine metabolism, such as ornithine and citrulline (Figure 3.6).

Societal and Ethical Biochemistry

Are nutritional supplements foods or drugs?

Nutritional products have always captured the attention of those looking to improve their health or physique. These products have progressed from herbal extracts to vitamins, minerals, amino acids, and small organic cofactors, and they are now readily available from a variety of outlets, ranging from specialty supplement shops to corner gas stations. Are these molecules drugs, intended to relieve the symptoms of an illness, or are they foods? Do these molecules do what they claim to do?

We often think of drugs as eliciting some physiological or psychological effect in the body, for example, altering blood pressure, making someone more alert or drowsy, or causing the release of a hormone. Based on this definition, almost any molecule can be defined as a drug.

The U.S. Food and Drug Administration (FDA) defines drugs in the 2006 Food Drug and Cosmetics Act (FD&C Act) as follows:

> … in part, by their intended use, as "articles intended for use in the diagnosis, cure, mitigation, treatment, or prevention of disease" and "articles (other than food) intended to affect the structure or any function of the body of man or other animals." [FD&C Act, sec. 201(g)(1)]

This legal definition contains loopholes. For example, if a bodybuilder takes amino acid supplements, these would probably "affect the structure and function of the body," but possibly the same could be said if that bodybuilder was eating egg whites. Furthermore, not all molecules found in foods have been isolated and identified. For example, cranberries are eaten as a food, but what if an extract of cranberries was found to be beneficial in treating some cancers. Would that extract not be considered a drug?

Likewise, the caffeine in coffee or tea is clearly a drug because it stimulates our nervous system and has no value as a source of energy or building block for other biological molecules.

Therefore, the question of whether a substance is a drug, a pharmaceutical, a supplement, or a food often comes down to intent and dose. These factors need to be determined before a molecule can be marketed as a drug or as a supplement.

Regulations govern the use of dietary supplements. For example, if a new molecule that was not marketed before 1994 is introduced into a supplement, companies are required to notify the FDA of the new ingredient. Also, companies cannot make the type of claims about efficacy with supplements that they can for drugs developed and marketed to treat a specific disorder. The rules for introducing supplements are more lenient and do not need to demonstrate the same level of effectiveness or safety. With supplements, when it comes to safety, the burden of proof is on the FDA rather than on the company marketing the compound. If safety concerns do arise, the FDA can, in some instances, issue warning letters and seize compounds.

Because many nutritional supplements are viewed as "natural" and are available without a prescription, people have an unfounded confidence and trust that these molecules will be at best helpful and at least not harmful. Pharmaceuticals and drugs, on the other hand, are perceived as being synthetic or unnatural in some way and therefore less beneficial. These impressions do not hold up under the test of scientific scrutiny. For instance, many people take an extract of St. John's wort as a nutritional supplement to relieve mild depression. However, this supplement has been shown to alter certain metabolic processes in the liver that result in significantly more rapid clearing of some drugs, including some compounds found in birth control pills. This can reduce efficacy and potentially lead to unplanned pregnancies.

Despite not being incorporated into proteins, these amino acids are clearly important in biochemistry and metabolism.

Often, molecules we consume in our diet have effects that are like those of drugs. This topic is examined in **Societal and Ethical Biochemistry: Are nutritional supplements foods or drugs?**

WORKED PROBLEM 3.1 | The acid–base properties of amino acids

You have a sample of the amino acid histidine at pH 2 and you begin to titrate it with NaOH. Draw a predicted titration curve for histidine.

Strategy Examine the structure of histidine. There are three groups that can ionize: the backbone amino and carboxyl groups, and the side chain amino group. What are the pK_a values of those groups? What happens to each of these groups as the pH increases?

Solution

Follow-up question Would alanine act as a buffer at pH 4.1?

3.1 Summary

- Amino acids are small organic molecules containing both an amino group and a carboxyl group. Most are chiral and, in nature, the L enantiomer predominates.
- Twenty amino acids are commonly found as components of proteins.
- The amino acids found in proteins can be categorized by their side chains, which have diverse structures and chemistry, and contribute to the overall structure and properties of proteins.
- Amino acids serve other roles in biochemistry. For example, they act as metabolic intermediates and signaling molecules.

3.1 Concept Check

- Describe the stereochemistry of these amino acids.
- Categorize the amino acids by property or functional group.
- Describe how each amino acid is unique with regard to its structure and chemistry.
- Identify which parts of an amino acid are ionizable and give the pK_a of those groups.
- Explain on a chemical level why and how the immediate environment contributes to the pK_a of a group.

3.2 | Proteins Are Polymers of Amino Acids

Amino acids play several important roles in biochemistry but are chiefly used as building blocks for peptides and proteins. This section begins with a discussion of the peptide bond and its properties, and then discusses cofactors and modifications to amino acids found in proteins.

3.2.1 | Both peptides and proteins are polymers of amino acids

Two amino acids can join via an amide linkage between the carboxyl group of one amino acid and the amino group of the next (**Figure 3.7**). This linkage is referred to as a **peptide bond**, and the resulting molecule is termed a dipeptide. Three linked amino acids are referred to as a tripeptide, four as a tetrapeptide, and so on. **Oligopeptides** are generally 4 to 20 amino acids long, and peptides of more than 20 amino acids are usually referred to as **polypeptides**, although these terms are not strictly defined. Short stretches of amino acids are referred to as **peptides**, and longer chains, generally greater than 100 amino acids long, are referred to as **proteins**.

Both peptides and proteins are linear polymers of amino acids, and the amino acids they are made from have both amino and carboxyl groups. Therefore, when assembled into a peptide or protein, the sequence of amino acids can be described, proceeding from the **amino** (or N) **terminus** to the **carboxy** (or C) **terminus**.

Proteins are large, complex molecules. The average protein is a polymer of about 450 amino acids and a molecular weight of nearly 50,000 g/mole (amino acids in a peptide or protein have an average molecular weight of 110 g/mole). Instead of using these unwieldy numbers, biochemists refer to the molecular weight of a protein in terms of the mass of the individual molecule. Hence, a molecular weight of 50,000 g/mol can be expressed in Daltons, or in the case of proteins, kilo-Daltons (kDa), as 50 kDa. About 80% of proteins fall between 30 and 80 kDa in mass, although peptides can

FIGURE 3.7 **Peptide bond.** The peptide bond is the amide bond that connects the carboxyl group of one amino acid to the amino group of the next. In this process, water is formed. (Black, *Microbiology: Principles and Explorations*, 8e, copyright 2012, John Wiley & Sons. This material is reproduced with permission of John Wiley & Sons, Inc.)

be as small as a few amino acids. For example, the hormone oxytocin is an octapeptide with a molecular weight of 1 kDa. Proteins can be as large as thousands of amino acids, such as the protein titin, which has 34,350 amino acids and a molecular weight of 3,816 kDa.

We might expect proteins with greater mass to be physically larger. While this is often the case, the shape of the protein also plays an important role. **Figure 3.8** shows some representative proteins and their Stokes radius, a property of their size and shape. As we might expect, if we were to assume that these proteins are spherical, the ratio of their diameters is proportionally less than the ratio of their masses. This is not necessarily the case if the protein adopts some other conformation.

In the simplest scenario, a protein is a **monomer**, comprised of a single chain of amino acids folded into an active protein; however, in reality, proteins are often **multimers** consisting of several subunits. When assembled into its active complex, a protein may have the same subunits repeated several times, for example, a homotetramer with four identical subunits, or several different subunits, like a heterotrimer that has three different subunits. Often, subunits of a protein are labeled with regard to their function, such as regulatory and catalytic, or with Greek letters to assist in identifying them (**Figure 3.9**). The stoichiometry of the subunits is treated as in a chemical formula; thus, a tetrameric protein comprising two copies of each subunit would have the designation $\alpha_2\beta_2$.

Many of the techniques we employ in studying proteins are shared with the ones that are used to study synthetic polymers. These are discussed in **Biochemistry: Polymer chemistry**.

Protein	MW (kDa)	Stokes radius (nm)
IgM pentamer	1048	6.70
Apoferritin band 1	720	5.91
Apoferritin band 2	480	5.17
β-phycoerythrin	242	4.11
Lactate dehydrogenase	146	3.46
Bovine serum albumin	66	2.66
Soybean trypsin inhibitor	20	1.78

FIGURE 3.8   **Sizes of proteins.**   A comparison of the overall molar mass and relative size (Stokes radius) of proteins of differing sizes. The ratio of the Stokes radii of the IgM pentamer to soybean trypsin inhibitor is 3.7:1, while the ratio of their masses is 52.4:1. Note that this assumes that these proteins are roughly spherical in shape, which is not the case for all proteins.

Aspartate transcarbamoylase
(α6β6)

FIGURE 3.9   **Multimeric proteins.**   Many proteins have multiple subunits or are found in solution as multimers. Aspartate transcarbamoylase has six regulatory and six catalytic subunits in the holoenzyme. The second three catalytic subunits are found behind the three shown in this image. (PDB ID 1Q95, Huang, J., Lipscomb, W.N. (2004) Aspartate Transcarbamylase (ATCase) of Escherichia coli: A New Crystalline R-State Bound to PALA, or to Product Analogues Citrate and Phosphate, *Biochemistry* 43: 6415–6421)

Biochemistry

Polymer chemistry

Many important molecules in biochemistry are polymers, including proteins and the nucleic acids DNA and RNA. Many carbohydrates can also form polymers that can play structural roles, store energy, or contribute to protein trafficking and cell–cell recognition. Lipids do not typically form polymers, but they are built in a modular fashion from smaller building blocks and aggregate using many of the same weak forces that govern the behavior of larger molecules. Relevant lessons can be learned by comparing polymer chemistry and biological molecules.

Polymers are either linear or branched chains built of smaller molecules termed monomers. In most synthetic polymers, the monomeric units are small, simple organic molecules that join together through addition reactions between alkenes, or through condensation reactions to form polyamides or polyesters. These last two reactions are found in biochemistry, where proteins are an example of a polyamide and nucleic acids are an example of a polyphosphodiester.

The properties of polymers are partially dependent on the monomers that make up the polymer and partially dependent on the size of the polymer. In synthetic polymers, the desired qualities are often the ability to be drawn into filaments, such as nylon or Kevlar; the clarity of the material, for example, polycarbonate or Plexiglas; and the moldability or strength of the material, such as most plastics including polystyrene, polyethylene, and polypropylene. Proteins and carbohydrates display some of the same properties as synthetic polymers. However, because of the variety of side chains in the amino acids of proteins and the different types of weak forces involved, there is a greater variety of conformations that a protein can adopt and different types of roles it can play.

Polymer chemistry tools can be applied to answer biochemical questions. Low resolution techniques to determine the general overall size and shape of a protein include size exclusion chromatography, dynamic light scatter, fluorescence anisotropy, analytical ultracentrifugation, electron microscopy, or soft ionization mass spectrometry. Although such techniques do not provide the same information as X-ray diffraction or nuclear magnetic resonance (NMR) studies, two effective techniques for determining the structure of a molecule, they do provide important information about how the molecule behaves in solution and whether it forms multimeric assemblies.

A.

B.

p orbitals   **π bond between carbon and nitrogen**

FIGURE 3.10 **Nature of the peptide bond.** **A.** An analysis of a Lewis structure of the peptide bond reveals resonance states that contribute to the overall structure. **B.** Because of *p* orbital overlap, the C–N bond is shorter and more stable, and the peptide unit is planar, all supportive of the predicted structure.

3.2.2 The peptide bond has special characteristics

The amide bond formed between two amino acids is referred to as a peptide bond. The nature of the peptide bond has several interesting and important characteristics. Although this structure is often depicted as containing a double bond between the oxygen and carbon, it is actually more complex. Analysis of a peptide bond's Lewis structure indicates that the double bond could also be drawn between the carbonyl carbon and nitrogen. This contributes to the peptide bond structure to a small but significant extent (**Figure 3.10**).

Sketching the molecular orbitals forming the peptide unit shows that there is a pi (π) cloud that extends through the carbonyl oxygen and carbon, as well as the nitrogen. Therefore, according to molecular orbital theory, there is double bond-like character to the C–N peptide bond. The peptide bond is shorter than an ordinary C–N bond, and it has a higher bond enthalpy, requiring more energy to break. Finally, because the C–N bond has overlap of these π orbitals, we would anticipate that this would limit rotation around the C–N bond axis. Peptide units are planar with the peptide bond fixed in either a *cis* or *trans* conformation. In most instances, the conformation observed in proteins is *trans*, due in part to steric clashes between the carbonyl oxygen and the hydrogen attached to the peptide nitrogen.

Since the peptide is planar, it can be thought of as a fixed unit (**Figure 3.11**). Based on this information, it is possible to start to determine the crude structure of a protein and tease out how these planar units are interconnected. However, the torsional angles between the peptide units are also required. Imagine laying a series of cards down flat on a table and connecting them with flexible connectors such as pieces of string. If the torsional bond angles (the twist found between two cards) on either side of the card (the peptide unit) angles are known, it is possible to start to see how these flat units can form a three-dimensional structure. These angles are termed the phi (Φ) and psi (Ψ) angles.

Peptide bonds are rather stable. In the absence of enzymes, peptide bonds are generally resistant to base-catalyzed cleavage, although they can be broken with acid. Enzymatic degradation of proteins and peptides is catalyzed by proteases and peptidases, that is, enzymes that employ nucleophilic attack on the peptide carbon to cleave these bonds.

FIGURE 3.11 **Phi and psi bond angles.** **A.** The phi (Φ) and psi (Ψ) angles are the torsional bond angles located on either side of the peptide bond. **B.** Newman projections show the view down the nitrogen–carbon or carbon–carbon bond. Knowing these angles enables investigators to solve the structure of the protein structure at low resolution. (Adapted from drawings created by Jason D. Kahn, Univ. Maryland.)

3.2.3 Many proteins require inorganic ions or small organic molecules to function

Many proteins require other groups for binding or activity; these "non-protein" groups are termed **cofactors** or **prosthetic groups**. A protein missing its cofactor is referred to as an **apoprotein**, whereas a **holoprotein** contains both the protein and its cofactor. Apoenzymes or holoenzymes are enzymes that are analogous to apoproteins or holoproteins. Cofactors can be broadly divided into metal ions and small organic groups.

Divalent metal ions are a common cofactor Many proteins use divalent metal ions as cofactors in enzymatic reactions, either to initiate conformational changes in the protein, to bind and transport electrons, or to facilitate binding of the protein to other proteins or nucleic acids. Such ions include Ca^{2+}, Mg^{2+}, Zn^{2+}, Fe^{2+}, and Cu^{2+}. Other oxidation states of these metals, such as Fe^{3+} or Cu^+ may also be observed as cofactors; less commonly found metal ions include Sr^{2+}, Cr^{3+}, Ni^{2+}, or Mn^{2+}. Nutritionally, all of these ions are referred to as minerals.

Small organic molecules are often used as cofactors   Another type of cofactor used by proteins is small organic molecules (**Figure 3.12**). As with divalent metal ions, this group includes molecules involved in oxidation–reduction reactions, catalysis, binding, and transport. Examples of small organic cofactors are the redox active nicotine adenine dinucleotide (NAD^+) and flavin adenine dinucleotide (FAD); pyridoxal phosphate, which is used in amino acid metabolism; and heme, a functional group that combines both an organic molecule (the protoporphyrin ring), and an inorganic group (the iron ion found in its center). In the diet, these cofactors or their precursors are often referred to as vitamins.

3.2.4 | Amino acids can be modified within proteins

Most of the amino acids founds in proteins are the 20 common amino acids discussed above; however, amino acids can be modified within a protein (**Figure 3.13**). Several of the common modifications can have major effects; they can covalently cross-link proteins, alter activity, or change the location of proteins within the cell. Such modifications include covalent attachment of a carbohydrate through a glycosylation, or a lipid by an acylation or acetylation, or by phosphorylation or hydroxylation of key amino acids.

NAD⁺

FAD

Heme

FIGURE 3.12 **Examples of cofactors.**   These molecules are examples of common cofactors found in proteins. NAD^+ and FAD are both involved in redox reactions and are important electron carriers. Heme is used in oxygen transport, oxidation reactions, and as an electron carrier.

FIGURE 3.13 **Amino acid modifications.**   Many amino acids are regulated through post-translational modifications. Shown are examples of acetylation, phosphorylation, and hydroxylation.

Lipid modifications often change the subcellular localization or function of a protein

Lipids are largely nonpolar hydrophobic molecules. Binding or attachment of a lipid often results in a protein being localized to a lipid bilayer. This is the case when the fatty acids myristate or palmitate are attached covalently to serine residues of a protein through the serine hydroxyl group, generating an ester linkage between the serine hydroxyl and the carboxyl of the lipid, or when the steroid precursor farnesyl couples through a cysteine residue, forming a thioether.

Other lipid modifications can alter the function of a protein. Histones are small, positively charged proteins that organize DNA. Acetylation of lysine residues in histones neutralizes the positive charge on the amino group and decreases the interaction between the histone protein and the DNA backbone, increasing accessibility of enzymes to DNA and subsequently altering gene expression.

Carbohydrates are often found on secreted proteins

Many secreted proteins have carbohydrate modifications. The modifications may be short stretches of carbohydrate or massive carbohydrate complexes. Carbohydrates link to proteins either through the nitrogen of the asparagine side chain (termed an *N*-linked carbohydrate) or through the oxygen of the hydroxyl groups of serine or threonine (termed an *O*-linked carbohydrate).

Phosphorylation can alter protein function

One of the most common protein modifications is the addition of a phosphate. The phosphorylation is through enzymes known as **kinases**, and ATP is typically the source of the phosphate. Phosphates can be added to the hydroxyl groups of serine, threonine, or tyrosine residues via a phosphoester linkage. The incorporation of a phosphate can dramatically change the activity of an enzyme or cause the translocation or movement of a protein within a cell. Both phosphorylation and dephosphorylation are often thought of as switches in the cell, whereby a pathway or reaction is turned on or off. One example of this is lipolysis, the breakdown of stored fat in the cell. Lipolysis is mediated via protein kinase A, which phosphorylates several key enzymes and regulators of triacylglycerol storage, activating lipid breakdown.

Proteins of the extracellular matrix may be hydroxylated

Hydroxylated amino acids are often contained in the secreted structural proteins of the extracellular matrix, such as collagen. In these proteins, proline or lysine residues may be hydroxylated by prolyl or lysyl hydroxylases. In proline, hydroxylation occurs on either the γ carbon, C-4 of the side chain, or β carbon, C-3 of the side chain; the resulting amino acid is in 4-hydroxy or 3-hydroxyproline. Hydroxylations of lysine occur on the δ carbon. Elemental oxygen, O_2, is the oxygen source in both of these reactions. Ascorbate, also known as vitamin C, is used by the enzymes catalyzing these reactions to complete their catalytic cycle and become trapped in an oxidized state; in the absence of vitamin C, these enzymes are unable to operate and cannot hydroxylate proteins. The dietary-deficiency disease scurvy is marked by weakened connective tissue, bleeding, and tooth loss and results from the body's inability to modify these proteins.

WORKED PROBLEM 3.2 | Myoglobin structures

Using the Protein Data Bank (PDB), access a protein structure for myoglobin, the oxygen-binding protein found in muscle. Does myoglobin have a cofactor?

Strategy Access the PDB online (http://www.rcsb.org/pdb/home/home.do). Search for "myoglobin" (it will appear numerous times). Read the page and examine these structures. Do any of the structures have groups that are not comprised of protein?

Solution Myoglobin contains a heme group: a large planar heterocyclic structure with a single iron atom in the center. Heme groups are common prosthetic groups found in many proteins. They are important in the binding of oxygen, electron transport, and redox chemistry.

Follow-up question Is myoglobin a small, average, or large protein?

3.2 Summary

- Proteins are polymers of amino acids, averaging 450 amino acids in length (approximately 50 kDa).
- Proteins can have one or more subunits, and these subunits can be repeats of the same polypeptide or multiple different polypeptides.
- The peptide bond joining amino acids in the protein is planar because it has partial double bond character.
- Proteins may contain cofactors in the form of metal ions or small organic prosthetic groups.
- Proteins may have modifications such as acetylations or farnesylations (lengthy hydrocarbon chains), phosphorylations or hydroxylations.

3.2 Concept Check

- Describe what a protein is like chemically.
- Describe the peptide bond and explain why the peptide unit is planar.
- Name several different prosthetic groups.
- Describe the different types of post-translational modifications to proteins.

3.3 Proteins Are Molecules of Defined Shape and Structure

Proteins are varied in terms of both function and structure. As proteins are synthesized in the cell, they spontaneously and, in most cases, independently fold into the proper conformation. This is an amazing phenomenon, given that a molecule with over 5,000 atoms and an equal number of covalent bonds snaps into a single structure with near perfection. This section discusses the complex structures that proteins form. Proteins are organized into four levels of organization: primary, secondary, tertiary, and quaternary.

3.3.1 The primary structure of a protein is its amino acid sequence

At one level, a polymer of amino acids is like a charm bracelet, with each amino acid being one of the charms or beads. There can be multiples of a particular type of charm or bead in the bracelet, but they are placed in a specific order. The order or sequence of the amino acids in a protein is the **primary structure** of that protein (**Figure 3.14**). Just as alterations to the number, type, or position of charms in a bracelet might change the appearance, changes to the number of amino acids, the types of amino acid, or even the specific order of amino acids can alter the properties of a protein.

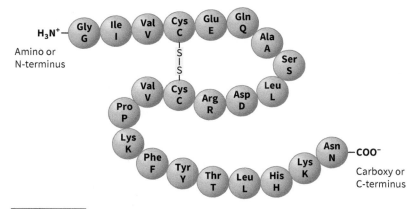

FIGURE 3.14 Primary sequence of a protein. The primary sequence of a protein is the sequence of amino acids from the amino to carboxy terminus (the N-to-C terminus).

If a single hydrophobic amino acid valine (Val or V) is substituted for a similar hydrophobic amino acid such as isoleucine (Ile or I), there may be no observed difference in the new protein. This type of substitution is termed a **conservative substitution**. A more radical substitution, such as the bulky hydrophobic tryptophan (Trp, W) for the small negatively charged aspartate (Asp, or D) may result in a more substantial change to protein conformation or function.

Here are two examples of how proteins may vary with regard to amino acid sequence and the ramifications of these changes. The peptide hormone insulin regulates carbohydrate and lipid metabolism and is used to treat type 1 diabetes, also known as diabetes mellitus. It is made as a single polypeptide that is then cleaved into two fragments termed the A and B chains. From its discovery in 1923 until the early 1980s, the insulin used to treat type 1 diabetes was derived from dogs or pigs rather than humans. The insulin from dogs or pigs is similar to the human hormone but differs at several sites (**Figure 3.15**). These differences were not sufficient to render the hormone ineffective but did lead to immunological reactions in some people.

An example of a more harmful amino acid change is found in the disease cystic fibrosis. Although many different mutations can lead to cystic fibrosis, one of the most common is ΔF508 in the *CFTR* gene. This gene codes for a protein that allows the passage of water and chloride ions through the plasma membrane of cells (**Figure 3.16**). This mutation results in a protein where the amino acid phenylalanine (F) at position 508 in the protein has been deleted (Δ). As a result of this single change in the amino acid sequence, the chloride channel fails to move to the plasma membrane and is retained in the endoplasmic reticulum following synthesis. This causes a lack of chloride ion transport, leading to the formation of thick, viscous mucus in the lungs of people with this disorder.

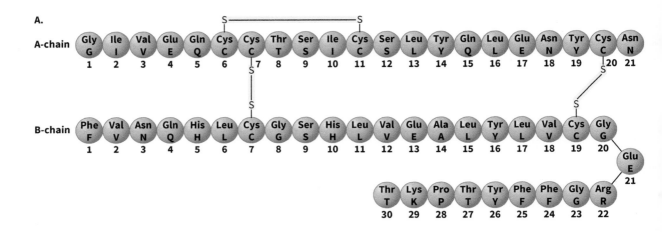

B.

	Insulin B-chain	Insulin A-chain
Human	FVNQHLCGSHLVEALYLVCGERGFFYTPKT	GIVEQCCTSICSLYQLENYCN
Great apes	FVNQHLCGSHLVEALYLVCGERGFFYTPKT	GIVEQCCTSICSLYQLENYCN
Macaque	FVNQHLCGSHLVEALYLVCGERGFFYTPKT	GIVEQCCTSICSLYQLENYCN
Rabbit	FVNQHLCGSHLVEALYLVCGERGFFYTPKS	GIVEQCCTSICSLYQLENYCN
Dog	FVNQHLCGSHLVEALYLVCGERGFFYTPKA	GIVEQCCTSICSLYQLENYCN
Horse	FVNQHLCGSHLVEALYLVCGERGFFYTPKA	GIVEQCCTGICSLYQLENYCN
Pig	FVNQHLCGSHLVEALYLVCGERGFFYTPKA	GIVEQCCTSICSLYQLENYCN
Cat	FVNQHLCGSHLVEALYLVCGERGFFYTPKA	GIVEQCCASVCSLYQLEHYCN
Rat	FVKQHLCGPHLVEALYLVCGERGFFYTPKS	GIVDQCCTSICSLYQLENYCN
Mouse	FVKQHLCGPHLVEALYLVCGERGFFYTPKS	GIVDQCCTSICSLYQLENYCN
Cattle	FVNQHLCGSHLVEALYLVCGERGFFYTPKA	GIVEQCCASVCSLYQLENYCN

FIGURE 3.15 **Differences in insulin sequence.** **A.** The sequence of the native human insulin is shown. **B.** An alignment of the A and B chains are compared for different species.

FIGURE 3.16 **Cystic fibrosis.** There are numerous mutations that can lead to cystic fibrosis, all of which affect the CTFR protein, a chloride channel found in lung and gastric mucosa. Mutations to this protein block the secretion of chloride, which results in the formation of thick mucus in the lung and gastrointestinal tract.

The primary structure of a protein is one of the most important aspects of protein structure; however, it is currently not possible to determine the more complex structure of a protein based solely on the amino acid sequence.

3.3.2 The secondary structure of a protein is comprised of a few conserved structures

The next level of organization of protein structure is **secondary structure**, which consists of two major structural elements: the α helix and β sheet. In addition, there are **turns**, tight connectors between two other structural elements, and **coils** or **loops**, larger regions without defined secondary structure.

The alpha helix is the most common element of secondary structure

The α **helix** is formed by the peptide backbone of a protein wrapping into a right-handed spiral (**Figure 3.17**). This spiral is held together by lone pairs of electrons on carbonyl oxygens forming hydrogen bonds with the hydrogen attached to the peptide nitrogen four amino acids in front of it. Because the first amino acid is bound to the fifth, the second to the sixth, the third to the seventh, and so on, this bonding is referred to as i+4. Since the groups involved in hydrogen bonding are not at the end of a whole amino acid unit, it takes 3.6 amino acids to complete one turn of an α helix. Because there are 360 degrees in a circle, and the α helix has 3.6 amino acids per turn, there are 100 degrees of turn per amino acid. The helix's pitch, or vertical distance required to make one rotation is 5.4 Å. Due to the tight turning of the α helix, the core of the helix is almost solid; that is, there is no space in the middle of the helix and nothing can pass through its core. Although often depicted as pipes, the α helix is more rod-like. The diameter of the α helix's core is 6 Å, but the addition of the amino acid side chains

A.

B.

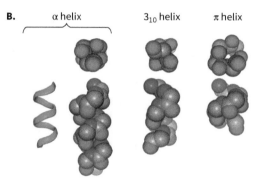

FIGURE 3.17 **Alpha helix.** **A.** The α helices are the most common structure observed in proteins. They are right-handed helices with an i+4 hydrogen bonding pattern. (Allison: *Fundamental Molecular Biology*, 2e, copyright 2011, John Wiley & Sons. This material is reproduced with permission of John Wiley & Sons, Inc.) **B.** The 3:10 helix (i+3) and the π helix (i+5) are tighter or looser, respectively. (PDB ID 2QD1 Medlock, A.E., Dailey, T.A., Ross, T.A., Dailey, H.A., Lanzilotta, W.N. (2007) A pi-Helix Switch Selective for Porphyrin Deprotonation and Product Release in Human Ferrochelatase. *J. Mol. Biol.* 373: 1006–1016)

increases the value to approximately 12 Å. Because of the arrangement of the peptide units in an α helix and the twist of the helix, the amino acid side chains are found only on the outside of the central structure.

Although hydrogen bonding in an α helix follows the pattern i+4, other patterns are found in nature. For example, the 3_{10} **helix** follows an i+3 pattern, resulting in a tighter helix, and the π **helix** has a looser i+5 pattern. The π helices are often short, containing seven amino acids on average (slightly more than a single turn) and are embedded within a stretch of α helix. Because this structure introduces a bulge to the helix, it is sometimes referred to as an α aneurism. The length of an average α helix is ten amino acids, encompassing about three turns. The influenza protein hemagglutinin is the largest helix found to date, at 104 amino acids in length.

Most amino acids can be found in α helices, but there are two notable exceptions. Glycine's small side chain, comprised of a single hydrogen atom, is floppy and discourages helix formation. In proline, the side chain links back onto the amino group, preventing the Φ and Ψ bond angles from forming the geometry necessary for an α helix. This leads either to a kink in the helix or, more often, termination of the helix at the proline. Proline also lacks the proton necessary for hydrogen bonding, which would destabilize the helix.

The α helix aligns the carbonyl groups in a single direction, resulting in a dipole moment for the entire structure, which yields a partial positive charge on the amino-terminal end and a partial negative charge on the carboxy-terminal end of the helix. In addition, the handedness of the helix (α helices are right-handed) means that the overall structure is chiral. This chirality can be experimentally measured with a technique called circular dichroism, which provides a percent of residues in an α helix in the protein.

The beta pleated sheet is a major element of secondary structure

The other major element of secondary structure is the β **pleated sheet** or β **sheet**. Unlike the more compact form of the α helix, in a β sheet the individual strands are extended. The sheet is named "β" because it was the second structure to be determined (**Figure 3.18**). As in the α helix, the bonding unit in a β sheet is formed by hydrogen bonding between carbonyl oxygens and the peptide hydrogen and nitrogens, although here it occurs in the plane of the sheet between different strands. This means that the amino acid side chains attached to these backbones alternate on either side of the sheet, perpendicular to the plane created by the backbones. Numerous individual strands can contribute to a single β sheet. Although β sheets are often depicted as being short and flat, in reality, they are often twisted or flowing, and they may even circle back upon themselves to form a barrel-like structure.

There are two distinct types of β sheet: **parallel** β sheets in which the two strands forming the sheet run in the same direction, and **antiparallel** β sheets in which the two strands run in opposite directions. This does not alter the positioning of the side chains of the amino acids, but it does change the pattern of hydrogen bonding between the backbones. Instead of a simple rectangular pattern of hydrogen bonding seen in parallel β sheets, antiparallel sheets have a trapezoidal shape. There is no apparent difference in hydrogen bond strength or structural stability between these two types of β sheet, and all amino acids can participate in these structures.

Hairpin turns, and loops or coils are minor but important elements of secondary structure

Alpha helices and β sheets are connected to each other using either hairpin turns (or loops) and coils (**Figure 3.19**). Nine different types of hairpin turns exist. These are categorized based on the Φ and Ψ bond angles they form and the overall hydrogen

A.

Secondary protein structure

Peptide bond

Hydrogen bonds

β pleated sheet

7.0 Å

B.

Parallel

C-terminus

C-terminus

Antiparallel

C-terminus

N-terminus

N-terminus

N-terminus

FIGURE 3.18 **Beta sheet.**
A. In β sheets there are hydrogen bonds between the backbone carbonyl groups and amino protons of adjacent sheets. Side chains (R) emerge from the top and bottom sides of the sheet. (Allison: *Fundamental Molecular Biology*, 2e, copyright 2011, John Wiley & Sons. This material is reproduced with permission of John Wiley & Sons, Inc.) **B.** A β pleated sheet can be broadly categorized as parallel, where the strands run in the same direction, or antiparallel, where the strands run in opposite directions.

bonding pattern. Hairpin turns comprise only three or four amino acids, and again are stabilized by hydrogen bonding in the backbone. Loops or coils may be as short as five or six amino acids, or can be composed of tens of amino acids, but they lack elements of α helix or β sheet and in the past were therefore referred to as "random coils." Today, the term *random coil* is no longer used because it is recognized that despite the lack of regular elements such as α helix and β sheet, the coils are probably organized into a discrete structure.

Hydrogen bonds stabilize secondary structures
Both helix and sheet are stabilized by hydrogen bonds in the peptide backbone. This is a critical feature in protein structure: repeated and regular hydrogen bonding contributes significantly to the overall stability of both elements of secondary structure and the overall stability of the protein. The contribution made by hydrogen bonding can be observed experimentally. Synthetic peptides comprised of a variety of amino acids can fold into either helix or sheet conformations. These proteins denature in response to similar experimental conditions indicating that the side chains are not contributing to the overall stability of the secondary structure.

A.

Type I

Type II

B.

Coil or loop

FIGURE 3.19 **Turns and coils.** Turns and coils link other pieces of secondary structure. **A.** Hairpin turns require a minimum of four residues to complete the turn and are stabilized by a single backbone hydrogen bond. **B.** A coil or loop, which is a longer connection between two elements of secondary structure. (PDB ID 3WFT Mizohata, E., Morita, Y., Oohora, K., Hirata, K., Ohbayashi, J., Inoue, T., Hisaeda, Y., Hayashi, T. (2014) Co(II)/Co(I) reduction-induced axial histidine-flipping in myoglobin reconstituted with a cobalt tetradehydrocorrin as a methionine synthase model. *Chem.Commun.(Camb.)* 50: 12560–12563)

Medical Biochemistry

Protein folding and disease

Despite their remarkable complexity, proteins fold into a single conformation and generally do this consistently, without assistance, and almost instantaneously. However, some proteins have more than one stable conformation.

In the mid-twentieth century there was an epidemic of a neurological disease among the Fore people of eastern Papua New Guinea. This disease is called kuru, also known as the shivering disease. People affected, who were typically the elder women of the group, suffered muscle weakness followed by shaking and tremors or truncal ataxia. As the disease developed over the course of a year, patients gradually lost control of their musculature, eventually becoming unable to take care of themselves or eat. They also lost control of their emotions, undergoing bouts of depression and of uncontrollable laughter. The disease always resulted in death.

Kuru has now been identified as a type of spongiform encephalopathy—a degradation of the brain related to Creutzfeldt–Jakob syndrome; bovine spongiform encephalopathy (also known as BSE or mad cow disease); and scrapie, a degenerative disease of sheep and goats. These diseases are all caused by prions—infectious protein particles that have, for reasons that are not totally clear, folded into an alternative conformation that causes disease. In all of these instances, the protein found in the healthy state is largely α helical, but in disease states it mostly adopts a β sheet conformation. It is now believed that when it is in the β sheet conformation, the protein polymerizes and forms insoluble plaques that lead to neurodegeneration. Exposure of a properly folded protein to the protein in the prion conformation will stabilize or catalyze the refolding of the healthy protein to the diseased one.

Exactly how the prion enters the body is unclear, but it is clear that consumption of diseased tissue increases the risk. In the case of the Fore, kuru was partially spread through funerary rituals. As a sign of respect for the dead, the Fore practice transumption; that is, cannibalism of the dead by the remaining village members. In this practice, women were more likely to eat neurological tissue and thus had a greater chance of exposure.

The study of this disease may provide important clues to many other disorders. In the United Kingdom in the late 1980s and early 1990s, over 4.4 million cattle were destroyed in an attempt to contain an epidemic of BSE. Over 180,000 cattle were found to be infected, and over 175 people contracted Creutzfeldt-Jakob syndrome as a result of exposure, through consumption of infected meat.

More broadly, the issue of protein folding as a cause of disease is becoming more widely accepted. It may be that other neurological diseases, including Alzheimer's disease, are the result of neuronal damage caused by insoluble plaques of misfolded protein.

Changes to secondary structure of a protein can have serious implications on protein folding and protein function. Some of these implications are discussed in **Medical Biochemistry: Protein folding and disease**.

3.3.3   The tertiary structure of a protein is the organization of secondary structures into conserved motifs

The **tertiary structure** of a protein often gives the overall shape of the protein (**Figure 3.20**). As the structures of more proteins have been solved, it has become clear that, as with the α helix and β sheet, some elements of tertiary structure are repeated in different proteins. These combinations of secondary structure are termed **motifs**. Motifs should not be confused with **domains**, which are pieces of a protein that retain their structure in the absence of the rest of the protein; that is, a domain is a discretely folding structure whereas a motif may be part of a domain. This section examines several of the most common structural motifs and reviews the forces involved in stabilizing these structures.

Alpha motifs contain predominantly helical domains
Several common motifs are mostly helical (**Figure 3.21**). They include the helix-turn-helix motif, the three-helix bundle, and the four-helix bundle. The globin fold, which comprises at least eight helices, is an example of a more complex motif that has been retained in evolution.

Beta motifs are arrangements of either parallel or antiparallel beta sheets   Other common motifs contain largely or solely β structures (**Figure 3.22**). These include the Greek-key motif,

Tertiary structure combines elements of secondary structure.

Sheet

Helix

FIGURE 3.20   Tertiary structures.   The tertiary structure of a protein gives the overall shape of the protein, in other words, how elements of the secondary structure (helix and sheet) are joined together to give the structure of a single polypeptide chain in a protein. (PDB ID 1AV5 Lima, C.D., Klein, M.G., Hendrickson, W.A. (1997) Structure-based analysis of catalysis and substrate definition in the HIT protein family. *Science* 278: 286–290)

Helix-turn-helix   **Four-helix bundle**   **Globin fold**
                                                                (eight helices)

FIGURE 3.21 **Alpha structures.**   Examples of all α structures include the helix-turn-helix, four-helix bundle, and globin fold. (Left: PDB ID 4DO2 Amprazi, M., Kapetaniou, E.G., Kokkinidis, M. (2013) Structural plasticity of 4-alpha-helical bundles exemplified by the puzzle-like molecular assembly of the Rop protein. *Proc.Natl.Acad.Sci.*USA 111: 11049–11054; Middle: PDB ID 1SZI Hickenbottom, S.J., Kimmel, A.R., Londos, C., Hurley, J.H. (2004) Structure of a Lipid Droplet Protein: The PAT Family Member TIP47 *Structure* 12: 1199–1207; Right: PDB ID 3WFT Mizohata, E., Morita, Y., Oohora, K., Hirata, K., Ohbayashi, J., Inoue, T., Hisaeda, Y., Hayashi, T. (2014) Co(II)/Co(I) reduction-induced axial histidine-flipping in myoglobin reconstituted with a cobalt tetradehydrocorrin as a methionine synthase model. *Chem.Commun.(Camb.)* 50: 12560–12563)

an arrangement of four strands of β sheet; the β barrel, a β sheet that has been closed to form a barrel-like structure; and the β propeller, a β sheet that is twisted from a central point until it has the appearance of a propeller. The immunoglobulin fold is an example of a more complex motif consisting of flattened β barrel structures.

Protein folds are conserved   Protein folds are conserved throughout evolution, although the folds may be made with different combinations of amino acids. Therefore, in addition to other databases you may be familiar with, there are structural databases and tools for proteins, such as Structural Classification of Proteins (SCOP), and the Class, Architecture,

FIGURE 3.22 **Beta structures.**   **A.** The Greek key is a four-strand β sheet. **B.** A β barrel has a β sheet wrapped up on itself. **C.** The β propeller structure has from four to eight blades, each of which is twisted like a fan blade. **D.** An immuno-globulin fold has strands of β sheet sandwiched on top of one another. (B: PDB ID 5EB6 Close, D.W., Langan, P.S., Bradbury, A.R.M. (2016) Evolution and characterization of a new reversibly photoswitching chromogenic protein, Dathail. *J.Mol.Biol.* 428: 1776–1789; C: PDB ID 3UVL Zhang, P., Lee, H., Brunzelle, J.S., Couture, J.F. (2012) The plasticity of WDR5 peptide-binding cleft enables the binding of the SET1 family of histone methyltransferases. *Nucleic Acids Res.* 40: 4237–4246; D: PDB ID 1IGT Harris, L.J., Larson, S.B., Hasel, K.W., McPherson, A. (1997) Refined structure of an intact IgG2a monoclonal antibody. *Biochemistry* 36: 1581–1597)

Topology, Homologous superfamily (CATH), which can be used to categorize, organize and search for conserved structural motifs. Both of these databases are freely accessible on the internet.

Numerous weak forces (and one covalent one) dictate tertiary structure

The covalent peptide bond links amino acids together in a protein. However, weak forces dominate the assembly of secondary and tertiary structures (**Figure 3.23**). These are the weak interactions that are studied in both general and organic chemistry; however, when studied as part of biochemistry, there are specific aspects of these forces that need to be considered.

Hydrogen bonding is, in many ways, the most important interaction in protein folding and in many other phenomena, including formation of phospholipid bilayers and the formation of the DNA double helix.

FIGURE 3.23 **Forces involved in stabilizing proteins.** **A.** The main side chain interactions found in proteins are shown. **B.** The different ways that side chains contribute to hydrogen bonding are shown.

To briefly review, a hydrogen bond forms when a hydrogen attached to a highly electronegative atom, usually an oxygen, nitrogen, or fluorine, is polarized to the point at which it will interact with the lone pair of electrons of a nearby molecule, again often a molecule of oxygen, nitrogen, or fluorine. In biochemistry, hydrogen bonds do not typically occur with hydrogen atoms bound to carbon, sulfur, or any other atoms, because these atoms lack the electronegativity required to sufficiently polarize the hydrogen. Hydrogen bonds are strongest, approximately 5 kcal/mol in biological systems, when the groups are arranged linearly and are within 2.2 Å of one another. Electronegativity also plays a role in hydrogen bond strength. The fluorine-based hydrogen bonds are stronger than those made with oxygen, and the oxygen-based structures are stronger than the structures using nitrogen.

Hydrogen bonds can be considered in one of two ways: first between amino acids within the protein, and second between the solvent molecules.

Hydrogen bonds are common and are found in every protein. Most of the polar amino acids contain groups such as hydroxyl groups, amines, and carboxamides that can participate in hydrogen bonding. In addition, the peptide backbone has lone pairs of electrons on the carbonyl carbon and peptide nitrogen that can participate in hydrogen bonding. The tertiary structure of proteins depends mainly on interactions of side chains with each other or with the backbone, whereas secondary structure depends mainly on interactions that occur within the peptide backbone itself.

The second way that hydrogen bonds affect protein structure is by hydrogen bonding within the solvent water molecules. This type of bonding is part of the hydrophobic effect, the phenomena in which hydrophobic groups cluster together. The hydrophobic effect does not depend on hydrophobic residues being attracted to one another. For example, hydrophobic molecules, such as oil or hexane, spread out to coat surfaces; thus, on a rainy day a drop of oil will spread out and form a slick on a puddle. In a hydrophobic liquid, such as hexane, London dispersion and van der Waals forces are at work in the molecules of the liquid, but these forces are 10 to 1,000 times weaker than hydrogen bonds. Therefore, although there are interactive forces between hydrophobic side chains, they are not strong enough to explain how hydrophobic residues group together in the core of the protein.

Water has strong intermolecular interactions, and it can form multiple hydrogen bonds at any time. When a hydrophobic molecule such as hexane or a hydrophobic side chain is introduced into water, the water molecules rearrange to accommodate the hydrophobic group. There is no hydrogen bonding possible between water and a hydrophobic molecule. Instead, water molecules organize into cages around hydrophobic molecules. The organization and formation of these cages to preserve hydrogen bonding in water results in a decrease in entropy, making this process generally unfavorable. Clustering hydrophobic molecules means that more can be caged with less surface area, resulting in fewer water molecules needed to form the cage. The overall result is an increased freedom of water molecules and an overall increase in entropy. This is the basis of the hydrophobic effect.

Dipole–dipole interactions are also found in proteins. Several polar side chains have the potential to participate in a dipole interaction, either with other polar residues or with the peptide backbone. In addition, an α helix has its own dipole and can generate enough of an electric field to interact with other side chains or helices.

Salt bridging describes the interaction of a positively and a negatively charged amino acid. A salt bridge is basically an electrostatic interaction; therefore, the energetics of the interaction of the positive and negative charge can be described using Coulomb's law:

$$F = \frac{kq_1q_2}{r^2D}$$

In this expression, the force of the interaction is dependent on Coulomb's constant (k) and the magnitude of the charges q_1 and q_2, and is inversely dependent on the square of the distance between the two charges (r^2) and the dielectric constant of the media, D. The charge on ionized amino acid side chains is always + or −1; therefore, q_1 and q_2 are constant in proteins, and the strength of the interaction depends on the square of the distance between the charges and the strength of the dielectric constant. The dielectric constant of water is high, almost 80 Debye units, whereas the dielectric constant of a nonpolar solvent such as hexane is only about 1 to 5 Debye units, so the strength of an electrostatic interaction is decreased by a factor of 80 in water, but by a much smaller value in a nonpolar solvent.

Coulombic interactions have several interesting ramifications and tend to lead to some misunderstandings in biochemistry. A common misconception is that adding a charged group, such as a phosphate, will cause a protein to translocate across the cell based on electrostatics alone. A quick analysis of the distance covered and the strength of the force shows that this is not the case.

Biochemical systems are aqueous, leading some to assume that *all* electrostatic interactions are weakened by the dielectric constant of water. The core of proteins where many salt bridges are found is also the location of many hydrophobic amino acid side chains. Thus, in many ways, the core of a protein is an oily droplet, so the strength of a salt bridge may be high in the core of the protein owing to the absence of water. Further complicating matters, the low dielectric constant and the close proximity of charged groups to one another in the core of the protein create the possibility that all charged species in the core of the protein interact with one another. Finally, although salt bridges can be viewed as an attractive force between positive and negative side chains, the rules that apply to salt bridges also apply to side chains with the same charge, which repel one another.

Cation-π interactions occur between the positively charged amino acids arginine, lysine, and histidine and a π bond, as shown in Figure 3.23. Pi bonds are seen in any double-bond system. Although the amino acids typically found in these interactions are tyrosine, tryptophan, phenylalanine, or histidine, weak cation-π interactions have been observed between a positively charged side chain and the peptide backbone carbonyl. Cation-π interactions are akin to a hydrogen bond, in that the bond strength decreases with the square of the distance between the two molecules involved ($1/r^2$). Also, the bond is stronger when the cation and π cloud approach each other at a 90° angle, that is, orthogonal to each other. Cation-π interactions are as strong as hydrogen bonds and as common as salt bridges, with anywhere from 5 to 12 bonds in an average protein.

Disulfide bonds are the only covalent force involved in the formation of tertiary structure. In a disulfide bond, two cysteine residues undergo redox chemistry to form a disulfide linkage. Disulfides are more oxidized than a pair of cysteine residues, and will form spontaneously in oxidizing environments. To keep cysteine residues from reacting with each other, a reducing agent is used. In the laboratory, compounds such as β-mercaptoethanol (βME) or dithiothreitol (DTT) are often used to accomplish this task. In the cell, the cytosol is a reducing environment owing to the presence of the peptide glutathione. These compounds will reduce any disulfides that form. Proteins containing disulfide bonds are synthesized and folded in the endoplasmic reticulum (ER).

Three identical subunits (homotrimer, α3)

FIGURE 3.24 **Quaternary structure.** The structure of purine nucleotide phosphorylases is an example of quaternary structure. This protein is a homotrimer with α3 stoichiometry. This enzyme has three identical subunits, each shown here in a different color. Note how the subunits are in close contact with each other in this example. (PDB ID 4EAR Haapalainen, A.M., Ho, M.C., Suarez, J.J., Almo, S.C., Schramm, V.L. (2013) Catalytic Site Conformations in Human PNP by (19) F-NMR and Crystallography. *Chem.Biol.* 20: 212–222)

3.3.4 The quaternary structure of a protein describes how individual subunits interact

Most proteins exist in a complex, either with other subunits of a protein or with different proteins. This is termed the **quaternary** structure of the protein (**Figure 3.24**). The forces that govern the interactions of these individual subunits are the same as those involved in the formation of tertiary structure.

WORKED PROBLEM 3.3 | Protein structure and disease

Sickle cell anemia is a common genetic disorder. The causal mutation in sickle cell anemia is E6V, that is, the substitution of a glutamic acid for valine in the sixth position of the β chain of hemoglobin, a tetrameric protein with the stoichiometry α2β2. In the deoxygenated state, the mutant hemoglobin can polymerize, causing erythrocytes (red blood cells) to form a sickled shape and lyse, leading to the symptoms of this disease. How might this mutation affect all four levels of protein structure?

Strategy   Examine the information we have been given in the question and think about the four levels of protein structure. How could this alteration in amino acid sequence lead to the observed phenotype and disease?

Solution   Hemoglobin is a tetrameric protein. The mutation has altered the primary sequence of the β chains of hemoglobin by replacing a negatively charged glutamic acid with a hydrophobic valine residue. It is not apparent from the information provided in the question how this might affect the secondary and tertiary structure of the protein. However, we do know that the protein is functional in the oxygenated state; that is, the mutation is not lethal, and therefore we may assume that the secondary and tertiary structures have not been significantly disrupted. Functional studies have borne out this hypothesis. However, the quaternary structure of the protein has been somewhat altered. Although the hemoglobin is still able to act as a tetramer, in the deoxygenated state, the hydrophobic valine enables the protein to assemble into polymers, leading to symptoms of the disease.

Follow-up question   A protein has an α helix with an isoleucine residue facing the core of the protein. Compare isoleucine to each of the other amino acids. Hypothesize which mutations would be more deleterious to the protein and which would be less.

3.3 Summary

- Protein structure can be described on four levels—primary through quaternary.
- The basic unit of protein structure is the peptide bond.
- Secondary structure describes higher order structures: α helices, β sheets, turns, and coils.
- Secondary structures are stabilized by hydrogen bonds in the peptide backbone, and can be formed by many different amino acids.
- Tertiary structures describe the interaction of different elements of helix and sheet to form a complex structure.
- Tertiary structure represents the complete folding of a single polypeptide into a functional protein.
- Examples of tertiary motifs include the four-helix bundle and the Greek key motif.
- Tertiary structures are stabilized by a combination of many weak forces; these include hydrogen bonding, dipole–dipole interactions, salt bridges, disulfide bonds, cation–π interactions, and a phenomenon known as the hydrophobic effect.
- Many proteins exhibit quaternary structure interactions between and among different polypeptide chains.

3.3 Concept Check

- Describe the four levels of structure of a protein, and explain the forces involved in the stabilization of each level.
- Provide examples of secondary and tertiary structure, and draw them in molecular detail.

3.4 | Examples of Protein Structures and Functions

As might be expected from a group of molecules composed of 20 different building blocks, proteins have a vast diversity in terms of both structure and function. This section describes seven different proteins, each of which exemplifies some interesting aspect of protein structure-function and plays an important role in the life of a cell or organism. All of the molecules discussed in this section are highly conserved throughout evolution.

FIGURE 3.25 Aquaporin. The aquaporins permit the passage of water through the plasma membrane. **A.** View from above looking down on the four subunits. **B.** In this side view, the plane of the plasma membrane is shown as yellow lines and the subunits of the aquaporin are shown in magenta. Water takes a path through the channel in each subunit formed by the six helices. (PDB ID 3D9S Horsefield, R., Norden, K., Fellert, M., Backmark, A., Tornroth-Horsefield, S., Terwisscha Van Scheltinga, A.C., Kvassman, J., Kjellbom, P., Johanson, U., Neutze, R. (2008) High-resolution x-ray structure of human aquaporin 5. *Proc.Natl.Acad.Sci.* USA 105: 13327–13332)

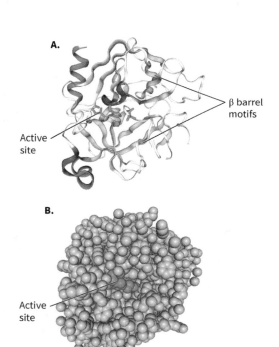

FIGURE 3.26 Chymotrypsin.

A. Chymotrypsin is mainly comprised of β sheets. At the interface of the two regions of sheet is the active site of this enzyme. **B.** In this space-filling model the catalytic residues are located in the middle of the structure. (A, B: PDB ID 1T7C Czapinska, H., Helland, R., Smalas, A.O., Otlewski, J. (2004) Crystal structures of five bovine chymotrypsin complexes with P1 BPTI variants. *J.Mol.Biol.* 344: 1005–1020)

3.4.1 Aquaporin, a transmembrane pore

Aquaporins are proteins that act as pores in the membrane, selectively allowing the passage of water into or out of the cell (**Figure 3.25**). Lipid bilayers have low permeability to water, and the aquaporins are necessary to rapidly transport water and for cells to function normally. Aquaporins are so specific that they will permit the passage of water but not the passage of acid (hydronium ion, H_3O^+).

Aquaporins consist of six transmembrane α helices pitched at a slight angle to each other in a single bundle. The center of this bundle forms the pore through which water passes. The outside of the helices are hydrophobic and are exposed to the acyl chains of the lipid bilayer.

Aquaporins are pores or channels rather than transporters. Channels allow for the transport of molecules down either a chemical or electrical gradient. They have much higher transit rates than transporters and do not require the input of energy for transport.

3.4.2 Chymotrypsin, an enzyme

Chymotrypsin is an enzyme; it is a small (26 kDa) globular protein that is produced by the pancreas and secreted into the intestinal lumen, where it cleaves dietary proteins into peptides. It is comprised predominantly of two compressed β barrel structures and one short α helix (**Figure 3.26**).

Chymotrypsin has two structural features that are common to most enzymes. First, its active site, where catalysis occurs, is relatively small compared to the rest of the structure. Only three amino acid side chains are directly involved in the catalytic steps of the reaction, although several other side chains are involved in the binding and recognition of the protein that is cleaved. This is in stark contrast to the other 242 amino acids found in the protein which are important for forming the scaffold on which the essential residues reside. These other parts of the protein may also play roles in regulation or localization of an enzyme in the cell. Second, the active site of chymotrypsin is found relatively close to the surface. Active sites are often near the surface of a protein but found in a canyon, trench, or other crevice. Frequently, amino acids found in turns or coils are found in an active site. In the example given here, binding of substrate and catalysis occurs at the interface of the two β structures.

3.4.3 | Collagen, a structural protein

Collagen is the protein in greatest abundance in the body (**Figure 3.27**). **Isoforms** are related proteins encoded by the same genes. Several isoforms of collagen are found in the body, and their expression varies in different organs and tissues.

Collagen is secreted by fibroblasts and assembles as part of the extracellular matrix. It is most concentrated in muscle and connective tissue and was one of the first protein structures to be elucidated. However, in several ways, collagen is unlike other proteins discussed in this chapter. Collagen is a fibrous protein forming extended strands and is helical, but not α helical. Instead, it has a structure known as a collagen helix in which three helical filaments twist around each other. In addition, collagen has an unusual amino acid composition, with a high proportion of residues of glycine (up to 33%), hydroxyproline, and proline (16% each). Hydroxyproline is a modified amino acid; select proline residues are modified by the enzyme prolyl hydroxylase. This enzyme uses molecular oxygen to complete the modification but

FIGURE 3.27 **Collagen.** Individual collagen molecules enriched in glycine, proline, and hydroxyproline form a collagen helix, a less compact, more gently spiraling left-handed helix. Three of these molecules twist around each other to form a collagen triple helix. Hydrogen bonding and steric interactions of the side chains stabilize this structure. Five triple helices form a collagen microfibril. (Middle: Karp, *Cell and Molecular Biology: Concepts and Experiments*, 7e, copyright 2013, John Wiley & Sons. This material is reproduced with permission of John Wiley & Sons, Inc.)

A.

Heme groups

Heme groups

B.

β subunits

α subunits

FIGURE 3.28 **Hemoglobin.** Hemoglobin is depicted in two different ribbon depictions. **A.** Hemoglobin is comprised of eight α helices connected by turns. **B.** Hemoglobin is a tetrameric molecule consisting of two α chains, shown in red and yellow, and two β chains, shown in green and blue, each of which has a heme functional group. Oxygen can bind to each of the heme groups. The four subunits are in close contact with one another, which facilitates communication between the four heme groups. (A, B: PDB ID 4YU4 Abubakkar, M.M., Maheshwaran, V., Ponnuswamy, M.N. (2015) Crystal structure of Mongoose (Helogale parvula) hemoglobin at pH 7.0.)

requires ascorbate, vitamin C, to reduce the enzyme back to the active form. In the absence of vitamin C, the enzyme is unable to operate properly, and hydroxylation does not occur. Consequently, collagen lacks hydroxyl groups and lacks structural integrity, leading to the disease scurvy, marked by weakened connective tissue, bleeding, and tooth loss. Glycine-rich patterns of amino acids and proteins containing modified amino acids such as hydroxylproline are also found in other filamentous proteins of the extracellular matrix.

3.4.4 Hemoglobin, a transport protein

Hemoglobin is a tetrameric protein found in erythrocytes or red blood cells (**Figure 3.28**). Each subunit of hemoglobin contains one molecule of heme: a large heterocyclic ring system surrounding a central iron atom. Oxygen binds to this central iron and that binding is at the core of oxygen transport, which is hemoglobin's primary function. A single molecule of oxygen can bind to each molecule of heme; thus, a single molecule of hemoglobin can transport up to four molecules of oxygen. However, the interaction of oxygen with the heme group is not simple; the four subunits of the protein cooperate, altering the affinity of oxygen for the heme group.

An examination of the structure of hemoglobin reveals that it is a globular protein that is predominantly made up of α helices joined by turns. As might be expected, the four subunits interact tightly, facilitating communication between them. Likewise, there are several places in the hemoglobin holoenzyme where other molecules can bind to alter the binding affinity of oxygen. These other molecules are termed **allosteric regulators**, because they act at sites removed from where the chemistry is occurring

3.4.5 Immunoglobulins, binding proteins

Immunoglobulins are molecules of the immune system that recognize and bind to antigens, which are small pieces of a molecule that the body recognizes as foreign (**Figure 3.29**). Usually, an immune reaction is provoked by an infection such as a bacterial or viral infection, but it could be from other sources such as a food (for example, peanuts) or any sort of foreign molecule in the body. In effect, immunoglobulins act as adapter molecules between the foreign molecule and the immune system cells required to neutralize it. To accomplish this,

FIGURE 3.29 **Immunoglobulins.** **A.** The immunoglobulins are a family of proteins that have an immunoglobulin fold, a series of β sheet structures stabilized by four interchain disulfide bonds. (Karp, *Cell and Molecular Biology: Concepts and Experiments*, 7e, copyright 2013, John Wiley & Sons. This material is reproduced with permission of John Wiley & Sons, Inc.) **B.** The basic structure seen in immunoglobulin gamma (IgG) is a dimer of dimers or a tetramer. Each dimer is comprised of a heavy chain and a light chain. The Fc and Fab domains are connected by a flexible hinge region. (PDB ID 1IGT Harris, L.J., Larson, S.B., Hasel, K.W., McPherson, A. (1997) Refined structure of an intact IgG2a monoclonal antibody. *Biochemistry* 36: 1581–1597)

immunoglobulins require an amazing amount of diversity to recognize an array of potential pathogens, but they also require a common portion to communicate with the cells of the immune system; these different parts of the molecule, performing different functions, are located at either end of the immunoglobulin.

An examination of the structure of immunoglobulin gamma (IgG) shows how it accomplishes its tasks. The molecule has four subunits: two identical heavy chains (50 kDa each) and two identical light chains (23 kDa each), all of which are held together by disulfide bonds. IgG can be split into three main fragments: two identical variable fragments (Fab) that bind to foreign molecules and a constant fragment (Fc) that binds to cells of the immune system and elicits an immune response. Having multiple variable regions within the same IgG molecule increases the interaction with the antigen, allows for binding to more than one copy of the foreign molecule at once, and increases the overall binding efficiency. The Fab and Fc fragments are connected by a hinge region that allows the molecule to be flexible and thus bind more easily. In terms of structure, immunoglobulins are comprised mainly of β sheet domains joined by turns and coils. The generic term **antibody** is often used to describe IgG.

3.4.6 Insulin, a signaling protein

Insulin is a small protein hormone made by the β-cells of the pancreas (**Figure 3.30**). Hormones bind to protein receptors in target cells and tissues to elicit a response. Insulin is a growth factor, signaling cells to store energy and divert energy to growth, but it is best known for its role in diabetes. Insulin signals cells to absorb glucose from the circulation. Interrupted or impaired insulin signaling results in diabetes. An autoimmune attack on the β-cells of the pancreas or on insulin itself results in a lack of the insulin signal, leading to type 1 diabetes. Type 2 diabetes develops in situations where there is an insulin signal, but the response of tissues is blunted or absent due to a problem with the insulin receptor or a post receptor defect.

Insulin is first synthesized as a single polypeptide of 104 amino acids, which is cleaved multiple times in the ER to yield a single protein of 51 amino acids comprised of two polypeptide chains, termed A and B, held together by disulfide bonds. The protein itself adopts an α helical configuration. It is unclear if insulin forms higher order structures (trimers or hexamers) joined through a common metal ion (Zn^{2+}) while in the circulation.

Insulin monomer   **Insulin dimer**   **Insulin hexamer**

FIGURE 3.30 **Insulin.** Insulin is a small (51 amino acid) protein hormone. Only the monomeric form of insulin is active, but the hormone will assemble into dimers and hexamers. The central atom in the hexamer is a zinc ion, chelated by histidine residues. (PDB ID 1ZEH Whittingham, J.L., Edwards, E.J., Antson, A.A., Clarkson, J.M., Dodson, G.G. (1998) Interactions of phenol and m-cresol in the insulin hexamer, and their effect on the association properties of B28 pro → Asp insulin analogues. *Biochemistry* 37: 11516–11523)

3.4.7 Myosin, a molecular motor

Myosins are a family of proteins that act as molecular motors, using the energy of ATP hydrolysis to elicit muscle contraction and transport vesicles in the cell (**Figure 3.31**). Myosins have heavy and light types of chains. The myosin heavy chain consists of three domains, a bulky globular head, a flexible neck, and a lengthy coiled α helical tail. The head domain interacts with the cytoskeletal protein actin, and it moves the myosin down the strand to the positive end of the actin fiber. The neck of myosin acts as a hinge, providing the head with flexibility. The tail of myosin can interact with adapter or cargo proteins; it can also form large bundles with other myosin tails. The light chains of myosin wrap around the neck region of myosin, potentially to provide stability to this flexible region. The light chains of myosin are structurally conserved with the calcium binding protein calmodulin; they may also play a role in the binding of Ca^{2+}.

WORKED PROBLEM 3.4 | Structural analysis of a protein

Examine the structure of the protein illustrated below. Which of the proteins discussed above is most similar to the protein shown here? What does this suggest about the function of the protein?

Strategy How does the overall structure of the protein shown compare to the other proteins depicted in this chapter? Do you recognize any of the elements of secondary or tertiary structure, or any domains?

Solution This image shows a protein with two domains enriched in β sheet. Comparing this structure to the seven proteins discussed in this section, or using software to compare this fold to all other structures determined to date, we see that it forms an immunoglobulin fold. This structure is deposited in the Protein Data Bank, and like all proteins there it has a four digit alphanumeric identifier number, such as PDB ID 1IGT.

Follow-up question Examine the structure of this protein.

How does this structure compare to the other proteins discussed in this section? Use your comparison to hypothesize a function for this protein. How would the differences in structure from the proteins discussed in this section result in different functions for this protein?

(Left: PDB ID 1IGT Harris, L.J., Larson, S.B., Hasel, K.W., McPherson, A. (1997) *Biochemistry* 36: 1581–1597; Right: PDB ID 3WFT Hayashi, T., Morita, Y., Mizohata, E., Oohora, K., Ohbayashi, J., Inoue, T., Hisaeda, Y. (2014) Co(II)/Co(I) reduction-induced axial histidine-flipping in myoglobin reconstituted with a cobalt tetradehydrocorrin as a methionine synthase model. *Chem.Commun.(Camb.)* 50: 12560–12563)

A.

Head

ATP

Light chains

Neck

α helical tail
150 nm

B.

ATP

Actin binding

Heavy chain (globular domain)

Head

Heavy chain (filamentous domain)

Light chains

Neck

C.

Ca²⁺

1 Calcium binds to thin filaments exposing actin active site.

Actin

Ca²⁺

Head

Neck

Light chains

ADP P

ADP P

Myosin

2 Myosin heads react to actin active site, creating crossbridges.

P P

ATP ATP

ADP ADP

ATP ATP

Power stroke

ADP ADP

4 Myosin head picks up fresh ATP, drops actin, and resets to again form crossbridges.

3 The myosin head groups flex.

FIGURE 3.31 **Myosin.** Myosin is an example of a molecular motor. **A.** and **B.** The heavy chain consists of a globular domain containing the actin binding region and ATP binding site and an extended filamentous domain. Myosin heavy chains bundle together joined by two other subunits (the light chains). (A: Karp, *Cell and Molecular Biology: Concepts and Experiments*, 7e, copyright 2013, John Wiley & Sons. This material is reproduced with permission of John Wiley & Sons, Inc.; B: PDB ID 1S5G Risal, D., Gourinath, S., Himmel, D.M., Szent-Gyorgyi, A.G., Cohen, C. (2004) Myosin subfragment 1 structures reveal a partially bound nucleotide and a complex salt bridge that helps couple nucleotide and actin binding. *Proc. Natl. Acad. Sci. USA* 101: 8930–8935.) **C.** Myosin functions in movement. (Ireland, *Visualizing Human Biology*, 4e, copyright 2012, John Wiley & Sons. This material is reproduced with permission of John Wiley & Sons, Inc.)

The mechanism by which myosin mediates movement starts with the binding of ATP to the active site of myosin; this elicits a conformational change that releases actin from myosin. As the ATP is hydrolyzed, the head of myosin is moved back, resulting in myosin binding elsewhere on the actin molecule. Release of phosphate from myosin causes a conformational change in myosin so that the head rocks, moving closer to the tail in a movement termed "the power stroke." Finally, ADP dissociates from the active site.

When an animal dies, cells exhaust the supply of ATP. In the absence of ATP, myosin is unable to release, resulting in muscle rigidity (rigor mortis).

3.4 Summary

- Proteins are the most diverse of the basic classes of biological molecules. They vary in size, structure, and function.

- Transmembrane proteins pass through the phospholipid bilayer. Some proteins are simply anchored in the membrane, whereas others, such as the aquaporins, form channels for specific molecules to pass through.

- Chymotrypsin is a classic example of an enzyme. Structural studies have made it possible to identify and characterize the side chains involved in intermolecular interactions and catalysis.

- Collagen, a fibrous protein found in the extracellular matrix, is one of the most prevalent proteins in the body. It is exceptional in that it possesses highly modified amino acids such as hydroxyproline and forms an unusual structure, referred to as the collagen helix.

- Hemoglobin is the red, heme-containing protein found in erythrocytes. Hemoglobin is responsible for oxygen binding and transport and is an illustration of allosterism; that is, it is regulated at sites distant from where the chemistry is occurring.

- Immunoglobulins are examples of how the diversity of protein structure solves interesting challenges. These proteins need to be able to bind to innumerable different foreign antigens, including some that are yet to evolve, and yet have a common portion that can interact with the cells of the immune system to elicit an immune response. To do this, IgG has regions that are highly variable linked to a domain that is common to all IgG molecules. Having multiple variable regions within the same IgG molecule increases the interaction with the antigen.

- Insulin is an example of a protein that acts as a signaling molecule. The relatively small insulin molecule is produced in the pancreas and travels through the bloodstream, signaling cells to increase uptake of glucose; it also acts as a growth factor and plays other roles in cell signaling.

- Myosin is a muscle protein that is partially responsible for muscle contraction. It is a type of molecular motor, using the energy of ATP hydrolysis to generate motion.

3.4 Concept Check

- Describe the proteins discussed in section 3.4 in terms of both their structure and their function, on a macromolecular level and an atomic level.

- Describe the elements of secondary structure seen in these proteins.

- Explain how each of these proteins fills a niche in nature.

The Bigger Picture

Proteins are the largest and most diverse class of biological molecules. They are linear polymers of amino acids that fold into complex shapes that are responsible for carrying out many of the jobs in the cell. This chapter discusses the structure of amino acids and the diverse roles these molecules play in biochemistry, both in and out of proteins. It then discusses the different levels of organization of protein structure. Finally, it examines seven different proteins, each of which highlights a different feature of protein structure.

Bioinformatics Exercises

Exercise 1 Drawing and Analyzing Amino Acids and Peptides

Exercise 2 Amino Acid and Chemical Properties of Green Fluorescent Protein

Exercise 3 Visualizing and Understanding α Helices

Exercise 4 Visualizing and Understanding β sheets

Exercise 5 Visualizing and Identifying Supersecondary Structures

Exercise 6 Visualizing and Analyzing Cytochrome *c*

Exercise 7 Visualizing and Analyzing Hemoglobin

Problems

3.1 Amino Acid Chemistry

1. With the exception of glycine, all amino acids are chiral. Which amino acids have more than one chiral carbon?

2. Why it is that proline is considered to disrupt a helix but histidine does not?

3. Amino acids, like all molecules in biochemistry, are selected for through the process of evolution. The ancestry of a gene or protein can be traced through evolutionary time using common ancestors. Is it possible to do the same thing with amino acids? Why or why not?

4. Examine the side chains of the amino acids. Based on their structures, which ones will absorb light? In which part of the electromagnetic spectrum might they absorb?

5. Examine the structures of the amino acids. Based on their structure, what might they appear like in the purified state? What would most proteins look like when purified?

6. Like the amino acids from which they are made, proteins are chiral. Circular dichroism is a technique that is used to determine how much a sample of a protein will rotate plane-polarized light. The amount of rotation correlates with the degree of α helicity of a protein. Why does an α helix rotate plane-polarized light but a β sheet does not?

7. The amino acid glycine is a common component in many buffers. Draw a titration curve of 100 mM glycine titrated with 1 M NaOH.

8. Calculate the percentage ionization in these amino acid side chains at the pH values specified:

   i. aspartate at pH 5.4
   ii. glutamate at pH 11.8
   iii. histidine at pH 8.0
   iv. tyrosine at pH 8.0

9. Tyrosine is generally listed as a polar amino acid. How else could this amino acid be categorized?

10. Which amino acids have aromatic side chains? Recall from organic chemistry that organic molecules follow Huckle's rule (the $4n+2$ rule). Show that each of the proposed aromatic amino acids follows this rule.

11. Which amino acids absorb in the UV? Why do other amino acids not absorb in the UV?

12. Based on the properties of the side chain, which amino acid would you predict to be most soluble in water? Least soluble in water?

13. Selenocysteine and selenomethionine are alternative amino acids found in some organisms. Examine the periodic table. How would the chemistry of these seleno amino acids compare to sulfur- or oxygen-containing amino acids?

3.2 Proteins Are Polymers of Amino Acids

14. With few exceptions, such as proline, how is it that most amino acids can form either an α helix structure or a β sheet structure?

15. How many different ways can the 20 common amino acids combine to form a protein 450 amino acids long?

16. The average mass of an amino acid in a protein is 110 g/mol. Dividing the mass of titin (3,816 kDa) by the number of amino acids (34,350) does not give the exact figure of 110. Why?

17. How could the alteration of a protein sequence lead to a change in the location of a protein in the cell?

18. Recently, there have been reports of college students being diagnosed with scurvy. What is scurvy, and how is it treated? Why do most Americans not get scurvy, and why might these college students have developed it?

19. ATP is usually the source of the phosphate in biochemical reactions, such as phosphorylation of proteins. Why is this the case? Could other molecules serve as the source? Which of the phosphates on ATP is the source of the phosphate? Why, in terms of energy and of equilibrium, does ATP have this role?

20. Cation-π interactions are predicted from electrostatics. Based on this statement, how would you expect the strength of the interaction to vary with the distance between the atoms in the interaction?

3.3 Proteins Are Molecules of Defined Shape and Structure

21. The four-helix bundle is one of the most commonly found tertiary motifs, and it is found in a wide variety of proteins. Describe how this motif could arise in two different proteins. Explain your observation first using divergent evolution and then using convergent evolution. Given that the four-helix bundle is found in thousands of different proteins, which instance, convergent or divergent evolution, is more likely?

22. Why are enzymes so large in comparison to the molecules in the reactions they catalyze?

23. Given the importance of structure in biochemistry, it would seem that obtaining the structure of a protein might be a good first step in investigating its properties. Think of other chemistry courses you have taken. If you know the structure of a molecule, what other information does that provide about the molecule?

24. Many amino acids have similar structures. Which amino acids can substitute for one another? That is, which amino acid substitutions are conservative mutations that potentially preserve function of a protein, rather than being radical and eliminating function?

25. Human serum albumin (a plasma protein that binds hydrophobic molecules like fatty acids) has 585 amino acids. What is its approximate molecular weight?

26. What is the core of a protein generally like compared to the surface? What types of amino acid side chains would you expect to find in these two environments?

27. If a protein were chemically synthesized in hexane instead of water, would it retain the same structure? Of the levels of structure discussed, which would be the most likely to be affected?

3.4 Examples of Protein Structures and Functions

28. Examining the structures of the seven proteins discussed in section 3.4, are there regions of each of these proteins where a mutation would be more or less harmful to the function of the protein?

29. Collagen is a fibrous protein found in the extracellular matrix. What challenges does this present when attempting to study collagen? What advantages are present?

30. Sickle cell anemia is a genetic disease resulting from a single amino acid substitution (glutamate to valine in the sixth position, or E6V) in the hemoglobin β chain. This mutation causes hemoglobin to polymerize into strands in the deoxygenated state, leading to the erythrocytes forming a sickled shape. Speculate as to why the mutation leads to the polymerization of hemoglobin and why this only happens in the deoxygenated state.

31. Before the 1980s, the insulin used to treat diabetes was obtained from pigs (porcine insulin) or cattle (bovine insulin). These molecules differ by only three amino acids in the 104 amino acid sequence, as shown in the table. Based on this comparison, which would you anticipate to be the better treatment for diabetes in humans, porcine or bovine insulin?

Insulin	A chain, position 8	A chain, position 10	B chain, position 30
Human	Threonine	Isoleucine	Threonine
Porcine	Threonine	Isoleucine	Alanine
Bovine	Alanine	Valine	Alanine

32. In chymotrypsin, only three amino acids are involved in catalysis, but there are almost 200 amino acids in the entire protein. What is the function of the other amino acids?

33. How does myosin use the chemical energy stored in ATP to generate motion?

34. What special features of aquaporin permit it to cross the plasma membrane? How does aquaporin allow water to flow through the membrane?

35. Immunoglobulins all have a similar structure but bind to different antigens. What is it about their structure that makes this possible?

Data Interpretation

36. Kwashiorkor is a type of malnutrition characterized by dietary protein deficiency. Examine the map shown below. The darker the color, the higher the prevalence of kwashiorkor. Where is the deficiency most prevalent? What is its likely cause, and how could this theory be tested? Why is the rate higher in France than in other countries in Europe? Why is the rate higher in the United States than in Australia or Canada? What other data would be useful in interpreting this figure and answering these questions? What other questions arise after thinking about this data?

37. A protein is loaded into a gel containing a pH gradient at pH 7. An electric field is applied and the protein migrates as shown. What does this data indicate about the protein?

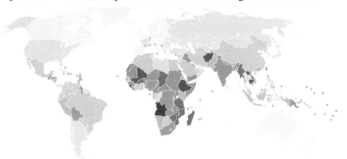

38. Chitinase is an enzyme that degrades the carbohydrate chitin. Samples of chitinase were separated using nondenaturing gel electrophoresis. In this experiment, pure chitinase was loaded in lanes 1 and 3, and chitinase treated briefly with a dilute solution of a protease was loaded in lanes 2 and 4. Lanes 1 and 2 were stained for protein, whereas lanes 3 and 4 were treated with a chitin solution that yielded a colored product when hydrolyzed. How would you interpret the results shown below?

39. A cytosolic enzyme is hypothesized to transiently interact with a protein cofactor found in the membrane of the endoplasmic reticulum. Cells containing these proteins are lysed and then mixed with a protein cross-linking agent. Following the reaction, the samples are analyzed by immunoblotting, a means of detecting a specific protein, also known as Western blotting, with an antibody directed against the enzyme. Explain the following result:

1. protein, no crosslinker
2. protein + crosslinker
3. protein + detergent + crosslinker
4. protein + Mg^{2+} + crosslinker
5. protein + Mg^{2+} no crosslinker
6. protein + Mg^{2+} + detergent + crosslinker

What are the strengths and weaknesses of this experimental approach? Which lanes are controls? What other controls (if any) could be used? How could you verify that the enzyme was interacting with the protein in the ER?

40. A protein has a predicted molecular weight of 47 kDa based on the amino acid sequence, an apparent molecular weight of 50 kDa by SDS-PAGE, and an approximate molecular weight of 95 kDa by size exclusion chromatography. Each of these techniques is described in the appendix. Why do the results vary between the different techniques? In particular, why is there such a difference between size exclusion chromatography and the other techniques? Which technique is likely to be most accurate and why?

Experimental Design

41. What techniques do you know of from other chemistry courses that could be used to determine the structure in solution of peptides 10 to 20 amino acids in length?

42. The amino acid proline disrupts the regular pattern of the α helix. How could you demonstrate this experimentally?

43. Most proteins fold into a single conformation and do so almost instantaneously and without assistance. How could you test this statement experimentally?

44. Examine the experimental technique appendix. Which experimental techniques are used to provide details about the structure of a protein? At which level of resolution are these techniques used; that is, which techniques could indicate that a protein is active as a hexamer in solution and which could indicate which side chains are involved in an active site?

45. You are studying a protein that consists of two domains: one catalytic and one regulatory. How could you test to see whether these domains can fold independently or whether they are dependent on one another for folding?

Ethics and Social Responsibility

46. Amino acids are freely available in purified form in vitamin and health food stores. Many amino acids and other naturally occurring molecules have distinct physiological effects in the body. Research the following question: When is a molecule considered a food item and when is it considered a drug? Do you agree with the definition you found in your research?

47. Most people with diabetes who need insulin currently use recombinant human insulin; however, for the first 70 years after the discovery of insulin, people were often treated with porcine insulin. Many people do not consume pork for personal, religious, or ethical reasons. Should those beliefs change when the choice is for a lifesaving treatment instead of a food source?

48. It has been estimated that seven times more energy is required to produce 1 kcal of beef protein than 1 kcal of soybean protein. Given rising energy costs, should beef receive government subsidies to make it more affordable or should we eat less meat?

49. Several prion-based diseases seem to be acquired through the consumption of neurological tissue. Is it ethical to prohibit the consumption of these tissues based on the potential for causing or transmitting disease?

50. Proteins in the diet can include beef, chicken, and soybeans. What does it mean for these items to be labeled as "organic"? Does each food source need to adhere to the same standard to be labeled as organic?

Suggested Readings

Amino Acids and the Basics of Protein Structure

Branden, C., and J. Tooze. *Introduction to Protein Structure.* New York, NY: Garland Science, 1999.

Buxbaum, E. *Fundamentals of Protein Structure and Function.* New York, NY: Springer, 2007.

Kessel, A., and N. Ben-Tal. *Introduction to Proteins: Structure, Function, and Motion.* Boca Raton, FL: CRC press, 2011.

Williamson, M. *How Proteins Work.* New York, NY: Garland Science, 2011.

Protein Architecture and Examples of Protein Structure

Fersht, A. M. *Structure and Mechanism in Protein Science.* New York, NY: W.H. Freeman, 1998.

Lesk, A. M. *Introduction to Protein Science Architecture, Function, and Genomics.* Oxford, UK: Oxford University Press, 2010.

Lesk, A. M. *Introduction to Proteins: The Structural Biology of Proteins Architecture.* Oxford, UK: Oxford University Press, 2001.

Liska, K. *Drugs and the Human Body.* Upper Saddle River, NJ: Pearson/Prentice Hall, 2004.

Petsko, G. A., and D. Ringe. *Protein Structure and Function.* Sunderland, MA: Sinauer Associates, Inc. 2003.

Proteins I

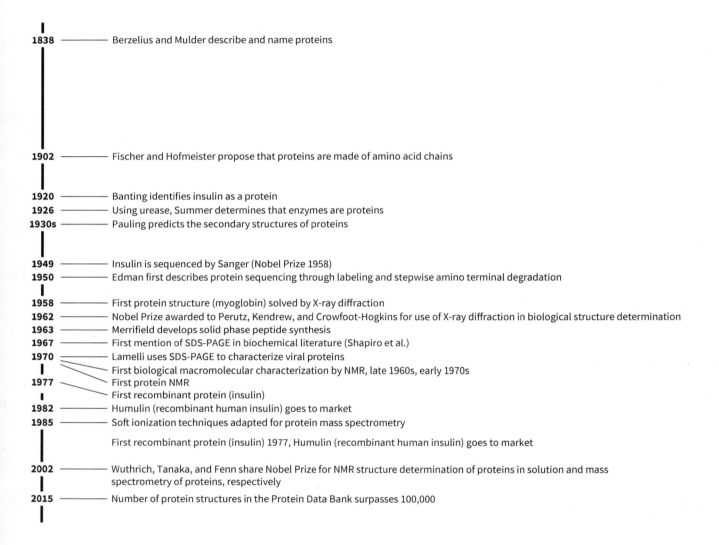

1838 ———— Berzelius and Mulder describe and name proteins

1902 ———— Fischer and Hofmeister propose that proteins are made of amino acid chains

1920 ———— Banting identifies insulin as a protein
1926 ———— Using urease, Summer determines that enzymes are proteins
1930s ———— Pauling predicts the secondary structures of proteins

1949 ———— Insulin is sequenced by Sanger (Nobel Prize 1958)
1950 ———— Edman first describes protein sequencing through labeling and stepwise amino terminal degradation

1958 ———— First protein structure (myoglobin) solved by X-ray diffraction
1962 ———— Nobel Prize awarded to Perutz, Kendrew, and Crowfoot-Hogkins for use of X-ray diffraction in biological structure determination
1963 ———— Merrifield develops solid phase peptide synthesis
1967 ———— First mention of SDS-PAGE in biochemical literature (Shapiro et al.)
1970 ———— Lamelli uses SDS-PAGE to characterize viral proteins
        ———— First biological macromolecular characterization by NMR, late 1960s, early 1970s
1977 ———— First protein NMR
        ———— First recombinant protein (insulin)
1982 ———— Humulin (recombinant human insulin) goes to market
1985 ———— Soft ionization techniques adapted for protein mass spectrometry

        First recombinant protein (insulin) 1977, Humulin (recombinant human insulin) goes to market

2002 ———— Wuthrich, Tanaka, and Fenn share Nobel Prize for NMR structure determination of proteins in solution and mass spectrometry of proteins, respectively
2015 ———— Number of protein structures in the Protein Data Bank surpasses 100,000

CHAPTER 4

Proteins II

Enzymes

iStock/Getty Images

Just as different tools perform different jobs, enzymes also can be grouped by function and form.

Enzymes in Context

In a toolbox, there are a wide variety of tools to choose from—screwdrivers, wrenches, hammers, and saws—each with a specific structure and function. If we imagine the tool section of a large hardware or home improvement center, we may encounter unusual tools, such as a giant wrench. Even though this particular tool may be unfamiliar, it is easy to imagine a function for it, based on its appearance (the structure) and how other similar tools act (the mechanism). It is also easy to appreciate the need for a wide range of tools; for example, the differences between a nail and a screw mean that both hammers and screwdrivers are necessary. Looking at the bigger picture, we can see how tools can be grouped according to their function, that is, whether they cut, fasten, bend, hold, and so on. We can categorize, make generalizations, note exceptions and specificities, and build on our knowledge of tools.

Just as tools can be grouped, enzymes can be broadly characterized based on the reactions they catalyze and the chemistry they conduct. Alternatively, they can be categorized based on protein conformation or structure. Armed with a knowledge of structure, we can amass other data that can help in determining a possible reaction mechanism for an enzymatically catalyzed reaction. We can then build on this knowledge to probe the types of reactions that an enzyme will catalyze and those it will not, and explain those differences. With these differences in mind, it is then possible to identify different types of inhibitors, alter biochemical processes, develop new drugs, and diagnose and treat disease. These properties of enzymes are discussed in **Dynamic Figure 4.1**.

CHAPTER OUTLINE

4.1 Regarding Enzymes

4.2 Enzymes Increase Reaction Rate

4.3 The Mechanism of an Enzyme Can Be Deduced from Structural, Kinetic, and Spectral Data

4.4 Examples of Enzyme Regulation

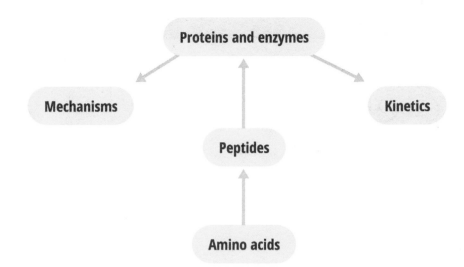

DYNAMIC FIGURE 4.1 This chapter discusses the general properties, kinetics, and mechanisms of enzymes, and how they are regulated.

COMMON THEMES

Evolution's outcomes are conserved.	• Mutations to DNA sequences may alter an enzyme's amino acid sequence. The new enzyme may act normally (a silent mutation), have a slightly altered function, such as a change in rate or binding of a different substrate, or be completely nonfunctional. If a mutation benefits the organism, there is an increased likelihood that it will be transmitted to the organism's progeny.
	• As organisms have become more complex and organs and systems have evolved, enzymes have evolved functions or regulatory mechanisms specific to that organ or tissue.
	• The mechanisms enzymes employ to catalyze reactions are themselves repeated and conserved throughout nature; this is an example of evolution at the chemical level.
	• Analysis of mechanisms and structures of enzymes illustrate both convergent and divergent evolution.
	• The regulatory mechanisms employed by enzymes have coevolved with catalytic mechanisms.
Structure determines function.	• The structure of an enzyme and the position of amino acid side chains in the active site provide important biochemical information that can be used to help elucidate an enzymatic mechanism.
	• Regulatory mechanisms (e.g., proteolytic cleavage, phosphorylation, or binding of a small regulatory molecule) lead to changes in the tertiary or quaternary structure of the enzyme, modifying substrate binding or the geometry of the active site, and ultimately altering activity.
Biochemical information is transferred, exchanged, and stored.	• Many enzymes play important roles in transmitting and carrying out biochemical signals in the cell.
	• The regulation of enzymes (through either covalent modification or allosteric mechanisms) regulates both the rates of biochemical reactions and flux through biochemical pathways.
Biomolecules are altered through pathways involving transformations of energy and matter.	• Most biochemical reactions are catalyzed by enzymes.
	• The use of enzymes affords a means to regulate biochemical reactions and a way to couple energetically unfavorable reactions with favorable ones.
	• Data about the rate at which a catalyzed reaction proceeds can be used to describe the reaction mathematically.
	• Spectroscopic, structural, and kinetic data can be used to describe the mechanism of an enzymatically catalyzed reaction.

4.1 | Regarding Enzymes

Most of the thousands of reactions that occur in the cell require a catalyst to run at biologically significant rates.

At room temperature, a bag of sugar (sucrose) is reacting with oxygen in the air, gradually forming CO_2 and H_2O. This reaction is happening far too slowly for us to see; even so, it is possible to measure this reaction chemically and understand from general chemistry that it is happening. The energetics of the reaction indicates that the reaction is exothermic; that is, heat is given off in the process. Examining other thermodynamic parameters, we find that there is a negative free energy (ΔG) for this reaction, indicating spontaneity in the forward direction. Finally, as this reaction runs, there is an increase in the entropy—the number of possible microstates or the disorder of the system. All of these thermodynamic parameters are true, yet they reveal nothing of the speed or rate of the reaction. If you were to leave a bag of sugar exposed to oxygen in your kitchen and return even several years later, you would see no appreciable change.

If that same bag of sugar were dissolved in water and incubated with yeast, the same net reactions would occur. Sucrose would be consumed, and CO_2 and H_2O would be generated, as would some heat from the making of chemical bonds. The entropy of the system would increase, and the reaction would proceed favorably. However, this reaction would be visible to the naked eye because the microbes would generate CO_2 so quickly that it would bubble out of solution. The same overall reaction is happening in the two cases, and the thermodynamics are unchanged. However, what *has* changed is that a biological system has contributed a catalyst (or, in this case, multiple catalysts) to increase the rates of reactions to the point where the yeast can use these reactions at room temperature. The catalysts are protein molecules termed **enzymes**.

4.1.1 | Enzymes are protein catalysts

Enzymes are the cell's solution to most of its catalytic problems. Enzymes are usually globular proteins, although some have irregular shapes, or form filaments. Some enzymes are monomeric, meaning they contain a single subunit, while others are multimeric; that is, they have two or more subunits (**Figure 4.2**). Multimeric enzymes may have both **catalytic subunits** and **regulatory subunits**, or may have multiple catalytic subunits that interact and help to regulate one another, an example of allosteric regulation.

The reactants in an enzymatically catalyzed reaction are referred to as **substrates**, and the molecules produced are referred to as **products**. Although this chapter focuses on reactions that have a single substrate, over 60% of reactions use more than one substrate and have more than one product. The substrate binds to the enzyme at the location where catalysis occurs, termed the **active site**. This site is on the surface of the enzyme but is often in a cleft, pocket, or trench. The residues that make up the surface of the active site are responsible for substrate binding and for catalysis, although some residues have more specialized functions. The active site is generally formed by residues on turns or coils, although sometimes sections of helixes or sheets may also participate in the reaction.

Several models are used to describe the interaction of the substrate with the enzyme. Some substrates interact with enzymes like a key in a lock, known as the **lock and key** model (**Figure 4.3**). In this analogy, only the correct key will fit the lock; that is, the correct steric interactions are needed for the substrate to fit into the enzyme's active site. This model explains some aspects of enzyme-substrate interactions particularly well. For example, enzymes are generally quite specific in terms of what substrates they will bind to, being able to distinguish, for example, between glutamate and aspartate or between the carbohydrates glucose and galactose (which differ only in the chirality of a single chiral center). In this regard, enzymes may indeed be like a key in a lock. However, other aspects of enzyme molecules do not fit this model. In **induced fit**, the interaction of the substrate with the enzyme helps to form the active site. An analogy for this is a latex or nitrile laboratory glove. The glove itself is roughly hand shaped, but in the absence of a hand, the glove is flat and floppy. The hand filling the glove is like a substrate in an active site. The induced fit interaction helps

A.

Carbonic anhydrase
(monomeric)

B.

Calcium-calmodulin II kinase
(multimeric)

FIGURE 4.2 General topology of enzymes.   Enzymes can be **A.** monomeric with a single subunit or **B.** multimeric with several subunits. (A: PDB ID 1CA2 Eriksson, A.E., Jones, T.A., Liljas, A. (1988) Refined structure of human carbonic anhydrase II at 2.0 A resolution. *Proteins* 4: 274–282; B: PDB ID 2UX0 Rellos, P., Pike, A.C.W., Niesen, F.H., Salah, E., Lee, W.H., von Delft, F., Knapp, S. (2010) Structure of the CaMKIIdelta/Calmodulin Complex Reveals the Molecular Mechanism of CaMKII Kinase Activation. *Plos Biol.* 8: 426)

A.

Active site

Substrates (S)

Enzyme

B. Substrate

Sucrose

Products

Glucose Fructose

Active
site

(sucrase)

H_2O

Enzyme conforms
to the shape of
substrate.

Enzyme

FIGURE 4.3 **Models of substrate binding.** **A.** In the lock and key model, the substrate fits in the active site like a key fitting into a lock. (Karp, *Cell and Molecular Biology: Concepts and Experiments*, 7e, copyright 2013, John Wiley & Sons. This material is reproduced with permission of John Wiley & Sons, Inc.) **B.** In induced fit, the substrate fits into the enzyme like a hand inserting into a glove. (Alters, *Biology: Understanding Life*, 1e, copyright 2006, John Wiley & Sons. This material is reproduced with permission of John Wiley & Sons, Inc.) **C.** Enzymes are specific enough to discern the difference between very similar structures, such as glucose and galactose.

C.

CH₂OH

O OH

OH

OH

OH

Glucose

CH₂OH

OH O OH

OH

OH

Galactose

to describe many enzyme-substrate interactions, as well as some conformational changes the enzyme may undergo as a result of substrate binding.

The active site is a tight fit. Binding of substrate usually fills the site entirely. Even water is excluded. If water molecules are present, they are usually involved in substrate binding or the reaction mechanism rather than being passive bystanders. This observation explains several reactions that would otherwise make no sense. Reactions such as transesterifications occur only because there is no water available to hydrolyze a bond, whereas other reactions add a hydroxyl group stereospecifically, through the specific positioning of a water molecule by the enzyme. The enzyme hexokinase catalyzes the transfer of a phosphate group from ATP to a hydroxyl group in glucose. To accomplish this, the enzyme binds both substrates and closes down around them, excluding water or any other molecule from the active site before catalysis occurs (**Figure 4.4**).

FIGURE 4.4 **Topology of the active site.** Shown is the enzyme glucokinase and a close-up view of its active site. Once the substrate is bound, the enzyme closes around it like the two halves of a clam shell, excluding all molecules except the two substrates. This is an example of induced fit. (PDB ID 1V4T, 1V4S Kamata, K., Mitsuya, M., Nishimura, T., Eiki, J., Nagata, Y. (2004) Structural basis for allosteric regulation of the monomeric allosteric enzyme human glucokinas. *Structure* 12: 429-438)

Substrate
(glucose)

Active site

Glucose
concealed
in active site

Glucokinase

**Glucokinase with
bound substrate**

4.1.2 Enzymatically catalyzed reactions can be categorized

Tens of thousands of different reactions can occur in an organism. However, these reactions can be divided into six different classes, each having different subclasses, based on the type of substrate and the mechanism of action of the enzyme involved (Table 4.1). The classes are:

1. Oxidoreductases—catalyze reactions involving the gain or loss of electrons.
2. Transferases—transfer one group to another.
3. Hydrolases—cleave a bond with water.
4. Lyases—break double bonds using some other means than oxidation or hydrolysis.
5. Isomerases—catalyze a rearrangement of the molecule.
6. Ligases—join two molecules.

These groups were decided upon by the Enzyme Commission (EC) of the International Union of Biochemistry and Molecular Biology (IUBMB), and are called **EC numbers**. Every enzyme has a unique EC number, based on its category and further subclassifications. For example, adenylate cyclase, the enzyme that catalyzes the formation of the signaling molecule cyclic AMP from ATP, is a lyase (Class 4) but is then further subclassified into a phosphorus-oxygen lyase that acts on ATP.

One way our understanding of enzyme chemistry has assisted in the clinic through the measurement of enzyme activity in the blood is discussed in **Medical Biochemistry: Enzymes in diagnosis**.

TABLE 4.1   **Classes of Enzymes Production**

Class	General reaction	Important subclasses	Examples
1. Oxidoreductases	$A_{Red} + B_{Ox} \leftrightarrows A_{Ox} + B_{Red}$	Dehydrogenases Oxidases, peroxidases Reductases Monooxygenases Dioxygenases	Cytochrome oxidase Lactate dehydrogenase
2. Transferases	$A\text{-}B + C \rightarrow A + C\text{-}B$	C-1 Transferases Glycosyltransferases Aminotransferases Phosphotransferases	Acetate kinase Alanine deaminase
3. Hydrolases	$A\text{-}B + H_2O \rightarrow A\text{-}H + B\text{-}OH$	Esterases Glycosidases Peptidases Amidases	Lipase Sucrase
4. Lyases ("synthases")	$A\text{-}B \leftrightarrows A + B$ (reverse reaction: synthases)	C-C-Lyases C-O-Lyases C-N-Lyases C-S-Lyases	Oxalate decarboxylase Isocitrate lyase
5. Isomerases	$A\text{-}B\text{-}C \leftrightarrows A\text{-}C\text{-}B$	Epimerases *cis trans* Isomerases Intramolecular transferases	Glucose-phosphate isomerase Alanine racemase
6. Ligases ("synthetases")	$A + B + ATP \rightarrow A\text{-}B + ADP + P_i$	C-C-Ligases C-O-Ligases C-N-Ligases C-S-Ligases	Acetyl-CoA synthetase DNA ligase

Medical Biochemistry

Enzymes in diagnosis

Physicians often request blood work on a patient to aid in a diagnosis. A comprehensive metabolic panel (referred to as a CHEM-20) is a commonly requested battery of blood tests. Many parameters will be already familiar: pH and the concentrations of different ions and metabolites, such as glucose and urea. These values provide the clinician with a general view of the function of various organs and systems. Other values, such as the activities of several enzymes typically found in the liver or muscle, can probe deeper. Because these enzymes are not typically found in blood, their appearance indicates organ damage. Such enzymes include lactate dehydrogenase, alanine transaminase, aspartate aminotransferase, and creatine phosphokinase.

Lactate dehydrogenase (LDH) is usually localized to specific tissues, including the heart, the liver, the muscle, and/or the kidney. If LDH is released from those tissues, it will accumulate in the blood rather than being excreted by the kidney. LDH is therefore used as a marker for general tissue damage.

Alanine transaminase (ALT) and aspartate aminotransferase (AST) are localized to the liver; hence, as with LDH, elevated levels of these enzymes in blood indicate liver damage. Similarly, the liver enzyme gamma-glutamyl transpeptidase (gamma-GT) is a marker for liver damage. Among its multiple functions, gamma-GT catalyzes the transfer of the gamma-linked glutamate from glutathione to an acceptor molecule.

One final molecule that is often included on chemistry panels is creatine phosphokinase (CPK). This enzyme is specifically found in muscle tissue and the liver, where it functions in creatine metabolism. Elevated levels of CPK indicate muscle damage or, more frequently, heart attack.

4.1.3 How do enzymes work?

Enzymes are catalysts. All catalysts work by decreasing the **activation energy** (E_a or $\Delta G^{\ddagger}$) of a reaction. As mentioned above, enzymes do not change the thermodynamic parameters of a reaction. Those are equations of state, and they do not depend on *how* reactants are transformed into products, merely that they *are* transformed. Likewise, catalysts do not affect equilibrium. If an equilibrium for a reaction lies heavily to the left or to the right, it will still be that way in the presence of an enzyme; the only difference is that the reaction will achieve that equilibrium more quickly in the presence of a catalyst than without.

Catalysts increase reaction rate by lowering the energy of the transition state (**Figure 4.5**). General chemistry indicates that the number of molecules that can cross the energy barrier from reactants, or substrate, to products is limited by the height of the barrier, known as the activation energy, through the Arrhenius equation:

$$k = Ae^{-\frac{E_a}{RT}}$$

FIGURE 4.5 **Enzymes lower activation energy.** Shown is a reaction coordinate with energy on the *y*-axis and the progress of the reaction on the *x*-axis. All reactions have an energetic barrier they need to cross (the activation energy, E_a). Enzymes work by lowering this barrier. This makes both the forward and reverse directions more favorable. (Karp, *Cell and Molecular Biology: Concepts and Experiments*, 7e, copyright 2013, John Wiley & Sons. This material is reproduced with permission of John Wiley & Sons, Inc.)

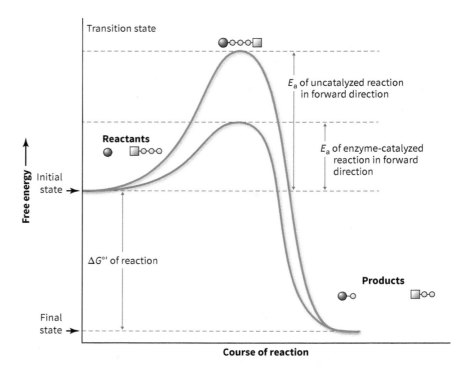

In this instance, the higher the barrier (E_a, the activation energy), the slower the reaction. Catalysts work by lowering this barrier and thus increasing the reaction rate. A quick calculation shows how significant this can be. A 36 kJ/mol change in the activation energy results in an astounding 10^6-fold change in the **rate constant** (k) at the same temperature.

As an analogy, think about living in one town in the mountains and wishing to go to a second town, located in a nearby valley. We would be limited by the height of the mountain we need to climb to go to the second town; a tunnel through the mountain would facilitate our travel.

Enzymes lower activation energy in both a surprisingly simple and terribly complex way. Enzymes bind substrates using a combination of weak forces and steric interactions that align functional groups, polarize bonds, promote electron flow, constrain molecules, and otherwise place molecules in a favorable geometry for reactions to occur. That is, enzymes literally form a pocket that brings groups together or pulls them apart to form a structure similar to the transition state. Once at the peak of this energetic barrier some fraction of molecules will decompose back into substrates, while the remainder will convert into products.

WORKED PROBLEM 4.1 | Describing an enzymatically catalyzed reaction

Lysozyme is an enzyme that breaks bonds in the carbohydrate chains found in bacterial cell walls. Describe this reaction using the vocabulary found in this section.

Strategy   Examine the image and the reaction shown. Describe in your own words what is going on. Next, determine whether there are specific terms or names for what you have described, and put what you have written into scientific terms.

Solution   Lysozyme is a monomeric enzyme that catalyzes the hydrolytic cleavage of carbohydrate chains in the bacterial cell wall; thus it belongs to EC classification 3, hydrolases. The carbohydrate chains are the substrate, and they bind to the active site of the enzyme using induced fit. This binding stabilizes the transition state, lowering the activation energy—the barrier to catalysis. The broken fragments of the carbohydrate chain are the products of the reaction.

Follow-up question   Choose any three enzymatically catalyzed reactions you can think of (either from this text or from other sources). Categorize these reactions based on the six types of reactions found in section 4.1.2.

4.1 Summary

- Enzymes are protein catalysts that increase rates of reaction by lowering activation energy.
- Enzymes are often globular proteins that may be monomeric or multimeric.
- Substrates (the reactants) are converted to products in the active site of the enzyme, a surface cleft that specifically binds the substrate.
- The active site binds substrate like a key in a lock or a hand in a glove. The binding is specific and tight, with solvent often being excluded.
- Enzymes can be categorized based on the type of reaction they catalyze.
- Enzymes do not alter equilibrium, but they do allow systems to achieve equilibrium more quickly than would be the case in the absence of a catalyst.

4.1 Concept Check

- Describe what generally happens in an enzymatically catalyzed reaction.
- Describe the interactions of substrate and enzyme using the proper biochemical terminology.
- Describe the two models (lock and key and induced fit) that are used to describe these interactions.
- Use a simple thermodynamic argument to describe why enzymes increase the rate of a reaction.

4.2 | Enzymes Increase Reaction Rate

Rates of enzymatically catalyzed reactions can be derived from rates of chemical reactions and are powerful tools for describing reactions.

4.2.1 | A review of chemical rates

The rate of a chemical reaction is defined as the change in concentration of a reactant or product over time. Using square brackets to denote molar concentrations and the notation of calculus gives:

$$\frac{d[R]}{dt} \quad \text{or} \quad \frac{d[P]}{dt} \tag{4.1}$$

If this is the simplest reaction, where a single molecule of reactant is being changed into product, then the loss of reactant will equal the gain in product:

$$\frac{-d[R]}{dt} = \frac{d[P]}{dt} \tag{4.2}$$

In the simplest chemical reaction, such as an isomerization, a single molecule of A reacts to form a molecule of B.

$$A \rightarrow B \tag{4.3}$$

If we determine experimentally that this is a first-order reaction overall, we can express this mathematically using an equation termed a **rate law**:

$$\text{Rate} = \frac{d[B]}{dt} = k[A] \tag{4.4}$$

In this expression, the rate is equal to a rate constant (k) multiplied by the concentration of A. This constant is unique for any individual reaction. The reaction rate also varies with the concentration of reactant A. In this example, the rate varies linearly with A. If the concentration of A were to double, the rate would double; if the concentration were to go up five times, the rate would increase five times. This indicates that the rate is first order with regard to A and first order overall; that is, it varies linearly with A and nothing else. It also indicates that, on a physical level, the reaction does not require two molecules of A to collide; rather, it proceeds when a single molecule of A rearranges into B.

A reaction in which two molecules of A need to collide to generate a molecule of B is second order with regard to A:

$$2A \longrightarrow B \tag{4.5}$$

$$\text{Rate} = \frac{d[B]}{dt} = k[A]^2 \tag{4.6}$$

Here, the rate of the reaction varies with the square of the concentration of A. Thus, if the concentration of A were to double, the rate would increase by four times. If the concentration were tripled, the reaction would go nine times faster.

If the reaction rate did not vary at all with regard to the concentration of A, we would say that the reaction is zeroth order with regard to A

$$\text{Rate} = k \tag{4.7}$$

None of these rate laws relates concentration and time. To do that, the integrated rate law for each equation is required. For a first-order reaction, the equation is first rearranged and then integrated:

$$\frac{d[A]}{[A]} = -k \, dt \tag{4.8}$$

$$\int_{[A]_0}^{[A]_t} \frac{d[A]}{[A]} = -k \int_0^t dt \qquad (4.9)$$

This gives:

$$ln[A]_t - ln[A]_0 = -kt \qquad (4.10)$$

which can be rearranged to give:

$$ln[A]_t = ln[A]_0 - kt \qquad (4.11)$$

or

$$[A]_t = [A]_0 e^{-kt} \qquad (4.12)$$

The integrated form of the second-order rate law can be derived in a similar fashion and gives:

$$\frac{1}{[A]_t} = \frac{1}{[A]_0} + kt \qquad (4.13)$$

The integrated form of the zeroth-order rate law is

$$[A]_t = [A]_0 - kt \qquad (4.14)$$

By integrating the rate law, it is possible to express product concentration as a function of time.

The rate constant (k) relates the concentration to the rate. It has two main components. First is the frequency factor, A, which describes the percentage of collisions that result in a favorable reaction, that is, the number of times that molecules must collide before they collide in the proper orientation to cause chemistry to occur. The second term is an exponential term that relates the activation energy, E_a; the temperature (measured in Kelvin), T; and the gas law constant, R. Here, e is being raised to the negative activation energy (E_a) power. Hence, the higher the E_a, the lower the value of the exponential, the lower the value of k, and the lower the rate. However, as the temperature increases, it can modify the exponential term to increase k and thus increase the reaction rate. This is a variation of a Boltzman–Maxwell distribution and describes the fraction of molecules with enough energy to overcome the activation energy barrier (**Figure 4.6**). Combining the frequency factor A and the exponential term gives the Arrhenius equation you may recall from general chemistry:

$$k = Ae^{-\frac{E_a}{RT}} \qquad (4.15)$$

When a chemical reaction is catalyzed, the catalyst takes part in the reaction but is not consumed. Rather, it provides an alternative path for a reaction to occur, and this alternative mechanism has a lower activation energy.

4.2.2 The Michaelis-Menten equation relates enzymatic rates to measurable parameters

Before examining an enzymatically catalyzed reaction, it is helpful to define the terms used. In such a reaction, the starting material is termed the substrate (S), and it is converted by the enzyme (E) to the product (P). The rate of an enzymatically catalyzed reaction is referred to as a velocity (v).

In some of the first experiments to determine enzymatic rate, Adrian Brown, a professor of malting and brewing, determined that invertase (an enzyme that breaks down sucrose) is

FIGURE 4.6 Boltzmann distribution. A Boltzmann distribution shows the distribution of particles with different energies.

independent of sucrose concentration provided that the concentration of the substrate is much higher than that of the enzyme.

$$\text{Sucrose} \xrightarrow{\text{invertase}} \text{glucose} + \text{fructose}$$

From this finding, Brown surmised that catalysis must take at least two steps, the formation of an enzyme–substrate complex (*ES*), and the formation of product, and that the product-forming step does not involve sucrose.

$$E + S \underset{k_{-1}}{\overset{k_1}{\rightleftharpoons}} [ES] \overset{k_2}{\rightarrow} E + P \tag{4.16}$$

If there were enough substrate available to bind the entire free enzyme (saturation), then k_2 would become the rate-determining step of this reaction. This is consistent with the observation that increasing substrate concentration past a certain point fails to elicit an increase in reaction rate. When this is the case, and the enzyme is saturated with substrate, the rate law becomes:

$$v = \frac{d[P]}{dt} = k_2[ES] \tag{4.17}$$

Here, the rate of formation of [*ES*] is the total of the rates that build up the concentration of [*ES*] minus those that break it down:

$$\frac{d[ES]}{dt} = k_1[E][S] - k_{-1}[ES] - k_2[ES] \tag{4.18}$$

This form of the rate law cannot be integrated simply; instead, assumptions are needed to proceed further. The first assumption, made by Leonor Michaelis and Maude Menten, was that k_2 is much slower than k_{-1}, enabling an equilibrium to be established between *E*, *S*, and the *ES* complex:

$$K_s = \frac{k_{-1}}{k_1} = \frac{[E][S]}{[ES]} \tag{4.19}$$

where K_s is the dissociation constant of the *ES* complex. In honor of their work, the *ES* complex is referred to as the **Michaelis complex**.

The second assumption, termed the **steady state assumption**, assumes that the *ES* complex forms rapidly from free enzyme and substrate, and it exists at a relatively unchanging concentration as the reaction proceeds until substrate is depleted:

$$\frac{d[ES]}{dt} = 0 \tag{4.20}$$

Both of these approximations are useful in expressing enzyme rate in terms of measurable quantities. Describing enzymatic catalysis requires the use of terms that can be readily measured. Although *ES* and *E* are not easily measured, total enzyme is:

$$[E] + [ES] = [E]_{\text{tot}} \tag{4.21}$$

To calculate rate, we need to be able to rearrange these expressions to determine [*ES*]. Combining equations 4.18 and 4.21 gives:

$$k_1([E]_{\text{tot}} - [ES])[S] = (k_{-1} + k_2)[ES] \tag{4.22}$$

Distributing k_1 and *S* across the first term yields:

$$k_1[E]_{\text{tot}}[S] - k_1[ES][S] = (k_{-1} + k_2)[ES] \tag{4.23}$$

This can be rearranged to:

$$k_1[E]_{\text{tot}}[S] = (k_{-1} + k_2)[ES] + k_1[ES][S] \tag{4.24}$$

Grouping terms gives:

$$k_1[E]_{\text{tot}}[S] = [ES](k_{-1} + k_2 + k_1[S]) \tag{4.25}$$

Solving for [ES] gives:

$$[ES] = \frac{[E]_{tot}[S]}{\left\{ \dfrac{(k_{-1}+k_2)}{k_1} \right\} + [S]} \tag{4.26}$$

Defining the ratio of the rate constants $(k_{-1}+k_2)/k_1$ as $\mathbf{K_M}$, the Michaelis constant, gives:

$$[ES] = \frac{[E]_{tot}[S]}{K_M + [S]} \tag{4.27}$$

To express this equation as a velocity or rate instead of simply in terms of [ES], it is necessary to use the equation $v = d[P]dt = k_2[ES]$ (equation 4.17). Substituting gives:

$$v_0 = \frac{d[P]}{dt} = k_2[ES] = \frac{k_2[E]_{tot}[S]}{K_M + [S]} \tag{4.28}$$

The maximal rate achievable (V_{max}) occurs when the entire enzyme is saturated with substrate, $[ES] = [E]_{tot}$. This can be substituted into equation 4.28 as shown:

$$v_0 = \frac{V_{max}[S]}{K_M + [S]} \tag{4.29}$$

This is the **Michaelis-Menten equation**, the central equation of **enzyme kinetics** that relates substrate concentration [S] to two fundamental properties of the enzyme: the theoretical maximal velocity for a given concentration of enzyme (V_{max}) and the Michaelis constant (K_M). A plot of this curve, substrate concentration versus **initial rate** or **initial velocity**, gives a characteristic saturation kinetic: a rectangular hyperbola rotated 45° (**Figure 4.7**).

4.2.3 | The Michaelis constant has several meanings

The Michaelis constant (K_M) has several meanings in biochemistry, all of which are equally valid. First, it can be seen as a ratio of rate constants. This ratio describes the rate constant of formation of the ES complex, divided by the rate constants of the breakdown of the complex. This provides a second way of thinking about the Michaelis constant, that is, as an equilibrium constant that describes the interaction of E, S, and ES. Therefore, the Michaelis complex also describes the affinity of substrate for enzyme (how tightly substrate and enzyme interact), which is an important and distinct parameter of enzyme kinetics. The lower the K_M value, the higher the affinity of the pair for each other. There are enzymes that have low K_M values and therefore bind substrate well but also have low k_2 values and do not rapidly catalyze reactions. These enzymes act as molecular timers, binding to substrate but then taking seconds to minutes to catalyze the reaction. The signaling proteins known as G proteins employ this mechanism; while bound to GTP, they activate other proteins but the effect stops once GTP has been hydrolyzed.

Finally, K_M can be also thought of as the concentration at which the enzyme operates at one-half of maximal velocity at a given concentration of enzyme $(V_{max}/2)$. While this is a commonly used explanation for introductory students, please be aware that the K_M value for any enzyme is not defined by the V_{max} value and K_M is independent of enzyme concentration. This definition can be seen either on a plot of substrate concentration versus velocity or by analyzing the Michaelis-Menten equation as shown in Figure 4.7.

FIGURE 4.7 **Saturation kinetic curve.** Shown is a graph of initial reaction velocity (reaction rate) versus substrate concentration. This curve illustrates saturation kinetics, the observation that, above a certain concentration of substrate, the rate cannot increase any further. Many enzymes will obey these kinetics.

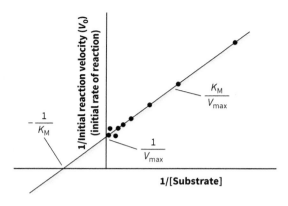

FIGURE 4.8 **Lineweaver-Burke plot.**
A Lineweaver-Burke plot is a different means of graphing the Michaelis-Menten equation. In this graph, $1/v_0$ on the y-axis is graphed versus $1/[S]$ on the x-axis. The y-intercept is $1/V_{max}$ and the x-intercept is $-1/K_M$.

4.2.4 Kinetic data can be graphically analyzed

It is difficult to obtain meaningful data by looking at a graph of substrate concentration versus initial velocity. As computational tools have advanced, it has become easy to use software to perform a nonlinear curve fit to the dataset, to obtain the asymptote that represents V_{max}, and from there to calculate K_M from the $V_{max}/2$ value.

The classical way to interpret Michaelis-Menten kinetic data is to construct a **Lineweaver-Burke plot**.

$$\frac{1}{v_0} = \left(\frac{K_M}{V_{max}}\right)\frac{1}{[S]} + \frac{1}{V_{max}} \tag{4.30}$$

This is a double reciprocal plot of the data, with the point slope form of the line ($y = mx + b$) (**Figure 4.8**). The inverse of the substrate concentration is plotted against the inverse of the velocity. The resulting data give a straight line with a y-intercept of $1/V_{max}$ and an x-intercept of $-1/K_M$. The slope of this line is K_M/V_{max}.

The Lineweaver-Burke plot is the most common means of representing kinetic data. While it is relatively easy to read compared to a saturation kinetic curve, it has its own shortcomings. Rate data collected over the concentrations typically associated with enzyme kinetics experiments are often compressed near the x-axis. Second, points taken at lower concentrations (and therefore found farther down the x-axis in the reciprocal plot) can distract the viewer and skew the result, although this is not as significant a problem if the curve is being fit by a graphing program. Finally, the reciprocal nature of the axis means that any errors in the experiment become amplified in the graph.

4.2.5 k_{cat}/K_M is a measure of catalytic efficiency

So far we have been working with the approximation that k_2 is the catalytic step of the enzymatic reaction. In the simple reaction model shown in equation 4.16, k_2 is sometimes called k_{cat}. The k_{cat} value is calculated by dividing V_{max} by $[E]_{tot}$. The value k_{cat} is also known as the **turnover number** of the enzyme, that is, the number of reactions that the enzyme can catalyze per unit time (k_{cat} is a first-order rate constant with the units sec^{-1}).

At less than saturating conditions, most of the enzyme is found as free E rather than ES. In this instance, dividing k_{cat}/K_M gives the catalytic efficiency: a second-order rate constant that describes how often a reaction occurs for every encounter of enzyme and substrate.

4.2.6 Some enzymes approach catalytic perfection

Some enzymes catalyze a reaction nearly every time they encounter a substrate molecule. In these cases, the rate-limiting step becomes the diffusion of enzyme and substrate together, a number termed the **diffusion controlled limit**. This value is on the order of 10^8 to 10^9 M^{-1} sec^{-1}, depending on the enzyme and substrate. Interestingly, several enzymes have achieved this limit, suggesting they have achieved some form of chemical and evolutionary perfection (**Table 4.2**).

While these are optimal values, the average value of most enzymes is on the order of 10^{-5} M^{-1} sec^{-1}, with a k_{cat} of 10 s^{-1}, far lower values. Furthermore, the catalytic competence of enzymes seems to vary with their task. Studies have shown that the enzymes found in central metabolism are far more efficient (30-fold more) than those in secondary metabolism.

TABLE 4.2 **Examples of Highly Efficient Enzymes**

Enzyme	Reaction	K_{cat}/K_m
Superoxide dismutase	$O_2^- \rightarrow O_2$	2×10^9
Fumarase	Fumarate + $H_2O \rightarrow$ Malate	1×10^9
Catalase	$2\,H_2O_2 \rightarrow 2\,H_2O + O_2$	4×10^8
Acetylcholinesterase	Acetylcholine $\rightarrow$ Acetate + choline	2×10^8
Carbonic anhydrase	$CO_2 + H_2O \rightarrow H_2CO_3$	7×10^7

DIFP
(diisopropylfluorophosphonate)
insecticide

Sarin
(isopropyl methyl
phosphonofluoridate)
nerve gas

MAFP
(methyl arachadonylfluorophosphonate)
laboratory reagent

FIGURE 4.9 **Irreversible enzyme inhibitors.** Examples of suicide enzyme inhibitors include the nerve gas sarin, the protease inhibitor DIFP (diisopropylfluoro-phosphate), and MAFP (methyl arachadonylfluorophosphonate). Each of these inhibitors includes a fluorophosphonate. In each of the enzymes, there is nucleophilic attack on the phosphorus. The fluoride (a good leaving group) departs, leaving the enzyme forever covalently bound to the active site nucleophile.

4.2.7 | Enzymatic reactions may be inhibited through one of several different mechanisms

Numerous small molecules can act as **enzyme inhibitors**. This section discusses the three major mechanisms through which such molecules can inhibit an enzyme, and the effect they have on kinetics. There are other means through which enzymes can be inhibited. For example, some enzymes can be directly poisoned through an **irreversible inhibitor**, also termed a **suicide substrate**. These inhibitors covalently modify the active site of the enzyme, irrevers-ibly blocking its further function. In terms of a kinetic study, as more inhibitor is added, the enzyme seems to disappear: in effect, the catalyst has been inactivated. In terms of biology these inhibitors can have very serious effects. For example, many pesticides and nerve agents are potent irreversible inhibitors of acetylcholinesterase (**Figure 4.9**). Acetylcholinesterase is found in the synapse between neurons and muscle cells and functions to inactivate the neu-rotransmitter acetylcholine following a signal. Blocking this enzyme results in rigid muscle contraction, paralysis, and eventual death.

Competitive inhibition Many enzymes recognize a single small molecule as their substrate, yet other small molecules with similar shape can also bind in the active site, competing directly with the substrate. These competitors, known as **competitive inhibitors**, may or may not be converted to a product by the enzyme, but they tie up the enzyme and prevent the conversion of the substrate into product.

$$E + S \rightleftarrows ES \rightarrow E + P$$
$$+$$
$$I$$
$$\downarrow\uparrow$$
$$EI$$

where I is the inhibitor, and EI is the enzyme inhibitor complex. The competitive inhibitor ties up free enzyme but can be outcompeted with added substrate. In other words, if the substrate concentration is high enough, all of the free E will be saturated with substrate and become ES. Because the inhibitor cannot bind ES, it loses efficacy. Hence, competitive inhibitors do not affect V_{max}, but they do raise K_M.

The Michaelis-Menten equation for a system with a competitive inhibitor is:

$$v_0 = \frac{V_{max}[S]}{\alpha K_M} + [S] \tag{4.31}$$

where α is $1 + [I]/K_I$, $[I]$ is the concentration of I, and K_I is the dissociation constant of the EI complex:

$$K_I = \frac{[E][I]}{[EI]} \tag{4.32}$$

Plots including reactions with these inhibitors illustrate the change they have on V_{max} (**Figure 4.10**). The double reciprocal form of the Michaelis-Menten equation for a competitive inhibitor is:

$$\frac{1}{v_0} = \left(\frac{\alpha K_M}{V_{max}}\right)\frac{1}{[S]} + \frac{1}{V_{max}} \tag{4.33}$$

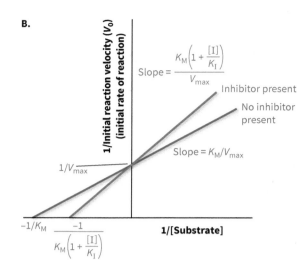

FIGURE 4.10 **Competitive inhibition.** **A.** In the presence of a competitive inhibitor, V_{max} is unchanged, and K_M is lowered. **B.** In a Lineweaver-Burke plot, the y-intercept is unchanged, but the slope is changed.

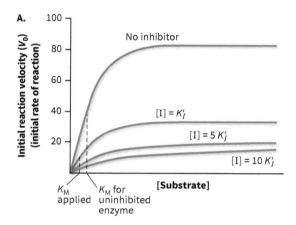

FIGURE 4.11 **Uncompetitive inhibition.** **A.** Shown is a graph of a saturation kinetic plot. **B.** Graphing 1 over the substrate concentration versus 1 over the velocity gives a double reciprocal or Lineweaver-Burke plot. In the presence of an uncompetitive inhibitor, V_{max} and K_M are both altered, leading to parallel lines on a Lineweaver-Burke plot.

Uncompetitive inhibition

In contrast to competitive inhibitors, **uncompetitive inhibitors** bind only to the ES complex.

$$E + S \rightleftarrows ES \rightarrow E + P$$
$$+$$
$$I$$
$$\downarrow\uparrow$$
$$ESI$$

By binding only to the ES complex, these inhibitors decrease V_{max} because they are lowering ES; however, they also increase K_M by depleting ES complex.

The Michaelis-Menten equation for an uncompetitive inhibitor is:

$$v_0 = \frac{V_{max}[S]}{K_M} + \alpha'[S] \tag{4.34}$$

where

$$\alpha' = 1 + \frac{[I]}{K_I'} \tag{4.35}$$

with

$$K_I' = \frac{[ES][I]}{[ESI]}. \tag{4.36}$$

Please note that in uncompetitive inhibition, the inhibitor constant is α' instead of α.

The double reciprocal form of the Michaelis-Menten equation in this instance is:

$$\frac{1}{v_0} = \left(\frac{K_M}{V_{max}}\right)\frac{1}{[S]} + \frac{\alpha'}{V_{max}} \tag{4.37}$$

Here, both $1/V_{max}$ and $-1/K_M$ are altered by α', resulting in a y-intercept of α'/V_{max} and an x-intercept of $-\alpha'/K_M$ (**Figure 4.11**). When the substrate concentration in an uncompetitive situation is low, there is little ES complex and the uncompetitive inhibitor loses effectiveness. This is the opposite of the situation seen in competitive inhibition.

FIGURE 4.12 **Mixed inhibition.** **A.** In the case of a mixed inhibitor, both V_{max} and K_M are altered. **B.** Lineweaver-Burke plots of these data show the lines intersecting somewhere in the plane to the left of the y-axis.

Mixed inhibitors

Mixed inhibitors bind to the enzyme in the presence or absence of substrate:

$$E + S \rightleftharpoons ES \rightarrow E + P$$
$$+ \qquad +$$
$$I \qquad I$$
$$\updownarrow \qquad \updownarrow$$
$$EI \qquad ESI$$

The Michaelis-Menten equation for mixed inhibition is:

$$v_0 = \frac{V_{max}[S]}{\alpha\, K_M} + \alpha'[S] \qquad (4.38)$$

Mixed inhibitors act as a combination of competitive and uncompetitive inhibitors, and they are effective regardless of substrate concentration.

The Lineweaver-Burke equation for a mixed inhibitor is:

$$\frac{1}{v_0} = \left(\frac{\alpha\, K_M}{V_{max}}\right)\frac{1}{[S]} + \frac{\alpha'}{V_{max}} \qquad (4.39)$$

The Lineweaver-Burke plot of this equation gives a series of lines that intersect at a point left of the y-axis but above the x-axis (**Figure 4.12**). In situations where $\alpha = \alpha'$, the line will intersect on the x-axis, in which case the inhibition is referred to as noncompetitive or pure mixed inhibition.

A summary of how these inhibitors act is found in **Table 4.3**.

An example of enzyme inhibition and how it applies to modern medicine can be found in **Societal and Ethical Biochemistry: Enzyme inhibitors as lifesavers-antiretroviral drugs.**

TABLE 4.3 **Effects of Enzyme Inhibitors on Kinetic Parameters**

Inhibitor	Apparent K_m	Apparent V_{max}
None	K_m	V_{max}
Competitive	αK_m	V_{max}
Uncompetitive	$K_{m/\alpha'}$	$V_{max/\alpha'}$
Mixed	$\alpha K_{m/\alpha'}$	$V_{max/\alpha'}$

Societal and Ethical Biochemistry

Enzyme inhibitors as lifesavers-antiretroviral drugs

This chapter discusses enzyme inhibitors and the different mechanisms of inhibition. Enzyme inhibitors are a useful laboratory tool for probing enzyme function and mechanism, but their benefits are much wider than that; for example, many everyday drugs, including the antiretroviral drugs used to treat human immunodeficiency virus (HIV) are enzyme inhibitors.

HIV (the virus that causes acquired immunodeficiency syndrome or AIDS) is a retrovirus, meaning that it uses RNA rather than DNA as its genetic material. As part of its life cycle, HIV uses reverse transcriptase (RT) to copy the viral genome into a DNA copy inserted into the host's genome. The viral genome contains the code for all viral proteins. Several of these proteins are transcribed as a single protein that is then cleaved into mature proteins by a specific viral protease. Healthy mammalian cells lack both RT and the viral protease; therefore, these two enzymes are suitable targets for pharmaceutical treatments aimed at blocking the spread of the virus.

Several different classes of drugs are used in antiretroviral therapy, but this section focuses on the three most common and well-established classes: RT inhibitors (RTIs) and non-nucleoside RT inhibitors (NNRTIs), both of which inhibit RT; and protease inhibitors, which inhibit the viral protease.

RTIs are analogs of the deoxynucleosides used as a substrate by RT. Nucleoside analogs typically lack the 3′ hydroxyl group on the ribose or deoxyribose ring, making it impossible for RT to extend the sequence of the DNA after incorporating one of these molecules. These analogs compete with deoxynucleosides for the active site; as such, they are competitive inhibitors. NNRTIs also inhibit RT but do not bind in the active site. Rather, these drugs bind elsewhere on RT and are noncompetitive inhibitors.

Protease inhibitors block the viral protease, preventing cleavage of the viral proteins and synthesis of mature virus. A notable feature of these inhibitors are the peptide bonds apparent in their structure. Protease inhibitors bind in the active site of the viral protease and are potent competitive inhibitors of the protease. Newer variants of these drugs have modifications—tetrahedral transition-state analogs or structures that use linkages other than peptides—that make them more resistant to breakdown and metabolism in the body, increasing the half-life and efficacy of the drug.

Azidothymidine (AZT)
(nucleoside analog)

Ritonavir
(protease inhibitor)

Because the HIV virus mutates rapidly, more than one of these drugs is usually used in treatment. This is termed "cocktail therapy" or "highly active antiviral treatment" (HAART). The latest drugs used in the treatment of HIV target other aspects of the viral life cycle, such as the entry of the virus into the host cell or integration of the viral genome into the host's genome.

As we move into the fourth decade of the AIDS epidemic, HIV infection has become a disease that can be managed, but it is still a significant health threat. In 2016 the World Health Organization (WHO) reported that over 36.7 million people are infected with HIV, including 2.1 million children. It still causes over a million deaths annually.

4.2.8 | Many reactions have more than one substrate

This chapter has focused on **Michaelis-Menten kinetics** with a single substrate and a single product. However, most reactions have more than one substrate and more than one product. Similar equations describe the behavior of enzymes that have two substrates and two products, but the basic parameters (K_M and V_{max}) are still observed. These reactions can be defined by the order in which substrates bind and products leave.

WORKED PROBLEM 4.2 | Calculating kinetic parameters

An enzyme is reacted with its substrate, A, for 1 minute at 37°C and yields the following rates.

[A], (mM)	Initial velocity, v_0 (µMol/min)
1	1.2
2	1.9
5	3.1
12.5	4.1
20	4.5
40	4.8

What are K_M and V_{max} for this enzyme?

Strategy Given the kinetic data, how could you transform it to get K_M and V_{max}?

Solution

Lineweaver-Burke Plot

$y = 0.6449x + 0.1934$

(plot: x-axis labeled 1/[S] ranging from −0.4 to 1.2; y-axis labeled $1/v_0$ ranging from 0.1 to 0.9)

A Lineweaver-Burke plot of the data will give the values of V_{max} (the y-intercept is $1/V_{max}$, 5.2) and K_M (the x-intercept is $-1/K_M$, 3.33 mM).

Follow-up question What other information would you need to calculate k_{cat}?

The equations and concepts outlined in the study of Michaelis-Menten kinetics have been used to describe many situations in which it might be anticipated that these kinetics would not work, and yet they often do. Such situations include the metabolism of ethanol by the liver, protein–protein interactions, and growth of bacteria. Despite the usefulness and flexibility of the Michaelis-Menten equation, caution must be employed to ensure that the assumptions made in the analysis of any system do not confound the actual biochemistry occurring.

4.2 Summary

- The rates of enzymatically catalyzed reactions can be examined mathematically.
- Analysis of the rate of a chemical reaction provides important data that are useful in elucidating the mechanism of the reaction.
- Kinetic parameters such as V_{max} and K_M can be obtained from plots of kinetic data.
- The efficiency of an enzyme can be calculated as the ratio of k_{cat}/K_M.
- Some enzymes have achieved catalytic perfection; they carry out a reaction almost every time they encounter a substrate molecule.
- Enzymes can be inhibited by several different mechanisms.
- Competitive inhibitors compete with substrate for the active site; they increase K_M but do not affect V_{max}.
- Uncompetitive inhibitors bind solely to the ES complex; they decrease V_{max} and modify K_M.
- Mixed inhibitors bind to either the free enzyme or the ES complex; they decrease V_{max} and modify K_M.
- Noncompetitive inhibition occurs where both α and α' are equal in a mixed inhibitor.
- Many reactions have more than one substrate and product. These reactions can be classified and their kinetics defined by the number of substrates and products and by the order in which they bind and leave.

4.2 Concept Check

- Describe the Michaelis-Menten equation and the meaning of the various components such as V_{max} and K_M.
- Use the terms V_{max} and K_M to describe how enzymes behave.
- Construct and interpret a double reciprocal plot to extract K_M and V_{max} from raw kinetic data.
- Using graphs and equations, explain the difference between the three types of inhibition in terms of how these small molecules act on the enzyme and how they affect kinetic parameters.

4.3 The Mechanism of an Enzyme Can Be Deduced from Structural, Kinetic, and Spectral Data

From a chemical perspective, the mechanism of any reaction is a valuable piece of information. The mechanism gives us information about how the reaction proceeds (or does not) at one of the most fundamental levels. It explains why some products and not others are seen. The information found in a chemical mechanism provides basic information that helps in predicting what will happen in future experiments. The same is true for biochemistry. An enzymatic mechanism ties together numerous pieces of chemical and structural data to give a concise explanation of the chemistry that is believed to occur. To clarify, mechanisms are models; although data can be consistent or inconsistent with a mechanism, they cannot be proven. Nevertheless, understanding the fundamental chemistry occurring in an enzyme is valuable when it comes to understanding why some substrates will react and others will not, or in designing enzyme inhibitors or drugs.

One other point of clarification: the term mechanism has more than one use in biochemistry. When we are discussing how an enzyme catalyzes a reaction, we refer to the mechanism by which that enzyme catalyzes the reaction. This is a typical organic or inorganic reaction mechanism shown with arrows pushing electrons. There is, however, a broader use of the term mechanism in biochemistry. When discussing how a drug elicits an effect, a mechanism of action of that drug (for example, signaling through a G protein coupled receptor) may be mentioned. This use of the term mechanism uses a pathway, a series of reactions, or an accepted chain through which proteins interact. In this regard, the term mechanism does not include the atomic level of detail in a reaction mechanism, but it is nevertheless a valid use of the term.

4.3.1 Enzymatically catalyzed reactions have common properties

In thinking about organic reaction mechanisms, we may consider the general categories of mechanisms (S_N1 or E2), or something more involved (4+2 cycloaddition). Other questions arise, such as the effect of leaving groups, solvent selection, bond polarity, electron withdrawing or donating groups, or the effects of stereochemistry. Collectively, all these contribute to the overall reaction and the type of mechanism that occurs.

In examining an enzymatically catalyzed reaction, many of the same conditions arise, but there are several important distinctions. Because enzymes lower activation energy, several general principles and guidelines are followed, and relatively few types of catalysis can occur.

The general principles are as follows:

- Enzymes bind substrate and orient substrates properly for chemistry to occur. Hence, they favor reactions by organizing and positioning groups to prime them for reactions. This lowers entropic contributions (ΔS) to the free energy of the transition state.

- Enzymes bind substrates using a large number of weak forces. This is sometimes referred to as electrostatic catalysis and is the sum total of the weak forces acting on the substrate to effect chemical change.

- Using induced fit, enzymes bind substrates in a way that favors the transition state. If we think of the hand-in-glove analogy, the glove is more of a baseball glove that positions the hand to properly catch the ball.

In relation to general chemical mechanisms, there are three distinct categories for these types of catalysis. However, there are many instances where more than one type of mechanism is employed; for example, a metal ion may activate an acid-base catalyst, or a combination of covalent catalysis and acid-base catalysis may be found in a single mechanism. The general chemical mechanisms are as follows:

- **General acid-base catalysis**, in which an amino acid side chain either donates or accepts a proton, causing reactions to occur. The polar and charged amino acids play important roles in this form of catalysis.

- **Metal ion catalysis**, in which an active site metal ion can act as a redox active center, or as a Lewis acid or base (donating or accepting electrons as needed), or can assist in the polarization of water molecules to generate hydroxide. Metal ions are found in a third of all enzymes; the metals include zinc, magnesium, iron, calcium, copper, nickel, cobalt, and other polyvalent metal ions.

- **Covalent catalysis**, in which nucleophilic or electrophilic attack on an atom results in a covalent intermediate formed between the enzyme and substrate. The mechanistic steps in forming and breaking the intermediate are at lower transition state energies than the uncatalyzed reaction. The completion of the catalytic cycle releases the products and regenerates the active site residues. Serine, histidine, aspartate, cysteine, lysine, tyrosine, and the cofactors thiamine pyrophosphate and pyridoxal phosphate often participate in covalent catalysis.

A review of chemical reaction mechanisms and how they are used to describe enzymatic catalysis can be found in **Biochemistry: Chemical reaction mechanisms**.

Biochemistry

Chemical reaction mechanisms

Chemical reaction mechanisms indicate how scientists believe electrons flow and the details of how a reaction occurs. Mechanisms are valuable because they provide a way to explain how a reaction proceeds, and they connect structural, chemical, and kinetic data to give an elegant picture of what is happening at the molecular level.

Chemical mechanisms will be familiar from organic chemistry. In these mechanisms, the flow of a pair of electrons is depicted with a two-headed arrow:

Electrons flow from regions of high-electron density (a double bond, lone pair of electrons, or other electron-rich center) to regions of low-electron density (a polarized hydrogen in a hydroxyl group or a carbonyl carbon):

Movement of a single electron can be depicted using a single-headed arrow. The same rules apply for reactions using inorganic centers (metal ions), observed in some oxidation reactions and in the electron transport chain in mitochondria.

> **Single-headed arrows represent movement of a single electron.**

In biochemistry, the same rules apply, but there are several other things to keep in mind. Most reactions in biochemistry are catalyzed; thus, the geometry and topology of the active site plays a key role in the catalytic mechanism. Likewise, because of the positioning of nucleophiles and electrophiles in the active site, pK_a values can be significantly altered within the enzyme. An example of this is water. Activated water molecules that are coordinated and polarized in a mechanism become potent nucleophiles, a phenomenon that is not observed when water is in bulk solution.

> **A coordinated and polarized water molecule becomes a nucleophile and attacks the phosphorous.**

A second consideration for enzymatically catalyzed reactions is their complexity. A biochemically catalyzed mechanism may well have upward of 10 to 15 arrows and multiple steps. Do not be intimidated by this. If you can explain the hydration of an alkene, you can use the same logic and rules (electron flow, electronegativity, bond polarity, and geometry) to explain an enzymatically catalyzed reaction.

4.3.2 | Examining examples of enzymatic reaction mechanisms illustrates underpinning principles

Mechanisms are known for many enzymes, and three representative examples are discussed here to illustrate the underpinning principles.

Acid–base catalysis: lysozyme
Lysozyme is a natural antibiotic found in mucus and tears, and at high levels in egg white. Lysozyme is a hydrolase and cleaves a link between carbohydrate chains found in the cell wall of bacteria. When this cell wall loses structural integrity, the bacteria lyse and die.

Lysozyme is a compact enzyme, only 128 amino acids in length (14.3 kDa). The structure is slightly oblong and consists of two domains, one with several short helical stretches and one with a short portion of β sheet, connected by an α-helical linker. The active site is found in a trench that runs the length of the enzyme between the two domains and accommodates the carbohydrate substrate.

The active site of lysozyme has two negatively charged residues that are necessary for catalysis: an aspartate in position 52 (Asp 52) and a glutamic acid in position 35 (Glu 35) (**Figure 4.13**). In the mechanism shown, the glutamic acid is protonated and the aspartate is not. The mechanism can only proceed if this is the case.

It took nearly 60 years from the initial discoveries of lysozyme activity to the elucidation of its structure. A mechanism was first proposed in 1966 and was debated for over 35 years until an alternative mechanism was proposed in 2001. Both of these mechanisms have merit and have data in support of them. Indeed, years later they are still being debated.

A.

B.

Chair conformation

Half-chair conformation

Lysozyme

C.

1. Substrate binds. Strain leads to attack by aspartate.

2. The first product leaves; the remaining substrate is bound in a carbohydrate-enzyme adduct.

3. Water enters the active site and is polarized for attack by glutamate.

4. Release of the second product.

FIGURE 4.13 **Mechanism of lysozyme.** **A.** Shown is the structure of lysozyme with the active site residues and substrate highlighted in a ball and stick depiction. **B.** Binding of carbohydrate to lysozyme results in a conformational change in the carbohydrate ring (from chair to half-chair). **C.** Lysozyme induces strain in the molecule, then uses an activated water for catalysis. (PDB ID 9LYZ Kelly, J.A., Sielecki, A.R., Sykes, B.D., James, M.N., Phillips, D.C. (1979) X-ray crystallography of the binding of the bacterial cell wall trisaccharide NAM-NAG-NAM to lysozyme. *Nature* 282: 875–878)

FIGURE 4.14 **Carbonic anhydrase structure and reaction.** **A.** The active site of carbonic anhydrase is found at the bottom of a trench lined by a β sheet. **B.** His 64 acts as a proton shuttle moving protons out of the active site. **C.** Carbonic anhydrase catalyzes the reaction of water and carbon dioxide to form carbonic acid, which ionizes to form bicarbonate ion. (A, B, Left: PDB ID 1CA2 Eriksson, A.E., Jones, T.A., Liljas, A. (1988) Refined structure of human carbonic anhydrase II at 2.0 A resolution. *Proteins* 4: 274–282; B, Right: PDB ID 1CAM Xue, Y., Liljas, A., Jonsson, B.H., Lindskog, S. (1993) Structural analysis of the zinc hydroxide-Thr-199-Glu-106 hydrogen-bond network in human carbonic anhydrase II. *Proteins* 17: 93–106)

The currently accepted mechanism for lysozyme proceeds as follows. The carbohydrate substrate of lysozyme is a polymer of six-membered rings. These rings have a similar conformation to cyclohexane and normally exist in a chair conformation. Binding of the carbohydrate to lysozyme distorts the first ring of the carbohydrate, changing it from a chair conformation to a half-chair conformation. The oxygen forming the linkage between the first and second rings attacks the proton of the active site glutamate. This results in cleavage of the bond between the rings and release of the second ring side of the carbohydrate chain. The first ring can exist in several resonance states, including that of an oxonium ion. This transition state is attacked by the active site aspartate, which forms a covalent adduct with the first ring. Water then enters. The active site glutamate orients the water and deprotonates it, generating a hydroxyl ion, which then attacks the intermediate at the linkage between the first ring and the aspartyl group of the enzyme. This causes release of the first-ring side of the carbohydrate chain, and regeneration of the active site.

Metal based catalysis: carbonic anhydrase

Carbonic anhydrase is a relatively small enzyme of 29 kDa (**Figure 4.14**). It is found in numerous cells, including erythrocytes (red blood cells), the kidney, and the stomach where it catalyzes the conversion of CO_2 into H_2CO_3, (carbonic acid), which rapidly ionizes into H^+ and HCO_3^- (bicarbonate). Bicarbonate serves as the most important buffering system in the body, but it is also involved in kidney function and in maintaining the hydrostatic pressure in the eye. The direction of this reaction depends on the concentrations of substrates available.

Carbonic anhydrase is largely spherical in shape. It has one large β sheet that dominates the structure. Part of this sheet is the floor of the active site, which lies in a deep (15 Å) crevice formed by several short stretches of helix, and several turns and coils.

The active site of carbonic anhydrase contains a Zn^{2+} ion, held in place by the imidazole rings of three histidine residues (**Figure 4.15**). The fourth coordination site of the Zn^{2+} binds a water molecule. Two other residues (a glutamate and a threonine, not shown) help to position and polarize the water molecule through hydrogen bonding. Another residue important to the mechanism is histidine 64. While the other residues position either the zinc ion or water, His 64 is important in shuttling protons out of the active site.

The mechanism begins by the zinc ion binding to water. Binding polarizes the water to the point of deprotonation, generating a hydroxyl ion, which is stabilized by the zinc ion. This nucleophile attacks the carbon of carbon dioxide, generating HCO_3^-, which is released. The proton released from the water molecule in the first step is shuttled out of the active site through binding to a network of two intervening hydrogen-bonded water molecules, ultimately transferring to His 64. The ring of His 64 can pivot on the methylene group to transfer these protons out of the active site cleft to buffers in the surroundings of the enzyme.

1. **Water binds the active site zinc to generate the active enzyme.**

2. **Active site zinc polarizes water. Protons are shuttled out by histidine.**

3. **Carbon dioxide binds; the hydroxyl group from water attacks.**

4. **Bicarbonate is stabilized through the zinc ion prior to departure.**

FIGURE 4.15 **Mechanism of carbonic anhydrase.** Carbonic anhydrase uses an active site zinc complexed to three histidines to polarize a water molecule. Protons from the active site are shuttled through two fixed water molecules to transfer the proton to a histidine residue that shuttles the proton out of the active site.

Carbonic anhydrase is found in almost all species, from corals to plants to mammals, but in each case it serves different functions ranging from carbonate deposition to carbon fixation in photosynthesis, to acid–base balance. Although these enzymes differ in structure, each employs a Zn^{2+} ion chelated in place by three highly conserved histidine residues. This is an example of convergent evolution—taking different evolutionary paths to arrive at a structure that performs the same chemistry.

Covalent catalysis: chymotrypsin, a serine protease

Proteases are enzymes that degrade proteins, cleaving peptide bonds. Some proteases are specific, cleaving only a select sequence; such proteases are important in protein maturation, blood clotting, trafficking of proteins in the cell, and disease. Other proteases are more generic and important in digestion; among these is the digestive enzyme chymotrypsin (**Figure 4.16**). Chymotrypsin is secreted from the pancreas and cleaves dietary proteins in the duodenum.

Chymotrypsin is a small (25.6 kDa) globular protein. It is structurally characterized as a trypsin fold—a structure comprised of two β barrel domains, the active site being at the interface of the two. This structure is found in many proteases. Chymotrypsin is synthesized as a single polypeptide (chymotrypsinogen), which itself is proteolytically processed. The final active form of chymotrypsin contains three polypeptide chains held together by five disulfide bonds and weak forces.

Chymotrypsin does not indiscriminately cleave proteins; instead, it cuts selectively on the carboxyl side of bulky hydrophobic residues such as tyrosine, phenylalanine, and tryptophan. This provides an important clue as to the topology of the active site but is more important in substrate recognition than in catalysis. This substrate recognition pocket (termed the S1 pocket) is large enough to accommodate the bulky residue, and it is lined with hydrophobic residues that also facilitate binding of the substrate.

Adjacent to the substrate recognition pocket are two regions important in catalysis. One of these is the charge relay system (also known as the catalytic triad), which consists of three

FIGURE 4.16 **Chymotrypsin structure and reaction.** Chymotrypsin is a protease, an enzyme that cleaves a peptide bond. The enzyme consists of two distinct β sheet domains. The active site is found at the interface of these two domains. (Tortora; Derrickson, *Principles of Anatomy & Physiology*, 14e, copyright 2013, John Wiley & Sons. This material is reproduced with permission of John Wiley & Sons, Inc.; PDB ID 1T7C Czapinska, H., Helland, R., Smalas, A.O., Otlewski, J. (2004) Crystal structures of five bovine chymotrypsin complexes with P1 BPTI variants. *J.Mol.Biol.* 344: 1005–1020)

key residues: aspartate, histidine, and serine, with the latter being the nucleophile in the catalytic mechanism. Also nearby is a glycine residue that participates in the oxyanion hole, the other important region which is formed by a gap created by the peptide backbone and glycine which stabilizes intermediates as the reaction proceeds.

The mechanism of chymotrypsin employs a nucleophilic attack and a covalently bound intermediate

The reaction mechanism of chymotrypsin begins with the binding of a protein in the active site (**Figure 4.17**). The hydroxyl group of the serine residue would probably be protonated if this amino acid were on the surface of the protein or free in solution; however, this is not the case in the active site, where the serine is adjacent to the histidine and aspartate of the charge relay system. Rather than existing as a deprotonated imidazole and protonated hydroxyl, the pair share the proton through a low-barrier hydrogen bond. Therefore, the interaction with the histidine means that the serine hydroxyl group has far more of an alkoxide-like character than would otherwise be possible. This deprotonated serine hydroxyl becomes the nucleophile that attacks the carbonyl carbon of the peptide.

As electrons flow from the hydroxyl into the carbonyl carbon and oxygen, the formerly planar sp^2 carbonyl center changes to a tetrahedral sp^3 center. The peptide is now covalently linked to the enzyme through the serine residue. The reaction is stabilized by the oxyanion hole. The stabilization of this transition state is one of the most important steps in the catalytic mechanism.

The tetrahedral oxyanion intermediate is short-lived, however. As it collapses and electrons flow back out of the oxygen through the bond network, the carbon-nitrogen bond breaks, and nitrogen acquires a proton from the histidine of the catalytic triad. The fragment of the substrate protein with the new amino terminus leaves the active site.

Water now enters the active site. The active site histidine deprotonates this water, and the resulting hydroxyl group attacks the acyl-enzyme intermediate (the ester linking the carboxyterminus of the substrate protein to the active site serine). Again, electrons flow up through the carbonyl group, forming a tetrahedral intermediate stabilized by the oxyanion

FIGURE 4.17 Mechanism of chymotrypsin. The active site of chymotrypsin has three critical residues for catalysis (the catalytic triad or charge transfer system). A deprotonated serine attacks the peptide carbon forming an acyl enzyme intermediate. Then water enters the active site and cleaves the acyl enzyme intermediate.

hole. As electrons flow back through this center and this intermediate collapses, the carbon–oxygen bond is broken, and the serine hydroxyl returns to share its proton with histidine. The protein containing the newly generated carboxyl terminus leaves, and the catalytic cycle is complete.

Armed with this information, it is possible to probe the structure and mechanism of chymotrypsin further. If specific site-directed mutants of the enzyme were generated, the effects of these mutations on the kinetics or mechanism of an enzyme could be studied. Creating a mutation in the S1 pocket might affect K_M (affinity of substrate for enzyme) but not catalysis, whereas inserting a bulky residue in place of the glycine in the oxyanion hole might do the reverse, affecting catalysis (V_{max}, k_2, or k_{cat}) but not substrate binding (K_M). In reality, mutations designed to alter the specificity of chymotrypsin by placing charged residues in the S1 pocket resulted in an enzyme that had no catalytic activity. In this instance, the mutation may have affected protein folding, or it may be that the binding of substrate is more complex than is currently thought.

Other proteases share some properties with chymotrypsin. Trypsin and elastase both have substrate-recognition pockets, but these enzymes have different substrate specificities. Trypsin's S1 pocket is specific for basic residues, and its substrate-recognition pocket contains an aspartate residue, whereas the S1 pocket of elastase is specific for short-chain hydrophobic residues and is hydrophobic.

Chymotrypsin is a member of a class of proteins termed **serine proteases** because of their active site serine (Figure 4.18). Other enzymes (typically proteases or esterases) also employ an active site serine that is nucleophilically primed by a catalytic triad. Cysteine proteases are among the enzymes that use an active site cysteine as the nucleophile to attack the carbonyl carbon. In this instance, a neighboring amino acid increases the nucleophilicity

A.

| Serine protease | Aspartyl protease | Metalloprotease | Cysteine protease |

B.

Chymotrypsin (bovine)   Elastase (porcine)   Trypsin (streptomyces)

FIGURE 4.18 **Different classes of proteases.** **A.** Serine proteases, aspartyl proteases, metalloproteases, and cysteine proteases all employ similar chemistry: nucleophilic attack on the carbonyl carbon. **B.** Note that these enzymes not only employ similar nucleophiles, they have a conserved topology and overall structure, although not necessarily the same amino acid sequence. (Left: PDB ID 1T7Z Delker, S.L., West Jr., A.P., McDermott, L., Kennedy, M.W.,

Bjorkman, P.J. (2004) Crystallographic studies of ligand binding by Zn-alpha2-glycoprotein. *J.Struct.Biol.* 148: 205–213; Middle: PDB ID 1QNJ Wurtele, M., Hahn, M., Hilpert, K., Hohne, W. (2000) Atomic Resolution Structure of Native Porcine Pancreatic Elastase at 1.1 A. *Acta Crystallogr.*, Sect. D 56: 520; Right: PDB ID 1SGT Read, R.J., James, M.N. (1988) Refined crystal structure of Streptomyces griseus trypsin at 1.7 A resolution. *J.Mol.Biol.* 200: 523–551) of the attacking thiolate through deprotonation. Other proteases include aspartyl proteases and metalloproteases, both of which use an activated water molecule (a hydroxyl group) as the nucleophile. In this regard they are similar to carbonic anhydrase.

4.3.3 Mechanisms are elucidated using a combination of experimental techniques

Enzyme mechanisms cannot be truly proven. There is simply the presence or absence of data to support a proposed mechanism. A combination of structural, kinetic, spectral, and other biochemical data combine to validate a proposed mechanism. That mechanism may still be called into question if new data arise, but a combined body of data reduces the likelihood of this happening. As an example, let us briefly review the data in support of the mechanism of chymotrypsin. The main data are based on affinity labeling, structural studies, and kinetics, as outlined below.

Diisopropylfluoridate (DIPF) is an affinity label, that is, a molecule that will specifically label only one of the serine residues of chymotrypsin (**Figure 4.19**). This suggests that the labeled serine is different than the other serine residues in the protein; that is, it is implicated in the catalytic mechanism—a prediction that is corroborated by other data. Another affinity label, tosyl-L-Phenylalanine chloromethyl ketone (TPCK), irreversibly derivatizes only one histidine residue in the entire protein, the histidine residue of the active site. Labeling with both of these molecules fails to occur if the protein is denatured, and labeling can be blocked by competitive inhibitors. Now that we have seen the mechanism of chymotrypsin, these data should begin to make sense. Of all of the serine and histidine residues available in chymotrypsin, the two found in the active site are specifically labeled because they participate in the hydrolysis reaction. This does not explicitly lead us to a mechanism, but it does implicate these two residues in the process.

In terms of structural studies, the structure of chymotrypsin has been solved by X-ray diffraction, which provides the coordinates of the atoms used in proposing these mechanisms. Other proteins that interact with chymotrypsin have had their structures solved by either X-ray diffraction or nuclear magnetic resonance (NMR) and can be shown to interact with chymotrypsin as predicted.

Chymotrypsin has an acyl-enzyme intermediate in which the carboxy terminus of the cleaved peptide bond is transiently bound to the active site serine. This can be demonstrated with the artificial substrate paranitrophenylacetate, which is colorless until the acetate moiety is cleaved, giving paranitrophenol, which has a yellow color. When paranitrophenylacetate is incubated with chymotrypsin, there is a rapid release of paranitrophenol as the enzyme undergoes the initial step of catalysis. However, to degrade more molecules, the enzyme needs to finish the catalytic cycle and resolve the existing acetyl-enzyme intermediates. This is seen in kinetic studies as a biphasic curve. In the first segment of the curve, the rapid hydrolysis and release of paranitrophenol is shown (**Figure 4.20**). This is followed by a second phase in which the enzyme is operating at the steady state. The slopes of these lines indicate the relative rates of each of the steps of the mechanism with the burst phase having a steeper curve followed by the slower steady state.

There are other ways to probe the mechanism of enzymes. These include examination of spectra as enzymatic reactions proceed, to look for evidence of different states. An examination of the rates of reaction using substrates isotopically labeled in specific positions is termed an isotope effect.

Diisofluorophosphate (DIFP)   **Tosyl-l-phenylalanine ketone** (TPCK)

FIGURE 4.19 **Affinity labels diisofluorophosphate (DIFP) and tosyl-L-Phenylalanine chloromethyl ketone (TPCK).** DIFP and TPCK are both used as affinity labels, molecules that specifically derivatize key amino acid residues in the active site, such as this active site serine.

A.

B.

Para nitrophenyl acetate
(clear)

Para nitrophenol
(yellow)

FIGURE 4.20 **Biphasic kinetics.** **A.** When examined over short timeframes (less than a second), chymotrypsin and many other enzymes demonstrate biphasic kinetics. The amount of product is measured in units of concentration (nanomolar). **B.** Reactions like this can be studied through the use of a colorimetric substrate, such as paranitrophenyl acetate.

WORKED PROBLEM 4.3 | A proposed chemical mechanism

You identified a novel metalloprotease and obtained its structure. Propose a mechanism for this reaction.

Strategy Examine the active site. What molecules are present, and how might they participate in catalysis? How is this active site similar to ones we have seen previously? How does a metalloprotease function?

Follow-up question If the active site glutamate in this mechanism were mutated to an aspartate, how might that effect the mechanism?

Solution The proposed mechanism is shown. Experimental data would be needed to validate this proposed mechanism.

4.3 Summary

- Enzymes catalyze chemical reactions through transition state stabilization, which is achieved through decreased entropy, increased weak interactions, and induced fit.

- Enzymes use some combination of general acid–base, metal ion, or covalent catalysis to complete reactions.

- Lysozyme, carbonic anhydrase, and chymotrypsin are provided as examples of enzyme mechanisms. Each of these illustrates several of the principles of enzymatic catalysis.

- Proposed enzyme mechanisms are built up from several different sources of data; they present a rich picture of the steps of a chemical reaction in an enzyme. They can also provide important information to guide drug design, explain disease, and further scientific understanding.

4.3 Concept Check

- Describe how enzymes generally catalyze reactions, including the forces involved.
- Describe how lysozyme, carbonic anhydrase, and chymotrypsin catalyze reactions.
- Identify the nucleophiles and electrophiles found in each mechanism.
- Explain how these mechanisms differ and how are they similar to one another.
- Explain the data that support the proposed mechanism for chymotrypsin.

4.4 Examples of Enzyme Regulation

Tools can be useful in accomplishing a job, but only if they can be controlled. Most tools have controls that turn them on or off, or perhaps change their speed. The same applies to enzymes. Evolution has produced complex means of regulating the rate at which enzymes catalyze reactions.

Enzyme activity can be regulated by altering gene expression (altering levels of the enzyme itself), sequestering the enzyme in one compartment of the cell or one organ of the organism, or limiting the access of the enzyme to substrate (potentially also through compartmentalization). This section describes two specific means of regulating enzyme activity: **covalent modification** and **allosteric regulation**.

4.4.1 Covalent modifications are a common means of enzyme regulation

Covalent modification of proteins includes any covalent addition or removal of groups from the proteins. Two common means of activation, discussed here, are **proteolytic cleavage** and **phosphorylation**.

Proteolytic cleavage An example of an enzyme activated through proteolytic cleavage is chymotrypsinogen, the zymogen form of chymotrypsin (**Figure 4.21**). **Zymogens** are inactive enzyme precursors that require proteolytic activation. In the case of chymotrypsinogen, the active form of the protein (chymotrypsin) is a protease that could degrade proteins in the acinar cells of the pancreas in which it is made, harming the cell and the organism. To avoid this, chymotrypsin is synthesized as a zymogen. The full-length peptide (chymotrypsinogen) has 245 amino acids. Once secreted into the digestive tract, it is attacked by trypsin, which cleaves the zymogen between an arginine and an isoleucine residue in the amino terminus, facilitating two important structural changes. First, the peptide nitrogen of the arginine residue is now free to interact with the aspartate of the active site, stabilizing the glycine residue lining the pocket that stabilizes the tetrahedral oxyanion intermediate. This change in conformation allows the oxyanion hole to form and thus allows catalysis to proceed. Second, the cleavage between the arginine and isoleucine alters the conformation of the protein, exposing a sequence that is recognized by other molecules of chymotrypsin and leading to optimally activated enzyme. The three polypeptides found in chymotrypsin are linked together by disulfide bonds.

Phosphorylation **Protein kinases** are enzymes that add phosphates to the hydroxyl groups of serine, threonine, or tyrosine residues of proteins. Often, the phosphate comes from a donor molecule such as ATP or GTP. Phosphates are removed by a second family of enzymes termed **phosphatases**.

A phosphorylation event can be seen as throwing a switch with regard to protein function: turning an enzyme either on or off. This can happen and cause an effect in less than a millisecond, or it can take several hours depending on the process. In considering the chemical changes going on at the surface of the protein that is being phosphorylated, it is possible to hypothesize how and why alterations in enzyme activity occur. Adding a phosphate group to

Chymotrypsinogen

Chymotrypsin

FIGURE 4.21 **Chymotrypsinogen and chymotrypsin.** Chymotrypsinogen is the zymogen form of chymotrypsin. Proteolytic cleavage leads to activation of the enzyme. Note the movement of isoleucine 16 relative to the active site aspartate 194, both shown highlighted with green spheres. (Top: PDB ID 1EX3 Pjura, P.E., Lenhoff, A.M., Leonard, S.A., Gittis, A.G. (2000) Protein crystallization by design: chymotrypsinogen without precipitants. *J.Mol.Biol.* 300: 235–239; Bottom: PDB ID 1T7C Czapinska, H., Helland, R., Smalas, A.O., Otlewski, J. (2004) Crystal structures of five bovine chymotrypsin complexes with P1 BPTI variants. *J.Mol.Biol.* 344: 1005–1020) a serine, threonine, or tyrosine residue adds a bulky group. This may cause steric hindrance between domains of a protein, between subunits, or between different polypeptides that need to interact for catalysis to occur. The phosphate also incorporates a negative two charge, which can participate in coulombic interactions, to a previously uncharged part of the protein. However, these interactions are tempered by the solvent between the two charges. The charge added to a protein through phosphorylation would probably interact with and influence many of the other charged groups in that protein, but would be unlikely to attract another charged molecule from across the cell. Nevertheless, if two proteins need to bind together for catalysis to occur, adding a negative charge to one protein could increase the likelihood of an interaction with the second protein. This would be dependent on the latter having a region of positive charge near the surface that could interact with the phosphate. Finally, the oxygen atoms bound to the phosphate have the potential to participate in more hydrogen bonds than the unphosphorylated side chain.

An example of regulation by phosphorylation is the signaling protein src (pronounced sark), a regulatory kinase originally identified and named for the Rous sarcoma virus (**Figure 4.22**). The regulation of kinases and phosphatases occurs through a series of

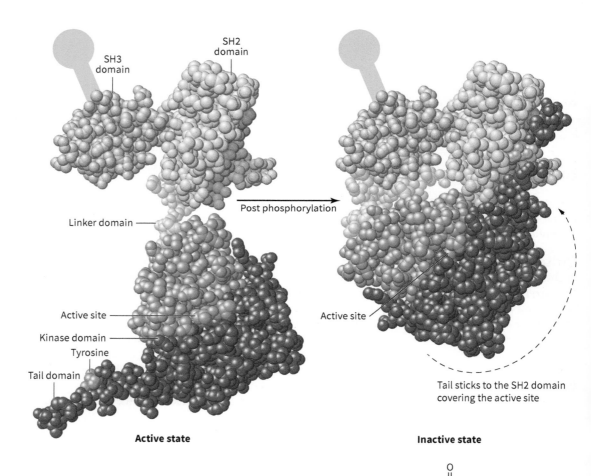

Active state

Inactive state

Tail sticks to the SH2 domain covering the active site

FIGURE 4.22 **Src is regulated by phosphorylation.** Phosphorylation of a tyrosine residue in the tail of src causes increased electrostatic interactions with residues in the SH2 domain. This results in binding of the phosphotyrosine in the tail by SH2 domain, generating the inactive state of the protein. (Image from the RCSB PDB July 2003 Molecule of the Month feature by David Goodsell [doi:10.2210/rcsb_pdb/mom_2003_7])

Tyrosine

Phosphotyrosine

signaling steps termed a **signaling cascade**. Src is a kinase and an important player in several signaling cascades. The kinase has several domains: two SH domains (src homology domains), SH2 and SH3, that are important in binding to other proteins and substrate recognition; a flexible linker that acts as a hinge; a catalytic kinase domain; and a tail that contains a specific tyrosine residue. In the active state, the tail-domain tyrosine is not phosphorylated, the protein hangs open, and the active site is accessible to substrate. However, when the kinase is phosphorylated, the tail domain wraps around the kinase domain and the phosphotyrosine residue docks to one of the SH domains, closing off the active site to substrate.

Active form (R)   **Inactive form (T)**

FIGURE 4.23 **Allosteric regulation.**   Allosteric regulators bind to the enzyme (or complex) at a site called the allosteric site. Binding of inhibitors stabilizes the T state while binding of activators stabilizes the R state. Shown here is a single subunit, although there can be multiple subunits influencing each other (Black, *Microbiology: Principles and Explorations*, 8e, copyright 2012, John Wiley & Sons. This material is reproduced with permission of John Wiley & Sons, Inc.).

4.4.2 | Allosteric regulators bind at sites other than the active site

Allosteric regulators act to increase or decrease the activity of an enzyme by binding at a site other than the active site (**Figure 4.23**). The term "allosteric" comes from Greek and literally means "other place." Allosteric regulators are most often small molecules, in some instances as small as a proton. Proteins that are allosterically regulated are classically thought of as being multimeric and cooperative, although this view is currently being reconsidered. It is clear that allosteric regulation is far more common than was once thought.

In classical allosteric models, there are two states: a tense state (T) in which the enzyme is inactive or inhibited and affinity for substrate is low, and a relaxed state (R) in which the enzyme is active and affinity for the substrate is high. An easy way to remember this is that you do not get any work done when you are tense. The names of these states are slightly misleading, because the name correlates with the *activity* rather than with the *conformation* of the protein. The binding of an allosteric regulator shifts the conformation from one state to the other, altering the activity. Only these two states, T and R, exist—there is no middle ground. Binding of allosteric activators favors the R state, while binding of allosteric inhibitors favors the T state.

Enzymes that are allosterically regulated exhibit sigmoidal (S-shaped) activity curves (**Figure 4.24**). These curves are the result of two different types of binding, T and R. The high-affinity, high-activity R state resembles a saturation curve that is shifted to the left, while the lower affinity, lower activity T curve is shifted to the right. When these curves are summed together, the resulting graph is sigmoidal and represents the mixed population of enzyme molecules found in the cell or test tube. The addition of an activator shifts this curve to the left, meaning that the enzyme is more active at a lower concentration of substrate whereas an inhibitor conversely shifts it to the right. Allosteric regulators work acutely and instantaneously, in contrast to some other forms of regulation that require a cascade of events or induction of gene expression. Allosteric regulation is the most rapid form of regulation and the most direct.

Aspartate transcarbamoylase is an example of an allosterically regulated enzyme One of the best studied examples of an allosteric enzyme is aspartate transcarbamoylase or ATCase (**Figure 4.25**). This enzyme catalyzes the formation of *N*-Carbamoyl aspartate from aspartate and carbamoyl phosphate—the rate-determining step in pyrimidine biosynthesis in *E. coli*. Rate-determining steps are frequently highly regulated; ATCase is no different, having at least three allosteric regulators.

The ATCase holoenzyme is a dodecamer with six catalytic and six regulatory subunits. If envisioned as a globe, the catalytic subunits are arranged as a trimer on either pole of the enzyme, largely separated by

FIGURE 4.24 **Allosteric enzymes have sigmoidal kinetics.**   Cooperativity between active sites in an allosteric enzyme leads to sigmoidal (S-shaped) kinetics. Addition of an allosteric inhibitor shifts the curve to the right, requiring a higher concentration of substrate for the same level of activity, while addition of an activator shifts the curve to the left.

A.

1. Amino group of asp attacks carbonyl of carbamoyl phosphate.

2. Tetrahedral intermediate collapses, eliminating phosphate.

3. Forming *N*-Carbamoyl aspartate and free phosphate.

B. T-state   R-state

Side view

Top view

E.

C.

Catalytic subunits

Regulatory subunits

D.

Phosphono linkage

FIGURE 4.25 **ATCase regulation.**
A. Aspartate transcarbamoylase catalyzes the addition of a carbamoyl group to the amine moiety of aspartate, the rate-determining step of pyrimidine biosynthesis. **B.** The active enzyme is a dodecamer consisting of six catalytic and six regulatory subunits. **C.** The catalytic subunits form two triads at either end of the molecule largely separated by a band of six regulatory subunits (in three pairs). **D.** Binding of the transition state analog PALA shifts the equilibrium between the T-state and R-state and results in inhibition of the enzyme. **E.** PALA, shown in the box, binds using numerous hydrogen bonds in the ATCase active site. (B, Left: PDB ID 1RAH Kosman, R.P., Gouaux, J.E., Lipscomb, W.N. (1994) Crystal structure of CTP-ligated T state aspartate transcarbamoylase at 2.5 A resolution: implications for ATCase mutants and the mechanism of negative cooperativity. *Proteins* 15: 147–176; B, Right: PDB ID 1Q95 Huang, J., Lipscomb, W.N. (2004) Aspartate Transcarbamylase (ATCase) of Escherichia coli: A New Crystalline R-State Bound to PALA, or to Product Analogues Citrate and Phosphate. *Biochemistry* 43: 6415–6421)

Arg105A
His134A
Arg54A
Arg167A
Thr53A
Ser52A
Arg229A
Leu267A
Thr55A
Gln231A

a belt of regulatory subunits at the equator. The active site of ATCase is unusual in that it is found at the interface of two of the catalytic subunits and involves both subunits. Analysis of the mechanism and regulation of ATCase has been facilitated by crystallographic studies, which have been advanced in part through the discovery and use of the transition-state analog *N*-phosphonoacetyl-L-aspartate (PALA). ATCase is unable to cleave the phosphono linkage in this molecule. Instead, it binds tightly in the active site, stabilizing the enzyme in the R state. This has enabled investigators to obtain structures of ATCase in both the T (unoccupied) and R states, and compare the two.

ATCase is the rate-determining step in pyrimidine biosynthesis, and it is regulated by molecules downstream in the pathway; this is an example of feedback control. The three best studied allosteric regulators of ATCase are ATP, CTP, and UTP. As you may recall, the adenine moiety of ATP is not a pyrimidine but a bicyclic purine. Both cytosine (from CTP) and uracil (from UTP) are downstream products of this pathway. All three nucleoside triphosphates (NTPs) bind to the regulatory subunits, but there are only two **binding sites**: a high-affinity binding site that can only bind to ATP and CTP, and a low-affinity binding site that preferentially binds to UTP. Complicating matters further, when UTP binds to the low-affinity site, it results in preferential binding of CTP at the high-affinity site. Therefore, only ATP and CTP can bind to the high-affinity site, and these molecules compete with one another for the site. However, if concentrations of all three NTPs are high enough, UTP can bind to the low-affinity site, resulting in preferential CTP binding at the high-affinity site.

High levels of CTP indicate that the cell has enough CTP and that further synthesis of pyrimidines should be slowed. When CTP binds to the regulatory subunit, the sigmoidal kinetic curve for the synthesis of *N*-carbamoyl aspartate is shifted to the right and the enzyme's activity falls by 50%–70% (**Figure 4.26**). Binding of CTP favors the T state. If UTP is also added, this inhibition increases to 95%.

FIGURE 4.26 **Effect of allosteric regulators on ATCase.** ATCase activity in the presence of the allosteric activator ATP shifts the rate curve to the left, while binding of the allosteric inhibitor CTP shifts the curve to the right.

In contrast to the pyrimidine NTPs, binding of ATP activates the enzyme, shifting the curve to the left and favoring the R state. High levels of ATP could indicate that the cell has an excess of energy and can thus promote growth and biosynthesis of DNA and mRNA; alternatively, it could indicate that there is an excess of purine nucleotides compared to pyrimidines. In either case, the regulatory mechanism should make biological and chemical sense to us.

Binding of these allosteric regulators results in a shift to either the T or R state, as noted. In ATCase, this leads to a large conformational change in the enzyme that involves complex interactions between numerous residues. The catalytic subunits of ATCase have a high degree of interaction with each other. Part of this interaction involves a loop of amino acids termed the 240's loop, named for its location within the protein (amino acids 230-245). The switch from T to R causes a large movement of the 240's loop, which decreases the interaction between the adjacent subunits. Furthermore, the 240's loop and two other residues are adjacent to the active site of ATCase. When they move, they change the topology of the active site, moving key residues away from one another, and hence decreasing activity.

The movement and interactions of the 240's loop are only part of the story of how ATCase functions. However, they illustrate how structural information, combined with activity and other data, help to paint a detailed picture of how enzymatic reactions occur and are regulated.

The regulation of enzymes is also under the selective pressures of evolution
Evolution can be illustrated at many different levels in biological systems, as discussed previously throughout this work. Biochemists often focus on the conservation of a particular nucleotide or amino acid sequence, whereas organismal biologists may focus on an aspect of morphology (beak shape or skull size); however, evolution covers all aspects between these extremes. The examples of protein regulation given here have undergone hundreds of millions of years of natural selection. An enzyme does not simply evolve as a catalyst. In some instances, the substrate for the enzyme may also be changing over time, and the regulatory mechanisms that dictate enzymatic rate are also under selective pressure. The selective pressures on a multimeric enzyme complex regulated by several different phosphorylation sites or allosteric regulators illustrates the complexity of this scenario.

WORKED PROBLEM 4.4 | Regulation of an enzyme

Lactate dehydrogenase catalyzes the conversion of pyruvate to lactate. It is a tetrameric enzyme that is allosterically activated in some species of bacteria by fructose-1,6-bisphosphate (FBP). What would a graph of pyruvate concentration versus rate look like in the presence and absence of FBP? Would FBP stabilize the T or the R state?

Strategy Describe allosteric regulation. What have our previous examples of allosteric regulation looked like?

Solution

Acting as an activator means that FBP stabilizes the R state and shifts the curve to the left.

Follow-up question The allosteric regulators discussed so far have been heterotropic; that is, they are not substrates for the enzyme in question. In contrast, homotropic allosteric regulators are substrates for the enzyme. How can a substrate for an enzyme also be a regulator?

4.4 Summary

- In many cases, the rate at which an enzyme operates can be manipulated by the cell, the system, or the organism.

- The many examples of regulation can be grouped into covalent modification and allosteric regulation.

- Two examples of covalent modification are proteolytic cleavage and phosphorylation.

- Proteolytic cleavage works by removing domains of the pro-enzyme that inhibit activity. This type of regulation is irreversible.

- Phosphorylation is the addition of a phosphate group, usually from a high-energy phosphate donor such as ATP, and usually to the hydroxyl group of a serine, threonine, or tyrosine residue.

- Phosphorylations are mediated by a group of enzymes called kinases. These mutations are reversible because the phosphate group can be removed by the action of a phosphatase.

- Allosteric regulation occurs when small molecules bind to sites on the enzyme distal to the active site. The action of these regulators is often cooperative, with multiple regulatory sites acting on multiple active sites.

4.4 Concept Check

- Provide examples of each type of mechanism.

- Describe how each type of mechanism works.

- Explain which of the regulatory mechanisms are reversible, which are not, and why this is the case.

- Describe the advantages and disadvantages of each of these control systems.

The Bigger Picture

Enzymes are the tools responsible for catalyzing most of the reactions that occur in the cell. A working knowledge of how enzymes function is critical and fundamental to an understanding of biochemistry. This chapter introduces enzymes and the language used to describe them. It gives a mathematical description of how enzymes behave (enzyme kinetics) and how they are affected by inhibitors. The next section discusses enzyme mechanisms, that is, the proposed means by which an enzyme actually carries out the chemistry it performs. Finally, the chapter discusses several mechanisms that regulate enzyme function and activity.

Bioinformatics Exercises

Exercise 1 Introduction to Enzyme Informatics

Exercise 2 Cofactor Chemistry

Exercise 3 Interactions in the Serine Protease Active Site

Exercise 4 Enzyme Cofactors and Kinetics

Exercise 5 Survey of Enzyme-Inhibitor Complexes

Problems

4.1 Regarding Enzymes

1. Examine this structure. Based only on this information, where might you find the active site on this enzyme? (PDB ID 1V4T Kamata, K., Mitsuya, M., Nishimura, T., Eiki, J., Nagata, Y. (2004) Structural basis for allosteric regulation of the monomeric allosteric enzyme human glucokinase. *Structure* 12: 429–438)

2. The burning of sugar in air is chemically similar to the enzymatically catalyzed oxidation of sugar. Draw a reaction coordinate diagram for the reaction of sucrose ($C_{12}H_{22}O_{11}$). What are the different thermodynamic parameters of this reaction (such as free energy)? How do these change when the reaction is catalyzed?

3. Restriction enzymes are used in laboratory manipulations to cut DNA; many of these enzymes can be inactivated by incubating them at 80°C for 30 minutes. Why would this incubation inactivate the enzyme? Why do enzymes not simply operate better at higher temperatures, as other catalysts do?

4. Like proteins, RNA molecules can be catalytic. Examine the structure of a short sequence of RNA. What types of functional groups are there in RNA molecules that could participate in catalysis in the way that amino acid side chains do?

5. Based on your knowledge of DNA, RNA, and proteins, propose a reason why catalytic RNA and protein molecules have been observed but catalytic DNA molecules have not.

6. Contaminating proteases are a common problem in protein or enzyme purification. These enzymes degrade the very proteins the scientist is attempting to isolate, but they can be inhibited with a mixture of protease inhibitors. What would such a mixture be likely to contain? What would be the properties of that group of inhibitors?

7. Efavirenz is one of the NNRTI class of drugs used to treat HIV infection. Drug-resistant HIV has undergone mutations which lead to drug resistance. The most common mutation observed after efavirenz treatment is K103N, which is also observed with other NNRTIs. Examine the genetic code. Why might this particular mutation predominate rather than others?

8. Azidothymidine (AZT) is an example of an antiretroviral drug used to treat HIV infection. Its structure is shown below. What class of drug is this (NNRTI, RTI, or protease inhibitor)?

Azidothymidine

9. Norvir is an HIV protease inhibitor. Based on the structure of Norvir, what amino acids might you predict to bind in the active site of the protease?

Norvir

10. Would the antiretroviral drugs developed and used to treat HIV be useful for treating other viral infections? Why or why not?

4.2 Enzymes Increase Reaction Rate

11. The Eadie-Hofstee plot is another means of obtaining a linear graph of Michaelis-Menten data, and has the equation $v = K_m(v/[S]) + V_{max}$. Velocity is plotted on the y-axis, and velocity over substrate concentration is plotted on the x-axis. What are the values of the slope and y-intercept of this graph? What is the advantage of this graph over a Lineweaver-Burke or a saturation kinetic (Michaelis-Menten) plot? Can you derive the Eadie-Hofstee form of the equation from the Michaelis-Menten equation?

12. Acetazolamide (Diamox) is a diuretic used to treat conditions ranging from glaucoma to altitude sickness. Diamox is an inhibitor of carbonic anhydrase. Examine the structure of Diamox given below. What kind of inhibitor might this be? Explain the reasoning behind your answer. What part of Diamox might bind carbonic anhydrase?

Acetazolamide

13. If you propose that an enzyme is proceeding through a S_N2 mechanism, what is the simplest way to test that mechanism?

14. Bis(sulfosuccinimidyl)suberate (BS3) is a cross-linking reagent. It will react with primary amines to cross-link them, forming new amide linkages. Draw a diagram of how this reaction may occur. How could this reagent be used to help determine whether an enzyme has multiple subunits? Which amino acids would be affected?

BS3

15. Aspartate transcarbamylase will also bind to succinate, shown below. What would this lead you to predict about the aspartate binding site?

Succinate

16. Many enzymes employ metal ions for catalysis. Often these are divalent, bearing a 2+ charge. This chapter examines one example where Zn^{2+} is held in place by the imidazole rings of three histidine residues. In what other ways can metal ions be tethered to a protein? How does the binding of these metal ions affect their catalytic properties?

17. Carbonic anhydrase is said to have achieved catalytic perfection. Could this enzyme be artificially improved? If so, how?

4.3 The Mechanism of an Enzyme Can Be Deduced from Structural, Kinetic, and Spectral Data

18. Examine the mechanism of carbonic anhydrase. If the Zn^{2+} were removed from the active site, and replaced with either Cu^+, Cd^{2+}, or Fe^{3+} would you expect the enzyme to still be functional? Why or why not?

19. Examine the structure and mechanism of lysozyme. If the glutamate and aspartate residues were reversed, would you expect the enzyme to still be active? Why or why not?

20. Examine the substrate binding site of lysozyme. If there were a mutation to the region distant from the bond that is cleaved, would you expect that this mutation would be more or less harmful to the enzyme than a mutation that was closer to the bonds that are cleaved?

21. We often speak of some residues of an enzyme being more highly conserved than others (for example, the active site serine). Explain what "highly conserved" means and why some residues are more highly conserved than others.

22. The active site residues in some proteins seem to be "ultimately conserved," meaning that any change to that residue results in a complete lack of activity. Is it possible for the gene coding for that enzyme to evolve? Explain your answer.

23. Based on the mechanism of a serine protease, propose a mechanism for a transacylase, an enzyme that transfers an acyl group from one hydroxyl group to another.

24. If the glycine residue in the oxyanion hole of chymotrypsin were mutated to an alanine residue, how might this affect the kinetics of the reaction? Which parameters would be affected more significantly: K_M or k_{cat}?

25. If the glycine residue in the oxyanion hole of chymotrypsin were mutated to a tryptophan residue, how might this affect the kinetics of the reaction? Which parameters would be affected more significantly: K_M or k_{cat}?

26. If the substrate binding pocket of chymotrypsin were mutated to include a lysine residue, how might this affect the kinetics of the reaction? Which parameters would be affected more significantly: K_M or k_{cat}?

27. Identify and describe three techniques that could be used to determine whether a protein is phosphorylated or not.

4.4 Examples of Enzyme Regulation

28. In thinking of enzymes and evolution, the focus is often on the binding of substrate or catalysis, with regulation seen as a secondary event. What sorts of selective pressures are at work in regulating enzyme function in enzymes such as the ones discussed in this chapter?

29. This chapter discusses the regulation of proteins by allosterism, phosphorylation, or proteolytic cleavage. Compare these three types of regulation with regard to level of control. Which are reversible,

and which are not? How quickly does each type of control take effect? How fine-tuned is each level of control?

30. Biochemical pathways are molecular assembly lines where numerous enzymes each catalyze a single step. Where might you anticipate that such a process would be controlled?

31. The strength of an electrostatic interaction can be estimated using a version of Coulomb's law: $\Delta E = A\,k\,q_1 q_2/D\,r$ where A is Avogadro's number (6.02×10^{23}), k is 9.0×10^9 joules/coulomb^2, q_1 and q_2 are the charges on the groups measured in coulombs (1.6×10^{-19} joules per electron), D is the dielectric constant of the media, and r is the distance in meters. How strong is the coulombic attraction between a phosphoserine residue (charge 2−) and a histidine residue (charge 1+) on the other side of a protein 20 angstroms away? Assume the core of the protein is similar to hexane, with a dielectric constant of 4. What if the histidine were on an adjacent protein 20 angstroms away, with water ($D = 80$) separating them?

32. PALA competes for binding in the active site of ATCase, yet it acts as an allosteric inhibitor and stabilizes the R state. Explain this phenomenon.

33. Allosteric enzymes are thought to function in one of two states, tense or relaxed. Could you envision a model where there are other intermediate states? Please explain.

34. Some enzymes have been shown to polymerize or form multimers upon the addition of an allosteric regulator. How could you test whether an enzyme had formed some sort of higher-order structure upon the addition of an allosteric regulator?

35. Small molecules that affect allosteric sites are a growing area of drug development. Speculate as to why development of an allosteric regulator may have advantages over other types of inhibitors.

Data Interpretation

36. An experiment yields the kinetic data shown below:

[Substrate], mM	Rate (μM/min/mg enzyme), substrate, no inhibitor	Rate (μM/min/mg enzyme) [substrate] + 7 nM inhibitor
0.02	0.8	1.5
0.04	1.5	2.9
0.10	3.7	6.9
0.25	8.6	15
1.00	24	36
2.50	41	50

- Graph this data and provide values of V_{max} and K_M for this enzyme.
- How is the inhibitor acting on this enzyme?
- What information would you need to be able to calculate K_I for this inhibitor?

37. You identified a new protein and obtained the amino acid sequence, but you lack structural data. Mutation of a serine of interest to alanine results in a partial loss of activity, but mutation of the same serine to aspartate returns activity to wild-type levels. What explanation could link these observations?

38. Phosphofructokinase is an enzyme in the glycolytic pathway (which the cell uses to break down glucose). Phosphofructokinase uses ATP to add a phosphate group to C-1 of fructose-6-phosphate, generating fructose 1,6-bisphosphate. Explain how ATP and AMP are acting in this graph.

39. A pure sample of chymotrypsin gives three bands that are smaller than the expected 25.6 kDa when examined on SDS-PAGE, but elutes from a size exclusion column somewhere between 25 and 27 kDa. Explain this finding.

Experimental Design

40. You are studying an enzyme you believe to be regulated by phosphorylation. Design an experiment to test whether this enzyme is more active in the phosphorylated state. Include proper controls in your design.

41. You have identified a previously undiscovered family of enzymes. Examination of related sequences in Genbank shows a group of three histidine residues that are conserved in all related species. Design an experiment to see whether this enzyme employs a metal ion in its active site.

42. Chymotrypsin is related to trypsin, another digestive enzyme. Soybeans synthesize a small protein (the soybean trypsin inhibitor) that binds tightly to trypsin but is not cleaved. Look up the structures for trypsin bound to its inhibitor in the Protein Data Bank (PDB). Design an experiment to test which residues of the inhibitor molecule are essential for binding to the enzyme.

43. You discovered a small molecule you believe may be an inhibitor of the HIV protease. How could you determine the type of inhibitor?

44. ATCase is a dodecameric enzyme comprising six regulatory and six catalytic subunits. Design an experiment to show that ATCase is a functional dodecamer.

Ethics and Social Responsibility

45. Most antibiotics are inhibitors of bacterial enzymes. Antibiotics are a hugely successful category of drugs, yet generally, they are not as profitable for pharmaceutical companies as other types of medications. The lack of profitability, coupled with the difficulty of identifying new antibiotics, has limited discoveries of new classes of antibiotics. Should the government create incentives to increase the number of new antibiotics under development?

46. Many enzymes are used commercially in cleaning products. Based on your knowledge of chemistry and biology, is this a "green" approach to cleaning, or would it be better to use synthetic detergents?

47. Some of the older types of contact-lens solutions use hydrogen peroxide to clean and decontaminate lenses and use the enzyme catalase or a metal catalyst to break down the hydrogen peroxide. What is the difference between these two catalysts, and why would you choose one over the other?

48. The study of enzymes and enzyme mechanisms by itself is not of interest to most people, but disease-resistant crops, antibiotics, and antivirals are of interest. Look up the terms "basic research," "applied research," and "translational research." How do these fields differ, and how do they complement each other? Can any of these fields exist without the others?

49. WHO keeps a list of medicines that it considers essential for all healthcare systems. Based on your current knowledge, what types of drugs (for example, pain relievers or antibiotics) would you anticipate might be included in this list? Look up a current copy of the list (it is reviewed biannually) on the WHO Web site. Are there inclusions or omissions you find surprising?

Suggested Readings

4.1 Regarding Enzymes

Branden, C., and J. Tooze. *Introduction to Protein Structure.* New York, NY: Garland Science, 1999.

Buxbaum, E. *Fundamentals of Protein Structure and Function.* New York, NY: Springer, 2007.

Kessel, A., and N. Ben-Tal. *Introduction to Proteins: Structure, Function, and Motion.* Boca Raton, FL: CRC Press, 2011.

Petsko, G. A., and D. Ringe. *Protein Structure and Function.* Sunderland, MA: Sinauer Associates, Inc., 2003.

Williamson, M. *How Proteins Work.* New York, NY: Garland Science, 2011.

4.2 Enzymes Increase Reaction Rate

Cook, P. F., and W. W. Cleland. *Enzyme Kinetics and Mechanism.* New York, NY: Garland Science, 2007.

Copeland, R. A. *Enzymes: A Practical Introduction to Structure, Mechanism, and Data Analysis.* 2nd ed. Weinheim, Germany: Wiley-VCH, 2000.

Cornish-Bowden, A. *Fundamentals of Enzyme Kinetics.* Hoboken, NJ: Wiley Blackwell, 2012.

4.3 The Mechanism of an Enzyme Can Be Deduced from Structural, Kinetic, and Spectral Data

Bar-Even, A., E. Noor, Y. Savir, W. Liebermeister, D. Davidi, D. S. Tawfik, and R. Milo. "The Moderately Efficient Enzyme: Evolutionary and Physicochemical Trends Shaping Enzyme Parameters." *Biochemistry* 50, no. 21 (2011): 4402–4410.

Eisenthal, R., M. J. Danson, and D. W. Hough. "Catalytic Efficiency and kcat/KM: A Useful Comparator?" *Trends in Biotechnology* 25, no. 6 (June 2007) 247–249.

Ferscht, A. M. *Structure and Mechanism in Protein Science.* New York, NY: W.H. Freeman, 1998.

Xie, F., J. M. Briggs, and C. M. Dupureur. "Nucleophile Activation in PD...(D/E)xK Metallonucleases: An Experimental and Computational pKa Study." *Journal of Inorganic Biochemistry* 104, no. 6 (1998): 665–672.

4.4 Examples of Enzyme Regulation

Hammes, G. G. *Enzyme Catalysis and Regulation.* Cambridge, MA: Academic Press, 1982.

Kantrowitz, E. R. "Allostery and Cooperativity in Escherichia Coli Aspartate Transcarbamoylase." *Archives of Biochemistry Biophysics* 519, no. 2 (2012 March): 81–90.

Proteins II

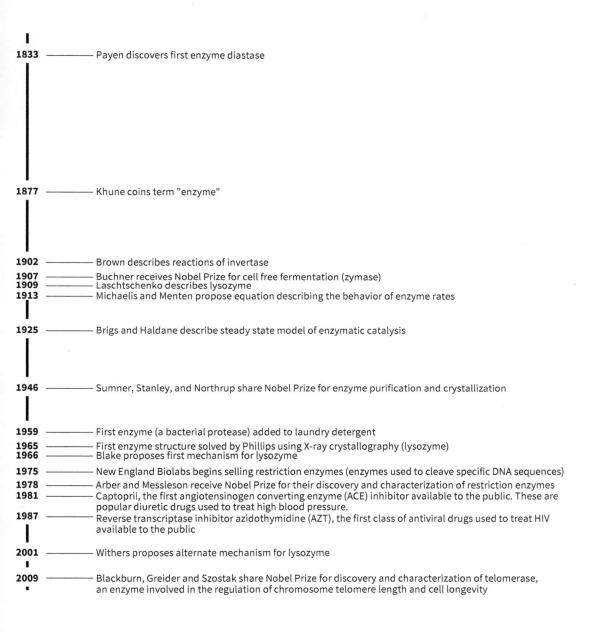

1833 ——————— Payen discovers first enzyme diastase

1877 ——————— Khune coins term "enzyme"

1902 ——————— Brown describes reactions of invertase
1907 ——————— Buchner receives Nobel Prize for cell free fermentation (zymase)
1909 ——————— Laschtschenko describes lysozyme
1913 ——————— Michaelis and Menten propose equation describing the behavior of enzyme rates

1925 ——————— Brigs and Haldane describe steady state model of enzymatic catalysis

1946 ——————— Sumner, Stanley, and Northrup share Nobel Prize for enzyme purification and crystallization

1959 ——————— First enzyme (a bacterial protease) added to laundry detergent
1965 ——————— First enzyme structure solved by Phillips using X-ray crystallography (lysozyme)
1966 ——————— Blake proposes first mechanism for lysozyme
1975 ——————— New England Biolabs begins selling restriction enzymes (enzymes used to cleave specific DNA sequences)
1978 ——————— Arber and Messleson receive Nobel Prize for their discovery and characterization of restriction enzymes
1981 ——————— Captopril, the first angiotensinogen converting enzyme (ACE) inhibitor available to the public. These are popular diuretic drugs used to treat high blood pressure.
1987 ——————— Reverse transcriptase inhibitor azidothymidine (AZT), the first class of antiviral drugs used to treat HIV available to the public

2001 ——————— Withers proposes alternate mechanism for lysozyme

2009 ——————— Blackburn, Greider and Szostak share Nobel Prize for discovery and characterization of telomerase, an enzyme involved in the regulation of chromosome telomere length and cell longevity

CHAPTER 5

Membranes and an Introduction to Signal Transduction

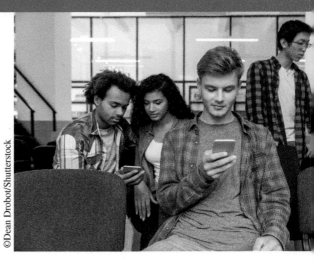

©Dean Drobot/Shutterstock

Communication between cells and organs is as important as it is between people.

Biochemistry in Context

We live in an age of communication. We can imagine how difficult it would be if we could not communicate with each other. Communicating means that we need to cross some sort of barrier, be it distance, or time, or a physical separation between the two parties.

Cells, too, need to communicate with other cells and respond to their surroundings. All cells have a membrane that delineates and separates the inside from the outside. These membranes define the boundaries of the cell and its organelles, and are important in how these units function, but the cell also needs some way to receive messages across this barrier.

This chapter discusses two aspects of biochemistry that we will use to help understand the regulation of metabolism. It begins with a description of the structure of the plasma membrane and a short introduction of the components of that membrane, including the structures and functions of some associated proteins. The chapter concludes with an introduction to signal transduction, that is, the way that cells respond to chemical signals with changes in enzyme function, flux through a metabolic pathway, or gene expression. Both the structure of the membrane and how signals are transmitted through it are described in **Dynamic Figure 5.1**.

CHAPTER OUTLINE

5.1 Membrane Structure and Function

5.2 Signal Transduction

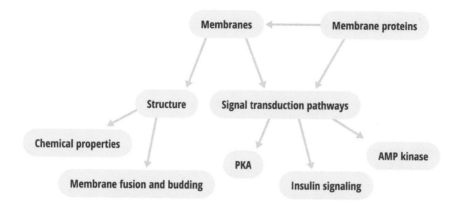

DYNAMIC FIGURE 5.1
Membranes composed of phospholipids and proteins form the barrier between the inside of the cell and the external environment. They also delineate the boundary of organelles. Signal transduction allows cells to communicate across this barrier.

COMMON THEMES

Evolution's outcomes are conserved.	• The structure of membranes and the molecules involved in their formation are conserved throughout evolution. As a result, many of the pathways involved in the biosynthesis of these molecules are also conserved.
	• The themes discussed in signal transduction are conserved in other pathways, cells, organs, tissues, and organisms.
	• Many of the signaling pathways in this chapter are conserved throughout evolution.
Structure determines function.	• The hydrophobic nature of the plasma membrane excludes small hydrophilic organic molecules and ions.
	• Molecules are transported across the plasma membrane by protein transporters, channels, or pumps.
	• The highly dynamic nature of the plasma membrane is important in its function.
	• Proteins associated with the plasma membrane are either integral (requiring detergent for dissociation) or peripheral (able to be dislodged without disrupting the lipid bilayer).
	• The hydrophobic effect and other weak forces explain the spontaneous assembly of the lipid bilayer and the association of proteins with the bilayer.
Biochemical information is transferred, exchanged, and stored.	• Signal transduction employs a series of signaling proteins and kinases to transmit information from a chemical signal outside the cell that causes an effect inside the cell.
	• Chemical signals can lead to alterations in metabolic pathways, enzyme activation, or gene regulation.
Biomolecules are altered through pathways involving transformations of energy and matter.	• As with all processes, the laws of thermodynamics apply to both membrane formation and the association of proteins with membranes.

5.1 | Membrane Structure and Function

Before studying biochemistry, people often see membranes as something static, such as the skin of an onion or the thin layer of connective tissue on a piece of meat. Those are not membranes in the biochemical sense. Instead, membranes are the submicroscopic barriers that surround and define cells and many organelles. These structures are dynamic, fluid, and only a few molecules thick.

5.1.1 The chemical properties of the membrane components dictate the characteristics of the membrane

Membranes in the cell are comprised of two main components: lipids and proteins. Lipids are hydrophobic molecules. The lipids found in cell membranes are characterized as **polar lipids**, containing polar, water-soluble functional groups in addition to their hydrophobic component. This combination makes these molecules **amphipathic**, having both water soluble and water insoluble properties, an important property in forming a membrane (**Figure 5.2**).

The predominant lipids in membranes are glycerophospholipids. These lipids have two acyl chains, long-chain fatty acids, esterified to a glycerol backbone. The third position on the glycerol backbone has a phosphate group. Finally, an alcohol is linked to the phosphate, forming a phosphodiester linkage. The phosphate group and alcohol are polar hydrophilic groups, whereas the acyl chains are hydrophobic, making the overall molecule amphipathic. Phospholipids vary both in terms of the length and degree of unsaturation of the acyl chains, and the type of alcohol found in the head group.

The membrane lipid **cholesterol** is the most common steroid found in the body. Cholesterol is largely hydrophobic, but it has a single hydroxyl group; within a membrane,

FIGURE 5.2 **Plasma membrane.** The plasma membrane consists of two sheets of amphipathic lipids (phospholipids and cholesterol) and numerous proteins. Both phospholipids and cholesterol have polar (hydrophilic) and nonpolar (hydrophobic) groups in the same molecule. (Ireland, *Visualizing Human Biology*, 4e, copyright 2012, John Wiley & Sons. This material is reproduced with permission of John Wiley & Sons, Inc.)

this hydroxyl group is oriented away from the core of the membrane. Structurally, cholesterol is planar, a property that allows cholesterol to disrupt interactions of the acyl chains of phospholipids, resulting in a higher degree of membrane fluidity at lower temperatures. However, once the percentage of cholesterol in the membrane increases past a certain point, fluidity decreases. Therefore, the levels of cholesterol found in the membrane must be tightly regulated.

The membrane consists of two sheets or leaflets of phospholipids. As seen in Figure 5.2, the molecules have the same orientation in each leaflet, with the head groups found in one plane and the acyl chains in another. The two leaflets are arranged so that the acyl chains of one adjoin the acyl chains of the other, forming a sandwich of acyl chains with polar head groups on either side of the membrane. This structure is termed a **phospholipid bilayer**, also known as **the lipid bilayer**. Cholesterol is inserted into the bilayer so that its hydroxyl group is oriented toward the head groups of one side or another and the remainder of the molecule is buried in the hydrophobic acyl chains.

Lipid bilayers are typically 45 Å (4.5 nm) thick and contain on the order of 10^6 lipid molecules per square micron (10^{-6} m) of membrane. Lipid bilayers are permeable to gases such as O_2, CO_2, and N_2, which can diffuse through the membrane. Although not readily soluble in water, hydrophobic molecules can pass fairly easily through the lipid bilayer. The solubility of molecules decreases with increasing size such that larger molecules are less soluble than smaller ones. Ions are generally unable to cross the membrane without some type of protein channel or pore to pass through. Likewise, small polar organic molecules including most biological molecules require proteins for transport into or out of the cell. Water and urea can both diffuse through the membrane, into and out of the cell, although it is thought that this transport is mainly through aquaporins. In the case of water, this diffusion through the hydrophobic membrane is particularly enigmatic and is still under investigation.

Membrane permeability and pharmaceuticals

An important aspect of drug design is solubility. A challenge for drug developers is that drugs need to be sufficiently soluble to dissolve and be transported in the blood but also sufficiently hydrophobic to pass through the lipid bilayer. It has been estimated that 80% of compounds that are effective drug candidates (molecules that will elicit the desired effect in the lab) will never become marketable drugs because of solubility issues.

Membranes are dynamic, spontaneously assembling structures

A property that scientists often look for in nanotechnology is self-assembly (the ability to form without external assistance). Due to the hydrophobic effect, the **lipid bilayer** is one of these self-assembling structures. An individual phospholipid molecule is amphipathic, having both hydrophobic and hydrophilic moieties in the same molecule. Thus, solvating each phospholipid molecule individually would require the organization of many more water molecules than would be the case if the hydrophobic tails of phospholipid molecules were clustered together. Therefore, membrane assembly is driven not by the attractive forces between acyl chains, nor by the attractive forces between head groups (in fact, the charged groups often repel one another), but by the phospholipids being "pushed" together as water molecules hydrogen-bond with each other.

Diffusion is the movement of particles down a concentration gradient. An example is a solution of dye or food coloring dropped into a container of water, or a strong smelling molecule in air, but it also could be the lateral movement of proteins in a lipid bilayer. Over time, without any forces to prevent it, the molecule will become randomly distributed throughout the solvent.

The diffusion of any molecule depends on several factors, including the molecule's size and shape, solvent viscosity, and the temperature. These factors combine to give a diffusion constant, a value that varies for each type of molecule. Because the diffusion constant is partially dependent on viscosity, it also varies with regard to solvent. When a molecule such as a protein is constrained in the lipid bilayer, the solvent may be the lipid molecules themselves. Smaller molecules like lipids move more quickly than larger ones, such as proteins, and molecules can move more rapidly through a medium with lower viscosity than one with higher viscosity.

Molecules will diffuse through a medium until they are randomly distributed and entropy has been maximized. This diffusion of molecules down a concentration gradient is an illustration of the second law of thermodynamics—that is, the entropy of a system tends to increase. The reverse process, the segregation or concentration of molecules in one area or compartment, is a violation of the second law, unless energy (ΔH) is expended somewhere else to drive transport.

Lipid bilayers are not static structures; they are constantly in motion. The term "fluid mosaic" has been used to describe the plasma membrane. In this analogy, the lipid molecules in the membrane are analogous to balls floating on the surface of a swimming pool. They are free to rotate and to move laterally but are generally unable to rise out of the pool or sink to the bottom. The same can be said for the phospholipids of the lipid bilayer. They have high rates of rotational and lateral diffusion (because only weak London-dispersion forces hold these molecules next to one another). A single phospholipid molecule can cross the length of the cell in less than a second. However, without enzymatic assistance, lipids cannot readily leave the lipid bilayer or flip from one side to the other.

Membranes in the cell also contain proteins

While half of the cell membrane's mass is comprised of lipid, the other half is protein. Membrane-associated proteins are diverse in structure and in function, and they give the membrane many of its properties. These proteins can be broadly categorized as **integral** or **peripheral membrane proteins** (**Figure 5.3**).

Integral membrane proteins are proteins that are somehow imbedded in the plasma membrane. These proteins can be further subclassified as **monotopic**, inserted into only one leaflet of the lipid bilayer, or **ditopic**, spanning both leaflets. Ditopic integral membrane proteins are also known as **transmembrane proteins**; they may have a single hydrophobic α helix spanning the membrane, or a series of helices or β sheets forming some type of anchor or pore. Other structures that tether monotopic integral membrane proteins to a membrane are hydrophobic "fingers," or loops of hydrophobic amino acids or hydrophobic domains that enter the membrane but do not pass completely through it. By definition, integral membrane proteins require detergent to remove them from the membrane. Detergents are amphipathic molecules with both polar and nonpolar ends to them that can disrupt and solubilize membrane proteins and lipids.

An example of a membrane-spanning protein is the seven-transmembrane (7TM) family of receptors, each of which has seven transmembrane α helices that span the membrane. Extracellular signals bind to the outside of the membrane and transduce signals to the interior of the cell through conformational changes to the receptor.

Integrins are structural proteins that anchor a cell in the extracellular matrix. They have both an α and β subunit, each of which has a single α helix passing through the plasma membrane of the cell.

Aquaporins are an example of pore-forming proteins. They have a series of α helices that span the membrane and twist about each other to form a selective pore through which particular molecules (such as water) can pass.

In contrast to integral membrane proteins, peripheral membrane proteins are associated with the surface of the membrane, either with the polar head groups of specific phospholipids or with other membrane proteins. Peripheral membrane proteins can also be associated with membranes through a hydrophobic anchor such as a myristoyl, palmitoyl, or farnesyl group. The G protein α subunit is associated with the plasma membrane through a hydrophobic anchor. Peripheral membrane proteins are not imbedded in the plasma membrane, and can be dissociated from the membrane by changes to pH, or by treatment with salt or concentrated solutions of molecules like urea or guanidinium hydrochloride that disrupt hydrogen bonding and the hydrophobic effect.

Multiple protein domains are involved in membrane interaction. For example, C1 and C2 domains are found in some kinases (enzymes that join a phosphate to a hydroxyl group) and lipases (enzymes that hydrolyze lipids). These domains recognize specific phospholipid head

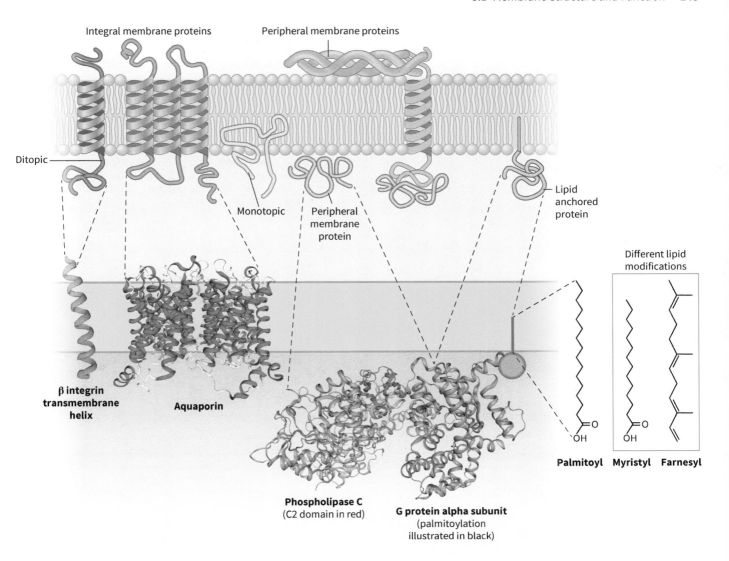

FIGURE 5.3 **Membrane proteins and the plasma membrane.**
In addition to the mechanisms listed for tethering to the cell
membrane, proteins can be conjugated to hydrophobic groups
(myristoyl, palmitoyl, or farnesyl, shown in enlarged view).
Aquaporins and integrins are examples of integral membrane
proteins. Phospholipase C and the G protein alpha subunit are
examples of peripheral membrane proteins. (Karp, *Cell and Molecular
Biology: Concepts and Experiments*, 7e, copyright 2013, John Wiley &
Sons. This material is reproduced with permission of John Wiley &
Sons, Inc.; Left: PDB ID 2M3E Surya, W., Li, Y., Millet, O., Diercks, T., Torres, J.

The Integrin Alpha L Transmembrane Domain in Bicelles: Structure
and Interaction with Integrin Beta 2; Middle: PDB ID 3D9S Horsefield, R.,
Norden, K., Fellert, M., Backmark, A., Tornroth-Horsefield, S., Terwisscha
van Scheltinga, A.C., Kvassman, J., Kjellbom, P., Johanson, U., Neutze,
R. (2008) High-resolution x-ray structure of human aquaporin 5. *Proc.
Natl.Acad.Sci.Usa* 105: 13327–13332; Right: PDB ID 3OHM Waldo,
G.L., Ricks, T.K., Hicks, S.N., Cheever, M.L., Kawano, T., Tsuboi, K.,
Wang, X., Montell, C., Kozasa, T., Sondek, J., Harden, T.K. (2010) Kinetic
Scaffolding Mediated by a Phospholipase C-(beta) and Gq Signaling
Complex. *Science* 330: 974–980).

groups and are important in recognition and binding of the phospholipid bilayer, but not necessarily in binding to individual substrate molecules and catalyzing reactions.

Proteins regulate the passage of most molecules through the membrane

Because lipid bilayers are virtually impenetrable to ions and most biological molecules, some way is needed for these molecules to pass in and out of the cell or organelle.
This passage is accomplished through several different types of proteins and mechanisms. If a
single ion is pumped or diffuses in a single direction, the protein is termed a **uniporter**. If two
or more ions are transported in the same direction across the membrane, the protein is termed
a **symporter**. If two or more ions are transported in different directions across a membrane,
the protein is termed an **antiporter** (**Figure 5.4**).

A. Uniporter — Symporter — Antiporter

B. Ligand gated

C. Voltage gated

FIGURE 5.4 **Transporters, pumps, and channels.**
A. Uniporters enable the transport of a single molecule or ion; symporters use one ion or molecule to drive the transport of a second in the same direction, while antiporters use a gradient of one molecule or ion to drive the transport in the opposite direction. There are two classes of ion channels: ligand gated or voltage gated.
B. Ligand-gated ion channels open when a ligand binds.
C. Voltage-gated ion channels open when there is enough of an electrochemical potential across the membrane. (B, C: Ireland, *Visualizing Human Biology*, 4e, copyright 2012, John Wiley & Sons. This material is reproduced with permission of John Wiley & Sons, Inc.)

Passage through a membrane can be broadly classified as either active or passive. In **active transport**, energy must be expended to move a molecule from one side of the membrane to another. Usually this is done to transport a molecule up a concentration gradient. In primary active transport, the energy of ATP hydrolysis is used directly to drive ions across a membrane. An example is the gastric proton pump that acidifies the stomach. This protein (the hydrogen/potassium ATPase) was originally named an ATPase because it catalyzes the breakdown of ATP. In **secondary active transport**, a gradient of other molecules (often ions) is used to pump a second molecule across the membrane. An example is the sodium–chloride symporter in the kidney, which helps to reabsorb these ions from glomerular filtrate in the nephron.

In **passive transport**, **transporter proteins** (the glucose transporters or aquaporins), permit the passage of molecules down a concentration gradient or electrochemical gradient. The transporter proteins are largely α helical and have a central pore that selectively permits the passage of a single specific molecule or a closely related group of molecules. Passive transport can also occur via **channels**, which are similar to transporters but differ in that channels are gated and are regulated. As shown in Figure 5.4, channels open and shut either through binding of a ligand (ligand-gated ion channels) or a change in the voltage across a membrane (voltage-gated ion channels). Both transporters and channels are important in the nervous system and in neurotransmission of signals.

A lipid bilayer devoid of channels is impermeable to ions; therefore, membranes can have an uneven distribution of chemicals on either side. This is a potential energy difference that the cell employs to generate ATP in mitochondria, drive various transport processes, and generate action potentials in neurons.

Osmosis is the movement of solvent (water in biochemical systems) through a semipermeable barrier from a region of low solute concentration (the hypotonic side) to a region of high concentration (the hypertonic side). We can visualize osmosis as a system that is moving toward an equilibrium in which solvent and solute concentrations are the same on both sides, although a barrier prevents this from ever truly happening. Like diffusion, the movement of molecules in osmosis is random, does not require the input of energy, and tends toward maximal randomness, driven by entropy.

5.1.2 | Other aspects of membrane structure

Membrane proteins also may be glycosylated, that is, modified by conjugation to carbohydrates (**Figure 5.5**). Inside eukaryotic cells, small carbohydrate modifications are important in trafficking of proteins to the correct location in the cell. Secreted proteins or proteins in the extracellular leaflet of the plasma membrane of the cell often have larger carbohydrate modifications that contribute to the function of the protein.

Cholesterol and sphingolipids can transiently and loosely aggregate in the plasma membrane to form a structure termed a **lipid raft**, shown in Figure 5.5. These structures are involved in cell signaling and tethering of membrane proteins.

Membranes vary throughout an organism or cell   The composition of a membrane is not uniform throughout the cell, or even from one leaflet of the lipid bilayer to another. Rather, membranes are asymmetric and have an uneven distribution of lipids.

Figure 5.6 shows how the lipid composition of membranes differs among different cell types and organelles. This is consistent with the principles of both biochemistry and evolution. Just as specialized cells or organelles contain different proteins, they also have a different lipid composition.

The leaflets of membranes in the cell are also diverse and asymmetrical. The asymmetry helps to maintain the structural integrity of the cell, and it has a role in cell signaling. The cytosolic face of the plasma membrane is enriched in phospholipids (phosphatidylinositol, phosphatidate, and phosphatidylserine) that act in cell signaling pathways.

Asymmetry is generated and maintained in the membrane by the action of phospholipid translocases (also known as flippases). These enzymes alter the composition of lipid bilayers by catalyzing the movement of phospholipids from one leaflet to another.

FIGURE 5.5   **Other aspects of membrane biology.** Some membrane proteins are clustered in transient segments of membrane, termed lipid rafts. Rafts are enriched in specific phospholipids and cholesterol. Rafts are thought to play roles in cell signaling and membrane transport. (Karp, *Cell and Molecular Biology: Concepts and Experiments*, 7e, copyright 2013, John Wiley & Sons. This material is reproduced with permission of John Wiley & Sons, Inc.)

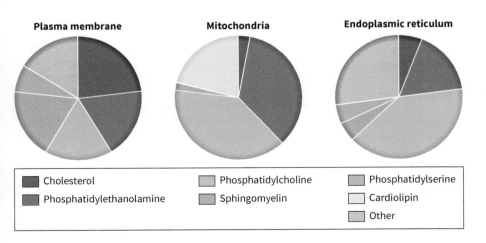

FIGURE 5.6   **Composition of lipid bilayers.**   The lipid composition of a membrane varies from cell type to cell type and from organelle to organelle. Shown is the composition for three different membranes. The lipids shown are cholesterol, phosphatidylethanolamine (PE), phosphatidylcholine (PC), sphingomyelin (SM), phosphatidylserine (PS), cardiolipin (CL), and all other lipids.

The structure of the lipid bilayer is so common we may forget that there was a time before this structure was known. How the structure of the plasma membrane was elucidated is discussed in **Biochemistry: Numerous techniques converge to give a picture of the plasma membrane.**

5.1.3   Membrane fusion and membrane budding

Membranes can increase in size through the addition or breakdown of single molecules of phospholipid, but this is not the accepted means by which large aggregates of lipid molecules move between pools within the cell. Membranous structures can either fuse together when a hormone or neurotransmitter is secreted from the cell or they can bud or bleb off from an existing structure (**Figure 5.7**).

Membrane fusion begins with two membranes coming into close proximity; as they approach one another, water is excluded. Some destabilization of one or both membranes causes the formation of a stalklike structure (the fusion pore), which then grows and spreads as the two membranes fuse.

Studies of the plasma membrane and membrane fusion and countless other scientific investigations have been facilitated by the use of cultured cells. The development and use of these cells is discussed in **Societal and Ethical Biochemistry: Cultured cell lines.**

Biochemistry

Numerous techniques converge to give a picture of the plasma membrane

The fluid mosaic model of the cell membrane is familiar to those studying the biological sciences. Students are taught that the surface of the cell is a membrane barrier, the surface of which, viewed from above, looks like a mosaic (an art form comprising numerous small pieces of tile). They are also taught that, unlike a mosaic, the membrane is fluid, with its "tiles" (the phospholipids and proteins in the membrane) able to freely rotate and move about within the membrane. Models of the plasma membrane are sometimes used to illustrate this structure, for example, using small balls floating on the surface of water. The term "fluid mosaic" is a wonderful name, in that it is memorable and generates a picture in the mind, but how do we know that this model describes the plasma membrane?

The fluid mosaic model was proposed by Singer and Nicholson in 1972. It had the basic familiar structure of two sheets of phospholipids oriented to form a hydrophobic barrier, with their polar head groups facing away from the hydrophobic core. Singer and Nicholson also proposed that integral membrane proteins were amphipathic and had structures that helped them to anchor in the membrane. Key to this model was the dynamic interactions of the components rather than the components themselves.

Since the late 1800s it has been known that proteins and phospholipids are components of the cell. However, advances in technology, such as chemical analysis, electron microscopy, light microscopy, and ultracentrifugation, were needed before scientists could combine numerous results to produce the currently accepted model. The amphipathic structures of phospholipids—part of the foundation of the fluid mosaic model—were elucidated in the late 1950s and early 1960s. An attractive aspect of the Singer and Nicholson model is that it is consistent with the restrictions imposed by thermodynamics; in other words, it makes chemical sense. The arrangement and orientation of phospholipid molecules to form the membrane, and the way that proteins float in the membrane, are easily explained by chemistry and do not violate any of the basic rules of thermodynamics. Furthermore, knowing the basic structure of the lipid bilayer, it makes sense that the phospholipid and protein molecules in the membrane can rotate and move laterally (there are few weak forces preventing them from doing so) but cannot readily flip from one leaflet to the other without some sort of enzymatic assistance.

Using these basic paradigms, Singer and Nicholson built a case for their model using experiments ranging from the more biophysical (differential calorimetry of membrane lipids) to the more biological (microscopy illustrating the clustering of membrane proteins when tethered to a divalent antibody). Other evidence included studies involving fusion of human and mouse cells and the diffusion of membrane proteins across the resulting hybrid cell. Further, using both their data and the broader literature, Singer and Nicholson showed that these phenomena were not specific to single circumstances, but rather they were found in various species and membranes, with various proteins. They were careful not to be proscriptive, and they pointed out weaknesses or exceptions to their model (including myelin sheaths of neurons), but collectively their data made a compelling case.

Since the original proposal of the fluid mosaic, there have been other techniques that also validate the model, and it is difficult now to imagine a time when the nature of the plasma membrane was considered controversial.

Fusion point

Hemifusion with stalk formation between two membranes

Fusion pore

Small vesicle fusing with membrane

Membrane fusion

FIGURE 5.7 **Fusion and budding.** When membranes fuse or bud, bends in the membrane facilitate the initial steps. As the structures approach each other, water is excluded between them. Membranes fuse at a single point forming an unstable stalk-like structure (hemifusion) and then the two membranes zipper together or apart at a fusion pore. Alterations to the phospholipid composition facilitate these changes in geometry and lipid packing.

Social and Ethical Biochemistry

Cultured cell lines

By its very nature, biochemistry involves studying living systems or molecules derived from living systems. Although study of isolated molecules can provide useful and meaningful data, studying a molecule in situ in the cell, tissue, or organism can provide a much richer picture of what the molecule is doing and how it affects overall biology.

Historically, studies were conducted in model organisms: bacteria, yeast, plants, and animals, or in human volunteers. However, such models are not applicable in some situations. For example, imagine attempting to study a disease that affects avocado trees; these trees take years to mature, so they are difficult to study directly. Model organisms such as bacteria or mice might not give meaningful results in this case, but cultured cells could provide a useful alternative.

Cells have been cultured since antiquity in the processes of making fermented foods such as cheese, bread, wine, and beer. In the laboratory, the culture of eukaryotic cells dates back to the early 1900s. These initial experiments helped scientists to develop an understanding of the conditions cells require for growth but were limited in their scope. For example, most of the experiments used tissue obtained from animal sources, a type of culture now referred to as primary culture. Such cells have a preset number of divisions they can undergo before they become senescent and stop dividing, and they often die after several days or weeks in culture. In addition, antibiotics were generally not available at that time, and cultures frequently became contaminated with microbes.

From the late 1940s onward, advances in tissue culture helped to set the stage for the widespread use of cultured cells; these advances included antibiotics, the use of serum as a source of growth factors, and standardized culture conditions. The final advances that made cell culture possible were the cells themselves.

Advances in virology and cancer biology led to the discovery that certain cells were transformed or immortalized (able to divide without limits), providing an almost endless source of cells that could be used to develop vaccines, express proteins, and study cellular processes.

The use of cultured cells might seem like a simple bypass around the potential ethical quagmire of using either animals or humans in biomedical research, but actually the use of such cells itself raises ethical concerns. At the time when some of the most popular cell lines were derived, there was little use of the current practice of informed consent, the concept that an experiment can only go ahead if the patients are informed of what is happening to them and give their permission. Patients had little idea that they were donating samples of tumors to be used in biomedical research, and at that time no one—patient, physician, or researcher—had any idea about the potential of these tools. There were no laws governing such decisions and the laws that have been written since are ambiguous at best or vary from jurisdiction to jurisdiction. In addition, science continues to advance and use these tools in research. At present, there are concerns that the genomes of these cell lines contain personal information about the family of the original donor, including relatives and descendants who are still living and may not want that information shared.

The history of the discovery of one cell line (HeLa cells) and the lasting impact this has had on the family of the donor (Henrietta Lacks) is described in *The Immortal Life of Henrietta Lacks* by Rebecca Skloot.

Cell culture has been an important part of biochemistry for many years, and it will continue to be so for the foreseeable future, but researchers should know and take into account the source of cells and the conditions under which they were generated. The extent to which descendants of donors should have a voice in the use of these cell lines is a question that remains to be answered.

WORKED PROBLEM 5.1 | Interpreting a FRAP experiment

FRAP is a technique used to determine the mobility of a molecule in a membrane. This is accomplished by measuring the time it takes for a fluorescent molecule to diffuse back into a photobleached region of the membrane. Photobleaching is the fading or bleaching of a fluorescent or chromogenic molecule with light.

A membrane-bound receptor is labeled with the fluorescent protein tag mCherry, and functional studies indicate that the labeled receptor still operates normally. The diffusion of the receptor is measured using fluorescence recovery after photobleaching (FRAP), in the presence and absence of ligand, giving the result shown below.

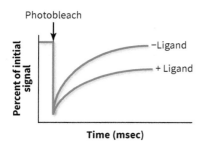

What can be said qualitatively about these results? What quantitative information can be obtained from this type of information?

Strategy Compare the experimental condition (+ ligand) to the control (− ligand). What is the difference between the two curves? What is happening in the experiment?

Solution A comparison of the two curves indicates that in the presence of ligand the fluorescent signal returns to the bleached region more slowly than in the unbound state. This correlates to a slower diffusional coefficient for the complex with the bound ligand. The results correlate percentage of original signal as a function of time. The half-life of recovery and the recovery rate can be modeled using several equations that are beyond the scope of this chapter, but they are not difficult to comprehend. Based on these data, a diffusional coefficient (D) can be determined. The diffusional coefficient can be used to calculate parameters such as the hydrodynamic radius or the diameter of the protein or complex if it were modeled as a sphere.

Follow-up question Why do you think the diffusional constant of the receptor in the previous question might change in the presence of ligand?

5.1 Summary

- Membranes are dynamic semipermeable barriers that compartmentalize the cell and separate it from the external environment.
- The membrane is a lipid bilayer, that is, two sheets of phospholipids arrayed with their hydrophobic acyl chains oriented to the middle of the membrane and their polar head groups oriented away from the membrane core.
- Membranes are about 50% protein by mass. These proteins provide many of the functions of the membrane, including permeability for ions and organic molecules, ligand binding, protein trafficking, endocytosis, and exocytosis.
- Proteins associated with the membrane can be classified as either peripheral or integral. Peripheral membrane proteins can be dissociated from the membrane with alterations to pH or salt concentration, whereas integral membrane proteins require detergent to remove them from the phospholipid bilayer.
- Membranes are dynamic structures and can fuse with one another or bud new membranous structures; this process is highly regulated and involves numerous trafficking proteins.

5.1 Concept Check

- Describe the general topology and behavior of a membrane.
- Discuss the ways in which proteins bind to membranes and the forces, functional groups, and energies involved.
- Analyze the generic structure of a phospholipid, and comment on why it aligns in the plasma membrane as it does.
- Describe in qualitative terms how membranes fuse or bud.

5.2 | Signal Transduction

Imagine that you are planning a party and need to notify your friends. There are numerous ways you could try to contact them: calling, texting, using social media, and so on. You could also ask some friends to tell others. If planning a large event, you could make flyers and hang them around campus. All of these means of communication involve conveying some type of information from a sender to a receiver. This is analogous to signal transduction—the means by which cells and tissues in the body communicate with one another.

5.2.1 | General principles underlie signal transduction

In a signal transduction pathway, also known as a cascade, a chemical signal (a hormone or neurotransmitter) binds to a protein receptor found in the plasma membrane of the cell (Figure 5.8). This causes a conformational change in the receptor that initiates a chain of events on the cytosolic face of the membrane. Often, a second chemical signal, or **second messenger**, is produced inside the cell. This is analogous to a flyer posted on campus being seen inside a dorm; although it was not the original signal, it still propagates the message. A signal transduction cascade activates or inhibits protein kinases, the enzymes that add phosphates to proteins. The addition of phosphate can result in conformational change, activating or inhibiting enzymes. Often, multiple rather than single kinases are acted upon, with each being activated or inhibited either by a specific signaling event or by a specific kinase.

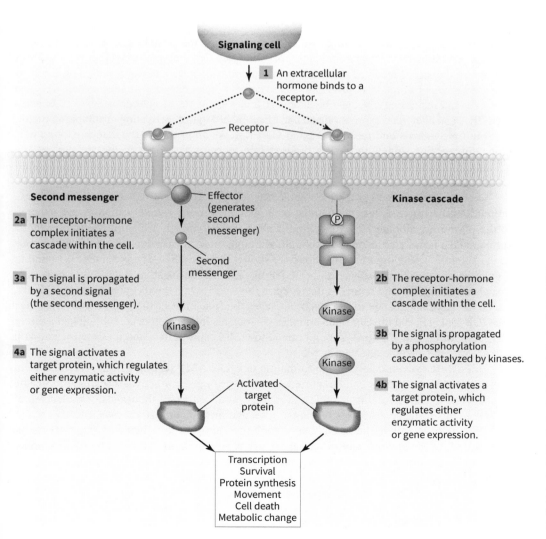

FIGURE 5.8 **Signal transduction fundamentals.** At its most basic, signal transduction occurs when a signal (a hormone, neurotransmitter, or extracellular stimulus) binds to a receptor. This causes changes inside the cell to produce other signaling molecules (second messengers) or a cascade of kinases. Ultimately, this results in a change to some protein, altering its function in the cell. (Karp, *Cell and Molecular Biology: Concepts and Experiments*, 7e, copyright 2013, John Wiley & Sons. This material is reproduced with permission of John Wiley & Sons, Inc.)

There are many advantages to this system. For example, signal transduction can be at once both general and highly specific. One signal may have multiple different outcomes in different tissues, based on the types of receptor and downstream signaling pathways activated. Conversely, multiple chemical signals may bind to a single receptor, eliciting the same response. The multiple steps in these pathways provide multiple points at which the system can be controlled and fine-tuned, either by other proteins or through allosterism.

The use of a second messenger provides an additional opportunity to amplify the signal. To continue the analogy given above, if you were to text one friend about your party, she would receive your message; however, if you gave her a flyer and she posted it in a dorm, hundreds of people might see it, so the signal has been amplified. Because second messengers are typically small organic compounds that are enzymatically synthesized and degraded, there is an opportunity for significant amplification at this step. One molecule of signal binds to a single receptor, which activates a single enzyme, but this enzyme may rapidly make tens of thousands of copies of a second messenger.

Finally, signal transduction allows for a range of outputs over a range of time frames. The cascades can be as simple as the activation of an enzyme or as complex as the activation of a family of genes. They function in processes ranging from neurotransmission to development of an organism and can therefore operate in time frames ranging from milliseconds to hours or days.

Three common signaling pathways discussed in this section are chosen as representative pathways to illustrate the general principles of signal transduction and for their relevance to intermediary metabolism.

5.2.2 The protein kinase A (PKA) signaling pathway is activated by cyclic AMP

One of the most common signaling pathways in the cell is the **protein kinase A** (also known as **PKA**, cAMP dependent protein kinase, or A-kinase) signaling pathway (Figure 5.9). PKA transduces the signal received into actions in numerous cellular pathways, including lipolysis (the breakdown of stored fats), glycogen (stored carbohydrate) metabolism (decreasing glycogen synthesis and increasing glycogen breakdown), and some types of neurotransmission. In addition, PKA can alter gene expression and can target other kinases, activating or inhibiting them.

Multiple ligands and receptors signal via PKA. As an example, the catecholamine hormone epinephrine signals through a β-adrenergic receptor and binds to the receptor on the extracellular side of the plasma membrane. Like the interactions of an enzyme with its substrate, binding of hormone induces a conformational change in the receptor.

On the cytosolic face of the membrane, the receptor is complexed to a heterotrimeric G protein that has three different subunits: α, β, and γ. Both the α and γ subunits are tethered to the plasma membrane by a lipid modification, most typically a palmitoylation on the α subunit and a farnesylation on the γ subunit, although this can vary depending on the subclass of the subunit. These lipid modifications are shown in Figure 5.3. The α subunit is bound to a guanine nucleoside phosphate, either GDP or GTP. In the inactive state, the G protein is associated with GDP and bound to the receptor; however, when the receptor binds to a ligand, the conformational change to the receptor causes the α subunit of the G protein to exchange the GDP for GTP, and the G protein complex dissociates into an active G_α subunit and a dimer consisting of G_β and γ. The G_α subunit bound to GTP is now active, and it can associate with and activate the enzyme adenylate cyclase.

Adenylate cyclase catalyzes the formation of **cyclic AMP (cAMP)** from ATP. This is an illustration of how signals can be amplified. A single G protein activates a single molecule of adenylate cyclase, but this enzyme can rapidly produce tens of thousands of molecules of cAMP. In this instance, cAMP is serving as a second messenger that activates PKA.

PKA is a heterotetrameric enzyme complex comprised of a dimer of regulatory subunits found between two catalytic subunits. Each regulatory subunit has two cAMP binding sites (four sites in the holoenzyme complex), and the binding of cAMP is cooperative and allosteric. Binding of cAMP releases the catalytic subunits, which are then free to phosphorylate their cellular targets. These targets include enzymes which regulate carbohydrate and lipid metabolism, ion channels in the plasma membrane, and the transcription factor CREB (the cAMP response element binding protein).

FIGURE 5.9 **PKA signaling pathway.** The PKA pathway was one of the first elucidated. In this example of the pathway, a hormone signals through a β-adrenergic receptor to stimulate a heterotrimeric G protein. This results in activation of adenylate cyclase and production of cAMP. The cAMP (a second messenger) binds to PKA, activating the enzyme.

There are numerous ways in which this pathway is regulated. First, when GTP is hydrolyzed, the G_α subunit needs to re-associate with the $G_{\beta\gamma}$ dimer and then to a ligand-bound receptor in order to reactivate. Therefore, hydrolysis of GTP is one of the fundamental ways this system is regulated. Second, the ligand can be removed from the receptor or degraded, or the entire ligand-receptor complex can be removed from the plasma membrane by receptor-mediated endocytosis. Removal of the signal or the signaling complex brings signaling to a halt. The final means by which signaling can be regulated is by modulation of the concentration of cAMP, which can be enzymatically degraded by phosphodiesterase. This enzyme cleaves cAMP to form AMP. Molecules that inhibit phosphodiesterase lead to elevated levels of cAMP and therefore to increased PKA signaling.

Once the role of G proteins and PKA in β-adrenergic signaling was established, this finding was used to elucidate several aspects of disease. One such example is cholera (**Figure 5.10**), a bacterial disease spread by drinking contaminated water. Cholera kills by dehydrating its victims. The toxin produced by these bacteria cause people with cholera to produce as much as a liter per hour of watery diarrhea. The catalytic subunit of the toxin is

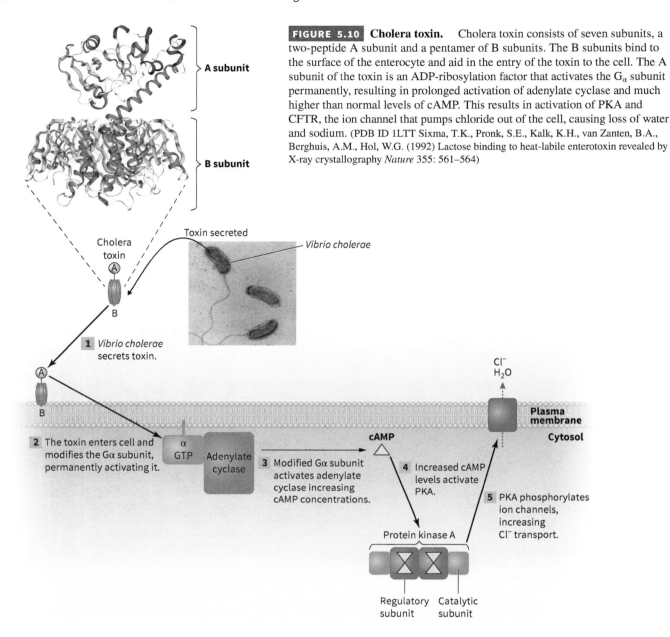

FIGURE 5.10 **Cholera toxin.** Cholera toxin consists of seven subunits, a two-peptide A subunit and a pentamer of B subunits. The B subunits bind to the surface of the enterocyte and aid in the entry of the toxin to the cell. The A subunit of the toxin is an ADP-ribosylation factor that activates the G_α subunit permanently, resulting in prolonged activation of adenylate cyclase and much higher than normal levels of cAMP. This results in activation of PKA and CFTR, the ion channel that pumps chloride out of the cell, causing loss of water and sodium. (PDB ID 1LTT Sixma, T.K., Pronk, S.E., Kalk, K.H., van Zanten, B.A., Berghuis, A.M., Hol, W.G. (1992) Lactose binding to heat-labile enterotoxin revealed by X-ray crystallography *Nature* 355: 561–564)

an enzyme (an ADP-ribosylation factor) that catalyzes the transfer of an ADP-ribose group to the G_α subunit of the G protein. This modification to the G_α subunit locks it in the active conformation, making it chronically active and unable to hydrolyze GTP and switch off. This leads to elevated cAMP levels and overactive PKA, resulting in activation of a chloride channel in the cells lining the intestine. The opening of this channel causes the accumulation of chloride in the lumen of the intestine. As these ions leave the cell, they draw water and sodium with them. The cell is unable to reabsorb these molecules, so dehydration and loss of electrolytes follows.

G proteins are an interesting and unexpected example of enzymatic catalysis and of how evolution can result in unexpected changes. There is a common perception that processes evolve to become faster and more efficient, but in G proteins this is not the case. The G protein complex was first identified as a GTPase, an enzyme that breaks down GTP. The G_α subunit binds strongly to GTP (it has a low K_M value). Once bound to GTP, it is in the active state and does not readily hydrolyze the GTP (the enzyme has a relatively low value of k_{cat}). Therefore, the G_α subunit has evolved to act as a molecular timer. It can bind to substrate (GTP), but the hydrolysis of this substrate can take seconds to minutes to occur.

5.2.3 | Insulin is an important metabolic regulator and growth factor

Insulin is a protein hormone that is synthesized in the pancreas and is best known for its role in glucose metabolism and diabetes. While it is true that insulin plays seminal roles in these processes, it is also a growth factor and can affect gene expression.

Insulin signaling begins with insulin binding to the insulin receptor (**Figure 5.11**). This binding causes the receptor to dimerize, binding another copy of the insulin receptor. The insulin receptor is itself a kinase that phosphorylates tyrosine residues in the other copy found in the homodimer. This type of receptor is a **receptor tyrosine kinase (RTK)**, a type of receptor architecture often found in growth factor signaling.

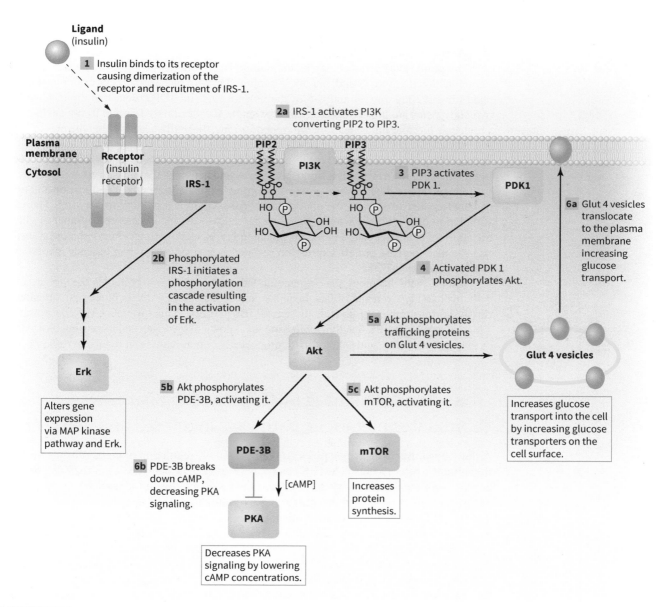

FIGURE 5.11 **Insulin signaling pathway.** Insulin binds to the insulin receptor, which undergoes dimerization and autophosphorylation. The receptor, now an active kinase itself, phosphorylates the insulin receptor substrate (IRS). Phosphorylated IRS interacts with the PI3 kinase complex which phosphorylates a specific phospholipid (phosphatidylinositol) into more highly phosphorylated forms (PIP2 and PIP3). The different phosphoinositides produced activate PDK1 (phosphoinositide dependent kinase) which in turn phosphorylates and activates Akt. Akt can affect numerous targets in the cell leading to changes in gene expression, cell growth, and differentiation, and changes to glucose metabolism.

Next, the phosphorylated insulin receptor binds to and phosphorylates the insulin receptor substrate (IRS-1), which is a scaffolding protein. On a building, scaffolding acts a framework around which other things can be positioned and hung. Similarly, **scaffolding proteins** act as a molecular framework that forms an assembly point for other proteins.

In the case of IRS-1, there are several groups of proteins that bind and activate. One of these groups is the series that leads to activation of the Erk proteins of the MAP kinase cascade. This cascade ultimately affects gene expression, regulating cell growth and differentiation.

The other major pathway through which insulin signals is the phosphoinositide or PI cascade. Phosphatidylinositol is a phospholipid found on the cytosolic face of the plasma membrane. One of the proteins that phosphorylated IRS recruits is phosphatidyl inositol-4,5-bis phosphate 3 kinase (PI3K). Phosphatidylinositol is found in the lipid bilayer and has the polar alcohol inositol as its head group. Inositol has six different hydroxyl groups, each of which can be phosphorylated, and alterations to these are important in cellular signaling. The PI cascade is the series of enzymatic modifications that can occur to this phospholipid head group.

PI3K is a kinase that phosphorylates an already phosphorylated form of phosphatidylinositol (phosphatidylinositol-4,5-bisphosphate, also known as PIP2) on C-3 to produce phosphatidylinositol-3,4,5-trisphosphate (PIP3).

The prefixes *bis* and *tris* may be unfamiliar. Bis refers to a compound that has two of the same functional groups added, but not in conjunction with one another. For example, the phosphates in PIP2 are on C-4 and C-5 of the inositol ring. In ADP (adenosine diphosphate), the two phosphates are linked together from the single C-5 of ribose. Tris and tri are analogous. If a molecule has four phosphates on different positions, the prefix used is either "tetra-" or "kis-."

PIP3 activates phosphoinositide dependent kinase 1 (PDK1), an enzyme that has several roles in the cell, and it acts in part to regulate cross talk between several signaling pathways. In this instance, however, PDK1 phosphorylates and activates the kinase Akt.

Akt phosphorylates several proteins in a complex that initiates the translocation and fusion of Glut4-coated vesicles to the plasma membrane. Glut4 is a glucose transporter. Therefore, stimulation of Akt via the insulin signaling cascade results in an increased number of glucose transporters being deposited in the plasma membrane, leading to increased glucose transport. Akt can also increase protein expression and production via a signaling cascade involving the protein complex mTOR.

Insulin is the hormone that signals the fed state. As such, it promotes the storage of the carbohydrate glycogen and of fats. Insulin signaling also plays a role in blocking fat breakdown (lipolysis) by stimulating phosphodiesterase 3B (PDE3B). This lowers cAMP concentrations, which in turn lowers PKA activity, blocking breakdown of glycogen and increasing biosynthesis of glycogen and fatty acids. All of these processes are coordinated and regulated through Akt.

5.2.4 | The AMP kinase (AMPK) signaling pathway coordinates metabolic pathways in the cell and in the body

A third signaling pathway that plays critical roles in the regulation of metabolism is the **AMP dependent protein kinase (AMPK)** pathway (**Figure 5.12**). AMPK is *not* the PKA pathway, and it is *not* stimulated by cAMP. Rather, AMPK is a cytosolic kinase, which is activated not by a receptor or second messenger but by binding of AMP or phosphorylation by other kinases. In the cell, levels of total adenosine nucleoside phosphates are relatively constant. When the cell has abundant energy, the levels of AMP and ADP will be low, and levels of ATP will be high. Conversely, when the cell has a low energetic state, there is relatively less ATP and more ADP and AMP. AMPK acts as an energy sensor. If the insulin signaling pathway signifies the fed state and promotes growth and energy storage, signaling through the AMPK pathway indicates a low energy level and stimulates the oxidation of molecules for ATP production. Elevated levels of AMP will activate AMPK, activating pathways that increase fatty acid oxidation, and glucose uptake, glycolysis (the breakdown of glucose for energy), and block glucose storage (glycogen synthesis). AMPK also blocks gluconeogenesis (the synthesis of new glucose), steroid biosynthesis, and fatty acid biosynthesis. Overall, AMPK promotes oxidation of fatty acids and carbohydrates for ATP production. The AMPK pathway is one of the principal regulators of homeostasis in the organism.

- Increases lipid mobilization:
  - Fatty acid breakdown (β-oxidation)
    via acetyl-CoA carboxylase-2 (ACC2)
    Blocks fatty acid synthesis via ACC-1
- Inhibits steroid biosynthesis
    via HMG CoA reductase

- Increases carbohydrate mobilization:
    Stimulates glucose uptake (glucose transporters)
    Stimulates glycolysis (glucose breakdown)
    via phosphofructokinase
- Inhibits glycogen synthesis via glycogen synthase
- Inhibits production of new glucose (gluconeogenesis)

FIGURE 5.12 **AMP kinase signaling.** AMP kinase is a heterotrimeric protein that is implicated in several metabolic pathways. It is directly stimulated by a high AMP:ATP ratio and the kinases CaMKK, Akt, and LKB1. (PDB ID 4CFF Xiao, B., Sanders, M.J., Carmena, D., Bright, N.J., Haire, L.F., Underwood, E., Patel, B.R., Heath, R.B., Walker, P.A., Hallen, S., Giordanetto, F., Martin, S.R., Carling, D., Gamblin, S.J. (2013) Structural Basis of Ampk Regulation by Small Molecule Activators. *Nat.Commun.* 4: 3017)

AMPK is also regulated by several other kinases and signaling pathways including PKA and insulin signaling. PKA phosphorylates a second kinase called liver kinase B-1 (LKB1), which in turn can phosphorylate and activate AMPK. Insulin can act through the insulin receptor to activate the PI cascade, ultimately resulting in the activation of the kinase Akt. Akt can also phosphorylate and activate AMPK. Again, this is an example of how cellular communication pathways intersect and influence one another.

A third means of regulating AMPK is through the calcium calmodulin kinase kinase (CaMKK). This kinase normally regulates the calcium calmodulin kinase (hence the name "kinase kinase"). In the presence of elevated levels of cytosolic calcium ions, CaMKK can phosphorylate AMPK, activating it. Several small molecules are known to interact with AMPK, including the drugs metformin and 5-aminoimidazole-4-carboxamide ribonucleotide (AICAR, pronounced "a-car").

Metformin is a biguanide, an oral antidiabetic agent that acts as an insulin sensitizer, making cells respond to lower levels of insulin. This drug also decreases the hyperglycemia (high blood sugar) in people with diabetes by decreasing hepatic gluconeogenesis. Metformin acts by stimulating AMPK, which in turn increases the response of the cell to insulin and blocks gluconeogenesis. These effects occur in addition to the metabolic benefits of activating AMPK, such as increased fat burning and decreased cholesterol biosynthesis.

ACIAR is a small molecule that acts as an AMPK agonist, and it was developed as a drug to prevent cardiac damage during heart surgery and ischemia (low blood flow). Like metformin, ACIAR acts to stimulate AMPK, but it has found an additional use. In 2011, the World Anti-Doping Agency listed AICAR as a performance-enhancing drug of abuse and a banned substance in international competitions. People who take AICAR as a performance enhancer hope to gain the benefits of exercise in pill form.

Perhaps the most intriguing way of activating AMPK is through exercise itself. It is not clear whether this activation is due to a combination of elevated Ca^{2+} concentrations, increased AMP levels, or activation of kinases, nor is it clear that AMPK is the key regulatory enzyme in this process.

As the examples of metformin and AICAR illustrate, numerous small molecules affect signal transduction and therefore how the cell and organism function. This is discussed in **Medical Biochemistry: Signal transduction and pharmaceuticals.**

Medical Biochemistry

Signal transduction and pharmaceuticals

Signal transduction pathways are not an esoteric aspect of biochemistry. Understanding signal transduction is important and has many practical uses. In any research question involving a complex system such as a cell or organism, a researcher has a duty to understand how signaling pathways work, because simple changes to a system may elicit a signaling response, complicating results. It is often easiest to biochemically shut down some pathways with specific inhibitors to simplify results.

Beyond biomedical research, molecules that affect signal transduction are some of the world's most popular and widely used pharmaceuticals, and at one time it was said that approximately 80% of all drugs affected cell signaling in some way. Although recent estimates suggest that number is closer to 30%, a quick analysis of the most widely used drugs shows just how important

these pathways can be. Of the over-the-counter medications sold in 2016, six of the ten highest selling medications (cough and cold remedies, analgesics, heartburn medications, sleep aids, anti-itch medications, and smoking cessation aids) all affect signaling in some way, as do five of the ten most widely used prescription drugs. These drugs can be as common as aspirin or nicotine, or as cutting edge as recombinant protein hormones.

This section introduces signal transduction and starts to lay the groundwork for how signaling affects metabolism. Each of these pathways plays a significant role in biochemistry and metabolism. The interactions and phosphorylation events presented here are meant to form a foundation from which to build an understanding of the basics of signal transduction and provide several examples relevant to metabolism. The interactions of these proteins are far more complex than presented here, and new interactions and cross talk between existing pathways are being discovered daily.

WORKED PROBLEM 5.2 | The effect of caffeine on signal transduction

Caffeine (3,5,7-trimethyl xanthine) is the world's most commonly used stimulant; it acts as a phosphodiesterase inhibitor. How would caffeine affect the three signaling pathways discussed in this section?

Strategy If a compound inhibits phosphodiesterases, how would that affect the products of the phosphodiesterase reaction? Examine the pathways for insulin, PKA, and AMPK signaling. In which of these pathways does phosphodiesterase play a role, and what is that role?

Solution By inhibiting phosphodiesterase (the enzyme that breaks down cAMP), caffeine allows cAMP levels to increase.

This means that PKA is active with a lower level of stimulation, or that the background activity of PKA is elevated, and PKA signaling is increased.

Phosphodiesterases are found in multiple signaling pathways involving cAMP, and other cyclic nucleotides; however, they are not known to play a central role in either insulin signaling or AMPK signaling (despite structural similarities, AMP and cAMP are involved in very different pathways).

Follow-up question What are the physiological effects of caffeine on the body? What does this say about the signal process involved in the regulation of those processes?

5.2 Summary

- Signal transduction is the study of how cells communicate with each other.
- Most signal transduction pathways are complex, involving chemical signals (hormones or neurotransmitters), receptors, enzymes, kinases, and regulatory proteins.
- The complex nature of signal transduction pathways provides considerable variability, both in terms of how a signal arrives at the cell and the cellular response to that signal. There are also multiple levels of control, multiple places for pathways to interact, and multiple opportunities for amplification of signals.
- PKA is a kinase that is activated by the second messenger cAMP. It figures prominently in several cellular processes including some aspects of neurotransmission, several metabolic pathways, and gene transcription.
- The insulin signaling pathway responds to the protein hormone insulin. This pathway employs a receptor tyrosine kinase (RTK) to transduce signals into the cell. Although insulin signaling is best known for increasing the transport of glucose into the cell, it also regulates several important metabolic pathways and alters gene expression.
- AMPK is another important metabolic regulator. Unlike the first two pathways, no extracellular ligand leads to the activation of AMPK. Rather, the activation is induced by an elevated AMP:ATP ratio, exercise, and the activation of other kinases (calcium-calmodulin kinase kinase and LKB1).

5.2 Concept Check

- Describe the general principles involved in signal transduction.
- Draw the steps of the three signal transduction pathways discussed in this section.
- Compare these different pathways in terms of how they regulate metabolism.
- Predict what would happen if these pathways were altered by disease, such as cholera, or pharmacological intervention, such as caffeine.

The Bigger Picture

This chapter discusses two important aspects of the cell. Each cell is separated from other cells and from its external environment by membranes, and membranes also divide and define the margin of subcellular compartments called organelles. The chapter also introduces signal transduction, the process through which cells communicate with each other and use chemical signals to alter cellular processes.

Bioinformatics

Exercise 1 Properties of Membrane Proteins

Exercise 2 Porins: Maltoporin and OmpF

Problems

5.1 Membrane Structure and Function

1. If the ratio of protein mass in the membrane to lipid mass is 1:1 (50/50), what is the approximate molar ratio of the two to each other?

2. Peripheral membrane proteins disassociate from the membrane with changes in pH, increasing ionic (salt) concentrations, or by the addition of chaotrophic agents (urea). Are all of these treatments acting in the same manner? In other words, what is the mechanism by which proteins separate from the membrane for each treatment? Will any of these agents remove the protein from the membrane, or will some proteins disassociate only with a pH change whereas others respond only to urea?

3. An average cell has a diameter of 15 microns, and the thickness of the plasma membrane is 4.5 nm. Imagine that your campus represents a cell. How thick would be its plasma membrane?

4. Examine the structure of the head group of a phospholipid. What sorts of weak forces could form between those phospholipid head groups and a peripheral membrane protein? What amino acids would need to be involved in those noncovalent bonds (e.g., what functional groups)?

5. Examine the thermodynamic parameters (ΔG, ΔH, ΔS) behind the association of an integral membrane protein with the plasma membrane. How must these parameters change for a protein to be removed from the plasma membrane? Draw two illustrations, one with a protein in the plasma membrane and one with a protein separate from the plasma membrane. How does your thermodynamic model explain what is going on in the illustration?

6. The plasma membrane is fluid in all cells. Cattle and salmon live in very different environments. Cite one way in which these two organisms maintain membrane fluidity in the face of their different environmental challenges.

7. The perilipins (a family of lipid droplet proteins) were originally identified as proteins that stayed associated with the lipid droplet when washed with sodium carbonate (100 mM, pH 9.0). Based on this observation, describe a model for the association of the perilipins with the lipid storage droplet.

8. Head group packing in phospholipids describes the density or arrangement of phospholipid head groups in a monolayer or bilayer. Examine the Langmuir-Blodgett trough technique from the appendix. Using words or drawings, how would you describe head group packing to someone who has not seen this page or experiment?

9. If cells are disrupted by physical or chemical means, then sealed spherical compartments surrounded by a membrane forms instead of sheets of membrane because the exposed edges of a membrane are energetically unfavorable. What does "energetically unfavorable" mean here? Use thermodynamic arguments to describe why vesicles will form instead of sheets.

10. Describe the movement of lipids and proteins in a lipid bilayer. How can these molecules diffuse, and in what ways are their movement restricted?

11. Generally speaking, how does tethering molecules together in the plasma membrane affect the speed of their diffusion in the membrane? How can this alter their biochemical properties with regard to function, such as binding to a ligand?

12. The presence of two membranes in some organelles has been interpreted as meaning that eukaryotic cells arose through a symbiotic relationship between two prokaryotic cells. Describe in basic terms how this could happen. Would this be an example of punctuated equilibrium or phylogenetic gradualism? If you are unfamiliar with these terms, please consult a resource on evolutionary biology.

13. Describe what happens to membranes when two membranous compartments fuse together or when one membranous compartment pinches off to form a new compartment.

5.2 Signal Transduction

14. Describe two ways in which insulin can affect gene expression.

15. Metformin is an antidiabetic agent but it does not work through effects on insulin signaling. Explain this finding.

16. Why is AICAR a banned substance for athletic competitions but caffeine is not?

17. This chapter cited several examples of proteins that are targets for PKA. Look up a review article on PKA. What other proteins are phosphorylated by this kinase?

18. This chapter discusses caffeine as a phosphodiesterase inhibitor, but caffeine is also an adenosine receptor antagonist. What does the term "antagonist" mean in this instance? Look up the structure of caffeine. How does the structure of caffeine help to explain these two functions in the body?

19. Examine the signaling pathways discussed in this chapter. Describe two ways that these pathways can interact (e.g., one signaling pathway influencing the outcome of another).

20. Many drug companies are interested in formulating compounds that act on the kinase Akt, but far fewer are interested in compounds that act on the insulin receptor. What are the reasons for different levels of interest in Akt and insulin?

21. If a drug increased the activity of Akt, what would be the outcome in the cell with regard to glucose metabolism?

22. Phosphodiesterase inhibitors increase signaling through PKA. How does this work? Why does the presence of an inhibitor increase signaling, and what does this say about background levels of signaling in this pathway.

Data Interpretation

23. You have identified a rare condition in which, under certain unknown circumstances, a protein (termed "imstudyin") accumulates, leading to increased cognitive development. It is not clear whether this is an inherited condition, although environmental factors (exposure to the library and deprivation from videogames) seem to increase the risk of this condition.

Parts a–e pertain to this scenario.

a. To begin your investigations on imstudyin accumulation, you need a model system. Three have been proposed: a mouse model in which mice have repeatedly solved mazes, leading to increased accumulation of the protein; a sample of cells from an undergraduate's liver (obtained with written permission and informed consent) that has been transformed and is being cultured in the lab; and brain samples from a graduate student cadaver (which has been used in previous studies). Cite the strengths and weaknesses of each of these models for a biochemical study on imstudyin.

b. You would like to know where in the cell imstudyin accumulates. A sample of cells is disrupted by homogenization, and the resulting cellular lysate is subjected to density gradient ultracentrifugation. The results are shown below.

Lysosomes (d = 1.12 g/ml)
Smooth endoplasmic reticulum (d = 1.15 g/ml)
Mitochondria (d = 1.18 g/ml)
Nuclei (d = 1.4 g/ml)

Control   Experimental

Based on the results of this experiment, where would you hypothesize that imstudyin is accumulating? How else could you test this?

c. The fraction containing imstudyin from the previous experiment was treated with either 250 mM NaCl, 50 mM glycine (pH 3.0), or 0.1% Tween 20 (a detergent). The sample density was adjusted to 1.05 g/mL. The samples were centrifuged again and the results are shown below.

Control   NaCl   Glycine   Tween-20
                    (low pH)   (detergent)

Is imstudyin found in the lipid bilayer of this organelle? How can you tell? Use the data to support your hypothesis.

d. Samples were prepared as they were for part b. Following isolation of the region corresponding to imstudyin, some of the sample was treated with a protease. Samples were then subjected to immunoblotting (western blotting) and probed with an antibody to imstudyin. The results are shown below.

1   2   3   4   5

Lane 1, control, no protease

Lane 2, control, with protease

Lane 3, NaCl, with protease

Lane 4, glycine, with protease

Lane 5, Tween-20, with protease

Describe these results as you would if you were writing a scientific manuscript. What conclusions can you draw from the results of this question? How do these data align with your observations from questions b and c?

e. Other studies have noted that treatment with caffeine and glucose helps to increase the effects of imstudyin in some students. Cells were treated with caffeine, glucose, insulin, or some combination of these agents, and the amount of imstudyin found in the organellar fraction was quantitated using immunoblotting. Results are shown below.

Lane 1, control, no treatment

Lane 2, glucose

Lane 3, caffeine

Lane 4, insulin

Lane 5, insulin, glucose, and caffeine

Top panel-cytosol

Bottom panel-organelle

How is each compound affecting the distribution of the protein? What can this data tell you? Is this protein phosphorylated by either pathway? In other words, what does the data actually show you, and where are we extrapolating or drawing conclusions based on the outcomes shown?

Experimental Design

24. You are studying a novel protein thought to be involved in carbohydrate metabolism. Describe two experiments you could use to determine where in the cell this protein can be found.

25. Membranes are asymmetric. Design an experiment to test this hypothesis. What techniques would you employ, and what would you use as controls?

26. Examination of the primary sequence of a novel protein reveals three consensus PKA recognition sites. Describe an experiment to test the hypothesis that the protein is a target of PKA, including appropriate controls.

27. Several factors contribute to the fluidity of a membrane, one of which is the degree of saturation of the lipids comprising the membrane. Membranes made with unsaturated lipids generally have a lower melting point and are more fluid. Design an experiment to test this hypothesis.

28. FRAP is a technique used to determine the mobility of a molecule in a membrane. Design a FRAP experiment to test the mobility of an insulin receptor. Would you expect the receptor to be more mobile before or after insulin binding?

29. The insulin receptor is an example of an RTK and a representative member of the growth factor receptor family of receptors. Design an experiment to test the hypothesis that other growth factors will bind to the insulin receptor. Design a second experiment to determine whether EGF will activate the insulin receptor.

Ethics and Social Responsibility

30. Tens of thousands of people are on waiting lists for donated organs. Are you a registered organ donor? Explain why you are or are not a registered donor.

31. The drug caffeine is discussed in this chapter. Caffeine is generally not considered harmful, and its sale is not restricted in any way to minors, whereas other drugs, such as ethanol and nicotine, are restricted. Briefly research this topic. Why are some substances restricted and others not?

32. Many people believe that cultured cell models can take the place of animals in biomedical research. Based on your background knowledge and what you have learned in this chapter, is that a true statement? Do animals still have a place in biomedical research?

33. Many human cell lines were originally obtained without the donor's permission or with a vaguely worded statement of permission. Since those times, there has been a re-examination of the ethics surrounding informed consent. Should these donors' families be compensated for their ancestor's contributions?

34. Stem cells, especially embryonic stem cells (those derived from embryonic tissue) have been a topic of ethical debate in the United States since their discovery. It is now known that many tissues in the body harbor stem cells, and that other cells can be reprogrammed into stem cells. Many people still have a visceral reaction to the term "stem cell," without considering the source of those cells. Is their response valid? Is the use of stem cells (or all cultured cells for that matter) forever tainted by knowledge originally obtained in ways we may currently deem unethical?

Suggested Readings

5.1 Membrane Structure and Function

Ehnholm, C., ed. *Cellular Lipid Metabolism*. New York, NY: Springer, 2009.

Gurr, I. M. *Lipid Biochemistry: An Introduction*. 3rd ed. New York, NY: Springer, 1980.

The AOS lipid library retrieved from http://lipidlibrary.aocs.org/index.html

Vance, D. E., and J. E. Vance. *Biochemistry of Lipids, Lipoproteins, and Membranes*. 5th ed. New York, NY: Elsevier, 2008.

5.2 Signal Transduction

Dennis, E. A., S. G. Rhee, M. M. Billah, and Y. A. Hannun. "Role of Phospholipase in Generating Lipid Second Messengers in Signal Transduction." *FASEB Journal* 5, no. 7 (1991): 2068–77.

Gomperts, B. D., I. M. Kramer, and P. E. R. Tatham. *Signal Transduction*. San Diego, CA: Academic Press, 2003.

Milligan, G., ed. *Signal Transduction: A Practical Approach*. Oxford, NY: Oxford University Press, 1999.

Schönbrunner, N., J. Cooper, and G. Krauss. Translated by G. Weinheim. *Biochemistry of Signal Transduction and Regulation*. New York, NY: Wiley-VCH, 2000.

Sitaramayya, A. ed. *Introduction to Cellular Signal Transduction*. Boston, MA: Birkhauser, 1999.

Membranes and an Introduction to Signal Transduction

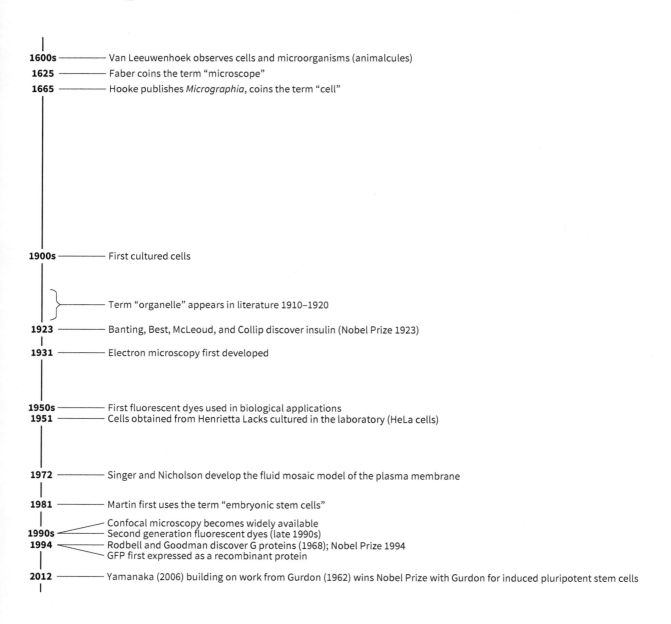

1600s —— Van Leeuwenhoek observes cells and microorganisms (animalcules)
1625 —— Faber coins the term "microscope"
1665 —— Hooke publishes *Micrographia*, coins the term "cell"

1900s —— First cultured cells

—— Term "organelle" appears in literature 1910–1920

1923 —— Banting, Best, McLeoud, and Collip discover insulin (Nobel Prize 1923)

1931 —— Electron microscopy first developed

1950s —— First fluorescent dyes used in biological applications
1951 —— Cells obtained from Henrietta Lacks cultured in the laboratory (HeLa cells)

1972 —— Singer and Nicholson develop the fluid mosaic model of the plasma membrane

1981 —— Martin first uses the term "embryonic stem cells"

—— Confocal microscopy becomes widely available
1990s —— Second generation fluorescent dyes (late 1990s)
1994 —— Rodbell and Goodman discover G proteins (1968); Nobel Prize 1994
—— GFP first expressed as a recombinant protein

2012 —— Yamanaka (2006) building on work from Gurdon (1962) wins Nobel Prize with Gurdon for induced pluripotent stem cells

CHAPTER 6

Carbohydrates I

Mono- and Disaccharides, Glycolysis, Gluconeogenesis, and the Fates of Pyruvate

bitt24 / Shutterstock.com

While sugar and starch are examples of carbohydrates, so are the cellulose in wood or the chitin in insect shells.

Carbohydrates in Context

Many people without biochemistry backgrounds can name foods rich in carbohydrates. Sugar, rice, bread, and pasta are good examples of carbohydrates, but many other molecules are also carbohydrates. Carbohydrates play structural roles, such as cellulose in cotton and wood, or chitin in the shells of crabs and insects. Carbohydrates make up part of the sugar phosphate backbone of 2-deoxyribose in DNA and ribose in RNA. Polymers of carbohydrate are found in the synovial fluid of joints, in mucus, and in some secreted extracellular matrix molecules. Even the ABO blood group antigen system is caused by carbohydrate modifications to proteins on the surface of cells. All of these molecules and their relationships and reactions are described in **Dynamic Figure 6.1**.

This chapter introduces the study of metabolism—the reactions through which organisms transform one molecule into another and provide the energy and intermediates for other reactions. While many questions in metabolism were solved decades ago, there are current questions, such as the effect of high fructose corn syrup in the diet, that remain unanswered.

This chapter discusses the properties and functions of simple carbohydrates and how they can be joined to one another to form more complex molecules. Also discussed is how glucose can be catabolized into pyruvate when needed for energy through the process known as glycolysis, and how new glucose is synthesized in animals in times of need. The chapter concludes with a discussion of the fates of pyruvate—the three-carbon α-keto acid produced at the end of glycolysis.

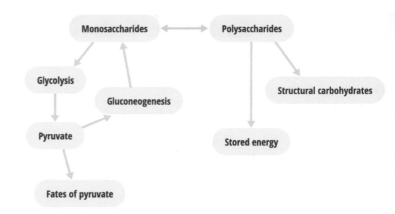

DYNAMIC FIGURE 6.1
Carbohydrates can be simply classified as monosaccharides (single building blocks) or polysaccharides (polymers of monosaccharides). Polysaccharides can serve structural roles or can serve as a stored form of energy. Monosaccharides can be catabolized into pyruvate. Likewise, pyruvate can be used to synthesize new glucose through gluconeogenesis.

COMMON THEMES

Evolution's outcomes are conserved.	• Many of the pathways we will see in this chapter are conserved throughout evolution.
	• In contrast to genes discussed in other chapters, such as the genes involved in eicosanoids and steroid metabolism, the genes coding for enzymes involved in glycolysis are found throughout biology and are therefore more ancient in origin.
	• Because glycolysis is so basic to the existence of an organism, mutations that disrupt this pathway are often lethal or put organisms at such an evolutionary disadvantage that they generally fail to pass on these genes.
Structure determines function.	• Monosaccharides are a family of molecules that are largely related through stereochemistry.
	• Monosaccharides are frequently depicted in Fischer projections to highlight their stereochemical differences. However, in solution, these molecules adopt a cyclic hemiacetal or hemiketal structure; this structure is best seen in a Haworth projection.
	• In the broadest sense, polysaccharides can be functionally characterized as being energy stores or as providing structure to the organism.
	• Energy-storing polysaccharides can either be linear like amylose or highly branched like amylopectin or glycogen. The branched forms enable the mobilization of monosaccharides at a higher rate, because release can happen simultaneously from several sites.
	• Structural polysaccharides are generally linear molecules, with multiple places where the strands can interact with one another through weak forces (typically hydrogen bonding, dipole–dipole, and electrostatic interactions).
	• The structure of many enzymes is conserved throughout biology, and many of the same chemical reactions are employed in the breakdown and biosynthesis of carbohydrates in divergent species.
Biochemical information is transferred, exchanged, and stored.	• Carbohydrate metabolism is regulated by several allosteric regulators and kinases that inhibit or activate key enzymes in the glycolytic pathway.
Biomolecules are altered through pathways involving transformations of energy and matter.	• In this as in other chapters, we will see that energetically unfavorable reactions become favorable when coupled to reactions with very negative $\Delta G°$ values. Although we typically think of this in terms of ATP hydrolysis, reactions of other groups such as phosphoesters or thioesters are common in biochemistry. Likewise, reactions that have $\Delta G°$ values close to zero can be tipped to move in either direction by changing the concentrations of substrates or products.
	• The synthesis of glucose and the degradation of monosaccharides use similar reactions but different pathways. Key steps are different, and compartmentalization is important. A similar theme is seen in fatty acid metabolism.

6.1 Properties, Nomenclature, and Biological Functions of Monosaccharides

Carbohydrates are a group of biological molecules with the basic formula $C_x(H_2O)_x$, hence the name "carbo-hydrate." At their most basic level, carbohydrates have the equivalent of one molecule of water for every carbon atom. This means that carbohydrates are polyhydroxy aldehydes or polyhydroxy ketones, that is, molecules in which one carbon bears a carbonyl group (C=O) and the others all carry hydroxyls (—OH). They also contain at least three carbons. We will first discuss the basic structures of carbohydrates and different ways we can represent these molecules on paper, and then we will move into modifications of these molecules.

$C_x(H_2O)_x$

Generic formula

$C_6H_{12}O_6$

Formula of a carbohydrate

Bond-angle depiction of a carbohydrate

Fischer projection of a carbohydrate

6.1.1 Monosaccharides are the simplest carbohydrates

This section focuses on the simplest carbohydrates, the **monosaccharides**. Monosaccharides can be linked together to form more complex carbohydrates. Monosaccharides all end in the suffix -ose to designate them as carbohydrates. They can be classified based by the number of carbons in the molecule, the presence of an aldehyde or a ketone, and the stereochemistry at the **penultimate carbon** (the chiral center farthest from the carbonyl). In terms of size, monosaccharides contain three to nine carbons but most contain five, six, or seven carbons (**Table 6.1**). The reasons for this are rooted in organic chemistry. A numbering system can be combined with the "-ose" suffix to provide a generic name for a group of carbohydrates; for example, five-carbon monosaccharides are **pentoses** and six-carbon monosaccharides are **hexoses**. Thanks to the carbonyl moiety, a monosaccharide contains either an aldehyde or a ketone and can therefore be broadly categorized as **aldoses** or **ketoses**. These terms can be combined with the numbering system mentioned previously. Thus, for example, fructose is a ketohexose and ribose is an aldopentose.

Carbohydrates can also be classified by the stereochemistry of the chiral carbons in the molecule. To do this, we examine the chiral center that is farthest from the carbonyl moiety. This chiral center is termed the penultimate carbon. The carbon farthest from the carbonyl —the last or ultimate carbon— has two hydrogens. Therefore, it has a plane of symmetry and is *achiral*—that is, not chiral. In categorizing monosaccharides, the molecule is first drawn in a **Fischer projection**. Recall that in a Fischer projection bonds are represented as horizontal and vertical lines where the horizontal lines project out toward the viewer and the vertical lines project back through the plane of the illustration. Next, a comparison is made between the penultimate carbon in the monosaccharide in question and glyceraldehyde, the simplest monosaccharide. If the hydroxyl group is found on the right, the molecule is given the stereochemical designation D; if it is on the left, it is given the designation L. Nearly all carbohydrates found in nature have D stereochemistry. It may be tempting to relate the D, L nomenclature of monosaccharides to other stereochemical systems, such as the *d, l* dextrorotary/levorotary system or the *R, S* system. However, the D, L system is merely

Anomeric carbon

Penultimate carbon

Achiral carbon

Fructose
(ketohexose)

Anomeric carbon

Penultimate carbon

Achiral carbon

Ribose
(aldopentose)

TABLE 6.1   Names of Monosaccharides

Number of carbons	Name
3	Triose
4	Tetrose
5	Pentose
6	Hexose
7	Heptose

CHO
H—C—OH
CH₂OH
D-Glyceraldehyde

CHO
H—C—OH
H—C—OH
CH₂OH
D-Erythrose

CHO
HO—C—H
H—C—OH
CH₂OH
D-Threose

CHO
H—C—OH
H—C—OH
H—C—OH
CH₂OH
D-Ribose

CHO
HO—C—H
H—C—OH
H—C—OH
CH₂OH
D-Arabinose

CHO
H—C—OH
HO—C—H
H—C—OH
CH₂OH
D-Xylose

CHO
HO—C—H
HO—C—H
H—C—OH
CH₂OH
D-Lyxose

CHO
H—C—OH
H—C—OH
H—C—OH
H—C—OH
CH₂OH
D-Allose

CHO
HO—C—H
H—C—OH
H—C—OH
H—C—OH
CH₂OH
D-Altrose

CHO
H—C—OH
HO—C—H
H—C—OH
H—C—OH
CH₂OH
D-Glucose

CHO
HO—C—H
HO—C—H
H—C—OH
H—C—OH
CH₂OH
D-Mannose

CHO
H—C—OH
H—C—OH
HO—C—H
H—C—OH
CH₂OH
D-Gulose

CHO
HO—C—H
H—C—OH
HO—C—H
H—C—OH
CH₂OH
D-Idose

CHO
H—C—OH
HO—C—H
HO—C—H
H—C—OH
CH₂OH
D-Galactose

CHO
HO—C—H
HO—C—H
HO—C—H
H—C—OH
CH₂OH
D-Talose

FIGURE 6.2   First fifteen D-aldoses.   The most common of these molecules found in biochemistry are glucose, mannose, galactose, ribose, and glyceraldehyde.

D-Glyceraldehyde

L-Glyceraldehyde

D-Mannose

D-Glucose
(dextrose)

a means of grouping molecules by comparing them to a standard, in this case, glyceraldehyde. The *R, S* names of carbohydrates and their ability to rotate plane polarized light are not related to the D, L system. The smallest ketose (dihydroxyacetone) is symmetric and lacks a chiral center.

Figure 6.2 and Figure 6.3 are Fischer projections showing the degree of relatedness of aldoses and ketoses, respectively. In a Fischer projection, placement of a group on one side of the carbon or the other indicates that these molecules are different stereoisomers. For example, the aldotetroses erythrose and threose are stereoisomers of one another, differing only in the stereochemistry around C-2. Carbohydrates that differ at one stereocenter, for example, the C-4 of the aldohexoses glucose and galactose, are termed **epimers** of one another. Different stereoisomers give the molecule a different final shape or conformation. Because they differ in conformation, these molecules will bind differently to enzymes and produce different products.

Although carbohydrates can be named according to the number of carbons and the presence of an aldehyde or ketone, most have common names. Since these molecules often differ only in their stereochemistry, it becomes problematic to refer to them using systematic names. For example, it is easier to refer to a molecule as "mannose" than as "(3S,4S,5S,6R)-6-(hydroxymethyl)oxane-2,3,4,5-tetrol." Glucose or blood sugar is the most prevalent monosaccharide and the building block of many complex carbohydrates. Because it is the most common D carbohydrate, glucose is also called **dextrose**, particularly in clinical situations.

6.1.2 Monosaccharides form hemiacetals and hemiketals

Fischer projections are used to depict monosaccharides because they make it easier to view the stereochemical differences between the different molecules. However, the projections are not an accurate reflection of these molecules in the cell nor do they provide an easily identifiable shape. One of the hydroxyl moieties in the monosaccharide can participate in nucleophilic attack on the carbonyl carbon to form a new structure—a hemiacetal or hemiketal. Hemiacetals and hemiketals are often unstable. However, tethering both the hydroxyl and carbonyl groups within the same molecule increases the likelihood of bond formation, and leads to a much greater proportion of the molecules existing as hemiacetals or hemiketals than would be the case if the carbonyl and hydroxyl were in separate molecules. In other words, intramolecular hemiacetal and hemiketal bonds form much more readily than intermolecular bonds.

FIGURE 6.3 **Seven D-ketoses.** The most common of these molecules found in biochemistry are fructose, xylulose, and dihydroxyacetone.

When a hemiacetal or hemiketal forms, the carbonyl group is converted from a trigonal planar sp^2 hybridized carbon to a tetrahedral sp^3 center. This carbon is now a new chiral center, and the carbonyl oxygen is converted to a hydroxyl group (**Figure 6.4**). The new hydroxyl can be found on either the bottom face or the top face of the ring. The former carbonyl carbon is now referred to as the **anomeric carbon**. If the hydroxyl group is found on the bottom face of the ring, the monosaccharide is designated α; if the hydroxyl group is on the top face, it is designated β. The α and β structures of a monosaccharide are termed **anomers** of one another. Although α and β anomers have different stereochemistry and conformation at the C-1, this is not usually a problem in biochemistry. The hemiacetal or hemiketal linkage is highly labile; it opens and recloses, and as it recloses it can form either of the anomers. However, the odds of forming one anomer over another are not 50:50. For any given monosaccharide, a particular ratio of anomers is observed at equilibrium. For glucose, the ratio of α to β is 36:64. The process of converting from one anomeric form to the other is known as **mutarotation**.

6.1.3 Monosaccharides form heterocyclic structures

To depict monosaccharides in their cyclic form, it is best to use **Haworth projections**. Compared to a Fischer projection, a Haworth projection more accurately depicts what the molecule looks like in solution, but it lacks some details of the molecule's conformation. Based on the number of hydroxyl groups present, it would seem that numerous rings of different sizes are possible. In reality, owing to ring strain and steric hindrances, five- and six-membered rings are the most common. Some carbohydrates can adopt either of these structures, each of which exists as a heterocyclic ring containing an oxygen (a hemiacetal or hemiketal). Based on their similarity to cyclic ethers (furan and pyran), a five-membered ring is designated as a **furanose**

FIGURE 6.4 **Most monosaccharides will form hemiacetal or hemiketal structures.** **A.** The formation of a new chiral center (from the old carbonyl carbon) results in an uneven mix of α and β anomers. **B.** Cyclic structures can open and reclose, rearranging from one anomer to another, a process known as *mutarotation*.

and a six-membered ring as a **pyranose**. However, the size of the ring is not necessarily a reflection of the number of carbons in the molecule: some pentoses can adopt a pyranose conformation, and some hexoses can be furanoses (because of the oxygen in the ring).

Furanoses often adopt an envelope conformation, in which four of the atoms of the ring are in one plane. When the ring oxygen is part of this plane, it reduces some of the steric clashes of ring substituents, but it increases torsional strain on the ring (**Figure 6.5**).

Pyranoses are six-membered rings, and they obey many of the same conformational rules that govern cyclohexanes. These molecules typically adopt chair conformations (the boat conformer is rarely seen due to steric clashes between substituents on the ring). When pyranoses adopt a chair structure, they tend to have the bulkier ring substituents arranged in an equatorial position rather than an axial position, predominantly due to steric hindrance.

6.1.4 Monosaccharides can be chemically modified

The monosaccharides discussed so far are polyhydroxy aldehydes and ketones; however, carbohydrates can also undergo chemical modifications through oxidation, reduction, or substitution reactions.

Glucosamine   ***N*-Acetylglucosamine**   **Xylitol**

Glucuronic acid   **2-deoxyribose**

In **amino sugars**, a hydroxyl group has been replaced by an amine. Frequently, these amines are further modified, for example, being acetylated to form an amide. The amino derivative of glucose (2-aminoglucose) is commonly known as **glucosamine**. Both glucosamine and the acetyl derivative (*N*-Acetylglucosamine) are found in important biological polymers, including chitin, extracellular matrix and insect exoskeletons.

In **sugar alcohols**, the carbonyl group is reduced to an alcohol. Without the carbonyl group it is impossible for sugar alcohols to form a hemiacetal or hemiketal linkage and form a cyclic structure.

Sugar alcohols can bind to taste receptors on the tongue and therefore still taste sweet; however, they cannot form cyclic structures and therefore cannot be absorbed by glucose transporters in the intestine. Because of this they have no caloric value; instead, sugar alcohols pass through the gut, where they are either fermented by bacteria or pass undigested. In nature, sugar alcohols are found in seaweed and some other plants, but they are also easy to make in the laboratory through the chemical reduction of the carbonyl group of monosaccharides. Xylitol, mannitol, and glucitol are sugar alcohols that are found in dietetic candy and gum.

Several monosaccharides can be oxidized to form a **sugar acid**, a carboxylic acid modification. Glucuronic acid (glucuronate) is a molecule of glucose in which C-6 has been enzymatically oxidized to a carboxylic acid. The liver employs glucuronic acid to detoxify foreign compounds known as xenobiotics. These compounds range from pharmaceuticals to the pigments and flavoring agents found naturally in all foods. These molecules often require modification to facilitate their removal from the body. An acetal is formed to a hydroxyl or an amino group on the foreign substance, and the complex is eliminated in the urine.

Deoxy sugars are formed by the removal of a hydroxyl moiety on one or more carbons of a monosaccharide. While the namesake carbohydrate in DNA is deoxyribose and is the most common and best known of these, hundreds of different deoxy sugars have been identified in bacteria, several of which are found in important antibiotics. In humans, deoxyribose is not made directly but is rather synthesized from ribonucleotide diphosphates by ribonucleotide reductase.

Monosaccharides can be attached to each other or to proteins, lipids, and peptides forming acetals and ketals. These linkages can occur through amines or hydroxyls and are referred to as **glycosidic bonds**. Compared to hemiacetals

A.

Furanose envelope structure

B.

Chair form   **Boat form**

C.

All axial
(not observed)   **All equatorial**

FIGURE 6.5 **Conformation of furanoses and pyranoses.** **A.** Furanoses adopt an envelopelike structure with one member of the ring out of the plane. **B.** Pyranoses can adopt a number of conformations. Shown are the chair and boat forms. In B, "a" indicates axial substituents and "e" indicates equatorial substituents. Note that the boat conformer is rarely seen due to steric clashes between axial substituents on the ring. **C.** When pyranoses adopt a chair structure, equatorial positions are favored to axial ones, again predominantly due to steric hindrance.

and hydroxyls the acetals and ketals found in glycosidic bonds are fairly stable and robust structures that require specific enzymatic degradation or strong acids to disassemble them.

Methyl α-D-Glucopyranoside   Methyl β-D-Glucopyranoside

6.1.5 Carbohydrates can be classified as reducing sugars or nonreducing sugars

All aldehydes are prone to oxidation to carboxylic acids. When one molecule is oxidized, another is reduced. Classically, carbohydrates were often categorized by their ability to reduce a particular reagent such as Cu^{2+} or Ag^+. The ability to reduce metals was a useful assay for aldehydes, and this was often used to measure aldose levels. Aldoses are reducing sugars, but some ketoses such as fructose will isomerize under the assay conditions and are also reducing sugars. Complicating matters further, some disaccharides have a free hemiacetal carbon. These hemiacetals are capable of opening, creating an aldehyde moiety that can undergo redox chemistry. Complex carbohydrates generally lack enough free aldehyde groups to be considered reducing sugars (**Figure 6.6**).

The ability of glucose to reduce metals figured prominently in the development of some of the first clinical tests for glucose (see **Medical Biochemistry: The interesting history of glucose testing**).

FIGURE 6.6 Reducing sugars.   A. Sugars like glucose that have free aldehyde groups or ketoses that can isomerize to aldoses have the ability to reduce metal ions, such as Cu^{2+}, becoming oxidized in the process. **B.** Disaccharides, such as maltose, are able to open to an aldehyde form and, therefore, also are considered reducing sugars.

A.
α-D-Glucose (hemiacetal)   Glucose (aldehyde) $+ Cu^{2+} + 5 OH^-$ Cu^{2+} ion reduced to Cu_2O $+$ $2 Cu_2O + 3 H_2O$ Aldehyde oxidized to carboxylic acid

B.
Maltose   Reducing end

Medical Biochemistry

The interesting history of glucose testing

Nearly 2,000 years ago, the Greek physician Areteus of Cappadocia described diabetes as "…a melting down of the flesh and limbs into urine…." Indeed, copious urination is one of the hallmarks of diabetes mellitus. In diabetes, cells are unable to absorb glucose from the plasma, owing to either a lack of insulin (type 1 diabetes) or a post-receptor signaling defect (type 2). As glucose levels rise,

transporters in the kidney that reabsorb glucose from the filtrate are overwhelmed, and glucose literally "spills over" into the urine. The extra glucose carries water with it, hence the increased urinary output. Since antiquity, it has been known that the urine of people with diabetes contains glucose. By the middle of the nineteenth century it was appreciated that a test for urinary glucose could be beneficial in the clinic, both as a diagnostic test for diabetes and as a way to determine how well the patient is responding to different treatments.

Such tests were available, but they were primitive. Some bold clinicians were apparently willing and able to taste the sugar in the urine of their patients, an unpleasant approach that clearly cannot produce a quantitative result. A more common technique was to collect a liter of urine, boil it dry, and then measure the mass of the residue that was left behind. This approach also had its drawbacks. Several different salts and solids can be found in urine, and these can vary depending on the composition of the diet and the disease state of the patient. The test was also unpleasant; it took some time to boil the sample dry, and it was difficult not to scorch or lose any of it.

The most significant advance in glucose testing at this time was made by Stanley Rossiter Benedict, a clinical biochemist credited with developing Benedict's solution: an alkali solution of carbonate, citrate, and, most importantly, Cu^{2+} ions. Benedict knew both from his work and from that of his competitor Otto Folin that the aldehyde moiety found in glucose could reduce Cu^{2+} to Cu^+. The reagent would change from a brilliant blue solution of Cu^{2+} to a brick red precipitate as the Cu^+ formed Cu_2O. Benedict published his findings in the *Journal of Biological Chemistry* in 1908.

Benedict's test was quickly adopted by clinicians as a rapid, simple, and semiquantitative means of determining urinary glucose concentrations. Perhaps the greatest endorsement came from Dr. Elliot Joslin, director of the Joslin Diabetes Center in Boston, Massachusetts. Joslin directed his patients to use the reagent daily to track their urinary glucose and to record their results in a diary.

This simple test resulted in several major paradigm shifts in medicine. For one of the first times, it gave clinicians the ability to measure the rate of progression of disease and make alterations to a treatment—medicine was evolving from an art to a science.

Also, people could now be active participants in their own healthcare. People with diabetes were not subjects treated by the physician, but were partners who could directly affect their urinary glucose levels through diet and who could record the findings.

Benedict's test remained the standard test for more than 50 years. In more recent times, it has been replaced by enzymatic assays based on glucose oxidase. A significant difference between these tests is the sample tested. Older tests assay glucose in urine. This roughly correlates with plasma glucose levels in people with diabetes, but the results can be influenced by diet, volume of urine, and several other factors. The urine tests do not give an accurate picture of blood glucose at a particular moment in time. Enzymatic assays give a snapshot of blood glucose level at the time the blood is drawn. In the clinic, these assays are colorimetric (producing a colored product in the presence of glucose).

In the home setting, testing is now accomplished by a modification of the enzymatic assay, using a glucometer, which uses a disposable test strip impregnated with a stabilized sample of glucose oxidase. When blood is drawn into the strip, the glucose oxidase converts the glucose to glucuronic acid, and the electrons that are captured are transferred to a device that measures changes in current. The more glucose available for oxidation, the more current flows. The current is compared to standard values, and the device gives a concentration of glucose in the blood. One drawback of using glucometers is that blood must be drawn (using a fingerstick); however, the advantage of knowing the blood glucose concentrations in real time outweighs the inconvenience and pain of a fingerstick. As glucometer design improves, the devices require less blood; the newest ones use as little as 0.3 μl of blood.

WORKED PROBLEM 6.1 | The structures of monosaccharides

Shown below is the Fischer projection of D-galactose. Draw the Haworth projection of β-D-galactopyranose.

D-Galactose

Strategy Review the cyclization of glucose discussed in this section. Which hydroxyl groups would be likely to contribute to a ring structure? Which hydroxyl group would have to contribute to

form a pyranose? What do the designations α and D tell you about the structure?

Solution The structure of β-D-galactopyranose is shown below. Compare the position of the hydroxyl groups in the Fischer and Haworth projections to those of glucose. Note the position of the hydroxyl group on the anomeric carbon. The position of each hydroxyl group is essential in how this molecule functions in biochemistry.

β-D-Galactopyranose

Follow-up question Galactose can also form a furanose. Draw α-D-galactofuranose.

6.1 Summary

- Carbohydrates have the basic formula $C_x(H_2O)_x$; as a result, they are polyhydroxyaldehydes or polyhydroxyketones.
- The simplest building blocks of carbohydrates are termed monosaccharides.
- Due to the presence of hydroxyl and carbonyl groups in the same molecule, monosaccharides cyclize to form intramolecular hemiacetals or hemiketals.
- Monsaccharides can be modified to form amino sugars, sugar alcohols, and sugar acids.
- Sugars with free aldehyde groups can be oxidized and are therefore referred to as reducing sugars.

6.1 Concept Check

- Name and describe (at the chemical level) several different examples of monosaccharides.
- Analyze and identify the different anomers these molecules can adopt.
- Describe the different chemical modifications of monosaccharides.
- Explain how the structure of these molecules contributes to their function.
- Explain how these molecules are similar to one another or to other biological molecules, and how they are different.

6.2 Properties, Nomenclature, and Biological Functions of Complex Carbohydrates

Examining the structures of monosaccharides highlights limitations to the size and diversity of these molecules. Their small size and relative lack of different functional groups present fewer opportunities for interesting chemistry and function than, for example, the amino acids. Fortunately, monosaccharides have several structural features that work in their favor. Most contain a hemiacetal or hemiketal linkage, and all contain multiple hydroxyl groups. These functional groups can combine with other hydroxyl groups to form acetals or ketals. These linkages are more stable than hemiacetal or hemiketal bonds, and they facilitate the synthesis of more complex and diverse structures. Likewise, the multiple hydroxyl groups found on monosaccharides allow multiple acetals and ketals to branch off the same molecule, resulting in linear or branched polymers of the monosaccharide. In biochemistry, we refer to these types of bonds as glycosidic bonds, and molecules with carbohydrates attached are often referred to as glycosides.

Polysaccharides can be classified by the number of monomeric units they contain. **Disaccharides** contain two monosaccharides, **trisaccharides** contain three. If the molecule contains more than three monosaccharides, it may be referred to as an **oligosaccharide**, although larger assemblies are commonly referred to as **polysaccharides**.

The number of monosaccharide units in the polysaccharide is important, but equally important are the bonds joining those monosaccharides. Specific enzymes catalyze the formation and breakdown of these bonds. The presence or absence of these enzymes dictates the ability of an organism to use one of these molecules as a fuel source. Bonds between monosaccharides describe the position of the carbon involved in the linkage as well as the α or β face from which the acetal or ketal involved in the linkage originates. Thus, a β-1,4 linkage connects an acetal or ketal from the β face of the C-1 of one monosaccharide to C-4 of a second monosaccharide. The rest of this section discusses the structure and function of several important disaccharides, trisaccharides, and polysaccharides.

α-1,4 linkage

6.2.1 Common disaccharides include lactose, sucrose, and maltose

A disaccharide is composed of two monosaccharides joined together. The types of monosaccharides and the linkage between them dictate some of the properties of the disaccharide. This section discusses three simple examples: lactose, sucrose, and maltose (**Figure 6.7**).

Lactose   **Lactose** (milk sugar) is a disaccharide comprised of one molecule of glucose and one molecule of galactose, connected via a β-1,4 linkage (β-D-Galactopyranosyl-(1→4)-D-glucose). As its name suggests, lactose is commonly found in milk; however, the concentrations of lactose vary depending on the species. For example, the lactose concentration is higher in the milk of humans (9%) than in that of cows (4.7%), goats (4.7%), or sheep (4.6%).

In the stomach, lactose is degraded by lactase, releasing molecules of glucose and galactose. All humans possess this enzyme activity at birth, and some ethnic groups with lengthy histories of dairy farming, for example Europeans and some African and Central American groups, have retained the ability to express this enzyme throughout their lives. Therefore, they can continue to consume milk as adults. Worldwide, however, most people lose this enzyme by the end of childhood, and they are unable to digest the lactose found in milk. Instead, the lactose is fermented by microbes in the digestive tract, resulting in nausea, cramps, bloating, and diarrhea. People who are lactose intolerant have, in the past, needed to avoid most milk products. Recently, however, scientists have developed alternatives for those who are lactose intolerant but wish to consume milk. These include milk that has been treated with lactase and capsules of recombinant lactase, which can be consumed before eating a meal that contains milk. The lactase in these products takes the place of the endogenous enzymes that infants and children produce because it degrades the lactose into harmless monosaccharides for subsequent metabolism.

People who are lactose intolerant do not need to avoid all dairy products. In many products, for instance, those that are fermented such as yogurt and some cheeses, the lactose that was originally present has been catabolized by the microbes that produced the food, or has been lost in the curding process. These foods can be eaten without undesirable side effects.

FIGURE 6.7 Examples of common disaccharides. The structures of **A.** lactose, **B.** sucrose, and **C.** maltose are shown.

Sucrose

Sucrose (table sugar) is one of the most commonly consumed carbohydrates worldwide. Sucrose is a 1,2-linked disaccharide of glucose and fructose (α-D-Glucopyranosyl-(1→2)-β-D-fructofuranoside). Plants synthesize sucrose as a way to temporarily store energy and to attract organisms to help pollinate a plant or disperse its seeds. The taste of sucrose is characteristically sweet, and it is used as the basis of comparison for all other sweeteners.

Table sugar is crystalized sucrose often obtained from sugar cane or sugar beets. Sucrose can also be found in honey and maple syrup. The United States Department of Agriculture estimates that, by the mid-2000s, Americans were consuming close to 90 pounds of sugar per year as either sucrose or high fructose corn syrup.

The chemistry and controversy of high fructose corn syrup is discussed in **Societal and Ethical Biochemistry: The ongoing debate over high fructose corn syrup.**

Maltose

Maltose (malt sugar) is a dimer of glucose molecules connected in an α-1,4 linkage (α-D-Glucopyranosyl-(1→4)-β-D-Glucopyranoside). Maltose is the major breakdown product formed when plants catabolize starch. When hearing the term "malt," most people think of malted milk balls or malted milk; however, the molecule plays a central role in the brewing industry.

Grains such as barley store energy as starch (polymers of glucose). When barley grains germinate, they mobilize the energy stored in starch as maltose. An early step in beer production is malting of grain, in which the grains are kept damp and warm and are allowed to germinate. During the malting process, enzymes cleave maltose, a dimer of glucose, from starch polymers. Following malting, the grains are roasted, and the soluble maltose is then removed from the grain by steeping in warm water. This is the actual brewing step. These soluble carbohydrates provide the fuel source for yeast in the subsequent steps in beer production. During Prohibition in the 1920s and early 1930s, when the sale, manufacture, and transport of alcohol was banned in the United States, brewers stayed in business by producing malt for candy, cereal, and as a milk additive.

Not all grains lend themselves to malting. Barley is the main grain used in beer production and can be malted, but corn cannot because it lacks the necessary enzymes. There are two options for extracting soluble carbohydrates from corn. In North America, the corn is often

Societal and Ethical Biochemistry

The ongoing debate over high fructose corn syrup

Over the past 30 years, increased attention has been focused on the composition of the American diet. One of the molecules under the greatest scrutiny is high fructose corn syrup (HFCS).

HFCS is a sweetener prepared from corn. The corn is dried and milled, and to liberate glucose the resulting corn starch is treated with either dilute hydrochloric acid or amylase from bacteria or mold. The glucose is passed over a solid support to which glucose isomerase has been bound. The enzyme converts approximately 42% of the glucose to fructose. This product is HFCS-42, which is found in numerous processed foods. Some of the fructose is used to make an enriched product, HFCS-55 (55% fructose), which is used in soft drinks.

HFCS is desirable from a food-production perspective for several reasons. First, it is more economical than sucrose on a per-kilogram basis, and is even cheaper if we take into account that fructose is 1.7 times sweeter than sucrose. Second, HFCS is a liquid and is therefore easier than solid sucrose to handle in an industrial setting. Finally, the United States grows a lot of corn. The USDA reports that in 2017 over 14 billion bushels were grown. The conditions that are needed to grow corn and the diseases that affect it are well studied and understood. HFCS is used in a wide range of products, from baked goods to beverages to ketchup. In 2016, the average American consumed over 40 pounds of HFCS.

Commercially, HFCS is a success. Unfortunately, as HFCS consumption has increased in the American diet, so have

obesity and type 2 diabetes. Is HFCS the cause? The science is unclear. Consumption of HFCS has increased over the past 30 years, but so have other factors that may also be implicated in obesity and diabetes, such as increased consumption of fats (including *trans* fats), decrease in exercise, and an overall increase in the total number of calories consumed due to larger portion sizes. If we include in the analysis changes in how we eat, for example, in the car, on the run, or late at night, we see a complex problem with no simple answer.

Focusing on the biochemistry, we know that fructose is metabolized partially through glycolyis, discussed in section 6.3, but also through the fructolysis pathway. In this pathway fructose is phosphorylated to fructose-1-phosphate and then cleaved by an aldolase to yield DHAP and glyceraldehyde, both of which ultimately enter glycolysis as GAP. However, other details may add to this story. Consumption of glucose elicits a release of insulin from the pancreas, whereas consumption of fructose does not. Likewise, glucose triggers responses in the brain that blunt the appetite, whereas fructose does not. Finally, consumption of HFCS has been associated with increased levels of uric acid—a by-product of purine metabolism and a causal molecule in the disease gout. It may be that fructose metabolism provides a link between glycolysis and uric acid production.

None of these observations offers a clear answer. As is often the case, complex problems have equally complex solutions.

combined with malted barley or other grains. The enzymes found in the malted barley can hydrolyze the starches found in corn, in a process known as mashing. If the microbes from a previous mash are added to assist in the starch breakdown, this is known as a sour mash. The product of the fermentation of malt and corn is far from palatable, so it cannot be consumed as beer; instead, it is filtered and distilled to produce whiskey. Ancient cultures used different sources of enzymes to obtain similar results. In Central America, fermentable monosaccharides and disaccharides are released from corn by treating it with amylase from human saliva. Corn was communally chewed and spat into a pot; it was then fermented into a beer-like beverage called chicha, which was common in the Inca culture. Modern chicha drinks use other malting techniques to liberate fermentable carbohydrates from grains.

WORKED PROBLEM 6.2 | Drawing a disaccharide

Draw the disaccharide cellobiose, a dimer of two glucose molecules in a β-1,4 linkage.

Strategy Think about the structures of the monosaccharides that make up this molecule. Draw both in Haworth projections. Which carbons are involved in the linkage, and which face of the ring (α or β) would be involved in the acetal bond?

Solution The structure of cellobiose is shown here. Examine the structures of the monosaccharides comprising the disaccharide, and look at how they are connected.

Cellobiose

Follow-up question How would the structure and properties of this molecule change if it had an α linkage?

6.2.2 | Trisaccharides and oligosaccharides contain three or more monosaccharide units bound by glycosidic linkages

Trisaccharides and oligosaccharides are connected in a similar fashion to disaccharides through glycosidic bonds. As with disaccharides, both the composition of the building blocks and the connections between them impart properties to the final molecule (**Figure 6.8**). Oligosaccharides are typically between 7 and 20 monomers in length, although the delineation between larger oligosaccharides and shorter polysaccharides is a point of debate.

Raffinose—a trisaccharide   *Raffinose* is a trisaccharide composed of linked molecules of galactose, glucose, and fructose. Raffinose is effectively a molecule of galactose linked via an α-1,6 linkage to the glucose moiety of sucrose. It is commonly found in the *brassica* family—broccoli, cabbage, Brussels sprouts and also some legumes. Humans cannot digest raffinose because we lack α-galactosidase activity. Gut microbes can metabolize raffinose, resulting in the production of gaseous by-products (CO_2, H_2, and CH_4) in some individuals who ingest these vegetables. As with people who are lactose intolerant, an enzyme (in this case an α-galactosidase) can be taken in tablet or capsule form together with the food, to help prevent these side effects.

Inulin—an oligosaccharide   Inulin (not to be confused with the peptide hormone *insulin*) is a plant oligosaccharide consisting predominantly of polymers of fructose capped by glucose units, and contains 20–1,000 monomeric units. Plants use inulin as a storage form of energy. As with several other carbohydrates, humans lack the enzymes necessary to mobilize inulin and are therefore unable to digest it. As a result, inulin in the diet passes largely undigested into the intestine, where it is partially digested by gut microbes. Inulin represents one of several molecules broadly characterized as a soluble fiber, and is thought to be beneficial to the health of the gastrointestinal tract. It is found in high concentrations in plants such as chicory, and it is sometimes added to processed foods to elevate their fiber content.

A. motorolka/Getty Images

B. Premium Stock Photography GmbH/Alamy Stock Photo

FIGURE 6.8 **Examples of a trisaccharide and oligosaccharide.** Shown are the structures of **A.** raffinose (found in broccoli, beans, and cabbage) and **B.** inulin (a polysaccharide found in chicory and added to many foods). Neither molecule is digestible by humans due to the linkages between the monosaccharide subunits.

6.2.3 Common polysaccharides function to store energy or provide structure

Polysaccharides are typically made up of simple building blocks with a repeated linkage and are larger than oligosaccharides. Often these molecules act as stores of energy or as a structural matrix for the organism.

Stored sources of energy Plants use sugar for energy and store this sugar as starch. This starch can be found in roots and rhizomes underground, as in potatoes, or in grains like wheat or rice. Starch takes several different forms.

Amylose is a linear polymer of several hundred to several thousand glucose monomers linked by α-1,4 glycosidic bonds. It adopts a helical shape, but it can also form several other higher order structures. Amylose is relatively insoluble in water.

Amylopectin is a branched polymer of several thousand to several hundred thousand glucose monomers with α-1,4 linkages, with a branch point (linked α-1,6) about every 24–30 residues along the main chain. Because amylopectin is branched, it has numerous ends from which enzymes can degrade it. Hence, glucose monomers can be released from amylopectin more quickly than from amylose.

Häggström, Mikael (2014). "Medical gallery of Mikael Häggström 2014". Wiki Journal of Medicine 1 (2). DOI:10.15347/wjm/2014.008. ISSN 2002-4436.

Amylose

Amylopectin or glycogen

Glycogen and glycogenin

Amylose helical structure

Due to its linear nature, amylose, which composes up to 30% of the mass of starch, is harder to metabolize than amylopectin, the other component. Amylases, the enzymes responsible for breaking down amylose, can only attack the molecule from one end, cleaving either single glucose molecules or glucose dimers (maltose) from the molecule.

Differences in the ratio of amylose to amylopectin result in different forms of starch with different properties that are noticeable in food. This explains why some varieties of potato are good for baking and others are good for salads, and why some varieties of rice are good for sushi while others are good for risotto.

Glycogen is the storage form of carbohydrate in animals. Like amylopectin it is a highly branched polymer of glucose with α-1,4 and α-1,6 linkages, but the molecules differ in several important aspects. First, glycogen is generally larger than amylopectin: a single molecule of glycogen can be composed of several tens of thousands of glucose monomers. Second, glycogen is branched at every 6–12 glucose residues instead of every 24–30. This creates even more branch points and results in a molecule that can be rapidly degraded, mobilizing glucose molecules for energy. Third, a glycogen granule has a protein molecule (glycogenin) at its core.

Glycogen is found in granules in the cytosol of cells. Although low levels of glycogen are found in the kidneys and the intestine, the main glycogen stores in animals are in the liver and skeletal muscle. The liver has the highest concentration of glycogen (at least 10% of tissue weight), whereas muscle has only 1%–2%. However, because overall there is much more muscle by weight, muscles contain more than double the mass of glycogen in liver.

Glycogen serves as a reservoir to moderate levels of plasma glucose. When plasma glucose levels drop, liver glycogen is mobilized to provide energy for tissues and cells in need. Chief among these are erythrocytes and the cells of the brain.

Structural polysaccharides

There are numerous examples of secreted carbohydrates that different organisms use to provide structure or to act as an extracellular matrix (**Figure 6.9**).

Cellulose is a structural polysaccharide found in plants. It is the most abundant biological molecule on Earth. Cotton is nearly 90% cellulose fiber by mass. It is similar to amylose in that it consists of linear polymers of hundreds to thousands of glucose monomers connected via a 1,4 linkage. However, the linkage in cellulose is β, rather than the α linkage found in amylose. This has significant ramifications for the structure and reactivity of cellulose. Cellulose forms extended chains (in contrast to the helical structure found in amylose). Due to the orientations of the numerous hydroxyl groups on the cellulose, there are many places where hydrogen bonding can occur between chains, forming strong interactions between aligned adjacent polymers, thus giving this material its tough fiber-like characteristics.

The β linkage imparts other properties to cellulose. As with most animals, humans lack a β-glucosidase and are thus unable to digest cellulose. Some animals, notably ruminants such as cows, goats, and sheep; hind-gut fermenters including horses and turtles; lagomorphs (rabbits); and some insects, such as termites, harbor bacteria in their gut that can break down the cellulose found in grass or wood, releasing glucose, which the host organism can absorb.

Cellulose is not a source of human food, but it is a by-product of most food production. Concerns about the availability of petrochemicals and the environmental impact of burning petrochemicals has resulted in efforts focused on developing cellulosic ethanol—ethanol biochemically derived from cellulose. Current research in the United States is concentrating on these by-products (husks of corn, wheat, and rice) or on other crops that grow quickly and with minimal input (such as switch grass). Currently, ethanol production plays a small but important part in the U.S. energy strategy. Using ethanol in place of gasoline is feasible. Brazil fuels most of its vehicles with ethanol. However, using ethanol presents some engineering challenges. Unlike diesel vehicles, which can use either traditional or biodiesel, ethanol-fueled vehicles need to be built with fuel systems designed to handle the more hydrophilic ethanol. Ethanol has been seen as a "green" energy source that does not increase atmospheric CO_2, but the current form of production of ethanol is not truly clean. The CO_2 that was fixed in the cellulose of a plant grown last summer and converted to ethanol is released back into the atmosphere when the fuel is burned. Additionally, there are concerns that diverting a food crop (corn) to ethanol production results in higher food prices.

Chitin is a structural carbohydrate found in the cell wall of fungi and in the exoskeleton of arthropods such as insects and crustaceans. Chemically similar to cellulose, chitin is made of β-1,4 linked polymers of *N*-Acetylglucosamine rather than glucose. Due to the added *N*-Acetyl group, this molecule can more easily form hydrogen bonds between strands; hence, it has greater strength than other polysaccharides. Chitin is slow to break down in nature, and accumulation of chitin waste is a concern at seafood processing plants. Several commercial products are now made from chitin or its derivatives, including sutures, wound dressings for burn victims, and dietary supplements.

A. Cellulose

β-1,4 linkage

Glucose polymer

Martin Ruegner/Getty Images

B. Chitin

β-1,4 linkage

N-Acetyl group

N-Acetylglucosamine polymer

Cyndi Monaghan/ Getty Images

C. Alginate

β-1,5 linkage

Guluronate and mannuronate copolymer

Daniel Poloha Underwater/ AlamyStock Photo

D. Cross-linking in alginate

FIGURE 6.9 **Structures of cellulose, chitin, and alginate.** Shown are the repeating units of the structural carbohydrates **A.** cellulose, **B.** chitin, and **C.** alginate. Note how these molecules can cross-link with one another through hydrogen bonding (A, B, or C) or **D.** electrostatic interactions with a bridging metal ion.

Alginate is a structural polysaccharide found in the cell walls of brown algae and kelp. Unlike the other polysaccharides discussed here, alginate is a **copolymer**: a combination of two monomeric units. In the case of alginate, these monomers are guluronate and mannuronate (the deprotonated forms of guluronic and mannuronic acid). These molecules are themselves the enzymatically oxidized forms of gulose and mannose, with carboxyl moieties found on the number 6 carbon of each. The resulting alginate polymer is highly anionic and readily absorbs water, one of its most notable properties. Alginate is commercially used as a diet aid, food thickener, and absorbent owing to its ability to absorb water.

Having numerous negative charges, alginate will react with cations, particularly Ca^{2+} ions. The strands of alginate become linked, resulting in the formation of a gel. The food and beverage industry is now creating pearls or spheres of food or drink encased in a thin layer of alginate: a novel application of polysaccharide chemistry.

WORKED PROBLEM 6.3 | The properties of a polysaccharide

Pectins are a family of structural polysaccharides found in fruit. While there is considerable variability among pectins, most consist of a D-1,4 linked galacturonic acid (with methanol esterified to the carboxyl group in some cases). Pectins can be classified as high ester or low ester, depending on the degree of esterification. They will form gels (highly hydrated networks of carbohydrate and water) and are used as gelling agents in the production of jams, jellies, and candy. Both high- and low-ester pectins can be used in this process, with different pectins used in different applications. Based on your knowledge of polysaccharides and the descriptions of pectins provided, describe the forces that are involved in gelling high- and low-ester pectins.

Strategy Think about the structures of pectin. How does the structure and what you know of other polysaccharides fit with the observations in the question?

Solution Both high- and low-ester pectins are capable of inter-strand hydrogen bonding. Low-ester pectin also has a greater number of carboxyl groups that can bind to metal ions. In the case of divalent metal ions, such as Ca^{2+}, this can lead to bridging between strands of pectin (increasing the ability to gel). Hence, the ability to gel depends on both the metal ion content and the pH of the sample.

Follow-up question Acetylated pectins are also found in nature. These varieties fail to act as gelling agents. Propose a chemical reason why this is so.

6.2 Summary

- Monosaccharides can be joined to form disaccharides, trisaccharides, oligosaccharides, and polysaccharides.
- The acetal or ketal linkage formed between monosaccharide units can be described based on the positions of the carbons involved in the bond.
- Polysaccharides often serve as stores of energy or provide structure for an organism.
- The properties of complex carbohydrates are based on the monomeric units (glucose or galactose) and the connection between those units (β-1,4).

6.2 Concept Check

- Name and describe at the chemical level several different examples of disaccharides, trisaccharides, oligosaccharides, and polysaccharides.
- Describe the biochemical function of these molecules.
- Explain how the structure of these molecules contributes to their function.
- Explain how these molecules are similar to one another or to other biological molecules, and how they are different.

6.3 | Glycolysis and an Introduction to Metabolic Pathways

FIGURE 6.10 Overview of metabolic pathways. Any metabolic pathway consists of intermediates (A, B, C, D, and F) converted to one another by enzymes (E1, E2, E3). Some steps may be reversible, others may not. Pathways may branch or be linear.

This section discusses the breakdown of glucose into pyruvate, a process called **glycolysis**. In this pathway, as in any metabolic pathway, a small molecule (a metabolite) is transformed into a different molecule through a series of enzymatic reactions (**Figure 6.10**). This section describes what is meant by a metabolic pathway and some general themes to look for in any pathway, as well as how to apply this information to a discussion of glycolysis.

Because glycolysis is a catabolic pathway, one that breaks molecules down, the process is oxidative, and thus the final products are more oxidized than the starting materials. This means that the overall process gives off energy. However, glycolysis requires an initial energetic investment to initiate the process.

6.3.1 ## Metabolic pathways describe how molecules are built up or broken down

The sum total of all the chemical reactions in an organism constitutes that organism's metabolism. These reactions can be classified as **anabolic** (buildup molecules) or **catabolic** (breakdown molecules). The molecules in question are small organic molecules generically known as **metabolites**. They include amino acids, carbohydrates, lipids, and nucleotides, and other small molecules that fit somewhere in between these four groups. As a general rule, the overall breakdown of a metabolite yields energy and is oxidative, whereas reactions that build up metabolites require an input of energy and are reductive.

Some of the reactions that enzymes employ may not look familiar at first, but once examined, they reveal themselves to be reactions first encountered in organic chemistry. An example of this is the retro aldol condensation. A review of the retro aldol condensation from organic chemistry and its applications in biochemistry are found in **Biochemistry: The retro aldol reaction**.

Biochemistry

The retro aldol reaction

The controlled and direct formation or cleavage of carbon–carbon bonds presents an interesting conundrum in biochemistry. Given the sheer number of carbon–carbon bonds in nature, it might seem as though these bonds could form in many different ways, but that is not the case. In reality, there are relatively few ways to make or break carbon–carbon bonds. This box discusses the aldol reaction, a key reaction of glycolysis and gluconeogenesis. (This reaction is related to the Claisen condensation, found in organic chemistry.)

Aldols, as the name suggests, are organic molecules containing a carbonyl group such as an aldehyde with a hydroxyl moiety β to the carbonyl. Aldols are formed by the addition of one aldehyde to another:

The aldol (a β-hydroxy aldehyde) can then undergo elimination to form an enone. That reaction is known as an aldol condensation, and water is eliminated in the reaction.

In the organic laboratory, an aldol can be made via either an acid- or base-catalyzed mechanism:

The reverse reaction is a retro-aldol reaction, which results in bond cleavage:

The β-hydroxyl is deprotonated.

Resulting in collapse of the alkoxide, and reformation of the carbonyl.

This leads to loss of the enolate.

In biochemistry, retro-aldol reactions are central to the cleavage of F-1,6-bP in the fourth step of glycolysis, and to the reverse reaction in gluconeogenesis.

If we examine the Fischer projection of F-1,6-bP, we see that it fits the definition of an aldol.

The enzymes that carry out these reactions are known as aldolases, and they employ a Schiff base in carrying out this chemistry. A Schiff base is simply a carbon–nitrogen double bond in which the nitrogen is also bound to one other carbon.

The Schiff base forms between the carbonyl carbon of F-1, 6-bP, and a lysine side chain in the active site of the aldolase. In the retro-aldol cleavage, the Schiff base acts as an electron sink, assisting in electron withdrawal and cleavage of the α–β carbon–carbon bond; the positive charge on this Schiff base makes it drive the reaction to an even greater extent. In the laboratory, the enolate that forms on the carbon α to the carbonyl is stabilized by tautomerism and resonance. Although the reaction may look different, similar chemistry, such as the stabilization of the enolate, is occurring with the Schiff base.

1. F-1,6-bP substrate binds. Lysine forms Schiff base with carbonyl.

2. Aspartate deprotonates hydroxyl. Electrons flow into Schiff base.

Glyceraldehyde-3-phosphate
(product 1)

Some metabolic pathways appear to be linear, but most are actually branched. For example, there may be places along a pathway where other metabolites can enter or leave, or where metabolites from other pathways can regulate the initial pathway. Frequently, the interconnections of these metabolic pathways are depicted as a complex roadmap that includes hundreds or thousands of reactions and their interconnections. Metabolic pathways divide the process of conversion from one molecule to another into discrete steps. Multiple steps provide added places where a pathway can be controlled.

Metabolic pathways are regulated in multiple ways, including:

- The expression of genes encoding for the enzymes and other proteins involved in the pathway can be upregulated or downregulated, leading to higher or lower levels of enzymes.
- Genes coding for enzymes may be differentially expressed in one tissue over another, for example, liver versus muscle, leading to specialized functions for these tissues.
- Inside the cell itself there may be compartmentalization of processes such as those that occur in cytosol versus in mitochondria. This allows pathways with reciprocal functions to operate in the same cell.
- Key enzymes in pathways can be regulated via post-translational modification, for example, through the addition or loss of a phosphate group.
- Many enzymes in metabolism are allosterically regulated by small molecules, some of which have very different structures from the substrates and products of the reaction being catalyzed.
- Many reactions have a ΔG value that is close to zero; thus, the direction of the reaction is easily reversed by changing the levels of substrate or product.

Glucose

Pyruvate

Acetyl-CoA

Glycolosis   Gluconeogenesis

Fatty acid synthesis
or ATP generation

FIGURE 6.11 **Pyruvate in
metabolism.** Glucose and other
monosaccharides are catabolized through
glycolysis into pyruvate. Pyruvate can
be decarboxylated and enter the citric
acid cycle, producing other metabolic
intermediates or contributing to ATP
production.

Thermodynamics govern the direction and favorability of reactions in metabolism, and reactions only proceed downhill energetically. The best term for discussing the favorability of these reactions is Gibbs free energy, ΔG. Often, in metabolism, reactions are coupled, with an energetically favorable reaction making an unfavorable reaction favorable. An example of this is the addition of a phosphate group to a molecule. If the phosphate reactant were a free phosphate anion (HPO_4^{2-}) in solution, it would be energetically unfavorable to add that phosphate to an alcohol group, such as a serine or threonine side chain. Hence, this type of reaction does not occur. However, if that phosphate is donated in a reaction from a donor with a greater transfer potential, such as ATP, the overall reaction can proceed favorably with a negative ΔG value.

6.3.2 Glycolysis is the process by which glucose is broken into pyruvate

Glycolysis is the process used by almost all organisms to break down glucose into a three-carbon metabolite called **pyruvate** (**Figure 6.11**). The process provides energy to the organism in terms of both ATP and NADH/H$^+$, but also provides entry points for other molecules, such as fructose and glycerol, to be metabolized. The end-product, pyruvate, is often oxidized into acetyl-CoA and moves on to the citric acid cycle to provide even more energy. This same pyruvate can, however, be used to synthesize new amino acids or new molecules of glucose in other tissues, or it can be converted into acetyl-CoA and reduced into fatty acids. Clearly, glycolysis has a number of different functions.

The fact that glycolysis is found in almost all organisms from *E. coli* to humans indicates that this pathway has been in use for billions of years. Because of its central importance to metabolism, there are relatively few inherited mutations associated with glycolysis. Any major mutations would be extremely harmful to the organism.

Reactions of glycolysis   The glycolytic pathway is composed of ten reactions, which are generally put into two groupings. In the first five reactions of the pathway, energy in the form of two molecules of ATP needs to be "invested" in glucose. This investment energetically primes the energy-yielding reactions that occur in the last five reactions. This situation is analogous to a roller coaster in that the initial investment of energy (towing the train of cars to the top of a hill) provides the energy for the remaining trip.

The steps of glycolysis, shown in **Figure 6.12**, are as follows:

1. **Glucose is phosphorylated to glucose-6-phosphate, trapping it in the cell and maintaining a concentration gradient.** In the first step, glucose is phosphorylated on C-6 (the carbon outside the ring) to form glucose-6-phosphate. One molecule of ATP is consumed in this reaction. Because glucose-6-phosphate has a charge associated with it and a different structure than glucose, this molecule is unable to pass back through the glucose transporter and is thus trapped within the cell. This helps maintain a gradient of glucose, facilitating the diffusion of glucose into the cell.

    The enzyme responsible for catalyzing this reaction is one of several isoforms of the enzyme hexokinase. We might ask why multiple enzymes can be used to catalyze this reaction. The answer has to do with the properties of these enzymes and regulation of glucose metabolism in different tissues (such as the liver versus muscle) and at different metabolic states (for example, immediately after eating).

2. **Glucose-6-phosphate is isomerized to fructose-6-phosphate, generating a free hydroxyl group on the number 1 carbon for subsequent reactions.** Fructose is an isomer of

Energy investment stage

1. Glucose is phosphorylated to glucose-6-phosphate, trapping it in the cell and maintaining a concentration gradient.

2. Glucose-6-phosphate is isomerized to fructose-6-phosphate, generating a free hydroxyl group on the 1 carbon for subsequent reactions.

3. Fructose-6-phosphate is phosphorylated to fructose-1,6-bisphosphate, priming the molecule for subsequent cleavage.

4. Fructose-1,6-bisphosphate is cleaved into glyceraldehyde-3-phosphate and dihydroxyacetonephosphate.

5. Dihydroxyacetonephosphate is isomerized to glyceraldehyde-3-phosphate, ensuring that all carbons of glucose are available for oxidation.

Energy yielding stage

6. The 1 carbon of glyceraldehyde-3 phosphate is oxidized to a carboxyl group and phosphorylated with free phosphate to generate a molecule of NADH/H+ and 1,3-bisphosphoglycerate.

7. 1,3-bisphosphoglycerate transfers a phosphate from the 1 carbon to ADP making ATP and generating 3-phosphoglycerate.

8. 3-phosphoglycerate is isomerized to 2-phosphoglycerate, facilitating the subsequent dehydration of the 3 carbon.

9. 2-phosphoglycerate is dehydrated to generate phosphoenolpyruvate.

10. Phosphoenolpyruvate transfers its phosphate to ADP making ATP. The dephosphorylated enol tautomerizes to a keto group.

Pyruvate has multiple fates in the cell.

FIGURE 6.12 **Reactions of glycolysis.** There are ten reactions in glycolysis. The first five are the investment stage, and the final five are where energy is yielded.

glucose. In the second reaction, G-6-P is isomerized to F-6-P by phosphoglucose isomerase. The formation of F-6-P facilitates subsequent phosphorylation and cleavage reactions.

3. **Fructose-6-phosphate is phosphorylated to fructose-1,6-bisphosphate, priming the molecule for subsequent cleavage.** Fructose-6-phosphate undergoes another round of phosphorylation, this time on the newly exposed C-1. This process, catalyzed by phosphofructokinase (PFK), is also ATP dependent and generates the product fructose-1,6-bisphosphate.

4. **Fructose-1,6-bisphosphate is cleaved into glyceraldehyde-3-phosphate and dihydroxyacetone phosphate.** In this step, the hexose fructose-1,6-bisphosphate is cleaved by aldolase in a retro aldol reaction into two 3-carbon intermediates: an aldehyde (glyceraldehyde-3-phosphate) and a ketone (dihydroxyacetone phosphate). Both of these triose phosphate intermediates are used as glycolysis proceeds (**Figure 6.13**).

The mechanism of aldolase employs a Schiff base. This structure, which is used in several enzyme mechanisms, forms when a primary amine attacks a carbonyl carbon. The result is a carbon with a double bond to a nitrogen. In aldolase, a protonated Schiff base forms. This acts as an electron sink, withdrawing electrons from adjacent bonds and facilitating bond cleavage, in this case between the α and β carbons. Following bond cleavage, electron flow reverses out of the sink, resulting in protonation of the remaining

1. Fructose-1,6-bisphosphate binds.

2. Amine reacts with carbonyl to form protonated Schiff base.

3. Hydroxyl beta to the Schiff base is deprotonated. Electrons flow into the protonated Schiff base, cleaving the aldol in the process. The first product (GAP) leaves.

Glyceraldehyde-3-phosphate

4. Electron flow reverses out of the Schiff base and into the enamine intermediate. The carbon reprotonates.

5. The Schiff base is hydrolyzed regenerating the carbonyl and releasing the second product (DHAP).

Dihydroxyacetone phosphate

FIGURE 6.13 **The mechanism of aldolase.** The aldol cleavage reaction begins with the formation of a Schiff base intermediate on C-2 of F-1,6-bP. Following deprotonation of the hydroxyl on the β carbon, the Schiff base acts as an electron sink, withdrawing electrons and facilitating bond cleavage between the α and β carbons.

product. Hydrolysis of the Schiff base forms the new carbonyl and regenerates the free amine form of the enzyme.

5. **Dihydroxyacetone phosphate is isomerized to glyceraldehyde-3-phosphate, ensuring that all carbons of glucose are available for oxidation.** The remainder of the pathway proceeds with only glyceraldehyde-3-phosphate. Keto groups are unable to be oxidized further, and therefore dihydroxyacetone phosphate cannot be oxidized via the same pathway as GAP. Instead, DHAP is isomerized into GAP in a reaction that involves an enediol intermediate and is catalyzed by triose phosphate isomerase (TIM) (**Figure 6.14**). In this mechanism, DHAP is bound in the active site between two key residues: a deprotonated glutamate and a histidine. Abstraction of a proton from the carbon bearing the free hydroxyl results in electron flow into the carbon–carbon bond, forming a new double bond and causing protonation of the old carbonyl oxygen. This molecule containing both a double bond and two adjacent hydroxyl groups is called an *enediol*. In the final step of the mechanism, reversal of electron flow causes deprotonation of the terminal hydroxyl generating the new aldehyde found in the final product.

Glyceraldehyde 3-phosphate
+
Dihydroxyacetone phosphate

5 triose phosphate isomerase (TIM)

converts

Both molecules of GAP, the one coming from the aldol cleavage and the one resulting from the isomerization of DHAP, continue through glycolysis.

1. Substrate binds. Glutamate deprotonates carbon, resulting in enediol formation.

2. Enzyme changes conformation. Histidine deprotonates primary alcohol.

3. Electrons flow back the through a double bond into aspartate to generate aldehyde product.

FIGURE 6.14 **The mechanism of triose phosphate isomerase.** In this mechanism, the isomerization of DHAP to GAP proceeds through an enediol intermediate stabilized through the pyrolic nitrogen of the histidine ring. Both molecules of GAP, the one coming from the aldol cleavage and the one resulting from this reaction (the isomerization of DHAP), continue through glycolysis.

Therefore, from one 6-carbon glucose molecule we generate two 3-carbon intermediates (DHAP and GAP) and the DHAP is converted into a second molecule of GAP, which proceeds through the second phase of glycolysis.

This is the end of the investment phase of glycolysis. To summarize, in this phase glucose is absorbed by the cell, phosphorylated, isomerized, phosphorylated again, and cleaved; the resulting fragments are isomerized to yield two molecules of GAP. The cost is two molecules of ATP. During the second phase of glycolysis (the energy-yielding stage) the cell regains energy expended in the first phase.

6. **The number 1 carbon of glyceraldehyde-3 phosphate is oxidized to a carboxyl group and phosphorylated with free phosphate to generate a molecule of NADH/H$^+$ and 1, 3-bisphosphoglycerate.** In this step, C-2 of GAP is oxidized from a hydroxyl to a keto group (**Figure 6.15**). This process yields one molecule of NADH/H$^+$. In addition, a phosphoester is formed on C-1 of the molecule. Inorganic phosphate (HPO_4^{2-}) is used in this reaction.

Some aspects of the mechanism of glyceraldehyde-3-phosphate dehydrogenase may look familiar to you. As substrate binds, a base assists in the deprotonation and nucleophilic attack on the carbonyl carbon of the substrate. We have seen similar chemistry in the mechanism of chymotrypsin, but here the nucleophile is the thiolate anion generated by deprotonating cysteine. This results in the formation of a thiohemiacetal intermediate, again analogous to the tetrahedral oxyanion intermediate observed in chymotrypsin. At this point the mechanisms differ. Electrons from the thiohemiacetal intermediate are transferred to NAD$^+$, resulting in the formation of a covalently bound acyl thioester. The reduced NADH is exchanged for a new molecule of NAD$^+$. The mechanism resolves and the enzyme is regenerated through the attack of a phosphate ion on the thioester carbon. In chymotrypsin, water

1. Substrate binds.

2. Carbonyl of GAP is attacked by cysteine, forming thiohemiacetal.

3. Thiohemiacetal is oxidized to a thioester by NAD⁺.

4. Thioester intermediate.

5. Phosphate binds and attacks thioester. Product (1,3-bPG) is released; NAD⁺ exchanges for NADH regenerating enzyme.

1,3-bisphospho-glycerate (1,3-bPG)

FIGURE 6.15 **The mechanism of glyceraldehyde-3-phosphate dehydrogenase.** In the mechanism of glyceraldehyde-3-phosphate dehydrogenase, the binding of substrate (glyceraldehyde-3-phosphate) causes nucleophilic attack of the active site cysteine on the carbonyl carbon, resulting in the formation of a thiohemiacetal intermediate. Electrons from this unstable intermediate are transferred to NAD⁺, resulting in the formation of an acyl thioester intermediate. The reduced NADH is exchanged for a new molecule of NAD⁺ and phosphate attacks the thioester, regenerating the enzyme and releasing 1,3-bisphosphoglycerate.

was used to attack the acyl-enzyme intermediate and regenerate the free hydroxyl found in the active site serine. Thioesters are considerably less stable than their oxygen-containing counterparts and have a strongly negative ΔG of hydrolysis. This thermodynamically drives the reaction and generates the 1,3-bisphosphoglycerate product.

This reaction is the first example of NAD⁺ used in a reaction (**Figure 6.16**). NAD⁺ is a small organic molecule (nicotinamide adenine dinucleotide) that is used by biological systems as an electron acceptor. NAD⁺ will accept two electrons and a proton (the chemical equivalent of a hydride) to form NADH. A second proton accompanies NADH, balancing out the charge of the reaction. The pair is cited as NADH/H⁺ in the reduced state.

7. 1,3-bisphosphoglycerate (1,3-bPG) transfers a phosphate from the number one carbon to ADP, making ATP and generating 3-phosphoglycerate. In this step, phosphoglycerate kinase removes a phosphate from 1,3-bPG and transfers it to ADP to create a molecule of ATP. This is a substrate-level phosphorylation, the direct formation of a nucleotide triphosphate by a coupled reaction, rather than an oxidative phosphorylation as seen in mitochondria. It may seem odd that a kinase removes a phosphate, but this enzyme also can remain true to its name: in the presence of phosphoglycerate and ATP it will generate 1,3-bPG and ADP. This is an example of how an enzyme lowers the activation energy and enhances

Oxidized: NAD⁺

Nicotinamide
Ribose
2P
Adenosine

$+ H^+$
$+ 2 e^-$

Reduced: NADH

Ribose
2P
Adenosine

$$NAD^+ + H^+ + 2\,e^- \rightleftharpoons NADH$$

FIGURE 6.16 **Numerous molecules participate in redox chemistry in biochemistry.** NAD⁺ is a small redox active organic molecule that is a critical cofactor in many enzymatic reactions. Electrons transferred to NAD⁺ are used in subsequent reactions, such as the electron transport chain.

the rate of both the forward and the reverse reaction. As we will see in gluconeogenesis, this reaction also highlights how altering the concentrations of substrate and product can alter the reaction quotient Q and tip the free energy of a reaction, ΔG, to the negative.

8. 3-phosphoglycerate is isomerized to 2-phosphoglycerate, facilitating the subsequent dehydration of C-3. This reaction is catalyzed by phosphoglycerate mutase (**Figure 6.17**) and proceeds through a phosphoenzyme intermediate (2,3-bPG), coupled via a histidine residue. As with most isomerizations seen in metabolism, this neither costs nor provides energy.

Mutase catalyzes the isomerization of 2-phosphoglycerate to 3-phosphoglycerate. Exchange of a phosphate between C-2 or C-3 and the active site histidine results in the formation of 2, 3-bisphosphoglycerate, an intermediate in this reaction and an important regulator of hemoglobin.

FIGURE 6.17 **The mechanism of mutase.** Mutase catalyzes the isomerization of 2-phosphoglycerate to 3-phosphoglycerate. Exchange of a phosphate between C-2 or C-3 and the active site histidine results in the formation of 2,3-bisphosphoglycerate (an intermediate in this reaction and an important regulator of hemoglobin).

9. 2-phosphoglycerate (2-PG) is dehydrated to generate phosphoenolpyruvate (PEP). In this reaction, the hydroxyl group from C-3 is removed by enolase to give the dehydrated form. We often think of ATP as being readily able to transfer a phosphate and participate in chemical reactions because the hydrolysis of the phosphate has a large, negative ΔG value; however, the phosphate bond in PEP has an even more negative ΔG of hydrolysis and can easily transfer this phosphate group to ADP to form ATP in the next step (**Table 6.2**).

(2) 2-phosphoglycerate (2PG)

(2) $HO-CH_2-\overset{\overset{\displaystyle ^{-2}O_3P-O}{|}}{\underset{\underset{\displaystyle H}{|}}{C}}-C\overset{\displaystyle O^-}{\underset{\displaystyle O}{\diagup}}$

9 enolase

H_2O

(2) Phosphoenolpyruvate (PEP)

(2) $CH_2=\overset{\overset{\displaystyle ^{-2}O_3P-O}{|}}{C}-C\overset{\displaystyle O^-}{\underset{\displaystyle O}{\diagup}}$

TABLE 6.2	Standard Free Energies of Hydrolysis of Some Molecules with a High Phosphate Transfer Potential (Strongly Negative $\Delta G^{\circ\prime}$ of Hydrolysis)	
Intermediate	**kJ/mol**
Phosphoenolpyruvate	−61.9
1, 3–bisphosphoglycerate to 3-phosphoglycerate + Pi	−49.3
Phosphocreatine	−43.0
ATP to AMP and PPi	−45.6
ADP to AMP and Pi	−32.8
Acetyl-CoA	−31.4
ATP to ADP and Pi	−30.5
Glucose-3-phosphate	−20.9
PPi to 2 Pi	−19.2
Fructose-6-phosphate	−15.9
AMP to adenosine and Pi	−14.2
Glucose-6-phosphate	−13.8
Glycerol-3-phosphate	−9.2

10. Phosphoenolpyruvate (PEP) transfers its phosphate to ADP, making ATP. The dephosphorylated enol tautomerizes to a keto group. In this reaction, catalyzed by pyruvate kinase, PEP is converted to the three-carbon α-keto acid pyruvate. Again, in this process, a molecule of ATP is generated via substrate-level phosphorylation.

Step 10 marks the end of the energy-yielding phase of glycolysis. Because two 3-carbon intermediates were generated in the energy-investment phase, and pass through steps 6–10, the payoff phase generates two molecules of NADH/H$^+$ in step 6 and four molecules of ATP, two in step 7 and two in step 10. Overall, given that two molecules of ATP were used in the investment phase of glycolysis, and two molecules of NADH/H$^+$ and four molecules of ATP were generated in the payoff phase, each round of this metabolic pathways provides a net gain of two NADH/H$^+$ and two ATP.

Energetics of glycolysis
The relative free energies of reaction for each of the steps of the glycolytic pathway are shown in **Figure 6.18**. Upon analyzing the relative values and

FIGURE 6.18 **Energetics of glycolysis.** **A.** In the standard state six of the steps of glycolysis are energetically unfavorable and would proceed in the reverse direction. **B.** Due to the concentrations of metabolites found in the cell, these reactions proceed favorably with much lower ΔG values.

signs of these reactions, some patterns begin to emerge. Steps where energy is invested, such as where molecules of ATP are expended, have strong negative $\Delta G^{\circ\prime}$ values, indicating spontaneous reactions under standard state conditions. These reactions are driven by the reactions of intermediates that can readily transfer a phosphate group, such as ATP, 1,3-bPG, or PEP. Isomerization reactions typically have $\Delta G^{\circ\prime}$ values close to zero, indicating that these reactions are near equilibrium in the standard state.

In the cell, these reactions (especially the concentrations of the reactants) are *not* found in standard state conditions. Also, changing the concentrations of reactants changes the ΔG of a reaction, making a reaction favorable that would normally be unfavorable. This is vividly illustrated in the fourth step of glycolysis, in which F-1,6-bP is cleaved to DHAP and GAP. Under standard state conditions, $\Delta G^{\circ\prime}$ has a strong positive value (23 kJ/mol), indicating that this reaction proceeds strongly in the reverse direction, favoring F-1,6-bP. However, in a cell undergoing glycolysis, the concentrations of F-1,6-bP, DHAP, and GAP are such that the reaction proceeds in the forward direction ($\Delta G = -0.23$ kJ/mol).

Free energies (ΔG values) can be used to predict *favorability* or *direction* of a reaction, but they have no bearing on the *rate* of a reaction (how quickly it proceeds). Several reactions of glycolysis, most notably the isomerization of DHAP to GAP, are near equilibrium in the cell, but they proceed at rates near the upper limit of enzymatic reactions.

Regulation of glycolysis: an overview

Metabolic pathways can be thought of as being analogous to a factory. If we wanted to control how fast the assembly line is going, we could do this in several ways. We could control how much material comes into the assembly line, or we could control how much leaves at the other end, causing backups. Alternatively, we could try to control the process through the slower or irreversible steps of the assembly. Thus, if one step takes longer than the other steps, it may be an ideal place to control the entire process.

The situation in the factory is similar to that of a metabolic pathway. Three different steps in glycolysis (steps 1, 3, and 10) are committed steps or irreversible steps, both good places to control flux through a pathway (**Figure 6.19**). Glycolysis is regulated to some extent at each of these points. Multiple control points allow different metabolites to enter the pathway at different places, for example, glucose coming from outside the cell or glucose-1-phosphate derived from glycogen. Hexokinases regulate the phosphorylation of glucose and entry into glycolysis. The major enzymes that are regulated in the glycolytic pathway are phosphofructokinase and pyruvate kinase. They each provide some measure of regulation, depending on the tissue and metabolic state in question, and each can be regulated in several different ways. Enzyme activity can be modulated by post-translational modifications, such as phosphorylations. Shorter-term regulation can be accomplished through allosteric regulators, whereas changes in the expression of a gene coding for an enzyme can account for longer-term changes in the flux or flow of metabolites through a pathway.

Regulation of glycolysis: hexokinases

Trapping of glucose in the cell and the entry into glycolysis is accomplished by one of several enzymes, generically categorized as hexokinases. In mammals, there are four hexokinase isoforms designated as I, II, III, and IV. The latter is also known as glucokinase. All tissues express at least one of these enzymes. The II isoform is increased in cancer cells and may be partially responsible for the Warburg effect, which is an increased level of glycolysis seen in some tumors.

Hexokinases I, II, and III are almost ubiquitously expressed, and all have a high affinity for glucose at subphysiological concentrations, that is, below 1 mM. The normal range of plasma glucose is 5.0–7.8 mM. These hexokinases are strongly inhibited by the product G-6-P and obey Michaelis–Menten kinetics.

Hexokinase IV (glucokinase) differs from the other isoforms in several ways. First, it is expressed in only a few tissues that regulate carbohydrate metabolism, including the liver, insulin-secreting β cells of the pancreas, and the hypothalamus. Second, it has a far lower affinity for glucose than the other members of the family. Despite being called "glucokinase," hexokinase IV can also phosphorylate other hexoses. Third, it is an allosteric enzyme and therefore does not obey Michaelis–Menten kinetics; however, the active sites in glucokinase are half saturated at approximately 8 mM glucose. Finally, hexokinase IV is not inhibited by the product of the reaction; this enables the pancreatic β cell to use G-6-P as a sensor of plasma glucose, which it uses to trigger insulin secretion. In addition, after meals, the liver uses different levels of hexokinase I and IV to absorb more glucose and store it as glycogen.

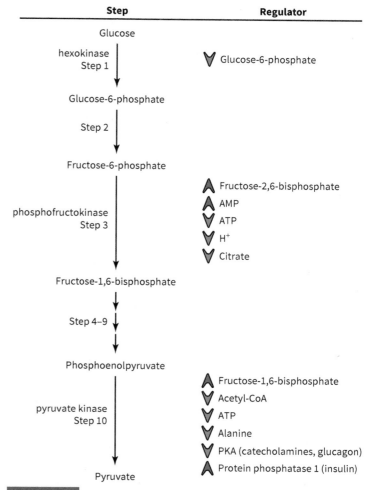

FIGURE 6.19 **Regulation of glycolysis.** The regulation of glycolysis occurs at several points in the pathway and through a variety of mechanisms, including both post-translational modification and allosteric regulation.

Regulation of glycolysis: phosphofructokinase

Phosphofructokinase (PFK) which catalyzes the phosphorylation of F-6-P to F-1,6-bP, is the first committed step that is unique to glycolysis. The G-6-P formed in step 1 can alternatively be directed to glycogen biosynthesis, a stored form of carbohydrate. This is also the rate-limiting step of glycolysis, and the key regulatory step. PFK is regulated at the level of gene expression and by allosteric regulators, but not directly by phosphorylation.

PFK is a homotetramer in mammals and has several allosteric regulators. The enzyme has two binding sites for ATP: a catalytic site that is used in the production of F-1,6-bP and a regulatory site. Binding of ATP signals that the cell is in a high-energy state and inhibits the enzyme. In contrast AMP and to some extent ADP can also bind in the regulatory site. Binding of AMP signals that the cell is in a low-energy state and stimulates the enzyme by stabilizing the active (R) conformation.

PFK is also inhibited by low pH. Anaerobic metabolism produces lactic acid, inhibiting PFK; this inhibition stops glycolysis and prevents further accumulation of damaging acidic by-products.

Glycolysis produces precursors for other metabolic pathways, such as the citric acid cycle. High levels of citrate indicate that these precursors are in abundance. Citrate is another inhibitor of PFK.

The strongest activator of PFK is fructose-2,6-bisphosphate (F-2,6-bP), which is not part of glycolysis but is made by a second enzyme, PFK-2 (**Figure 6.20**). When glucose is abundant, F-6-P levels are high. PFK-2 generates F-2,6-bP from F-6-P; in turn, the F-2,6-bP activates PFK. This is an example of **feed forward activation**, a type of regulation where the products of a reaction act to further activate the pathway. PFK-2 is a bifunctional enzyme composed of

FIGURE 6.20 **Regulation of phosphofructokinase-2 (PFK-2).** PFK-2 has both kinase and phosphatase activities. The activity of PFK-2 is regulated by PKA and AMPK.

both the kinase that generates F-2,6-bP and a second domain containing the phosphatase that breaks it down. The switch between these two activities is largely regulated by phosphorylation, mediated by PKA. However, the regulation of this enzyme differs in different tissues. Hormones such as glucagon or epinephrine act to increase levels of cAMP in the liver cell, activating PKA, which in turn phosphorylates PFK-2. Phosphorylation of PFK-2 favors the phosphatase activity of this enzyme, breaking down F-2,6-bP, inhibiting PFK and slowing glycolysis. AMP-dependent protein kinase (AMPK) can phosphorylate a different site in the cardiac and inducible isoforms of PFK-2, increasing kinase activity and leading to increased levels of F-2,6-bP and therefore increased glycolysis. All other isoforms of PFK-2, such as the one found in skeletal muscle, lack the AMPK phosphorylation site and are not thought to be regulated by AMPK.

The Tp53 induced glycolysis and apoptosis regulator (TIGAR) is a multifunctional protein that inhibits glycolysis by acting as a fructose bisphosphatase, reducing cellular levels of both F-2,6-bP and F-1,6-bP. Originally identified as a protein that prevented the development of cancer, TIGAR blunts glycolysis and shuttles monosaccharides toward the pentose phosphate pathway. This lowers reactive oxygen species (ROS) in the cell (oxygen-containing molecules such as hydrogen peroxide that have been implicated in DNA damage). Expression of TIGAR also appears to regulate DNA damage-induced *apoptosis* (programmed cell death), although the mechanism by which TIGAR does this is still unknown. TIGAR is downregulated in some cancers, which may help explain some of the etiology of the Warburg effect.

Regulation of glycolysis: pyruvate kinase

Pyruvate kinase (PK) catalyzes the transformation of PEP into pyruvate in the final step of glycolysis. Isoforms of the enzyme are found in different tissues, but this section focuses on the differences between the liver-specific isoform and those found in other tissues: predominantly skeletal muscle, the brain, and erythrocytes. All of the isoforms are regulated at the level of gene expression, and allosterically by small molecules. The liver isoform is also regulated by phosphorylation.

The liver form of PK is activated by insulin and inhibited by glucagon and epinephrine. All of these hormones act at least partially via a protein kinase A (PKA)-mediated mechanism. For example, glucagon and epinephrine inhibit PK via protein kinase A-mediated phosphorylation. Insulin, in contrast, acts by stimulating phosphodiesterase to decrease levels of cAMP and blunt the action of protein kinase A. Insulin also stimulates phosphoprotein phosphatase I, promoting dephosphorylation of PK, which is also allosterically stimulated by F-1,6-bP. Binding of F-1,6-bP increases the affinity of the PK for its substrate, PEP. PK is also inhibited by ATP, acetyl-CoA, and alanine. When glucose is abundant, levels of F-1,6-bP are high and PK is stimulated; when glucose is scarce, the reaction is inhibited. These molecules increase the rate of conversion of PEP to pyruvate when glycogenic metabolites are high. When there is abundant energy or when there are high levels of alanine, the rate is decreased.

The regulation of the other isoforms of PK is less complicated; they are simply stimulated by F-1,6-bP. This gives the organism a means of differentiating liver metabolism from the rest of the organ systems. When glucose is low and glucagon levels are high, PK and therefore glycolysis will be inhibited in the liver, but not in the other tissues of the body including the brain, erythrocytes, and muscle tissue.

Other molecules also use the glycolytic pathway

Glycolysis is often seen simply as a means of breaking down glucose and generating ATP or pyruvate for subsequent energy production. Although these are important functions of the pathway, there are others. For example, glycolysis provides a pathway for other carbohydrates and glycerol to enter metabolism (**Figure 6.21**). Glucose, like all monosaccharides, is relatively reactive, forming acetal linkages with random hydroxyl groups. In addition, changes in the concentration of glucose can influence the osmolarity of plasma or cytosol. Glycolysis provides a way to regulate and dispose of glucose, minimizing both of these potential problems.

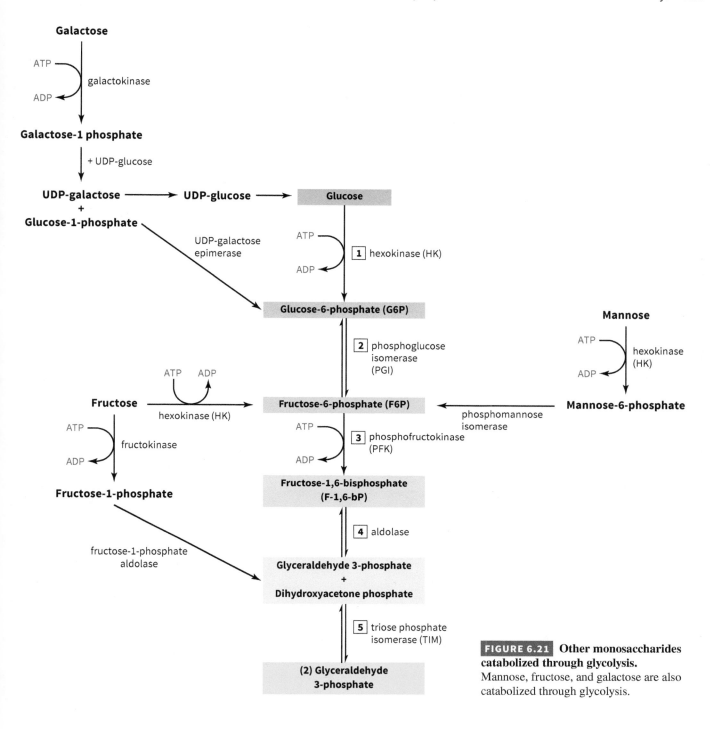

FIGURE 6.21 **Other monosaccharides catabolized through glycolysis.** Mannose, fructose, and galactose are also catabolized through glycolysis.

Galactose is phosphorylated by galactokinase to form galactose-1-phosphate, which then reacts with uridinediphosphate glucose (UDP-glucose) to yield glucose-1-phosphate (G-1-P) and UDP-galactose. The G-1-P released here is used in the final step of the pathway. The enzyme UDP-galactose epimerase catalyzes the isomerization (epimerization) of UDP-galactose to UDP-glucose. This inversion of the stereochemistry at C-4 occurs by first oxidizing the carbon to a planar carbonyl group, followed by reduction of the carbonyl to the new stereochemistry. Finally, phosphoglucomutase isomerizes the G-1-P to G-6-P, where it can enter glycolysis.

Mannose is phosphorylated by hexokinase to form mannose-6-phosphate (M-6-P), which is then acted on by phosphomannose isomerase to form F-6-P. From there, it proceeds through glycolysis.

Fructose is metabolized via one of two different pathways, depending on the tissue in which it occurs. In muscle, fructose is phosphorylated by hexokinase to F-6-P, which can then directly enter glycolysis. In liver, the scenario is somewhat different. Liver has higher levels of glucokinase than hexokinase, and the affinity of glucokinase for fructose is low. Here, fructose is phosphorylated by fructokinase to form F-1-P. However, F-1-P cannot be phosphorylated further and enter glycolysis; rather, it is acted on by an aldolase to yield DHAP and glyceraldehyde. As discussed above, the DHAP is isomerized to GAP by triose phosphate isomerase and enters glycolysis, but the glyceraldehyde generated has several paths it can follow. Glyceraldehyde kinase can phosphorylate the glyceraldehyde to GAP, which can enter glycolysis. Glyceraldehyde can also reenter glycolysis as DHAP. Glyceraldehyde is first reduced to glycerol by alcohol dehydrogenase. The glycerol can be phosphorylated on C-3 by glycerol kinase to form glycerol-3-phosphate, which can be oxidized by glycerol phosphate dehydrogenase to form DHAP. DHAP in turn is isomerized by triose phosphate isomerase to GAP and enters glycolysis. The catabolism of fructose to GAP and entry into glycolysis has recently been referred to as fructolysis by some researchers.

WORKED PROBLEM 6.4 | Glycolysis and galactose?

Imagine that you are studying a novel strain of bacteria that can grow on galactose. You assume that the metabolism of galactose in this strain occurs through glycolysis. Using radiolabeled carbohydrates, design an experiment to show how galactose is being metabolized.

Strategy We need a means of following galactose through metabolism. Using a radiolabeled galactose in which one carbon has been labeled with C^{14} should allow us to trace this molecule as it is metabolized.

Solution Galactose can enter glycolysis through several different pathways. In mammals, galactose is phosphorylated to galactose-1-

phosphate. A uridine monophosphate group is transferred from UDP-glucose to galactose, resulting in UDP-galactose and G-1-P. UDP-galactose is then epimerized to UDP-glucose, which liberates G-1-P as this cyclic pathway continues. If galactose were using a similar pathway to enter glycolysis, we would expect to see the radiolabel accumulate in those pools.

Follow-up question If galactose (rather than glucose) is entering glycolysis, what would be the product?

6.3 Summary

- Metabolic pathways consist of enzymatically catalyzed steps through which molecules are transformed.
- Glycolysis is the pathway through which glucose is converted into two molecules of the three-carbon α-keto acid pyruvate.
- Steps 1 and 3 of glycolysis are energetically possible due to the ability of ATP to donate phosphate groups to glycolytic intermediates.
- F-1,6-bP is cleaved into two 3-carbon intermediates (DHAP and GAP).
- DHAP is isomerized to GAP.
- GAP is changed into pyruvate in the final four steps of the pathway, producing a molecule of ATP in the process.
- Regulation of glycolysis occurs through both gene expression and allosteric regulation.

6.3 Concept Check

- Describe in general what it means for something to be called a metabolic pathway.
- Glycolysis is the breakdown of glucose, but it is also used to metabolize several common monosaccharides.
  - Describe the reactions of glycolysis at the chemical level.
  - Explain the energetics of glycolysis.
  - Explain which steps of glycolysis require energy and which yield energy.
  - Show how the structures and names of the glycolytic intermediates relate to one another.

Gluconeogenesis

The cells and organ systems of the body differ in terms of metabolism. For example, some run almost exclusively on glucose as fuel. These include erythrocytes, the brain, and the central nervous system. During times of fasting or starvation, plasma glucose and glycogen stores may not be able to meet the demands of these organs. To deal with such situations, organisms have evolved the ability to produce glucose from other metabolites—a process known as **gluconeogenesis**.

Not all molecules can be made into glucose. Pyruvate, lactate, glycerol, and some amino acids all contribute to gluconeogenesis (**Figure 6.22**). However, acetyl-CoA cannot undergo this process. Once pyruvate has been decarboxylated to acetyl-CoA, its fate is sealed. It can enter the citric acid cycle, undergo fatty acid biosynthesis, or contribute to ketone body formation, but it cannot form carbohydrates.

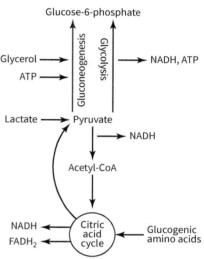

FIGURE 6.22 **Pathways that flow through gluconeogenesis.**   Glucogenic precursors include lactate, pyruvate, glycerol, and glucogenic amino acids.

| 6.4.1 | Gluconeogenesis differs from glycolysis at four reactions

We might expect gluconeogenesis to simply be the glycolytic pathway running in reverse. This is partially the case, but several reactions of glycolysis are energetically unfavorable when running in the reverse direction (**Figure 6.23**). These steps are the formation of glucose-6-phosphate (G-6-P), the formation of fructose-1,6-bisphosphate (F-1,6-bP), and the conversion of phosphoenolpyruvate (PEP) to pyruvate. These are also the most highly regulated steps of glycolysis. Different enzymes catalyze these reactions and couple them to other reactions, overcoming the energetic barriers. Likewise, different pathways for glycolysis and gluconeogenesis are controlled independently of one another: when one is turned on, the other can be turned off. The other reactions of glycolysis have ΔG values close to zero, and thus can be more readily tipped in the forward or reverse direction by modulating the concentrations of substrates or products.

Gluconeogenesis is a biosynthetic pathway, but it is often thought of as occurring during times of fasting, starvation, or in different disease states. As a synthetic pathway, gluconeogenesis requires energy and is in fact rather costly. To synthesize a single molecule of glucose from pyruvate requires six energetic equivalents of ATP (four ATP and two GTP).

Gluconeogenesis occurs predominantly in the liver but also in the cortex of the kidney and small intestine. The glucogenic fuel sources for these tissues vary. Lactate and alanine are used by the liver while lactate and glutamine are used by the kidneys, but the function of providing glucose for tissues in times of need is the same.

Conversion of pyruvate to phosphoenolpyruvate   The first step of gluconeogenesis involves the synthesis of PEP from pyruvate. This two-step process involves two different enzymes. First, pyruvate is converted to oxaloacetate by pyruvate carboxylase; this process occurs in the mitochondria and requires one molecule of ATP. The next step, generation of PEP from oxaloacetate, requires the enzyme phosphoenolpyruvate carboxykinase (PEPCK). A molecule of GTP is expended in this process, and the CO_2 fixed in the first step is lost. The cellular localization of PEPCK varies depending on the species. In humans, the enzyme is found in both mitochondria and cytosol. Specific transporters shuttle PEP out of the mitochondria, but no such transporters exist for oxaloacetate. In species that lack mitochondrial forms of PEPCK, oxaloacetate must first be transaminated into aspartate or reduced into malate, both of which can be transported to cytosol for PEP biosynthesis.

Following the synthesis of PEP, steps 4–9 of glycolysis are reversible and will proceed in the reverse direction if the concentration of glycolytic products exceeds substrates. All these steps (as well as the two remaining steps of gluconeogenesis) occur in the cytosol.

Liberation of glucose   The conversion of F-1,6-bP to F-6-P is carried out by fructose-1,6-bisphosphatase. Like glucose-1-phosphate, glucose-6-phosphate is trapped and unable to leave the cell. The conversion of G-6-P to glucose is catalyzed by glucose-6-phosphatase, an enzyme that is only found in tissues that export glucose for use elsewhere. Liver expresses

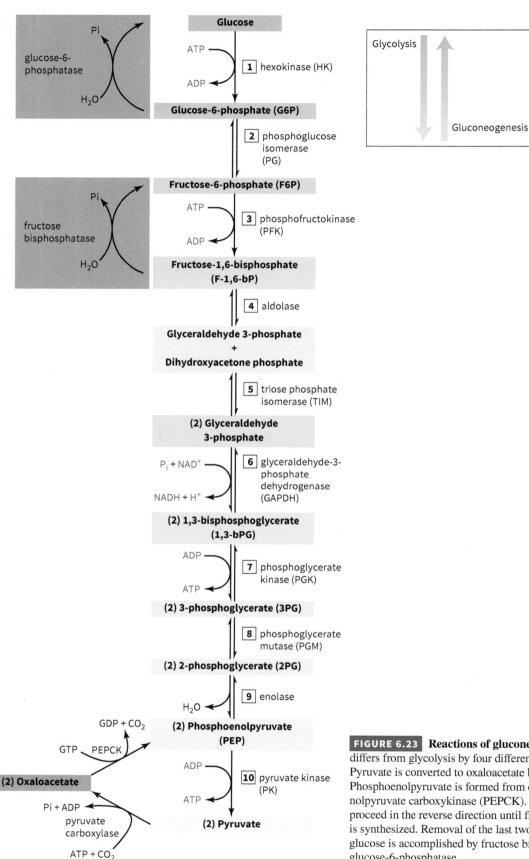

FIGURE 6.23 **Reactions of gluconeogenesis.** Gluconeogenesis differs from glycolysis by four different reactions (three steps). Pyruvate is converted to oxaloacetate by pyruvate carboxylase. Phosphoenolpyruvate is formed from oxaloacetate by phosphoenolpyruvate carboxykinase (PEPCK). The steps of glycolysis now proceed in the reverse direction until fructose-1,6-bisphosphate is synthesized. Removal of the last two phosphates to yield glucose is accomplished by fructose bisphosphatase and glucose-6-phosphatase.

this enzyme; as a result, it releases the glucose synthesized in the liver for use by other tissues (particularly the brain). Muscle lacks this enzyme; as a result, it fixes any G-6-P generated through gluconeogenesis as glycogen.

Glycerol enters gluconeogenesis as DHAP   Glycerol liberated from the breakdown of triacylglycerols is transported in the bloodstream to the liver, where it is metabolized, somewhat like hexoses. First, it is phosphorylated by glycerol kinase to yield glycerol-3-phosphate, which is then oxidized on C-2 to dihydroxyacetone phosphate by glycerol-3-phosphate dehydrogenase, an FAD-dependent enzyme. Triose phosphate isomerase then isomerizes dihydroxyacetone phosphate to glyceraldehyde-3-phosphate. Many other molecules (most notably many amino acids) can also enter gluconeogenesis.

6.4.2 The regulation of gluconeogenesis takes place at several different levels

The regulation of gluconeogenesis occurs through compartmentalization, allosteric regulation, phosphorylation, and changes in gene expression (**Figure 6.24**). The steps specific to gluconeogenesis are all points of control. As seen previously, irreversible or rate-determining steps are often the places where control over a pathway is exerted. This section focuses on

FIGURE 6.24 **Regulation of gluconeogenesis.** The regulation of gluconeogenesis is in many ways the reciprocal of glycolysis. In addition, the first two reactions of gluconeogenesis are compartmentalized to the mitochondria.

three of these steps (pyruvate carboxylase, phosphoenolpyruvate carboxykinase [PEPCK], and fructose-1,6-bisphosphatase). However, control of gluconeogenesis and glycolysis is reciprocal. Thus, when the energetic level of the cell is low, glycolysis proceeds and gluconeogenesis is inhibited, but when plasma glucose is low, the reverse occurs—that is, gluconeogenesis proceeds and glycolysis is inhibited.

The first level of control is compartmentalization. Pyruvate carboxylase and PEPCK are found in the mitochondria. These reactions are kept separate from the reactions occurring in cytosol by the mitochondrial membranes.

Allosteric control is employed in the regulation of both pyruvate carboxykinase, which is stimulated by high levels of acetyl-CoA and fructose-1,6-bisphosphatase, which is inhibited by elevated levels of AMP and F-2,6-bP. High AMP levels indicate to the cell that energy levels are low and that energy should be replenished if possible. F-2,6-bP is a positive regulator of glycolysis, and it reciprocally controls gluconeogenesis.

WORKED PROBLEM 6.5 | Potential side effects

Metformin is a drug that is used to treat type 2 diabetes, and it works in part by inhibiting gluconeogenesis. A potential danger of taking metformin is lactic acidosis, the accumulation of excess lactic acid in the body. Why could taking metformin lead to lactic acidosis?

Strategy Review the steps of gluconeogenesis. How is lactate linked to gluconeogenesis?

Solution Lactate can act as a substrate for gluconeogenesis. If gluconeogenesis is inhibited or blocked, lactate levels in blood can increase, leading to lactic acidosis.

Follow-up question If you were going to try to design a drug to inhibit gluconeogenesis, which step would you target and why?

6.4 Summary

- Gluconeogenesis is the synthesis of new glucose molecules. Only some metabolic precursors can be made into glucose.
- Gluconeogenesis differs from glycolysis at three steps. This means that both pathways can be independently controlled and are thermodynamically favorable.
- The regulation of gluconeogenesis occurs through compartmentalization, allosteric regulation, phosphorylation, and changes in gene expression.

6.4 Concept Check

- Describe how glucose can be synthesized from different metabolic precursors.
- Describe the gluconeogenic pathway and compare it to glycolysis.
- Explain how the reactions of gluconeogenesis allow the cell to synthesize glucose under energetically unfavorable conditions and how compartmentalization facilitates this process.
- Explain how gluconeogenesis is regulated, outlining which steps are regulated, and the molecules that regulate those steps.

6.5 | The Fates of Pyruvate

The pyruvate created at the end of glycolysis can have several different metabolic fates, depending on the tissue of origin and metabolic state of the organism. This section details five different fates of pyruvate, four of which occur in animals (**Figure 6.25, Table 6.3**).

FIGURE 6.25 **Fates of pyruvate.** There are five fates of pyruvate discussed in this section, four of which are carried out in animals (decarboxylation is only carried out by microbes, such as some yeast and bacteria).

TABLE 6.3 **Enzymes That Use Pyruvate as a Substrate**

Enzyme	Pathway	Product
Alanine transaminase	Transamination	Alanine
Pyruvate dehydrogenase	Entry to citric acid cycle	Acetyl-CoA + CO_2
Pyruvate decarboxylase	Anaerobic glycolysis (microbes)	Acetaldehyde
Pyruvate carboxylase	Gluconeogenesis	Oxaloacetate
Lactate dehydrogenase	Anaerobic glycolysis (animals)	Lactate

6.5.1 Pyruvate can be decarboxylated to acetyl-CoA by pyruvate dehydrogenase

Under aerobic conditions, most pyruvate is converted to acetyl-CoA. This reaction yields one additional molecule of NADH/H$^+$ and one molecule of acetyl-CoA, which can be used for either fatty acid biosynthesis or the citric acid cycle. Pyruvate dehydrogenase, the enzyme catalyzing this reaction, is the committed step between carbohydrate metabolism and lipid metabolism. Although this is a decarboxylation reaction, and CO_2 is released from pyruvate, it is catalyzed by pyruvate dehydrogenase rather than by pyruvate decarboxylase (which produces acetaldehyde in facultative anaerobes). Once decarboxylated to acetyl-CoA, the carbons cannot be reconstituted to carbohydrates.

Pyruvate dehydrogenase is a large multienzyme complex that is found in the mitochondrial matrix (**Figure 6.26**). The functional unit is comprised of three enzymes: a

A.

B.

E1

E2

E3

CO_2

$CH_3-\overset{OH}{\underset{|}{C}}-TPP$

Hydroxyethyl-TPP

pyruvate dehydrogenase (E_1)

TPP

Pyruvate

$CH_3-\overset{O}{\underset{||}{C}}-\overset{O}{\underset{||}{C}}-O^-$

1

2

Lipoamide

dihydrolipoyl transacetylase (E_2)

$CH_3-\overset{O}{\underset{||}{C}}-S$

HS—

HS—

R

3

CoA

$CH_3-\overset{O}{\underset{||}{C}}-S-CoA$

Acetyl-CoA

Acetyl-dihydrolipoamide

FAD

—SH

—SH

NAD$^+$

dihydrolipoyl dehydrogenase (E_3)

5

NADH + H$^+$

FAD

—S

—S

4

FIGURE 6.26 **Topology of pyruvate dehydrogenase.** **A.** Pyruvate dehydrogenase is a large multienzyme complex with up to 60 subunits in some species. (Image from the RCSB PDB September 2012 Molecule of the Month feature by David Goodsell (doi: 10.2210/rcsb_pdb/mom_2012_9)) **B.** The basic reactions of pyruvate dehydrogenase are catalyzed by three enzymes: pyruvate dehydrogenase (E1), dihydrolipoyl transacetylase (E2), and dihydrolipoyl dehydrogenase (E3). The reactions that happen in each enzyme of the complex and their relationship to each other are shown.

pyruvate dehydrogenase (E1), a dihydrolipoyl transacetylase (E2), and a dihydrolipoyl dehydrogenase (E3). Sixty copies of E2 are found in the core of the complex, surrounded by a coating of 30 copies of E1, and 12 copies each of E3 and an E3 binding protein that links E2 and E3. In addition, E1 is a tetramer with $\alpha_2\beta_2$ stoichiometry, and E3 is a homodimer. Clearly, the topology of the collective assembly is complex.

The mechanism by which acetyl-CoA is generated from pyruvate is equally elegant and complex, employing both thiamine pyrophosphate (TPP) and lipoamide prosthetic groups (**Figure 6.27**). These cofactors and mechanisms are conserved throughout biochemistry and will be seen in other reactions. First, E1 removes a proton from TPP, generating a carbanion. This structure containing both positive and negative charges in the same molecule is known as a ylid. The carbanion then attacks the carbonyl carbon of pyruvate, resulting in protonation of the carbonyl oxygen. Electrons then flow out of the carboxyl moiety of pyruvate into the positively charged thiazole ring of TPP, resulting in decarboxylation of pyruvate. Further assisting this step is the resonance stabilization of the intermediate that exists following departure of the CO_2. The remaining molecule is hydroxyethyl-TPP.

The hydroxyethyl carbanion on TPP next reacts with the disulfide bond found in the lipoamide group of E2, resulting in a cleavage of the disulfide. One sulfur links to the carbanion; the other abstracts a proton to form a thiol. The former carbanion carbon is then oxidized back to a carbonyl, forming a thioester and cleaving the bond to TPP in the process. The new thioester is transferred from lipoamide to coenzyme A, forming acetyl-CoA and leaving lipoamide as a dithiol. Lipoamide is on a long flexible arm, which permits it to move between distant sites in an enzyme complex. This theme occurs in other areas of biochemistry, most notably with the biotin coenzyme in fatty acid biosynthesis.

The lipoamide arm moves to the E3 subunit where the dithiol form of lipoamide is reoxidized to the disulfide, regenerating the active site of the enzyme. The two electrons and two

1. Base deprotonates TPP carbon.

2. Substrate binds. Carbanion attacks carbonyl carbon.

3. Electron flow back into TPP results in loss of CO_2.

4. Resonance stabilization of carbanion.

5. Resonance stabilization of carbanion.

6. Carbanion attacks disulfide of lipoamide.

7. Base deprotonates hydroxyl generating carbonyl and cleaving bond to TPP.

8. Thiol of CoA attacks carbonyl, generating acetyl CoA.

9. Product released, lipoamide reprotonated to reduced form.

Acetyl CoA

FIGURE 6.27 **The mechanism of pyruvate dehydrogenase.** The mechanism of pyruvate dehydrogenase proceeds through three different phases, each catalyzed by a different subunit. The two phases which generate acetyl-CoA are shown.

protons are used to reduce a disulfide bond in E3. Finally, the disulfide in E3 is oxidized as the electrons and protons are transferred to FAD to form $FADH_2$. $FADH_2$ is oxidized by transfer of the electrons to NAD^+, yielding $NADH/H^+$.

Pyruvate dehydrogenase is directly regulated through product inhibition and phosphorylation (**Figure 6.28**). In terms of product inhibition, both NADH and acetyl-CoA inhibit the enzyme. In terms of phosphorylation, it is inactivated by pyruvate dehydrogenase kinase, a process that is reversed by a specific phosphatase (pyruvate dehydrogenase phosphatase). The phosphatase itself is highly regulated, being stimulated by insulin, phosphoenolpyruvate, and AMP, but inhibited by ATP, NADH, and acetyl-CoA. Muscle-specific isoforms of the enzyme are also stimulated by Ca^{2+}. These regulators make biochemical sense, in that molecules that indicate a low energetic state push the system toward increased formation of acetyl-CoA, whereas those that are plentiful in energetic abundance do the opposite. In active muscle tissue, Ca^{2+} ions are released and thus increase the rate of conversion of pyruvate into acetyl-CoA. But why does insulin, a hormone associated with the fed state, stimulate the conversion of pyruvate to acetyl-CoA? In this instance, the acetyl-CoA is destined not for the citric acid cycle but for fatty acid biosynthesis.

Subunit	Regulation
E1	▲ Dephosphorylation by pyruvate dehydrogenase phosphatase
	▲ Insulin
	▲ Phosphoenolpyruvate
	▲ AMP
	▲ Ca^{2+}
	▼ NADH
	▼ Acetyl-CoA
	▼ ATP
	▼ Phosphorylation by pyruvate dehydrogenase kinase
E2	▼ Acetyl-CoA
E3	▼ NADH/H^+

FIGURE 6.28 **Regulation of pyruvate dehydrogenase.** E1, E2, and E3 indicate the subunits of the pyruvate dehydrogenase complex. The numbers on arrows represent the individual reactions. Pyruvate dehydrogenase is regulated through substrate availability and product inhibition and through phosphorylation of the E1 subunit. Pyruvate dehydrogenase kinase and phosphatase regulate the activity of the E1 subunit and are regulated by many small molecules including ATP, pyruvate, and acetyl-CoA.

6.5.2 Pyruvate can be converted to lactate by lactate dehydrogenase

In vigorously active muscle, there is often a greater need for energy (ATP) than can be generated by oxidative metabolism (ATP synthesis in the presence of oxygen). In this state of anaerobic metabolism, muscle cannot make enough ATP, so muscle pyruvate is generated as glycolysis proceeds to generate ATP. Unfortunately, this is a limited process. The muscle cell (myocyte) will quickly deplete its supply of NAD^+; once this has happened, glycolysis will grind to a halt. To keep glycolysis moving forward and generating ATP, a means is needed to reset these electron carriers. One way in which animal metabolism resets these carriers is through the conversion of pyruvate into lactate. This process temporarily allows glycolysis to proceed, but only in the short term. Imagine someone who has sprinted for as long as she or he can and reached the point of collapse, or someone who has been rock climbing and has completely spent his or her arm strength hanging onto a cliff face; in both cases, we can see both the need for limited anaerobic metabolism and the aftereffects of prolonged muscle activity in the absence of oxygen.

Lactate is produced in tissues by the action of lactate dehydrogenase (LDH), which exists in five different isoforms (**Figure 6.29**). Interestingly, there are only two different genes for the enzyme: LDHA, which encodes the muscle-specific isoform, and LDHB, which encodes the heart-specific isoform. The heart isoform is referred to as "H," and the muscle and liver isoform as "M." The holoenzyme consists of a combination of four subunits which can be all M, all H, or a mix of the two isoforms. The products of LDHA and LDHB are found in different ratios (M4, M3H, M2H2, MH3, and H4) in different tissues, with M4 being found in muscle and the liver, and H4 in the heart. The M4 isoform has a lower affinity for pyruvate and is not inhibited by pyruvate, whereas the H4 isoform has a higher affinity for pyruvate and is allosterically inhibited by pyruvate. Therefore,

A.

Isoform	H4	MH3	M2H2	M3H	M4
Heart	X	x			
RBC	x	X			
Brain	x	X	x		
Muscle			x	x	X
Liver				x	X

B.

NADH attacks the carbonyl carbon of pyruvate, leading to protonation of the carbonyl oxygen and formation of lactate.

FIGURE 6.29 **Lactate dehydrogenase.** **A.** Monomers of lactate dehydrogenase assemble and function as tetramers. The two genes for this enzyme are differentially expressed, leading to isoforms with different combinations of the M and H subunits, which are found in different tissues. A large X indicates the most prevalent combination in those tissues, and a small x indicates less prevalent combinations. **B.** Pyruvate is reduced to lactate in lactate dehydrogenase by transfer of electrons from NADH. Two arginines in the active site play a key role in the orientation of the pyruvate while an active site histidine acts as a proton donor to form the hydroxyl group on lactate.

the H isoform is better adapted to function in the conversion of lactate to pyruvate, and the M isoform is better suited to the reverse reaction.

The mechanism of lactate dehydrogenase employs two arginine residues in the active site. These residues play key roles in the orientation of the pyruvate substrate. Electrons flow from NADH to the carbonyl carbon of pyruvate and into the carbonyl oxygen. An active site histidine acts as a proton donor to complete formation of the hydroxyl group, forming lactate.

Lactate produced in active muscle can diffuse from the myocyte into the bloodstream. In the liver, lactate can be oxidized back to pyruvate by LDH (at the cost of one molecule of NADH/ H+). The liver can use this pyruvate to produce glucose via gluconeogenesis; it can then release the glucose for use by other tissues (presumably back to skeletal muscle). This is an example of how different organs have evolved and adapted to metabolically complement each other.

6.5.3 | Pyruvate can be transaminated to alanine

Throughout this chapter, we have seen examples of how different organs and tissues evolved to have specialized functions. This situation is readily apparent on a macroscopic level. The functions of intestine and bone are clearly different. Similar dramatic differences are seen in metabolism at the biochemical level. One such difference is the means by which pyruvate and alanine are metabolized in liver and muscle.

Pyruvate can be transaminated into alanine. Transamination reactions exchange an amine and hydrogen for an oxygen, generating a carbonyl group. Pyruvate undergoes a transamination with the amino acid glutamate to generate the amino acid alanine. Several amino acids (serine, cysteine, threonine, and glycine) also proceed through an alanine intermediate during catabolism.

Alanine is released from muscle and passes through the circulation to the liver. Hence, alanine is serving two important metabolic functions in this situation. First, it is shuttling carbons to the liver for pyruvate production. Second, it is shuttling potentially toxic amino groups to the liver to be detoxified into urea. In the liver, a second transamination reaction generates pyruvate from the carbon skeleton of alanine. The liver typically uses this pyruvate to generate glucose via gluconeogenesis. The resulting ammonia is eventually detoxified via the urea cycle.

Again, alanine metabolism illustrates the level of specialization of metabolism in different tissues that perform specific tasks. By shifting to the liver the metabolic burden of detoxifying ammonia (via transamination, oxidative deamination, and urea synthesis) and generating glucose from pyruvate (via gluconeogenesis), muscle is freed to perform other tasks such as motility and mobility.

6.5.4 | Pyruvate can be carboxylated to oxaloacetate by pyruvate carboxylase

Pyruvate can enter gluconeogenesis. The first step in this process is the formation of oxaloacetate from pyruvate and CO_2, a process known as carboxylation. The energy for this reaction is provided by the hydrolysis of ATP. This happens in the mitochondria, and the oxaloacetate produced is transaminated into aspartate, pumped out of the mitochondria, then transaminated back into oxaloacetate in the cytosol, where it serves as a substrate for PEPCK, and proceeds through gluconeogenesis. However, there is another role for oxaloacetate: as part of the citric acid cycle, it serves as a metabolic crossroads for several molecules, including the catabolism of several amino acids. The formation of oxaloacetate in this situation can act as an **anaplerotic** reaction, which are reactions that build up levels of citric acid cycle intermediates and restore levels of oxaloacetate.

6.5.5 | Microbes can decarboxylate pyruvate into acetaldehyde

Under short-term, limited anaerobic conditions, animals can survive by temporarily converting pyruvate to lactate, allowing glycolysis to proceed and produce ATP. This is, at best, a stopgap measure. In contrast, yeast and some other microbes can survive in the absence of oxygen. When oxygen is available, it is used as a terminal electron acceptor. Water is formed, and the reducing equivalents NADH and FADH$_2$ are reset to NAD$^+$ and FAD. In the absence of oxygen, organisms need some way to produce ATP. Although ATP can be made through glycolysis, this requires a mechanism for oxidizing NADH and FADH$_2$ back to NAD$^+$ and FAD. In yeast, this is accomplished by the oxidative decarboxylation of pyruvate catalyzed by pyruvate decarboxylase (**Figure 6.30**). Pyruvate decarboxylase uses pyruvate produced at the end of glycolysis to produce acetaldehyde and CO$_2$. This is a TPP-dependent enzyme with a Mg^{2+} cofactor. The mechanism begins with the formation of a covalent adduct between pyruvate and the ylid form of TPP. The nitrogen in the TPP acts as an electron sink drawing electrons into the thiazole ring and away from pyruvate. This facilitates the decarboxylation of pyruvate and cleavage of the carbon–carbon bond, releasing CO$_2$. The resulting carbanion is stabilized through resonance. Electron flow back into the ylid electron sink causes formation of the carbonyl group and cleavage of the carbon–carbon bond between the substrate and TPP. Acetaldehyde is released, and the ylid form of the enzyme is regenerated.

Alcohol dehydrogenase then generates ethanol from the acetaldehyde. The cofactor in this redox reaction is NADH/H$^+$, which is reset to NAD$^+$ in the process. Effectively, acetaldehyde takes the place of oxygen as the terminal electron acceptor in this series of reactions.

Many strains of yeast found in nature can tolerate concentrations of ethanol as high as 14% v/v. These strains are responsible for the relatively high concentrations of ethanol found in some wines. Generation of spirits with higher concentrations of ethanol requires chemical concentration (distillation). Over the past 40 years, yeast strains that can tolerate higher concentrations of ethanol have been selected for or generated in the laboratory. Although these strains have found some use in the food and beverage industry, they are of potentially much greater value in the production of biofuels (notably bioethanol).

FIGURE 6.30 **The mechanism of pyruvate decarboxylase.** The mechanism of pyruvate decarboxylase is also a TPP-dependent mechanism. As we have previously seen, pyruvate forms an adduct through the ylid form of TPP (1). The nitrogen in the TPP acts as an electron sink, facilitating the decarboxylation of pyruvate (2). The resulting carbanion is stabilized through resonance. The anion protonates, permitting electron flow back from the hydroxyl group to reform the ylid (3). In the process, acetaldehyde is released (4).

WORKED PROBLEM 6.6 | Fates of pyruvate in a strain of bacteria

A strain of bacteria form pyruvate after metabolizing galactose through glycolysis. These bacteria grow under aerobic conditions without any apparent inhibition, using galactose as a carbon source. They can also grow under anaerobic conditions, albeit slowly and with the gradual acidification of the media. Suggest one mechanism through which these bacteria are conducting anaerobic metabolism.

Strategy   The question tells us that the bacteria can degrade galactose through glycolysis and live under both aerobic and anaerobic conditions. If the media these cells live in acidifies under anaerobic conditions, what is one likely fate of the pyruvate produced in glycolysis?

Solution   The bacteria may be producing lactate (lactic acid) with the pyruvate that results from glycolysis. Remember that the electron carrier NADH/H$^+$ needs to be reset for glycolysis to proceed. Under aerobic conditions, this is usually accomplished through the use of oxygen and the formation of water. Under anaerobic conditions, the bacteria need another mechanism to oxidize NADH back to NAD$^+$. Microbes such as yeast often reduce pyruvate to acetaldehyde and CO_2, and then to ethanol; however, many other microbes will produce other wastes, such as lactate.

Follow-up question   How could you test your hypothesis about the production of lactate using both a chemical approach and a genetic approach?

6.5 Summary

- Pyruvate has distinct fates depending on the type of cell (or organ) and the metabolic state of the organism.
- Pyruvate can be decarboxylated to acetyl-CoA by pyruvate dehydrogenase.
- Pyruvate can be converted to lactate by LDH.
- Pyruvate can be transaminated to alanine via alanine aminotransferase.
- Pyruvate can be carboxylated to oxaloacetate by pyruvate carboxylase.
- Microbes can decarboxylate pyruvate into ethanol.

6.5 Concept Check

- Describe the fates of pyruvate in both higher organisms and in some microbes, and explain:
  ○ what pyruvate is transformed into in each of these cases.
  ○ the function of pyruvate in each of these cases.
  ○ pyruvate's role in the organism in a biochemical sense.

The Bigger Picture

Carbohydrates are clearly more than just an energy currency for organisms. The simplest carbohydrates (monosaccharides) and some polymers of carbohydrates (polysaccharides) are used by an organism as a source of stored energy. However, carbohydrates can also be structural molecules—for example, in the formation of the extracellular matrix, and they also function in cell-cell recognition. This chapter introduces the basic structure of monosaccharides, discusses how monosaccharides can be joined into polysaccharides, and describes how the most common monosaccharide (glucose) can be catabolized into pyruvate (glycolysis). Within the chapter, gluconeogenesis is described, outlining how new glucose can be formed from smaller molecules. The chapter concludes with a discussion of the metabolic fates of pyruvate, a molecule that is found at the junction of several metabolic pathways and serves several functions in the organism.

Bioinformatics Exercises

Exercise 1 Drawing Monosaccharides

Exercise 2 Introduction to Glycomics

Exercise 3 Oligosaccharides, Polysaccharides, and Glycoproteins

Exercise 4 Glycolysis and the KEGG Database

Exercise 5 Metabolism and the BRENDA and KEGG Database

Problems

6.1 Properties, Nomenclature, and Biological Functions of Monosaccharides

1. Describe these carbohydrates as

   a. aldose or ketose.

   b. triose, tetrose, pentose, hexose, or heptose

   c. α or β

   d. furanose or pyranose

2. Given the following Fischer projections, draw the Haworth projection for either a furanose or pyranose.

3. Given the following Haworth projections, draw the Fischer projections.

4. Draw the structures below as pyranoses.

5. Draw the following structures as a furanose.

6. Draw the following structures in a chair or envelope projection, noting which anomer you believe would be most stable and explaining why.

7. Draw the structures of the following modified monosaccharides.

   I. *N*-Acetylgalactosamine

   II. mannitol

   III. glucuronic acid

6.2 Properties, Nomenclature and Biological Functions of Complex Carbohydrates

8. Describe these disaccharides chemically using the vocabulary terms found in this chapter.

a. sucrose

b. maltose

c. lactose

9. Can humans digest chitin? Explain why or why not, using biochemical evidence.

10. American currency is printed on high-quality cellulose-based paper. Most paper consists of lower levels of cellulose and higher levels of starches and other carbohydrates. Pens used to detect counterfeit bills contain an iodine-based dye. What should the dye look like on an authentic bill?

11. In making simple cheese, milk is treated with vinegar (acetic acid) to denature proteins; this creates a curd (the solid fraction containing fats and precipitated proteins) and whey (the liquid fraction). Based on this simple procedure, if the curd were separated from the whey, could someone who is lactose-intolerant consume this cheese (the curd) without suffering the complications of lactose intolerance?

12. Beano and Lactaid are both over-the-counter products that contain enzymes to relieve discomfort associated with being unable to digest some foods.

a. Can they replace one another?

b. Would taking these products the day before help?

c. Would taking either Beano or Lactaid decrease the nutritional value of the food?

13. In organic chemistry we are taught that increasing the temperature of a liquid–solid extraction increases the yield. In many cases, solvents are refluxed with a solid to extract the desired materials. Why is this not done in most biochemical extractions?

6.3 Glycolysis and an Introduction to Metabolic Pathways

14. If a glucose molecule were labeled using ^{14}C on C-1, and the molecule were metabolized through glycolysis, where would you expect to find the label in pyruvate?

15. The energetics of glycolysis can be described using a roller coaster analogy. Initial energy is invested in glycolysis through phosphorylation (and hydrolysis of ATP). This is analogous to pulling the roller coaster up the hill. If glycolysis were a roller coaster, how would you envision the rest of the ride?

16. Would you anticipate that all the enzymes of glycolysis to be essential for life? Could a bacteria or yeast strain live without these enzymes?

17. Drug companies are seeking compounds that act on F-2,6-bP. Why is this molecule being considered as a potential target?

18. If a transgenic mouse overexpressed glucokinase in liver, how might this affect monosaccharide metabolism in the body as a whole?

19. Bacterial fructose-1,6-bisphosphate aldolase lacks the critical lysine in the active site; instead, it has two divalent metal ions bound. Based on this information, provide a mechanism for this enzyme.

20. If there were a mutation to aldolase in which the active site aspartate was mutated to tyrosine, how might the mutation affect the kinetics of the aldolase? Would the enzyme be catalytically competent? Which kinetic parameters would you expect to be affected and how?

6.4 Gluconeogenesis

21. How could breakdown of triacylglycerols (a glycerol backbone with three fatty acids esterified to it) contribute to gluconeogenesis?

22. The amino acid aspartate is a glucogenic amino acid, meaning it can contribute carbons to gluconeogenesis. If the amino group were removed from aspartate, how could the remaining carbon skeleton contribute to gluconeogenesis?

23. If a molecule of pyruvate were labeled using ^{14}C on all three carbons and went through gluconeogenesis, where would those labels be found in the final molecule of glucose?

24. Coffee and many diet soft drinks and energy drinks contain caffeine. Caffeine is a phosphodiesterase inhibitor and blocks the breakdown of cAMP. How does caffeine affect glycolysis and gluconeogenesis?

25. Most tissues, including muscle, the kidneys, and the liver, are capable of some of the reactions of gluconeogenesis, but only liver tissue exports glucose. What does this say about the role of gluconeogenesis in the liver?

26. If the serine phosphorylated by PKA on PFK-2 were mutated to an aspartate, how might this affect gluconeogenesis?

27. Examine the mechanisms of mutase and pyruvate decarboxylase. The free energy of the reaction of pyruvate decarboxylase is –20.6 kCal/mol, while the free energy of the mutase reaction is close to zero. Are the proposed mechanisms substantiated or unsupported by the thermodynamic data?

6.5 The Fates of Pyruvate

28. Pyruvate stands at a metabolic crossroads. Draw the structure of pyruvate and describe how pyruvate is made into the five different products.

29. If a person were on a high-fat diet, would you expect pyruvate levels to be high in liver? If so, where would those carbons originate?

30. If a molecule of pyruvate was labeled on the carboxyl carbon with ^{14}C and was used to make each of the five products discussed in the fates of pyruvate, where would be the label in each product?

31. Describe how the molecules that regulate pyruvate dehydrogenase make sense in the bigger picture of metabolism.

32. Describe how expression of the two different isoforms of LDH allows the different organs of the body to cooperate under hypoxic states, that is, under low oxygen concentration.

33. In describing the mechanism of pyruvate dehydrogenase, the designation "B" is used several times to designate a base. What types of functional groups, amino acids, or cofactors could serve as a base in this reaction?

34. How could the mechanism of pyruvate dehydrogenase be probed and assayed spectrophotometrically? What techniques could be used to test this mechanism? Could all parts of the mechanism be tested using this technique?

Data Interpretation

35. Imagine that you have isolated a slimy matrix secreted by a species of algae. The sample is retained by dialysis membrane with a pore size of 10 kDa. If treated with strong base, the sample yields a mixture of acetate, glucose, and glucosamine in a 1:1:1 molar ratio. Based on this information, propose three potential structures for this molecule.

36. You are investigating a small molecule that may potentially have use as a novel antidiabetic agent. The assay system consists of primary hepatocytes (liver cells) in a culture medium supplemented with serum to provide needed hormones and growth factors, but it is devoid of glucose. You incubated dishes of cells with various molecules and measured glucose release into the media as a function of time and treatment. The data obtained are shown below.

A. vehicle control

B. 10 mM drug

a. What do these data show?

b. What is the effect of this drug?

c. Why were hepatocytes chosen as the experimental model system? Would you expect a different result with other cell types?

d. Why was the assay run in media and serum rather than in saline or a buffered salt system? How could the use of media or serum complicate the assay?

e. If this drug had a molecular weight of 451 g/mol and a 10 mM concentration was needed to achieve the desired effect, would it ever make a good drug?

37. You have a friend who is a marine biologist. She is trying to determine the composition of the shell of a new species of shrimp she has discovered. Samples sent for elemental analysis indicate high levels of nitrogen (7.8%) in the shells. Based on these data, she has hypothesized that the shells are made of a keratinlike protein. How would you advise her? What other compounds might the shells contain?

Experimental Design

38. How would you test to see that shrimp shells your friend is studying are made of proteins, carbohydrates, or some other material?

39. You have isolated a white crystalline solid from tree sap that gives a positive Molisch test. Research the Molisch test and design a series of simple experiments to test the properties of this molecule.

40. You are investigating the kinetic properties of glyceraldehyde-3-phosphate dehydrogenase. Provide two ways by which you could ensure that this enzyme is not hindered by exhausting the supply of NAD^+.

41. Design an experiment to test whether gluconeogenesis is increased in mice treated with an experimental drug. How would this experiment differ if you wanted to test the effect of the drug in cultured cells or in humans?

42. There are multiple fates of pyruvate. If you were studying pyruvate entering the citric acid cycle, what considerations would you need to take into account to ensure that pyruvate was not lost to other pathways?

Ethics and Social Responsibility

43. Recently, some municipalities have called for a tax on foods containing high fructose corn syrup (HFCS), based on the public health threat posed by obesity and associated diseases (type 2 diabetes and heart disease). Given that the United States taxes tobacco products, is it in the public interest to use this approach to curb obesity?

44. Significant public and private funds are being directed toward the development of cellulosic ethanol (fuel ethanol derived from nonfood sources). Should more public or private funds be spent on this endeavor? Investigate how much oil companies and governments worldwide are investing in this research. Do you feel this is a good distribution of funds? Find a student who disagrees with you and debate the points about this spending.

45. Brazil uses limited petrochemicals and instead fuels its cars with ethanol derived from sugarcane. What are the ethical considerations of fueling a car with ethanol derived from sugarcane versus petrochemicals?

46. Agriculture has progressed to the point where a 10-pound bag of sugar can be purchased for only a few dollars. Humans have a clear preference for sweet foods; this is built into our biology. At the same time, modern lifestyles have made it possible for people to exercise less and less. One could argue that we have progressed to the point where humans are the first species that needs to consciously think about food consumption and exercise. Other species hoard food for consumption over the winter or hibernate, and burn off fat they have stored over the summer months. Have humans lost the ability to seasonally regulate food consumption and metabolic output?

47. Prohibition was the time in U.S. history when the production and consumption of ethanol was prohibited. Although there were clearly some good intentions in Prohibition, it generally failed to work. For example, organized crime increased, tax revenues decreased, and there was a general disregard for the ban. Prohibition was lifted in 1933 with the passing of the Twenty-first Amendment, but the sale of ethanol is currently tightly regulated. One could argue that ethanol is a natural food product and has been in the human diet since antiquity. Are there other foods that should be regulated? Are there other drugs that are currently illegal but should be legalized? Explain your views on these questions.

Suggested Readings

General and 6.1 Properties, Nomenclature, and Biological Functions of Monosaccharides

Gabius, H. J., ed. *The Sugar Code*. Weinheim, Germany: GmbH & Co. KGaA, 2009.

Gard, H.G., M. K. Cowman, and C. A. Hales, eds. *Carbohydrate Chemistry, Biology, and Medical Applications*. Amsterdam, The Netherlands: Elsevier Sciences, 2008.

McNaught, A. D. "Nomenclature of Carbohydrates." *Advances in Carbohydrate Chemistry and Biochemistry*. 52 (1997): 43–177.

Pigman, W., and D. Horton. *The Carbohydrates: Chemistry and Biochemistry*, 2nd ed. New York, New York: Academic Press, 1972.

Stick, R.V., and Spencer, W. *Carbohydrates, Essential Molecules of Life*. 2nd ed. Amsertdam, The Netherlands: Elsevier Science, 2008.

Taylor, M. E., and K. Drickamer. *Introduction to Glycobiology*. New York, New York: Oxford University Press, 2011.

Thisbe, K. Lindhorst. *Essentials of Carbohydrate Chemistry and Biochemistry*. Weinham, Germany: GmbH & Co. KGaA, 2007.

Varki, A. *Essentials of Glycobiology*. 2nd ed. New York, New York: Cold Spring Harbor Press, 2008.

6.2 Properties, Nomenclature, and Biological Functions of Complex Carbohydrates

Cornish-Bowden, A. "Provisional International Union of Pure and Applied Chemistry and International Union of Biochemistry Joint Commission on Biochemical Nomenclature Symbol for Specifying the Conformation of Polysaccharide Chains." *Provisional Pure and Applied Chemistry*. 55, no. 8 (1983): 1269–72.

Genauer, C. H., and H. F. Hammer. "Maldigestion and Malabsorption." Chap. 101 in *Sleisenger & Fordtran's Gastrointestinal and Liver Disease*, edited by M. Feldman, L. S. Friedman, and M. H. Sleisenger. Philadelphia, Pa.: Saunders Elsevier, 2010.

Gupta, B., A. Arorab, S. Saxena, and Alam M. Sarwar. "Preparation of Chitosan–Polyethylene Glycol Coated Cotton Membranes for Wound Dressings: Preparation and Characterization." *Polymers for Advanced Technologies* 20, no.1 (2008): 58–65.

"Lactose intolerance." *The National Digestive Diseases Information Clearinghouse (NDDIC)*. NIH Publication No. 09–2751. 2009. https://www.metsol.com/assets/sites/2/Foods_containing_lactose.pdf

Shahidi, F., J. Kamil, V. Arachchi, and Y. J. Jeon. "Food Applications of Chitin and Chitosans." *Trends in Food Science & Technology* 10 (1999): 37–51.

6.3 Glycolysis and an Introduction to Metabolic Pathways

Baggetto, L. G. "Deviant Energetic Metabolism of Glycolytic Cancer Cells." *Biochemie* 74, no. 11 (1992): 959–74.

Bayley, J. P., and P. Devilee. "The Warburg Effect in 2012." *Curr Opin Oncol*. 24, no.1 (2012): 62–7.

Cárdenas, M. L., A. Cornish-Bowden, and T. Ureta. "Evolution and Regulatory Role of the Hexokinases." *Biochim. Biophys. Acta*. 1401 (1998): 242–264.

de Souza A. C., G. Z. Justo, D. R. de Araújo, and A. D. Cavagis. "Defining the Molecular Basis of Tumor Metabolism: A Continuing Challenge Since Warburg's Discovery." *Cell Physiol Biochem*. 28, no. 5 (2011): 771–92.

Fothergill Gilmore, L. A., and P. A. M. Michels. "Evolution of Glycolysis." *Progress in Biophysics and Molecular Biology* 59, no. 2 (1993): 105–235.

Gatenby, R.A., and R. J. Gillies. "Why Do Cancers Have High Aerobic Glycolyis?" *Nature Reviews Cancer* 4, no. 11 (2004): 891–899.

Heinisch, J. "Isolation and Characterization of the Two Structural Genes Coding for Phosphofructokinase in Yeast." *Mol. Gen Genet*. 202 (1986): 75–82.

Hers, H. G., and L. Hue. "Gluconeogenesis and Related Aspects of Glycolysis." *Annual Review of Biochemistry* 52 (1983): 617–653.

Hue L., and M. H. Rider. "Role of Fructose 2,6-Bisphosphate in the Control of Glycolysis in Mammalian Tissues." *Biochemical Journal* 245, no. 2 (1987): 313–324.

Kim, J., and S. D. Copley. "Why Metabolic Enzymes Are Essential or Nonessential for Growth of Escherichia coli K12 on Glucose." *Biochemistry* 46, no. 44 (2007): 12501–11.

Kolwicz, S. C. Jr., and R. Tian. "Glucose Metabolism and Cardiac Hypertrophy." *Cardiovasc Res*. 90, no. 2 (2011):194–201.

Koppenol, W. H., P. L. Bounds, and C. V. Dang. "Otto Warburg's Contributions to Current Concepts of Cancer Metabolism." *Nat Rev Cancer*. 11, no. 5 (2011): 325–37.

Mor, I., E. C. Cheung, and K. H. Vousden. "Control of Glycolysis through Regulation of PFK1: Old Friends and Recent Additions." *Cold Spring Harb Symp Quant Biol*. 76 (2011): 211–6.

Munoz, M. E., and E. Ponce. "Pyruvate Kinase: Current Status of Regulatory and Functional Properties." *Comparative Biochemistry and Physiology Part B: Biochemistry and Molecular Biology* 135 (2003): 197–218.

Pilkis, S. J., and D. K. Granner. "Molecular Physiology of the Regulation of Hepatic Gluconeogenesis and Glycolysis." *Annual Review of Physiology* 54 (1992): 885–909.

Scrutton, M. C., and M. F. Utter. "Regulation of Glycolysis and Gluconeogenesis in Animal Tissues." *Annual Review of Biochemistry* 37 (1968): 249–258.

Sola-Penna, M., D. Da Silva, W. S. Coelho, M. M. Marinho-Carvalho, and P. Zancan. "Regulation of Mammalian Muscle Type 6-Phosphofructo-1-kinase and Its Implication for the Control of the Metabolism." *IUBMB Life* 62, no. 11 (2010): 791–6.

Sugden, M. C., and M. J. Holness. "The Pyruvate Carboxylase-Pyruvate Dehydrogenase Axis in Islet Pyruvate Metabolism: Going Round in Circles?" *Islets* 3, no. 6 (2011): 302–19.

Wilson, J. E. "Isozymes of Mammalian Hexokinase: Structure, Subcellular Localization and Metabolic Function." *Journal of Experimental Biology* 206, no. 12 (2003): 2049–57.

6.4 Gluconeogenesis

Exton, J. H. "Gluconeogenesis" *Metabolism-Clinical and Experimental* 21, no. 10 (1972): 945–990.

Friedmann, N. "Hormonal Regulation of Hepatic Gluconeogenesis." *Physiological Reviews* 64, no. 1 (1984): 170–259.

Pilkis, S. J., and D. K. Granner. "Molecular Physiology of the Regulation of Hepatic Gluconeogenesis and Glycolysis." *Annual Review of Physiology* 54 (1992): 885–909.

Pilkis, S. J., M. R. El Maghrabi, and T. H. Claus. "Hormonal Regulation of Hepatic Gluconeogenesis and Glycolysis." *Annual Review of Biochemistry* 57 (1988): 755–783.

6.5 The Fates of Pyruvate

Dienel, G. A., and L. Hertz. "Glucose and Lactate Metabolism During Brain Activation." *Journal of Neuroscience Research* 66, no. 5 (2001): 824–838.

Gladden, L. B. "Lactate Metabolism: A New Paradigm for the Third Millennium." *Journal of Physiology-London* 558, no. 1 (2004): 5–30.

Pronk, J. T., H. Y. Steensma, and J. P. vanDijken. "Pyruvate Metabolism in *Saccharomyces cerevisiae*." *Yeast* 12, no.16 (1996): 1607–1633.

Stacpoole, P. W. "The Pyruvate Dehydrogenase Complex as a Therapeutic Target for Age-Related Diseases." *Aging Cell* 11, no. 3 (2012): 371–377.

Sugden, M. C., and M. J. Holness. "The Pyruvate Carboxylase-Pyruvate Dehydrogenase Axis in Islet Pyruvate Metabolism: Going Round in Circles?" *Islets* 3, no. 6 (2011): 302–319.

Yadav, A. K., A. B. Chaudhari, and R. M. Kothari. "Bioconversion of Renewable Resources into Lactic Acid: An Industrial View." *Critical Reviews in Biotechnology* 31, no.1 (2011): 1–19.

Carbohydrates I

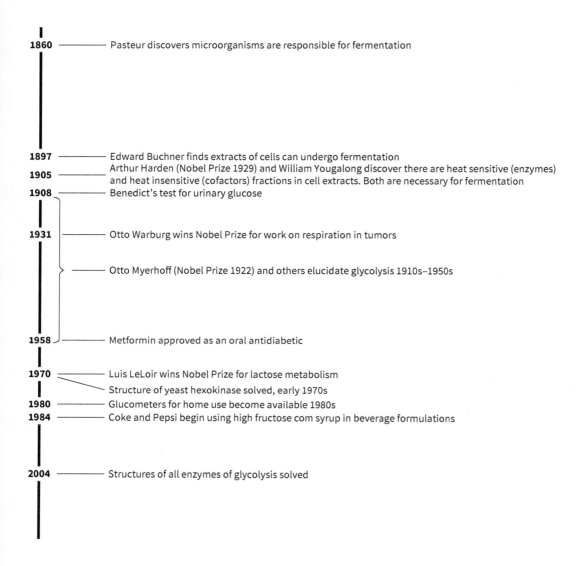

1860 —————— Pasteur discovers microorganisms are responsible for fermentation

1897 —————— Edward Buchner finds extracts of cells can undergo fermentation

1905 —————— Arthur Harden (Nobel Prize 1929) and William Yougalong discover there are heat sensitive (enzymes) and heat insensitive (cofactors) fractions in cell extracts. Both are necessary for fermentation

1908 —————— Benedict's test for urinary glucose

1931 —————— Otto Warburg wins Nobel Prize for work on respiration in tumors

—————— Otto Myerhoff (Nobel Prize 1922) and others elucidate glycolysis 1910s–1950s

1958 —————— Metformin approved as an oral antidiabetic

1970 —————— Luis LeLoir wins Nobel Prize for lactose metabolism

—————— Structure of yeast hexokinase solved, early 1970s

1980 —————— Glucometers for home use become available 1980s

1984 —————— Coke and Pepsi begin using high fructose com syrup in beverage formulations

2004 —————— Structures of all enzymes of glycolysis solved

CHAPTER **7**

The Common Catabolic Pathway

Citric Acid Cycle, the Electron Transport Chain, and ATP Biosynthesis

©Terry Smith Images/Alamy Stock Photo

Just as banks have different ways to exchange money, the mitochondrion uses the citric acid cycle and electron transport chain to convert different chemical forms of energy into the bonds of ATP.

Electron Transport in Context

Money, it has been said, makes the world go 'round. Under a barter system, trade is difficult to conduct over distances with any predictability. Paper money is not always the best medium for trade either. For example, it would be inconvenient or even dangerous to be paid weekly in cash or to make a large purchase, such as a car or house, using cash. Therefore, alternatives to money, such as credit cards or checks, have been developed. Money in all of its forms provides the potential to build things and do work.

This is analogous to the situation in the cell. Using the energy from one reaction to perform another is difficult if there is no common intermediate. Hence, the work of the cell—in the form of glycolysis, and now the citric acid cycle—gets paid in checks (NADH and $FADH_2$), which are cashed into ATP during oxidative phosphorylation.

Reducing equivalents (essentially electron carriers such as NAD^+) capture electrons in the citric acid cycle. These electrons move down a series of redox active centers, also electron carriers, ultimately forming water when they react with molecular oxygen. As the electrons move through these centers, the energy of their transfer is used to pump protons out of the mitochondrial matrix. This proton gradient (lower pH outside, higher pH inside) powers a tiny molecular motor—ATP synthase, the enzyme responsible for most of a cell's ATP production. This is shown in **Dynamic Figure 7.1**.

DYNAMIC FIGURE 7.1 The citric acid cycle uses acetyl-CoA from catabolic pathways to generate the reducing equivalents NADH and FADH$_2$. It also serves as a central hub for metabolism of small carbon-containing molecules. These reducing equivalents and others produced in catabolic pathways such as glycolysis are oxidized in the electron transport chain. The electrons are passed from carrier to carrier in the chain, ultimately being used to form water. The energy of electron transfer is used to form a proton gradient across the inner mitochondrial membrane which is used to drive ATP synthesis.

COMMON THEMES

Evolution's outcomes are conserved.	• The citric acid cycle, electron transport, and ATP synthase are conserved throughout evolution.
	• Cytochrome *c* is used as a marker gene to track evolution and demonstrate degrees of relatedness between species.
	• ATP synthase has evolved for specialized functions such as ion transport or flagellar motility.
Structure determines function.	• The structure of the intermediates in the citric acid cycle dictates in part how these molecules react.
	• The structure of the mitochondria and the electron transport apparatus allows for the development of a proton gradient across the mitochondrial membrane.
	• ATP synthase acts as a molecular motor, using the energy of the proton gradient to drive ATP production.
	• The entire electron transport chain and ATP synthase reside in one supercomplex (the respirasome), which allows for substrate channeling.
Biochemical information is transferred, exchanged, and stored.	• Substrate availability, feedback inhibition and allosteric regulators control specific steps of the citric acid cycle.
Biomolecules are altered through pathways involving transformations of energy and matter.	• Energetically unfavorable reactions become favorable when coupled with reactions that have a highly negative ΔG value. Although we typically think of this in terms of ATP hydrolysis, other highly favorable reactions (such as those involving thioesters) are common in biochemistry. Likewise, reactions that have $\Delta G°$ values close to zero can be tipped to move in either direction by changing the concentrations of substrates or products.
	• Electrons in bonds of intermediates of the citric acid cycle are transferred to oxygen through a series of electron carriers, ultimately forming water. These electrons transfer from one electron carrier to another in the different electron transport complexes.
	• Electrons from the reduced form of nicotine adenine dinucleotide (NADH) or flavin adenine dinucleotide (FADH$_2$) are transferred through a series of redox active electron carriers, ultimately being consumed in the production of water.
	• The energy of electrons flowing through the electron transport complexes is used to pump protons out of the mitochondrial matrix.
	• ATP synthase uses the energy of the proton gradient to drive ATP production.

7.1 | The Citric Acid Cycle

Acetyl-CoA is an important metabolic intermediate in several pathways. Chapter 6 describes how glucose and other monosaccharides are catabolized into pyruvate. Under aerobic conditions, the fate of most pyruvate is decarboxylation into acetyl-CoA. Likewise, Chapter 9 describes how fatty acids are catabolized into acetyl-CoA. Under normal conditions most of this acetyl-CoA enters the **citric acid cycle** (also known as the tricarboxylic acid cycle or the Krebs cycle) (**Figure 7.2**). The chemical bonds of acetyl-CoA are still energetically rich. The acetyl group of acetyl-CoA is ultimately oxidized in the citric acid cycle into CO_2, and the electrons obtained in these reactions are used to reduce the electron carriers NAD^+ and FAD to NADH and $FADH_2$. The electrons are used in subsequent reactions in the **electron transport chain** to generate a proton gradient, which subsequently drives ATP production in a process known as **oxidative phosphorylation**. A second

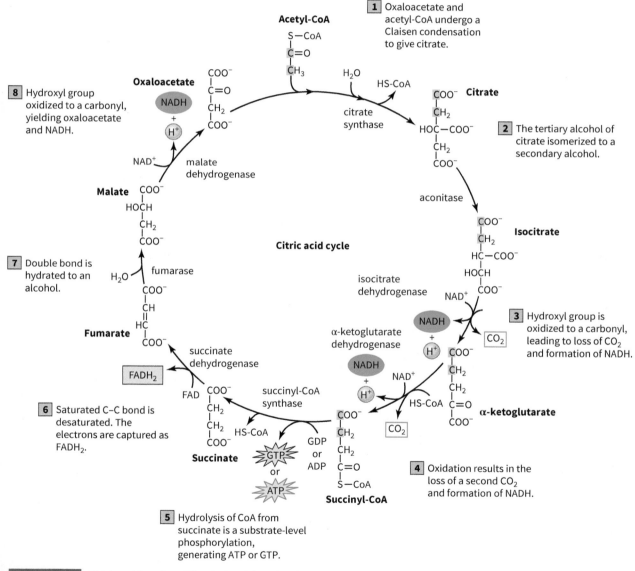

FIGURE 7.2 **Citric acid cycle.** The citric acid cycle (also known as the tricarboxylic acid cycle or the Krebs cycle) is the central hub of metabolism. While it oxidizes the carbons of acetyl-CoA to CO_2, it captures the electrons as NADH and $FADH_2$ for use in electron transport. Various pathways feed into and out of the cycle, linking central metabolism with other pathways. (Karp, *Cell and Molecular Biology: Concepts and Experiments*, 7e, copyright 2013, John Wiley & Sons. This material is reproduced with permission of John Wiley & Sons, Inc.)

and equally important function of the citric acid cycle is to serve as a central metabolic hub. Many molecules, such as the carbon skeletons of amino acids, are also metabolized through the citric acid cycle.

7.1.1 | There are eight reactions in the citric acid cycle

The citric acid cycle begins with a condensation of acetyl-CoA with oxaloacetate, generating the six-carbon tricarboxylic acid citrate.

Citrate is formed from acetyl-CoA and oxaloacetate in an aldol condensation. Acetyl-CoA forms the enolate.

Citrate contains a tertiary alcohol that cannot be oxidized. In the next reaction, citrate is isomerized to the secondary alcohol isocitrate by the enzyme aconitase, and the isocitrate is then oxidized to α-ketoglutarate by isocitrate dehydrogenase.

This is a combined dehydration-hydration reaction, which isomerizes the tertiary alcohol citrate to the secondary alcohol isocitrate.

The secondary alcohol in isocitrate is oxidized (dehydrogenated) to give the intermediate oxalosuccinate, which decarboxylates to give α-ketoglutarate.

In this process, a molecule of CO_2 is lost, and electrons from isocitrate are captured by NAD^+, generating $NADH/H^+$. Recall that in these reactions the equivalent of a hydride ion is transferred to NAD^+ forming NADH. The proton is released as a second reaction product and maintains charge balance. Thus the term $NADH/H^+$ represents this pair of reaction products generated in this way. In the next step, α-ketoglutarate is oxidized to succinyl-CoA by α-ketoglutarate dehydrogenase.

Alpha-ketoglutarate undergoes oxidative decarboxylation, a concerted reaction in which the carboxyl group closest to the carbonyl is lost as CO_2 and succinyl-CoA is formed.

Again, a molecule of $NADH/H^+$ is generated; however, in addition to the loss of CO_2, some energy is retained by the creation of a thioester bond between succinate and CoA. Some of this energy is used in the next reaction: the generation of succinate from succinyl-CoA.

The multienzyme complex α-ketoglutarate dehydrogenase is homologous to pyruvate dehydrogenase, seen in section 6.5. There are three different subunits to the enzyme: E1, a thiamine pyrophosphate (TPP) dependent decarboxylase; E2, a dihydrolipoyl transferase; and E3, a dihydrolipoyl dehydrogenase which employs NAD^+ and FAD. The reactions and chemistry that occur between these two oxidative decarboxylations are also conserved.

This oxidation is a substrate-level phosphorylation, a reaction that directly generates ATP or GTP.

Two isoforms of succinyl-CoA synthetase exist. One will form a molecule of guanosine-5′-triphosphate (GTP) from guanosine diphosphate (GDP) and inorganic phosphate (P_i) while the other will form ATP from ADP and P_i. Because GTP is a nucleoside triphosphate, it is energetically equivalent to ATP. Also, because GTP or ATP was generated directly by phosphorylating a nucleoside, this is a **substrate-level phosphorylation**, as opposed to an oxidative phosphorylation (one involving the oxidation of metabolites). Succinate and the remaining molecules in the cycle all have four carbons. The remaining reactions recycle these four carbons back to oxaloacetate, with two of the steps forming reducing equivalents. Succinate is a four-carbon dioic acid; there are no other functional groups, and the two central carbons are simply methylene units.

The remaining three reactions work together to incorporate a keto group onto one of the two central carbons. This keto group in oxaloacetate is necessary to provide the carbonyl group for the condensation reaction between acetyl-CoA and oxaloacetate in the first step of the cycle. The simplest way to think of this is to picture it as a series of simple organic reactions. An alkane can be oxidized into an alkene, which can be hydrated to an alcohol; the resultant alcohol can then be oxidized to a carbonyl group. The citric acid cycle works in the same way.

Succinate has two saturated central carbon atoms. These are desaturated to yield the *trans*-unsaturated dioic acid, fumarate.

In this oxidation, electrons from succinate are transferred to FAD to form the *trans* dioic acid fumarate.

Only the *trans* isomer is formed by succinate dehydrogenase. The natural selection of fumarate may have evolved due to steric hindrance, but it is more likely that the *trans* fumarate was selected over the *cis* isomer for other reasons. The *cis* isomer is more reactive and might participate in unwanted Diels-Alder (2 + 4 cycloaddition) reactions. The reducing equivalent involved in this two-electron reduction is FAD bound to succinate dehydrogenase; however, this FAD is tightly bound to the enzyme and quickly passes these electrons to the mobile electron carrier ubiquinone (Q) producing reduced ubiquinone (QH_2) for the electron transport chain. Fumarate is hydrated to malate, generating a hydroxyl group on one of the two carbons formerly found in the double bond, with water being the source of the hydroxyl group in this reaction.

The alkene moiety of fumarate is hydrated to form the secondary alcohol in malate.

As in most hydration reactions, energy is neither consumed nor produced to an appreciable extent (ΔG is close to zero). Finally, malate is oxidized to oxaloacetate: a four-carbon dioic acid with a keto group adjacent (α) to one of the carboxyls.

The hydroxyl group of malate is oxidized to the carbonyl of oxaloacetate. The electrons are harvested to NAD^+ in the process. This step is also reversible.

Again NAD^+ acquires electrons and is reduced to NADH. The cycle starts again using oxaloacetate.

To briefly review, the citric acid cycle takes a two-carbon intermediate (acetyl-CoA) and condenses it with a four-carbon intermediate (oxaloacetate), forming a six-carbon tricarboxylic acid (citrate). Citrate cannot be metabolized further and so is isomerized to isocitrate (moving from a tertiary to a secondary alcohol). Isocitrate is oxidized at this alcohol, first to α-ketoglutarate (five carbons) and then to succinyl-CoA (four carbons). At each of these oxidations, energy is harvested in the form of $NADH/H^+$. Succinyl-CoA is cleaved to liberate succinate, generating a molecule of GTP or ATP in the process. The final three reactions—dehydrogenation, hydration, and oxidation—regenerate oxaloacetate.

Desaturations often employ the cofactor FAD (as succinate dehydrogenase does in this reaction), whereas the second oxidation (malate dehydrogenase) uses NAD^+. Overall, the cycle generates two molecules of CO_2, one molecule of GTP or ATP, three molecules of $NADH/H^+$, and one molecule of $FADH_2$ (**Figure 7.3**).

Many of the cofactors employed in the citric acid cycle or other biochemical pathways are the vitamins and minerals we consume in our diet. A brief history of these molecules is found in **Societal and Ethical Biochemistry: Vitamins in human health and disease.**

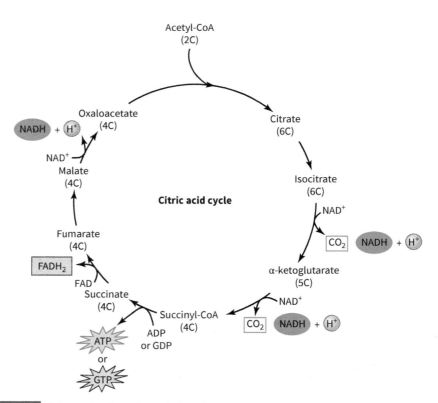

FIGURE 7.3 **Schematic view of the citric acid cycle.** This simplified view of the citric acid cycle shows the number of carbons in each intermediate as well as where energy is siphoned off as NADH, $FADH_2$, or GTP or ATP.

Societal and Ethical Biochemistry

Vitamins in human health and disease

There are several molecules such as NAD^+, FAD, biotin, and cobalamin that do not readily fit into the simple categories of amino acid, carbohydrate, fatty acid, and nucleotide. These molecules are derived from essential nutrients known as vitamins.

The term "vitamin" was coined by the Polish–American biochemist Casimir Funk, who merged the terms "vital" and "amine" (at the time, the compounds under investigation all contained amine moieties). Vitamins are small organic molecules produced by organisms, often by bacteria or plants.

Thiamine (vitamin B1)

Riboflavin (vitamin B2)

Nicotinamide (vitamin B3)

Hydroxycobalamin (X=OH) (vitamin B12)

Pantothenic acid (vitamin B5)

Pyridoxol (vitamin B6)

Biotin (vitamin B7)

Ascorbic acid (vitamin C)

Folic acid (vitamin B9)

Tocopherol (vitamin E)

Currently, 13 vitamins are recognized as necessary for human health: A, C, E, D, K, and the eight B vitamins. Humans cannot synthesize most of these compounds, except for small amounts of vitamins D and K. Vitamin B12 is generally obtained from animal sources in the diet; thus, vegetarians often have to take a vitamin B12 supplement. Vitamins themselves are not categorized as exclusive chemical species but rather as families of related molecules that can be biochemically converted from one form to another. Hence, "vitamin A" contains the active molecule retinal, but also contains retinol, lutein, and several other provitamins. Vitamins can be crudely categorized as being either fat soluble (A, D, E, and K) or water soluble (the B vitamins and vitamin C). Some of the chemical names of the vitamins in this list may be familiar as molecules encountered previously or as precursors for molecules studied; examples include vitamin B7 (biotin) seen in CO_2 binding, and vitamins B3 and B2 (niacin and riboflavin), which are precursors to NAD^+ and FAD.

When these compounds are lacking in the diet, it is hard if not impossible to perform the reactions they help to catalyze. This explains why a shortage or lack of vitamins in the diet leads to vitamin deficiencies and disease.

Vitamin deficiencies hold an odd niche both in medicine and in military history. Since the beginning of time, people have suffered from vitamin deficiencies based on poor diet or lack of

particular vitamins at certain times of the year. Under the obligation and confinement of military service, these effects become more pronounced and obvious. British sailors in the 1700s often developed scurvy, which is caused by vitamin C deficiency. At that time, the diet of sailors was comprised of grains, fish, and dried meat, all of which lack vitamin C. Vitamin C is needed for the development of collagen. The vitamin is essential in the formation of hydroxyproline, one of the modified amino acids of collagen. Lacking vitamin C, sailors suffered from anemia, general lethargy, failure to heal wounds, loss of teeth and hair, bleeding from mucus membranes, and jaundice. Scurvy was often fatal, and it was of great concern to the Royal Navy. The Scottish physician James Lind published a paper in 1753 in which he proposed treating scurvy with citrus fruits. The Royal Navy adopted the idea and began using limes as part of a sailor's daily rations. Limes were useful because they were resistant to rot, but by themselves they were difficult to stomach, so sailors took a mixture of lime juice with cane sugar and rum, which is now the basis of the daiquiri cocktail. British sailors became known as "limeys," which entered the vernacular. Although the consumption of citrus helped to prevent scurvy in sailors, it was another 180 years before vitamin C was finally identified as the essential nutrient needed to prevent this disease.

Vitamin B12 deficiency leads to beriberi, a painful neurological and muscle disorder that can be fatal. Takaki Kanehiro, a physician in the Japanese Imperial Navy, noted that enlisted sailors who ate a diet of white rice suffered from this disease, whereas officers aboard the same ships who ate a Western diet did not. This led to an experiment in which sailors on one ship were given a diet of white rice only, and those on a second ship were given a diverse diet. Among the sailors on the traditional diet of white rice, there were 161 cases of beriberi and 25 deaths, whereas, among the sailors on the diverse diet, there were 14 cases of beriberi and no deaths. Although the results showed that the disease was probably linked to the diet, the results were unfortunately misinterpreted as being due to a protein deficiency and not to low vitamin B12 levels.

The United States also has a military link to vitamin deficiencies. On entering World War I and instituting the draft, many recruits were unfit for basic training because of malnutrition leading to rickets, pellagra, and goiters. This led to two major civilian initiatives. First, many foods in America (especially foods made with wheat flour) were "enriched"; that is, they were supplemented with B vitamins. The idea was that because Americans consume bread with most meals, adding vitamins to the bread would reduce malnutrition. The other initiative was the recommended daily allowance (RDA) of vitamins and minerals. Interestingly, the National Institutes of Health (NIH) does not oversee the RDA. Rather, the United States Department of Agriculture (USDA) does, an organization whose role is to promote the production and consumption of U.S. agricultural products both at home and abroad. The RDA has changed over the years. Initially, its purpose was research into the daily consumption of vitamins needed to prevent disease in young, adult Caucasian males. Stemming from that research, scientists began to question whether the absence of disease equates to health. More recently, the RDA has been amended to reflect the findings from more detailed research, for example, into how quickly vitamins and minerals pass through the body. Also, the values now take into account the different nutritional needs of various other groups of people: women, teenagers, children, pregnant women, and the elderly.

Vitamins are often conflated with minerals. However, minerals (calcium, chlorine, cobalt, copper, iodine, iron, magnesium, molybdenum, phosphorus, potassium, selenium, sodium, sulfur, and zinc) differ from vitamins in that they are all the ions of inorganic elements and are typically found in the diet as simple salts or as cofactors in the proteins of food. As discussed, these molecules are important in several enzymes and proteins. Other minerals that may have roles in biochemistry include arsenic, boron, chromium, and silicon, although the dietary need for any of these elements is likely to be exceedingly low as elevated levels of many of these compounds is toxic.

Today, many people consume vitamins as a dietary supplement. Although the efficacy of dietary supplements has not been wholeheartedly embraced by the medical field, most (but not all) physicians believe that limited supplements are not harmful to health. When taken in large quantity, however, supplements can lead to health problems. Several case studies have been published of people believing that it was healthy to consume massive amounts of carrots, carrot juice, or vitamin A (in some reports, patients consumed upwards of several pounds of carrots a day). Often, these patients have an orange skin tone, due to either excess carotenoid consumption or jaundice, and the effects can sometimes be fatal. Autopsies of these patients often reveal fatty liver and cirrhosis as a result of the vitamin A burden placed on their livers.

Exactly how much Americans spend on vitamins and minerals is unknown, but estimates range from $22 to $40 billion a year, more than the total amount the U.S. government spends on biomedical research. These numbers do not include nutritional supplements and alternative health practices, each of which is estimated at twice what is spent on vitamins and minerals.

Clearly, vitamins are big business, and many stores specialize in these compounds; however, what is less clear is whether vitamin supplements are necessary and in what doses. Questions also remain about the bioavailability of these molecules. Do vitamins in tablet form have the same bioavailability as those found naturally in food?

In many ways, the central importance of the citric acid cycle and its resulting popularity has been to its detriment. Many students first encounter the citric acid cycle in middle or high school, where it has been stripped of all chemical information and is merely a series of boxes. This is often repeated in biology classes leading all the way into biochemistry. The citric acid cycle is a series of chemical reactions; if you wish to memorize the pathway you can, but eventually your memory will fail, and the names and shapes, without any underlying chemistry or structure, are meaningless. However, if you take the time to study the reactions involved and look at the chemistry occurring, understand why a reaction has to proceed in the way that it does, and identify in detail what the structures are, it should make the cycle a lot easier to learn and much easier to understand. This approach applies to all biochemical pathways and all metabolism, not just the citric acid cycle (**Table 7.1**).

The citric acid cycle is an example of a **metabolon**: a group of enzymes performing reactions with a common purpose. These enzymes may be localized in an organelle or part of an organelle. This differs from a pathway in that the individual enzymes of the metabolon may function in multienzyme complexes, and there may be interactions between individual proteins or complexes of proteins. In a metabolon, **substrate channeling** may occur, that is, the diversion of the product of one enzymatic reaction directly into a subsequent reaction, to increase reaction rate and efficiency. As purification techniques and biophysical and analytical techniques improve, enzymes and reactions that were formerly thought to function in isolation are increasingly being identified as part of a larger system. Metabolons have been associated with glycolysis, glycogenolysis, fatty acid biosynthesis, and the electron transport chain. In this regard, these complexes are similar to the multienzyme systems involved in cellular processes such as DNA replication, transcription, translation, signal transduction, and vesicular trafficking.

TABLE 7.1   **Reactions of the Citric Acid Cycle**

Reaction	Structure	Enzyme	$\Delta G^{\circ\prime}$ (kJ/mol)	ΔG (kJ/mol)
Acetyl-CoA + oxaloacetate + $H_2O \rightarrow$ CoASH + citrate		Citrate synthase	−31.4	−53.9
Citrate $\rightarrow$ isocitrate		Aconitase	+6.7	+0.8
Isocitrate + $NAD^+ \rightarrow \alpha$-ketoglutarate + $NADH + CO_2$		Isocitrate dehydrogenase	−8.4	−17.5
α-ketoglutarate + CoASH + $NAD^+ \rightarrow$ succinyl-CoA + $NADH + CO_2$		α−ketoglutarate dehydrogenase	−30	−43.9
Succinyl-CoA + GDP or ADP + $P_i \rightarrow$ succinate + GTP or ATP + CoASH		Succinyl-CoA synthetase	−3.3	~0
Succinate + FAD $\rightarrow$ fumarate + $FADH_2$		Succinyl-Co A dehydrogenase	+0.4	~0
Fumarate + $H_2O \rightarrow$ malate		Fumarase	−3.8	~0
Malate + NAD $\rightarrow$ oxaloacetate + $NADH + H^+$		Malate dehydrogenase	+29.7	~0

WORKED PROBLEM 7.1 | The citric acid cycles?

Some view the citric acid cycle as two separate linear pathways that have joined through evolution. Can you identify these two pathways? What would be their function if they were independent of one another?

Strategy   Examine Figure 7.2. Where are reasonable places to divide the citric acid cycle in half? Do any of the reactions seem to chemically fit together better than others?

Solution   We can view the citric acid cycle as having two parts. One part, an initial oxidative part, is where citrate is gradually oxidized to α-ketoglutarate and then to succinyl-CoA. A secondary oxidative part is where succinate is gradually oxidized back into oxaloacetate to continue the cycle.

Evolutionary biochemists who study primitive bacteria have hypothesized instances where the second half of the citric acid cycle runs in reverse, that is, from oxaloacetate to malate to fumarate to succinate. This path would enable anaerobic bacteria to regenerate NAD^+ to keep glycolysis moving forward and generating ATP. The first half of the citric acid cycle could keep running to generate intermediates for amino acid production or other metabolic pathways.

Follow-up question   If the two proposed pathways did evolve earlier in the history of life on Earth, what does this say about the other reactions of the citric acid cycle, the proteins that catalyze these reactions, and the genes that code for these proteins?

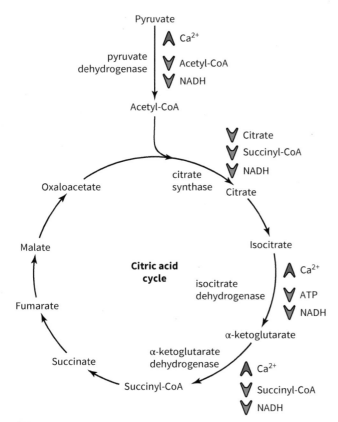

7.1.2 The citric acid cycle is regulated at multiple places and by several different mechanisms

In any metabolic pathway, we anticipate that the committed steps—those in which metabolites enter or leave the pathway or the rate-determining steps—are regulation points through the pathway. The citric acid cycle is no different, but because of its cyclic nature and the multiple substrates that feed into it, there are several enzymes and mechanisms of control. See **Figure 7.4** and Table 7.1.

The energetics of the citric acid cycle   Examining the reactions of the citric acid cycle shows that, as expected, several of the reactions have large negative standard free energies ($\Delta G^{\circ\prime}$). The cleavage of the thioester bond in acetyl-CoA by citrate synthase helps to drive this reaction and give it a highly negative ΔG value. Likewise, the release of CO_2 in the reactions catalyzed by isocitrate dehydrogenase and α-ketoglutarate dehydrogenase increases the entropy of the system and helps to drive ΔG down, thus making the reaction more favorable.

Note that two values are provided in Table 7.1, ΔG and $\Delta G^{\circ\prime}$. Recall from Chapter 1 that $\Delta G^{\circ\prime}$ is established under standard concentrations and conditions which vary widely from the actual concentrations and conditions in the cell (section 1.1). In the cell, or in any reaction that is running under nonstandard conditions, the free energy change of a reaction, denoted here as ΔG, is equal to the standard free energy change, plus a term describing the reaction concentrations and temperature: $\Delta G^{\circ\prime} + RT \ln Q$, where Q is the reaction quotient (the concentration of the products over the reactants raised to the power of the coefficient preceding each substance in the balanced chemical equation).

The other reactions of the citric acid cycle have standard free energy values relatively close to zero. Therefore, in the cell under physiological conditions, these reactions are driven in the forward direction by manipulating concentrations of the substrate and product.

FIGURE 7.4 Regulation of the citric acid cycle.   The citric acid cycle is regulated primarily by levels of substrates and products (such as citrate and succinate). The main allosteric regulator is AMP, but Ca^{2+}, ADP, and ATP regulate steps as well.

Substrate availability   Flux through the citric acid cycle is largely regulated by levels of substrates. Increased levels of substrates generally increase flux through the pathway and most of the reactions are inhibited by their products. Therefore, a stoppage at any point in the pathway can lead to inhibition of most of the prior steps. NADH is a product of three of the four dehydrogenases of the citric acid cycle, and it inhibits all three of these enzymes: isocitrate dehydrogenase, α-ketoglutarate dehydrogenase, and malate dehydrogenase.

Several other products inhibit the enzymes that generate them. For example, succinyl-CoA inhibits α-ketoglutarate dehydrogenase, and citrate inhibits citrate synthase.

Allosteric regulation   Because the citric acid cycle is central in the production of energy in the cell, it is also expected that molecular indicators of a low energy state will stimulate the pathway. High levels of adenosine diphosphate (ADP) indicate that energy (in the form of ATP) is in demand in the cell. Although the total concentration of all adenine nucleotides ([ATP] + [ADP] + [AMP]) in the cell is fairly constant, the balance between them shifts, based on the energetic state of the cell. Two reactions of the citric acid cycle are activated by increased concentrations of ADP: citrate synthase and isocitrate dehydrogenase.

Whether ATP inhibits the enzymes of the citric acid cycle is somewhat unclear. High concentrations of ATP will inhibit isolated enzymes from specific tissues (for example, isocitrate dehydrogenase from the heart) but not others (α-ketoglutarate dehydrogenase). Further complicating matters is the general observation that, in the transition from fully fed and rested to maximally exerted, total ATP concentrations change little (by less than 10%). Because of this relatively small change in concentration, it is unlikely that ATP can act as an allosteric regulator. ATP inhibition of the citric acid cycle has not been observed in isolated mitochondria. This highlights another complicating factor: the setting in which the enzymes function. In the mitochondrial matrix, these proteins are present at high concentration. In the purified state, devoid of the other molecules involved in the citric acid cycle, these enzymes may not behave as they do *in vivo*. Finally, structural data have not found an ATP binding site in either individual subunits or complexes of the enzymes of the citric acid cycle. The ATP/ADP ratio or energetic state of the cell is clearly involved in the regulation of the citric acid cycle, but which enzymes are interacting and involved is a matter of debate.

Ca^{2+} is an allosteric regulator that activates isocitrate dehydrogenase and α-ketoglutarate dehydrogenase. Calcium ions are important signaling molecules in the cell: they moderate vesicle fusion and muscle cell contraction (both of which require energy). Therefore, it makes chemical sense that these same signals also directly tell the citric acid cycle to feed more molecules toward ATP biosynthesis.

A final allosteric regulator that is worthy of mention is succinyl-CoA. Although this molecule inhibits the enzyme that makes it (α-ketoglutarate dehydrogenase), it also serves as an inhibitor of citrate synthase.

There are several other ways in which products of the citric acid cycle can increase or decrease flux though the pathway. Citrate inhibits the glycolytic enzyme phosphofructokinase, slowing glycolysis, which thus slows the production of pyruvate (and therefore of acetyl-CoA for the citric acid cycle). Pyruvate dehydrogenase (the committed step in the conversion of pyruvate to acetyl-CoA) is inhibited by its products NADH and acetyl-CoA and is activated allosterically by Ca^{2+}. The regulation of this step directly prevents the formation of acetyl-CoA (see section 6.5).

Hypoxia describes low oxygen levels in a cell, organ, or tissue. A family of transcription factors, known as hypoxia inducible factors (HIFs), is involved in the regulation of cellular processes such as angiogenesis (growth of new blood vessels), glycolysis, and the electron transport chain. HIFs respond to low oxygen levels. At high levels of oxygen, a hydroxyl group is added to a proline residue on HIF. The hydroxylation initiates assembly of a complex of proteins on HIF, including a ubiquitin ligase. Ubiquitin is a small protein that marks proteins for destruction through proteosomal degradation. At low levels of oxygen (hypoxia), there is less hydroxylation of HIF, which allows the transcription factor to move to the nucleus where it binds to DNA, triggering a cascade of transcriptional events that increase the amount of oxygen available to tissues.

Hydroxylation of prolines promotes interaction of HIF with the E3 ubiquitin ligase complex. The citric acid cycle intermediates succinate and fumarate inhibit prolyl 4-hydroxylases; therefore, high levels of these intermediates block the hydroxylase and thus block the interaction with E3 ubiquitin ligase, and the ubiquitination and degradation of HIF.

7.1.3 Anaplerotic reactions of the citric acid cycle replenish intermediates

If the only function of the citric acid cycle were to oxidize acetyl-CoA to CO_2, we could ignore the levels of the other intermediates in the cycle. However, numerous pathways converge on the citric acid cycle, either contributing to or depleting levels of the intermediates. Such pathways include biosynthesis and degradation of amino acids, gluconeogenesis, and biosynthesis of porphyrin and nucleotides. **Anaplerosis** is the scientific term for "filling up." Anaplerotic reactions replenish levels of citric acid cycle intermediates through a number of mechanisms, four of which are highlighted here: one that replenishes α-ketoglutarate, one that replenishes succinyl-CoA, and two that replenish oxaloacetate (**Figure 7.5**).

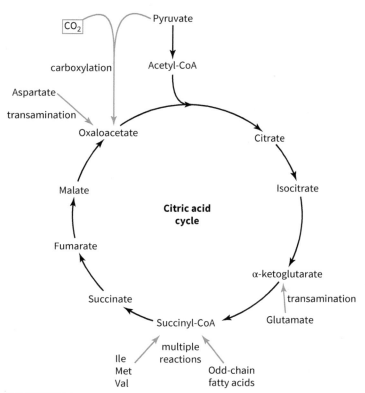

Alpha-ketoglutarate

Levels of α-ketoglutarate can be replenished by removal of the amine moiety from the amino acid glutamate. This reaction is catalyzed by glutamate dehydrogenase and is a key reaction of anaplerosis, the detoxification of amine groups, and the catabolism of amino acids. Amine groups are often shuttled to α-ketoglutarate (a process called transamination) to generate glutamate and a new α-keto acid from the old amino acid. The new molecule of glutamate can be transported in the blood to the liver for deamination to α-ketoglutarate. The resulting amino group is detoxified via the urea cycle, which is discussed in section 11.3.

$$\begin{array}{ccc} COO^- & & COO^- \\ | & & | \\ CH_2 & \quad NAD^+ \; NADH \quad & CH_2 \\ | & & | \\ CH_2 & & CH_2 \\ | & & | \\ NH_2-CH-COO^- + H_2O & \rightleftharpoons & NH_3 + O=CH-COO^- \\ \textbf{Glutamate} & & \textbf{Ammonia} \;\; \textbf{α-ketoglutarate} \end{array}$$

Succinyl-CoA

Levels of succinyl-CoA can be replenished through several intermediates that converge on the three-carbon fatty acid propionyl-CoA. Propionyl-CoA can be generated via catabolism of odd-chain fatty acids, branched-chain amino acids (leucine, isoleucine, and valine), or the amino acids threonine and methionine (via α-ketobutyrate) (Figure 7.6).

In propionyl-CoA carboxylase, a molecule of CO_2 is added to propionyl-CoA in a reaction employing a biotin functional group (Figure 7.7). Enzymes that add CO_2 to a molecule often employ a biotin functional group. In this particular reaction, CO_2 first reacts with the γ phosphate of ATP to form a carboxyphosphate. The lone pair of electrons on one of the ring nitrogens of biotin attacks the carbon of the carboxyphosphate, forming a carboxybiotin adduct as phosphate leaves. Next, the propionyl-CoA attacks the carboxyl carbon, facilitated by resonance stabilization and the anionic character of the α carbon of the propionate group. Methylmalonyl-CoA is released as the product. The S isoform is racemized into the R isomer by methylmalonyl CoA racemase (also known as methylmalonyl-CoA epimerase). Methylmalonyl-CoA mutase converts methylmalonyl-CoA to succinyl-CoA through a process that depends on cobalamin (vitamin B12). As with the biotin-dependent carboxylation described earlier in this chapter, this isomerization reaction also occurs in fatty acid biosynthesis (Figure 7.8).

FIGURE 7.5 **Central role of the citric acid cycle in metabolism.** Numerous pathways converge on the citric acid cycle. Anaplerotic reactions such as the carboxylation of proprionyl-CoA to succinyl-CoA build up intermediates of the cycle, while cataplerotic reactions (transaminations with α-ketoglutarate, for example) deplete the cycle of intermediates.

FIGURE 7.6 **Conversion of propionyl-CoA to succinyl-CoA.** Propionyl-CoA is derived from the catabolism of some amino acids and from fatty acids with odd numbers of carbons. Propionyl-CoA is carboxylated to methylmalonyl-CoA in a biotin-dependent process. Methylmalonyl-CoA is isomerized to succinyl-CoA by a vitamin B12 (cobalamin)-dependent enzyme.

1. Carbonate oxygen attacks γ-phosphate of ATP.

2. Electrons flow out of biotin and into carbonyl phosphate.

3. Generating carboxybiotin.

4. Base abstracts proton from α-carbon, generating enolate.

5. Carboxybiotin decarboxylates.

6. Enolate attacks carbon dioxide, generating methylmalony-CoA.

7. Biotin reprotonates regenerating enzyme.

FIGURE 7.7 **Mechanism of propionyl-CoA carboxylase.** Most carboxylases have a similar mechanism. Carbonate attacks the γ phosphate of ATP generating a carbonyl phosphate. The carbonyl phosphate is then attacked by one of the ring nitrogens of biotin. Phosphate departs and carboxybiotin is left. Carboxybiotin donates a CO_2 which is then attacked by the carbanionic form of propionyl-CoA. The product reprotonates to form malonyl-CoA.

1. Homolytic bond cleavage between Co and C leaves C radical.

2. Substrate binds and donates H to C radical, forming bond to Co^{2+}.

3. Bonds rearrange.

4. Bonds rearrange.

5. Product abstracts H from Ado C.

6. Product released, C-Co bond reforms.

FIGURE 7.8 **Mechanism of methylmalonyl-CoA mutase.** Methylmalonyl-CoA mutase catalyzes the rearrangement of methylmalonyl-CoA to succinyl-CoA. This enzyme uses a cobalamin (vitamin B12) cofactor for catalysis.

| 1. Base abstracts proton from β-carbon. | 2. Carboxybiotin decarboxylates. | 3. Electron flow from the enolate attacks carbon dioxide. |
| 4. Product (oxaloacetate) departs. | 5. Electron flow reverses reprotonating biotin. | 6. Regenerated biotin. |

FIGURE 7.9 **Mechanism of pyruvate carboxylase.** The carboxylation of pyruvate proceeds similarly to the carboxylation of propionate. First, carboxybiotin must be formed. This step requires ATP and formation of a carboxyl phosphate to provide energy and a leaving group to couple the carboxyl group to biotin (shown previously in Figure 7.6). In the model shown, the terminal carbon of pyruvate is deprotonated to generate an enolate. The enolate, in turn, attacks the CO_2 carbon, forming a new carboxyl group off C-3. The ring ketone of biotin is regenerated by protonation from the same base that deprotonated pyruvate earlier.

Oxaloacetate

Oxaloacetate can be synthesized from either pyruvate or the amino acid aspartate (**Figure 7.9**). Pyruvate can be acted on by pyruvate carboxylase to generate the oxaloacetate used in gluconeogenesis. Like propionyl-CoA carboxylase, pyruvate carboxylase is biotin dependent. Oxaloacetate generated by this process is retained in the mitochondrial matrix for use in the citric acid cycle, whereas oxaloacetate used for gluconeogenesis is first reduced to malate, then exported from the mitochondrial matrix and reoxidized back to oxaloacetate.

In the same way that α-ketoglutarate can be generated from glutamate, oxaloacetate can be generated by the transamination of aspartate (**Figure 7.10**). Aspartate aminotransferase catalyzes the exchange of amino groups between aspartate and α-ketoglutarate, generating oxaloacetate and glutamate. Both of these enzymes employ a pyridoxal phosphate cofactor to carry out catalysis.

The reactions that replenish citric acid cycle intermediates also highlight the role of the citric acid cycle as a central metabolic hub. Many molecules are either broken down into citric acid cycle intermediates or synthesized from them. Taken a step further, not all metabolites need to completely participate in the citric acid cycle. For example, the carbon skeletons of amino acids that enter the citric acid cycle as α-ketoglutarate can exit as succinyl-CoA and contribute to heme biosynthesis.

FIGURE 7.10 **Transamination of aspartate.** Aspartate can undergo a transamination reaction, effectively swapping an amino group with α-ketoglutarate to yield glutamate and oxaloacetate.

| Glutamate | | Oxaloacetate | | α-ketoglutarate | | Aspartate |

WORKED PROBLEM 7.2 | Anaplerotic reactions

Acetyl-CoA contributes directly to the formation of citrate, but acetate is not considered an anaplerotic intermediate. Explain why this is the case.

Strategy   Review the reactions of the citric acid cycle. What does "anaplerosis" mean?

Solution   Anaplerotic reactions "build up" levels of citric acid cycle intermediates, replenishing them. The intermediates most often discussed include α-ketoglutarate, succinyl-CoA, and oxalo-acetate. The reactions of the citric acid cycle themselves are not thought of as anaplerotic because they do not lead to an increase in

the concentration of that intermediate; the product of the reaction is immediately used by the next step. Because the formation of citrate from acetyl-CoA and oxaloacetate is part of the citric acid cycle, this step does not really elevate to the concentrations of intermediates and it is not anaplerotic.

Follow-up question   In several neurodegenerative processes, fluctuations of glutamate and glutamine levels lead to low energy levels in the cell by slowing down the citric acid cycle. Suggest how depletion of cellular glutamate could reduce flux through the citric acid cycle.

7.1 Summary

- The citric acid cycle is an oxidative pathway that enables the organism to harvest electrons from carbon-containing intermediates (with the electrons captured in the reducing equivalents NAD^+ and FAD, and energy captured in the form of a molecule of GTP or ATP).

- The cycle is:

  o regulated by levels of substrates and allosteric regulators such as ADP and citrate.

  o the entry point of many molecules other than acetyl-CoA into metabolism, including many amino acid skeletons.

  o the source of the building blocks of many molecules, including many amino acids.

- Anaplerotic reactions act to build up levels of citric acid cycle intermediates that may have been drained by other metabolic needs.

7.1 Concept Check

- Trace the reactions of the citric acid cycle in terms of the chemistry occurring in each step, the structures of the intermediates, and in terms of where NADH and $FADH_2$ are harvested.

- Show which steps of the citric acid cycle are regulated and how they are regulated. (This should make biochemical sense: when energy (in the form of ATP) is abundant, the cycle is slowed, but when there is a lack of energy, flux through the pathway is increased.)

- Identify which reactions act to build up citric acid cycle intermediates, and explain the chemistry of these reactions.

7.2   The Electron Transport Chain

In the metabolism covered so far in this chapter, a lot of chemistry has occurred, many carbons have been oxidized and numerous electrons have been harvested, but relatively little ATP has been generated. In the catabolism of glucose, glycolysis generated two molecules of ATP and captured four electrons in two molecules of NADH (**Figure 7.11**). Decarboxylation of pyruvate to form acetyl-CoA generated another two molecules of NADH, and oxidation of two molecules of acetyl-CoA into CO_2 produced another six molecules of NADH, two molecules of $FADH_2$, and

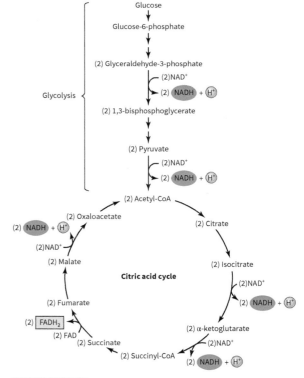

FIGURE 7.11   **Reducing equivalents come from multiple metabolic pathways.**   The reducing equivalents derived from glycolysis, the citric acid cycle, and other metabolic pathways such as β-oxidation (section 9.2) are oxidized in the electron transport chain.

FIGURE 7.12 **Overview of the electron transport chain.** The electron transport chain consists of four complexes that oxidize NADH and FADH$_2$ back to NAD$^+$ and FAD. The electrons from these complexes are passed through a series of redox centers ultimately being consumed in the formation of water in complex IV. The passage of electrons through these complexes provides energy to pump protons from the mitochondrial matrix to the intermembrane space. This proton gradient is used to synthesize ATP by the ATP synthase. Molecular weights and number of subunits provided are for the mammalian electron transport chain. (Complex I: PDB ID 5LDW Zhu, J., Vinothkumar, K.R., Hirst, J. (2016) Structure of mammalian respiratory complex I. *Nature* 536: 354-358; Complex III: PDB ID 3CX5 Solmaz, S.R., Hunte, C. (2008) Structure of complex III with bound cytochrome c in reduced state and definition of a minimal core interface for electron transfer. *J.Biol.Chem.* 283: 17542-17549; Complex II: PDB ID 1NEN Yankovskaya, V., Horsefield, R., Tornroth, S., Luna-Chavez, C., Miyoshi, H., Leger, C., Byrne, B., Cecchini, G., Iwata, S. (2003) Architecture of succinate dehydrogenase and reactive oxygen species generation *Science* 299: 700-704; Complex IV: PDB ID 5B1A Yano, N., Muramoto, K., Shimada, A., Takemura, S., Baba, J., Fujisawa, H., Mochizuki, M., Shinzawa-Itoh, K., Yamashita, E., Tsukihara, T., Yoshikawa, S. (2016) The Mg^{2+}-containing Water Cluster of Mammalian Cytochrome c Oxidase Collects Four Pumping Proton Equivalents in Each Catalytic Cycle. *J.Biol.Chem.* 291: 23882-23894; ATP synthase: PDB ID 5ARA Zhou, A., Rohou, A., Schep, D.G., Bason, J.V., Montgomery, M.G., Walker, J.E., Grigorieff, N., Rubinstein, J.L. (2015) Structure and conformational states of the bovine mitochondrial ATP synthase by cryo-EM. *Elife* 4: e10180-e10180)

two molecules of GTP or ATP. Thus, starting from a single molecule of glucose, at this point, metabolism has generated four ATP or their equivalent, but ten NADH, and two FADH$_2$.

Although relatively little ATP has been generated, the chemical energy of reactions has been stored in electron carriers, primarily NADH. This section describes the electron transport chain and how it uses that energy and those electrons to pump protons out of the mitochondrial matrix. Section 7.3 shows how the energy of the proton gradient created in this step drives ATP synthase.

The electron transport chain occurs in the matrix and inner mitochondrial membrane of eukaryotic cells. Protons are pumped out of the mitochondrial matrix and NADH and FADH$_2$ are oxidized back to NAD$^+$ and FAD. Four complexes—named I, II, III, and IV—are involved in this process. One of these complexes we have already seen. Complex II is succinate dehydrogenase from the citric acid cycle and was discussed in section 7.1.1. This section outlines the means by which electrons are transported through the complexes and discusses the structure and functions of each of the four complexes (**Figure 7.12**).

7.2.1 Electron transport occurs through a series of redox active centers from higher to lower potential energy

As glucose is metabolized through glycolysis, it is converted from one intermediate to the next. Almost all of these intermediates are stable molecules that can be isolated. Hence, it is possible to imagine glycolysis as an assembly line in which one molecule is transformed to the next, or as a cafeteria where one chooses a lunch, a drink, and finally a dessert from a range of alternatives. No matter how we envision these reactions occurring, the analogy falls woefully

TABLE 7.2   Reduction Potentials of Electron Carriers Found in Biochemistry

Component	Reduction Potential $(E^{\circ\prime})$, V	Component	Reduction Potential $(E^{\circ\prime})$, V
NADH	−0.315	Ubiquinone	0.045
Complex I (NADH:coenzymeq oxidoreductase, ~900 kDa, 45 subunits)		**Complex III (UQ-cytochrome _c_ oxdoreductase, 450 kDa, 9–11 subunits)**	
FMN	−0.380	Heme b_H	0.030
[2Fe-2S]N1a	−0.370	Heme b_L	−0.030
[2Fe-2S]N1b	−0.250	[2Fe-2S]	0.280
[4Fe-4S]N3, 4, 5, 6a, 6b 7	−0.250	Heme c_1	0.215
[2Fe-2S]N2	−0.150	Cytochrome _c_	0.235
Succinate	0.031	**Cytochrome IV (cytochrome _c_ oxidase, ~410 kDa 8–13 subunits)**	
Complex II (succinate-CoQ oxidoreductase, ~140 kDa, 4 subunits)		Heme _a_	0.210
FAD	−0.040	Cu_A	0.245
[2Fe-2S]	−0.030	Cu_B	0.340
[4Fe-4S]	−0.245	Heme a_3	0.385
[3Fe-4S]	−0.060	O_2	0.815
Heme b_{560}	−0.080		

short when considering electron transport, which can seem more akin to a gymnastic routine. A gymnast cannot simply stop during a routine and hold a pose for a prolonged period; rather, the routine is dynamic and controlled with great precision. Similarly, it is the precise control of electron flow that permits electron transport to occur.

As with a gymnast performing a routine, electrons flow smoothly down a gradient of reduction potentials, moving from one electron carrier to another, and changing the oxidation state of that carrier as they do so (Table 7.2). In some instances, this change can be blocked and the reduced intermediate isolated, but often it cannot. Disruption of the complex would lead to oxidation or reduction of other carriers, and a loss of the signal. Unlike molecules, electrons cannot be isotopically labeled; instead, they are often tracked spectrophotometrically as they perform chemistry on a chromophore, or as their spin state changes. Electron spin can be determined using electron paramagnetic resonance (EPR).

Each electron carrier involved in the electron transport chain has a different reduction potential, dependent on both the carrier and its environment. Therefore, changes in protein conformation can help to fine-tune the affinity of the carrier for electrons and keep the flow of electrons unidirectional. The electron carriers found in the electron transport chain are listed in (Figure 7.13).

- Flavins, such as FAD (flavin adenine dinucleotide) and FMN (flavin mononucleotide (FMN), employ the tricyclic isoalloxazine ring to bind electrons on the N-5 position. Flavins can transport different numbers of electrons: none (fully oxidized), one (partially reduced), or two (fully reduced).

- Quinones, such as ubiquinone, have a six-membered aromatic dione structure. Electrons can be exchanged between the ring and the structure to be reduced or oxidized. Like flavins, quinones can be fully reduced (dihydroquinone), partially reduced (a semiquinone), or fully oxidized (quinone).

- Heme groups employ an active metal center, usually iron in electron transport, bound to a porphyrin ring in a planar, heterocyclic cofactor. The iron ion is bound by the four nitrogens of the porphyrin ring. Heme proteins bind to the porphyrin ring through either

A.

B.

Ubiquinone

FAD

C.

Heme

D.

2Fe-2S

3Fe-3S

4Fe-4S

FIGURE 7.13 **Electron carriers in the electron transport chain.** Shown are some of the electron carriers employed by the electron transport chain. **A.** In FAD, the reduction occurs on the N-1 and N-5 positions. **B.** In ubiquinone (also known as coenzyme Q 10), the carbonyl groups are reduced to hydroxyl groups. **C.** Shown is an example of a heme group. The iron ion in the core of the organic complex (a protoporphyrin ring) carries the electrons. **D.** In iron-sulfur centers, the electrons are delocalized throughout the complex. The reduction potentials of each of these centers can be tuned by the local environment, so that electrons flow from one electron carrier to the next, moving from higher to lower reduction potential.

cysteine or histidine groups. Amino acid side chains of the protein (typically histidine or cysteine residues) also chelate (bind) the metal ion center above or below the plane of the porphyrin ring. Although this section focuses on heme proteins in the context of electron transport, heme groups also figure prominently in oxygen transport and in binding and catalysis. Heme groups bind a single electron, with the central iron ion fluctuating between Fe^{2+} and Fe^{3+} states.

- **Iron-sulfur centers** are found in iron-sulfur proteins. There are three different types: 2Fe-2S, 3Fe-3S, and 4Fe-4S. In each of these centers, there is a specific geometric arrangement of sulfur and iron atoms. Each iron-sulfur center can bind a single electron, delocalized across the entire center. Cysteine residues bind the iron-sulfur center in place in the protein. Often, multiple iron-sulfur centers are found in a single protein or protein complex.

- Copper centers found in cytochrome oxidase also act in electron transport. There are two such centers: Cu_A, which has two Cu^{2+} ions, and Cu_B, which has a single Cu^{2+} ion. The single electron transferred between these centers is delocalized over both copper ions in Cu_A, but it is bound exclusively by the single copper center in Cu_B.

The electrons flowing through the electron transport chain can be pictured as following little arrows as they move, but in reality, the electrons use the quantum mechanical property of **tunneling** to "hop" from one center to another. Tunneling is the ability of a small particle with sufficient energy, such as an electron, to pass through a barrier that is otherwise impenetrable. This may seem irrational on a macroscopic scale, but the probability of it happening can be predicted using quantum mechanics, and observed results validate the predictions.

While this section focuses on the electron carriers commonly found in electron transport, there are other electron carriers, many of which employ similar chemistry, although they may use different elements to carry these electrons. For example, plastocyanin proteins are small electron carriers used in photosynthesis; they are analogous to cytochromes in several ways but use copper ions rather than a heme group to store electrons. Ferredoxin is also an important electron carrier in several reactions; it employs an iron-sulfur center to store electrons. Other examples include the magnesium-containing center in chlorophyll, and the manganese and calcium atoms in the water-splitting enzyme of photosystem II. Clearly, biology has evolved numerous ways to transport and harness the power of electrons. A review of reduction potential and some of the roles it plays in biochemistry can be found in **Biochemistry: Electrochemistry in biochemistry**.

Biochemistry

Electrochemistry in biochemistry

Electrochemistry is important in biochemistry but is often poorly understood. In this chapter, electrochemistry figures prominently in two different ways: reduction potential and membrane potential. This section examines each in detail.

Reduction potential is a property of all materials but is often encountered in general chemistry as a series of reduction reactions of metals and metal ions. It is the property of all materials to gain or lose an electron or electrons; however, by convention, it is expressed as a reduction (gain of electrons). Reduction potential is measured in volts and is what we typically think of in terms of a battery or wet electrochemical cell. Materials with different reduction potentials will pass electrons from one material to another in a lower energy state (from a more negative reduction potential to a more positive one).

$$Zn^{2+} + 2e^- \rightarrow Zn\,(s) - 0.762$$

All molecules have reduction potentials, even though we commonly think of metals in relation to this type of electrochemistry. In biochemistry, we encounter reduction potentials in electron transport. As electrons pass from one electron carrier to another in the electron transport chain, they move down a series of reduction potentials, culminating in the reduction of oxygen (the formation of water).

$$O_2\,(g) + 4\,H^+ + 2\,e^- \rightarrow 2\,H_2O\,(l) + 1.229\ V$$

The electrochemical potential of protons, also known as the proton motive force or pmf, is the ability of a proton gradient to do work. Electrochemical potential has two components: the *chemical potential* and the *electrostatic potential*.

Chemical potential is the ability of a system of chemicals to do work. Imagine a system in which there is a beaker of water and a dye diffusing from the top of the beaker through the water. The dye molecules will diffuse as the system spontaneously becomes more disordered.

Electrostatic potential is the potential energy of a charged particle in an electric field, divided by the charge on the particle. The units of electrostatic potential are therefore joules/coulomb or volts. In biochemistry, we often see this as a disequilibrium of ions, an uneven concentration of ions across an impermeable or semipermeable membrane. In effect, this is the electronic component known as a capacitor. By segregating more ions on one side of the membrane than another, we create a difference in charge that can be expressed as an electrostatic potential. In biochemistry we term this specific example of electrostatic potential the membrane potential, which is essentially the voltage drop across a membrane.

The combination of membrane potential (electrostatic potential) and chemical potential results in the electrochemical potential, that is, the overall potential of an ion gradient to do work. This chapter discusses the electrochemical potential of the inner mitochondrial membrane, and in biochemistry there are frequent references to the electrochemical potential of cells, such as neurons or cardiomyocytes; however, most cells have an electrochemical potential across their membranes. Most cell types do not have a *polarizable* membrane with pumps and channels to create and use a gradient of ions such as those found in neurons, but most cell membranes are polarized.

Cytosolic NADH is shuttled into the mitochondrial matrix Glycolysis occurs in the cytosol and produces NADH, but complex I (NADH dehydrogenase) oxidizes NADH in the mitochondrial matrix. For NADH to be oxidized, it must be imported to the mitochondrial matrix. The inner mitochondrial membrane is impermeable to NADH, but the cell has evolved several means of transporting other reduced molecules into the mitochondria where they are oxidized (**Figure 7.14**).

The **glycerophosphate shuttle** converts the glycolytic intermediate dihydroxyacetone phosphate (DHAP) to glycerol-3-phosphate. On the inner mitochondrial membrane, a flavoprotein (flavoprotein dehydrogenase) transfers electrons from glycerol-3-phosphate to the FAD center, generating $FADH_2$. The electrons are then passed on to ubiquinone, where they can continue to participate in electron transport. In the process of this reaction, the glycerol-3-phosphate is converted back to DHAP, which can continue to participate in glycolysis.

The **malate-aspartate shuttle** is another means of transporting electrons into the mitochondria. In this shuttle, two exchange proteins (the α-ketoglutarate-malate carrier and the aspartate-glutamate carrier) transport molecules across the inner mitochondrial membrane. The α-ketoglutarate-malate carrier exports α-ketoglutarate from the matrix and imports malate. Once in the mitochondrial matrix, malate can be converted to oxaloacetate through the citric acid cycle, generating NADH. Oxaloacetate can be transaminated to aspartate (exchanging amino groups with glutamate to generate α-ketoglutarate). The aspartate is exchanged from the matrix for glutamate. In the cytosol, aspartate is transaminated with α-ketoglutarate to yield oxaloacetate and glutamate. Unlike the glycerophosphate shuttle, the malate–aspartate shuttle is reversible.

A.

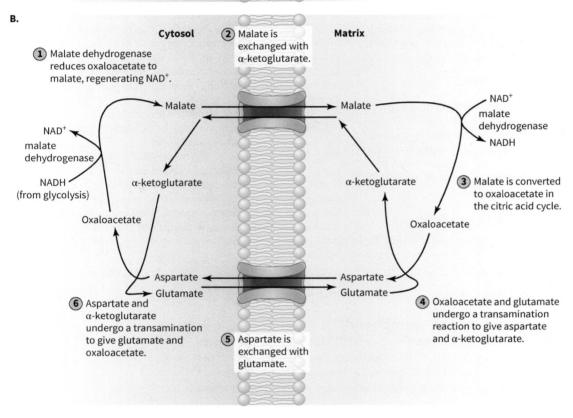

FIGURE 7.14 **Mitochondrial shuttles.** **A.** The glycerol phosphate shuttle uses DHAP to oxidize NADH, generating glycerol-3-phosphate in the process. These electrons are then transferred to FAD when glycerol-3-phosphate is oxidized back to dihydroxyacetone phosphate. **B.** In the malate-aspartate shuttle, glutamate and oxaloacetate undergo a transamination reaction to generate aspartate and α-ketoglutarate. In the cytosol another transamination regenerates glutamate and oxaloacetate. The oxalo-acetate is reduced to malate, which is shuttled back into the mitochondrial matrix where it is oxidized to oxaloacetate, delivering electrons to the matrix in the process.

B.

WORKED PROBLEM 7.3 | Electron flow

Working in the laboratory, you isolated an electron-transfer complex from a microbe that contains the following cofactors: a quinone, a heme complex, Cu^{2+}, and Zn^{2+}. Which of these cofactors are likely to be involved in electron transport? How might electrons flow through this complex?

Strategy Examine Table 7.2. Although all of these cofactors are found in biochemistry, some are more common in electron transport. Redox potentials depend partially on the carrier itself and partially on the microenvironment created by the protein around the center. What are the commonly accepted values for the centers listed in this problem?

Solution It is likely that the three-electron carriers are the quinone, the heme, and the copper ion. Zinc ions figure prominently

in biochemistry, and they are often used as an example when discussing electrochemistry in a general chemistry class, but zinc ions do not usually participate directly in redox chemistry in biochemistry.

In terms of the order, examination of the reduction potentials of the centers shows that the quinone has the lowest value, followed by the heme, and then the copper ion. This is one potential pathway; however, as we have seen, the environment of these redox centers can be altered by their environment.

Follow-up question How could you use spectroscopy to test your hypothesis about the flow of electrons?

Complex I (NADH dehydrogenase) transfers electrons from NADH to ubiquinone via a series of iron-sulfur centers

Complex I is the site of NADH oxidation to NAD^+. This 980 kDa, L-shaped complex is comprised of two large domains: a helical domain buried in the inner mitochondrial membrane, and a second globular domain on the matrix side. In eukaryotes, this complex contains more than 43 polypeptide chains, a tightly bound flavin mononucleotide (FMN) group, and nine different iron-sulfur centers that are used to transfer electrons from NADH, ultimately to the membrane electron carrier **ubiquinone**. The transmembrane domain of the complex is important in pumping protons out of the mitochondrial matrix, and the second domain is where reduction of NADH and transport of electrons occurs (**Figure 7.15**).

Electron transfer in complex I   The precise mechanism of NADH dehydrogenase is still being elucidated, but several important aspects of the enzyme have yielded clues about

A.

Molecular surface

Ribbon structure

Ribbon, electron carriers highlighted

B.

FIGURE 7.15 Complex I.   A. Complex I (NADH dehydrogenase) consists of a large membrane-bound domain where proton pumping occurs and a cytosolic arm responsible for electron transport. Electrons are trafficked from NADH to a flavin center (FMN), through a series of iron-sulfur centers ultimately being used to reduce ubiquinone. A ribbon diagram of the NADH dehydrogenase shows the overall structure and the numerous transmembrane α-helical domains. Movement of electrons through the complex causes a conformational change that results in the pumping of four protons from the matrix to the cytosolic side of the inner mitochondrial membrane. **B.** A transparent view of complex I showing the electron carriers FMN and Fe-S centers and the site of ubiquinone binding. (PDB ID 5LDW Zhu, J., Vinothkumar, K.R., Hirst, J. (2016) Structure of mammalian respiratory complex *I. Nature* 536: 354-358) its function. First, electrons are transferred from NADH in the mitochondrial matrix to the bound FMN cofactor. The isoalloxazine ring of FMN has three different oxidation states: fully reduced, semiquinone (one extra electron), and fully oxidized (two extra electrons). The ability of FMN to function in more than one oxidation state enables the transfer of electrons from the two-electron carrier (NADH). From FMN, the electrons flow through several (up to nine) iron-sulfur centers, including both Fe2-S2 and Fe4-S4.

Ultimately, electrons are transferred to the two-electron carrier ubiquinone. As with FMN, ubiquinone can exist in three different oxidation states: fully reduced (Q), the partially oxidized semiquinone (Q$^-$), and fully oxidized (QH$_2$) (**Figure 7.16**). In addition to its multiple oxidation states, ubiquinone has another feature essential to electron transport: its hydrophobic isoprenoid tail anchors the carrier in the inner mitochondrial membrane and prevents it (and the electrons it is carrying) from diffusing throughout the matrix. Instead, ubiquinone transfers electrons from complex I to complex III. As explained in section 7.2.3, ubiquinone is also used to transfer electrons from complex II to complex III. A different soluble carrier (cytochrome c) is used to transfer electrons from complex III to complex IV (see section 7.2.4).

Complex I pumps protons out of the mitochondrial matrix

As mentioned in section 7.1, electron transport serves two important functions: it oxidizes electron carriers back to their initial states, and it uses the energy of transferring these electrons to pump protons out of the mitochondrial matrix against their concentration gradient, that is, moving protons from lower H$^+$ concentration inside the matrix to higher H$^+$ concentration outside the matrix. Instead of wasting this surplus energy as heat, the electron transfer reactions are coupled to proton transfers across the inner mitochondrial membrane. The protons are transferred against their concentration gradient, and therefore the proton transfers on their own would be energetically unfavorable. However, the overall process, which combines the favorable electron transport processes with the unfavorable proton pumping processes, adds up to a net favorable combined process. In other words, the surplus energy from electron transfer drives the formation of the proton gradient.

The cell uses the proton gradient to synthesize ATP. Complex I contributes to the proton gradient by pumping four protons out of the mitochondrial matrix. Analysis of a bacterial iso-

FIGURE 7.16 **Redox states of ubiquinone and FAD.** **A.** Ubiquinone has a long, hydrophobic isoprenoid tail that anchors it in the inner mitochondrial membrane, but the redox chemistry happens at the quinone end of the molecule. **B.** Ubiquinone can be fully oxidized (the quinone), partially reduced (the semiquinone), or fully reduced (the hydroquinone). **C.** FAD consists of a tricyclic flavin ring connected to the polyol ribitol and then ADP. **D.** The redox chemistry occurs on the nitrogens at positions 1 and 5 on the flavin ring.

form of this protein (a simpler version than the mitochondrial isoform) reveals several features that help to elucidate the process. The bacterial isoform has three domains, each of which has architecture similar to Na^+/H^+ antiporters. These subunits are strongly helical, and they are buried in the inner mitochondrial membrane; they are connected to one another by a single helical segment that is orthogonal (rotated 90°) to the transmembrane helices. This single helix is thought to move back and forth like a piston, opening and shutting the ion channels and pumping protons out of the matrix as electrons flow through the complex.

7.2.3 | Complex II is the citric acid cycle enzyme succinate dehydrogenase

Complex II is succinate dehydrogenase from the citric acid cycle (this enzymatic complex is discussed earlier in this chapter). This enzyme catalyzes the oxidation of succinate (a four-carbon dioic acid) to fumarate (a *trans* unsaturated dioic acid). In the process, two electrons are removed and transferred to FAD, generating $FADH_2$. Ultimately, the electrons from this reaction are transferred to ubiquinone and shuttled to complex III. No protons are pumped out of the matrix by complex II (**Figure 7.17**).

A.

Molecular surface   **Ribbon structure**   **Ribbon, electron carriers highlighted**

B.

FIGURE 7.17 **Complex II.** Complex II is succinate dehydrogenase. **A.** Complex II does not transfer any protons from the matrix to the intermembrane space. Instead, it transfers electrons from the bound FAD cofactor through a series of iron-sulfur centers to a heme *b* group where they are transferred to ubiquinone. The panel on the right shows the arrangement of the electron carrying complexes in complex II. **B.** A transparent view of complex II showing the FAD, Fe-S, and heme centers. (PDB ID 1NEN Yankovskaya, V., Horsefield, R., Tornroth, S., Luna-Chavez, C., Miyoshi, H., Leger, C., Byrne, B., Cecchini, G., Iwata, S. (2003) Architecture of succinate dehydrogenase and reactive oxygen species generation *Science* 299: 700-704)

Complex II is comprised of four protein subunits: two transmembrane and two hydrophilic. The two hydrophilic proteins contain the FAD group (covalently attached to the protein via a histidine side chain), and an iron-sulfur protein containing three different iron-sulfur centers (2Fe-2S, 4Fe-4S, 3Fe-4S). Transfer of electrons from the iron-sulfur centers to ubiquinone is mediated by a heme center.

Electron transfer in complex II   As with complex I, the mechanism of electron carrier oxidation is not completely clear; however, X-ray crystallographic studies have provided some potential leads as to how these reactions occur (**Figure 7.18**). There are two potential mechanisms for the formation of fumarate and the transfer of electrons to FAD: a concerted, E2 type of elimination reaction or a stepwise reaction (E1) with an enolate intermediate. If the reaction were to proceed via an E2 mechanism, a base (presumably a basic residue, such as histidine or deprotonated arginine) would deprotonate one of the α carbons of succinate. Electrons would then flow through the carbons, generating the double bond through the transfer of a hydride (H$^-$) to the N-5 atom of the FAD group (generating FADH$_2$). The coplanar geometry needed for an E2 reaction helps to explain why the product (fumarate) is in a *trans* configuration. In the proposed E1 mechanism, a base abstracts an α proton (as it did in the E2); however, the electrons flow into one of the carbonyl oxygens, generating an enolate. Electron flow is then reversed, and FAD acquires a hydride ion to give the products. There is some experimental data to support both of these mechanisms.

Electrons from FADH$_2$ are passed through the iron-sulfur centers to the heme *b* group. It is unclear at this point whether the heme group is actually oxidized in this reaction (existing as a short-lived intermediate and essentially holding the electrons as they are passed), or helps to stabilize the semiquinone form of the ubiquinone as electrons are moving down the chain.

E1 mechanism

| 1. Base abstracts proton. Electrons flow into carbonyl forming enolate transition state. | 2. Electron flow then reverses and a hydride is acquired by FAD. | 3. Fumarate is formed and released. |

E2 mechanism

| 1. Concerted loss of proton and formation of double bond through a periplanar transition state. | 2. Fumarate is formed and released. |

FIGURE 7.18 **Two plausible mechanisms for succinate dehydrogenase.**   Two potential mechanisms for the formation of fumarate by succinate dehydrogenase exist. In the first, proton abstraction by base, formation of the double bond, and loss of a hydride ion to FAD forming FADH$_2$ occur in a concerted fashion through a classic E2 mechanism. The second proposed mechanism is basically an E1 reaction in which a basic residue abstracts a proton, and electrons flow into the carbonyl oxygen, forming an enolate transition state. Electron flow then reverses, and a hydride (H$^-$) is acquired by FAD. Experimental data exists that partially validates each mechanism.

Although this complex is called complex II, the reactions it carries out do not follow the reactions of complex I in any organized way. Both complex I and complex II independently generate ubiquinone, which transfers electrons to complex III.

7.2.4 | Complex III is ubiquinone/cytochrome *c* reductase

Complex III takes electrons from the membrane-bound electron transporter ubiquinone and transfers them to the soluble electron carrier **cytochrome *c*** (**Figure 7.19**). This presents the cell with a challenge, in that ubiquinone can carry two electrons, whereas cytochrome *c* and the carriers in the remainder of the electron transport chain can carry only one. Electrons are passed through several heme centers and an iron-sulfur center (termed a Rieske center after its discoverer John Rieske) as they are transferred to cytochrome *c*. The net result of the oxidation of one molecule of ubiquinone is the formation of two molecules of reduced cytochrome *c* and the pumping of four protons out of the mitochondrial matrix.

Complex III contains 11 subunits, three of which are cytochrome proteins containing heme groups, and one of which contains an iron-sulfur center (the Rieske center). The entire complex is dimeric; it has an α-helical region that spans the mitochondrial membrane and a globular complex on the matrix side of the inner mitochondrial membrane.

A.

Molecular surface   Ribbon structure   Ribbon, electron carriers highlighted

B.

FIGURE 7.19 Complex III. Complex III is the cytochrome *c*/ubiquinone oxidoreductase. **A.** Electrons in this complex are transferred from the two-electron carrier ubiquinone to the one-electron carrier cytochrome *c*. In the process, protons are pumped from the matrix, contributing to the proton gradient. **B.** The transparent view of complex III shows the several different heme groups that figure prominently in this process. (PDB ID 3CX5 Solmaz, S.R., Hunte, C. (2008) Structure of complex III with bound cytochrome c in reduced state and definition of a minimal core interface for electron transfer. *J.Biol.Chem.* 283: 17542-17549)

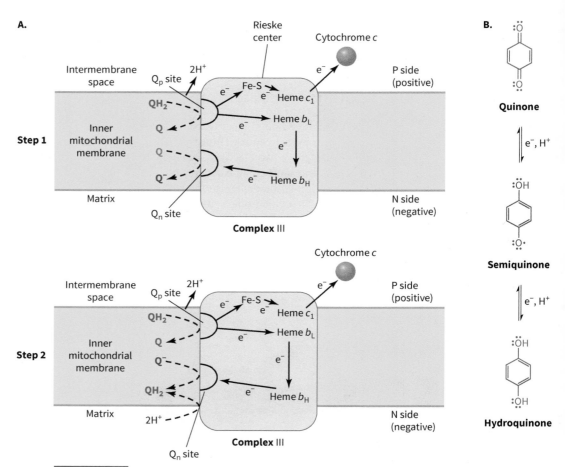

FIGURE 7.20 **Q cycle and electron transport.** The Q cycle switches electron transport from transporting pairs of electrons to transporting single electrons. **A.** In step 1 of the Q cycle, fully reduced ubiquinone (QH2) binds to complex III in the Q_p site. Two protons from coenzyme Q are released to the intermembrane space. One electron is transferred to cytochrome c while the other is shuttled via heme b_L and heme b_H to a fully oxidized molecule of ubiquinone (Q) bound in the Q_n site, generating a semiquinone (Q^-). In step 2 of the Q cycle, a new molecule of fully reduced ubiquinone binds in the Q_p site. Electrons are transferred and protons are pumped as in the first half; however, this results in the formation of a new molecule of fully reduced ubiquinone in the Q_n site. This molecule is released and can be subsequently oxidized in another cycle. **B.** Shown are the oxidation states of ubiquinone. (Illustration by Nicholas and Ferguson from *Plant Physiology and Development*, 6e, edited by Lincoln Taiz, Eduardo Zeiger, Ian Max Moller, and Angus Murphy, Copyright © 2014 by Sinauer Associates. Reprinted by permission of Oxford University Press, rights conveyed through Copyright Clearance Center, Inc.)

Electron transport in complex III and the Q cycle

As mentioned in the previous section, ubiquinone can carry two electrons, while the remainder of the electron transport chain can carry only one. Therefore, there needs to be some way to move from transporting electrons in pairs to transporting them singly; this mechanism is the **Q cycle** (Figure 7.20).

There are two ubiquinone binding sites in complex III: the Q_p site for the more positively charged intermembrane space, and the Q_n site for the more negative or matrix side. Fully reduced ubiquinone binds to complex III in the Q_p site. An electron is transferred first to the Rieske center and then to a heme (heme c_1), before passing to cytochrome c. In this process, the ubiquinone becomes partially reduced to the semiquinone form, and two protons are released to the intermembrane space side of the inner mitochondrial membrane.

The second electron is then transferred from the semiquinone to another heme (heme b_L). This electron tunnels to the final heme in this complex (heme b_H). H and L refer to high ($E^{\circ\prime} = 0.050$) and low ($E^{\circ\prime} = -0.100$) electron-transfer potential, with H being found closer to the matrix side of the membrane. The electron is passed from heme b_H to a different molecule of fully oxidized ubiquinone bound at the Q_n site, reducing it to the semiquinone form.

The second half of the Q cycle begins as the first did. A new molecule of fully reduced ubiquinone binds in the Q_p site and undergoes a one-electron reduction, passing that electron

FIGURE 7.21 **Cytochrome *c*.** Cytochrome *c* is a small soluble heme protein that acts to shuttle electrons from complex III to IV. The heme electron carrier is almost completely buried in cytochrome *c*. (PDB 3CYT Takano, T., Dickerson, R.E. (1980) Redox conformation changes in refined tuna cytochrome c. *Proc Natl Acad.Sci.USA* 77:6371-6375)

off to a Rieske center, then to heme c_1 and finally to cytochrome *c*, releasing two protons on the intermembrane space side. The second electron from the semiquinone bound at the Q_p site is transferred to heme b_L and heme b_H. Heme b_H then reduces the semiquinone bound at the Q_n site to form fully reduced ubiquinone, which is released into the inner mitochondrial membrane. This may seem like a redundant pathway because it regenerates one reduced ubiquinone for each two that enter the cycle, but in fact, it provides a relatively simple way to switch from carrying one electron to carrying two. The Q pool is the term for the combination of oxidized and reduced forms of ubiquinone found in the mitochondrial membrane.

7.2.5 │ Cytochrome *c* is a soluble electron carrier

Electrons from complex III are transferred to cytochrome *c*. This small heme protein (12 kDa) carries a single electron in the heme group (**Figure 7.21**). The heme group itself is bound to the protein via cysteine side chains, thus differing slightly from the heme groups discussed previously. The critical heme cofactor is found buried in the core of the protein, and it is inaccessible to solvent or substrates. The surrounding protein provides an environment that regulates the affinity of the heme group for its passenger electron, and permits loading and unloading of the electron by binding to complexes III and IV at an appropriate location and distance from other electron carriers. Although the heme group is responsible for carrying the electron, the surrounding protein dictates the path it will follow in moving from complex III to complex IV.

How can the electron reduce the heme group, when the heme group is buried in the core of the protein? The answer probably lies in quantum mechanics. The electron being transported is thought to tunnel from one electron carrier to another, allowing it to cross barriers that normally seem impassable, and appear on the other side.

Cytochromes are an ancient family of proteins and are highly conserved throughout evolution. Their small size (approximately 100 amino acids) and ubiquitous nature (they are found in nearly all species) have facilitated their use in studies of evolution and genetics, especially cladistics: the placement of organisms on the tree of life.

7.2.6 │ In complex IV, oxygen is the terminal electron carrier

In mammals, **complex IV** (also known as cytochrome oxidase) is a 410 kDa homodimer, each half of which contributes 13 subunits to the structure (**Figure 7.22**). A single molecule of the phospholipid cardiolipin is found at the interface of the dimer. Complex IV takes four electrons from four copies of cytochrome *c* and uses them to reduce a molecule of molecular oxygen (O_2) to

A.

2H$^+$

CuA

Heme a_3

Heme a

CuB

½O$_2$ + 2H$^+$

H$_2$O

2H$^+$

Molecular surface

Ribbon structure

CuA

Heme a_3

CuB

Heme a

Ribbon, electron carriers highlighted

B.

FIGURE 7.22 **Complex IV.** **A.** Complex IV is a dimeric complex that uses the electrons of cytochrome *c* to produce water with molecular oxygen. This process uses two heme groups and two copper centers, and it pumps four protons out of the matrix (only half of the dimer is shown pumping protons). **B.** A transparent view of both dimers showing the orientation of the heme and copper centers. (PDB ID 5B1A Yano, N., Muramoto, K., Shimada, A., Takemura, S., Baba, J., Fujisawa, H., Mochizuki, M., Shinzawa-Itoh, K., Yamashita, E., Tsukihara, T., Yoshikawa, S. (2016) The Mg^{2+}-containing Water Cluster of Mammalian Cytochrome c Oxidase Collects Four Pumping Proton Equivalents in Each Catalytic Cycle. *J.Biol.Chem.* 291: 23882-23894)

water (H$_2$O). To do this, it uses four different electron carriers: a bimolecular copper center (Cu$_A$), two heme groups (bound in cytochrome *a* and cytochrome *a$_3$*), and a second copper center (Cu$_B$).

Complex IV is comprised of 28 membrane-spanning α helices. The entire complex is predominantly helical, with two pieces of β sheet structure per monomer. Cytochrome *c* is thought to bind negatively charged residues near the β barrel structure on the intermembrane face of the complex through lysine side chains on cytochrome *c*.

Electron transport through complex IV and water formation

Once cytochrome *c* binds to complex IV, electrons are transferred from the heme of cytochrome *c* to the Cu$_A$ of the complex, through the heme of cytochrome *a*, to cytochrome *a$_3$* and then to Cu$_B$. In this final step, the electrons do not appear to completely move onto the second copper center (Cu$_B$); rather, they are shared between the copper, heme, and oxygen. This is where the formation of water occurs.

The binuclear Cu$_A$ center includes two cysteines, two histidines, a methionine and a glutamate residue. The cysteine residues in this complex give an overall geometry that is similar to a 2Fe-2S complex. Electrons tunnel from the heme of cytochrome *c* and are delocalized across the copper atoms in the Cu$_A$ complex. Both heme groups have distal histidines in the fifth coordinate position to the iron atom of the heme group. The heme of cytochrome *a$_3$* is coordinated to molecular oxygen in the sixth position. The other end of the oxygen molecule is coordinated to the Cu$_B$ copper. In turn, the Cu$_B$ copper is held in place by three histidines, one of which has a highly unusual covalent bond through the side chain to an adjacent tyrosine residue. This tyrosine is also thought to play a key role in catalysis.

1. The first electron reduces Cu^{2+}. The first water is released.

2. A second electron reduces Fe^{3+}. The second water is released.

3. Oxygen adds to the active site iron.

4. Oxygen is heterolytically cleaved and metal centers oxidized.

5. A third electron is added, generating water.

6. Addition of a fourth electron regenerates the Fe^{3+}-OH-center found in step 1.

FIGURE 7.23 **Mechanism of water formation.** Water is formed in complex IV between the heme 3_a and Cu_B centers. For each molecule of oxygen bound, four electrons and four protons are used to produce two molecules of water, released in the first two steps of the mechanism.

The bond formed by one of the ring carbons of tyrosine to histidine moves the tyrosine side chain, positioning it to become a donor of both H^+ and an electron during the reduction and cleavage of O_2. Formation of the bond to the nitrogen of the histidine lowers the pK_a of the phenolic proton, enabling proton donation; it also lowers the reduction potential, facilitating the formation of a tyrosyl radical.

The mechanism of water formation begins with the enzyme in the fully oxidized state (O), with the iron bound to a hydroxyl ion, the copper bound to water, and the tyrosine side chain in the deprotonated (phenolate) state (**Figure 7.23**). Both a proton and electron are transferred to the center, generating Cu^+ and a protonated phenol group, and water is released. A second proton and electron are transferred to the center. Water is formed again, this time on the iron center, and is then released, leaving behind the Fe^{2+} state. The enzyme is now in the fully reduced state (R). Next, oxygen binds to the iron in the heme group and electrons rearrange themselves such that the iron forms a Fe^{4+} center coordinated to an O^{2-} atom. The second oxygen is transferred to the copper center, forming a Cu^{2+} oxidation state. This oxygen atom also acquires a proton from the tyrosine, generating a tyrosyl radical and a hydroxyl group coordinated to the Cu^{2+} center. Another proton and a third electron are transferred to the center, with the electron joining the radical to form a phenolate ion and the proton forming water on the Cu^{2+} center. Finally, a fourth and final electron is added, reducing the iron center from Fe^{4+} to Fe^{3+}, which is complexed to a hydroxyl ion, returning the enzyme to the fully oxidized state.

Proton pumping in complex IV

As electrons are used to reduce oxygen to water, four protons are pumped out of complex IV into the mitochondrial matrix. Two channels in complex IV are involved: the K and D channels (each named for a key lysine or a key aspartate residue). Both are thought to use a proton wire, a series of bound water molecules, to rapidly transfer protons to where they are needed. Although the exact mechanism of proton pumping remains unclear, it is likely that slight changes in structure as electrons move through the redox centers alter the pK_a values of the side chains lining the channel, causing protons to bind to or be released from water molecules lining the channel; the net result is a loss of protons on the intermembrane space side.

7.2.7 The entire complex working as one: the respirasome

To this point, this chapter has described the parts of electron transport, pieced together each of the electron carriers and complexes, and shown how electrons travel through these complexes. However, in reality, the story may be more complicated. Although each complex is enzymatically active on its own, data now suggest that the individual complexes aggregate together into one supercomplex, termed the **respirasome** (Figure 7.24). Also, although this chapter depicts the stoichiometry of the complexes as 1:1:1:1, there may be other ratios (a ratio of 1:1:3:7 has been proposed). Aggregating complexes would assist in substrate channeling (where substrate concentrations are higher at some locations, or where substrate can be directed from one active site to another). Likewise, keeping intermediates in close proximity may help in moving electrons via quantum mechanical tunneling.

The respirasome may be one of the largest biochemical structures ever proposed, but it has parallels in biochemistry. Other structures that have a higher order of organization, and effectively concentrate chemical reactions and chemical reactants in a small area, include the ribosome, replisome, transcriptional complex, and signal transduction complexes, among others.

Many poisons inhibit electron transport or uncouple the proton gradient from electron transport
Not surprisingly, compounds that inhibit electron transport are potent poisons. There are multiple places in the electron transport chain where poisons can bind. Many poisons have been characterized in terms of where they bind and block electron transport. Although highly toxic, these molecules are powerful research tools in the laboratory. Some molecules (for example, demerol and amytal) inhibit electrons passing through the iron-sulfur centers of complex I but do not provide their clinical effect via this particular mechanism. Nevertheless, this inhibition may provide clues to some of the side effects or more toxic effects seen in these compounds, especially when taken in excess (Figure 7.25, Table 7.3).

FIGURE 7.24 **Respirasome.** The complexes of the electron transport chain are not thought to operate as single units but rather as a composite working in unison to facilitate reactions. This is termed the respirasome. Shown is a single unit comprised of complexes I, III, and IV. In this assembly, complex II is not seen, but other combinations of complexes have been observed. (PDB ID 5J4Z Letts, J.A., Fiedorczuk, K., Sazanov, L.A. (2016) The architecture of respiratory supercomplexes. *Nature* 537: 644-648)

Complex IV

Complex III

Complex I

FIGURE 7.25 **Poisons of electron transport.** There are numerous compounds that can inhibit electron transport. Some act as poisons and block electron transport irreversibly, whereas others bind less tightly and have found use as pharmaceuticals.

TABLE 7.3   **Drugs and Poisons and Where They Act in the Electron Transport Chain**

Drug or Poison	Complex	Carrier Bound
Rotenone (insecticide)	I	Fe-S
Amytal (amobarbital, barbituates)		
Demerol (meperidine)		
Carboxin (fungicide)	II	Ubiqinone binding site
2-thionyltrifluoroacetone		
Antimycin A1	III	Cyt b_H in the Q_n site
Cyanide (CN⁻)	IV	Heme cyt a_3
Azide (N_3^-)		
Carbon monoxide (CO)		
2,4-dinitrophenol (DNP)	ATP synthase	Uncoupling agent
Dicumarol		
FCCP		

A discussion of the effects of some proton gradient uncouplers can be found in **Medical Biochemistry: Uncoupling of the electron transport chain**.

Medical Biochemistry

Uncoupling of the electron transport chain

Imagine we had a magic pill to burn fat. We could consume whatever calories we wished and they would all burn away in our sleep. Although this sounds too good to be true, people are still searching for this magic pill.

Historically, there are multiple reports of munitions workers developing illnesses after being exposed to toxins in the course of their work. From the late 1880s until the late 1930s, munitions were often made with picric acid (2,4,6 trinitrophenol). Picrates are unstable molecules that form dangerous explosives. During World War II, picrate-based explosives were replaced with the more stable trinitrotoluene (TNT). During this period (and especially during wartime), working conditions were less than optimal, and munitions workers were frequently exposed to chemicals, including picrates. The exposure led to a set of symptoms including yellowed skin (picrates have a characteristic yellow color), elevated body temperature and respiration rate, profuse sweating, and weight loss in some cases resulting in death.

Breakdown products of picrates, particularly 2,4 dinitrophenol (DNP), are proton ionophores, molecules that can move specific ions across an otherwise impermeable barrier such as a plasma

2,4-dinitrophenol

Cytosol

2,4-DNP breaks down the proton gradient

Mitochondrion

membrane. In the case of DNP, a combination of aromaticity and electron-withdrawing nitro groups lowers the pK_a of the phenolic hydroxyl proton to 4.1. In the intermembrane space, the deprotonated phenolate acquires a proton. Once protonated it becomes less soluble in aqueous solution and more soluble in lipid; it then diffuses across the inner mitochondrial membrane, where it deprotonates. Thus, DNP transports protons back into the mitochondria.

In light of this data, the symptoms and fate of those poisoned with DNP becomes clear. DNP uncouples electron transport from ATP production. The cell goes into overdrive, burning carbohydrates and lipids, sending acetyl-CoA through the citric acid cycle, passing electrons through NADH and $FADH_2$ to the electron transport chain and through the chain to form water. All this effort to pump protons out of the matrix is for nothing, because DNP simply shuttles them back in. A lot of heat is generated and oxygen consumed, but no ATP is made. Those affected either overheat or expire due to a lack of ATP for basic cellular needs.

In spite of these side effects, researchers have attempted to employ a controlled use of DNP as a means of losing weight. Following publication of a series of papers describing the potential weight-loss benefits of DNP, drugs appeared in the 1930s with varying levels of the compound. Unfortunately, people vary in their response to DNP and it has a relatively narrow therapeutic index (the dose of drug that is beneficial is very close to the dose

that is harmful). DNP was officially withdrawn from diet pills in 1938, and it is not currently approved to treat any disease. However, it is available on the Internet and used illicitly by bodybuilders, boxers, and wrestlers to lose weight quickly. Web sites claim that this compound can be used safely, but the evidence, including deaths from DNP use, suggests otherwise.

Interestingly, nature has provided us with a potential alternative to DNP. Babies and hibernating animals express a protein in brown adipose tissue known as uncoupling protein-1 (UCP-1): a proton channel that is found in the inner mitochondrial membrane and serves to let protons back into the mitochondria. As seen in patients with DNP poisoning, such movement of protons can lead to increased burning of fat for energy and increased body temperature (which in the case of weight loss could be the desired effect). UCP-1 is responsible for nonshivering thermogenesis, which helps to keep babies and hibernating animals warm. The protein is only expressed in brown adipose tissue, but research is ongoing as to how this protein could be used to increase fat burning in obese or overweight humans.

(PDB ID 5ARA Zhou, A., Rohou, A., Schep, D.G., Bason, J.V., Montgomery, M.G., Walker, J.E., Grigorieff, N., Rubinstein, J.L. (2015) Structure and conformational states of the bovine mitochondrial ATP synthase by cryo-EM. *Elife* 4: e10180-e10180)

WORKED PROBLEM 7.4 | Mechanism of an antifungal agent

The antifungal agent myxothiazol binds to complex III and inhibits electron transport. Spectroscopic studies show that the absorbance spectra of cytochrome c_1, heme b_L, and cytochrome c all remain in the oxidized state (not reduced) when the drug is added. How might myxothiazol act?

Strategy Examine Figure 7.19. How do electrons travel through complex III? What is the purpose of the Q cycle?

Solution Crystallography shows that myxothiazol binds in the Q_p site, blocking the binding of ubiquinone and blocking transfer of electrons to the downstream electron carriers.

Follow-up question Cyanide (CN^-) binds tightly to the iron centers in some heme groups, but not all. Why?

7.2 Summary

- Electrons harvested from catabolic reactions are used in the electron transport chain to pump protons out of the mitochondrial matrix, generating a proton gradient.

- Electrons are passed from one redox active center to another center with higher reduction potential.

- The redox active centers used in electron transport include iron-sulfur centers, heme groups, and organic electron carriers such as quinones.
- The energetic equivalent of NADH is transported into the mitochondrial matrix via either the glycerophosphate or malate–aspartate shuttle.
- Four macromolecular protein complexes are involved in electron transport:
  o Complex I is NADH dehydrogenase. It oxidizes NADH to NAD^+, passing electrons to ubiquinone and pumping four protons out of the matrix for each molecule of NADH.
  o Complex II is succinate dehydrogenase. This enzyme of the citric acid cycle oxidizes succinate to fumarate, capturing the two electrons in a molecule of $FADH_2$. Electrons from $FADH_2$ are transferred through several redox centers to ubiquinone.
  o Complex III is ubiquinone oxidase. Complex III uses ubiquinone to take electrons from complexes I and II and other catabolic processes, and it transfers them to the soluble electron carrier cytochrome c. Four additional protons are transferred to the intermembrane side of the inner mitochondrial membrane for each molecule of ubiquinone.
  o Complex IV is cytochrome c oxidase. Complex IV oxidizes cytochrome c, transferring electrons to oxygen to generate water. Two final protons are pumped out of the mitochondrial matrix, one for each molecule of cytochrome c.
- Many toxic compounds act by blocking specific steps of electron transport.

7.2 Concept Check

- Analyze how the structure of each complex gives rise to its function.
- Describe the redox active centers found in each complex.
- Explain why electrochemistry is used to describe the reactions in this chapter more than reactions in glycolysis, for example, and the net effect of all of these reactions.
- Explain how different poisons can inhibit or block electron or proton transport.

7.3 | ATP Biosynthesis

Until this point, a great deal of chemistry has been used in breaking glucose down into CO_2, but little ATP has been produced. The enzyme that is largely responsible for ATP production is known by many different names, the most common of which are **ATP synthase** or the **F_0/F_1 ATPase**. This multimeric enzyme uses the electrochemical energy of the proton gradient established by the electron transport chain to synthesize ATP from ADP and inorganic phosphate, P_i.

7.3.1 | The structure of ATP synthase underlies its function

The general topology and structure of ATP synthases are conserved throughout biology. For simplicity, this section focuses on the bacterial form of the enzyme. ATP synthase can be divided into two complexes: F_0 and F_1. The membrane-bound F_0 complex is comprised of three different subunits (1 a, 2 b, and 10–15 c). The c subunits are arrayed in a disc that floats in bacterial plasma membrane or the inner mitochondrial membrane in eukaryotes. The a subunit acts as an adapter between the c subunits and the homodimer of b subunits. The b subunit spans the membrane and has an extended arm that cradles the F_1 complex (**Figure 7.26**).

The F_1 complex has nine subunits: three α, three β, one γ, one δ, and one ε. A hexameric globular domain composed of all the α and β subunits in an alternating pattern forms the catalytic portion of the complex. The γ subunit forms an axle that passes through the center of the α-β hexameric complex and connects it to the F_0 complex via the c subunits. The δ subunit caps the α-β hexamer and links it to the b homodimer of the F_0 complex. Finally, the ε subunit associates with the γ and c subunits, linking the complexes together.

Mitochondrial forms of this enzymatic complex have retained the same architecture and function but are more complex, comprising at least 17 different subunits, each with a specialized function.

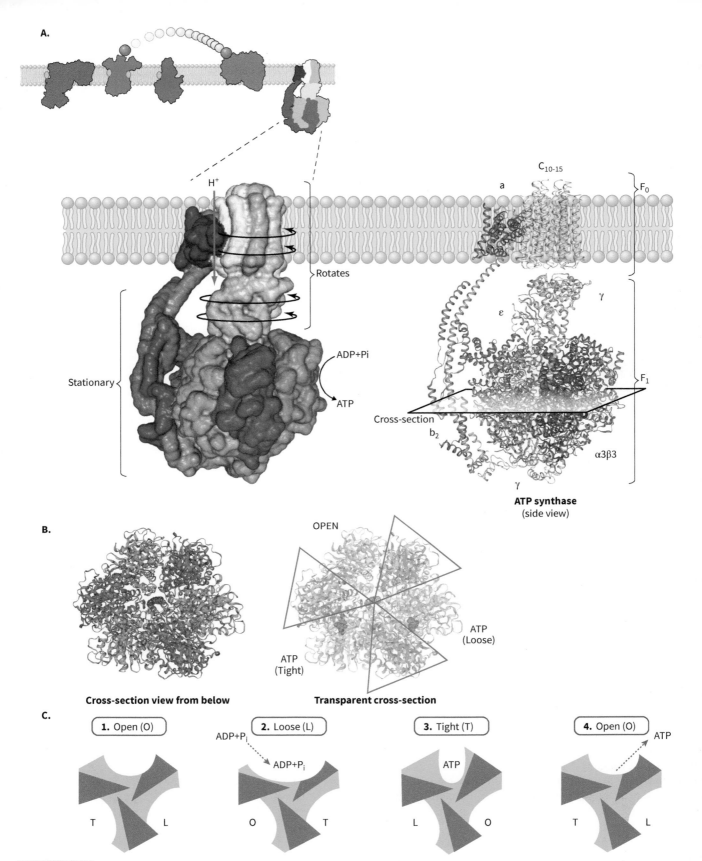

FIGURE 7.26 **Reactions of ATP synthase.** **A.** The ATP synthase consists of two larger fragments, the membrane-bound F_0 complex and the catalytic F_1 complex. (PDB ID 5ARA Zhou, A., Rohou, A., Schep, D.G., Bason, J.V., Montgomery, M.G., Walker, J.E., Grigorieff, N., Rubinstein, J.L. (2015) Structure and conformational states of the bovine mitochondrial ATP synthase by cryo-EM. *Elife* 4: e10180-e10180) **B.** As the F_1 complex rotates past the b subunits, the conformation of a and b change, resulting in binding of ADP and P_i and formation of ATP. (PDB ID 1BMF Abrahams, J.P., Leslie, A.G., Lutter, R., Walker, J.E. (1994) Structure at 2.8 A resolution of F1-ATPase from bovine heart mitochondria. *Nature* 370: 621-628) **C.** The complex consists of three active sites that progress through three different states: open, where nothing is bound; loose, where ADP and P_i bind; and tight, where the change in conformation generates ATP.

7.3.2 ATP synthase acts as a molecular machine driving the assembly of ATP molecules

We can visualize ATP synthase working as a tiny machine, in which protons slip down their electrochemical gradient back into the mitochondrial matrix. This movement of protons provides the energy for the synthase to generate ATP. As the protons move between the a and b subunits of the F_0 complex, they cause the ring of c subunits to rotate, which in turn causes the γ and ε subunits to also move. As the γ subunit passes through the hexamer of α and β subunits, a conformational change occurs, releasing newly generated ATP and binding to ADP and P_i. With each turn of the complex, a new molecule of ATP is released.

The mechanism of ATP synthase has not been observed directly, but there is much evidence to support the individual steps described above. Perhaps the most striking evidence comes from a paper that appeared in the journal *Nature* in 2004, in which investigators used chimeric proteins to fuse a fluorescent actin arm onto the F_0 subunit. A second modification of the F_1 subunit made it possible to mount the complex on a glass microscope slide. When ATP was added to this system, the position of the actin arm changed, providing evidence for the proposed mechanism (**Figure 7.27**).

The energetics of the proton motive force   The energy for ATP synthesis comes from the electrochemical potential created by the uneven distribution of protons across the inner mitochondrial membrane. This proton gradient is generated by protons being pumped out of the mitochondrial matrix during electron transport. The electrochemical potential can be separated into a chemical potential (a higher concentration of protons on the outside of the membrane than on the inside) and an electric potential (the added positive charge that accumulates on the outside of the membrane). These terms can be discussed quantitatively by describing each of the components (the chemical and the electrical) and by mathematically calculating their combined potential.

The electrical potential difference across a membrane is measured in volts or millivolts, and it is analogous to a weight lifted to some height or a car on the top of a hill. When describing

A.

Fluorescent actin filament

Streptavidin

Biotin

His tag

Source: Pratt and Cornely (2018). *Essential Biochemistry,* 4e (Wiley). Reproduced with permission of John Wiley & Sons, Inc.

B.

Source: Yoh Wada, Yoshihiro Sambongi, and Masamitsu Futai (2000). Biological nano motor, ATP synthase F_0F_1: from catalysis to $\gamma\varepsilon c_{10-12}$ subunit assembly rotation. *Biochimica et Biophysica Acta (BBA) - Bioenergetics* Volume 1459, Issues 2–3: 499–505. https://doi.org/10.1016/S0005-2728(00)00189-4. Reproduced with permission of Elsevier.

FIGURE 7.27   **Rotation of the ATP synthase can be demonstrated in the laboratory.**   **A.** In 2004, researchers used recombinant DNA techniques to produce an ATP synthase with two modifications, a histidine tag (His tag) on the a subunit and a biotinylation of the c subunit. Avidin binds very tightly to biotin. Therefore, a streptavidin tag fused to a fluorescent actin arm was used as a reporter. **B.** The modifications to the ATPase were minor enough to permit function of the complex but enable the use of the fluorescent actin arm as a reporter to follow rotation of the c subunit. The arm made a one-third rotation for every ATP molecule hydrolyzed. The modifications to the ATPase were minor enough to permit function of the complex but enable the use of the fluorescent actin arm as a reporter to follow rotation of the c subunit. The arm made a 1/3 rotation for every ATP molecule hydrolyzed. 4YXW 1 electrical potentials, an analogy to water is often used, with the potential difference seen as analogous to water flowing over a waterfall or traveling through a pipe. The height of the waterfall or the diameter of the pipe relate to the potential voltage difference across a membrane or in an electrical circuit. The amount of water flowing equates to the number of electrons or ions moving and is the amperage of the system (a different quantity than voltage). There may be tall waterfalls with little water flowing over them (equating to high voltage and low current) or short waterfalls with a flood of water moving across them (equating to low voltage and high current). In biological systems, voltages are typically measured in tens of millivolts, and amperages in the order of pico-amps. These values may seem small, but they can be readily measured across the plasma membrane of a cell. Also, given the size of the cell, the current density per unit area can be quite high.

The electrical component of the electrochemical potential can be envisioned as the voltage drop across the membrane. This is the potential difference or membrane potential:

$$\Delta\Psi_m = \Psi_{in} - \Psi_{out}$$

where $\Delta\Psi_m$ is the membrane potential, and Ψ_{in} and Ψ_{out} are the voltages on the inside and outside of the membrane, respectively. Electrical potential energy is related to the Gibbs free energy by the following constants:

$$\Delta G = n\mathscr{F}\Delta\Psi_m$$

where ΔG is the change in free energy of a process, n is the number of electrons per mole of product, $\mathscr{F}$ is the Faraday constant (96,485 coulombs mol^{-1} or 96.48 kJ/V · mol), and $\Delta\Psi_m$ is the potential difference. If the difference across the membrane is –0.040 volts, the free energy of the process is:

$$= (1)(96.48 \text{ kJ/V} \bullet \text{mol})(-0.040 \text{ V})$$

$$= -3.90 \text{ kJ/mol}$$

In this example, the membrane potential is positive on the outside, making the difference negative and the overall free energy negative, and thus favorable. This component of the total free energy of the reaction is due solely to the electrical potential.

The component of the free energy due to the difference in concentration created by pumping protons across the membrane also can be described using a version of the Gibbs free energy expression:

$$\Delta G = \Delta G^{\circ\prime} + RT \ln Q$$

in which, ΔG is the free energy for any reaction or process, $\Delta G^{\circ\prime}$ is the standard free energy exchange, R is the gas law constant, T is temperature in Kelvin, and $\ln Q$ is the natural log of the reaction quotient. The reaction quotient is the ratio of products to reactants for a system that is not at equilibrium. Although this equation is often applied to a chemical reaction, it can be applied just as easily to the imbalance of chemicals across a membrane. Here, it can be used to describe the concentration of protons on either side of the membrane:

$$\Delta G = \Delta G^{\circ\prime} + RT \ln ([H_{in}^+]/[H_{out}^+])$$

Since the proton concentration is often discussed in terms of pH, it is easy to transform the previous equation, changing from a natural log to a base-10 log by multiplying by 2.303.

$$\Delta G = 2.303 \, RT \log([H_{in}^+]/[H_{out}^+])$$

Substituting pH for the negative log of $[H^+]$ gives

$$\Delta G = -2.303 \, RT(pH_{in} - pH_{out})$$

or

$$\Delta G = -2.303 \, RT \, \Delta pH$$

where ΔpH is the difference in pH from the inside to the outside of the membrane ($pH_{in} - pH_{out}$).

If the change in pH from the inside to the outside of a membrane was 1 pH unit, the free energy available to a system from this chemical gradient would be:

$$\Delta G = -2.303 \, (8.315 \times 10^{-3} \text{ kJ/mol} \bullet \text{K}) \, (310 \text{ K}) \, (1.0) = -5.93 \text{ kJ/mol}.$$

As discussed earlier in this section, this is only one component of the total free energy. The combined total of the electrical potential and the chemical potential exclusively for protons (disregarding other ions) is referred to as the **proton motive force** (pmf). The free energy expression for pmf is:

$$\Delta G = -2.303 \, RT \, \Delta pH + n\mathscr{F} \, \Delta\Psi_m$$

At body temperature (37°C, 310 K), the equation simplifies to:

$$\Delta G = -5.9 \, \Delta pH + n\mathscr{F}\Delta\Psi_m$$

This equation gives the free energy available for work generated by the proton gradient across the membrane. The amount of energy required to generate this gradient is therefore the same magnitude with the opposite sign (ΔG of the reaction is positive).

WORKED PROBLEM 7.5 | Calculating the energy obtained from the pmf

In specific bacteria, there is a 140 mV potential drop across the membrane. The pH is 6.9 on the inside of the membrane and 7.4 on the outside. How much free energy is available for ATP biosynthesis?

Strategy Bacteria lack mitochondria but synthesize ATP using electron transport and an ATP synthase. What equation and information do we need to be able to calculate the free energy?

Solution If we use the free energy expression for pmf,

$$\Delta G = -5.9 \, \Delta pH + n\mathscr{F}\Delta\Psi_m$$

we need to know the pH gradient and voltage drop across the membrane. The difference across the membrane ($pH_{in} - pH_{out}$) is:

$$6.9 - 7.4 = -0.5 \text{ pH units.}$$

The voltage across the membrane is 140 mV or 0.140 V. The constants in the expression are $n = 1$ (the charge on a proton) and $F = 96.485 \text{ kJ} \cdot V^{-1} \cdot mol^{-1}$. The free energy is therefore:

$$\Delta G = -5.9 \, (-0.5) + (1) \, (96.485 \text{ kJ} \cdot V^{-1} \cdot mol^{-1}) \, (0.140 \text{ V})$$
$$\Delta G = 2.95 + 13.51$$
$$\Delta G = 16.45 \text{ kJ} \cdot mol^{-1}$$

The equation tells us that the free energy required to create the proton gradient is 16.45 kJ $\cdot$ mol^{-1}. It takes energy to generate the gradient; therefore, the sign on the free energy is positive. The energy produced by the gradient is of the same magnitude but has the opposite sign (-16.45 kJ $\cdot$ mol^{-1}).

Follow-up question If the free energy (ΔG) of the following reaction was 45 kJ/mol, how many protons would it take to synthesize one molecule of ATP?

$$ADP + P_i \rightarrow ATP + H_2O$$

ATP is transported out of the mitochondrial matrix by a translocase

ATP fuels many diverse reactions in the cell, and it is probably used in every organelle. Therefore, ATP must be released from the mitochondria to travel to its site of use. In return, ADP must travel to the mitochondrial matrix to be phosphorylated to ATP. The proteins responsible for this exchange are ATP:ADP translocases, 30 kDa monomeric transmembrane proteins found in the inner mitochondrial membrane.

The transmembrane domain of the translocase has six membrane-spanning α helices that form a cone-shaped depression. Binding of substrate in the cone causes the helices to move so that the opening shuts on one side of the membrane and opens on the other. After shuttling ATP from the matrix to the intermembrane space, the binding site will collect a molecule of ADP and reverse its conformation, completing the process. The binding site at the bottom of the funnel contains a conserved arginine-rich nucleotide-binding sequence. The ATP-ADP translocase is highly abundant in the inner mitochondrial membrane, comprising more than 12% of the protein found there. Once through the inner mitochondrial membrane, ATP is thought to pass unrestricted through pores in the outer mitochondrial membrane.

7.3.3 | Other ATPases serve as ion pumps

There are other ATP synthases, the most common of which are also often characterized as ATPases. These ATPases use ATP hydrolysis to perform their proscribed function in reverse. Based on their structure and function, ATPases can be broadly sorted into five categories: F-type, A-type, V-type, P-type, and E-type.

F-type ATPases F-type ATPases are those that have already been described in this section (F_0/F_1 ATPase). They are called "F" because of the isolation of a *factor* involved in phosphorylation of ADP.

A-type ATPases

A-type ATPases are found in the single-celled microorganisms *Archaea* (hence the name "A-type"). They serve a similar function and have a similar architecture to F-type ATPases.

V-type ATPases

V-type ATPases are found in *v*acuoles. These complexes work in reverse compared to ATP synthase, using the energy of ATP hydrolysis to pump protons, or in some instances Na$^+$ ions, into a vacuole. They have similar architecture to F-type ATPases. V-type ATPases have been implicated in several cellular processes including receptor-mediated endocytosis, protein trafficking, active transport of metabolites, and neurotransmitter release.

P-type ATPases

P-type ATPases are pumps that use ATP hydrolysis to move ions from one side of a phospholipid bilayer to another. They differ from the F-type, A-type, and V-type enzymes based on their architecture and proposed mechanism of action. Typically, P-type ATPases have a single transmembrane subunit that is responsible for both ATPase and ion-pumping activity. A *p*hospho-enzyme intermediate (an aspartyl phosphoanhydride) is conserved in all P-type ATPases.

E-type ATPases

E-type ATPases are *e*xtracellular ATPases, and they can be characterized further into ecto-ATPases, CD39-like ATPases, and ecto-ATP/ADPases. All these enzymes hydrolyze extracellular ATP but may also hydrolyze ADP or other nucleotide triphosphates. Typically, E-type ATPases are glycoproteins that depend on divalent metal ions for activity. They may play a role in platelet aggregation, transplant rejection, and parasite survival.

7.3.4 | Inhibitors of the ATPases can be powerful drugs or poisons

Given their central importance in energy production, it might seem that inhibition of ATP synthases and ATPases would be harmful. Several poisons (such as cyanide) work by inhibiting electron transport, thereby blocking ATP production in the cell. Often, however, the difference between a substance acting as a poison or a drug is a question of dosage. ATPases are also the target of several drugs and are an important field of research.

Oligomycin

Balifomycin

Aurovertin B

Apicularen

Lansoprazole

ATP synthase inhibitors Oligomycin is a natural antibiotic isolated from the bacterium *Streptomyces*. Oligomycin is a member of a family of molecules termed macrolide antibiotics that contain a large, macrocyclic lactone that the bacterium probably secretes to poison any bacterial competitors. Oligomycin acts by binding at the interface of the a and c subunits of ATP

WORKED PROBLEM 7.6 | Steely hair disease

Menkes syndrome (also known as steely hair disease) is a genetic disorder that effects plasma concentrations of Cu^{2+}. Although the copper is absorbed from the small intestine, in this syndrome it does not leave the enterocytes and enter the plasma. The copper deficiency manifests itself in several ways (kinky hair is one obvious way) but is usually fatal in early childhood. The causal mutation in Menkes syndrome is in a gene coding for an ATPase. Propose a mechanism for how a mutation of the gene coding for this protein might impair copper absorption. What class of ATPase might be involved?

Strategy Recall the structure of the intestine: enterocytes lining the intestinal lumen absorb nutrients and secrete them into the lymph or plasma, depending on the type of nutrient. If copper can enter these cells but not leave, it may be that the ions are somehow impaired from leaving the cell, or they become trapped in an organelle. What role might an ATPase play in this trafficking? Consider the different classes of ATPases.

Solution The gene coding for the ATPase ATP7A protein is mutated in Menkes syndrome. This enzyme is a P-type ATPase that is involved in movement of divalent metal ions in the cell. In the normal cell, the enzyme resides in the Golgi; however, when copper levels rise, it translocates to the membrane surface and pumps copper ions out of the cell and into the plasma. Exactly how and where the mutation (or mutations) prevents this process from happening is still being investigated.

Follow-up question The copper binding motif in ATP7A employs the sequence:

$$-DGMHCKSCV-$$

Think about which side chains interact with divalent metal ions. Which of these residues might be important for copper binding?

---

synthase, blocking proton translocation and rotation of the ring and the associated F_1 complex, hence blocking ATP production. Although oligomycin is too toxic to be used in the clinic to treat patients with bacterial infections, similar molecules are used (such as the macrolide antibiotics azithromycin and arithromycin); however, these molecules act via a different mechanism (blocking protein biosynthesis). Oligomycin may not have a clinical use, but it is commonly used in the research laboratory for the study of electron transport and energy production.

The reagent dicyclohexylcarbodiimide (DCC) is commonly used in solid-phase peptide synthesis but also happens to be an inhibitor of ATP synthase. In theory, DCC could couple with any carboxylate group found in the protein; in practice, it preferentially couples to an aspartate residue in the c subunit. When administered to functional (coupled) mitochondria, DCC prevents proton translocation and rotation of the c ring. As with oligomycin, DCC is of no clinical use, but it is a useful reagent for studying the function of ATP synthase.

Aurovertin B binds to the b subunit of the F_0 fragment, inhibiting ATP biosynthesis. It is being investigated as a potential anticancer agent. Inhibiting ATP synthesis in actively growing cancer cells can induce growth arrest and apoptosis.

Many polyphenolic molecules are thought to be beneficial to health, although distinct mechanisms for these benefits have not been demonstrated; one example is resveratrol, a phenolic compound found in grape skins and red wine. Polyphenols bind to and inhibit ATP synthase to differing degrees. It may be that this is one of the mechanisms by which polyphenols are beneficial.

P-type ATPase inhibitors
The hydrogen/potassium ATPase (H^+/K^+ ATPase) is responsible for the acidification of the stomach. Drugs such as omeprazole (Prilosec) and lansoprazole (Prevacid) inhibit the action of this ATPase, and are generically known as proton pump inhibitors. These drugs and others like them have been hugely successful in the treatment of heartburn and gastroesophageal reflux disease.

V-type ATPase inhibitors
V-type ATPases have been implicated in numerous biological processes and diseases including kidney failure (distal renal tubule acidosis), protein secretion, and several bone-density disorders. Numerous V-type ATPase inhibitors are under investigation as either research tools or potential drugs for the treatment of disorders associated with these proteins. Examples of such inhibitors include macrocyclic lactones (archazolid), plecomacrolides (bafilomycin and concanamycin), and benzolactones (apicularen and lobatamide). V-type ATPase inhibitors are produced by soil microbes and, as discussed for oligomycin, are used as a molecular defense against other microbes. Discovery of these molecules is another example of how studies in a field of biochemistry that may seem eccentric or obscure can yield important findings that have widespread implications for science and medicine (Table 7.4).

TABLE 7.4   **Drugs That Affect ATPases**

Drug	Class of ATPase	Effect
Apoptolidin	ATP synthase (F_0/F_1 ATPase)	Induces apoptosis; research tool
Bafilomycin B1	V-type inhibitor	Microbial antibiotic; research tool
Concanamycin C		Microbial antibiotic; research tool
Oligomycin B	F-type inhibitor	Microbial antibiotic; research tool
Ouabain	Na^+/K^+ ATPase inhibitor	Used in hunting (arrow poison); neuroscience research
Omeprazole/Lansoprazole/esomeprazole	H^+/K^+ ATPase inhibitor	Over-the-counter acid production blocker (proton pump inhibitor)

7.3 Summary

- The cell uses a tiny molecular motor to synthesize ATP.
- The energy of the proton gradient across the inner mitochondrial membrane can be described mathematically.
- Proteins related to ATP synthase work in reverse as ATPases, to generate ion gradients in vesicles or to pump ions across a cell membrane.
- Inhibitors of ATP synthase or ATPases can be potent poisons or beneficial drugs.

7.3 Concept Check

- Describe the overall conformation of the ATP synthase.
- Explain how the ATP synthase complex is thought to function, that is, how the potential of the chemiosmotic gradient is harnessed to make ATP.
- Describe mathematically the energetics of the proton gradient.
- Describe some of the other proteins that use ATP to generate an ion gradient (these are often thought of as ATP synthases running in reverse).
- Explain how inhibition of ATP synthase or ATPases can be used in the laboratory or clinic.

The Bigger Picture

All organisms require energy for the chemical reactions needed to survive. The common catabolic pathway is a general term that describes the funneling of molecules through different catabolic pathways into acetyl-CoA, which is oxidized in the citric acid cycle.

The reducing equivalents obtained in this process are used to produce a proton gradient, which is used to make ATP. This process is conserved throughout evolution and is used in different forms in all organisms.

Bioinformatics Exercises

Exercise 1 The Citric Acid Cycle and the KEGG Database
Exercise 2 Viewing and Analyzing Complexes I–IV

Exercise 3 Diversity of the Electron-Transport Chain and the KEGG Database

Problems

7.1 The Citric Acid Cycle

1. Examine these three citric acid cycle intermediates. Each has been labeled with C^{14}. Following one round of the citric acid cycle, where would the C^{14} be found?

2. Examine these three citric acid cycle intermediates. Each has been labeled with O^{18}. Following one round of the citric acid cycle, where would the O^{18} be found?

3. Without looking at a table of free energy values, what would you predict the free energies of reaction to be for the various reactions of the citric acid cycle? Which would be strongly positive, which negative, and which near zero?

4. Examine each of the reactions of the citric acid cycle. In your own words, what happens in each step? Compare this to the name of each enzyme. How does your description compare to the name?

5. Name the regulators of the citric acid cycle. At what point does each regulator affect the reactions? Which regulators are feedback inhibitors, and which are allosteric inhibitors? Examine the structure of these enzymes using the Protein Data Bank (PDB). Where is the active site of each enzyme, and where does the regulator bind?

6. Radioisotopes were instrumental to the elucidation of the citric acid cycle. Could fluorescent molecules have been used instead? How could you use a fluorescently tagged analog of isocitrate to help identify the next step in the citric acid cycle?

7. Based solely on the reactions of the citric acid cycle, could this pathway be used to fix CO$_2$ into acetyl-CoA or other molecules?

8. Examine the energetics of the citric acid cycle. Could this pathway be used to fix CO$_2$ into acetyl-CoA or other molecules?

9. If the citric acid cycle is so important to all of metabolism, why isn't there any redundancy to the pathway?

10. While some notable mutations exist, there are relatively few diseases that arise from complete deficiencies of any of the enzymes in the citric acid cycle. Why is this the case?

11. Why are structures available for some but not all citric acid cycle enzymes in the PDB?

12. Using an electronic resource, find papers that discuss the regulation of the citric acid cycle (such as the work of Gilvarg and Davis). When did this research take place? What sources did you use to research Gilvarg and Davis's work (for example, primary literature papers, review articles, books, online summaries)? How could you gauge the credibility of the work?

7.2 The Electron Transport Chain

13. Structures for the complexes of the electron transport chain can be found in the PDB. Look up some of these structures in the PDB. Which species are they from, and why?

14. Many of the structures of the electron transport chain and ATP biosynthesis have been imaged with electron microscopy. Why has such a low-resolution technique been used, when it is usually associated with cell biology and used to examine larger structures?

15. Could you block any one single step of electron transport completely and not kill an organism? Please explain.

16. Many biochemical reactions run at ΔG values close to zero but are reversible with slight changes in concentration. Is electron flow reversible through the electron transport chain? Is there a reason why electrons need to flow in the direction they do?

17. Radiolabeling facilitated many early metabolic studies and is still used today. Is there an equivalent for electrons? Is there a way to isotopically label an electron?

18. Some organisms use molecules as electron carriers other than the ones discussed. If there were a protein with a Cu center, a heme group, and a manganese-containing heme analog, and based on the data in Table 7.2, predict the order in which they might function in electron transport. Which carriers would be used, and when?

19. Describe three techniques that can be used to show that the electron transport chain is found on the matrix side of the inner mitochondrial membrane.

20. Cytochrome c is often used as a marker for evolutionary change. Can it be used for all organisms? What are the strengths and limitations of using this single gene? What assumptions about evolutionary change must be made to use this gene successfully?

21. We may not think of gases as reagents in reactions, but several enzymes in biochemistry fix CO$_2$ while others use O$_2$ for a variety of processes. Describe the cofactors and chemistry involved in some of these processes.

22. Succinate dehydrogenase was first discovered in the 1930s. Why was it not recognized as part of electron transport chain until the 1990s?

23. What is wrong with this proposed mechanism?

Oxaloacetate

24. Cyanokit is an injectable form of vitamin B12 (hydroxycobalamin). It is used to treat cyanide poisoning. Suggest how this drug might work.

7.3 ATP Biosynthesis

25. Both picric acid and DNP can act as uncoupling agents. Based on your knowledge of organic chemistry, which is likely to be the better uncoupling agent?

26. Examine the list of ATPase inhibitors in Table 7.4. Using these inhibitors, how could you determine whether an ATPase was of the V- or P-type?

27. Compare the structures of the different ATP synthases and ATPases discussed in section 7.3. How are they similar, and how are they different? Based on the structures alone, which would you expect to be part of the same evolutionary tree?

28. Many people take proton pump inhibitors for treatment of heartburn. These pumps are ATPases that are embedded in the plasma membrane. If these pumps are inhibited, how do their cells avoid high concentrations of ATP?

Questions 29–33 are concerned with ATPases that acidify vesicular structures in the cell.

29. How much ATP would you have to hydrolyze to cause a pH drop of 7.2 to 4.5 in a lysosome that has a diameter of 0.1 microns?

30. What assumptions would you need to make in performing this calculation?

31. If that change took three seconds, what would be the rate of acidification?

32. What is the turnover number of this enzyme if one pump was involved?

33. What is the turnover number of this enzyme if ten pumps were involved?

Data Interpretation

34. A new graduate student in your laboratory has added radiolabeled citrate to cultured cells in an attempt to generate radiolabeled succinate. Instead, when checked, the label was found almost everywhere in the cell. The student believes he "got a bad batch" of radiolabeled citrate. What has probably happened instead? Why has the label shown up in other pools?

35. The same student is also attempting to use radiolabeled succinyl-CoA to produce radiolabeled GTP. Will this work?

36. The cobalt center in vitamin B12 fluctuates between the Co^{2+} and Co^{3+} states. These two states can be detected spectrophotometrically and have different visible range spectra as well as EPR signals. Co^{3+} is red colored and has no unpaired electrons, whereas Co^{2+} is yellow and has unpaired electrons. Which spectra (A or B) would match these oxidation states? Would you expect the molecule that generated each of the following spectra to give an EPR signal? Why or why not?

37. You isolated a purported electron transport complex from fungi. The individual complexes have the following molecular weights:

Complex	Mass	Complex	Mass
I	950 kDa	III	130 kDa
II	250 kDa	IV	190 kDa

Size exclusion chromatography of the sample reveals a single peak with an expected molecular weight of 1.5 to 1.8 MDa (1500 to 1800 kDa). Electron microscopy of the same sample gives the following images:

Side

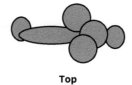

Top

Propose a stoichiometry for the subunits in this complex. Could you algebraically predict the stoichiometry without the electron microscopy data?

Experimental Design

38. The proton motive force used to synthesize ATP has both a concentration and charge dependence. Because of the charge on the proton, these values cannot be completely divorced from one another.

How could you tease out the chemical versus electrical component of pmf in mitochondria?

39. Many oxidation reactions occur in the absence of enzymes. Metal ions, for example, can oxidize many molecules in the presence of oxygen or water. Propose a simple control to show that the steps of the citric acid cycle are all enzymatically catalyzed.

40. Using electron transport inhibitors, design an experiment to demonstrate that cytochrome *c* transports electrons from complex III to complex IV.

41. The FAD cofactor found in succinate dehydrogenase/complex II is tightly bound to the protein. Design an experiment to test this hypothesis.

42. You have identified a new protein in a species of algae. Based on sequence similarity to ATPases, you believe it may be involved in acidifying a subcellular compartment in the algae. Design an experiment to test this hypothesis.

Ethics and Social Responsibility

43. Colony collapse syndrome is a recently occurring phenomenon in which large numbers of bees have mysteriously vanished or died. Neonicotinoid pesticides used in many applications such as treating crops and flea and tick sprays for dogs and cats, are far less toxic than other insecticides (such as rotenone) but have been implicated as the causal agent in bee death. Research this issue and debate the use of neonicotinoid pesticides from both perspectives.

44. In the 1930s, many diet pills contained proton uncoupling agents such as DNP. Occasionally these drugs resurface, and there are stories of people using them with negative side effects. If these or similar molecules could be rendered safe, should people take them, or should weight be controlled by other means, such as diet and exercise?

45. Cyanide is a potent electron transport inhibitor, binding irreversibly to cytochromes. Cyanide fishing is a process in which fishermen dump cyanide into waters to stun tropical fish. The fish are scooped up in nets and sold to aquarium hobbyists. However, the health of the fish is often adversely affected by the cyanide poisoning, and the coral reef is killed by the residual cyanide. What are the socioeconomic circumstances that lead to this type of fishing? Is one group more to blame than another?

46. Cyanide holds an infamous place in history as a poison. Spies supposedly carried cyanide pills under their tongues, so they could commit suicide in the event of capture. Although clearly a potent poison, cyanide has been used by scientists to probe electron transport and elucidate some of the more fundamental questions in biochemistry about ATP production. Drugs and molecules often become personified by society, and people develop strong positive or negative connotations with them. Are these views founded? Are some molecules beneficial and others simply not?

47. In 1982, a number of people in San Diego unintentionally poisoned themselves with MPTP, a synthetic drug they thought to be the drug "angel dust" (phencyclidine or PCP). The MPTP depleted key areas of their brain (the substantia nigra) of citric acid cycle intermediates, resulting in neuronal death. The loss of these cells manifested itself as Parkinsonism (the shaking and shuffling gait of people suffering from Parkinson's disease). These people inadvertently provided important clues as to how Parkinson's disease can occur. What rights and responsibilities do these patients have, both for themselves and to science, medicine, and society as a whole?

Suggested Readings

7.1 The Citric Acid Cycle

Brunengraber, H., and C. R. Roe. "Anaplerotic Molecules: Current and Future." *Journal of Inherited Metabolic Disease* 29, no. 2–3 (April-June 2006): 327–31.

Fandrey, J., T. A. Gorr, and M. Gassmann. "Regulating Cellular Oxygen Sensing by Hydroxylation." *Cardiovascular Research* 71, no. 4 (September 1, 2006): 642–51.

Kaelin, W. G., Jr., and P. J. Ratcliffe. "Oxygen Sensing by Metazoans: The Central Role of the HIF Hydroxylase Pathway." *Molecular Cell* 30, no. 4 (May 23, 2008): 393–402.

Lambeth, D. O., K. N. Tews, S. Adkins, D. Frohlich, and B. I. Milavetz. "Expression of Two Succinyl-CoA Synthetases with Different Nucleotide Specificities in Mammalian Tissues." *Journal of Biological Chemistry,* 279 (2004): 36621–4.

Lowenstein, J. M., ed. *Methods in Enzymology: Volume 13 Citric Acid Cycle.* Boston, Massachusetts: Academic Press, 1969.

Sazanov, L. A., and J. B. Jackson. "Proton-Translocating Transhydrogenase and NAD- and NADP-Linked Isocitrate Dehydrogenases Operate in a Substrate Cycle which Contributes to Fine Regulation of the Tricarboxylic Acid Cycle Activity in Mitochondria." *FEBS Letters* 344, no. 2–3 (May 16, 1994): 109–16.

Stobbe, M. D., S. M. Houten, A. H. van Kampen, R. J. Wanders, and P. D. Moerland. "Improving the Description of Metabolic Networks: The TCA Cycle as Example." *The FASEB Journal* 26, no. 9 (2012): 3625–36.

Sugden, M. C., and M. J. Holness. "The Pyruvate Carboxylase-Pyruvate Dehydrogenase Axis in Islet Pyruvate Metabolism: Going Round in Circles?" *Islets* 3, no. 6 (November–December 2011): 302–19.

Wan, B., K. F. LaNoue, J. Y. Cheung, and R. C. Scaduto, Jr. "Regulation of Citric Acid Cycle by Calcium." *Journal of Biological Chemistry* 264, no. 23 (1989): 13430–39.

7.2 Electron Transport Chain

Bertini I., G. Cavallaro, and A. Rosato. "Evolution of Mitochondrial-Type Cytochrome c Domains and of the Protein Machinery for Their Assembly." *Journal of Inorganic Biochemistry* 101, no. 11–12, (2007): 1798–1811.

Crofts, A. R., S. Hong, N. Ugulava, B. Barquera, R. Gennis, M. Guerrgova-Kuras, and E. Berry. "Pathways for Proton Release during Ubihydroquinone Oxidation by the bc1 Complex." *Proceedings of the National Academy of Sciences of the United States of America* 96, (1999): 10021–6.

Doherty, M. K., S. L. Pealing, C. S. Miles, R. Moysey, P. Taylor, M. D. Walkinshaw, G. A. Reid, and S. K. Chapman. "Identification of the Active Site Acid/Base Catalyst in a Bacterial Fumarate Reductase: A Kinetic and Crystallographic Study." *Biochemistry* 39, no. 35 (September 5, 2000): 10695–701.

Dudkinaa, N. V., M. Kudryashevb, H. Stahlbergb, and E. J. Boekemaa. "Interaction of Complexes I, III, and IV within the Bovine Respirasome by Single Particle Cryoelectron Tomography." *Proceedings of the National Academy of Sciences of the United States of America* 108, no. 37 (September 13, 2011): 15196–200.

Horsefield, R., V. Yankovskaya, G. Sexton, W. Whittingham, K. Shiomi, S. Ōmura, B. Byrne, G. Cecchini, and S. Iwata. "Structural and Computational Analysis of the Quinone-Binding Site of Complex II (Succinate-Ubiquinone Oxidoreductase): A Mechanism of Electron Transfer and Proton Conduction During Ubiquinone Reduction." *Journal of Biological Chemistry* 281, no. 11 (2006): 7309–16.

Johnson, D. C., D. R. Dean, A. D. Smith, and M. K. Johnson. "Structure, Function, and Formation of Biological Iron-Sulfur Clusters." *Annual Review of Biochemistry* 74 (2005): 247–81.

Lancaster, C. R., and A. Kröger. "Succinate: Quinone Oxidoreductases: New Insights from X-Ray Crystal Structures." *Biochimica et Biophysica Acta* 1459, no. 2–3 (August 15, 2000): 422–31.

Mowat, C. G., R. Moysey, C. S. Miles, D. Leys, M. K. Doherty, P. Taylor, M. D. Walkinshaw, G. A. Reid, and S. K. Chapman. "Kinetic and Crystallographic Analysis of the Key Active Site Acid/Base Arginine in a Soluble Fumarate Reductase." *Biochemistry* 40, no. 41 (2001): 12292–8.

Oyedotun, K. S., and B. D. Lemire. "The Quaternary Structure of the *Saccharomyces cerevisiae* Succinate Dehydrogenase: Homology Modeling, Cofactor Docking, and Molecular Dynamics Simulation Studies." *Journal of Biological Chemistry* 279, no. 10 (2004): 9424–31.

Palsdottir, H., Gomez-Lojero, B. L. Trumpower, and C. Hunte. "Structure of the Yeast Cytochrome bc1 Complex with a Hydroxyquinone Anion Q_o Site Inhibitor Bound." *Journal of Biological Chemistry* 278, no. 33 (2003): 31303–11.

Schägger, H., and K. Pfeiffer. "The Ratio of Oxidative Phosphorylation Complexes I–V in Bovine Heart Mitochondria and the Composition of Respiratory Chain Supercomplexes." *Journal of Biological Chemistry* 276, no. 41 (2001): 37861–7.

Solomon, Edward I., Uma M. Sundaram, and Timothy E. Machonkin. "Multicopper Oxidases and Oxygenases." *Chemical Reviews* 96, no. 7 (1996): 2563–2606.

Sun, F., X. Huo, Y. Zhai, A. Wang, J. Xu, D. Su, M. Bartlam, and Z. Rao. "Crystal Structure of Mitochondrial Respiratory Membrane Protein Complex II." *Cell* 121 (2005): 1043–1057.

Tran, Q. M., R. A. Rothery, E. Maklashina, G. Cecchini, and J. H. Weiner. "The Quinone Binding Site in *Escherichia coli* Succinate Dehydrogenase Is Required for Electron Transfer to the Heme b." *Journal of Biological Chemistry* 281, no. 43 (2006): 32310–7.

Yankovskaya, V., R. Horsefield, S. Törnroth, C. Luna-Chavez, H. Miyoshi, C. Léger, B. Byrne, G. Cecchini, and S. Iwata. "Architecture of Succinate Dehydrogenase and Reactive Oxygen Species Generation." *Science* 299, no. 5607 (2003): 700–4.

Zaunmüller, T., D. J. Kelly, F. O. Glöckner, and G. Unden. "Succinate Dehydrogenase Functioning by a Reverse Redox Loop Mechanism and Fumarate Reductase in Sulphate-Reducing Bacteria." *Microbiology* 152 (Pt 8) (August 2006): 2443–53.

Zhang, Z., L. Huang, V. M. Schulmeister, Y. I. Chi, K. K. Kim, L. W. Hung, A. R. Crofts, E. A. Berry, and S. H. Kim. "Electron Transfer by Domain Movement in Cytochrome bc1." *Nature* 392, (1998): 677–84.

7.3 ATP Biosynthesis

Huss, M., F. Sasse, B. Kunze, R. Jansen, H. Steinmetz, G. Ingenhorst, A. Zeeck, and H. Wieczorek. "Archazolid and Apicularen: Novel Specific V-ATPase Inhibitors." *BMC Biochemistry* 6 (August 4, 2005): 13.

Huss, M., and H. Wieczorek. "Inhibitors of V-ATPases: Old and New Players." *Journal of Experimental Biology* 212, (Pt 3) (February 2009): 341–6.

Ōmura, S. *Macrolide Antibiotics: Chemistry, Biology, and Practice.* 2nd ed. Boston, Massachusetts: Academic Press, 2002.

Plesner, L. "Ecto-ATPases: Identities and Functions." *International Review of Cytology* 158, (1995): 41–214.

Plesner, Liselotte, Terence L. Kirley, and Aileen F. Knowles, eds. *Ecto-ATPases: Recent Progress on Structure and Function.* New York, New York: Springer, 1997.

The Common Catabolic Pathway

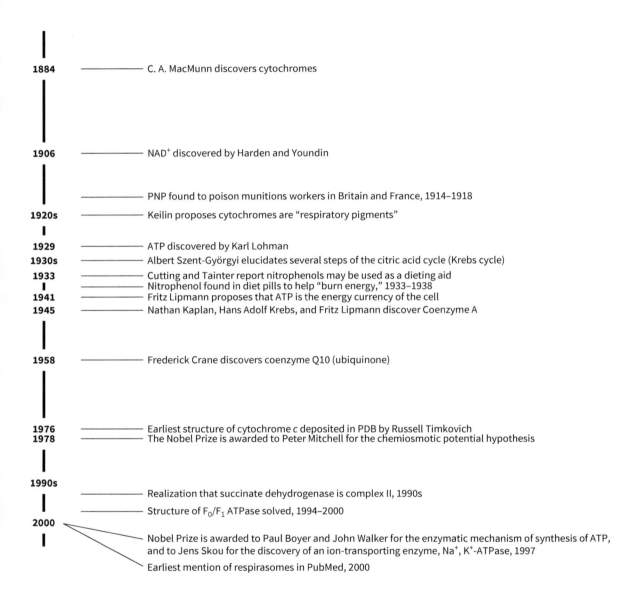

1884 ——————— C. A. MacMunn discovers cytochromes

1906 ——————— NAD$^+$ discovered by Harden and Youndin

——————— PNP found to poison munitions workers in Britain and France, 1914–1918
1920s ——————— Keilin proposes cytochromes are "respiratory pigments"

1929 ——————— ATP discovered by Karl Lohman
1930s ——————— Albert Szent-Györgyi elucidates several steps of the citric acid cycle (Krebs cycle)
1933 ——————— Cutting and Tainter report nitrophenols may be used as a dieting aid
——————— Nitrophenol found in diet pills to help "burn energy," 1933–1938
1941 ——————— Fritz Lipmann proposes that ATP is the energy currency of the cell
1945 ——————— Nathan Kaplan, Hans Adolf Krebs, and Fritz Lipmann discover Coenzyme A

1958 ——————— Frederick Crane discovers coenzyme Q10 (ubiquinone)

1976 ——————— Earliest structure of cytochrome *c* deposited in PDB by Russell Timkovich
1978 ——————— The Nobel Prize is awarded to Peter Mitchell for the chemiosmotic potential hypothesis

1990s
——————— Realization that succinate dehydrogenase is complex II, 1990s
——————— Structure of F_0/F_1 ATPase solved, 1994–2000
2000
Nobel Prize is awarded to Paul Boyer and John Walker for the enzymatic mechanism of synthesis of ATP, and to Jens Skou for the discovery of an ion-transporting enzyme, Na$^+$, K$^+$-ATPase, 1997

Earliest mention of respirasomes in PubMed, 2000

CHAPTER 8

Carbohydrates II

Glycogen Metabolism, the
Pentose Phosphate Pathway,
Glycoconjugates, and
Extracellular Matrices

EMMANUEL DUNAND/Getty Images

While many of the runners in this marathon may think
about their glycogen reserves helping them cross the
finish line, they are also relying on polysaccharides in
their connective tissue and extracellular matrices
to help literally hold them together.

Polysaccharides in Context

Carbohydrates are nearly as diverse as proteins, and what they lack in
functional group diversity and catalytic power, they make up for in overall diversity of form and structure. Starch and cellulose are polysaccharides, but so is glycogen, which acts as a store of energy in animals. Substances as diverse as mucus and connective tissue are largely comprised
of polysaccharides, or proteins decorated with lengthy carbohydrate
chains. These molecules are key to growth, development, and immunity;
they also impart structure to the organism as a major component of cartilage and connective tissue. The many roles that carbohydrates play in
biochemistry are just beginning to be understood.

This chapter starts with a discussion of the metabolism of glycogen.
It highlights the regulation of glycogen metabolism, particularly how it
differs from tissue to tissue, and its response to different chemical stimuli
(hormones). Section 8.2 looks at the pentose phosphate pathway, which
generates NADPH for lipid biosynthesis and redox needs of the cell,
generates ribose-5-phosphate for nucleotide biosynthesis, and provides
a way to catabolize other carbohydrates in the cell. Sections 8.3 and 8.4
discuss the properties and chemistry of the extracellular matrix: Section 8.3
focuses on polysaccharides in glycoproteins, glycolipids, proteoglycans,
and peptidoglycans, and section 8.4 discusses matrix proteins and their
assembly. The final section also looks at biofilms, analogous structures
to the extracellular matrix made by some strains of microbes. These processes are discussed in **Dynamic Figure 8.1**.

CHAPTER OUTLINE

8.1 Glycogen Metabolism

8.2 The Pentose Phosphate Pathway

8.3 Carbohydrates in Glycoconjugates

8.4 Extracellular Matrices and Biofilms

DYNAMIC FIGURE 8.1 Carbohydrates in animals are stored as glycogen. The synthesis and breakdown of glycogen is highly regulated. The pentose phosphate pathway coordinates production of NADPH and ribose in tissues that need these molecules for growth or redox chemistry. There are several types of molecules that are glycosylated. Many of these are found in the extracellular matrix.

COMMON THEMES

Evolution's outcomes are conserved.	• The pentose phosphate pathway evolved, in part, from the more primordial CO_2 fixation pathway used by photosynthetic bacteria and plants.
	• The eukaryotic extracellular matrix has its evolutionary origins in the secreted molecules made by microbes. Certain features of these structures, termed biofilms, are similar to those of the extracellular matrix, for example, group immunity due to secreted antibiotics, changes in phenotype and structure, and cell–cell communication.
	• Similar molecules (secreted glycoproteins and proteoglycans) are found in biofilms and the extracellular matrix.
	• Both biofilms and the extracellular matrix may have evolved from the bacterial cell wall, which has some similar features on a single-cell basis.
Structure determines function.	• The branched structure of glycogen provides numerous points at which glucose can be rapidly mobilized or incorporated.
	• The structure of extracellular matrix proteins and polysaccharides relates to their function. These molecules are often soft gels, but others provide some of the strongest structures in biochemistry. Many extracellular proteins are fibrous or filamentous, and they provide numerous locations for cross-linking.
	• Alterations of what we consider "normal" protein chemistry are often seen in the extracellular matrix. Such modifications include hydroxylated prolines and lysines, and cross-linked lysine and glutamine residues. These modifications lead to increased structural stability of the matrix.
Biochemical information is transferred, exchanged, and stored.	• Glycogen metabolism is tightly regulated by numerous kinases. These pathways are coordinated by hormones in the body.
	• Xylulose-5-phosphate, a product of the pentose phosphate pathway, is an important regulator of the transcription factor ChREBP (the carbohydrate response element-binding protein).
	• Hydroxy proline residues seen in collagen are also found in the transcription factor hypoxic inducible factor (HIF). When oxygen levels are low, HIF is not hydroxylated and is able to activate gene expression.
Biomolecules are altered through pathways involving transformations of energy and matter.	• As discussed in other chapters, energetically unfavorable reactions become favorable when coupled to reactions with a large, negative ΔG value (the hydrolysis or transfer of favorable leaving groups). We typically think of this in terms of adenosine-5′-triphosphate (ATP) hydrolysis or phosphate transfer; however, other reactions (such as hydrolysis of a thioester thioesters), are common in biochemistry. Similarly, reactions that have $\Delta G°$ values close to zero can be tipped to move in the forward or reverse direction by changing the concentrations of substrates or products.

- Addition of carbohydrates to a molecule involves energetic activation through the use of uridine-5′-triphosphate (UTP), to produce uridine diphosphate (UDP)-carbohydrates.
- Liberation of glucose monomers from glycogen is energetically favorable.
- Isomerization of monosaccharides found in the pentose phosphate pathway occurs with ΔG values close to zero and can be tipped in the forward or reverse direction by the concentration of substrates.

8.1 Glycogen Metabolism

If we think of carbohydrates as a form of stored energy analogous to money, then glycogen is money in the bank. Glycogen is a stored form of glucose. Certain cells and tissues in the body (particularly the brain and erythrocytes, and to some extent the kidneys) require glucose for energy. For a variety of reasons, the energy source of these tissues is limited to glucose. Glycogen acts as a buffer, storing glucose when glucose is plentiful and releasing it at other times as the body needs it.

Glycogen is a highly branched polymer of α-1,4 and α-1,6 linked glucose monomers, with a single molecule of the protein **glycogenin** at the core (**Figure 8.2**). In the same way that the starch amylopectin stores energy in plants, glycogen stores energy in animals. Cells cannot store monomeric glucose. The anomeric carbon in monomeric glucose could react with free hydroxyl groups, randomly glycosylating molecules in the cell. In addition, a significant amount of water is needed to hydrate the glucose, which would generate a high osmotic pressure in the cell. Glycogen is not transported in the body; instead, it is synthesized and degraded in situ. Skeletal muscle stores most of the body's glycogen (75%); the remaining glycogen is stored in the liver. Muscle glycogen cannot release glucose for use by the rest of the body and so uses that glucose in muscle cells, but the liver can and does release glucose, so that it can fuel other tissues. The synthesis of glycogen is termed **glycogenesis** and the breakdown is **glycogenolysis**.

FIGURE 8.2 **Glycogen is a storage form of glucose.** Glycogen granules can contain tens of thousands of α-1,4 and α-1,6 linked glucose monomers and have a single molecule of the protein glycogenin in their core. (Häggström, Mikael (2014). "Medical gallery of Mikael Häggström 2014". Wiki Journal of Medicine 1(2), DOI: 10.15347/wjm/2014.008. ISSN 2002–4436.)

FIGURE 8.3 **Synthesis of glycogen.** New glucose monomers are added to glycogen by glycogen synthase. The energy needed to drive the reaction comes from coupling glucose first to UDP. The bond to UDP joins the anomeric carbon of glucose (C-1) to C-4 of the growing glycogen chain.

8.1.1 | Glycogenesis is glycogen biosynthesis

Like the polymers discussed in other chapters (DNA, RNA, and proteins), glycogen is a polymer. However, glycogen differs from these other polymers in that glycogen is highly branched and has numerous termini—an important evolutionary adaptation. Biosynthesis and degradation can only occur at termini; hence, the large branched molecule of glycogen can be built up or broken down more rapidly than a linear molecule.

Glucose enters any cell via a glucose transporter, and it is rapidly phosphorylated to glucose-6-phosphate (G-6-P). Both of these steps were introduced in the discussion of glycolysis. When G-6-P levels are high, glycogenesis begins with G-6-P being isomerized into glucose-1-phosphate by the enzyme **phosphoglucomutase**. The addition of glucose monomers to glycogen is energetically unfavorable. Instead, carbohydrate metabolism is fueled by the formation of a molecule that has the ability to transfer glucose molecules to the growing chain. That molecule is uridine diphosphate-glucose or UDP-glucose (**Figure 8.3**). In many reactions, we think of ATP as providing energy for a reaction, such as transfer of a phosphate group, to occur. Here, the nucleotide phosphate is UDP instead of ATP, and the group that is transferred is a molecule of glucose.

UDP-glucose is formed when the phosphate on glucose-1-phosphate attacks the α phosphate of UTP, liberating pyrophosphate and generating UDP-glucose. Although this reaction is not in and of itself energetically favorable, it is coupled to the hydrolysis of pyrophosphate into two molecules of inorganic phosphate, which is extremely favorable ($\Delta G = -33$ kJ/mol), making the overall net reaction favorable. Using UDP-glucose, **glycogen synthase** can add glucose monomers to the hydroxyl on C-4 of a growing glycogen molecule via an α-1,4 glycosidic bond (an acetal).

The initiation of a completely new molecule of glycogen proceeds through a slightly different pathway. The glycogenin protein at the core of glycogen is a glycosyl transferase that adds glucose molecules (as UDP-glucose) to an active site tyrosine molecule. The new glycogen chain continues to be extended until it is between 4 and 13 glucose monomers long, at which point glycogen synthase takes over.

Although glycogenin has only been found in mammalian systems, there may be paralogs (genes produced by duplication which evolve new but related functions) that regulate the priming of other polysaccharides in other species. This may be a rare instance of mammalian biochemistry informing microbial or plant biochemistry, rather than using a simple model to learn about human systems.

The branches in glycogen are incorporated by a **branching enzyme** (amylo α-1,4 → α-1,6-transglycosylase) that transfers a chain of about seven glucose molecules to the

FIGURE 8.4 **Branching enzyme.** Branching enzyme transfers a 7-mer of glucose residues to the hydroxyl on C-6 of a glucose residue at least four glucose residues from the branch point.

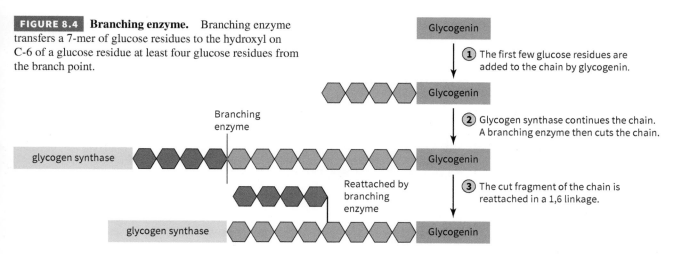

hydroxyl of C-6 in either the same chain or an adjacent chain (**Figure 8.4**). The branch point is at least four carbons from the end of the chain. The resulting reaction leaves behind two new termini, each of which has an exposed hydroxyl group on C-4 to which new molecules of UDP-glucose can be added.

WORKED PROBLEM 8.1 | Synthesizing polysaccharides

You identified a new strain of grass which, like some other grasses, stores polymers of fructose (inulin). When extracts of this grass are incubated with UDP-fructose or fructose alone, no new inulin is formed; however, incubation with sucrose and UDP-glucose or fructose and UDP-glucose produces new inulin. Based on this information and what you know of glycogen metabolism, how might the inulin polymers form?

Strategy What is the structure of glycogen? How is glycogen synthesized? What are the building blocks of glycogen, and how are they formed?

Solution Inulin is a β-1,2 linked polymer of fructose monomers. Formation of glycosidic bonds by the direct combination of two monosaccharides is energetically unfavorable. In glycogen, as in most carbohydrates, the reaction is made favorable by using UDP-glucose as a donor of one of the monosaccharides. This is

still the case with inulin, but by an indirect route. Synthesis of inulin involves fructose monomers, derived from sucrose, being added to the growing inulin chain. In the example of the grass, energy from UDP-glucose is used to drive sucrose production. Then fructose is transferred in a transglycosylation reaction to the growing inulin polymer.

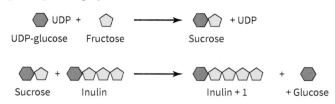

Follow-up question Secreted polysaccharides (known as exopolysaccharides) found in the extracellular matrix are often repeats of two monosaccharides. How might these form?

8.1.2 | Glycogenolysis is glycogen breakdown

Because energy is required to form glycogen, the reverse reaction (liberation of glucose monomers) occurs spontaneously without input of additional energy.

Glycogen is degraded one glucose unit at a time by **glycogen phosphorylase**. The enzyme removes glucose molecules at their α-1,4 linkages, liberating them into the cytosol as G-1-P, and leaving the glycogen shortened by one unit. Glycogen phosphorylase, which contains a pyridoxal phosphate cofactor, uses inorganic phosphate to complete this reaction. In this reaction, the inorganic phosphate serves as the nucleophile to attack C-1 of the terminal glucose monomer to generate glucose-1-phosphate. The phosphorylase cannot cleave branched termini. Instead, it stops four glucose residues before a branch point, and **glycogen**

debranching enzyme removes three of those four residues, transferring them to the free C-4 terminus of another branch and leaving one glucose monomer at the branch point. The debranching enzyme then liberates this glucose using a hydrolysis reaction (**Figures 8.5, 8.6**).

G-1-P has two possible fates, depending on the cell type. In muscle, phosphoglucomutase can interconvert G-1-P and G-6-P. Therefore, G-1-P liberated from glycogen can be isomerized

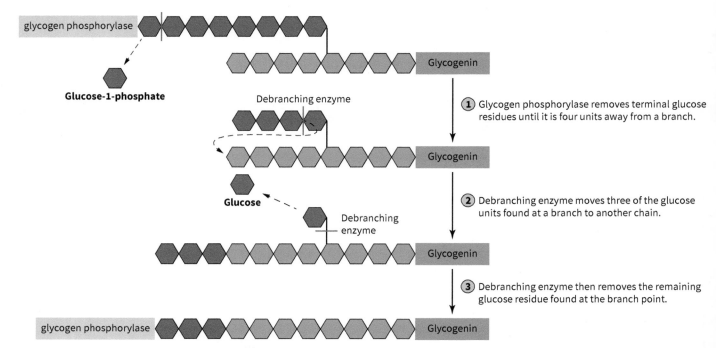

FIGURE 8.5   **Glycogen breakdown.**   Glycogen is degraded by glycogen phosphorylase. Phosphorylase removes glucose residues and releases them to the cytosol as glucose-1-phosphate. Phosphorylase stops four glucose residues before a branch point. At that fork, glycogen debranching enzyme removes three of the four residues and transfers them to the end of another chain. The debranching enzyme then removes the branch glycogen and releases it as free glucose.

FIGURE 8.6   **Mechanism of glycogen phosphorylase.**   Glycogen phosphorylase has an active-site pyridoxal phosphate used differently than we have seen previously. The phosphate moiety of PLP primes a molecule of inorganic phosphate for nucleophilic attack by the anomeric oxygen of the terminal glucose of glycogen. This results in cleavage of the anomeric linkage and formation of glucose-1-phosphate.

and enter into glycolysis, in the same way as any other molecule of G-6-P. In the liver, the story is somewhat different. G-1-P is still isomerized to G-6-P, but the liver also expresses glucose-6-phosphatase, which can cleave the phosphate from G-6-P, liberating glucose. Under these conditions, hexokinase and glucokinase cannot keep up with the glucose-6-phosphatase; this results in elevated levels of cytosolic glucose, which diffuses out of the cell, providing glucose for other tissues that need it.

Mutations to the enzymes involved in the synthesis or breakdown of glycogen lead to glycogen storage disorders (Table 8.1).

TABLE 8.1   Representative Glycogen Storage Disorders

Disease	Mutation	Hypoglycemia	Hepatomegaly	Hyperlipidemia	Muscle symptoms
Type I (Von Gierke)	Glucose-6-phosphatase	Yes	Yes	Yes	None
Type II (Pompe)	Acid α−glucosidase	No	Yes	No	Weakness
Type III (Cori/Forbes)	Debranching enzyme	Yes	Yes	Yes	Myopathy
Type V (McArdle)	Muscle glycogen phosphorylase	No	No	No	Exercise induced cramping
Type IV (Tarui)	Muscle phosphofructokinase	No	No	No	Exercise induced cramping
Type 0	Glycogen synthase	Yes	No	No	Occasional cramping

WORKED PROBLEM 8.2 | Glycogen storage disorder

Cori's disease is a rare autosomal recessive disorder in which the activity of debranching enzyme is defective. What effect would this have on glycogen metabolism? What might you expect for a phenotype?

Strategy   What role does debranching enzyme play in glycogen metabolism? How would the lack of this enzyme affect whole-body metabolism? What would change, and why?

Solution   Cori's disease is one of a family of more than 12 glycogen storage disorders. In these diseases, some aspect of glycogen metabolism is defective, and the body reacts to compensate. In the case of Cori's disease (also known as glycogen storage

disease type III) the absence of debranching enzyme means that glycogen cannot be debranched; thus, glycogen stores cannot be mobilized and the glycogen chains keep growing. This results in low fasting plasma glucose levels, elevated ketone bodies but high levels of glycogen storage in the liver and muscle (and, in some cases, the heart). These elevated levels result from the inability to catabolize glycogen properly. The clinical result of this disease is enlarged liver (hepatomegaly) and skeletal muscle weakness.

Follow-up question   Why are patients with this disorder often treated with high-protein diets?

8.1.3 | The regulation of glycogenesis and glycogenolysis

The regulation of glycogenesis and glycogenolysis is complex but can be distilled down to the regulation of two key enzymes: glycogen phosphorylase and glycogen synthase (Figure 8.7). Both of these enzymes are acutely regulated via the action of kinases and phosphatases and several allosteric regulators. As might be expected, the two proteins are reciprocally regulated. Protein kinase A is one of the main regulators of both glycogen synthase and glycogen phosphorylase, but other kinases and phosphatases also play a role in regulating glycogenesis and glycogenolysis.

Most kinases are regulated through a signaling cascade. This section discusses two of these cascades and then puts them into the context of glycogen metabolism. Among the various hormones involved in the cascades are insulin, which signals the fed state, and glucagon, which signals the fasted state. In these states, glycogen will either be synthesized or degraded,

FIGURE 8.7 **Overview of the regulation of glycogen metabolism.** Glycogen levels are regulated by the balance of two enzymes, glycogen synthase and glycogen phosphorylase. Phosphorylation of glycogen synthase blocks the action of this enzyme and conversely activates glycogen phosphorylase. Dephosphorylation of glycogen synthase activates that enzyme and deactivates glycogen phosphorylase.

as necessary. Glycogen storage is also regulated by the catecholamine hormones epinephrine and norepinephrine. These hormones signal the "fight-or-flight" response, that is, the hormonal response that animals use to remove themselves from danger. Under these conditions, energy is required by the organism, so glycogen is broken down into glucose-1-phosphate.

G protein coupled receptors
The peptide hormone glucagon and the catecholamines epinephrine and norepinephrine act via seven-transmembrane G protein-coupled receptors (GPCRs) as shown in **Figure 8.8**. Catecholamines or glucagon can bind to these receptors, which in turn activate a G protein. Tissue-specific expression of these receptors helps to fine-tune and integrate whole-body glycogen metabolism.

G proteins then activate adenylate cyclase. This membrane-bound enzyme catalyzes the conversion of ATP into the second messenger cyclic adenosine monophosphate (cAMP), which has several targets in the cell. Glycogen metabolism is dependent on the cAMP-dependent protein kinase (PKA). PKA is a tetrameric enzyme that is made up of a dimer of dimers. It

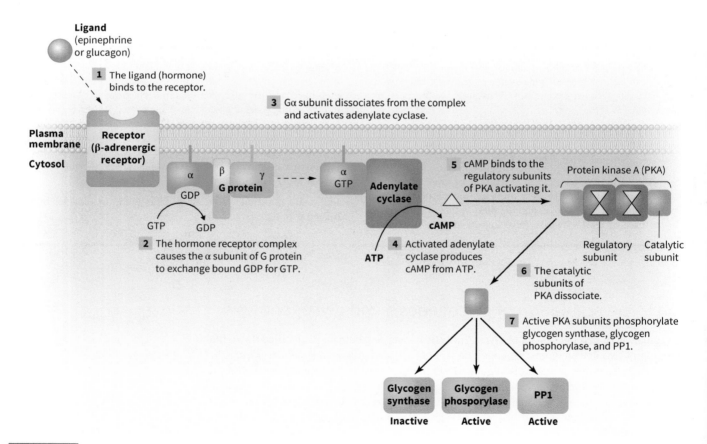

FIGURE 8.8 **Action of glucagon and epinephrine on the cell.** Glucagon and epinephrine signal through a seven-transmembrane G protein-coupled receptor to activate a heterotrimeric G protein. Once bound to GTP, the Gα subunit will activate adenylate cyclase, which will produce cAMP from ATP. The second messenger cAMP will in turn activate protein kinase A, which can phosphorylate many targets in the cell, including glycogen synthase, glycogen phosphorylase, and protein phosphatase 1.

1 Insulin binds to its receptor causing dimerization of the receptor and recruitment of IRS-1.

2 IRS-1 activates PI3K converting PIP2 to PIP3.

Plasma membrane

Cytosol

Receptor (insulin receptor)

IRS-1

PIP2

PI3K

PIP3

3 PIP3 activates PDK 1.

PDK1

4 Activated PDK 1 phosphorylates Akt.

Akt

5 Akt phosphorylates GSK-3, inactivating it.

GSK-3

GSK-3-P

6 Unphosphorylated GSK-3 phosphorylates glycogen synthase, inactivating it, but when GSK-3 is inactivated by Akt, glycogen synthase is active.

Glycogen synthase-P

Inactive

Glycogen synthase

Active

FIGURE 8.9 **Insulin signaling.** Insulin regulates both metabolism and growth. In metabolism, insulin signals through an insulin receptor to activate the phosphoinositide cascade via PI₃ kinase. This ultimately results in the activation of Akt, which phosphorylates and inhibits glycogen synthase kinase (GSK-3). Insulin also affects glycogen synthesis and degradation by activating phosphoprotein phosphatase 1 (not shown).

has two regulatory subunits that bind the cAMP, and two catalytic subunits that use ATP to catalyze the phosphorylation of numerous target proteins.

Insulin receptors

Insulin signaling occurs via a different mechanism than GPCRs (Figure 8.9). The hormone insulin binds to an insulin receptor, causing dimerization of that receptor and autophosphorylation on specific tyrosine residues (this is a receptor tyrosine kinase, or RTK). The binding results in nucleation of scaffolding proteins and kinases, which assemble into a macromolecular signaling complex. Among the kinases are PI₃ kinase, which initiates a phosphoinositide signaling cascade. PI₃ kinase phosphorylates phosphatidylinositol 4,5-bisphosphate into phosphatidylinositol 3,4,5-trisphosphate. These second messengers activate the kinase Akt. Akt in turn phosphorylates multiple proteins, including glycogen synthase kinase-3 (GSK-3), inactivating it.

Insulin also acts to stimulate glycogenesis and block glycogenolysis by stimulating protein phosphatase 1 (PP1).

Bringing signals together: the balance of covalent modification and allosteric regulators

Both glycogen synthase and glycogen phosphorylase are regulated by covalent modification and by allosteric regulators. In the case of these enzymes, the covalent modifications consist of the phosphorylation or dephosphorylation of key serine residues, and the allosteric regulators are ATP and glucose-6-phosphate.

The a/b naming convention is used for both glycogen synthase and glycogen phosphorylase. In this convention the enzyme can be modeled as existing in one of two states, an active state "a" and a less active state "b." Phosphorylation or dephosphorylation dictates whether an enzyme is in the a or b state, but the regulation of glycogen synthase and glycogen phosphorylase are the reciprocal of each other. This means that glycogen synthase is most active (the a state) while dephosphorylated, but that glycogen phosphorylase is most active (the a state) when phosphorylated.

The activity of glycogen synthase and glycogen phosphorylase is also modified by allosteric regulators. The effectiveness of these regulators varies with regard to both the

Phosphoprotein phosphatase 1 (PP1) dephosphorylates the b state of the enzyme and returns it to the more active a state. This is stimulated by the **insulin** signaling pathway.

Phosphorylation of glycogen synthase by PKA, GSK-3, or other kinases results in the enzyme adopting the less active b state. These kinases are stimulated by **epinepherine** and **glucagon** and inactivated by insulin.

Glucose-6-phosphate is an allosteric activator of glycogen synthase.

FIGURE 8.10 **Regulation of glycogen synthesis.** Phosphorylation of glycogen synthase through any one of a number of possible kinases converts it to the inactive form. Dephosphorylation by phosphoprotein phosphatase 1 activates the enzyme. Phosphoprotein phosphatase itself is activated by phosphorylation by PKA.

molecule itself (ATP vs. glucose-6-phosphate) as well as the phosphorylation state of the enzyme.

Bringing signals together: the effect on glycogen synthase

Glycogen synthase is activated by dephosphorylation and inactivated by phosphorylation (**Figure 8.10**). Therefore, any pathways that phosphorylate glycogen synthase will inactivate it, and any that dephosphorylate the enzyme will activate it. Glycogen synthase is phosphorylated by glycogen synthase kinase-3 or GSK-3, which is regulated by Akt. When Akt phosphorylates GSK-3, it inactivates GSK-3, thus favoring the dephosphorylated or active state of glycogen synthase. Glycogen synthase can be also directly phosphorylated by PKA and several other kinases.

Glycogen synthase is also regulated by phosphoprotein phosphatase 1 (PP1). The phosphatase removes phosphates from glycogen synthase, resulting in its activation. Interestingly, PP1 is also regulated by phosphorylation: it is inactivated by phosphorylation (catalyzed by PKA) and allosterically activated by G-6-P. This provides an added level of regulation of glycogen concentrations in the cell.

Glycogen synthase is also allosterically activated by G-6-P, which binds to the phosphorylated form of the enzyme. This makes metabolic sense in that, when glucose levels in the plasma are high, intracellular levels of glucose (and therefore of G-6-P) will increase, triggering the cell to store some of this G-6-P as glycogen.

Bringing signals together: the effect on glycogen phosphorylase

Glycogen phosphorylase is activated by phosphorylation and deactivated by dephosphorylation (**Figure 8.11**). The regulation of glycogen phosphorylase is similar to that of glycogen

Phosphoprotein phosphatase 1 (PP1) dephosphorylates the a state of the enzyme and returns it to the less active b state. This is stimulated by the **insulin** signaling pathway.

Phosphorylation of phosphorylase kinase by protein kinase A (PKA) results in phosphorylase kinase adopting the more active a state. PKA is stimulated by **epinephrine** and **glucagon.**

Glycogen phosphorylase is allosterically activated by AMP and inhibited by ATP and glucose-6-phosphate.

FIGURE 8.11 **Regulation of glycogen phosphorylase.** The activity of glycogen phosphorylase is regulated by both allosteric regulators (AMP, ATP, and glucose-6-phosphate) and phosphorylation state. A significant difference is that glycogen phosphorylase is active in the phosphorylated state. The phosphorylation of this enzyme is catalyzed by phosphorylase kinase, which in turn is regulated by PKA and Ca^{2+}. The dephosphorylation of glycogen phosphorylase is catalyzed by phosphoprotein phosphatase 1 (PP1).

synthase (although slightly less complex). Phosphorylation of glycogen phosphorylase is catalyzed by phosphorylase kinase. Phosphorylase kinase is activated by phosphorylation (mainly by PKA) and also by calcium ions.

Dephosphorylation of glycogen phosphorylase is catalyzed by PP1, as previously discussed.

TABLE 8.2 The Effect of Hormones on Glucose Metabolism

	Insulin		Glucagon		Epinepherine	
	muscle	liver	muscle	liver	muscle	liver
Glycogenesis	⋀	⋀	—	⋁	⋁	⋁
Glycogenolysis	⋁	⋁	—	⋀	⋀	⋀

PP1 is anchored in a complex with glycogen synthase and glycogen phosphorylase
PP1 is anchored within the cytosol in a complex with other proteins that regulate glycogen metabolism. These proteins include glycogen phosphorylase, phosphorylase kinase, and glycogen synthase. The protein that anchors the complex together with the phosphatase is G_M, which targets molecules to glycogen. G_M is itself phosphorylated at two different sites: one linked to insulin signaling and the other to catecholamine or glucagon signaling. Insulin-dependent phosphorylation of G_M results in activation of PP1 and dephosphorylation of the other members of the complex (phosphorylase kinase, glycogen phosphorylase, and glycogen synthase), leading to an increase in glycogen synthase activity, a decrease in glycogen phosphorylase activity, and an increase in overall glycogen storage.

Proteins that act as an organizing structure for other proteins are generically referred to as scaffolding proteins. **Scaffolding proteins** such as G_M are found in cell signaling, often with proteins that anchor kinases close to substrates, creating a locally elevated level of substrates and enzymes, and facilitating the signaling process.

Tissues respond to stimuli differently
Different tissues express different receptors, and thus may respond differently to a particular hormone (Table 8.2). An example of this is glycogen metabolism in the liver and muscle. Glucagon and epinephrine both elicit glycogenolysis in these tissues, but examination of the function of these tissues reveals clues as to what is happening in the underlying biochemistry. In a fight-or-flight response, muscle needs glucose to help remove the organism from danger, so muscle glycogen is depleted and used in glycolysis and the citric acid cycle to make ATP. In the liver, glycogen is mobilized, and glucose leaves the liver and travels to muscle, where again it is used to make ATP. In contrast, muscle uses its glucose in situ and does not release it. Also, muscle lacks glucagon receptors, whereas these receptors are present in the liver. When the body releases glucagon, which signals that blood sugar is low, muscle cannot respond, whereas the liver responds through glycogenolysis, releasing glucose.

WORKED PROBLEM 8.3 | Glycogen signals

A dog is brought into the veterinary clinic with weight loss. Analysis of blood samples indicates increased plasma glucose and decreased levels of plasma amino acids. Subsequent analysis reveals a pancreatic tumor and significantly elevated levels of glucagon in the plasma. How would elevated levels of glucagon affect glycogen metabolism?

Strategy In this scenario, we have an organism with elevated glucagon levels. How and where does glucagon signal in the body, and what is its ultimate effect on glycogen metabolism?

Solution Glucagon is a polypeptide (29 amino acids long) that is secreted from the α cells of the pancreas. It acts as an antagonist to insulin, raising blood glucose levels and promoting energy mobilization. Glucagon acts by binding to a G protein-coupled receptor that activates adenylate cyclase and elevates cAMP. This results in the activation of PKA, which will phosphorylate multiple targets in the cell, including phosphorylase kinase. Phosphorylase kinase is activated by phosphorylation and, in turn, activates

phosphorylase, causing glycogen breakdown and releasing more glucose into the bloodstream. PKA also targets glycogen synthase kinase and glycogen synthase. In the case of these last two enzymes, phosphorylation will block their activity, preventing the synthesis of more glycogen. This explains the elevated plasma glucose levels but not decreased concentrations of amino acids. Decreasing plasma amino acid concentrations are caused by an increasing contribution of these amino acids to gluconeogenesis to maintain plasma glucose levels in the absence of glycogen.

Glucagon receptors are predominantly expressed in the liver, but not in muscle.

This signaling cascade occurs in the context of many other processes. It is highly likely that there is cross talk between the glucagon signaling pathway and other pathways.

Follow-up question An energy drink contains both sucrose and caffeine (discussed in section 5.2). How might this combination affect glycogen metabolism?

8.1 Summary

- Glycogen is a highly branched storage form of glucose found in animals.
- Glycogen is built up from activated molecules of glucose (UDP-glucose) by the enzyme glycogen synthase.
- Glycogen phosphorylase catalyzes the release of glucose-1-phosphate (G-1-P) from glycogen.
- A complex series of kinases regulate glycogen storage. Insulin promotes storage of glycogen through a kinase cascade that results in phosphorylation of phosphoprotein phosphatase 1 (PP1) and dephosphorylation of glycogen synthase and glycogen phosphorylase. Glucagon and catecholamine hormones promote glycogen breakdown and mobilization, predominantly through PKA-mediated phosphorylation of glycogen synthase (inactivating it) and of glycogen phosphorylase (activating it).
- Glycogen synthase and glycogen phosphorylase are also regulated by allosteric mechanisms. Glycogen synthase is allosterically activated by glucose-6-phosphate. Glycogen phosphorylase is allosterically inhibited by glucose-6-phosphate and ATP, but activated by AMP.
- Changes to glycogen metabolism are tissue specific and are coordinated both by hormones and by kinase cascades.

8.1 Concept Check

- Analyze the structure of glycogen and compare it to other polysaccharides.
- Explain how glycogen formation is initiated and the reactions involved in the synthesis and breakdown of glycogen.
- Discuss which hormones are important in the regulation of glycogen stores and how they function.
- Discuss in molecular detail the kinases described in this section and the roles they play in glycogen metabolism.

8.2 | The Pentose Phosphate Pathway

The pentose phosphate pathway integrates the synthesis of three different types of molecules. Section 6.1 noted that there are no essential carbohydrates. As long as we have glucose we can produce all the other carbohydrates we need. The pentose phosphate pathway provides a mechanism by which we can produce those different monosaccharides including ribose—the sugar used to produce nucleotides. There are pathways in metabolism that require reducing equivalents to synthesize molecules. The pentose phosphate pathway also provides those in terms of NADPH. Finally, the pentose phosphate pathway provides a means through which we can have a replenishable supply of antioxidants. Some of the NADPH produced is used to reduce the antioxidant peptide **glutathione**, helping keep the cell in the reduced state. Both the rearrangement of carbohydrates and the generation of NADPH use the **pentose phosphate pathway**, which is also known as the pentose phosphate shunt, the hexose monophosphate shunt, or the phosphogluconate pathway. The pathway can be divided into an oxidative phase that produces NADPH, and a second, nonoxidative phase that alters the structure of carbohydrates. The entire pentose phosphate pathway takes place in the cytosol.

8.2.1 The oxidative phase of the pentose phosphate pathway produces NADPH and ribulose-5-phosphate

The starting material for the pentose phosphate pathway is glucose-6-phosphate (G-6-P). The enzyme glucose-6-phosphate dehydrogenase catalyzes the first step in the pathway (**Figure 8.12**). This committed step is also the rate-determining step. The enzyme catalyzes a dehydrogenation, which is technically an oxidation of G-6-P to 6-phosphogluconate. The electrons from C-1 of G-6-P are passed to NADP$^+$ to form NADPH. The hemiacetal carbon of G-6-P is

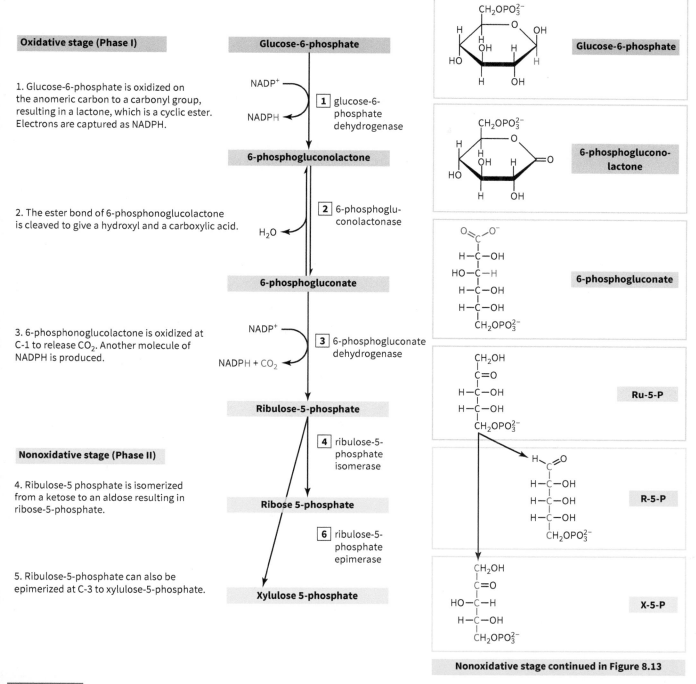

Oxidative stage (Phase I)

1. Glucose-6-phosphate is oxidized on the anomeric carbon to a carbonyl group, resulting in a lactone, which is a cyclic ester. Electrons are captured as NADPH.

2. The ester bond of 6-phosphonoglucolactone is cleaved to give a hydroxyl and a carboxylic acid.

3. 6-phosphonoglucolactone is oxidized at C-1 to release CO_2. Another molecule of NADPH is produced.

Nonoxidative stage (Phase II)

4. Ribulose-5 phosphate is isomerized from a ketose to an aldose resulting in ribose-5-phosphate.

5. Ribulose-5-phosphate can also be epimerized at C-3 to xylulose-5-phosphate.

Nonoxidative stage continued in Figure 8.13

FIGURE 8.12 **Oxidative steps of the pentose phosphate pathway.** The first three steps of the pentose phosphate pathway are referred to as phase I or the oxidative phase. In these steps, glucose-6-phosphate is oxidized first to a lactone, which is then opened to a carboxylic acid. Decarboxylation (loss of CO_2) generates a pentose (ribulose-5-phosphate). This process generates two molecules of NADPH. In the final step of this phase, ribulose-5-phosphate undergoes one of two different isomerizations to produce ribose-5-phosphate or xylulose-5-phosphate, as noted by the split arrows.

oxidized from a hydroxyl group to a carbonyl group forming a lactone. Next, gluconolactonase catalyzes hydrolysis of the lactone (the cyclic ester) to give the carboxylic acid found on the C-1 and the hydroxyl on C-5. The open-chain form of each carbohydrate is used in the rest of the pathway. The enzyme 6-phosphogluconate dehydrogenase oxidizes the carbohydrate further, oxidizing the C-3 to a keto group. The C-1 departs as CO_2, in a β keto-acid decarboxylation, producing the ketopentose ribulose-5-phosphate. The electrons removed in this reaction are shuttled to $NADP^+$, generating a second molecule of NADPH.

This is the end of the oxidative phase. So far, beginning with G-6-P, the pathway has generated two molecules of NADPH, one molecule of CO_2, and one molecule of ribulose-5-phosphate.

The nonoxidative phase of the pentose phosphate pathway results in rearrangement of monosaccharides

The second phase of the pentose phosphate pathway interconverts ribulose-5-phosphate with other monosaccharides (**Figure 8.13**). This provides a means to generate ribose from other carbohydrates and a way for other monosaccharides to enter carbohydrate metabolism. First, ribulose-5-phosphate isomerizes via an enediol intermediate to ribose-5-phosphate. This reaction is similar to phosphoglucose isomerase, which interconverts G-6-P and fructose-6-phosphate (F-6-P) in glycolysis. The ribose-5-phosphate produced in this step is used in nucleotide biosynthesis.

Nonoxidative stage

6. Transketolase transfers a two carbon group from xylulose-5-phosphate to ribose-5-phosphate, resulting in a molecule of glyceraldehyde-3-phosphate and sedoheptulose-7-phosphate.

7. Transaldolase transfers a three carbon group from sedoheptulose-7-phosphate to glyceraldehyde-3-phosphate resulting in fructose-6-phosphate and erythrose-4-phosphate.

8. A second reaction of transketolase combines xylulose-5-phosphate and erythrose-4-phosphate to yield fructose-6-phosphate and glyceraldehyde-3-phosphate.

FIGURE 8.13 **Nonoxidative reactions of the pentose phosphate pathway.** The second phase of the pentose phosphate pathway is the nonoxidative phase. In this phase, aldoses and ketoses react to generate a new aldose and a new ketose. Dashed arrows indicate the branch points in this pathway (aldoses and ketoses of different steps combine to form new products).

Ribulose-5-phosphate can also be acted on by phosphopentose epimerase to yield xylulose-5-phosphate. Epimers are a type of isomer that differ only in the stereochemistry about a single chiral center (glucose and galactose are 4-epimers), whereas isomers differ in other ways, such as the placement of a carbonyl group (glucose is an aldose, and fructose is a ketose). Inversion of stereochemistry of C-3 on ribulose-5-phosphate occurs through an ene-diolate intermediate.

The final three reactions of the pentose phosphate pathway interconvert ribose-5-phosphate and xylulose-5-phosphate with other monosaccharides. These two molecules can undergo a transketolase reaction, to give sedoheptulose-7-phosphate and glyceraldehyde-3-phosphate (G-3-P). Subsequently, the two molecules can undergo a transaldolase reaction, to give erythrose-4-phosphate and F-6-P. Finally, another molecule of xylulose-5-phosphate can react with erythrose-4-phosphate to give F-6-P and G-3-P.

There are several patterns that help to make sense of this part of the pathway. First, the total number of carbons that go into any reaction must equal the total number that comes out. For example, in the first reaction of the nonoxidative stage of the pentose phosphate pathway in (reaction 6) Figure 8.13, two 5-carbon substrates go in (ribose-5-phosphate and xylulose-5-phosphate) and one 7-carbon and one 3-carbon intermediate come out (sedoheptulose-7-phosphate and glyceraldehyde-3-phosphate). Altogether, the following reactions happen:

$$5 + 5 \rightarrow 7 + 3 \rightarrow 4 + 6 \text{ (reactions 6 and 7).}$$

In the final reaction, we have

$$4 + 5 \rightarrow 6 + 3 \text{ (reaction 8).}$$

The other pattern that may be useful is that each reaction contains both an aldose and a ketose and each reaction results in the formation of a new aldose and a ketose.

The mechanisms of transketolase and transaldolase   Two enzymes figure prominently in the nonoxidative phase of the pentose phosphate pathway: transketolase and transaldolase. When looking at the products and reactants, these reactions look similar and thus might be expected to employ a similar mechanism. In fact, they use different mechanisms: one proceeding through a **thiamine pyrophosphate (TPP)** mediated mechanism and the other through a **Schiff base**.

In transketolase, TPP can deprotonate to form a TPP carbanion, which attacks the carbonyl carbon of the ketose substrate, forming an adduct with the TPP (**Figure 8.14**). This addition compound collapses into aldose as electrons flow into the thiazole ring nitrogen of TPP. The aldose product is released, and the new aldose substrate binds. Electron flow now reverses from the ring nitrogen, back out through glycolaldehyde, attacking the carbonyl carbon of the aldose substrate and forming a new carbon–carbon bond. The product deprotonates, generating a new carbonyl group on the ketose product and regenerating TPP.

In transaldolase, an active site lysine forms a Schiff base with the ketose substrate (**Figure 8.15**). This base protonates, resulting in electron flow into the base nitrogen, formation of an enzyme–substrate adduct, and the release of the aldose product. Next, an aldose substrate binds. Electron flow reverses out of the protonated Schiff base, attacking the carbonyl carbon of the aldose substrate. The base deprotonates and is hydrolyzed to yield the ketose product and regenerate the active site lysine.

8.2.3 | Regulation of the pentose phosphate pathway

The pentose phosphate pathway occurs in the cytosol, together with glycolysis, most of gluconeogenesis, and several other pathways. Glucose-6-phosphate dehydrogenase catalyzes the committed step and entry into the pathway. If we consider only the oxidative phase of the pathway, this is also the rate-determining step. Because NADPH is used for biosynthetic pathways and NAD^+ is used in degradative ones, NADPH is found mainly in the reduced form (99 NADPH: $1NADP^+$), whereas NAD^+ is found mainly in the oxidized form (99 NAD^+: 1NADH). The activity of glucose-6-phosphate dehydrogenase is regulated by levels of the substrate $NADP^+$.

1. TPP deprotonates, generating a carbanion.

TPP

2. Ketose substrate binds. TPP carbanion attacks carbonyl carbon.

TPP carbanion   Ketose substrate

3. Base deprotonates hydroxyl group on carbon alpha to the carbonyl. Electrons flow into TPP. Aldose product released.

Addition compound

R—CHO

4. Aldose substrate binds. Electron flow out of TPP adduct attacks carbonyl carbon.

Activated glycoaldehyde

5. Hydroxyl bound to TPP adduct is deprotonated. Electrons flow into TPP.

6. Ketose product released.

TPP

Ketose product

FIGURE 8.14 Mechanism of transketolase. Transketolase employs an active site thiamine pyrophosphate (TPP) to attack the carbonyl carbon of the ketose substrate. This forms an addition product that rearranges to release the aldose product. The aldose substrate binds and electrons flow back out of TPP attacking the carbonyl carbon of the aldose, again forming a tertiary alcohol. The alcohol deprotonates and electrons flow back from the oxyanion into the carbon, generating the ketose product.

The pentose phosphate pathway also has the ability to convert molecules such as ribose into hexoses for entry into glycolysis and to oxidize carbohydrates into CO_2, although these are thought to play relatively minor roles compared to NADPH and ribose-5-phosphate production.

8.2.4 The pentose phosphate pathway in health and disease

Different cells have a greater need for the products of the pentose phosphate pathway than others, such as:

- Cells that are rapidly dividing, which require both NADPH (for biosynthetic reducing equivalents) and ribose (for production of nucleotides and RNA and DNA).
- Cells of the liver, lactating mammary gland, and gonadal tissue involved in fatty acid or sterol biosynthesis that require NADPH.
- Macrophages and neutrophils, the phagocytic cells of the immune system, which require NADPH to produce the superoxide (O_2^{2-}) used in killing pathogens.

As a result, any of the cells noted in these examples have high levels of expression of the enzymes of the pentose phosphate pathway. There is one other cell type that also requires

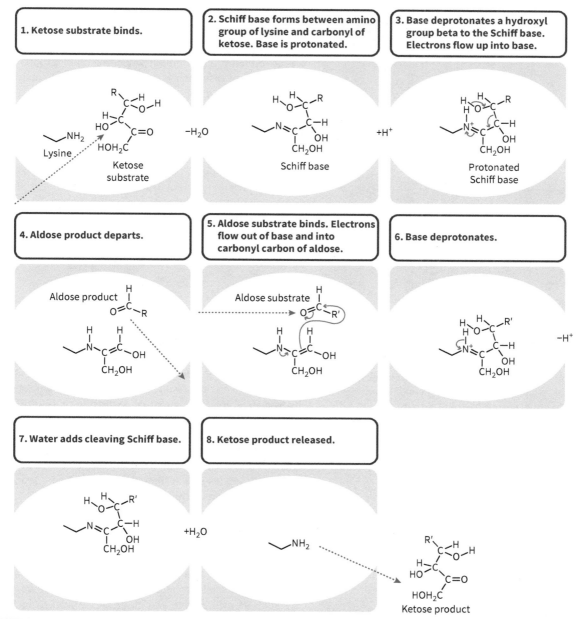

1. Ketose substrate binds.

2. Schiff base forms between amino group of lysine and carbonyl of ketose. Base is protonated.

3. Base deprotonates a hydroxyl group beta to the Schiff base. Electrons flow up into base.

4. Aldose product departs.

5. Aldose substrate binds. Electrons flow out of base and into carbonyl carbon of aldose.

6. Base deprotonates.

7. Water adds cleaving Schiff base.

8. Ketose product released.

FIGURE 8.15 **Mechanism of transaldolase.** Transaldolase catalyzes a similar reaction to transketolase but uses a very different mechanism. Rather than a thiamine pyrophosphate-dependent mechanism, transaldolase employs an active site lysine, which forms a Schiff base. In the first step of the mechanism, binding of the ketose substrate leads to a reaction of the active site lysine with the carbonyl carbon of the ketose, generating the Schiff base. The base is protonated and electrons flow down through an adjacent hydroxyl group, cleaving a carbon–carbon bond and leading to the release of the aldose product. Next, the aldose substrate binds and electron flow reverses from the Schiff base nitrogen up through the double bond to attack the carbonyl carbon of the aldose. Deprotonation of the Schiff base and addition of water regenerates the lysine and forms the final ketose product.

high levels of pentose phosphate pathway enzymes. Red blood cells (erythrocytes) require high levels of NADPH produced by the pentose phosphate pathway to help neutralize reactive oxygen species. In erythrocytes, as in macrophages and neutrophils, there are high levels of reactive oxygen species such as hydrogen peroxide, due to high concentrations of oxygen within these cells and the potential for side reactions as molecular oxygen is carried by the heme group. In macrophages and neutrophils, hydrogen peroxide is synthesized and used to destroy pathogens and invaders. In all three cell types, the redox active tripeptide glutathione is used as a means of neutralizing reactive oxygen species that are free in the cell before they can cause oxidative damage to proteins and lipids. NADPH is used to reduce glutathione following oxidation.

A.

Dr. Mae Melvin / CDC Public Health
Image Library

B.

Primaquine

Chloroquine

Primaquine and chloroquine. **A.** The malarial parasite *Plasmodium falciparum* (dark images in this micrograph) degrades hemoglobin as a source of amino acids. The heme waste products crystalize into a nontoxic form (hemozoin). **B.** Primaquin and chloroquine block the recrystallization, which leads to accumulation of heme by-products toxic to the parasite.

A.

JIANG HONGYAN/Shutterstock

B.

Vicine

Convicine

FIGURE 8.17 **Fava beans.** **A.** Fava beans (*Vicia faba*) are also known as broad beans. Despite their association with favism, they are a common component of the Mediterranean diet. **B.** Fava beans contain the glycosides vicine and covicine. When metabolized, these molecules lose their carbohydrate moieties. These compounds are toxic and induce hemolysis either by direct action on the erythrocyte membrane or by producing hydrogen peroxide, which in turn causes cell damage and death.

Glutathione is an antioxidant
Glutathione is a tripeptide comprised of a glutamate joined via an amide linkage through the γ-carboxyl group to a dipeptide of cysteine and glycine. The cytosol is a reducing environment (meaning thiol groups are typically found instead of disulfides), and glutathione helps maintain this balance. Glutathione is commonly found as a monomer, rather than as a dimer joined through a disulfide bridge between the cysteine side chains. Glutathione peroxidases are a family of enzymes that use two molecules of glutathione to oxidize peroxides to water and alcohols, leaving the oxidized, disulfide-bonded form of glutathione. Interestingly, glutathione peroxidase has an active site with an unusual amino acid: selenocysteine. This side chain is analogous to cysteine, but has selenium in place of the sulfur atom. To regenerate the reduced free thiol form of glutathione, glutathione dehydrogenases use NADPH to reduce the disulfide and form $NADP^+$.

Glutathione, therefore, serves as an antioxidant and redox buffer, helping to prevent oxidative damage in most tissues and cells of plants and animals. As one might expect, if the processes by which this system functions are mutated, damaged, or inhibited, oxidative damage and disease will result. Loss of function of glucose-6-phosphate dehydrogenase leads to impaired synthesis of NADPH, and hence the ability to reduce glutathione dimers. As a result, reactive oxygen species build up, and the lipids and proteins of erythrocytes become damaged. If this damage is sufficiently severe, it can result in the loss of the erythrocyte, eventually resulting in hemolytic anemia, a shortage of erythrocytes due to their loss or damage. Depending on the severity of the anemia, this condition can be fatal.

A partial deficiency of glucose-6-phosphate dehydrogenase can be advantageous in some instances, because it may lead to elevated levels of reactive oxygen species (and perhaps reduced erythrocyte life span). This mutation is commonly found in Mediterranean and African countries, and it is thought to provide some measure of resistance to the malarial parasite *Plasmodium falciparum*. Antimalarial drugs such as primaquine and chloroquine lead to increased levels of peroxides, which damage the erythrocyte in a similar fashion, making it less favorable to the parasite (**Figure 8.16**). Deficiencies in glucose-6-phosphate dehydrogenase can potentiate the effects of these drugs. Such deficiencies are thought to be the most common genetic defect in humans, affecting as many as 400 million people worldwide, although many people with the deficiency are asymptomatic.

Individuals with glucose-6-phosphate dehydrogenase deficiency can also have a reaction to other environmental factors. One such example is favism, a hemolytic response to consumption of fava beans (also known as broad beans, *Vicia faba*) (**Figure 8.17**). Fava beans are delicious and are commonly found in the diets of Mediterranean people but contain several molecules of the alkaloid glycosides class, such as vicine and covicine, which can damage erythrocytes by a mechanism similar to some antimalarial drugs.

Chronic granulomatous disease
Chronic granulomatous disease is another disorder affected by glucose-6-phosphate dehydrogenase activity. One of the functions of NADPH is to act as

an electron donor in the generation of large amounts of certain biologically useful reactive oxygen species, particularly in the phagocytic cells of the immune system. When the enzyme activity is low or absent, the ability to generate NADPH is limited. Without the ability to produce an oxidative burst of these chemicals to damage or kill intruders, these cells have a limited capacity to defend against pathogens, thus weakening the immune system and resulting in chronic infections.

The synthesis of reactive oxygen species and the response of phagocytic cells encompass a complex series of reactions involving multiple proteins. Production of NADPH is only one piece of that pathway. If any of the steps in peroxide production are in any way inhibited or defective, then chronic granulomatous disease can result. Hence, there are several classifications of the disease based on which enzymes are affected. The classifications may have different severities and pathophysiologies, but all have a similar set of symptoms.

WORKED PROBLEM 8.4 | Rapid cell growth

How would the pentose phosphate pathway respond if cells were rapidly dividing?

Strategy   What are the metabolic needs of a growing cell? What does the pentose phosphate pathway provide cells?

Solution   The pentose phosphate pathway serves multiple functions. One function is to generate reducing equivalents in the form of NADPH. The growing cell could use NADPH in the synthesis of new fatty acids for phospholipid biosynthesis or new amino acids. The pentose phosphate pathway also provides ribose-5-phosphate for nucleotides (for DNA and RNA biosynthesis), and for NAD^+, FAD, and other ribose-containing cofactors. In any growing cell,

there is a need for a balance between these metabolites; however, in a cell that is rapidly dividing, the need for ribose-5-phosphate for nucleotides will probably outweigh the need for reducing equivalents. In this case, the oxidative phase of the pathway can be bypassed by siphoning G-3-P and F-6-P out of glycolysis. Even though the final steps of the pathway are reversible, if these carbons are used for ribose-5-phosphate biosynthesis, they cannot be used in glycolysis or the citric acid cycle for energy.

Follow-up question   Based on the pathways we have been discussing, propose how an organism could live off ribose as its sole carbon source.

8.2.5 | Xylulose-5-phosphate is a master regulator of carbohydrate and lipid metabolism

Previously when we have discussed the regulation of metabolism we have focused on short-term regulation of enzyme activity modulated via phosphorylation or allosteric regulators. A third way that metabolism is regulated is by increasing the levels of enzymes through increased transcription of the genes that code for them. The proteins that regulate gene transcription are termed transcription factors. One such transcription factor is the **carbohydrate response element-binding protein (ChREBP)**, a transcription factor that responds to high levels of carbohydrates and regulates transcription of genes involved in carbohydrate and lipid metabolism. The most notable genes regulated by ChREBP are those for pyruvate kinase, as well as acetyl-CoA carboxylase and fatty acid synthase, both discussed in lipid metabolism.

In the absence of high levels of carbohydrate, ChREBP is found in the cytosol in the inactive form. When levels of G-6-P in the cell are high, the pentose phosphate pathway is active, generating NADPH for fatty acid biosynthesis. As flux through this pathway increases, it produces higher levels of xylulose-5-phosphate, which activates a phosphatase (protein phosphatase 2A). This dephosphorylates specific phosphoserine and phosphothreonine residues in ChREBP, activating the protein. The now-active transcription factor translocates from the cytosol to the nucleus, where it increases the expression of genes needed to store energy.

In summary, when G-6-P is plentiful in the cell, the pentose phosphate pathway product xylulose-5-phosphate signals to ChREBP via a phosphatase to increase the expression of the genes of glycolysis and fatty acid biosynthesis in order to store energy. If G-6-P levels are low, due to either a lack of glucose or high rates of flux through glycolysis and the citric acid cycle, the transcription factor remains phosphorylated in the cytosol, and gene transcription is not initiated (**Figure 8.18**).

FIGURE 8.18 **Carbohydrate response element binding protein (ChREBP).** The carbohydrate response element binding protein is a cytosolic transcription factor. In the inactive state, it is found phosphorylated on key residues (catalyzed by both PKA and AMPK). When levels of xylulose-5-phosphate rise, they activate phosphoprotein phosphatase 2A, which dephosphorylates the transcription factor. This leads to its translocation to the nucleus and activation of genes involved in energy storage. (Wessner, *Microbiology*, 2e, copyright 2017, John Wiley & Sons. This material is reproduced with permission of John Wiley & Sons, Inc.)

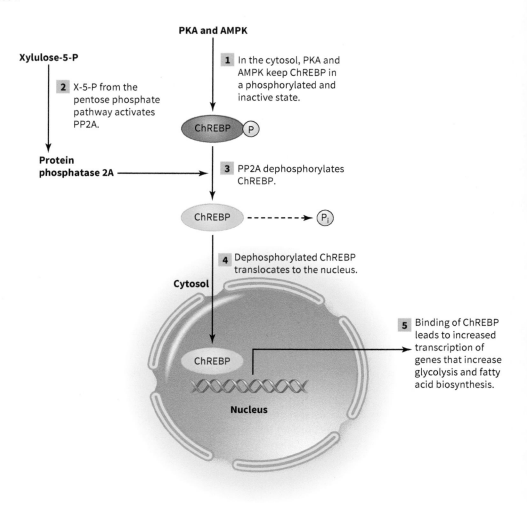

PKA and AMPK

1 In the cytosol, PKA and AMPK keep ChREBP in a phosphorylated and inactive state.

Xylulose-5-P

2 X-5-P from the pentose phosphate pathway activates PP2A.

ChREBP (P)

Protein phosphatase 2A

3 PP2A dephosphorylates ChREBP.

ChREBP ------→ (Pi)

4 Dephosphorylated ChREBP translocates to the nucleus.

Cytosol

ChREBP

Nucleus

5 Binding of ChREBP leads to increased transcription of genes that increase glycolysis and fatty acid biosynthesis.

WORKED PROBLEM 8.5 | Fructose redux

High-fructose corn syrup has been targeted as a cause of obesity. Section 6.3 discussed how fructose is catabolized via glycolysis (fructolysis). How could fructose be catabolized via the pentose phosphate pathway, and what might be the ramifications of elevated fructose levels in the cell?

Strategy To answer this question, we need to know how fructose is metabolized in glycolysis and fructolysis, and how the pentose phosphate pathway works. We should also think about other products of the pentose phosphate pathway, and how they may contribute to the overall metabolism of the cell or organism.

Solution F-6-P is one product of the pentose phosphate pathway. Section 6.2 explained that monosaccharides diffuse into the cell down a concentration gradient. Once inside the cell, the monosaccharide is phosphorylated, either through fructokinase (to yield F-1-P) or hexokinase (to yield F-6-P). F-6-P is usually catabolized via glycolysis or fructolysis; however, the transketolation and transaldolation reactions of the pentose phosphate pathway are reversible. Therefore, if F-6-P is in abundance,

it could react with G-3-P to give xylulose-5-phosphate and erythrose-4-phosphate. Another molecule of F-6-P could then react with the erythrose-4-phosphate to yield sedoheptulose-7-phosphate and glyceraldehyde-3-phosphate. As described in section 8.2, in the forward direction of the pathway these two molecules can react together to give ribose-5-phosphate and another molecule of xylulose-5-phosphate. Thus, from one molecule each of fructose and of glyceraldehyde-3-phosphate, it is possible to generate two molecules of xylulose-5-phosphate and hence alter gene expression via ChREBP.

Although it is unlikely that most fructose is metabolized through this pathway, a demonstration that elevated fructose leads to altered gene expression could validate this hypothesis. There are many ways to catabolize fructose in the cell, all of which occur simultaneously; therefore, discerning increased flux through a particular pathway is difficult.

Follow-up question How could you test whether exposure to fructose alters gene expression? What would you use for controls, both positive and negative?

8.2 Summary

- The pentose phosphate pathway coordinates three divergent needs of the cell: ribose synthesis, NADPH synthesis, and carbohydrate metabolism.
- In the first (oxidative) phase of the pentose phosphate pathway, G-6-P is oxidized into 6-phosphogluconate, and then into ribulose-5-phosphate and CO_2. One molecule of NADPH is produced at each step.
- In the nonoxidative second phase of the pentose phosphate pathway, a molecule of ribulose-5-phosphate is isomerized to xylulose-5-phosphate. The subsequent reactions of the second phase are transaldolase and transketolase reactions that allow the rearrangement of these two pentoses into other aldoses and ketoses.
- The pentose phosphate pathway provides a way for carbohydrates to enter metabolism other than through glycolysis or gluconeogenesis.
- The NADPH produced in the pentose phosphate pathway is used in lipid biosynthetic pathways. The NADPH is also important in the oxidative response of some cells of the immune system and in maintaining a reducing environment in the cell by reducing oxidized glutathione dimers. Disruptions of these pathways can result in disease.
- Xylulose-5-phosphate is an important metabolic regulator; it activates protein phosphatase 2A, which in turn dephosphorylates and activates the transcription factor ChREBP, activating several genes involved in energy storage.

8.2 Concept Check

- Generally, summarize the two stages of the pathway and what happens in each stage.
- Outline the reactions that occur in each stage and the products of those reactions.
- Explain how the flux through the pentose phosphate pathway coordinates diverse aspects of metabolism and provides for the different needs of the cell.
- Describe the roles that xylulose-5-phosphate and ChREBP play in carbohydrate metabolism.

8.3 Carbohydrates in Glycoconjugates

Carbohydrates are important as structural molecules, as ligands for protein receptors, and in signaling. They can be linked to proteins or lipids on the surface of the cell, and they are also found in macromolecular assemblies outside the cell. This section discusses four main classes of carbohydrate modifications, known as glycoconjugates. These include:

- **Glycoproteins**—membrane-bound or extracellular proteins with some amount of carbohydrate modification.
- **Glycolipids**—membrane phospholipids with an attached carbohydrate moiety.
- **Proteoglycans**—extensive mesh nets of polysaccharides joined to fibrous proteins.
- **Peptidoglycans**—lengthy chains of polysaccharides cross-linked by peptides and found in bacterial cell walls.

Section 8.4 discusses the assembly of these molecules into the extracellular matrix.

8.3.1 Glycoproteins

Glycoproteins are proteins with attached carbohydrate modifications. In eukaryotic cells, these modifications are made initially in the endoplasmic reticulum and are then continued in the Golgi complex. Most glycosylated proteins are secreted by the cell to the outside, or retained to lysosomes, or found as integral plasma membrane proteins; few glycosylated proteins are found in the cytosol or in other organelles.

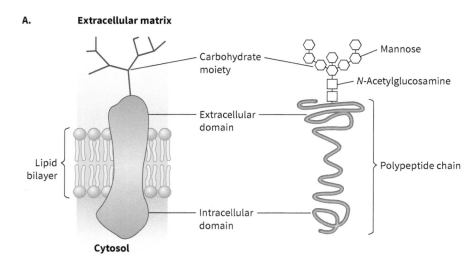

A. Extracellular matrix

Carbohydrate moiety

Mannose

N-Acetylglucosamine

Extracellular domain

Lipid bilayer

Polypeptide chain

Intracellular domain

Cytosol

B. (N-linkage) Asparagine

N-Acetylglucosamine linked to asparagine through N of asparagine

C. (O-linkage) Serine

N-Acetylgalactosamine linked to serine through O of serine

FIGURE 8.19 **An example of a glycoprotein.** **A.** Glycoproteins are typically found exposed on the outer leaflet of the plasma membrane. **B.** and **C.** Proteins have carbohydrates attached via an asparagine (*N*-linked) or via a serine or threonine residue (*O*-linked).

The carbohydrates found in glycoproteins can be either ***N*-linked** or ***O*-linked**. In *N*-linked glycoproteins, the carbohydrates are linked via an amide to the side chain of the amino acid asparagine. The **consensus recognition sequence**, the protein sequence that is recognized and glycosylated, is (Asn-X-Ser/Thr) where X is any amino acid. *O*-linked glycoproteins are linked via an acetal linkage between the sugar and the hydroxyl group of a serine, or threonine residue, or hydroxylated residues (hydroxylysine and hydroxyproline) (**Figure 8.19**).

Numerous types of monosaccharides can be attached to proteins (**Figure 8.20**). In addition to some of the more familiar monosaccharides discussed in section 6.1 (glucose, mannose, galactose), there are aldoses (fucose and xylulose) and acetylated amino sugars. This last group includes *N*-Acetylglucosamine (GlcNAc), *N*-Acetylgalactosamine (GalNAc), and *N*-Acetylneuraminic acid (Neu5Ac or NANA). Neuraminic acid and its derivatives are types of sialic acid. It has been estimated that half of all proteins are glycosylated and these modifications range from less than 1% to 60% carbohydrate by mass.

The roles of glycosylations in proteins are still being elucidated. Some regulate the activity of enzymes or stability of proteins, and may be involved in protein folding. Some modified carbohydrates, such as mannose-6-phosphate, are involved in protein trafficking, that is, the organized movement and marshaling of proteins in the cell. Prokaryotes have limited ability to glycosylate proteins, and among eukaryotic species, there is variation in ability to glycosylate proteins. This difference is important if using bacteria or an insect cell line to produce protein for study, where improper or missing glycosylation can (and does) lead to misfolded or inactive proteins.

Glucose
(β-D-Glc ⬢)

Galactose
(β-D-Gal ⬢)

Mannose
(β-D-Man ⬢)

N-Acetylglucosamine
(β-D-GlcNAc ◼)

N-Acetylgalactosamine
(β-D-GalNAc ◼)

Sialic acid
(α-D-Neu5Ac ⬟)

Fucose
(α-L-Fuc ◇)

Xylulose
(β-D-Xyl ⬤)

FIGURE 8.20 **Common carbohydrates found in glycoproteins.** Shown are common examples of monosaccharides found in glycoproteins and their abbreviations. Note the amino sugars *N*-Acetylglucosamine, *N*-Acetylgalactosamine, and neuraminic acid (*N*-Acetyl sialic acid). Dashed boxes highlight differences among these structures.

Examples of glycoproteins

There are thousands of glycoproteins, and their

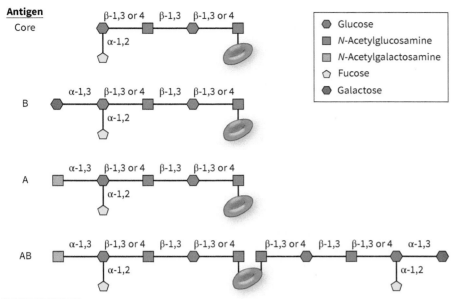

FIGURE 8.21 **ABO blood group antigens.** The ABO blood group antigens result from carbohydrate modifications on the surface of erythrocytes. People with the O antigen have the core carbohydrate shown. Those with the A blood type have an extra molecule of *N*-Acetylgalactosamine, while those with the B blood type have an extra molecule of galactose. People with the AB blood group have a mixture of glycoproteins with both modifications found.

functions in biochemistry are still being elucidated. This section discusses one example in which carbohydrate modification is important, the ABO blood groups.

ABO blood group antigens The ABO blood group antigens are a series of carbohydrate modifications predominantly on a transmembrane protein found on the extracellular surface of erythrocyte plasma membranes (**Figure 8.21**). In the ABO system there are four blood groups: A, B, AB, and O. People with the O blood type have glycoproteins bound to a core pentasaccharide. Those with type A blood have an additional molecule of *N*-Acetylglucosamine, whereas those with type B have an additional molecule of galactose. Those with type AB blood have a combination of proteins with the A glycosylation and proteins with the B glycosylation. People with blood type O are known as *universal donors* because their blood can be given to anyone; their proteins lack these modifications and just have the core modification. People with blood type AB type are known as *universal recipients* because they can receive blood from anyone; their immune system recognizes both modifications as those of the recipients.

Receiving the wrong blood type elicits an immune response against the blood cells that are recognized as foreign; this can be fatal.

Blood types are usually listed as an ABO letter or letters followed by a (+) or (−) symbol known as the Rhesus factor, Rh. The Rh is a different protein that is coded for by a different gene and is positive or negative, indicating the presence or absence of this protein.

One group of proteins that bind to and recognize specific glycosylations are lectins, plant glycoproteins that are discussed in **Biochemistry: Lectins**.

Biochemistry

Lectins

Glycoproteins are proteins with attached carbohydrates; in contrast, lectins are proteins that recognize and bind tightly to specific carbohydrate sequences.

Although lectins were first identified in plants more than 100 years ago, little is known about their function. Lectins may be important in cell adhesion to an extracellular matrix or in the defense of the host against a pathogen. In animals, lectins bind to mannose-6-phosphate residues on glycosylated proteins in the

Golgi complex, and they assist in the sorting of these proteins. This process, known as protein trafficking, is a field of intense investigation.

Lectins can be monomeric or multimeric proteins, and many are polyvalent (can bind to multiple carbohydrate chains at once). They are globular and have an average size of 40 to 75 kDa. Most lectins have at least one metal ion (either Mg^{2+} or Ca^{2+}). The lectin concanavalin A from jack beans was found to have an almost identical amino acid sequence to another protein found in the same plants, differing only at the amino and carboxyl termini. Concanavalin A exhibits a property called circular permutation. In this process, after translation and folding, the amino and carboxyl termini of the protein end up in close proximity to one another and then join via a process that is unclear, creating a circular loop through the amino acid backbone. Some other part of the backbone is cleaved, generating new amino and carboxyl termini.

In the laboratory, lectins have been used in affinity purification techniques (discussed in the techniques section). Many of the best characterized lectins come from legumes, an abundant starting material for purification. The lectin can be purified from a sample, affixed to a column or resin, and then used as a means of isolating or purifying other glycosylated proteins. The use of lectins in the laboratory decreased when advances in antibody production and molecular biology made it possible to add affinity tags to proteins of interest. However, more recently, fluorescently labeled lectins and advances in fluorescent technology have helped lectins regain their place in the laboratory.

Lectins have other applications. Many are categorized as agglutinins—compounds that make blood cells clump together. This happens as the lectins bind to the carbohydrate moiety of cell-surface glycoproteins. Because this binding is carbohydrate specific, lectins can be used to help identify the antigens, in this case, carbohydrate moieties, on the cell surface and perform blood typing.

Although lectins are a useful research tool, not all lectins are benign. One of the first lectins to be purified in 1888 was ricin from castor beans. Ricin binds to glycoproteins on the cell and thus gains entry to the cell through endocytosis. Once inside the cell, ricin is a potent inhibitor of ribosome function. One of the ricin subunits is a glycosidase that cleaves an N-glycosidic bond within the 28S subunit of the ribosome, removing an adenine. This irreversibly damages the ribosome, blocking protein synthesis. The turnover number for this enzyme is 1,777 per minute; that is, the enzyme can inactivate as many as 1,777 ribosomes per minute. Inactivation of the ribosomes results in cell death, and exposure to ricin is often fatal. The lethal dose in humans can be as little as 1.75 µg, which can be obtained from as few as five castor beans. Ricin is suspected of having been used as a poison in espionage. In one of the more infamous assassinations of the Cold War, Bulgarian dissident Georgi Markov was poisoned with a microscopic ricin-tipped dart fired into his leg from an umbrella as he waited for a bus in London. Four days later he was dead. Autopsy results found a microscopic pellet in his leg containing a 0.2 mg dose of ricin that had failed to completely dissolve.

8.3.2 | Glycolipids

Glycolipids are amphipathic membrane lipids containing either a glycerol or sphingosine backbone with carbohydrate modifications. Most of these molecules are found on the outer leaflet of the plasma membrane, with the acyl chains of the lipid embedded in the membrane and the carbohydrate moiety exposed to the external environment. This section discusses four examples of glycolipids: lipopolysaccharides, glycosylphosphatidylinositol (GPI), cerebrosides, and gangliosides.

Lipopolysaccharide **Lipopolysaccharide** is a component of the bacterial outer membrane. In gram-negative bacteria, it helps to maintain the integrity of the outer membrane; it also protects the outer membrane from lipases and makes it more resistant to attack from phages (bacterial viruses). In animals, however, lipopolysaccharide is toxic; it acts as a pyrogen, which induces fever and activates the immune system. Lipopolysaccharide is partially responsible for the septic shock that is sometimes seen in advanced infections.

Lipopolysaccharide has three parts: an outer polysaccharide termed the O antigen, a core oligosaccharide, and lipid A, which is a bacterial lipid comprised of a dimer of glucosamine molecules to which multiple (usually six) fatty acids are attached via ester or amide linkages. The core oligosaccharide acts as an adapter between lipid A and the O antigen. The core can vary considerably, but it often contains one, two, or three monosaccharides attached to lipid A through a glycosidic linkage to the glucosamine group. The outer O antigen also varies from species to species but typically consists of linear combinations of galactose, mannose, rhamnose, and other hexoses. The O antigen is also linked via a glycosidic bond to the core carbohydrate (**Figure 8.22**).

Glycosylphosphatidylinositol Glycosylphosphatidylinositol, or **GPI** anchors are used by eukaryotic cells to anchor proteins to the outer leaflet of the plasma membrane

FIGURE 8.22 **Structure of lipopolysaccharide.** Lipopolysaccharide is found in the outer membrane of bacteria. It consists of lipid A bound to a core series of carbohydrates, two ethanolamine groups (ETN), and a lengthy carbohydrate tail. (Wessner, *Microbiology*, 2e, copyright 2017, John Wiley & Sons. This material is reproduced with permission of John Wiley & Sons, Inc.)

(**Figure 8.23**). GPI contains a molecule of phosphatidyl inositol, a linker polysaccharide composed of glucosamine and several mannose residues, and a molecule of phospho-ethanolamine attached to the protein. As in other carbohydrate-containing molecules, the polysaccharides may be modified with other groups (in this case, other fatty acids or carbohydrates).

Proteins to be affixed to a GPI anchor are translated into the ER, where a hydrophobic sequence at the protein's carboxy terminus attaches the protein to the ER membrane. This sequence is cleaved, and the resulting carboxy terminus is linked via an amide to the amine moiety of phosphoethanolamine, forming the GPI anchor.

There are many different types of GPI-anchored proteins, for example, enzymes, adhesion molecules, and proteins found in cell–cell recognition. Several important signal transduction pathways employ GPI-anchored proteins to tether them to the plasma membrane.

Cerebrosides and gangliosides

Cerebrosides and gangliosides are glycosylated sphingolipids (**Figure 8.24**). Cerebrosides have a single sugar, usually glucose or galactose, attached to the free hydroxyl group of ceramide through a glycosidic linkage. Gangliosides have an additional three to seven monosaccharides; these are often not linear and include at least one molecule of *N*-Acetylneuraminic acid (Neu5Ac).

Cerebrosides containing galactose (galactocerebrosides) and gangliosides are highly enriched in the central nervous system but are found to some extent in most tissues. Cerebrosides and gangliosides are internalized and degraded in lysosomes. There are several inborn errors of metabolism (Gaucher's, Tay-Sachs, Nieman-Pick type C, and Fabry's diseases) that involve a deficiency in

FIGURE 8.23 **Structure of a glycosyl phosphoinositide (GPI) anchor.** GPI anchors are used in eukaryotic cells to anchor proteins in the outer leaflet of the plasma membrane. The anchor consists of a molecule of phosphatidyl inositol to which a mannose-rich carbohydrate linker is attached. The mannose adapter is also linked to a phosphoethanolamine group, which is bound to a protein via an amide link to the carboxy terminus of the protein.

FIGURE 8.24 **Structures of cerebrosides and gangliosides.** Cerebrosides and gangliosides are glycosphingolipids that are found in higher concentrations in nervous tissue. **A.** Cerebrosides have the phospholipid ceramide joined to a single simple carbohydrate, while gangliosides have an oligosaccharide modification. **B.** Dysfunction in the enzymes (shown in blue) that produce or break down these molecules, lead to a variety of human diseases (shown in red).

FIGURE 8.25 **Lysosomal storage disorder.** The lysosomes in the micrograph are filled with whorls of membrane, indicative of a lysosomal storage disorder.

H. Liapis, K. Foster, E. Theodoropoulou, et al. *Phenotype/Genotype Correlations in the Ultrastructure of Monogenetic Glomerular Diseases,* Journal Ultrastructural Pathology Volume 28, 2004 - issue 4, Taylor and Francis

cerebroside or ganglioside degradation. In these disorders, lysosomes fill with glycolipids; the result is developmental disorders and, in many cases, death (**Figure 8.25**).

The Neu5Ac and other sialic acid derivatives found in gangliosides also have a role in infectious disease. For example, influenza virus has a protein on the surface of the virus called hemagglutinin that binds to sialic acid residues on the surface of cells. The virus uses this protein to gain entry and infect the cell. Recently, drugs have been developed that attempt to treat the spread of the flu virus through attacking these pathways. These are discussed in **Medical Biochemistry: Neuraminidase inhibitors.**

Medical Biochemistry

Neuraminidase inhibitors

There is a disease that accounts for more than half a million deaths each year. It mutates out of control at such a rate that vaccination programs and health organizations constantly work to stay ahead of it. In any given year, this disease may infect as many as 20% of the population. It is easily transmitted through the air or contaminated surfaces, can jump from species to species, and may be transmitted and spread through agriculture and migrating birds. In 1918, an outbreak of this disease killed some 50 to 100 million people, more than half of whom were in their 20s and 30s. That outbreak killed more than 1% of the world's population and caused more deaths in its first 25 weeks than the AIDS pandemic did in its first 25 years. The disease is influenza, commonly known as the "flu."

Influenza is caused by the influenza A virus (*Orthomyxoviridae*), a single-stranded RNA virus that attacks the epithelial cells of the mucus membranes and respiratory tract. Release of pro-inflammatory cytokines such as tumor necrosis factor α (TNF-α) and γ-interferon cause some of the other symptoms of influenza, including fever, muscle aches, and overall tiredness. The influenza virus has an envelope—a lipid bilayer studded with glycoproteins—that surrounds an RNA core. The RNA is in about eight pieces, each of which codes for one or two genes. Two important glycoproteins, hemagglutinin and neuraminidase, are on the surface of the virus particle, or the virion. These two proteins are reflected in the name of the virus, such as H5N1 or H2N2. There are 17 different subtypes of hemagglutinin and 9 different subtypes of neuraminidase.

Hemagglutinin is a carbohydrate-binding glycoprotein; essentially, it is a lectin. Hemagglutinin has two main roles in viral pathogenesis. It binds to sialic acid residues on the cell surface (particularly red blood cells and the epithelial cells of the upper respiratory tract); this binding fastens the virion to the host cell. The host cell uses endocytosis to internalize pieces of membrane, and viruses bound to sialic acid are internalized in this process. Inside the cell, these endosomes are processed as they normally would be. That is, proton pumps begin to acidify the endosome in preparation for fusion with other vesicles and transformation into a lysosome. However, in this instance, acidification of the contents is a trap. As the endosome is acidified, hemagglutinin changes in structure, forming a single α helix more than 60 amino acids long. The formation of this helix exposes a short hydrophobic peptide sequence at the end, which is thought to act as a molecular grappling hook, fastening into the endosomal membrane and facilitating fusion with the virion, releasing the viral contents into the cytoplasm of the host cell.

Inside the host cell, ribosomes bind and translate the viral RNA into viral proteins, including an RNA-dependent RNA polymerase (viral polymerase). The viral polymerase and messages translocate to the nucleus, where the new viral messages are transcribed. These new messages are transported back to the cytosol, where they assemble with riboproteins and other viral proteins at the cell membrane. Viruses bud from the cell but are still bound to the membrane by hemagglutinin.

Neuraminidase, the other glycoprotein of interest in this story, is a hydrolytic enzyme that cleaves sialic acid residues from the surface of the viral envelope and the cell. The removal of sialic acid enables the virus to leave the cell and infect other cells nearby; it also prevents viruses from binding to one another.

One line of drug development for influenza is based on identifying and exploiting differences between the biology of the pathogen and the infected person. In the case of the influenza virus, the presence of neuraminidase is one of the differences. Drugs that inhibit neuraminidase act by blocking the function of the enzyme; that is, the drugs block cleavage of sialic acid groups. The four drugs for influenza currently on the market are competitive inhibitors of neuraminidase. The infected cells can still make mature viral particles, but the drugs render those particles unable to release and propagate the infection. Although these drugs are not cures for influenza, they tend to lessen the severity of the infection and reduce the time with symptoms by one day.

8.3.3 | Proteoglycans and non-proteoglycan polysaccharides

Proteoglycans are a major component of the extracellular matrix. They have two major parts: a glycosaminoglycan, or GAG, which is a large polysaccharide consisting in part of amino sugars, and a protein core. One significant difference between glycoproteins and proteoglycans is the overall amount of carbohydrate. Although glycoproteins can have extensive carbohydrate modifications, they are still predominantly proteins. Proteoglycans, on the other hand, have far more carbohydrate than protein. Cross-linking in proteoglycans between proteins and carbohydrate chains creates an extensive macromolecular network. One non-proteoglycan carbohydrate worthy of mention is hyaluronic acid. This lengthy polysaccharide is comprised of amino sugars but lacks the protein component found in proteoglycans.

Despite the amino groups on the carbohydrate moiety of proteoglycans, the molecule often carries an overall negative charge. This is due to oxidized carbohydrates via carboxylic acid groups, or sulfates being coupled to the carbohydrate. These negatively charged groups have sodium counter ions, which draw significant amounts of water into the structure. The ability to absorb water serves various functions, depending on the proteoglycan. Most proteoglycans are viscous, and many act as gels. Hence, some of these molecules can act as lubricants, keeping joints moving freely. Other proteoglycans form a much firmer gel and resist compaction, acting

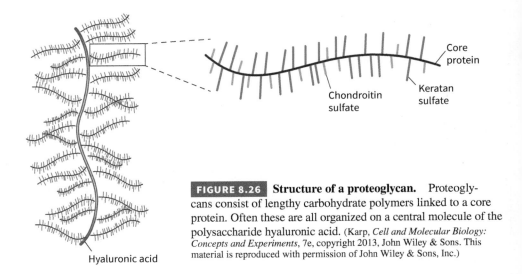

FIGURE 8.26 **Structure of a proteoglycan.** Proteoglycans consist of lengthy carbohydrate polymers linked to a core protein. Often these are all organized on a central molecule of the polysaccharide hyaluronic acid. (Karp, *Cell and Molecular Biology: Concepts and Experiments*, 7e, copyright 2013, John Wiley & Sons. This material is reproduced with permission of John Wiley & Sons, Inc.)

as shock absorbers. The layer of carbohydrate presents a partial barrier to both pathogens and cancerous cells, preventing or slowing their progression through a tissue (**Figure 8.26**).

Examples of glycosaminoglycans
Examples of common glycosaminoglycans found in humans include:

- **Heparan sulfate**—this linear polysaccharide is comprised of repeating disaccharides, usually glucuronic acid and *N*-Acetylglucosamine. The polysaccharide is sulfated at several locations in each disaccharide unit. Heparin is a related glycosaminoglycan that is enriched in iduronic acid and *N*-Acetylglucosamine. Heparan sulfate is found in the extracellular matrices of most animals.

Heparan sulfate

- **Chondroitin sulfate**—this linear polysaccharide is comprised of repeating glucuronic acid and *N*-Acetylgalactosamine disaccharides. As with heparan, it is multiply sulfated on each residue (typically on the 4 and 6 position of each *N*-Acetylglucosamine). Isomerization of glucuronic acid molecules into iduronic acid produces the molecule dermatan sulfate (a common component of epithelial tissues, such as skin and blood vessels). Chondroitin sulfate is found in materials of high tensile strength, such as tendons, cartilage, and the aorta. Many people currently take supplements of glucosamine and chondroitin for joint health, although their efficacy is debated.

Chondroitin

Glucuronic acid   *N*-Acetylglucosamine

- **Keratan sulfate**—this linear polysaccharide is a polymer of galactose and *N*-Acetyl-glucosamine. It is typically less sulfated than chondroitin or heparan sulfate, having a single sulfate on C-6 of either monosaccharide. Keratan sulfate is found in bone, horn, and cornea.

Keratan sulfate

Galactose   *N*-Acetylglucosamine
sulfate

These three polysaccharides have a far greater degree of variability than is seen in other classes of biological molecules. The sequence of a nucleotide or protein, although not set in stone, is highly invariant. Considerable biochemical effort is placed on making sure that DNA is copied with high fidelity—few to no mistakes—or that proteins are synthesized without error. The same does not seem to hold for proteoglycans. Depending on the tissue, organism, or even sample, there can be variability in characteristics such as degrees of sulfation, incorporation of other monosaccharides, isomerization or epimerization of monomers in the chain, and length of the chain. Whether this variability has a distinct purpose in biochemistry and what it is selected for are unclear, although it is known that tampering with these ratios can be harmful. In 2008, a batch of heparin was contaminated with chondroitin that had been chemically oversulfated. Patients given this heparin died rapidly from anaphylaxis, the severe allergic response commonly associated with bee stings or peanuts in those who are severely allergic. Further characterization revealed that this modified polysaccharide can elicit a release of the vasodilator bradykinin. Although the mechanism of the release of bradykinin is still unknown, this example shows that the interactions of cells with glycosaminoglycans can be harmful, and strongly suggests that the degree of sulfation of these polysaccharides is not random.

Hyaluronic acid is a non-proteoglycan matrix polysaccharide

Hyaluronic acid differs from the other polysaccharides discussed here, in that it is not a part of a proteoglycan. Rather, it is secreted as a lengthy linear polysaccharide of glucuronic acid and *N*-Acetylglucosamine. Molecules of hyaluronic acid can be huge, containing up to 25,000 monomers and ranging in molecular weight from several kilodaltons up to 20 million daltons. The average size ranges from 3 to 5 million daltons, depending on the tissue. Hyaluronic acid is synthesized by a complex in the plasma membrane and excreted from the cell as it is synthesized (whereas other glycosaminoglycans are added in the ER and Golgi complex).

Hyaluronic acid

Glucuronic acid   *N*-Acetylglucosamine

The protein components of proteoglycans vary widely

Numerous matrix proteins have been found to be involved in proteoglycan formation. We will discuss several fibrous proteins found in the matrix and other common components of proteoglycans in the next section.

FIGURE 8.27 **Structure of the peptidoglycan cell wall in gram-positive bacteria.** Peptidoglycans consist of lengthy linear carbohydrate chains cross-linked by short peptides. While the carbohydrate and amino acid composition varies slightly across different phyla of bacteria, the overall structure is conserved. (Wessner, *Microbiology*, 2e, copyright 2017, John Wiley & Sons. This material is reproduced with permission of John Wiley & Sons, Inc.)

8.3.4 Peptidoglycans

Peptidoglycans are the building blocks of the cell wall in bacteria. They are composed of a dimeric repeat of *N*-Acetylglucosamine (GlcNAc) and *N*-Acetylmuramic acid (MurNAc) in a β-1,4 linkage (**Figure 8.27**). Extending from each molecule of *N*-Acetylmuramic acid is a short (4 to 5 residue) peptide, linked through the oxygen on C-3. The amino acids found in the peptide vary by species, but include the L isomers of alanine and lysine, and the D isomers of glutamine, glutamic acid, and alanine. Please recall that the L isomers of amino acids are the common form found in proteins; D isomers are unusual and are found only in a few locations, such as the bacterial cell wall.

Cross-linking of these peptides with a pentaglycine linker by a transpeptidase provides a rigid net that gives the bacteria structure. Several antibiotics act by taking advantage of the chemistry of the bacterial cell wall. For example, penicillin and its derivatives irreversibly inhibit the transpeptidase, blocking formation of the peptide linkage between peptidoglycan chains in gram-positive bacteria (**Figure 8.28**). The chains of peptidoglycan in gram-negative

FIGURE 8.28 **Structure of penicillin G and other lactam antibiotics.** **A.** Lactam antibiotics like penicillin act by inhibiting transpeptidase, the enzyme that catalyzes the cross-linking of polypeptides in the peptidoglycan cell wall. The lactam ring is essential in this mechanism. **B.** The structures of other first-generation penicillin analogs differ in the organic functional groups that are fixed to the β-lactam and fit differently in the active site of transpeptidase. Cephalosporin is a second-generation penicillin analog. While this structure differs in some ways, it retains the β-lactam ring essential for this inhibition.

bacteria use a different mechanism to cross-link chains; as a result, they are not sensitive to penicillin. Other derivatives of penicillin ("illin" class antibiotics) have improved properties; for example, they have greater bioavailability and stability and are more widely tolerated. These derivatives include ampicillin, amoxicillin, and methicillin, as well as second-generation drugs such as carbenicillin and piperacillin. Newer types of penicillin-class drugs include carbapenems and cephalosporins. Although these drugs look quite different from the original compound, they all retain the β-lactam ring, which is key in the inhibitory mechanism.

Nature also exploits the bacterial cell wall. Many organisms express lysozyme, a naturally occurring β-glycosidase that cleaves the linkage between *N*-Acetylglucosamine and *N*-Acetylmuramic acid. This effectively dissolves the bacterial wall, leading to bacterial lysis. Lysozyme is present in human tears (helping to prevent bacterial infections of the eye), and it is abundant in the egg white of chicken eggs, where it helps to protect the yolk and embryo from bacterial contamination.

WORKED PROBLEM 8.6 | Sharing matrices

Experimental treatments are underway for people with severe muscle damage. In one such treatment, cells are scraped from pig bladder, and the tissue is sterilized and then transplanted into the damaged muscle. In time, new muscle grows into the transplanted matrix.

Explain why the transplanted pig bladder tissue did not turn into a new bladder. Also, why does the body fail to mount an immune response against this foreign object?

Strategy   Consider the matrix the cells are living in. How could these cells be prompted to grow and to grow properly? Why does one tissue (bladder) grow in one part of the body and a different tissue (muscle) in another? On a basic level, what causes an immune response?

Solution   When scraped free of cells, sterilized, and dried, the pig bladder resembles a piece of parchment paper or dried skin.

Essentially, it is just that, the remaining connective tissue or matrix devoid of living cells. The cells are what make this organ a bladder; most tissues of the body are rich in collagen and in the other proteoglycans discussed here and in the next section. There is too little molecular difference between these matrices to elicit an immune response, but there is an as-of-yet undetermined signal that tells muscle cells, or some type of pro-muscle stem cell, to migrate into this matrix and begin to regenerate the tissue.

Follow-up question   Pigs lacking α-1,3 galactosyltransferase have been suggested as a source of tissues for transplantation into human recipients. How might this mutation help to prevent rejection of these tissue grafts?

8.3 Summary

- Glycoproteins, glycolipids, proteoglycans, and peptidoglycans are all examples of glycosylated molecules.
- Glycoproteins are mainly extracellular proteins to which carbohydrate chains have been added.
- In glycoproteins, carbohydrates can be either *O*-linked (via a serine or threonine residue) or *N*-linked (through an asparagine residue).
- The ABO blood group antigens are examples of glycoproteins.
- Glycolipids are membrane lipids with attached carbohydrate groups.
- Lipopolysaccharide, glycosyl phosphoinositide (GPI) anchors, cerebrosides, and gangliosides are all examples of glycolipids.
- Proteoglycans are comprised of a protein linked to a glycosaminoglycan (a large carbohydrate polymer).
- Common examples of glycosaminoglycans, which are often sulfated, include:
  - heparan sulfate (glucuronic acid and *N*-Acetylglucosamine),
  - chondroitin sulfate (galactose and *N*-Acetylglucosamine),
  - keratan sulfate (iduronic acid and *N*-Acetylglucosamine).
- Hyaluronic acid is a non-proteoglycan glycosaminoglycan found in the extracellular matrix. Its structure consists of a repeating dimer of glucuronic acid and *N*-Acetylglucosamine.
- Gram-negative bacteria have a peptidoglycan cell wall made of chains of polysaccharides cross-linked by short peptides.
- The antibiotic penicillin blocks the cross-linking of the peptides. As a result, the bacterial cell wall loses integrity and the bacteria lyse.

8.3 Concept Check

- Describe the four types of glycosylated molecules mentioned in this section.
- Provide examples of the four glycosylated molecules' structures and functions.

8.4 Extracellular Matrices and Biofilms

Cells in eukaryotic systems are held together in a fibrous mesh of secreted polymers. These polymers (proteins and polysaccharides) form a gel that helps to give structure to and protect the underlying cells. Many prokaryotic systems also employ a secreted matrix of proteins and polysaccharides for similar protection and structure. This section discusses the secreted matrices of both eukaryotic and prokaryotic cells, and some recent discoveries and applications in this field.

8.4.1 Eukaryotic extracellular matrix proteins

The extracellular matrix of a tissue is made of proteins, glycoproteins, and proteoglycans in a fibrous, gel-like mesh (**Figure 8.29**). The composition and function of the matrix has not been fully elucidated; however, more than 100 proteins have been found in the matrix, and these have diverse functions, including structure, ligand binding, immune responses, and regulation of growth and development. In addition, the matrix varies in composition from tissue to tissue and as the organism develops; it can also change in response to disease.

In addition to the glycosaminoglycans discussed in section 8.3 (heparan sulfate, chondroitin sulfate, keratan sulfate, and hyaluronic acid), several fibrous proteins are important in the matrix. Examples of some of the more common fibrous proteins, discussed below, are collagen, elastin, fibronectin, and laminin.

Collagen Collagen is the protein found in the highest abundance in the extracellular matrix. It is present in almost every tissue of the body, and it has been estimated that as much as 25% of the protein in the body (by mass) is collagen. So far, 28 different types of collagen protein have been identified in the body, coded for by at least 42 different genes.

The structure of all collagens is similar. Collagens are helical, but unlike the α helix commonly seen in biochemistry, collagen adopts a structure known as the **collagen triple helix**.

A detailed examination of the structure of collagen I (the most prevalent collagen) shows that it is comprised of three polypeptide chains: two copies of α1 and one copy of α2. These three chains wrap around each other, forming a left-handed helix (α helices are right handed). Another significant difference between collagen and other proteins is the amino acid composition. Collagen is enriched in three amino acids: glycine, proline, and lysine. In addition, the proline and lysine residues are often chemically modified into hydroxyproline and hydroxylysine.

Collagen synthesis begins with translation of collagen mRNA. A signal sequence directs this protein to the ER for processing. In the ER, the signal sequence is removed, prolines and lysines are hydroxylated, and hydroxylysines are often glycosylated; the collagen monomers form into tropocollagen, adopting the collagen triple helix structure. Glycosylation continues in the Golgi complex as these proteins are processed. Once secreted, the termini of the helices are truncated by collagen peptidases. The enzyme lysyl oxidase catalyzes the final assembly of tropocollagen molecules. Cross-linking into the mature form by lysyl oxidase is discussed in the next section; hydroxylation of proline residues is a hallmark of collagen and is discussed here (**Figure 8.30**).

FIGURE 8.29 **Schematic view of the extracellular matrix.** Matrix glycoproteins and proteoglycans form a gel-like mesh for the cell.

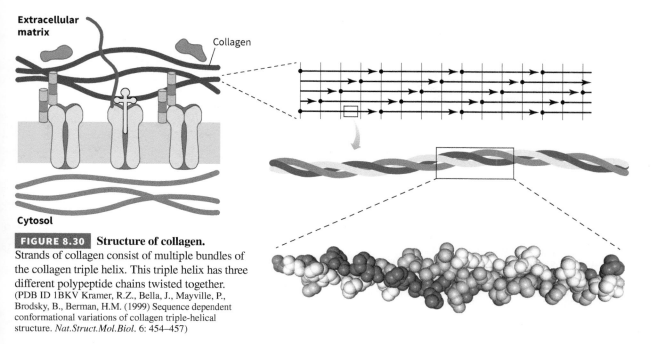

Extracellular matrix

Collagen

Cytosol

FIGURE 8.30 **Structure of collagen.**
Strands of collagen consist of multiple bundles of
the collagen triple helix. This triple helix has three
different polypeptide chains twisted together.
(PDB ID 1BKV Kramer, R.Z., Bella, J., Mayville, P.,
Brodsky, B., Berman, H.M. (1999) Sequence dependent
conformational variations of collagen triple-helical
structure. *Nat.Struct.Mol.Biol.* 6: 454–457)

The hydroxylation of proline is one of the key reactions in the formation of collagen. It requires L-ascorbate (vitamin C); thus, a deficiency of vitamin C causes disease, in the form of scurvy, as discussed in section 7.1. In scurvy, an inability to form extracellular matrix (connective tissue) leads to hair and tooth loss, bleeding from mucus membranes, and failure to heal wounds. Prolonged vitamin C deficiency is often fatal.

Prolyl hydroxylase is the enzyme responsible for the hydroxylation of proline. This enzyme is a tetramer with the stoichiometry $\alpha2\beta2$. The α subunits are a mixed-function oxidase that hydroxylates proline using molecular oxygen, iron, and ascorbic acid; the β subunits are identical to the protein disulfide isomerase (another enzyme involved in protein modification and remodeling). As proline is being hydroxylated, a second oxidation reaction is also occurring, in which α-ketoglutarate is oxidized to succinate and CO_2. In the citric acid cycle, the oxidation of α-ketoglutarate to succinate and CO_2 proceeds through succinyl-CoA, generating a molecule of GTP in the process. The energy released in the α-ketoglutarate oxidation in prolyl hydroxylase is instead used to drive the hydroxylation of proline.

Proline + **α-ketoglutarate** $\xrightarrow[\text{prolyl hydroxylase}]{\text{Ascorbate, } O_2, Fe^{2+}, CO_2}$ **4-hydroxyproline** + **Succinate**

Hydroxyproline residues are best known for their role in collagen, but they are also important in other proteins such as elastin (discussed below), prions, the ion-channel poison conotoxin, and the RNA-silencing complex protein argonaut. Finally, hydroxylation of a key proline in hypoxic inducible factor (HIF), discussed in section 7.1, directs the protein to ubiquitination and proteosomal degradation. Although not all of these reactions are catalyzed by the same enzyme, they all result in hydroxyproline residues.

Elastin   Elastin and fibrillin are the two proteins responsible for the elastic fibers found mainly in the skin and arteries. Elastin forms the core of these fibers, while fibrillin forms a mantle of microfibers coating the central core. Elastin is comprised largely of hydrophobic residues. It is enriched in proline and glycine, but these residues are not hydroxylated as they are in collagen. There are also repeated stretches that are rich in lysine

FIGURE 8.31 **Structure of elastin and the desmosine cross-link.** Elastin is normally a highly condensed protein, but it can be extended and snap back to its original shape (like a rubber band). The protein strands are cross-linked by desmosine bridges formed by lysine residues.

and alanine. The lysine residues in this region are cross-linked to one another or to fibrillin via two different routes (**Figure 8.31**). **Transglutaminase** catalyzes cross-linking between glutamine residues of fibrillin and lysine residues in elastin (**Figure 8.32**). Ammonia (NH_3) is split out in the process, and an unusual peptide bond is formed between the γ-carboxamide of glutamine and the ε-nitrogen of lysine. **Lysyl oxidase** polymerizes monomers of a soluble pro-protein (tropoelastin) secreted from cells near the matrix into mature elastin. In the lysyl oxidase reaction, the side chain of lysine is oxidatively deaminated, and subsequent reactions (potentially uncatalyzed spontaneous reactions) form cross-links to other amino acids. Although tropoelastin is about 75 kDa, mature elastin fibrils can be millions of daltons in size.

FIGURE 8.32 **Transglutaminase.** **A.** In the extracellular matrix, transglutaminase generates an unusual amide bond between the side chains of lysine and glutamine. **B.** Commercially, transglutaminase is used in the food industry as "meat glue" to join pieces of meat together, as is seen in this Pacific Yellowtail/Yellowfin Tuna sashimi.

Fibronectin Fibronectin is a dimeric, 440-kDa glycoprotein found in the extracellular matrix. However, unlike the other proteins discussed

FIGURE 8.33 **Structure of fibronectin.** Fibronectin is a dimeric protein that links the cell (via integrins) with the extracellular matrix (via collagen and some polysaccharides like heparin). The structure of fibronectin consists of multiple repeats of β structure repeated throughout the length of the structure. Fibronectin is also glycosylated through both *N*-linked and *O*-linked carbohydrate chains.

in this section, it is also found in a soluble form in the circulation where it functions in the clotting cascade (**Figure 8.33**). Fibronectin acts as an adapter between the cell and the matrix. Integrins, integral membrane glycoproteins, bind to fibronectin and link it to other proteins and polysaccharides of the extracellular matrix to the cytoskeleton.

As with several other fibrillar proteins, fibronectin is coded for by a single gene, but it has multiple repeats in the protein sequence, each formed by a single exon. This is indicative of partial gene-duplication events. Differential splicing of this gene gives rise to soluble and filamentous forms of the protein.

The fibronectin molecule is a homodimer that contains multiple copies of three distinct repeats, each of which has two antiparallel β sheets. Up to 15 of these different features are found in fibronectin in different combinations. Repeat I binds to matrix proteins (collagen and fibrin), and repeat III binds to the cell at least partially via interactions with the integrins.

Laminins
Laminins are a family of 15 different proteins that function in the basal lamina, which is a layer of the basement membrane, a fibrous layer of connective tissue found under the epithelial layers (**Figure 8.34**). Laminins are heterotrimeric, consisting of one subunit each of α, β, and γ. There are five different α isoforms, four β isoforms, and three γ isoforms that exist and assemble into the mature holoprotein. Laminin 211, for example, has one copy each of the α2, β1, and γ1 subunits.

Laminins are large proteins ranging from 900 kDa to over 1.5 MDa. They form a four-armed cruciform shape comprised of α-helical coiled-coil domains that link globular bulges. The assembly of the macromolecular complex is stabilized in part by the coiled-coil domain. Repeated domains in the coil interact through hydrogen bonding, salt bridging, and the hydrophobic effect to form the structure. The longest of the three chains of laminins (the α chain, comprised mainly of the coiled-coil domain) functions in cellular adhesion, whereas the short chains (β and γ) attach to other matrix proteins and polysaccharides.

Laminins are implicated in several diseases. Most notable among these is a form of congenital muscular dystrophy in which the genes coding for laminin 211 are in some way mutated. More than 28 mutations have been characterized, ranging from simple point mutations to large deletions; all of these mutations result in defective proteins. The rest of the basal lamina seems unaffected, but the end result for the patient is muscle cell death,

FIGURE 8.34   **Structure of the laminins.**   Like fibronectin, the laminins help link integrins to the extracellular matrix. The laminins consist of three polypeptide chains twisted around each other. Salt bridges and hydrophobic interactions hold these chains together. Laminins interact between integrins and fibronectin and collagen.

inflammation, and the invasion of other cell types (such as adipocytes) into the muscle tissue (**Figure 8.35**).

Because many molecules in the matrix are large and polyvalent, there are opportunities for multiple interactions between molecules. Matrix DB is software that tracks the interactions of the macromolecules of the extracellular matrix, based on what has been observed in the literature (**Figure 8.36**). More than 2,200 protein–protein and protein–glycosaminoglycan interactions have been mapped. The software also takes into consideration the multimeric nature of some members; for example, collagens and laminins function as multimers, enabling multiple interactions with other macromolecules. A group of molecules that interact with each other has been termed an interactome.

FIGURE 8.35   **Dysfunction of the laminins results in muscular dystrophy.**   Shown is a micrograph of a muscle tissue biopsy from a patient with muscular dystrophy. Note the large number of adipocytes (large open cells) in contrast to the muscle cells. Several different diseases (known as laminopathies) can arise from mutations of the laminins.

Cell culture and tissue engineering

Cells differ in the affinity with which they adhere to different surfaces. Over time, researchers discovered that surfaces usually need some sort of preparation to permit cell adherence. In plastic tissue-culture dishes, cultured cells adhere relatively poorly to untreated polystyrene. Thus, manufacturers treat the surface with an ionized gas or plasma creating oxidative modifications, for example, removing phenolic groups and incorporating hydroxyl, carbonyl, and carboxylic acid moieties. This simple treatment greatly improves the adherence of cells.

As different cell types have been adapted for culture, different surfaces have been developed, for example, a surface of biological molecules such as collagen, fibrin, fibronectin, or polymers of lysine. Such surfaces provide more of a native biological substrate for the cells to grow on. For some cell lines, this is still not enough; for example, embryonic stem cells require a layer of feeder cells to grow on. The feeder layer is a layer of cells grown to confluence: that is, the cells are grown to a contiguous monolayer of cells, then treated with pulses of electricity, radiation, or the DNA crosslinker and chemotherapeutic agent mitomycin C to stop the cells from dividing further (**Figure 8.37**). The feeder cells are metabolically active and thus still able to secrete the cytokines and hormones that the embryonic stem cells need to survive.

Despite these techniques for improved adhesion, there are still several drawbacks to cell culture. Eukaryotic cells prefer living systems to flat plastic surfaces. Primary cultures of cells, that is, cells that are directly derived from living tissue as opposed to transformed cultured cells, lose their phenotype after time in culture. For example, over time a hepatocyte (liver cell) will stop synthesis of the proteins that are typically found in the liver, making this model less valid for the study of liver processes.

The study of recreating tissues or organs lost through injury is *tissue engineering,* the growth of cultured cells in a three-dimensional matrix. Tissue engineering involves a combination of materials, matrices, and cells working to give a final product that has the desired mechanical, immunological, and biocompatible properties. In tissue engineering, the scaffold, which is the matrix to which the cells attach, needs to provide structure for the cells to grow. At the same time, the scaffold must allow the cells or host to reabsorb the matrix after the cells take

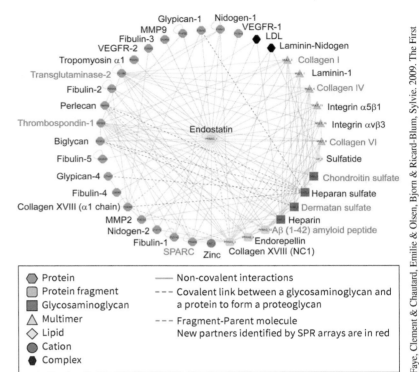

Faye, Clement & Chautard, Emilie & Olsen, Bjorn & Ricard-Blum, Sylvie. 2009. The First Draft of the Endostatin Interaction Network. *The Journal of Biological Chemistry.* 284. 22041-7. 10.1074/jbc.M109.002964.

FIGURE 8.36   **Interactions of matrix proteins can be studied *in silico.*** Shown is an image from Matrix DB, a web-based tool, that illustrates interactions of different molecules found in the extracellular matrix. This is a graphical interpretation of the interactome of these molecules.

hold. Hence, the scaffold is often made of proteins, such as collagen, or polyesters of lactic acid, glycolic acid, or caprolactone. As these molecules hydrolyze, they release monomers that are absorbed and used by the cell.

FIGURE 8.37   **Cultured cells.**   **A.** Cells in culture are often grown in flasks. **B.** The surface of the flask is treated to generate a more hydrophilic surface to which cells can adhere. **C.** Embryonic stem cells (the colony in the center of the micrograph) live on a layer of feeder cells. **D.** These "zombie cells" are metabolically active but are not capable of division due to treatment with mitomycin c.

To date, there have been limited but promising successes with engineered tissues being transplanted into humans. For the most part, the tissues have been epithelial in nature; they include skin grafts, vascular tissue grafts, and artificial bladders (**Figure 8.38**).

WORKED PROBLEM 8.7 | Characterizing matrix proteins

Sodium dodecyl sulfate polyacrylamide gel electrophoresis (SDS-PAGE) is a common technique used in the analysis of proteins. Why is it often difficult to characterize matrix proteins using SDS-PAGE?

Strategy How is SDS-PAGE performed, and what information does it provide?

Solution SDS-PAGE is discussed in detail in the techniques appendix. In SDS-PAGE, a protein sample is denatured by heating in the presence of the detergent SDS. Often, a sulfhydryl reducing agent such as β-mercaptoethanol (β-ME) or dithiothreitol (DTT) is added to cleave disulfide bonds. The SDS imparts a negative charge, and the proteins can be separated in an electric field through a gel matrix such as polyacrylamide (hence the "PAGE" in SDS-PAGE). The movement through this field varies inversely with molecular weight; that is, larger proteins move more slowly

than smaller ones. Typical ranges over which proteins can be separated run from several thousand up to several hundred thousand daltons, with 10 to 200 kDa being most common.

Analysis of matrix proteins by SDS-PAGE poses a range of problems. Often, matrix proteins are cross-linked to one another through covalent bonds that are not disulfides and are thus not susceptible to cleavage by β-ME or DTT. Also, matrix proteins form a polymer that is much too large to be analyzed using this technique. In addition, matrix proteins are often glycosylated, and glycosylations alter the migration of proteins in SDS-PAGE. Therefore, SDS-PAGE is a powerful technique but not necessarily the right one for analysis of matrix proteins.

Follow-up question How could some matrix proteins be processed so that they are suitable for analysis by SDS-PAGE?

BRIAN WALKER/APTN/ ASSOCIATED PRESS

FIGURE 8.38 **Engineered tissues.** Recent advances in tissue engineering include human bladders grown in culture.

Science Source/Science Source

Bacteria   Secreted matrix

FIGURE 8.39 **Structure of a biofilm.** In a biofilm, bacteria live in a secreted matrix of proteins and polysaccharides. The film can consist of only one species or can have multiple species living in symbiosis. This is an example of a biofilm obtained from the inner surface of a needle-less connector.

8.4.2 | Biofilms are composed of microbes living in a secreted matrix

Biofilms are associations of microbes (of a single species or multiple species) living in a secreted matrix (**Figure 8.39**). Biofilms are often found at an air–liquid or solid–liquid interface. The slime at the bottom of a pond can be an example of a biofilm, as can dental plaque, an infection in a tissue, or aggregations of microbes on a biomedical implant. They are also the primary methods used in sewage and wastewater treatment to remove contaminants and by the aquarium industry to remove ammonia from the water in fish tanks. Biofilms are responsible for fouling pumps and corrosion of equipment exposed to marine environments. Biofilms have been associated with almost 80% of chronic human infections, and they are thought to be responsible for tens of thousands of deaths a year. Hence, biofilms are of significant commercial, medical, and scientific interest.

Biofilms often form as thin films one microbe thick, but in some cases can grow to be several centimeters thick and as large as several meters across. Organisms in a biofilm have a different phenotype and thus express different genes (or express the same genes but to differing degrees) than they would when floating freely in suspension or living singly on a surface.

Biofilm development Biofilms undergo a distinct series of steps as they develop. In the earliest stage, single microbes begin to adhere to a surface or interface. As more members join the surface, they begin to alter gene expression and adhere irreversibly. At this point the microbes begin to secrete extracellular polysaccharides that form a matrix around the organisms. As the film begins to mature, more microbes are recruited; also, microbes already present in the film start to divide, increasing the size of the film. Matrix secretion continues and the film thickens. In the final stage of development, parts of the film may rupture, releasing its inhabitants to disperse and generate new films elsewhere (**Figure 8.40**).

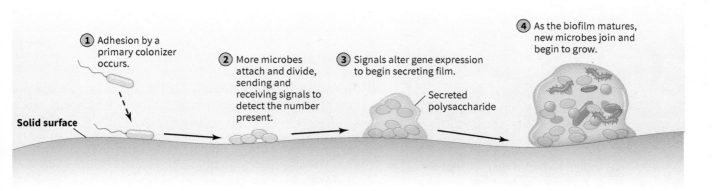

FIGURE 8.40 **Life cycle of a biofilm.** Biofilms house microbes in a secreted matrix. (Wessner, *Microbiology*, 2e, copyright 2017, John Wiley & Sons. This material is reproduced with permission of John Wiley & Sons, Inc.)

Bacteria can communicate with one another using chemical messengers through mechanisms similar to those found in eukaryotic cells. This approach, termed quorum sensing, enables bacteria to determine the density of like organisms in the immediate area and alter their gene expression in response. Quorum-sensing signaling molecules have been shown to have a role in biofilm initiation in numerous species.

The ability of microbes to form biofilms is almost universal. When in a biofilm, the growth of the bacteria slows because the diffusion of small molecules may be limited. Although it may seem as though the bacteria are putting themselves at a disadvantage in this situation, the biofilm provides a stable environment. For example, bacteria are often more antibiotic resistant in a biofilm. Also, some members of the colony may themselves secrete antibiotics that stop competitors from growing and competing for resources. The development of a biofilm is an evolutionary adaptation; the bacteria work together and expend energy for both their own good and that of the film. These observations have been extended beyond bacteria. Fungal biofilms have now been described in the scientific literature.

Given the diversity of microbes, the extracellular matrix forming the biofilm might be expected to be equally diverse, and it is. Common polymers found in biofilms include alginates (polymers of mannuronic and guluronic acids), chitin (polymers of *N*-Acetylglucosamine), and polymers rich in glucose or mannose, or several other common monosaccharides and disaccharides. In addition to exopolysaccharides, the matrix contains proteins, including lectin-like proteins that bind to polysaccharides, and amyloid-like fibrils, unusual polymers of amino acids such as polyglutamate, and extracellular DNA.

Biofilm decontamination and prevention   Removal of a biofilm is not as simple as washing off surface microbes, because the microbes forming the film are cloistered in the matrix of the film and the film itself may be attached to the surface. There is significant ongoing research into what combinations of detergents, antibiotics, and hydrolytic enzymes can disrupt biofilms, yet the films are notoriously hard to remove. One method being investigated is blasting films away using a jet of oxygen–helium plasma. This technique generates short-lived oxidative intermediates that are thought to eradicate the film without penetrating or damaging the tissue underneath. The treatment of surfaces with ozone is also being investigated. This technique may be useful in some cases but is not viable in a living organism. The ozone oxidizes the matrix polysaccharides, generating smaller fragments and creating hydrophilic modifications; it also kills the microbes in the film. This technique is often used in aquariums, pools, and spas.

An alternative to removing biofilms is to find ways to prevent their growth in the first place. Smooth surfaces with hydrophobic coatings discourage bacterial settling and biofilm initiation. Also, some polymers have been impregnated with antibiotics, hydrophobic oils,

FIGURE 8.41 **Micrograph of *Pseudomonas aeruginosa*.** *Pseudomonas* in the lung can form biofilms secreting viscous mucus that help bacteria survive. *Pseudomonas* is responsible for one of the opportunistic infections that takes hold in cystic fibrosis.

nanoparticles of silver, or positively charged groups such as *N*-Alkylpyridinium salts, and these techniques seem to be effective at reducing biofilm formation. In biomedical applications, low-energy sound waves have been found to prevent microbes from binding to the surface of devices such as catheters.

Biofilms in human health

Given that most microbes can form biofilms, it stands to reason that these structures will have a role in human health. This section discusses two biofilms implicated in health and disease: *Pseudomonas aeruginosa* and dental plaque.

Pseudomonas aeruginosa

Pseudomonas aeruginosa is a common environmental pathogen. This pathogen is usually not a danger to healthy individuals, but it participates in opportunistic infections, for example, in the lungs of individuals with cystic fibrosis (**Figure 8.41**). In cystic fibrosis, a defective chloride transporter (cystic fibrosis transmembrane conductance regulator, CFTR) causes numerous pathophysiologies leading to the formation of viscous, sticky mucus in the lungs. *Pseudomonas* infections can be treated with antibiotics; however, by their mid-20s, most people with cystic fibrosis harbor antibiotic-resistant strains. Often, people with cystic fibrosis are on prophylactic antibiotics and require percussive therapy, which involves thumping on the chest several times a day to clear mucus. Newer therapies for lung disease in cystic fibrosis include gene therapy to replace the defective CFTR, attempts to trigger other chloride channels to open (e.g., the experimental drug Desnufosol), or lung transplant.

Dental plaque

Dental plaque is a biofilm composed of microbes that live on the surface of teeth and gingival, or gum, tissues. The primary microbes are strains of *Streptococcus*; however, more than a thousand different strains of bacteria and yeast are thought to exist in dental plaque. The acidic waste products of these bacteria can damage the surface of the teeth, causing tooth decay and gum disease.

Although it is clear that bacteria secrete some of the matrix, it appears that another component of the matrix is salivary protein secreted by the human host perhaps to contain or otherwise control the growth or damage from the bacteria in the plaque.

The balance between health and disease in plaque is not dictated by the presence or absence of the biofilm; everyone has dental plaque. The difference between someone with advanced periodontal disease and someone with healthy teeth is more an issue of the types of microbes in the film and the extent of the plaque. Brushing and flossing are mechanical ways to control biofilms; various components of toothpaste and mouthwash also help to control the growth of mouth flora.

Symbiotic microbes: kefir and kombucha

Kefir and kombucha are ancient drinks that come from different parts of the world but have a similar biochemical makeup. Kefir is a fermented milk beverage from eastern Europe, whereas kombucha is a fermented tea drink thought to have originated in Mongolia and western China. While we may think of fermented beverages such as beer, mead, cider, and wine as being intoxicating, kefir lacks alcohol (lactate is the final fermentation product), and kombucha has only a low concentration of alcohol (0.5%). Similar to beer and wine, kefir and kombucha probably arose in antiquity as a way of preserving leftover milk or tea. Today, these drinks are consumed worldwide, both for their taste and their health benefits.

Whereas beer and wine are primarily the products of yeast-based fermentations, kefir and kombucha result from a combination of yeast and bacteria living symbiotically in an exopolysaccharide matrix. In kefir, these microbes form structures called kefir grains: lumpy, white-to-yellow aggregates ranging in diameter from less than a millimeter to over a centimeter. In kombucha, the bacteria and yeast form a mat that floats at the air–liquid interface, resembling a jellyfish or mushroom, and is thus referred to as a kombucha

A.

Stephanie Frey/iStock/Getty Images

B.

Brian Hagiwara/Photolibrary/Getty Images

FIGURE 8.42 **Kefir grains and kombucha mushrooms.** **A.** Kefir grains are colonies of different strains of bacteria and yeast that live in a secreted extracellular matrix. **B.** Kombucha "mushrooms" grow in tea. While they have different microorganisms and matrix components, the theme is similar to to kefir grains.

mushroom. In well-developed kombucha cultures, the leathery mat can be several centimeters thick (**Figure 8.42**).

In both kefir and kombucha, the cultures are maintained by removing some of the culture medium or liquid, and adding fresh milk or tea, depending on the beverage being made. Alternatively, a piece of the kombucha mat (termed a "baby") or some kefir grains can be added to fresh liquid.

While this section has focused on the extracellular matrix of animal and microbial cells, plants too have an extracellular matrix, typically one rich in cellulose. The stored carbohydrates found in plant material or other sources, such as algae, can be used by humans as a source of fuel for their machines. These sources of energy, termed biofuels, are discussed in **Societal and Ethical Biochemistry: Biofuels**.

Societal and Ethical Biochemistry

Biofuels

All animals are chemotrophs; that is, they require energy from food to sustain their metabolic processes. However, only humans use external energy to alter their environment. Even ancient people extended the geographic range in which they could live by using fire to keep warm. Today, we take advantage of automation and technology such as transportation, refrigeration, and modern agricultural methods for many of the services that are essential to our daily lives.

As global economies develop and the global population increases, there is a greater demand for devices that use fuel and therefore a greater demand for fuel. Building devices that are more fuel efficient makes sense, but this resolves only part of the problem. There has also been a shift in the past two centuries from fuels such as wood, whale oil, and dung to coal, oil, and gas. Some energy sources are considered to be carbon neutral; for example, the CO_2 released by burning wood is used by growing trees to make new glucose in photosynthesis and then transformed into cellulose, so there is no net increase in atmospheric carbon (although there is a carbon cost in harvesting and transporting the wood). Energy can come from other sources: in the past, energy came from wind and water, using windmills and watermills; today energy comes from sources such as wind turbines, hydropower,

nuclear, and solar. Some of these options are growing in popularity as alternatives to fossil fuels. However, the greatest need today for fuels worldwide is for cars and trucks, and the leading candidates to replace the petroleum products used in vehicles are biofuels, that is, products derived from biological sources. Biofuels currently fall into two categories, biodiesel and ethanol.

Biodiesel is formed by esterifying methanol or other short-chain alcohols to fatty acids. By forming an ester (which is far less polar than the carboxyl group) the resulting molecule has a lower boiling point, higher volatility, and lower viscosity, and is more hydrophobic—all desirable properties for this type of fuel. These fuels are often formed from vegetable oils, such as corn or soybean; they can also be made from recycled vegetable oils. Producing biodiesel is relatively easy; the reaction is a simple Fisher esterification using an acid or base catalyst. The difficulty in using biofuels is quality control. Although it is relatively simple for an individual to produce ten gallons of biodiesel in the garage, home-made biodiesel is highly variable in quality and may harm the performance of the vehicle, in contrast to the quality fuel bought at the pump. This challenge does not exist in commercial biofuels where large-scale engineering and quality control address these concerns.

Ethanol can be made easily by fermenting starches and sugars. In the United States, corn is the main source of ethanol. In some parts of the country, gasoline has up to 10% ethanol as an additive; in other parts, fuel (referred to as E85) contains 85% ethanol and 15% petroleum products. Ethanol production is now mandatory in the United States; in 2012, 13 billion gallons of ethanol were made, which is equivalent to 5 billion bushels of corn or nearly 50% of the feed corn crop. The decision to mandate ethanol production was a political one that has a far-reaching impact: If corn must be used to make ethanol and supply is low, it drives up the cost of the final product. Also, because corn used for fuel is then not available to feed livestock, these laws are likely to affect food prices as well as fuel prices.

To be a successful alternative, it would be beneficial if there were other ways to generate ethanol. Plant biomass that is left behind, such as corn husks and stalks, have a lot of unused cellulose that is broken down by microbes in the soil. Switchgrass (*Panicum virgotum*) is another plant that has recently been targeted as a source of cellulose for biofuel production. The fuel produced from plant biomass and switchgrass is cellulosic ethanol; essentially, this is the same as ethanol obtained by the fermentation of starches or sucrose.

Ethanol was being produced from wood chips more than 100 years ago. In the late 1800s, chemists were generating ethanol by treating the wood chips with a dilute solution of sulfuric acid and heating it for several hours. More recently, to assist in the cleavage of cellulose into sugar, enzymes obtained from molds or fungi have been included in the process. Although yeast is still the main microbe used to convert sugar to ethanol in the fermentation, the yeast and other microbes involved in ethanol production have now been genetically engineered to tolerate higher ethanol concentrations, higher temperatures, and lower pH values.

The advantages of biofuels are many, but they are not a panacea. Even though these biofuels use carbon that was recently in the atmosphere, and ideally they could be produced locally cutting down the cost of transport, they are not free. There are energetic and monetary costs to growing the plants and processing them into ethanol or biodiesel. In addition, the fuels are not necessarily good for the environment just because they are derived from plants. For example, the growing and harvesting of sugar cane for ethanol production in Brazil is far from environmentally friendly. A large acreage must be dedicated to growing the sugar cane, the crop is frequently treated with large amounts of fertilizer and pesticides, and slash-and-burn techniques are used to harvest the cane. On the other hand, most vehicles in Brazil run on 97% ethanol, and the country imports almost no oil. While it may seem strange to run a car using processed vegetable oil or corn in the gas tank, fossil fuels are actually biofuels, just from a different era.

8.4 Summary

- Collagen, elastin, fibronectin, and laminin are all examples of large, secreted matrix glycoproteins.
- Hydroxyproline is found in collagen and elastin. Its synthesis is catalyzed by prolyl hydroxylase, a mixed-function oxidase that uses molecular oxygen, α-ketoglutarate, and a catalytic iron center.
- Cross-linking of lysines and glutamine residues in matrix proteins is common. These reactions are catalyzed by lysyl oxidase and transglutaminase.
- Matrix proteins are involved in development, immunity, and wound healing; they also give structure to the organism.
- The interactome describes how large matrix proteins interact with other macromolecules.
- The field of tissue engineering attempts to grow new tissues from inert matrices and cells.
- Biofilms are groups of microbes growing in a secreted matrix; they provide similar functions to the extracellular matrix in eukaryotic organisms, including scaffolding and anchoring the cells, directing their growth, and in some cases development.
- Bacteria in biofilms exhibit a different phenotype and group immunity through secreted antibiotics.
- Considerable effort is spent on controlling or eliminating biofilms from surfaces, or preventing their formation.
- Kefir and kombucha are fermented drinks created by colonizing microbes. These microbes live in symbiosis with each other in a secreted matrix.

8.4 Concept Check

- Name and describe the molecules involved in the extracellular matrix.
- Describe the special properties of the molecules found in the extracellular matrix (for example, hydroxyproline), how these modifications are made, and how they give rise to function.
- Give examples of how changes in the extracellular matrix cause or contribute to disease.

The Bigger Picture

Carbohydrates are a diverse and fascinating set of biological molecules. We often focus on their role as a stored source of energy, but carbohydrates are clearly important in the formation of the extracellular matrix, as structural molecules, and as signaling molecules. This chapter discusses the storage and mobilization of glucose in glycogen, a highly branched polymer of glucose found in the liver and muscle tissue, and the regulation of glycogen. It also examines the pentose phosphate pathway. This multifaceted pathway answers several needs in the cell, including the metabolism of different carbohydrates, such as ribose, and the generation of NADPH for lipid biosynthesis. The final two sections discuss the polysaccharide and protein components that cells secrete. These complex mesh networks of polymers (extracellular matrix and biofilms) provide structure for an organism and help to regulate development and immunity.

Bioinformatics Exercises

Exercise 1 Glycogen Phosphorylase Structure and Activity

Exercise 2 Glucagon Control of Glycogen and Glucose Metabolism

Problems

8.1 Glycogen Metabolism

1. Glycogen is stored glucose. If a plant stored fructose as a polymer for energy, would you anticipate that it would cost energy to synthesize the stored form of these molecules?

2. Some glycogen-storage diseases are treated by giving patients cornstarch. Why?

3. Is glycogen a reducing sugar?

4. What proteins are activated by glucagon? What is the function of each of these proteins?

5. Muscle does not provide glucose for the brain during times of starvation. Why?

6. The brain is fueled almost exclusively by glucose. Using this fact, would it be a good idea to express glucose-1-phosphatase in muscle? What type of phenotype would be exhibited by a mouse expressing glucose-1-phosphatase in muscle?

7. Muscle does not express the glucagon receptor. If muscle did express the glucagon receptor, would muscle become responsive to glucagon? What would the response be? What would you hypothesize as a phenotype for a transgenic mouse expressing the glucagon receptor in muscle?

8.2 The Pentose Phosphate Pathway

8. Glucose-6-phosphate dehydrogenase catalyzes the first step of the pentose phosphate pathway. This enzyme is highly specific for $NADP^+$; the K_M for NAD^+ is about a thousand times that of $NADP^+$. What does this mean in terms of affinity of the enzyme for NAD^+ and $NADP^+$? How would being forced to use NAD^+ affect rate?

9. Why does the pentose phosphate pathway take place in the cytosol?

10. Examining the mechanism of transaldolase, is there any other amino acid that could be substituted for lysine in the active site and retain activity?

11. If high levels of fructose in the diet were influencing the pentose phosphate pathway, how might this alter flux through this pathway? What kinetic information would you need to know to determine flux through this path?

12. In what metabolic situation would you need more of one metabolite of the pentose phosphate pathway than another?

13. The pentose phosphate pathway serves multiple functions, and the genes coding for the enzymes of this pathway are differentially expressed in different tissues. In adipose, breast, macrophage, liver, and muscle tissues, would you expect the genes of the pentose phosphate pathway to be constitutively (all the time) or inducibly (turned on and off) expressed? Explain your reasoning. If the genes are inducibly expressed in any of these tissues, what environmental, developmental, or other changes might lead to expression?

14. Favism is caused by a mutation in the gene coding for glucose-6-phosphate dehydrogenase. This gene is on the X chromosome. Does this mean that more men or more women will be affected by favism? Is this a sex-linked trait?

15. Glutathione peroxidase has an active site selenocysteine rather than cysteine. How would the change from sulfur to selenium produce similar chemistry, and in what ways would the chemistry differ?

8.3 Carbohydrates in Glycoconjugates

16. Where in the cell would you expect to find GPI-anchored proteins?

17. How could you free a protein from a GPI anchor?

18. Mutation of an asparagine to a glutamine is usually considered a conservative mutation. Using glycoproteins as an example, provide an instance where such a mutation is not trivial.

19. Analyze the monosaccharides and disaccharides that make up the matrix polysaccharides discussed in this chapter. Based on your knowledge of glycogen metabolism, propose reactions by which these polysaccharides could be formed.

20. What are the components of the four matrix polysaccharides discussed in this chapter? What are the sources of those carbohydrates?

21. Describe for someone outside the sciences how blood typing works.

22. Several inborn errors of metabolism arise from dysfunctional glycolipid metabolism. Describe three of these disorders on the chemical level and how these diseases manifest themselves in patients.

23. Look up the mechanism of action of penicillin. How do penicillin and other drugs inhibit the cross-linking of the peptidoglycan coating? Why are these drugs more effective on some bacteria than others?

8.4 Extracellular Matrices and Biofilms

24. Prolyl hydroxylase has an iron redox active center. Could copper substitute for the iron? Why or why not?

25. Would prolyl hydroxylase be more likely to have a magnesium or a cobalt center? Explain your answer.

26. How could you test experimentally the proposed mechanism for prolyl hydroxylase? What technique would be most useful?

27. Could a kombucha mushroom produce kefir, or vice versa? Would you expect those cultures to be the same or to have the same matrix?

28. How are biofilms commonly removed?

29. Electron microscopy is a technique commonly used to analyze matrix proteins. Why is this technique chosen instead of others?

30. Given their plentiful nature, you might expect there to be more structural analysis (X-ray diffraction and nuclear magnetic resonance [NMR]) studies performed on matrix proteins. What technical issues have hindered these studies?

31. Lysyl oxidase catalyzes cross-links between lysine residues in the matrix. Examine the structure of desmosine and isodesmosine. Can you determine the source of the ring carbons? Could any amino acid other than lysine participate in this reaction? What forces are helping to stabilize this cross-link?

32. Cross-linking is commonly seen in disulfide bonds but rarely in lysines and glutamines. Suggest why it is that we only see these cross-linking reactions in the matrix.

Data Interpretation

33. Question 33 pertains to a series of three electron micrographs obtained from a paper that examines the effect of the drug cantospermine on glycogen metabolism. (Molyneux et al., PNAS 82 pp 93–97 1985.)

R Saul, J J Ghidoni, R J Molyneux, and A D Elbein / *Castanospermine inhibits alpha-glucosidase activities and alters glycogen distribution in animals* / Published January 1, 1985, National Academy of Sciences

The image is a control image of an electron micrograph of a rat liver stained with alkaline lead citrate and uranyl acetate.

  a. Lead acetate and uranyl acetate are not used in light microscopy. Why are they used in electron microscopy?

  b. Which organelles can you identify in this image? How do they compare to illustrations you have seen in print?

  c. Why do some structures in this image appear darker than others?

  d. What are the darkest images in this micrograph?

Molyneux et al., PNAS 82 pp 93–97 1985

This second image has been prepared in the same way, but it is from a rat given the drug castanospermine.

  e. How has the image changed?

  f. Which organelles can you recognize now?

  g. How has the staining changed?

Molyneux et al., PNAS 82 pp 93–97 1985

In this third image, castanospermine-treated liver samples were digested with amylase after the cells had been fixed and sliced.

  h. What role does amylase serve in the body?

  i. What reaction does amylase catalyze?

  j. How is amylase being used in this instance?

  k. How does this image differ from the other two?

  l. What does this data show?

  m. What is the effect of treating animals with castanospermine?

Experimental Design

34. Kefiran, the exopolysaccharide produced by bacteria in kefir grains, has a ratio of glucose to galactose of about 1:1. Based on what you know of other polysaccharides, what would you propose is the structure of kefiran? How might this molecule be synthesized by these bacteria? How could you test your hypotheses for the structure, and how could it be synthesized?

35. Design an experiment to determine the degree of glycosylation, the amount of carbohydrate, in a membrane glycoprotein you have been studying.

36. Propose a way to measure glycogen levels in a dish of cultured cells.

37. Design an experiment to test whether a protein of interest is bound to a membrane via a GPI anchor.

38. How could you show that two matrix proteins were interacting in the extracellular matrix?

Ethics and Social Responsibility

39. This chapter discussed tissue engineering. Currently, tens of thousands of people are on waiting lists for organ transplants. Are you an organ donor? If not, what keeps you from becoming one?

40. Given the involvement of biofilms in human disease, do you think that more funding should be dedicated toward basic research into biofilms? Propose a source of this funding.

41. Many athletes who run marathons take advantage of carbo-loading. That is, using a dietary plan, they deplete muscle glycogen leading up to a big race and then supposedly build large stores to use on race day. Using drugs or artificially increasing your red blood cell count is considered illegal in sporting events. Why is dietary manipulation of glycogen stores not illegal? At what point does training become doping?

42. Many of the inherited diseases mentioned in this chapter are incurable, despite advances in science. Often, we know what is wrong in a particular disease but cannot cure it. Does this situation give hope to people with such disorders, or does it simply make the problem more frustrating?

43. There are 14 common mutations for CFTR, the gene coding for the chloride channel that is defective in cystic fibrosis. Would you want to know whether you were a carrier for a CF mutation? How would you use that information? How might others use that same information?

Suggested Readings

8.1 Glycogen Metabolism

Chaikuad, A., D. S. Froese, G. Berridge, F. von Delft, U. Oppermann, and W. W. Yue. "Conformational Plasticity of Glycogenin and Its Maltosaccharide Substrate During Glycogen Biogenesis." *Proceedings of the National Academy of Sciences of the United States of America* 108 (2011): 21028–33.

Gibbons, B. J., P. J. Roach, and T. D. Hurley. "Crystal Structure of the Autocatalytic Initiator of Glycogen Biosynthesis, Glycogenin." *Journal of Molecular Biology* 319, no. 2 (2000): 463–77.

Juhlin-Dannfelt, A. C., S. E. Terblanche, R. D. Fell, J. C. Young, and J. O. Holloszy. "Effects of Beta-Adrenergic Receptor Blockade on Glycogenolysis During Exercise." *Journal of Applied Physiology* 53, no. 3 (September 1982): 549–54.

Whelan, W. "Pride and Prejudice: The Discovery of the Primer for Glycogen Synthesis." *Journal of Protein Science* 7, no. 9 (1998): 2038–41.

8.2 The Pentose Phosphate Pathway

Cappellini, M. D., and G. Fiorelli. "Glucose-6-Phosphate Dehydrogenase Deficiency." *Lancet* 371, no. 9606 (2008): 64–74.

Dentin R., J. Girard, and C. Postic. "Carbohydrate Responsive Element Binding Protein (ChREBP) and Sterol Regulatory Element Binding Protein-1c (SREBP-1c): Two Key Regulators of Glucose Metabolism and Lipid Synthesis in Liver." *Biochimie* 87, no. 1 (2005): 81–6.

Glogauer, M. "Disorders of Phagocyte Function." Chap. 175 in *Cecil Medicine*, 23rd ed. Edited by L. Goldman and D. Ausiello. Philadelphia, PA: Saunders Elsevier, 2007.

Iizuka, K., and Y. Horikawa. "ChREBP: A Glucose-Activated Transcription Factor Involved in the Development of Metabolic Syndrome." *Endocrine Journal* 55, no. 4 (2008): 617–24.

Uyeda, K., and J. J. Repa. "Carbohydrate Response Element Binding Protein, ChREBP, a Transcription Factor Coupling Hepatic Glucose Utilization and Lipid Synthesis." *Cell Metabolism* 4, no. 2 (2006): 107–10.

Uyeda K., H. Yamashita, and T. Kawaguchi. "Carbohydrate Responsive Element-Binding Protein (ChREBP): A Key Regulator of Glucose Metabolism and Fat Storage." *Biochemical Pharmacology* 63, no. 12 (2002): 2075–80.

8.3 Carbohydrates in Glycoconjugates

Adam, A., N. Montpas, D. Keire, A. Désormeaux, N. J. Brown, F. Marceau, and B. Westenberger. "Bradykinin Forming Capacity of Oversulfated Chondroitin Sulfate Contaminated Heparin in Vitro." *Biomaterials* 31, no. 22 (2010): 5741–8.

Guerrini, M., D. Beccati, Z. Shriver, A. Naggi, K. Viswanathan, A. Bisio, I. Ishan Capila, et al. "Oversulfated Chondroitin Sulfate Is a Contaminant in Heparin Associated with Adverse Clinical Events." *Nature Biotechnology* 26 (2009): 669–75.

Han, L., M. Monné, H. Okumura, T. Schwend, A. L. Cherry, D. Flot, T. Matsuda, and L. Jovine. "Insights into Egg Coat Assembly and Egg-Sperm Interaction from the X-Ray Structure of Full-Length ZP3." *Cell* 143, no. 3 (2010): 404–15.

Hang, H. C., and C. R. Bertozzi. "The Chemistry and Biology of Mucin-Type O-Linked Glycosylation." *Bioorganic & Medicinal Chemistry* 13, no. 17 (September 1, 2005): 5021–34.

Knudson, C. B., and W. Knudson. "Cartilage Proteoglycans." *Seminars in Cell and Developmental Biology* 12, no. 2 (2001): 69–78.

Monné, M., L. Han, T. Schwend, S. Burendahl, and L. Jovine. "Crystal Structure of the ZP-N Domain of ZP3 Reveals the Core Fold of Animal Egg Coats." *Nature* 456, no. 7222 (2008): 653–7.

Peter-Katalinić, J. "Methods in Enzymology: O-Glycosylation of Proteins." *Methods in Enzymology* 405 (2005): 139–71.

Rankin, T., and J. Dean. "The Zona Pellucida: Using Molecular Genetics to Study the Mammalian Egg Coat." *Reviews of Reproduction* 5, no. 2 (2000): 114–21.

Schrager, J. "The Chemical Composition and Function of Gastrointestinal Mucus." *Gut* 11, no. 5 (1970): 450–6.

Tian, E., and K. G. Ten Hagen. "Recent Insights into the Biological Roles of Mucin-Type O-Glycosylation." *Glycoconjugate Journal* 26, no. 3 (April 2009): 325–34.

Wassarman, P. M. "Zona Pellucida Glycoproteins." *Journal of Biological Chemistry* 283, no. 36 (2008): 24285–9.

8.4 Extracellular Matrices and Biofilms

Alkawareek, M. Y., Q. T. Algwari, G. Laverty, S. P. Gorman, W. G. Graham, D. O'Connell, and B. F. Gilmore. "Eradication of *Pseudomonas aeruginosa* Biofilms by Atmospheric Pressure Non-Thermal Plasma." *PLoS One* 7, no. 8 (2012): 44289.

Blanc, P. J. "Characterization of the Tea Fungus Metabolites." *Biotechnology Letters* 18, no. 2 (1996): 139–42.

Cao, Y., J. P. Vacanti, K. T. Paige, J. Upton, and C. A. Vacanti. "Transplantation of Chondrocytes Utilizing a Polymer-Cell Construct to Produce Tissue-Engineered Cartilage in the Shape of a Human Ear." *Plastic and Reconstructive Surgery* 100, no. 2 (1997): 297–302.

CNN. "Ricin Dart Fired by Umbrella Killed Bulgarian Envoy." Retrieved from http://edition.cnn.com/2008/US/02/29/ricin.cases/index.html

Colognato, H., and P. D. Yurchenco. "Form and Function: The Laminin Family of Heterotrimers." *Developmental Dynamics* 218, no. 2 (2000): 213–34.

Costerton, J. W., P. S. Stewart, and E. P. Greenberg. "Bacterial Biofilms: A Common Cause of Persistent Infections." *Science* 284 (1999): 1318–22.

Csiszar, K. "Lysyl Oxidases: A Novel Multifunctional Amine Oxidase Family." *Progress in Nucleic Acid Research and Molecular Biology* 70 (2001): 1–32.

Endo, Y., and K. Tsurugi. "The RNA *N*-Glycosidase Activity of Ricin A-Chain. The Characteristics of the Enzymatic Activity of Ricin

A-Chain with Ribosomes and with rRNA." *Journal of Biological Chemistry* 263, no. 18 (1988): 8735–9.

Epstein, A. K., T. S. Wong, R. A. Belisle, E. M. Boggs, and J. Aizenberg. "Liquid-Infused Structured Surfaces with Exceptional Anti-Biofouling Performance." *Proceedings of the National Academy of Sciences of the United States of America* 109, no. 33 (2012): 13182–7.

Garrote, G. L., A. G. Abraham, and G. L. De Antoni. "Chemical and Microbiological Characterization of Kefir Grains." *Journal of Dairy Research* 68, no. 4 (2001): 639–52.

Gorres, K. L., and R. T. Raines. "Prolyl 4-Hydroxylase." *Critical Reviews in Biochemistry and Molecular Biology* 45, no. 2 (2010): 106–24.

Hall-Stoodley, L., J. W. Costerton, and P. Stoodley. "Bacterial Biofilms: From the Natural Environment to Infectious Diseases." *Nature Reviews Microbiology* 2 (2004): 95–108.

Larivier, J. W., P. Kooiman, and K. Schmidt. "Kefiran a Novel Polysaccharide Produced in Kefir Grain by *Lactobacillus brevis*." *Archives of Microbiology* 59, no. 1–3 (1967): 269–70.

Lopez, D., H. Vlamakis, and R. Kolter. "Biofilms." In *Cold Spring Harbor Perspectives in Biology* (June 2010). doi: 10.1101/cshperspect.a000398

Marsh, P. D. "Contemporary Perspective on Plaque Control." *British Dental Journal* 212, no. 12 (2012): 601–6.

Mayser, P., S. Frommer, C. Leitzmann, and K. Gründer. "The Yeast Spectrum of the Tea Fungus Kombucha." *Mycoses* 38, no. 7–8 (1995): 289–95.

Miller, M. B., and B. L. Bassler. "Quorum Sensing in Bacteria." *Annual Review of Microbiology* 55 (2001): 165–199.

National Science Foundation (U.S.A.) (2004). The Emergence of Tissue Engineering as a Research Field. Retrieved from https://www.nsf.gov/pubs/2004/nsf0450/start.htm

Nerem, R. M. *Principles of Tissue Engineering*, 2nd ed. Edited by Joseph Vacanti, R. P. Lanza, and Robert S. Langer. Boston, MA: Academic Press, 2000.

Saul, R., J. J. Ghidoni, R. J. Molyneux, and A. D. Elbein. "Castanospermine Inhibits Alpha-Glucosidase Activities and Alters Glycogen Distribution in Animals." *Proceedings of the National Academy of Sciences of the United States of America* 82 no. 1 (January 1985): 93–7.

Seneviratne, C. J., C. F. Zhang, L. P. Samaranayake, and J. Chin. "Dental Plaque Biofilm in Oral Health and Disease." *Journal of Dental Research* 14, no. 2 (2011): 87–94.

Simova, E., D. Beshkova, A. Angelov, T. S. Hristozova, G. Frengova, and Z. Spasov. "Lactic Acid Bacteria and Yeasts in Kefir Grains and Kefir Made from Them." *Journal of Industrial Microbiology and Biotechnology* 28, no. 1 (2002): 1–6.

Singh, P. K., A. L. Schaefer, M. R. Parsek, T. O. Moninger, M. J. Welsh, and E. P. Greenberg. "Quorum-Sensing Signals Indicate That Cystic Fibrosis Lungs Are Infected with Bacterial Biofilms." *Nature* 407, no. 6805 (2002): 762–4.

Stoodley, P., K. Sauer, D. G. Davies, and J. W. Costerton. "Biofilms as Complex Differentiated Communities." *Annual Review of Microbiology* 56, (2002): 187–209.

Tada, S., Y. Katakura, K. Ninomiya, and S. Shioya. "Fed-Batch Coculture of *Lactobacillus kefiranofaciens* with *Saccharomyces cerevisiae* for Effective Production of Kefiran." *Journal of Bioscience and Bioengineering* 103, no. 6 (2007): 557–62.

Ullrich, M. *Bacterial Polysaccharides: Current Innovations and Future Trends.* Cambridge, MA: Caister Academic Press, 2009.

Carbohydrates II

5th century BCE —— Pythagoras commands followers to avoid fava beans, potentially due to favism

1888 —— Ricin is first lectin to be discovered and purified

1901 —— Karl Landsteiner discovers three different blood groups

1929 —— Von Gierke's disease is characterized
1930 —— Karl Landsteiner is awarded the Nobel Prize

1947 —— Carl and Gerty Cori win the Nobel Prize with Bernardo Houssay for hormonal control of carbohydrate metabolism

1960 —— Luis Leloir studies sugar nucleotides in polysaccharide biosynthesis in the 1960s
1970 —— Luis Leloir is awarded the Nobel Prize
1971 —— Earl Sutherland is awarded the Nobel Prize for cAMP

1991 —— Edwin Krebs wins the Nobel Prize for phosphorylase kinase

2000 —— Glycogen phosphorylase structure determined (PDB ID 1EM6)

2012 —— Lefkowitz and Kobilka win the Nobel Prize for G protein coupled receptors
First G protein coupled receptor structure published

CHAPTER 9

Lipids I

Fatty Acids, Steroids, and Eicosanoids; Beta-Oxidation and Fatty Acid Biosynthesis

© University of Georgia Research Foundation, Inc.

Lipids form the membranes of cells, are stored for future use as a fuel, or can serve as signaling molecules.

Lipids in Context

Lipids are perhaps the most maligned class of biological molecules. Many people consider fats the bane of those trying to lose weight. While many people may not know that cholesterol and steroids are lipids, they do associate them with negative thoughts. Cholesterol is viewed as a cause of blocked arteries, heart attacks, and stroke, whereas steroids are synonymous with disgraced athletes and are blamed for acne, mood swings, and unwarranted aggression. Yet, for all their bad press, we cannot live without these molecules: lipids are essential not only to human life but to *all* life.

Lipids are a diverse set of biomolecules unified by a single property: hydrophobicity. However, there is no single unifying structure among lipids. Lipids include cholesterol, corticosteroids, eicosanoids, fatty acids, and phospholipids and have a range of functions:

- Phospholipids in lipid bilayers separate the inside of the cell from the outside environment and form the defining perimeter of most organelles. They also can play important roles in signaling.
- Cholesterol is another membrane component in some cells where it helps maintain the fluidity of the lipid bilayer.
- Steroid hormones made from cholesterol are critical for sexual development, reproduction, and regulation of mineral balance in higher organisms.
- Fatty acids stored as triacylglycerols in adipose (fat) tissue serve to insulate and cushion vital organs.
- Eicosanoids and certain other lipids act as signaling molecules, regulating functions such as blood pressure, pain, inflammation, and labor and delivery.

This chapter begins with descriptions of the properties and functions of several of the major classes of lipids. We then discuss the degradation and biosynthesis of fatty acids, and the biosynthesis of ketone bodies and cholesterol. In each of these pathways, the discussion highlights the steps in the pathway, the mechanisms of reactions where applicable, and the regulation of the pathway. Finally, the chapter closes with the biosynthesis of eicosanoids and endocannabinoids, two important classes of signaling molecules. These molecules and their relationships are depicted in **Dynamic Figure 9.1**.

CHAPTER OUTLINE

9.1 Properties, Nomenclature, and Biological Functions of Lipid Molecules

9.2 Fatty Acid Catabolism

9.3 Fatty Acid Biosynthesis

9.4 Ketone Body Metabolism

9.5 Steroid Metabolism

9.6 Eicosanoid and Endocannabinoid Metabolism

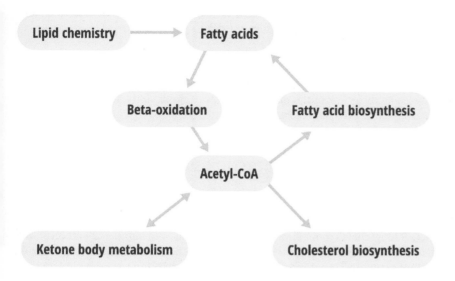

DYNAMIC FIGURE 9.1 Lipids are generically identified as hydrophobic biomolecules. Among the simplest lipids are the fatty acids. These molecules can be catabolized into acetyl-CoA through β-oxidation or can be found esterified to hydroxyl groups in cholesteryl esters, phospholipids, and triacylglycerols. Cholesteryl esters and triacylglycerols are the storage forms of cholesterol and fatty acids, whereas phospholipids form lipid bilayers and play roles in signal transduction. Fatty acids can be liberated from phospholipids to form eicosanoids, a powerful class of signaling molecules. Cholesterol, another membrane component, also serves as the precursor in the synthesis of bile salts and steroid hormones.

COMMON THEMES

Evolution's outcomes are conserved.	• Comparison of the major enzymes of fatty acid biosynthesis (acetyl-CoA carboxylase ACC and fatty acid synthase FAS) gives insights as to how this pathway has evolved.
	• Analysis of different species reveals that genes coding for the proteins and enzymes responsible for the synthesis of certain molecules, such as some steroids and eicosanoids, have evolved more recently; hence, these molecules may address needs that are lacking in simpler species.
Structure determines function.	• The structure of different lipids partially dictates their function; for example, amphipathic phospholipids form bilayers, whereas nonpolar triacylglycerols provide an anhydrous energy source.
	• The hydrophobic effect causes amphipathic lipids to form structures such as bilayers, micelles, and vesicles.
	• The structure of many enzymes in these pathways is conserved both within a single organism and between different species.
	• A common set of chemical reactions are used in the metabolism of lipids and in biosynthesis of different lipids.
Biochemical information is transferred, exchanged, and stored.	• Lipids can serve as important signaling molecules and second messengers.
Biomolecules are altered through pathways involving transformations of energy and matter.	• Reactions that are energetically unfavorable become favorable when coupled to reactions with large, negative ΔG values; we often think of this in terms of ATP hydrolysis, but other bonds with a large negative ΔG of hydrolysis, such as thioesters, are common in lipid biochemistry. Likewise, as we have seen elsewhere, reactions that have $\Delta G°$ values close to zero can be tipped to move in the forward or reverse direction by changing the concentrations of substrates or products.
	• Fatty acids and ketone bodies are synthesized and degraded using similar reactions. Different biochemical pathways and compartmentalization result in biosynthesis of fatty acids or β-oxidation. This is similar to the situation seen with glycolysis and gluconeogenesis.
	• Similar chemical patterns are found in β-oxidation, fatty acid synthesis, and ketone body synthesis and breakdown. Some of these reactions were discussed in the citric acid cycle.

9.1 Properties, Nomenclature, and Biological Functions of Lipid Molecules

This section provides an overview of the main categories of lipids: fatty acids, neutral lipids, phospholipids, steroids, bile salts, and eicosanoids.

9.1.1 Fatty acids are a common building block of many lipids

Fatty acids are components of neutral lipids, phospholipids, and eicosanoids. Typically, fatty acids are unbranched long-chain carboxylic acids, containing an even number of carbon atoms, generally between 12 and 26 with 16 and 18 carbons being the most common (**Figure 9.2**). Fatty acids are either **saturated** (no double bonds), **monounsaturated** (one double bond), or **polyunsaturated** (multiple double bonds). Unless otherwise noted, all double bonds in fatty acids can be assumed to be in the *cis* conformation. Figure 9.2 illustrates the notation system used to describe fatty acids. The number of carbon atoms and the number of double bonds are separated by a colon. The position of a double bond is designated by a superscript Greek delta, Δ, followed by the position of the first carbon of each double bond; for example, a double bond between C-9 and C-10 would be denoted Δ^9. Common polyunsaturated fatty acids do not have conjugated double bonds and instead have a single methylene unit between double bonded carbons.

Because of the way fatty acids are synthesized, elongated (extended beyond 16 carbons in length), and desaturated (how double bonds are incorporated), many fatty acids are also characterized by the position of the double bond farthest from the carboxyl group. The carbon farthest from the carboxyl group within that double bond is given the designation ω (omega, the last letter in the Greek alphabet); hence, we find **ω-3, ω-6**, ω-7, or ω-9 fatty acids, counting from the terminal carbon. The melting points of fatty acids vary widely, but some common

Oleic acid 18:1$^{\Delta 9}$

FIGURE 9.2 **Structure of oleic acid and major categories of fatty acids.** **A.** Fatty acids are long-chain, even-numbered carboxylic acids. They may be unsaturated (like oleic acid) in which instance they almost always have *cis* double bonds. **B.** Palmitic, palmitoleic, and linolenic acids are all fatty acids. Palmitic (16:0) is a saturated fatty acid, palmitoleic (16:1$^{\Delta 9}$) is a monounsaturated fatty acid, and linolenic (18:2$^{\Delta 9,12}$) is a polyunsaturated fatty acid. Note how the inclusion of *cis* double bonds introduces kinks into the carbon chain. Highly polyunsaturated fatty acids are kinked to the point of being almost circular in shape.

| Palmitic acid 16:0 | Palmitoleic acid 16:1$^{\Delta 9}$ | Linolenic acid 18:1$^{\Delta 9, 12}$ |

TABLE 9.1 Some Common Fatty Acids

Description	Common name	IUPAC name	Source	Melting point	ω-nomenclature
12:0	Lauric acid	Dodecanoic acid	Bay leaves	44.2	–
14:0	Myristic acid	Tetradecanoic acid	Coconut oil	53.9	–
16:0	Palmitic acid	Hexadecanoic acid	Palm oil	63.1	–
18:0	Stearic acid	Octadecanoic acid	Beef tallow	69.6	–
20:0	Arachidic acid	Eicosanoic acid	Peanut oil	76.5	–
$16:1^{\Delta 9}$	Palmitoleic acid	cis-9-hexadecenoic acid	Animal fats	1	ω-7
$18:1^{\Delta 9}$	Oleic acid	cis-9-octadecaenoic acid	Olive oil	13.4	ω-9
$18:2^{\Delta 9, 12}$	Linoleic acid	cis-, cis-9, 12-octadecadienoic acid	Safflower oil	−5	ω-6
$18:3^{\Delta 9, 12, 15}$	α-Linolenic	cis-, cis-, cis-9, 12, 15 octadecadienoic acid	Safflower oil	−11	ω-3
$20:3^{\Delta 8, 11, 14}$	DGLA, dihomogamma linolenic acid	Eicosatrienoic acid	Fish oil (rare)	~−5	ω-6
$20:4^{\Delta 5,8,11,14}$	Arachidonic acid	Eicosatetraenoic acid		−49.5	ω-6
$20:5^{\Delta 5,8,11,14,17}$	EPA	Eicosapentaenoic acid		~−50	ω-3
$22:6^{\Delta 4,7,10,13,16,19}$	DHA	Docosahexaenoic acid		−44	ω-3

trends emerge. As the fatty acid gets longer, the melting point increases. However, incorporation of double bonds greatly decreases the melting point (**Table 9.1**).

Fatty acids are typically known by their common name (stearic acid), or an International Union of Pure and Applied Chemistry [IUPAC] name such as octadecanoic acid, 18:0.

Fatty acids: acid-base properties
Because fatty acids contain a carboxyl group, they act as weak acids. The pK_a of the carboxyl group is about 4.5, similar to other carboxylic acids such as amino acids or the intermediates of the citric acid cycle. Fatty acids are generally ionized (approximately 99.9%) at pH 7.4. In the laboratory, to increase the percentage of ionized species and thus make the molecule more soluble in aqueous solutions, the acid is often reacted with a strong base to generate a carboxylic acid salt or a carboxylate. Carboxylic acids, the protonated species, are distinct from carboxylates, the deprotonated species, and it is not surprising that the two forms have different properties and reactivity.

Fatty acids are typically found as esters or amides. Amides are referred to as peptides in protein chemistry but as amides in the lipid literature. Both ester and amide linkages are

WORKED PROBLEM 9.1 | Characterizing a fatty acid

Linolenic acid is $18:3^{\Delta 9, 12, 15}$. What is the omega designation of linolenic acid?

Strategy Examine Figure 9.2. Think about what the omega designation tells us. It may be useful to draw the structure of linolenic acid.

Solution Linolenic acid has the following structure:

The omega carbon is the final carbon. The double bond closest to that carbon is on the third carbon from the end, making this a ω-3 fatty acid.

Follow-up question Using Table 9.1, identify this fatty acid:

frequently observed in lipid chemistry. The term **free fatty acid** is reserved for fatty acids that are not part of an ester or an amide.

With a long, nonpolar hydrophobic tail at one end of the molecule and a polar carboxylate group at the other end, fatty acids are considered **amphipathic**, literally meaning having "both feelings," because they contain both hydrophobic and hydrophilic groups and are thus both water-loving and water-hating. The term amphipathic is also used to describe α helices having both a polar and a nonpolar face.

Fatty acids: assembly into higher order structures
Like other amphipathic molecules, fatty acids exhibit interesting properties when dissolved in water. At a very low concentration, fatty acids are found as single molecules in solution, but at higher concentrations, they aggregate into a roughly spherical structure known as a **micelle** (**Figure 9.3**). Within the micelle, the hydrophobic tails are oriented toward the waterless core of the sphere and the hydrophilic head groups are oriented toward the solvent. This structure maximizes the interaction of the polar head groups with water while shielding the hydrophobic tails. Similar to protein folding, when hydrophobic molecules are clustered together, water molecules are effectively freed from having to cage these molecules. Formation of a micelle appears to result in an apparent gain of organization and loss of entropy; however, the reverse is true when looking at the larger picture. The gain in entropy as a result of liberating water makes the overall Δ*S positive*. The free energy (Δ*G*) of the assembly of micelles is therefore negative, and the process is spontaneous. This is another illustration of the **hydrophobic effect**.

The concentration at which micelles form is called the **critical micellar concentration** (or CMC). The CMC is a property of all amphipathic molecules, including all detergents and many lipids and differs for each molecule. For fatty acids, the CMC is typically in the range of 1 to 6 μM; below this concentration, fatty acids are found as monomers in solution, and above it, they spontaneously assemble into micelles. The micelles exist in a dynamic equilibrium with monomeric (single) fatty acids in solution. Increasing the concentration of fatty acids above the CMC increases the *number* of micelles found in a sample but not the *size* of the micelles. When working with an amphipathic molecule in the laboratory, it is useful to know

FIGURE 9.3 **Micelle formation results in increased degrees of freedom for water.** **A.** In a micelle, amphipathic molecules are oriented with their hydrophobic tails toward the center of the micelle and their hydrophilic head groups oriented toward the aqueous surroundings. Note that micelles have no water in their core. Micelles form as a result of the hydrophobic effect. **B.** Shown is an isolated amphipathic molecule surrounded by water molecules. Water molecules can hydrogen bond to the polar head group but form a cage around the hydrophobic tail. **C.** Fewer water molecules are organized around a micelle than around a similar number of monomeric amphiphiles. Despite the apparent gain of organization and loss of entropy in the organization of a micelle, the gain in entropy as a result of liberating water makes the overall Δ*S* positive. The free energy (Δ*G*) of the assembly of micelles is therefore negative, and the process is spontaneous.

A. Monoglycerides and diglycerides

B. Triacylglycerols

Monoacylglycerol   Diacylglycerol   Saturated fat   Monounsaturated fat   Polyunsaturated fat

FIGURE 9.4 **Other examples of glycerides.** **A.** Shown is an example of a monoglyceride and a diglyceride, or monoacylglycerol and diacylglycerol. **B.** The second example shows saturated, mono-unsaturated, and polyunsaturated triacylglycerols.

the CMC. Below the CMC, amphipathic molecules will partition into membranes; at concentrations above the CMC, membranes will begin to dissolve.

9.1.2 Neutral lipids are storage forms of fatty acids or cholesterol

Because fatty acids are carboxylic acids and are amphipathic, they can act as detergents and affect pH—properties that could be harmful to the organism. Therefore, fatty acids are stored as **neutral lipids**, which lack charged groups because the carboxylic acid group is esterified to either glycerol or cholesterol.

Fatty acids esterified to glycerol form a **monoacylglycerol** (one fatty acid), **diacylglyc-erol** (two fatty acids), or **triacyclglycerol** (three fatty acids); these molecules are also referred to as a **monoglyceride**, **diglyceride**, or **triglyceride**, respectively (**Figure 9.4**).

If a glyceride contains only saturated fatty acids (no double bonds), it is called a saturated fat; if it contains at least one fatty acid that has a single double bond, it is termed a monoun-saturated fat; and if it contains at least one fatty acid with multiple double bonds, it is known as a polyunsaturated fat. Glycerides can be crudely categorized as fats or oils based on their melting points; fats are solid at room temperature, whereas oils are liquid at room temperature. A saturated fat is solid at room temperature because the straight chains of the fatty acids allow the molecules to pack tightly together. Saturated fats commonly come from animal origins, such as tallow from cows or lard from pigs. Unsaturated fats are liquid at room temperature because the kinked *cis* double bonds prevent the molecules from packing tightly together. Common sources of unsaturated fats are vegetables, such as corn, soy, or canola, and cold-water fish, such as salmon.

Although plant oils are readily available, they are less desirable for some food and cook-ing applications than solid fats because of their physical properties. For example, solid fats are preferred for baked and fried products. Hence, vegetable oils used in processed foods are often hydrogenated, that is, chemically treated with hydrogen gas and a catalyst to convert some of the unsaturated fatty acids into saturated ones. The complete conversion of all the *cis* double bonds in a vegetable oil results in a product that has too high a melting point and a waxy taste and feel. Therefore, oils are often partially hydrogenated. This partial reaction can result in the naturally occurring *cis* fatty acids being isomerized to *trans* fatty acids, forming ***trans* fats**. The properties of *trans* fats are similar to those of saturated fats; they are metab-olized differently than either saturated or *cis* fatty acids. Although low quantities of *trans* fatty acids do occur naturally in some bacteria and ruminants, organisms have not evolved to metabolize large quantities of *trans* fats. It is possible to remove most of the *trans* fatty acids from processed foods. This is done by replacing the partially **hydrogenated fats** with blends of saturated and unsaturated fats that have similar physical properties to the hydrogenated fats.

trans Δ-9 double bond

FIGURE 9.5 **Structures of vitamins A and E.** Both vitamins A and E are fat-soluble vitamins and contain an ester moiety. For vitamin A (retinyl palmitate), this serves to protect the hydroxyl group from oxidation to an aldehyde or carboxylic acid until needed in the body. Vitamin E (tocopheryl acetate) is also frequently found as an ester—in this case an acetate. Again, this form of the vitamin is protected from premature oxidation by the ester. Vitamin A is found in foods such as tomatoes. Nuts are a rich source of vitamin E.

Vitamin A

Vitamin E

Fatty acids esterified to cholesterol yield **cholesteryl esters**, the main storage form of cholesterol. Cholesteryl esters form a large part of the plaque in arteries that leads to atherosclerosis and heart disease. Certain cells in the body also store cholesteryl esters as a cholesterol reserve, used to produce steroid hormones.

Fatty acids and cholesterol are not the only molecules stored as esters. Retinyl palmitate, a storage form of vitamin A, is an ester of retinol and palmitic acid. The esterification protects the hydroxyl group of retinol from oxidation to an aldehyde or carboxylic acid until the vitamin is needed in the body. Vitamin E is often administered in an esterified form, as tocopheryl acetate or succinate; the esterification prevents oxidation of the alcohol and thus helps to stabilize the compound (**Figure 9.5**). The ester bond is cleaved in the stomach, and the free alcohol (tocopherol) is absorbed and used by the body.

Another class of neutral lipids worth mentioning is the **waxes**. These molecules are long-chain fatty acids esterified to a long-chain alcohol termed a fatty alcohol; waxes are lengthy and hydrophobic (**Figure 9.6**). Organisms produce and secrete these molecules as protective coatings that provide some degree of natural waterproofing and prevent desiccation. The best known include bee's wax; carnauba wax; jojoba oil; lanolin; and spermaceti, the wax found in the head of sperm whales. Lanolin, also known as wool grease, is secreted by sheep to assist in waterproofing their wool and skin. Found in many skin creams and lotions, lanolin differs from the other waxes mentioned above because the alcohol forming the ester is cholesterol rather than a fatty alcohol.

9.1.3 Phospholipids are important in membrane formation

Phospholipids are lipid molecules that contain a phosphate moiety. The hydrophilic nature of the phosphate group and the hydrophobic nature of the aliphatic lipid make these molecules amphipathic. Phospholipids are considered **polar lipids** and are the main structural component of membranes. Many phospholipids are also involved in signal transduction and act as lipid signaling mediators.

Triaconatyl palmitate
(bee's wax)

FIGURE 9.6 **Structure of waxes.** Waxes, such as triaconatyl palmitate, consist of long-chain fatty acids esterified to long-chain alcohols. The highly hydrophobic nature of these molecules makes them useful as protectants against desiccation.

Phospholipids can broadly be divided into two categories, depending on the type of backbone they contain. **Glycerophospholipids** have a glycerol backbone, whereas **sphingolipids** have a sphingosine backbone. Because of their structure and geometry, some of these molecules can form micelles, but many will form other more complex structures, such as lipid bilayers, monolayers, or vesicles, a bilayer surrounding an aqueous compartment (**Figure 9.7**).

Micelle   **Bilayer**   **Vesicle**

FIGURE 9.7 **Examples of phospholipid structures.**   Phospholipids can form a variety of structures, depending on the head group, type of acyl chain, and number of acyl chains (one versus two). These structures can include some of the ones we have seen previously, for example, micelles and bilayers. Phospholipids can also form structures such as vesicles, a bilayer structure containing an aqueous core.

Glycerophospholipids   Glycerophospholipids feature two fatty acyl chains and a phosphoalcohol esterified to a glycerol backbone. Fatty acids are found esterified in the first two positions on the glycerol backbone. A phosphate group is in the final position, attached through a phosphoester linkage. Also connected to the phosphate is an alcohol, again through a phosphoester linkage. The alcohol gives rise to the common names of these lipids (**Figure 9.8**).

A.

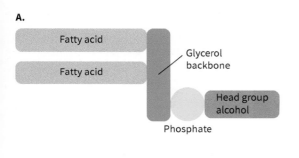

B.

C.

Glycerol—O—P—O[H]

Phosphatidate

Glycerol—O—P—O—CH_2—CH_2—NH_3^+

Phosphatidylethanolamine

Glycerol—O—P—O—CH_2—CH_2—N^+(CH_3)(CH_3)—CH_3

Phosphatidylcholine

Glycerol—O—P—O—CH_2—CH—NH_3^+ / COO^-

Phosphatidylserine

Glycerol—O—P—O—(inositol ring with OH OH HO OH OH)

Phosphatidylinositol

D.

Cardiolipin

FIGURE 9.8 **Structure of glycerophospholipids.**   **A.** and **B.** Glycerophospholipids feature two fatty acyl chains and a phosphoalcohol esterified to a glycerol backbone. The length and degree of unsaturation of the fatty acids may vary. The most significant difference between these molecules occurs in the head group alcohol. **C.** The five common most head groups of phospholipids. At physiological pH both the amine on the choline head group as well as the phosphate moiety are ionized making the molecule zwitterionic. **D.** Cardiolipin is a glycerophospholipid comprised of two molecules of phosphatidate connected by a central glycerol molecule. It is prevalent in mitochondrial membranes.

FIGURE 9.9 **Composition of lipid bilayers.** The lipid composition of a membrane varies from cell type to cell type and from organelle to organelle. Shown is the composition for three different membranes. The lipids shown are cholesterol, phosphatidylethanolamine (PE), phosphatidylcholine (PC), sphingomyelin (SM), phosphatidylserine (PS), cardiolipin (CL), and all other lipids.

Phosphatidylcholine and phosphatidylethanolamine both contain positively charged amine groups in addition to the negatively charged phosphate, and like amino acids they are zwitterionic at neutral pH. Phosphatidylinositol, phosphatidylserine, and phosphatidate are all important in signaling cascades. These molecules are termed anionic phospholipids or acidic phospholipids due to their net negative charge.

Phosphatidylcholine and phosphatidylethanolamine also form the bulk of the lipid in cell membranes (typically over 50%), although membrane composition varies within the cell (such as the plasma membrane compared to mitochondrial or ER membrane), within the organism (a hepatocyte compared to a rod or cone cell in the eye), and between different species (erythrocytes from a human and a cow) (**Figure 9.9**). Phospholipid concentrations are also different in the two bilayers of the plasma membrane. Typically, the cytosolic leaflet of the plasma membrane is enriched in acidic phospholipids: phosphatidate, phosphatidylserine, phosphatidylglycerol, and phosphatidylinositol.

A phospholipid containing a single acyl chain and a free hydroxyl group is termed a **lysophospholipid**.

Sphingolipids
Sphingolipids contain many of the same fatty acids and alcohols as glycerophospholipids but differ in the backbone alcohol. The backbone alcohol in sphingolipids is sphingosine, which has two free hydroxyls, an amine, and a long (16 carbons) monounsaturated hydrocarbon tail. The phosphate is esterified through the primary hydroxyl most distal from the fatty-acid tail. Fatty acids are attached via an amide linkage to the amine, and the secondary hydroxyl between the amide and the fatty tail is not usually modified in any way.

One of the first sphingolipids identified was sphingomyelin, a major component of the myelin sheath coating some neurons. More recently, sphingolipids have gained attention for their possible involvement in the regulation of apoptosis and anoikis (programmed cell death). In particular, ceramide, sphingosine, and sphingosine-1-phosphate generated from sphingomyelin have been shown to promote apoptosis (**Figure 9.10**).

WORKED PROBLEM 9.2 | Candy chemistry

Some candy bar labels state that the product contains soy lecithin, an emulsifier. Lecithin is another term for phosphatidylcholine. Describe how soy lecithin works as an emulsifier.

Strategy To answer this question we need to know what lecithin is and how an emulsifier works. We discussed phosphatidylcholine in this section, and we previously discussed emulsifiers. Drawing the structure of phosphatidylcholine will help us to explain which properties of this molecule make it an emulsifier.

Solution Emulsifiers are amphipathic molecules that act to suspend one type of molecule in another, such as a hydrophobic

molecule in an aqueous solvent. Soy lecithin is phosphatidylcholine obtained from soybeans. This phospholipid forms a micelle-like structure, coating and solubilizing fatty molecules in chocolate, for example. Within the micelles, the hydrophobic acyl chains are oriented toward the core of the particle and the polar head groups to the outside.

Follow-up question We have previously seen how other amphipathic molecules can act as detergents. Could soy lecithin be used as a detergent?

A.

Fatty acid

Sphingosine

Head group
alcohol

Phosphate

B.

C.

Sphingosine—O—P—O⋮H⋮

Phosphoceramide

Sphingosine—O—P—O—CH₂—CH₂—N⁺—CH₃

Sphingomyelin

FIGURE 9.10 **Structural examples of sphingophospholipids.** **A.** The backbone of these lipids is formed by the long-chain fatty alcohol sphingosine. **B.** A single fatty acid is attached via an amide linkage to sphingosine. **C.** Phosphoalcohols are attached via a phosphoester bond to the more terminal hydroxyl of sphingosine.

9.1.4 | All steroids and bile salts are derived from cholesterol

Steroids are a group of lipids with diverse functions but a common skeleton consisting of four fused rings. Variety among the steroids comes from incorporation of hydroxyl groups, carbonyl groups, and hydrocarbons around the ring system. **Cholesterol** is the most common steroid, and the one from which most other steroids are derived (**Figure 9.11**). It is an alcohol containing a single –OH group but is otherwise lacking in functional groups. The other steroids introduced in this section are steroid hormones (both sex hormones and corticosteroids) and bile salts.

In the cell, cholesterol is found within membranes and is oriented so that the hydroxyl moiety is away from the membrane core. Cholesterol is the master steroid, and it is found almost exclusively in animal tissue. Other organisms, such as plant sterols, have related compounds or employ other biochemistry, including modulating the fatty acyl composition of membranes to achieve the functions of cholesterol in animals. The fluidity of membranes is essential for a variety of functions including transport across the membrane, diffusion of proteins within the membrane, and membrane integrity; therefore, the concentration of cholesterol needs to be tightly controlled. At low concentrations, cholesterol maintains membrane fluidity by decreasing the interactions between lipids and proteins in the membrane; however, at higher concentrations, it decreases this fluidity.

Many steroids are also important signaling molecules. The two main classes of steroid hormones are the sex hormones and the corticosteroids. Cholesterol is converted into pregnenolone, and from that into a class of progestagens. The glucocorticoids, mineralocorticoids, and androgens are all derived from progestagens. Estrogens are derived from androgens, notably testosterone. All of these molecules share a common steroid skeleton, but they differ in the functional groups connected to that skeleton. A discussion of the role of steroid hormones in fertility and how hormones can be used to regulate fertility can be found in **Medical Biochemistry: Oral contraception.**

Steroid skeleton

Cholesterol

Estradiol

Testosterone

Cortisone

FIGURE 9.11 **Steroids.** All steroids have a common system of fused rings, and many steroids can be recognized by this characteristic shape. Shown are the steroid hormones estradiol, testosterone, and cortisone. Note the subtle differences in these structures that produce significant effects in growth and development or regulate fluid balance.

Medical Biochemistry

Oral contraception

Few drugs are as effective, successful, and controversial as oral contraceptives. Since their introduction in 1960, these drugs have been used by hundreds of millions of women worldwide. When used correctly, they are over 99.7% effective in preventing pregnancy, second only to surgical sterilization. The sheer number of people taking these drugs, combined with the issues surrounding their use—sexuality, morality, changing societal views, human rights, insurance coverage, and control of reproduction—continue to make these drugs among the most widely discussed and debated. It is little wonder that oral contraceptives are the one drug known as "The Pill."

Adam Hart-Davis/Science Photo Library/Getty Images

Progesterone

Norethindrone

Levonorgestrel

Mifepristone

From a biochemical perspective, human fertility is regulated by a cascade of both peptide and steroid hormones. Elevated progesterone levels from the ovary signal to the uterine lining (the endometrium) to prepare for an implanted embryo, should the egg become fertilized. If a fertilized egg does not implant in the endometrium, the cells in the ovary secreting hormones (the corpus luteum) die off, resulting in a drop in estrogen and progesterone levels. This also has the effect of shedding the endometrial lining, resulting in menstruation. However, if the egg is fertilized and implants in the endometrium, it begins to secrete human chorionic gonadotropin (a peptide hormone), which keeps the ovary secreting progesterone until later in the pregnancy when the placenta begins to play a larger role.

Oral contraceptives work by fooling the body into thinking that it is pregnant and thereby blocking or delaying ovulation. This is the only scientifically established mechanism of action of oral contraceptives; such methods do not work if an egg has been fertilized or if the woman is already pregnant. The drugs act by delivering a synthetic progesterone analog that blocks ovulation. The analog is needed because progesterone itself is poorly absorbed orally. Many oral contraceptives also contain estrogens, added to reduce adverse effects of the progesterone, such as breakthrough bleeding.

The development of oral contraceptives is a fascinating example of how biochemistry, and science in general, can influence history. It had been proposed in the early part of the twentieth century that steroid hormones might be able to regulate ovulation, and hence fertility, but these molecules were difficult and expensive to obtain from animal sources. The combined skills of chemists, biologists, and botanists led to the discovery of a species of Mexican yams that produced a precursor steroid that can be chemically converted in the lab into progesterone or progesterone analogs. This breakthrough, more than any other, permitted the development of oral contraception.

There are several alternative delivery systems for synthetic progesterone. In addition to the oral route, such contraception can be delivered via transdermal patches, subcutaneous implants, and intrauterine devices.

Recently, new drugs have arrived on the market, advertised as emergency birth control or the "morning after pill." It has been known for many years that taking larger than normal doses of regular birth control pills can block ovulation. The difference in these new formulations is that they are now in a single pill, and they can be purchased from a pharmacy without a clinical consultation. The medical value of this approach and the societal issues accompanying it continue to be debated.

Bile salts, such as cholic acid or taurocholic acid, are detergents synthesized from cholesterol by the liver, and stored in the gall bladder. The body uses bile (a combination of cholesterol, bile salts, and amphipathic proteins) to solubilize dietary lipids in the gut; the bile increases the surface area and facilitates the enzymatic degradation of the lipids.

Cholic acid

Taurocholic acid

Taurine

9.1.5 Eicosanoids are potent signaling molecules derived from 20-carbon polyunsaturated fatty acids

The term **eicosanoids** broadly describes molecules that are derived from 20-carbon polyunsaturated fatty acids. These fatty acids are arachidonic acid ($20:4^{\Delta 5,8,11,14}$), eicosapentaenoic acid

$(20:5^{\Delta 5,8,11,14,17})$ and dihomogamalinolenic acid $(20:3^{\Delta 11,14,17})$. Eicosanoids such as the prostaglandins and leukotrienes are potent signaling molecules that mediate distinct and diverse functions in the body. Although best known as mediators of pain and inflammation, they also help to regulate blood pressure, sleep–wake cycles, labor, and delivery. Nonsteroidal anti-inflammatory drugs (NSAIDs) block the production of these signaling molecules.

Arachidonic acid   **Prostaglandin E2**   **Leukotriene A4**

9.1 Summary

- Fatty acids are common components of many lipids. Their properties vary with their length and number of double bonds.
- Some lipids can be stored as esters. Triacylglycerols are stored fatty acids esterified to glycerol; cholesteryl esters are stored cholesterol esterified to a fatty acid.
- There are two major categories of phospholipids: glycerophospholipids (with a glycerol backbone) and sphingolipids (with a sphingosine backbone). Both are found in membranes and other similarly complex structures.
- Steroids are lipids with a common skeleton of four fused rings. Cholesterol, sex hormones, and bile salts are steroids. The properties and functions of these molecules vary depending on the functional groups attached to the skeleton. Steroids have diverse functions, including acting as a structural component of membranes, acting as signaling molecules, or acting as detergents.
- Eicosanoids are signaling molecules derived from 20-carbon polyunsaturated fatty acids.

9.1 Concept Check

- List those lipids that are polar and those that are nonpolar.
- Provide examples of each lipid and discuss the properties.
- Think about the lipid molecule's structure in a schematic way; for example, a triacylglycerol has three fatty acids esterified to a glycerol backbone.

9.2 | Fatty Acid Catabolism

The body's main store of energy is comprised of fatty acids esterified to glycerol as triacylglycerols. The highly reduced state and hydrophobic nature of triacylglycerols make them an ideal stored energy source. In contrast to carbohydrates, fats do not require water for hydration because they are stored in an anhydrous state. Compared to proteins and carbohydrates, the fats have the highest amount of energy per gram—9 Calories compared to the 4.5 Calories for proteins and carbohydrates.

The breakdown of fatty acids is known as **beta (β)-oxidation** because it occurs at the second carbon from the carboxyl functional group, that is, at the *beta* carbon or C-3. Beta-oxidation occurs in nearly every cell of the body; in some instances, for example, in the heart, it provides most of the energy requirements of the tissue. The oxidation occurs in the mitochondria. The process of moving fatty acids into the mitochondria requires them to be energetically activated. Activation for any molecule is achieved by coupling it to another molecule, which results in a product with different properties than the original. For example, in carbohydrate metabolism, glucose molecules need to be phosphorylated in the activation stage of glycolysis, before cleavage and energy return occur in subsequent stages. In the case of fatty acids, activation occurs through coupling to coenzyme A in the cytosol to form acyl-CoA. Once the acyl-CoA is formed, the reactions of β-oxidation are thermodynamically spontaneous, and no further energetic investment is required.

The energy to drive the formation of acyl-CoA comes from the hydrolysis of ATP into AMP and pyrophosphate (PPi), and the subsequent hydrolysis of PPi into two molecules of inorganic phosphate, P_i. The combined large negative $\Delta G°$ value of ATP and PPi hydrolysis is necessary to form the thioester linkage and makes this reaction essentially irreversible.

9.2.1 Fatty acids must be transported into the mitochondrial matrix before catabolism can proceed

Long-chain acyl-CoA (more than 16 carbons) are unable to penetrate the inner mitochondrial membrane. Instead, fatty acids are shuttled across the inner mitochondrial membrane as acylcarnitines. The fatty acid is transferred from CoA to carnitine (4-trimethylamino-3-hydroxybutarate). Carnitine palmitoyl transferase I (CPT I) catalyzes the transesterification from the thioester of the CoA to the ester of carnitine (**Figure 9.12**). Although CPT I catalyzes the transesterification of all long-chain acyl-CoA, the enzyme was first identified as catalyzing the transesterification of palmitoyl-CoA, and the name now represents the transesterification of all long-chain acyl-CoA. The formation of acylcarnitine by CPT I is thought to be the rate-determining step in β-oxidation. The transport of acylcarnitine into the mitochondria is mediated by carnitine carrier protein, also known as carnitine:acylcarnitine translocase, a membrane protein that exchanges free carnitine in the mitochondrial matrix for acylcarnitine in the intermembrane space. Once inside the mitochondrial matrix, a second transferase (CPT II) completes the reverse reaction to produce free carnitine and regenerate the acyl-CoA.

9.2.2 Fatty acids are oxidized to acetyl-CoA by β-oxidation

Each cycle of β-oxidation shortens a fatty acid by two carbon atoms. In each instance, a molecule of acetyl-CoA is removed from the fatty acid. Again, the group being oxidized is the β carbon. The process occurs in four steps:

1. **Formation of a double bond between the α and β carbons.** In the first step, a *trans*-Δ-2 double bond is incorporated between the α and β carbons in the fatty acyl-CoA. This is an oxidation reaction; the enzyme involved is acyl-CoA dehydrogenase, which uses FAD as a cofactor. FAD is often employed as a cofactor when a reaction incorporates a double bond, as happens in the citric acid cycle when succinate is oxidized to fumarate.

2. **Hydration of the double bond to an alcohol.** The second step of the pathway is a hydration reaction, in which enoyl-CoA hydratase adds a molecule of water in a hydration reaction to form an alcohol on the β carbon, yielding 3-L-Hydroxyacyl-CoA. The addition is stereospecific, and only the L isomer is formed.

3. **Oxidation of the alcohol to a ketone.** The third step is another oxidation reaction, as 3-L-Hydroxyacyl-CoA is converted to β-ketoacyl-CoA by 3-L-Hydroxyacyl-CoA dehydrogenase, an NAD^+-dependent enzyme. A molecule of $NADH/H^+$ is generated at this step.

4. **Cleavage of the carbon–carbon bond and formation of a new acyl-CoA linkage.** In the final step, a molecule of acetyl-CoA is cleaved from the β-ketoacyl-CoA by the enzyme β-ketothiolase. Although similar to other thiolases encountered in this chapter, this enzyme is specific for degradative pathways and preferentially uses the β-keto substrate. If the resulting acyl-CoA is four carbons or more in length, the molecule will undergo repeated cycles of β-oxidation until it has been oxidized into acetyl-CoA units. The final cycle of β-oxidation yields two molecules of acetyl-CoA.

In summary, the oxidation of a fatty acid proceeds in a stepwise fashion of oxidation, hydration, oxidation, and thiolysis that is similar to the citric acid cycle. If we examine the

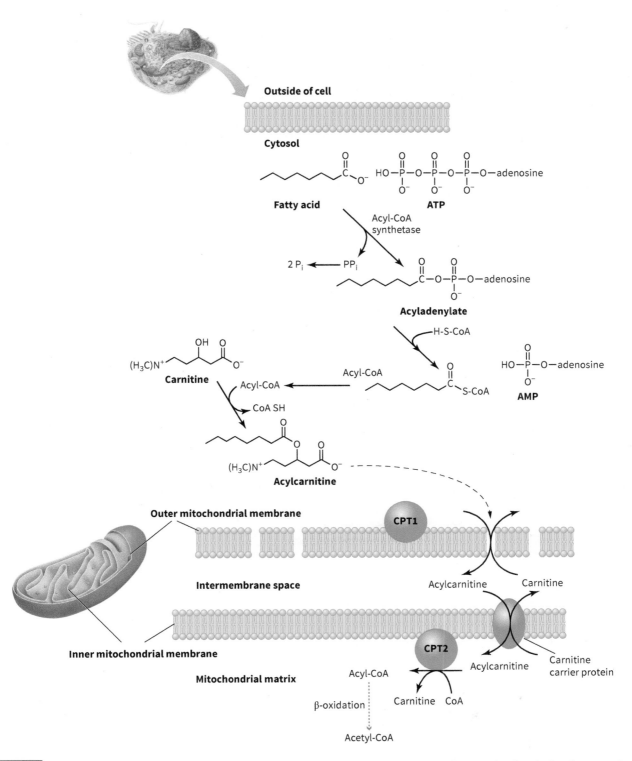

FIGURE 9.12 **Activation and delivery of fatty acids to the mitochondria.** Transfer of fatty acids into the mitochondrial matrix is a multistep process. First, fatty acids must be energetically activated by ATP and coupled to coenzyme A. Acyl-CoA is formed in a two-step process. A mixed anhydride is formed between the fatty acid and ATP. The energetic equivalent of two molecules of ATP (two phosphoanhydride bonds) are consumed in this process. Second, coenzyme A attacks the fatty acyl side of the anhydride to yield acyl-CoA and AMP. Energetic activation of molecules by ATP is also seen in glycolysis, glycogenesis, and protein synthesis. Following activation, the fatty acyl chains are transesterified to carnitine by carnitine palmitoyl transferase I (CPTI). The carnitine carrier protein can then shuttle these fatty acids into the mitochondrial matrix where carnitine palmitoyl transferase II (CPTII) can catalyze the reverse reaction (formation of a new acyl-CoA inside the mitochondrial matrix). Free carnitine is shuttled back through the membrane by carnitine carrier protein.

β-oxidation

1. The fatty acyl-CoA is oxidized, resulting in a double bond between the α and β carbons. Electrons are captured as $FADH_2$, and thus contribute to the electron transport chain.

2. The double bond of the enoyl-CoA is hydrated to yield a hydroxyl group.

3. The hydroxyl group is oxidized to a carbonyl, yielding a β-keto acyl group. Another molecule of NADH is produced in this reaction.

4. The remaining fatty acyl-CoA undergoes further rounds of β-oxidation. Acetyl-CoA is further metabolized by the citric acid cycle.

FIGURE 9.13 **Beta-oxidation of fatty acids.** In β-oxidation, the β carbon is oxidized in a stepwise fashion to form acetyl-CoA. The remaining acyl-CoA is shortened by two carbons on each cycle of β-oxidation. On each pass, one molecule each of $FADH_2$ and NADH/H+ is generated. These electron carriers pass electrons to the electron transport chain and are reduced to be used again.

final three steps of the citric acid cycle in detail (see section 7.1), we see that the chemistry is nearly the same as it is in β-oxidation. A saturated carbon–carbon bond is desaturated to an alkene, the alkene is hydrated to an alcohol, and the alcohol is oxidized to a ketone. Understanding how this stepwise oxidation occurs on the chemical level will help to clarify the overall pathway and the intermediates, enzymes, mechanisms, and energetics of the reactions. By repeating the four steps of β-oxidation multiple times, lengthy fatty acids can be broken into two-carbon acetyl-CoA units (**Figure 9.13**).

The metabolic purpose of β-oxidation goes beyond the generation of acetyl-CoA; in two of the steps, the oxidation also leads to the controlled harvesting of electrons (as $FADH_2$ in

FIGURE 9.14 **Oxidation of unsaturated fatty acids from the Δ-3 position.** The initial steps of β-oxidation proceed without difficulty until the unsaturation is at the Δ-3 position. The bond can be isomerized to a *trans*-Δ-2 double bond, and β-oxidation proceeds as usual.

the generation of the double bond, and as NADH/H$^+$ in the oxidation of the hydroxyl to a ketone). These electrons are used in oxidative phosphorylation to generate a proton gradient across the inner mitochondrial membrane, ultimately resulting in the generation of ATP, as seen in section 7.2.

Double bonds in unsaturated fatty acids need to be moved or removed before oxidation

Several problems arise when trying to metabolize unsaturated fatty acids (**Figure 9.14**). If the fatty acids are naturally occurring, then the bonds are almost always *cis* double bonds. Often, these originate on an odd-numbered carbon, most commonly in the C-9 position, although sometimes in the C-5 position as well. In this instance, β-oxidation proceeds through several rounds until a β–γ double bond exists (a *cis*-Δ-3 double bond, between the C-3 and C-4 positions). This *cis*-Δ-3 double bond is isomerized to a *trans*-Δ-2 double bond by 3,2 enoyl-CoA isomerase, and β-oxidation proceeds.

If a double bond is found between even-numbered carbons, the first step of β-oxidation, formation of a *trans*-Δ-2 double bond, results in a conjugated system (**Figure 9.15**). In mammals, the Δ-4 double bond is reduced, resulting in a *trans*-Δ-3 double bond, which is isomerized back to *trans*-Δ-2 and, again, β-oxidation proceeds.

Occasionally, the 3,2 enoyl-CoA isomerase will sporadically generate a Δ-3, Δ-5 conjugated pair of double bonds. This scenario is rectified in the same way that a Δ-4 double bond is; that is, the pair of double bonds is reduced to a single Δ-3 double bond, followed by isomerization to Δ-2.

FIGURE 9.15 **Oxidation of polyunsaturated fatty acids from the Δ-4 position.** If a Δ-4 double bond is encountered, β-oxidation begins, resulting in a conjugated Δ-2, Δ-4 system. This is reduced to a single Δ-3 double bond, which can then be isomerized to Δ-2 as previously seen, and oxidation proceeds.

To review, if there is a double bond beginning at an odd-numbered carbon (Δ-3) it can be migrated to the Δ-2 position by an isomerase. However, if there is a Δ-4 double bond, β-oxidation begins and the two double bonds are rearranged to a single *trans*-Δ-3 double bond, which is then isomerized to Δ-2.

Odd-numbered fatty acids result in propionate A small percentage of the fatty acids found in nature have an odd number of carbons. Such fatty acids are most commonly found in bacteria and ruminant tissues. They are degraded through β-oxidation until a three-carbon fatty acyl group (propionyl-CoA) is formed. Propionyl-CoA is then carboxylated to form D-Methylmalonyl-CoA (the enantiomer of the L form found in fatty acid biosynthesis). The D isomer is converted to the L form by methylmalonyl-CoA epimerase. In a rearrangement reaction, methylmalonyl-CoA mutase converts the L isomer to succinyl-CoA, which enters the citric acid cycle.

9.2.3 Beta-oxidation is regulated at two different levels

Beta-oxidation is primarily regulated through the availability of substrate. Elevated levels of free fatty acids in the cellular environment (such as the extracellular fluid) result in increased uptake of free fatty acids into cells. Likewise, hydrolysis of a cell's triacylglycerol stores increases levels of free fatty acids in the cytosol. The increased fatty acid concentrations from both extracellular and intracellular sources lead, in turn, to elevated levels of cytosolic acyl-CoA. Thus, the pathways that dictate the breakdown of triacylglycerols, freeing up fatty acids, and the transport and trafficking of free fatty acids inside or outside the cell, have a major impact on the levels of fatty acid substrates available for β-oxidation. In general, pathways that regulate triacylglycerol breakdown include the hormones insulin or glucagon and two kinases, protein kinase A (PKA) and AMP dependent protein kinase (AMPK) and are discussed in section 10.6.

The other way in which the cell regulates β-oxidation is through the compartmentalization of substrate. Importing fatty acylcarnitines from the cytosol into the mitochondria is a point of control; CPT I is the protein responsible for transport across the outer mitochondrial membrane. CPT I is inhibited by malonyl-CoA, a metabolite produced in the cytosol that is used in the *biosynthesis* of fatty acids. High levels of malonyl-CoA indicate that the cell is also producing metabolites for fatty acid biosynthesis. Therefore, the cell is in an energetically rich state and does not need to burn fatty acids in β-oxidation. Inhibition of CPT I by malonyl-CoA blocks fatty acids from entering the mitochondria and therefore blocks β-oxidation. This is another example of control being exerted on a rate-determining and committed step.

The energetics of fatty acid oxidation Fatty acid oxidation releases significant stores of energy. Let us examine the energetics of the oxidation of a single molecule of the 18-carbon fatty acid stearate (18:0). The activation of stearate costs a cell the energetic equivalent of two molecules of ATP since two phosphoanhydride bonds are cleaved. Stearate then goes through eight rounds of β-oxidation, with the final round yielding two molecules of acetyl-CoA. Each round of β-oxidation yields one molecule of NADH and one of $FADH_2$. Collectively, therefore, the oxidation of stearate has produced:

- eight molecules of NADH,
- eight molecules of $FADH_2$, and
- nine molecules of acetyl-CoA.

NADH and $FADH_2$ are oxidized to NAD^+ and FAD in the electron transport chain. As we have seen in section 7.3, the energetic yield for the oxidation of NADH and $FADH_2$ is approximately 2.5 ATP/NADH and 1.5 ATP/$FADH_2$. The acetyl-CoA will be further oxidized in the citric acid cycle, with each molecule of acetyl-CoA yielding the energetic equivalent of the hydrolysis of ten molecules of ATP. Collectively, this means that the catabolism of a single molecule of stearate will provide the energetic equivalent of the hydrolysis of 122 molecules of ATP (Table 9.2).

TABLE 9.2   **ATP Produced by the Oxidation of One Molecule of Stearate**

Molecule	Number per stearate	ATP per molecule	Total ATP
NADH	8	2.5	20
FADH$_2$	8	1.5	12
Acetyl-CoA	9	10	90
Total			122

WORKED PROBLEM 9.3 | Following carbons in β-oxidation

If a molecule of palmitate is radiolabeled with C^{14} on the C-9 and C-10 positions, will the C^{14} be released in one or two molecules of acetyl-CoA?

Strategy   Think about which carbons are oxidized in β-oxidation. Beta-oxidation takes place on the β carbon and effectively removes carbons from the fatty acid as two carbon fragments.

Solution   Examine how palmitate proceeds through β-oxidation; the fatty acid is shortened by two carbons on each round of oxidation. On the fifth round, the acetyl-CoA fragment containing C-9 and C-10 will be liberated. Thus, the C^{14} will come off in a single molecule of acetyl-CoA.

Follow-up question   If this same molecule of palmitate was completely oxidized through β-oxidation, how many ATP could be produced from the acetyl-CoA, NADH, and FADH$_2$ generated in these steps?

9.2 Summary

- Before catabolism, fatty acids must be activated by coupling to coenzyme A. The activation both requires energy (supplied by hydrolysis of ATP) and provides energy for subsequent steps.
- Activated fatty acids must be shuttled into the mitochondrial matrix (as acylcarnitines) for catabolism.
- Beta-oxidation is the stepwise process through which fatty acids are oxidized on the β carbon into two-carbon acetyl-CoA units.
- Beta-oxidation is regulated by substrate availability, compartmentalization within the cell, and inhibition of key steps in the pathway.

9.2 Concept Check

- Illustrate how fatty acids are activated in the cytosol, transported to the mitochondrial matrix, and catabolized through β-oxidation.
- Describe chemically what is happening in each of these steps and why these steps are necessary.
- Explain how the pathway differs if the fatty acid is unsaturated.
- Analyze the thermodynamics of the reactions (which reactions help drive the entire pathway forward or have ΔG values close to zero and are reversible).
- Describe how β-oxidation is regulated at the molecular level.

9.3 Fatty Acid Biosynthesis

We may associate fats and therefore fatty acids with adipose tissue. While the majority of the body's fats are stored in adipose tissue, fatty acid biosynthesis occurs most frequently in the liver or other tissues.

In this section, we first outline the process of fatty acid biosynthesis, using the example of palmitate (16:0), and then we show how longer or unsaturated fatty acids form from palmitate. The enzymes involved in the synthesis of palmitate are typically found in the cytosol; however, the enzymes involved in the elongation and desaturation of fatty acids are commonly found in the endoplasmic reticulum. Carbohydrate metabolism employs separate compartments (the cytosol and the mitochondria) for some of the steps of glycolysis and gluconeogenesis. This is done to ensure that the steps of these pathways are energetically favorable and to provide an additional means of regulating these pathways. Fatty acid metabolism employs a similar mechanism. While β-oxidation occurs in the mitochondria, fatty acid biosynthesis occurs in the cytosol.

Fatty acid biosynthesis requires an input of energy, which is provided by the reducing equivalent NADPH and the transfer potential of the thioester bonds found in the starting material, malonyl-ACP. ACP is acyl carrier protein, a small protein with a phosphopantetheine group. ACP in fatty acid biosynthesis acts in an analogous fashion to coenzyme A in fatty acid degradation and the citric acid cycle. Although fatty acids are built up from two-carbon subunits, and the reactions are similar, the process is not a simple reversal of β-oxidation.

Much of the early research on fatty acid biosynthesis was conducted in the bacterium *E. coli*, which differs from the mammalian enzymes and pathways described in this section. The differences are discussed as they arise in the text. Although *E. coli* is used as a model organism, different bacterial species may have other variations in fatty acid metabolism. Both the differences and similarities help illustrate how fatty acid metabolism continues to evolve.

9.3.1 Two major enzyme complexes are involved in fatty acid biosynthesis

Two, major, multifunctional enzyme complexes are responsible for the reactions of palmitate biosynthesis: **acetyl-CoA carboxylase (ACC)** and **fatty acid synthase (FAS)**. ACC synthesizes malonyl-CoA, a three-carbon building block that is the immediate precursor for fatty acid biosynthesis and a substrate for FAS. Regulation of fatty acid biosynthesis occurs through the regulation of both enzymes, but the rate-determining step is catalyzed by ACC.

Acetyl-CoA carboxylase synthesizes malonyl-CoA   ACC is a large, multifunctional enzyme complex that has three main domains: biotin carboxylase (BC), carboxyl transferase (CT), and the biotin binding (BB) domain (**Figure 9.16**). In bacteria such as *Escherichia coli*, the domains and any substrate binding sites are coded for by different genes, which give rise to different proteins that function in a multi-protein complex. In mammals, two different genes give rise to two different isoforms of ACC, each of which has all the binding sites and catalytic properties of the enzyme. The two isoforms, ACC1 and ACC2, catalyze similar reactions but have very different biological functions. ACC1 is found in all cells but particularly in lipogenic tissues, such as liver and adipose tissue; it is believed to be the isoform responsible for generating malonyl-CoA for fatty acid biosynthesis. This enzyme is associated with the cytoplasmic surface of the endoplasmic reticulum and releases its product (malonyl-CoA) into the cytosol. In contrast, ACC2 contains a mitochondrial targeting sequence and is found on the outer mitochondrial membrane. The production of mitochondrial malonyl-CoA is responsible for the inhibition of carnitine acyltransferase and is therefore more likely involved with blunting the β-oxidation of fatty acids than with their synthesis.

Both ACC isoforms synthesize malonyl-CoA through a multistep process, with biotin (a B vitamin) as the activated carrier (**Figure 9.17**). The biotin is attached via an amide linkage to the terminal ε-nitrogen of a lysine side chain. The length of the lysine–biotin complex provides an extended and flexible arm for the activated CO_2 group to be transferred from one active site to the next without being released from the protein. Biotin is carboxylated through the reaction of the bicarbonate anion and ATP. The hydrolysis of ATP provides the energy to drive the carboxylation reaction. The carboxybiotinylated enzyme then adds the carboxyl group to acetyl-CoA to form malonyl-CoA.

A.

Molecular surface   Ribbon diagram   Ribbon of one subunit

B.

FIGURE 9.16 **Structure of the biotin carboxylase domain of human acetyl-CoA carboxylase I from yeast.** **A.** ACC1 is a dimer (shown as a molecular surface and as a ribbon diagram in violet and purple). In the third structure, only one subunit is shown and the three key domains are colored blue (biotin carboxylase domain, BC), green (biotin binding domain, BB), and gold (carboxyl transferase domain, CT). **B.** The same three domains are shown in greater detail. The flexibility of the biotin-lysine arm (shown bound in the CT active site) allows this group to translocate between the CT and BC active sites (shown in pale blue and pale gold in the schematic view). ACC2 has a different structure and is not shown. (PDB ID 5CSL Wei, J., Tong, L. (2015) Crystal structure of the 500-kDa yeast acetyl-CoA carboxylase holoenzyme dimer. *Nature* 526: 723–727)

Fatty acid synthase makes palmitate from malonyl-CoA and acetyl-CoA

FAS is a large multifunctional enzyme complex. The homodimeric human form of the enzyme consists of two polypeptides, each with 2,511 residues. Extensive research has been dedicated to determining whether these subunits interact and, if so, how. In mammals, the subunits are arranged in a head-to-tail fashion; however, it is not clear how strongly, if at all, the subunits assist one another in catalysis. The scenario may be completely different for the *E. coli* form of the enzyme because enzymatic activities in *E. coli* are provided by six, discrete individual proteins rather than a long multifunctional polypeptide chain (**Figure 9.18**).

Collectively, FAS catalyzes seven different enzymatic reactions, four of which are analogous to the reactions of β-oxidation and three of which are novel. The three reactions

1. Carbonate oxygen attacks γ-phosphate of ATP.	2. Electrons flow out of biotin and into carbonyl phosphate.	3. Generating carboxybiotin.

4. Base abstracts proton from α-carbon, generating enolate.	5. Carboxybiotin decarboxylates.	6. Enolate attacks carbon dioxide, generating malony-CoA. Biotin reprotonates, regenerating enzyme.

FIGURE 9.17 **The overall reaction and mechanism of malonyl-CoA formation.** Malonyl-CoA is formed by the carboxylation of acetyl-CoA. The mechanism of this reaction begins with the activation of bicarbonate with ATP to form a carbonyl phosphate. The amine moiety of biotin then attacks the carbonyl phosphate forming a carbamate. An enolate generated by the deprotonation of acetyl-CoA attacks the carbamate carbon to form malonyl-CoA and regenerate biotin. The lengthy combination of the lysine side chain and the arm on biotin has led to the swinging arm hypothesis in which the combined length of these two units provides a means by which biotin can participate in both of these reactions as they occur at two distantly separated active sites.

specific to fatty acid biosynthesis, described below, occur in the first steps of the pathway. Like glycolysis and gluconeogenesis, biology exploits reactions with $\Delta G°$ values that are close to zero, such as the hydration of a double bond to form a hydroxyl group. In glycolysis those reactions can be viewed as nearly reversible, and the value of ΔG can be influenced by the concentration of products and reactants in the reaction. In fatty acid synthase, substrate channeling (passing of substrate from one subunit to the next) artificially raises the effective concentration of the substrate and increases the rate and efficiency of the entire process (**Figure 9.19**).

1. **Transfer of activated carbon units to acyl carrier protein.** To start synthesizing fatty acids, malonyl-CoA and acetyl-CoA must be transferred to fatty acid synthase; one to the condensing domain via a thioether to a cysteine residue, and the other to the ACP domain through the phosphopantetheinyl group. In the first reaction of fatty acid synthesis, acetyl-CoA is transferred from the thioester of CoA to the ACP domain of FAS. The name ACP is something of a misnomer. In bacteria such as *E. coli*, ACP is a separate protein, but the ACP functionality is only one domain of the FAS complex in birds and mammals. The transfer of this group to the thioester of ACP is catalyzed by malonyl-CoA/acetyl-CoA acyltransferase (MAT).

2. **Transfer of acetyl group to the KS domain of FAS.** The acetyl group does not stay bound to ACP for long. Instead, it is transferred to the catalytic domain of the β-ketoacyl-ACP synthase (KS) domain. In the remaining steps of this round of fatty acid biosynthesis, the growing fatty acyl chain stays bound to ACP, but the growing chain appears to be transferred to the KS domain.

3. **Transfer of malonyl group from malonyl-CoA.** The active donor of carbon units for fatty acid biosynthesis is malonyl-CoA made by ACC1. The first step in using this is the transfer of the thioester bond from CoA to the cysteine of ACP.

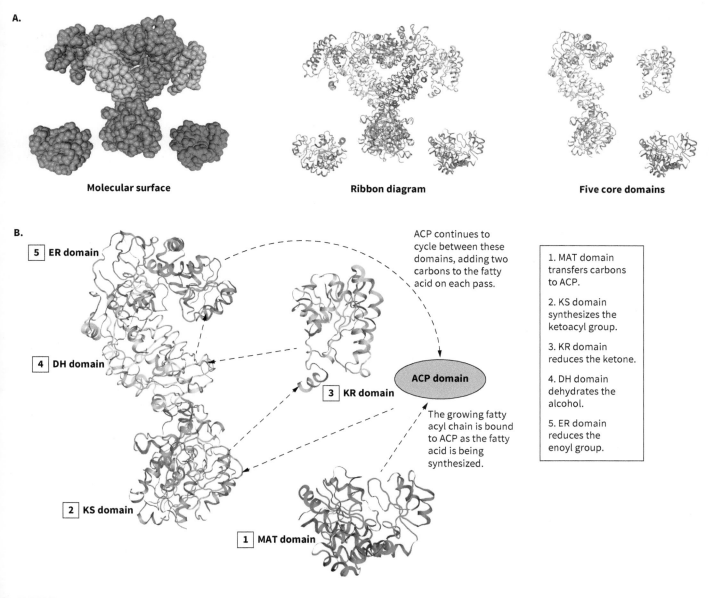

A.

Molecular surface   **Ribbon diagram**   **Five core domains**

B.

1. MAT domain transfers carbons to ACP.

2. KS domain synthesizes the ketoacyl group.

3. KR domain reduces the ketone.

4. DH domain dehydrates the alcohol.

5. ER domain reduces the enoyl group.

ACP continues to cycle between these domains, adding two carbons to the fatty acid on each pass.

The growing fatty acyl chain is bound to ACP as the fatty acid is being synthesized.

ACP domain

5 **ER domain**

4 **DH domain**

3 **KR domain**

2 **KS domain**

1 **MAT domain**

FIGURE 9.18 **The structure of mammalian fatty acid synthase (FAS).** Fatty acid synthase carries out the multiple reactions necessary to synthesize fatty acids. In prokaryotes, these are performed by a multi-subunit protein. **A.** In mammals, these are found in a single polypeptide. The holoenzyme is a homodimer with each half containing all of the necessary subunits for fatty acid synthesis. Shown in **B.** are five of the essential domains (MAT, KS, KR, DH, and ER). The growing fatty acid, attached to the ACP domain, flips between these sites as the nascent fatty acid grows. When it achieves 16 carbons in length (palmitate), it is cleaved by ketothiolase (KT, not shown). (PDB ID 2CF2 Maier, T., Jenni, S., Ban, N. (2006) Architecture of Mammalian Fatty Acid Synthase at 4.5 A Resolution. *Science* 311: 1258)

4. **Condensation of malonyl- and acetyl-ACP.** These two activated carbon carriers are then condensed together in a Claisen condensation catalyzed by the β-ketoacyl-ACP synthase (KS) domain to form acetoacetyl-ACP. The CO_2 used to synthesize malonyl-CoA is lost at this step. The resulting acetoacetyl group remains on ACP, which in turn delivers this substrate to the other reaction centers. Therefore, the final two carbons of any fatty acid come from acetyl-CoA while the others are derived from malonyl-CoA.

5. **Reduction of the β-keto group by NADPH/H$^+$ to a hydroxyl group.** The growing fatty acid has been elongated by two carbons, but it exists as a diketone instead of a hydrocarbon. It is reduced by a series of stepwise reactions. The first of these is the reduction of the ketone on the β carbon to a hydroxyl group catalyzed by the β-keto-ACP reductase (KR) domain. This enzyme requires NADPH/H$^+$ to reduce the carbonyl of the β-keto group to a hydroxyl group.

Fatty acid biosynthesis

1. Acetyl-CoA is transferred to acyl carrier protein (ACP).

2. Acetyl-ACP transfers the acetyl group to the active site cysteine of the KS domain.

3. Malonyl-CoA is transferred to acyl carrier protein (ACP).

4. Malonyl-ACP and acetyl-S-KS are condensed into a single molecule of acetoacetyl-ACP. The CO_2 used in the formation of malonyl-CoA is lost in this step.

5. The β-keto group is reduced by NADPH/H$^+$ to a β-hydroxyl group.

6. The alcohol is dehydrated leaving an α-β double bond.

7. The double bond is reduced by a second molecule of NADPH/H$^+$ leaving the newly extended fatty acid.

8. Steps 3 through 7 are repeated six more times to generate a palmitoyl-ACP.

9. Palmitoyl-ACP is cleaved by a thioesterase to release palmitate and ACP.

FIGURE 9.19 **Reactions of fatty acid synthase.** The reactions of fatty acid synthase are largely the reverse of β-oxidation with several notable exceptions. Acyl carrier protein is the handle used to manipulate the intermediates and NADPH is the reducing equivalent. Two carbon units are added through malonyl-ACP (carbon dioxide is lost to form the enolate required in this step).

6. **Dehydration of the alcohol to an α-β double bond.** The alcohol generated in the previous step is now dehydrated to a double bond by 3-hydroxyl acyl-ACP dehydratase (DH). This step requires no added input of energy and has a ΔG value close to zero.

7. **Reduction of the double bond by NADPH/H^{+}.** The final step in the addition of the acetyl group is the reduction of the double bond to a saturated hydrocarbon chain by NADPH/H^{+}. This is carried out by the enoyl-ACP reductase (ER) domain. This step finalizes the elongation of the growing acyl chain by two carbons.

8. **Steps 3 through 7 are repeated six more times to generate palmitoyl-ACP.** Six more two-carbon units are added to the growing fatty acyl chain as malonyl-ACP groups. Each undergoes all of the reactions of fatty acid synthesis to generate the 16-carbon fatty acid palmitate.

9. **Palmitoyl-ACP is cleaved by a thioesterase to release palmitate and ACP.** In the final reaction, palmitoyl thioesterase cleaves palmitate from ACP releasing a free fatty acid (palmitate) and acyl carrier protein. Palmitate may be acted on by elongases and desaturases to yield longer fatty acids or ones that contain double bonds.

While the steps of fatty acid biosynthesis employ reactions that are almost the reverse order of β-oxidation reactions, there are several significant differences (**Figure 9.20**).

First, the reducing equivalent used in steps 4 and 6 is NADPH/H^{+} rather than NADH and FADH$_2$. NADPH differs from NADH in that an additional phosphate has been esterified to the 2′ position of the ribose ring attached to the adenine group. Whereas NAD^{+}/NADH

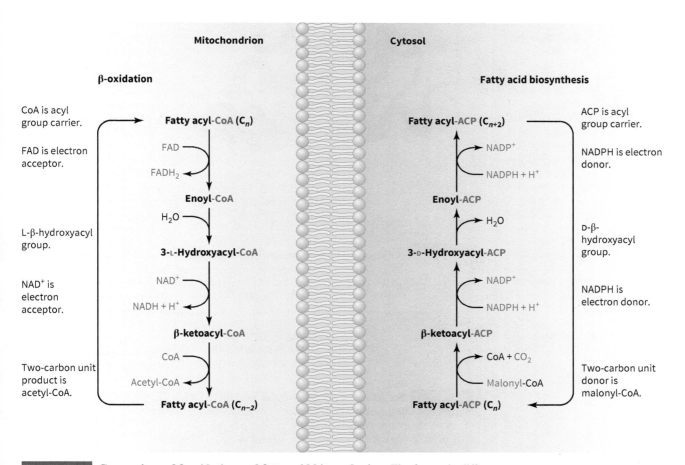

FIGURE 9.20 **Comparison of β-oxidation and fatty acid biosynthesis.** The five main differences between β-oxidation and fatty acid biosynthesis are shown.

Redox active
carbon

NADPH

is typically used in catabolic reactions, NADP/NADPH is often used in anabolic reactions, including fatty acid biosynthesis, cholesterol biosynthesis, and the reactions of the Calvin cycle in photosynthesis. NADPH is also the reducing equivalent used by the cytochromes, enzymes used by the liver to detoxify drugs and xenobiotics, and some of the reactions of bile salts and eicosanoid synthesis.

Second, the carbon units used in fatty acid biosynthesis are bound to ACP rather than CoA. In both ACP and CoA, acetate groups are bound via a thioester bond to the cysteamine end of a phosphopantetheine group (**Figure 9.21**). However, in contrast to CoA (in which the phosphopantetheine group is attached to AMP), the phosphopantetheine in the much larger ACP is linked to a serine residue.

A third difference between β-oxidation and fatty acid biosynthesis is the stereochemistry of the hydroxyl-bearing carbon. The D isomer is seen in biosynthesis (D-β-hydroxyacyl-ACP), whereas the L isomer (L-β-hydroxyacyl-CoA) is seen in β-oxidation.

The sequence of reactions in FAS is repeated six more times. In each round an additional two carbons are added onto the growing fatty acyl chain until the 16-carbon fatty acid palmitate is synthesized and palmitate is released.

The reactions of β-oxidation and fatty acid biosynthesis may seem new to you, but in many ways these reactions are ones that you have covered in organic chemistry. The critical step of these reactions is discussed in **Biochemistry: The Claisen condensation**.

Fatty acid biosynthesis differs in bacteria and mammals, presenting an opportunity to develop new antibiotics to treat diseases. An example of this is tuberculosis. Isoniazid is an antibiotic used to treat tuberculosis and other persistent bacterial infections. The skeleton of

FIGURE 9.21 **Structure of the acyl carrier protein (ACP).** The phosphopantetheine group (space-filling) shown in the center is covalently bound to a serine residue in the protein. In the image, the phosphopantetheine group is bound to a hexanoyl group in the cavity of ACP. Note that ACP is a small protein. It is much larger than the phosphopantetheine group (and much larger than coenzyme A). (PDB ID 2FAC Roujeinikova, A., Simon, W.J., Gilroy, J., Rice, D.W., Rafferty, J.B., Slabas, A.R. (2007) Structural Studies of Fatty Acyl-(Acyl Carrier Protein) Thioesters Reveal a Hydrophobic Binding Cavity that Can Expand to Fit Longer Substrates. *J. Mol. Biol.* 365: 135–145)

isoniazid was first synthesized in 1912, but its antibacterial properties were not discovered until 1951. The drug was highly effective, but the mechanism of action was unknown. In the early 1970s, it was discovered that the drug forms an adduct with NADP that inhibits the enoyl-ACP reductase, blocking fatty acid biosynthesis in bacteria, but not in mammals, resulting in slowing bacterial growth or in bacterial death. Recently, antibiotic-resistant tuberculosis

---

Biochemistry

The Claisen condensation

There are remarkably few ways in nature to generate carbon–carbon bonds, but the Claisen condensation is one exception. It is a classic reaction of organic chemistry and at the core of lipid biochemistry. The starting material for the reaction are two esters, and the final product is a β-diketone or, in the instance of lipid metabolism, a β-keto ester.

An enolate is necessary for the Claisen reaction to proceed. To form an enolate, there has to be a labile proton on the α carbon.

In the laboratory, a Claisen condensation is achieved using a strong base to remove the α proton and form the enolate. Enolate formation is the rate-limiting step in the reaction, and it is resonance-stabilized through the adjacent carbonyl group. In enzymatic reactions, an equivalent base forms in the active site in the enzyme to abstract the proton. One other limitation is that the base, in this case a proton acceptor in the active site of the enzyme, cannot be a strong nucleophile because it would add to the ester or a carbonyl carbon. This limitation is not typically a problem in biological systems.

A slightly different pathway is taken to obtain the enolate in fatty acid biosynthesis. Rather than generate the enolate by deprotonation, malonyl-CoA is decarboxylated to generate an enolate that can attack the ester carbon bound to fatty acid synthase, forming a covalently bound intermediate, before eliminating the synthase and the β-keto ester.

Another condition necessary for the reaction is that there needs to be a suitable leaving group adjacent to the enolate. Again, in the laboratory this is typically an alkoxide generated by one of the esters. In the instance of lipid biosynthesis, the leaving group is either the pantothenate group of coenzyme A or ACP.

Claisen condensations are found in fatty acid biosynthesis, ketone body biosynthesis, and the metabolism of some amino acids. The reverse reaction, a retro Claisen, or Claisen ester cleavage, is employed in β-oxidation. Aldol condensations and decarboxylation reactions of β-keto acids follow a similar scheme—formation of a resonance-stabilized carbanion intermediate, followed by nucleophilic attack.

Malonyl-CoA decarboxylates, yielding an enolate.

The enolate attacks the carbonyl carbon of acetyl-ACP yielding acetoacyl-ACP.

An alpha proton on the ester is removed by a base yielding an enolate.

Aldol condensation

Decarboxylation reaction

A.

Sutthaburawonk/Getty Images

B.

Isoniazid

CDC/ Ray Butler, MS

FIGURE 9.22 **Isoniazid and tuberculosis.** **A.** Tuberculosis is a bacterial infection that often affects the lungs. It can be diagnosed on an X-ray. **B.** Isoniazid is a fatty acid synthesis inhibitor used to treat persistent bacterial infections (such as *Mycobacterim tuberculosis*, shown in the micrograph). It binds to and blocks enoyl-ACP reductase, blocking subsequent steps in fatty acid biosynthesis.

has emerged (**Figure 9.22**). The structural analysis of proteins in these strains shows how individual mutations can lead to drug resistance and provides valuable data for designing new drugs. People often question why scientists spend so much time, effort, and resources on basic research that is not directly related to treating human disease. The development of isoniazid is a simple illustration that demonstrates how basic and applied research coupled together can unexpectedly lead to new treatments for human diseases and can serve as a guide in the development of new drugs.

9.3.2 Elongases and desaturases in the endoplasmic reticulum increase fatty acid diversity

As discussed above, the synthesis of palmitate (16:0) occurs in the cytosol, but elongation of palmitate to longer fatty acids and desaturation to unsaturated fatty acids occurs predominantly in the endoplasmic reticulum.

Fatty acids are elongated by two carbons through the addition of the activated carbons of malonyl-CoA. The first step in the elongation, the synthesis of a β-keto acyl-CoA, is catalyzed by various enzymes and is referred to as ELOVL (elongation of very long-chain fatty acids) that have different preferences for chain length and degree of unsaturation. A common set of enzymes then completes the process through reactions that are the same as those found in palmitate biosynthesis.

In mammals, fatty acids are desaturated by direct oxidative desaturation, predominantly by Δ-9 desaturase. This enzyme complex directly removes two electrons and associated hydrogens from stearoyl-CoA (18:0) to create oleyl-CoA ($18:1^{\Delta 9}$). The complex consists of three proteins: an NADH-cytochrome b5 reductase, cytochrome b5, and the desaturase. Electrons from both the fatty acid and NADH are transferred to the redox active iron centers in the cytochrome, and then to the desaturase. The final electron acceptor is molecular oxygen, generating two molecules of water. Inclusion of NADH in the reaction provides the two additional electrons needed to generate the second molecule of water, using up both atoms of oxygen in the process.

Because mammals lack desaturase activity at positions beyond the C-9 (for example, at Δ-12 or Δ-15), they are unable to add double bonds any farther down the fatty acid chain. Hence, fatty acids with double bonds in the ω-3 and ω-6 positions are considered essential fatty acids and must be supplied in the diet, typically in the form of $18:2^{\Delta 9,12}$ linoleic acid and $18:3^{\Delta 9,12,15}$ α-linolenic acid. Both of these polyunsaturated fatty acids are commonly found in plants, where Δ12 or Δ15 desaturases are responsible for their synthesis. Humans can elongate and desaturate these fatty acids into the more highly unsaturated ω-3 and ω-6 fatty acids

Molecular surface   **Ribbon diagram**   **Steroyl-CoA**   **Zn²⁺ ions**   **Kink in stearoyl group**

FIGURE 9.23 **Structure of Δ-9 desaturase.** Shown is the structure of Δ-9 desaturase from mouse (*Mus musculus*) in a molecular surface and ribbon depiction. The Δ-9 desaturase employs a pair of iron ions to generate the double bond, in this structure they have been replaced with zinc (shown in purple). Note the kink that the substrate binding site places on stearate. This ensures that the reaction happens with the proper stereo-chemistry. (PDB ID 4YMK Bai, Y., McCoy, J.G., Levin, E.J., Sobrado, P., Rajashankar, K.R., Fox, B.G., Zhou, M. (2015) X-ray structure of a mammalian stearoyl-CoA desaturase. *Nature* 524: 252–256)

needed for eicosanoid biosynthesis, using a combination of Δ-4, Δ-5, Δ-6, and Δ-9 desaturases and elongases (**Figure 9.23**).

9.3.3   The formation of malonyl-CoA by acetyl-CoA carboxylase is the regulated and rate-determining step of fatty acid biosynthesis

As seen in other pathways, the rate-determining or committed step in a pathway is often a place where control mechanisms are found. In fatty acid biosynthesis, acetyl-CoA carboxylase (ACC) catalyzes the rate-determining step and is the main point of regulation (**Figure 9.24**).

Allosteric regulators   Acetyl-CoA carboxylase is allosterically regulated by several molecules. For example, it is inactivated by acyl-CoA, a level of control that makes sense on both a chemical and biological level as an example of feedback inhibition. ACC synthesizes malonyl-CoA, which is used to synthesize fatty acyl-CoA. The allosteric regulation of ACC by fatty acyl-CoA provides a link to the energy level of the cell. If concentrations of acyl-CoA increase, their production is decreased, given that increased levels of acyl-CoA indicate either that triacylglycerols are being catabolized or that there is a block to their synthesis.

A second allosteric regulator of ACC is citrate, which binds to ACC1 and causes the enzyme to polymerize into lengthy strands (although the mitochondrial form of the enzyme does not polymerize). The individual complexes of ACC1 are less active than the polymer. Hence, although citrate does not participate in the conversion of acetyl-CoA to malonyl-CoA, it is still performing a regulatory function. Again, it should make both biological and chemical sense that elevated levels of citrate would prompt the cell to store energy. When energetic levels are high, the citric acid cycle will slow as ATP inhibits isocitrate dehydrogenase, and levels of citrate will rise. In turn, this results in more citrate

Active
⋀ Citrate
⋁ Acyl-CoA
⋀ Polymerization
Acetyl-CoA carboxylase-OH

Phosphoprotein phosphatase 2A (PP2A) dephosphorylates the enzyme and returns it to the active state. This is stimulated by the **insulin** signaling pathway.

⋀ PP2A   ⋁ AMPK

Phosphorylation of ACC I by AMP kinase (AMPK) or protein kinase A (PKA) results in ACC adopting the less active state. PKA is stimulated by **epinephrine** and **glucagon.**

Acetyl-CoA carboxylase-P
Less active

FIGURE 9.24 **Regulation of ACC.** ACC is regulated by phosphorylation and dephosphorylation, as well as polymerization, and two allosteric regulators (citrate and acyl-CoA).

being available for the tricarboxylic acid transport system, increasing levels of citrate in the cytosol. Thus, citrate is serving multiple functions; it acts as a chemical indicator of the energetic state of the mitochondria, helps shuttle carbons out of the mitochondria for fatty acid biosynthesis, and allosterically activates the enzyme that produces malonyl-CoA (the precursor of those fatty acids). Glutamate and other dicarboxylic acids also activate ACC through a similar mechanism. Hence, elevated levels of several small metabolites converge to signal the cell to store energy as fatty acids.

Regulation by phosphorylation

ACC is also regulated by phosphorylation. AMP activated protein kinase (AMPK) plays a central role as a regulator of metabolism in the cell. ATP is often converted to AMP through biochemical reactions. As we saw in Chapter 6, ATP can be regenerated from AMP through substrate level phosphorylation or the F_0/F_1 ATPase found in mitochondria. Concentrations of ATP and AMP therefore reflect the energetic state of the cell with high concentrations of ATP (and low concentrations of AMP), signifying an energy-rich state while the converse (high AMP/low ATP) indicates an energy deficit.

High concentrations of AMP activate AMPK, which will phosphorylate ACC1 and thus inactivate it. As with the other regulatory mechanisms discussed, this should make metabolic sense. When concentrations of AMP are high, such as during exercise, the cell needs energy and should not be spending it converting acetyl-CoA to malonyl-CoA for fatty acid biosynthesis. Likewise, high levels of malonyl-CoA will limit β-oxidation by inhibiting carnitine palmitoyl transferase I and decreasing fatty acid import. Hence, in low-energy states, it makes sense to constrain the enzyme involved in malonyl-CoA synthesis. In these instances, biosynthetic pathways such as fatty acid or cholesterol biosynthesis are blunted, whereas those that yield energy (β-oxidation) are increased. PKA can also phosphorylate ACC, although the biological significance of this event is unclear.

Regulation of ACC gene expression

A final level of regulation that is worthy of mention is that of ACC gene expression. Two transcription factors play notable roles. First, ACC is partially regulated by the sterol response element binding protein (SREBP). This transcription factor binds to a sterol response element in the promoter region of the ACC gene, activating transcription. This transcription factor is partially responsible for activating many genes involved in lipid metabolism. The other transcription factor involved in the regulation of ACC is the carbohydrate response element binding protein (ChREBP), which was discussed in section 8.2. In response to a high-carbohydrate diet, ChREBP activates genes containing a carbohydrate response element (ChoRE); this includes both the ACC and FAS genes.

Further regulation of lipid metabolism occurs in triacylglycerol storage and mobilization. This will be discussed further in Chapter 10.

WORKED PROBLEM 9.4 | Predicting a knockout phenotype

There are two isoforms of ACC: ACC1 and ACC2. If we were to knock out either of these genes in mice, what would you predict for a phenotype? How would lacking these genes affect the animal and its metabolism?

Strategy What are the isoforms of ACC, and what functions do they serve? What would happen if one or both were missing?

Solution The ACC1 knockout mouse is unable to produce fatty acids, a mutation that is lethal to an embryo early in its development. The phenotype of the ACC2 knockout is a bit more complicated. Because ACC2 regulates CPT I, knocking out ACC2 leads to an increase in fatty acid transport into the mitochondria and increased β-oxidation. ACC2 knockout mice develop normally, have a normal appearance, and reproduce with vigor (a basic sign of overall animal health); however, compared to normal mice, they can consume more food and burn more fat through β-oxidation, and they are resistant to weight gain, diet-induced obesity, and type 2 diabetes mellitus. On the cellular level, both β-oxidation and glycolysis are elevated. It appears that eliminating ACC2 increases flux through oxidative pathways.

Characterizing any genetically manipulated animal is complex. While there is often an overt phenotype, in order to identify peripheral effects, it is generally necessary to ask the right questions.

Follow-up question Many drug companies are pursuing compounds that affect AMPK. How would a drug affecting AMPK be likely to affect ACC? How might that in turn affect fatty acid metabolism? What might be the effects on the animal's overall metabolism?

9.3 Summary

- Fatty acid biosynthesis occurs primarily in the cytosol and involves two important multifunctional enzyme complexes (ACC and FAS).
- The first step in fatty acid biosynthesis is the production of the three-carbon intermediate malonyl-CoA. Acetyl-CoA carboxylase synthesizes malonyl-CoA from acetate in the cytosol.
- FAS synthesizes palmitate (16:0) from malonyl-CoA and acetyl-CoA, using energy provided by NADPH.
- Longer and unsaturated fatty acids are produced from palmitate in the endoplasmic reticulum.
- Fatty acid biosynthesis is regulated by substrate availability, compartmentalization within the cell, and inhibition of key steps in the pathway itself. This is accomplished through both allosteric regulators and phosphorylation of key enzymes.

9.3 Concept Check

- Describe the steps involved in fatty acid biosynthesis.
- Indicate how the steps in fatty acid biosynthesis are similar to or different from those of β-oxidation.
- Indicate which electron carriers are involved in biochemistry and how they affect the chemistry of the reactions.
- Describe how fatty acids longer than 16 carbons or containing double bonds are formed.
- Describe in both general and specific terms how fatty acid biosynthesis is regulated.

9.4 Ketone Body Metabolism

Fatty acids are an excellent source of stored energy, and evolution has produced elegant means for synthesizing, storing, and degrading these molecules. However, the organism must be protected from the detergent-like properties of fatty acids, properties that result from the amphipathic nature of fatty acids and would denature proteins and disrupt membranes. Fatty acids are released from adipose tissue and are mainly transported in the blood bound to albumin but are sometimes associated with plasma lipoproteins. In binding and sequestering fatty acids, albumin prevents them from acting as detergents. Although this system works well in delivering fatty acids to tissues such as the heart, the liver, and muscle, it is unable to deliver fatty acids to the brain.

The brain is protected and shielded by the blood–brain barrier, a semipermeable structure consisting of endothelial cells tightly joined together with an extracellular matrix that work together to exclude many metabolites. Large molecules and proteins including fatty acids bound to albumin are unable to cross the blood–brain barrier. Therefore, the brain cannot absorb or use fatty acids from the circulation.

Typically, the brain obtains most of its energy from glucose, which is transported across the blood–brain barrier. However, under fasting conditions, when there is low plasma glucose, or in certain disease states such as uncontrolled diabetes mellitus when the brain may be unable to use glucose as a fuel source, an alternative is needed. Under these conditions, the liver synthesizes **ketone bodies (acetone, acetoacetate and β-hydroxybutyrate)** to provide energy to the brain (**Figure 9.25**). Two of these three molecules (acetoacetate

FIGURE 9.25 Structure of ketone bodies. Shown are acetone, acetoacetate, and β-hydroxybutyrate. These are produced by the liver. The body, especially the brain, can use acetoacetate and β-hydroxybutyrate for fuel. Acetone is a breakdown product formed by the spontaneous decarboxylation of acetoacetate. (Liver: Tortora; Derrickson, *Principles of Anatomy & Physiology*, 15e, copyright 2016, John Wiley & Sons. This material is reproduced with permission of John Wiley & Sons, Inc.; Brain: Ireland, *Visualizing Human Biology*, 4e, copyright 2013, John Wiley & Sons. This material is reproduced with permission of John Wiley & Sons, Inc.)

Acetone

Acetoacetate   β-hydroxybutyrate

transported through blood

Produced in liver   Used by brain

and β-hydroxybutyrate) are small, water-soluble equivalents of fatty acids, which can also permeate the blood–brain barrier.

9.4.1 Ketone bodies are made from acetyl-CoA

Ketone bodies are synthesized when glucose levels are low but acetyl-CoA levels are high. This occurs when fatty acids in the liver have been broken down to acetyl-CoA, but there are insufficient intermediates of the citric acid cycle to catabolize the acetate.

The process begins by the condensation of two molecules of acetyl-CoA into a molecule of acetoacetyl-CoA (**Figure 9.26**). The reaction is catalyzed by the enzyme thiolase (which is also involved in β-oxidation). The energy for the reaction is provided by the cleavage of the thioester bond between coenzyme A and acetate.

A third molecule of acetyl-CoA condenses with acetoacetyl-CoA. This reaction is catalyzed by β-hydroxy-β-methylglutaryl-CoA synthase (HMG-CoA synthase) to produce β-hydroxy-β-methylglutaryl-CoA (HMG-CoA). The first two reactions of ketone body synthesis are also the first two reactions of cholesterol biosynthesis.

Next, HMG-CoA is acted on by HMG-CoA lyase, which cleaves acetyl-CoA and liberates acetoacetate, a molecule with two metabolic fates. It can be secreted directly by the liver or can be reduced by β-hydroxybutyrate dehydrogenase in the liver to yield the D isomer of β-hydroxybutyrate. This too is released by the liver and can be used as a fuel by the brain. Beta-hydroxybutyrate has a chemical advantage over acetoacetate. While acetoacetate can undergo a spontaneous decarboxylation reaction to form acetone and CO_2, the more highly reduced state of β-hydroxybutyrate prevents this reaction from occurring. Although acetone and CO_2 are not toxic in the concentrations normally found in people undergoing ketone body production, these molecules are no longer usable, and the energy they contain is lost to metabolism.

9.4.2 Ketone bodies can be thought of as a water-soluble fuel source used in the absence of carbohydrates

Once released from the liver, ketone bodies travel through the circulatory system to tissues where they are metabolized. Ketone body metabolism occurs primarily in the brain, although heart and skeletal muscle also have the ability to use ketone bodies.

The first step in the use of ketone bodies is the conversion of β-hydroxybutyrate to acetoacetate by β-hydroxybutyrate dehydrogenase. Acetoacetate undergoes a substitution reaction with succinyl-CoA, forming acetoacetyl-CoA and succinate. The liver lacks 3-ketoacyl-CoA transferase, the enzyme needed for this reaction and thus cannot use ketone bodies for fuel. Coupling to coenzyme A energetically activates acetoacetate for subsequent cleavage. In the next reaction, acetoacetate reacts with CoA and thiolase to produce two molecules of acetyl-CoA, which can be further metabolized through the citric acid cycle to generate NADH and $FADH_2$ for the electron transport chain to use in ATP production (**Figure 9.27**).

In the discussion of the citric acid cycle, it was noted that the conversion of succinyl-CoA to succinate also yields a molecule of GTP or ATP. Therefore, the use of succinyl-CoA effectively costs a molecule of GTP or ATP.

In states of prolonged fasting, starvation, or untreated diabetes the liver will produce ketone bodies to help provide fuel for the brain. This state, referred to as ketosis, can also be achieved if individuals subject themselves

FIGURE 9.26 **Synthesis of ketone bodies.** Ketone body synthesis proceeds in the cytosol when levels of acetyl-CoA are elevated. Acetyl-CoA molecules condense in a series of Claisen condensations to form β-hydroxy-β-methylglutaryl-CoA. Acetoacetate can be reduced by β-hydroxybutyrate dehydrogenase to give β-hydroxybutyrate, which is released from cells and travels through the circulatory system to tissues in energetic need.

to very low carbohydrate diets, such as Atkins, South Beach, or Paleo. Ketones can be detected on the breath or in the urine of subjects with ketosis.

Acetoacetate and β-hydroxybutyrate can provide energy, but high levels of these molecules can be dangerous. Both these molecules, and the fatty acids they come from, have carboxylic acid moieties; therefore, high concentrations of them can lower the pH of the blood, which can decrease hemoglobin's ability to carry oxygen.

Although high levels of ketone bodies are associated with disease states or states of starvation, low levels of ketones are found in the bloodstream at concentrations that vary over the course of the day. It is probable that a low level of ketone body production is a part of normal physiology.

Regulation of ketone body production

As with other pathways, ketone body biosynthesis is regulated through hormonal control, allosteric regulators, and substrate availability. These three levels of control work together to regulate ketone body synthesis by regulating fatty acid transport into the mitochondrial matrix. Increases in the catecholamine hormones epinephrine and norepinephrine and decreases in insulin elevate triacylglycerol breakdown, leading to elevated concentrations of fatty acids available for β-oxidation. Glucagon decreases levels of hepatic malonyl-CoA by inhibiting acetyl-CoA carboxylase (ACC), resulting in carnitine palmitoyl transferase I (CPT I) activation, which is the rate-determining step in β-oxidation and ketone body biosynthesis. Finally, oxaloacetate helps regulate ketone body biosynthesis. If oxaloacetate levels are low due to increased gluconeogenesis, there will be less oxaloacetate available to enter the citric acid cycle. In this instance, acetyl-CoA will instead be used for acetoacetate biosynthesis. This pathway also liberates CoA molecules from acetyl-CoA, which allows β-oxidation to continue.

FIGURE 9.27 **Breakdown of ketone bodies provides energy for tissues in energetic need.** Tissues, such as those found in the brain, can use β-hydroxybutyrate and acetoacetate for fuel. Beta-hydroxybutyrate is oxidized back to acetoacetate by β-hydroxybutyrate dehydrogenase (the same enzyme that catalyzed the reduction in ketone body production). Acetoacetate can combine with succinyl-CoA to liberate succinate and form acetoacetyl-CoA. Acetoacetyl-CoA is cleaved by thiolase to give two molecules of acetyl-CoA, again in a reverse of the synthetic pathway.

WORKED PROBLEM 9.5 | Ketones as a weight-loss agent

Ketone bodies are often elevated during periods of weight loss. Imagine that a drug is developed that increases the rate of acetoacetate decarboxylation into acetone. Would this drug be a good option for people who wish to lose weight?

Strategy Think about the chemical pathways involved in ketone body production and breakdown and the function of ketone bodies. Also think about why ketone bodies are produced during weight loss.

Solution Ketone bodies are produced by the liver during fasting; their function is to provide energy to brain tissue when glucose is not available. In some dietary states, carbohydrate intake is curtailed and, as a result, the liver increases ketone body production. Some fraction of acetoacetate spontaneously decarboxylates to form CO_2 and acetone. These carbons are either exhaled or are lost in the urine; they cannot be used for energy. Therefore, we might conclude that a molecule that increases this pathway would lead to carbons being wasted, and hence weight loss.

Follow-up question

In the preceding question, we concluded that increased acetoacetate breakdown would be beneficial. Can you suggest why this might *not* be the case?

9.4 Summary

- Ketone bodies (acetone, acetoacetate, and β-hydroxybutarate) are small, soluble molecules made from acetyl-CoA.
- Ketone bodies provide energy to tissues, most often the brain, that need it in times of fasting.

9.4 Concept Check

- Describe how ketone bodies are synthesized and broken down.
- Describe the biological function of ketone bodies and where in the organism and cell they are made.
- Describe how ketone bodies are helpful and how can they be harmful to the organism.

9.5 | Steroid Metabolism

Cholesterol holds an interesting place in biochemistry. Animals require cholesterol to maintain membrane fluidity and to act as a precursor of several essential molecules, for example, steroid hormones, some fat-soluble vitamins, and bile salts. However, elevated plasma cholesterol is linked to atherosclerosis and heart disease. As a result, there has been significant research into the regulation of cholesterol levels. Cholesterol is largely an animal product, but humans can synthesize all that they need (nearly 1 gram per day), so there is no need for those who do not eat animal products to take cholesterol supplements. Rather, most people consume too much cholesterol in the diet. Less than 300 mg cholesterol per day is the intake currently recommended by the United States Department of Agriculture (USDA) and the American Heart Association. For comparison, there are 12 mg of cholesterol in a glass of low fat milk, 90 mg in a scoop of ice cream, 190 mg in a single egg, and over 205 mg in an average fast-food bacon cheeseburger, two-thirds of the recommended daily intake.

Once cholesterol is synthesized or taken in through the diet, it does not undergo biodegradation in the body; rather, cholesterol and its derivatives are lost or excreted. A significant fraction of the daily requirement for cholesterol is to replace what is lost through the shedding of epithelial cells in skin and the lining of the gastrointestinal tract. Cholesterol derivatives also form bile salts that act as detergents in the gastrointestinal tract and form the basis for steroid hormones. Cholesterol levels are tightly regulated, both in the cell and in the body as a whole, but both loss of cholesterol through the GI tract and blocking biosynthesis of new cholesterol are ways that cholesterol levels can be pharmacologically manipulated.

9.5.1 | Cholesterol is synthesized in the liver through the addition of energetically activated isoprene units

Similar to fatty acids and ketone bodies, cholesterol is synthesized from acetyl-CoA; however, the synthesis of cholesterol from its immediate precursors is somewhat more modular than the synthesis of these other molecules. Energetically activated five-carbon alkenes are made from acetyl-CoA and then undergo condensation reactions to eventually form cholesterol. The first series of reactions used to form the two 5-carbon intermediates are known as the mevalonate pathway.

The first two reactions in the synthesis of cholesterol are the condensation of three molecules of acetyl-CoA. The condensation of the first two molecules, which is catalyzed by thiolase, forms acetoacetyl-CoA, the same reaction employed in the first step of ketone body biosynthesis, as shown in Figure 9.26. Although this is the same intermediate used in ketone body biosynthesis, the enzymes responsible for the synthesis of cholesterol precursors are found in the cytosol, while those responsible for the synthesis of ketone bodies are found in the mitochondria. It is the compartmentalization of these enzymes that regulates the metabolic fate of the products, determining whether they will form cholesterol or ketone bodies. The second reaction is addition of a third molecule of acetyl-CoA (catalyzed by HMG-CoA synthase) to form **β-hydroxy-β-methylglutaryl-CoA**, which is abbreviated as **HMG-CoA**. The name of this compound should help in deducing the structure. Both the hydroxyl group and the methyl group reside on the β carbon of glutarate. Glutarate is the deaminated form of the amino acid glutamate and is a five-carbon dioic acid. Both reactions involved in the synthesis of HMG-CoA are reversible. The next step is the reduction of HMG-CoA to **mevalonate** (**Figure 9.28**). This step requires NADPH to produce the primary alcohol found in mevalonate. Unlike the first two steps, the reduction of HMG-CoA is irreversible and results in the cleavage of the thioester bond to CoA. The enzyme responsible for this committed step in cholesterol biosynthesis is **HMG-CoA reductase**. Like many of the enzymes found in the biosynthesis of cholesterol, HMG-CoA reductase is a transmembrane protein found in the membrane of the endoplasmic reticulum and is the target of many of the most widely used and effective cholesterol-lowering drugs.

In cholesterol biosynthesis, mevalonate units are fused into activated isoprene units. These steps require energy from ATP. Mevalonate is first phosphorylated to 5-phosphomevalonate, which is further phosphorylated to give 5-pyrophosphomevalonate. This molecule gives rise to two important intermediates: Δ3 isopentenyl pyrophosphate and dimethyl allyl pyrophosphate. These molecules are both isoprenes, five-carbon alkenes that are coupled to readily hydrolyzable pyrophosphate groups. They are also isomers, differing only in the placement of the double bond.

Isopentenyl pyrophosphate → (isopentenyl pyrophosphate isomerase) → **Dimethylallyl pyrophosphate**

The next steps in the synthesis of cholesterol involve the condensation of these isoprene units (**Figure 9.29**). The two 5-carbon isomers (Δ3 isopentenyl pyrophosphate and dimethyl allyl pyrophosphate) are condensed by prenyl transferase to form a one 10-carbon molecule, geranyl pyrophosphate. Loss of pyrophosphate provides the energy for this reaction. In this pathway, as with glycolysis and β-oxidation, an early investment of energy provides the energy for subsequent reactions. Another five-carbon molecule (Δ3 isopentenyl pyrophosphate) is added to geranyl pyrophosphate to yield the 15-carbon farnesyl pyrophosphate, again, with energy provided by the loss of a pyrophosphate group. Condensation of two farnesyl pyrophosphate groups produces squalene, a 30-carbon intermediate. The final two pyrophosphates are lost in this reaction, which also requires reducing equivalents, provided by NADPH/H$^+$.

Squalene is highly branched, but it lacks the characteristic rings of a steroid. Two further steps are required to form that distinctive structure (**Figure 9.30**). First, squalene monooxygenase produces an epoxide between C-2 and C-3 of squalene. This process requires reducing equivalents that come from NADPH/H$^+$. Next, in one of the more amazing reactions in biochemistry, an enzyme known simply as cyclase catalyzes a concerted reaction in which all four rings of the steroid nucleus are formed, and the epoxide is cleaved to yield the molecule lanosterol. Nineteen additional steps are required to form the final cholesterol molecule.

Cholesterol is found at significant concentrations only in animal tissues. Plants and fungi employ different steroids as signaling molecules and vary the fatty acid composition of membranes to regulate fluidity.

Other unsaturated molecules are also produced from mevalonate
Cholesterol is not the only molecule produced through this pathway. Farnesyl groups are used by the cell to anchor some proteins in the plasma

FIGURE 9.28 **Mevalonate pathway.** HMG-CoA is reduced to mevalonate. In this reaction, the thioester to CoA is broken and the carboxyl is reduced to a hydroxyl. Mevalonate is sequentially phosphorylated to form 5-pyrophosphomevalonate, which is decarboxylated to form the five-carbon isoprenoid isopentenyl pyrophosphate.

Dimethylallyl pyrophosphate
(5 carbons)

Isopentenyl pyrophosphate
(5 carbons)

prenyltransferase
(head to tail)

PP$_i$

Geranyl pyrophosphate
(10 carbons)

prenyltransferase
(head to tail)

PP$_i$ (5 carbons)

Farnesyl pyrophosphate
(15 carbons)

squalene synthase
(head to head)

NADPH

NADP$^+$ + 2PP$_i$

Squalene
(30 carbons)

FIGURE 9.29 **Synthesis of squalene from isoprenes.** Squalene is formed by sequential condensation reactions fueled by the hydrolysis of phosphate groups. A molecule of each five-carbon isoprene condenses to form the ten-carbon geranyl pyrophosphate. An additional molecule of isopentenyl pyrophosphate adds to form the 15-carbon farnesyl pyrophosphate (pyrophosphate is lost in each of the first two reactions). Finally, two molecules of farnesyl pyrophosphate condense in a head-to-head fashion to form squalene.

membrane. **Figure 9.31** shows various isoprenes, such as ubiquinone, an antioxidant employed in the electron transport chain. Ubiquinone and other quinones are made from farnesyl pyrophosphate. Plants make a variety of molecules from the five-carbon building blocks isoprenyl pyrophosphate and dimethylallyl pyrophosphate, including the carotenoids retinol and beta carotene, numerous essential oils, and latex. Plants employ these molecules as both pigments and antioxidants. The molecules provide scents to attract some animals, for instance, those involved in pollination, or to poison others, such as those that would devour the entire plant. Many of the scents and flavors we commonly encounter in roses, geraniums, lemon, and clove, for example, are due to these compounds. Collectively, these molecules are termed terpenoids.

Regulation of cholesterol biosynthesis

The cell is faced with a complex problem when it comes to cholesterol biosynthesis. It needs to tightly regulate the levels of cholesterol production to match membrane biosynthesis, to generate isoprenoids, and to provide precursors for the formation of diverse molecules with a range of functions. Thus, the cell needs to exert a high level of control over this pathway.

FIGURE 9.30 **Cholesterol is formed from squalene.** Cyclase catalzyes the single step cyclization of squalene into lanosterol. An additional 19 steps are needed to form the final cholesterol molecule.

Ubiquinone
(UQ)

Geraniol

Limonene

Madlen/Shutterstock

angelo gilardelli/Shutterstock

FIGURE 9.31 **Structures of some other isoprenes.** Isoprenes form many diverse structures, especially in plant biochemistry. Shown are ubiquinone (an electron carrier found in mitochondria), geraniol (a scented compound found in geraniums and citronella), and limonene (responsible for lemon/lime flavor). Latex rubber (not pictured) is another example of isoprene chemistry.

Regulation of cholesterol biosynthesis happens at several levels (Figure 9.32). Nearly all of these control steps affect the level of HMG-CoA reductase or the committed step in cholesterol biosynthesis, and they act over different timeframes.

Allosteric control

The most rapid control of cholesterol biosynthesis happens through a negative feedback control loop. Mevalonate, the product of HMG-CoA reductase, can directly inhibit cholesterol biosynthesis. Therefore, if the cell has high levels of mevalonate, the reaction is blocked, providing the most rapidly acting level of control.

Post-translational modification

The next level of regulation is through post-translational modification of HMG-CoA reductase. The enzyme is inactivated by phosphorylation, a reaction mediated by AMP kinase. Although the key phosphorylation and dephosphorylation events are directly regulated by AMPK and a specific HMG-CoA reductase phosphatase, these proteins and their activities are regulated on a broader level by several kinases and phosphatases, including PKA and PP2A. Catecholamines and glucagon inhibit cholesterol biosynthesis by inhibiting phosphatases. In contrast, insulin activates protein phosphatases and therefore activates HMG-CoA reductase.

HMG-CoA reductase can be ligated to ubiquitin and targeted for degradation by a proteasome. As described above, high levels of cholesterol can bind to HMG-CoA reductase through the sterol-sensing domain. When cholesterol is bound, the structure of HMG-CoA reductase is altered, promoting ubiquitination. Therefore, another level of regulation of HMG-CoA reductase is protein degradation. If cholesterol levels are moderately high, cholesterol will bind the protein and inhibit activity; however, at higher concentrations, the equilibrium will shift and the cholesterol-HMG-CoA reductase complex will predominate, increasing the likelihood that the complex will be ligated to ubiquitin and targeted for degradation.

Transcriptional regulation

The final means of regulation available to the cell is to regulate the transcription of the HMG-CoA reductase gene. This occurs through the sterol response element binding protein (SREBP) transcription factor.

HMG-CoA reductase phosphatase dephosphorylates the reductase and returns it to the active state. This is stimulated by the **insulin** signaling pathway but blocked by **epinephrine** and **glucagon.**

Mevalonate
Active
HMG-CoA reductase-OH

HMG-CoA reductase phosphatase

AMPK

HMG-CoA reductase-P
Inactive

FIGURE 9.32 **Regulation of cholesterol biosynthesis.** Cholesterol biosynthesis is largely regulated at the level of HMG-CoA reductase. Phosphorylation of this enzyme results in deactivation, while dephosphorylation produces the opposite effect. Also shown are several of the kinases and phosphatases known to regulate HMG-CoA reductase.

The cell can obtain cholesterol from external sources via low-density lipoproteins (LDL). Additional regulation of the cell's free cholesterol levels happens through the LDL receptor, HMG-CoA synthase, and acyl-CoA cholesterol acyltransferase (ACAT, the enzyme responsible for the synthesis of cholesteryl esters).

The enzymes involved in the production of isoprenoids have a slightly higher affinity for their substrates; that is, they have lower K_m values than the enzymes leading to sterol production, meaning that isoprenoids can still be synthesized when mevalonate concentrations are low.

9.5.2 | Steroid hormones are derived from cholesterol

Steroid hormones are all derivatives of cholesterol (**Figure 9.33**). The first steps in steroid biosynthesis are the oxidative cleavage of the cholesterol side chain and the oxidation of the hydroxyl group to yield progesterone, the master sex hormone. While the cleavage of the side chain occurs in the mitochondria, most other reactions of steroid hormone biosynthesis happen in the smooth endoplasmic reticulum. Many of the enzymes involved are part of the cytochrome P450 family of enzymes, a group of oxidases that employ heme cofactors to carry out reactions.

FIGURE 9.33 Steroid hormone biosynthesis. Steroid synthesis is a highly branched and multistep series of pathways. Following synthesis of progesterone, there is a split between the sex hormones and the corticosteroids. This intermediate leads to the production of all other steroid hormones through the action of numerous enzymes, many of which employ cytochrome P450 to accomplish the chemistry in question.

WORKED PROBLEM 9.6 | Why this step?

Given all of the ways to control cholesterol levels, why would drug companies target HMG-CoA reductase as a way to regulate cholesterol levels?

Strategy Examine how cholesterol is synthesized. Is there anything different about HMG-CoA reductase?

Solution HMG-CoA reductase is an attractive molecule to target, for several reasons. First and foremost, it is the committed, irreversible, and rate-determining step in cholesterol biosynthesis. Such steps are often checkpoints for controlling flux through pathways. Also, HMG-CoA reductase is acted on by many different regulators. Any of these could, in theory, also be used to regulate

the enzyme (and thus the pathway), but modulating these molecules can have undesirable effects. Some of the signaling pathways that affect cholesterol biosynthesis (such as AMPK) also affect other physiological processes. Likewise, modulating other candidate molecules (such as mevalonate) directly can be problematic and may also have undesirable side effects.

Follow-up question Many proteins are joined to a farnesyl group (farnesylated) or otherwise prenylated. HMG-CoA reductase inhibitors may inhibit prenylation of some proteins. What does this say about how strongly these drugs inhibit the pathway? What does this also say about the cell's need for cholesterol versus the cells' need to prenylate proteins?

Progesterone has multiple fates. It can be further modified by hydroxylation and reduction to give the mineralocorticoids and glucocorticoids, such as aldosterone and cortisol. Progesterone also can be hydroxylated, leading to the synthesis of androgens. Androgens are the group of hormones associated with male sexual characteristics but are found in both males and females. Subsequent oxidations and reductions produce the rest of the androgens series, including testosterone. Estrogens are all derived from the androgens. The key step in this conversion is the aromatization of one of the rings of the steroid skeleton. Aromatization of the ring leads to estradiol if the precursor was testosterone.

As with most pathways, regulation of steroid hormone biosynthesis is tightly controlled at several levels. Pituitary signals trigger tissues to initiate production of steroid hormones. Chronic control of these steps occurs at the level of expression of the genes coding for proteins in the specific pathway of interest. At the acute level, a key regulatory step is the availability of cholesterol for conversion to progesterone. This step occurs in the inner mitochondrial membrane. The translocation of cholesterol from the outer to the inner mitochondrial membrane is regulated by the steroidogenic acute regulatory protein (StAR).

StAR is a 30 kDa phosphoprotein that has a hydrophobic channel with a curved β sheet structure (**Figure 9.34**). The molecule consists of a sheet topped by two helices and several turns. The hydrophobic channel is large enough to hold a single cholesterol molecule, but the exact mechanism of transfer—shuttling single molecules of cholesterol, acting as a channel for cholesterol, or facilitating temporary fusion of the inner and outer mitochondrial membranes—has yet to be elucidated.

Levels of precursor hormones can also affect levels of downstream hormones in steroid synthesis. For example, elevated levels of progesterone in the menstrual cycle or during pregnancy perturb levels of mineralocorticoids, resulting in changes in Na^+/K^+ mineral balance (and hence lead to water retention). Abuse of steroids by athletes can also lead to bloating. An extreme and dramatic illustration of the effects of precursor hormone levels is seen in diseases of the adrenal gland that affect mineralocorticoid production, which can lead to severe swelling and edema.

Steroid hormones are metabolized by cytochrome enzymes in the liver. Specifically, cytochrome P450 oxidases oxidize the steroid skeleton, adding hydroxyl groups to make the molecule more water soluble. The oxidized steroids are eliminated from the liver with bile.

FIGURE 9.34 **Structure of the steroid acute regulatory protein (StAR) domain.** StAR binds cholesterol and regulates its transport from the outer to inner mitochondrial membrane where it is acted on by cytochrome enzymes involved in the synthesis of steroid hormones. Cholesterol molecules bind inside the pocket formed by the helix to the left and the β sheet structure. (PDB ID 3FO5 Thorsell, A.G., Lee, W.H., Persson, C., Siponen, M.I., Nilsson, M., Busam, R.D., Kotenyova, T., Schuler, H., Lehtio, L. (2011) Comparative structural analysis of lipid binding START domains. *Plos One* 6: e19521-e19521)

9.5.3 | Bile salts are steroid detergents used in the digestion of fats

Bile salts are amphipathic molecules that act as detergents, helping to solubilize dietary fats in the small intestine, and facilitating their digestion and breakdown into free fatty acids and glycerol before absorption by the intestine. The amphipathic nature of bile salts can be difficult to visualize when examining the structure. Cholesterol is a planar molecule; once derivatized into a bile salt, the molecule has two faces: one polar, the other nonpolar. As a result, these detergents help to solubilize lipids but are gentle enough not to denature enzymes or disrupt plasma membranes of the cells lining the gastrointestinal tract. As with fatty acids, the deprotonated form of the molecule is referred to as a bile salt, while the protonated form is termed a bile acid.

Bile salts can be categorized as conjugated or unconjugated. Conjugation in this sense does not refer to the number and position of double bonds but rather to the covalent addition of an amino acid, typically either glycine or taurine, to the carboxyl group. Addition of such groups typically makes the bile salt much more soluble in water and thus a better emulsifier.

FIGURE 9.35 **Bile salt biosynthesis.** Bile salts are made through multistep pathways. Two initial reactions change cholesterol into 7-α-hydroxycholest-4-en-3one. At this point the pathways diverge. The path shown to the left leads to choloyl-CoA (cholate) (12 steps). The pathway to the right leads to chenodeoxycholoyl-CoA (chenodeoxycholate) and requires one fewer step. Both of these bile salts can be conjugated (coupled to an amino acid) to give the secondary bile salts glycocholate, taurocholate, glycochenodeoxycholate, and taurochenodeoxycholate.

Bile salts are synthesized in the liver (**Figure 9.35**). The rate-determining step in their synthesis is the action of cholesterol 7-hydroxylase, a cytochrome P450 enzyme that uses heme and molecular oxygen to incorporate a hydroxyl group on the C-7 of the cholesterol ring to form 7-α-hydroxycholest-4-en-3-one. The ring is often further hydroxylated at the C-12 position. Finally, the branched tail of cholesterol is oxidized to a carboxylic acid. In many instances, a highly hydrophilic group (glycine or taurine) is joined via an amide linkage to this carboxyl group.

Bile salts are secreted from the liver to the gall bladder, which stores bile (a mixture of bile salts, free cholesterol, and proteins) until it is needed for digestion. The body secretes upwards of 30 g of bile salts a day. Most of the bile salts in this mixture are reabsorbed via an intestinal, or ileal, bile acid transporter, and recycled to the liver. Bile acid sequestrants, that is, compounds that bind to bile salts in the small intestine and sequester them, can be effective at lowering plasma cholesterol, which is the precursor of bile salts. Two examples of these medications are cholestyramine and colsevelam.

Cholestyramine   **Colesevelam**

9.5 Summary

- Steroids are a class of lipids containing a planar systems of four fused rings.
- Cholesterol, the principal steroid from which all others are derived, is synthesized through the mevalonate pathway.
- Steroid hormones are derived from cholesterol and include the sex hormones, glucocorticioids, and mineralocorticoids.
- Bile is a biological detergent composed of cholesterol, proteins, and bile salts.

9.5 Concept Check

- Identify what makes a molecule a steroid.
- Explain the difference between a sex hormone and a bile salt based on their structure.
- Describe functions of steroids and isoprenes in biochemistry and biology.
- Describe the mevalonate pathway, cholesterol biosynthesis, and the regulation of cholesterol biosynthesis.
- Explain in general terms how steroid hormones are thought to act in the cell.
- Explain in general terms how steroids and bile salts are made in the body.

9.6 | Eicosanoid and Endocannabinoid Metabolism

The eicosanoids and **endocannabinoids** are a large family of potent signaling molecules derived from 20-carbon polyunsaturated fatty acids. The best characterized of the precursors is arachidonic acid (AA, $20:4^{\Delta5,8,11,14}$); others include eicosapentaenoic acid (EPA $20:5^{\Delta5,8,11,14,17}$) and dihomogamalinolenicacid (DGLA, $20:3^{\Delta8,\ 11,14}$).

In the cell, these fatty acids are typically esterified to the central hydroxyl group of phosphatidylcholine or phosphatidylethanolamine. Phospholipids with these fatty acids are found almost exclusively on the cytosolic side of the plasma membrane where fatty acids are released by the action of specific phospholipases.

Following its release, the fatty acid can be derivatized in several different ways as shown in for arachidonate.

9.6.1 | Eicosanoids are classified by the enzymes involved in their synthesis

In the linear pathway, arachidonate is acted on by a **lipoxygenase** (LOX) to form **leukotrienes**, as shown in Figure 9.36. These molecules are linear, and they differ from the other eicosanoids in that they lack rings. Leukotrienes are so named because they were first identified in white blood cells and have at least three conjugated double bonds.

In the cyclic pathway, arachidonate is acted on by one of the **cyclooxygenase** enzymes (COX I or COX II) to form prostaglandin H_2 or PGH_2. The name reveals some of the features of these molecules. PG refers to **prostaglandin**, which has a single five-membered ring. PGI refers to prostacyclin, which has a second, oxygen-containing heterocyclic ring. TX refers to a thromboxane, which has a six-membered ring and also contains an oxygen atom. The next letter refers to the order in which it was discovered, and the number refers to the number of double bonds in the molecule outside the ring. Therefore PGH_2 is a prostaglandin (PG) that was discovered eighth (H) and has two double bonds.

Following production of PGH_2, pathways diverge. All of the other prostaglandins, prostacyclins, and thromboxanes are derived from PGH_2. It is generally thought that a single type

FIGURE 9.36 **Major pathways of eicosanoid biosynthesis.** Arachidonate is released from phospholipids by a phospholipase. Once free, arachidonate can be acted on by cyclooxygenase (to yield the prostaglandins, prostacyclins, and thromboxanes), epoxidase (to give the epoxyeicosatrienoic acids) or 5-lipoxygenase (to yield the leukotrienes). All are important mediators of vasodilation, pain, and inflammation.

Drug	Inhibits	Used for
NSAIDS (aspirin, ibuprofen, ketoprofen, naproxyn)	COX I and II	Relief of pain, fever, inflammation
COX II inhibitors (rofecoxib, valdecoxib, celecoxib)	COX II	Chronic inflammation
Prostaglandin creams and suppositories	—	Induction of labor, vasodilation, ulcers
Leukotriene receptor agonist (inhibitors) (montelukast, zarfirlukast)	Leukotriene receptor	Asthma
5-LO inhibitors (zileuton)	5-LO	Asthma

of eicosanoid is produced in a given cell or tissue. The different eicosanoids are usually lipophilic and are thought to act as local signaling molecules, working over short distances in the body and binding to specific receptors. In some instances, eicosanoids can act as ligands for transcription factors such as the peroxisome proliferator-activated receptor (PPAR), although they more often act through a G protein coupled receptor (GPCR). Many details of eicosanoid signaling have yet to be elucidated (**Figure 9.36**).

There are two major isoforms of COX enzymes: COX I and COX II. COX I is constitutively expressed; that is, it is found at constant low levels in many cells and tissues. The products of COX I are used in the organism's day-to-day signaling pathways. Examples of such pathways include regulation of blood pressure, blood clotting, immune responses, labor and delivery, and sleep–wake cycles. In contrast, expression of COX II can be induced. When injury or inflammation damages a tissue, the gene coding for the COX II enzyme is activated and the enzyme is produced. Hence, this protein is involved with processes we typically think of as abnormal, such as pain and inflammation.

To summarize, the COX enzymes catalyze the production of PGH$_2$, which is the precursor of all other prostaglandins, prostacyclins, and thromboxanes. Also, the production of elevated levels of some of these eicosanoids is associated with pain and inflammation. Therefore, blocking the production of PGH$_2$ could block the production of these downstream products and thus decrease pain and inflammation—something that is accomplished with COX inhibitors.

NSAIDS are COX inhibitors

Forms of COX inhibitors have been used since antiquity; they are one of the most widespread of all classes of drugs (**Figure 9.37**). COX inhibitors include the nonsteroidal anti-inflammatory drugs (NSAIDs) aspirin, ibuprofen, ketoprofen, and naproxyn. The role of acetaminophen (Tylenol) as a COX inhibitor is still debated; it is used as an antipyretic (fever reducer) and analgesic (pain reliever) but is not commonly used as an anti-inflammatory drug.

Many people suffer from conditions that used to necessitate taking large doses of NSAIDs for significant periods of time, often resulting in adverse effects such as stomach ulcers. To help counter these effects, a new class of NSAIDs was developed. COX II inhibitors block the action of COX II, the isoform associated with pain and inflammation, but not the action of COX I. However, in 2004, VIOXX, a COX II inhibitor, was voluntarily withdrawn from the market after reports of a possible increased risk of heart attack associated with the drug. The significance of the risk is still a matter of controversy, but the drug has not returned to market. Interestingly, this does not seem to be the case for other COX II inhibitors.

FIGURE 9.37 **Structures of COX inhibitors.** Shown are **A.** the structures of the general COX inhibitors aspirin, ibuprofen, naproxen, and **B.** the COX II inhibitors rofecoxib, celecoxib, and valdecoxib (VIOXX, Celebrex, and Bextra, respectively). Note the structural similarities of these compounds.

9.6.2 | Endocannabinoids such as anandamide are also arachidonate derivatives

A second class of signaling molecules derived from arachidonate are the endocannabinoids. The best characterized of these is anandamide (*N*-Arachidonyl ethanolamine), "ananda," named from the Sanskrit word for bliss. This molecule and other related structures are endogenous ligands for both the cannabinoid and vanilloid receptors. They all contain derivatives of arachidonic acid and are highly insoluble in water. Endocannabinoids are small lipophilic signaling molecules that are thought to act over short ranges.

The cannabinoid receptors (CB1 and CB2) are transmembrane G protein coupled receptors. They were first identified as the receptors that bind to Δ9 tetrahydrocannabinol (THC), the active compound in marijuana. Activation of these receptors results in hypotension, decreased gastrointestinal tract activity, increased appetite (also known as orexia), and decreased pain perception or nociception. The effects on the central nervous system are complex and probably involve more than simply a single G protein signaling pathway.

The vanilloid receptor, transient receptor potential cation channel subfamily V member 1 (TRPV1), is a nonspecific cation channel found in the peripheral nervous system and involved

WORKED PROBLEM 9.7 | NSAIDs in pregnancy

Pregnant women are advised to avoid NSAIDs in the third trimester (the last third) of pregnancy. Why?

Strategy To answer this question, we need to examine the nature and functions of NSAIDs and the changes that occur in pregnancy that might be relevant for the use of NSAIDs.

Solution Although they are available over the counter and are typically thought of as innocuous, NSAIDs, as with any drug, can be dangerous in some circumstances. NSAIDs are general COX inhibitors, and they block the production of the prostaglandins

and prostacyclins associated with pain and inflammation. Prostaglandins of the PGE and PGF family are important in labor and delivery, specifically in uterine contractions and the softening of the uterine opening, referred to as cervical ripening. Inability to produce prostaglandins during this critical phase of pregnancy can lead to stalled labor and complications.

Follow-up question Prostaglandin creams are often used to induce labor. Why are the prostaglandins not administered orally or intravenously?

Compound	Receptor	Source	Effect	Structure
Anandamide or arachidonylethanolamine	Both	Endogenous ligand	Many, feelings of wellness	
Capsaicin	TRPV-1	Hot peppers	Burning sensations, pain relief	
Δ-9 tetrahydrocannabinol (THC)	CB1 and 2	Marijuana	Appetite stimulant, pain relief, antiemetic, treatment of glaucoma	
Rimonabant	CB1 (reverse agonist)	Synthetic	Appetite suppressant	
Vanillin	TRPV-1, likely others	Naturally occurring sources or synthetic	Agent responsible for vanilla flavor, biological effects unclear	

FIGURE 9.38 **Structure of some endocannabinoids and vanilloids** Shown are the structures of the endogenous ligand for the cannabinoid receptors (anandamide or arachidonyl ethanolamine), and two compounds found in plants (the vanilloid receptor ligand capsaicin and Δ-9 tetrahydrocannabinol, the active component in marijuana). Rimonabant is an inverse agonist of the CB1 receptor. The CB1 receptor is shown in blue, and the vanilloid receptor (TRPV-1) is in red and orange. (Vanilloid: PDB ID 5IRX C Gao, Y., Cao, E., Julius, D., Cheng, Y. (2016) TRPV1 structures in nanodiscs reveal mechanisms of ligand and lipid action. *Nature* 534: 347–351; Cannabinoid: PDB ID 5TGZ Hua, T., Vemuri, K., Pu, M., Qu, L., Han, G.W., Wu, Y., Zhao, S., Shui, W., Li, S., Korde, A., Laprairie, R.B., Stahl, E.L., Ho, J.H., Zvonok, N., Zhou, H., Kufareva, I., Wu, B., Zhao, Q., Hanson, M.A., Bohn, L.M., Makriyannis, A., Stevens, R.C., Liu, Z.J. (2016) Crystal Structure of the Human Cannabinoid Receptor CB1. *Cell* 167: 750–762.e14)

in nociception. The channel is stimulated by heat, low pH, and anandamide, but perhaps the best known ligand is capsaicin, the compound responsible for the burning taste of hot peppers.

Both the endocannabinoids and their receptors are the focus of intense scrutiny from researchers and pharmaceutical companies. Due to their role in the regulation of pain, blood pressure, and appetite, these molecules are potential targets for drug development (**Figure 9.38**).

Because the endocannabinoids are all highly lipophilic, they are thought to be generated in the plasma membrane and to function there as well. Unlike other receptors we have seen, the ligand-binding pocket for CB1 and CB2 is in the region of the protein that is buried within the plasma membrane.

Drugs that modulate the cannabinoid receptors are of potential interest to medicine. One such compound, rimonabant, shown in Figure 9.38, is a reverse agonist to the CB1 receptor; that is, it binds to the receptor but dulls the response to that receptor rather than activating or blocking it. Rimonabant was developed as an anorectic or appetite suppressant to help combat obesity. It drives down appetite but also blunts other urges; for example, it blocks cravings for nicotine and has therefore been studied as a smoking cessation aid. However, the drug was withdrawn soon after its introduction to the market due to concerns about adverse effects including increased depression and risk of suicide. Scientists are now focused on developing drugs that have similar positive effects in modulating cannabinoid receptors but with fewer adverse effects.

We've now seen a variety of ways in which lipids can act as signaling molecules. A discussion of how some of these molecules are used as drugs is found in **Societal and Ethical Biochemistry: Performance enhancing drugs**.

Societal and Ethical Biochemistry

Performance enhancing drugs

Throughout history, people have been aware that physical and mental performance can be enhanced biochemically. For example, in ancient times, athletes and warriors would ingest herbal concoctions, animal organs, wine, or opium in the hope of besting their opponents. During the twentieth century, sports medicine was more evidence-based, and it became clear that some drug combinations could measurably improve performance, albeit often with adverse effects for the athlete. To protect athletes, rules were enacted to limit, eliminate, or curtail the use of these compounds. At the same time, there was an increase in the development and use of drugs to give greater improvements in performance and avoid detection from regulatory agencies.

Doping may have first had a significant impact in the 1960s in what was then East Germany. Records at international competitions were shattered by athletes who owed more to the laboratory than the practice field. Steroids, one of the main drugs of choice of the times, became synonymous with cheating, grotesquely overgrown musculature, hair growth, and terrible acne. Other, less obvious adverse effects of steroids include impotence, gynecomastia (breast enlargement in males), gonadal atrophy, and uncontrollable bouts of aggression. This was seen in both male and female athletes abusing these drugs.

There are multiple classes of performance enhancing drugs that are used by athletes to help them excel. We tend not to think of ibuprofen or caffeine as performance enhancing, but without these drugs many people would have a harder time going on their daily run or training for a marathon. Performance enhancing drugs fall into the main categories of painkillers and stimulants, sedatives (used, for example, in shooting sports to steady a hand), diuretics (used by bodybuilders to increase muscle definition, and by boxers and wrestlers to lose water and thus qualify for a lower weight class), and those that promote muscle growth. Anabolic steroids such as methandrostenolone, which falls into this latter class, are synonymous with drugs in sport.

When people think of anabolic steroids, testosterone and its adverse effects is one of the first steroids that comes to mind. In addition to muscle growth, testosterone promotes hair growth, changes in voice, and acne. Women taking testosterone will experience virilization, or the development of male secondary sexual characteristics; men will experience testicular atrophy. Although testosterone will promote muscle growth, athletes are often looking for a specific type of muscle growth, for example, bulk versus definition or speed versus endurance. They also want a drug that is harder to detect than testosterone. In response to these challenges, biochemists developed several different approaches.

The pharmaceutical industry, as common practice, makes numerous derivatives of a parent compound and tests each to see which gives the desired effects. Some of these drugs have legitimate uses in veterinary medicine or as male hormone replacement therapy, but when abused these drugs can provide gains in performance.

A second approach used in drug design employs molecules that are not active as taken but are metabolized or activated by the body. For example, androst-4-ene-3α,17α-diol, or "andro" for short, is an endogenous testosterone precursor used by several professional baseball players in the 1990s. This drug was subsequently banned because of its testosterone elevating properties. Using this strategy, levels of particular precursors or important regulatory steps in the biosynthesis can be bypassed, leading to elevated levels of the hormone of interest. Additionally, some of these precursors may also have androgenic properties.

A new class of drugs that is emerging is the selective androgen receptor modulators (SARMs). These compounds are not steroids in the truest sense because they lack the steroid skeleton; rather, they act as specific agonists or antagonists of the androgen receptor. These drugs can be taken orally, have tissue-specific effects, and cause fewer adverse effects; thus, they may be suitable for treatment of diseases such as wasting, osteoporosis, and prostate cancers. However, they are also being abused by athletes.

All of these drugs work via a similar mechanism. They first bind to steroid receptors in the cytosol; the hormone-receptor complex then translocates to the nucleus, where it binds to specific DNA promoter sequences and affects gene transcription.

To counter some of the adverse effects of anabolic steroids and decrease the chances of detection, masking agents are often used. Such agents include inactive steroid precursors, taken to give the appearance of normal steroid precursor ratios in tests, and diuretics that assist in the elimination of compounds from the body.

Methandrostenolone
(anabolic steroid)

BMS-564-929
(selective androgen
receptor modulator)

Steroids are detected through blood or urine analysis. Typically, the analysis combines some sort of extraction or concentration step (such as a solid-phase extraction) with a chromatographic one (gas chromatography). As new types of drugs or combinations or dosages and patterns of use (termed cycles) are developed, new testing methods are also developed. Recent detection methods employ mass spectrometry and look for unnatural isotopic ratios in the body.

Whether or not steroid abuse is detected, biology will eventually catch up with those taking steroids; that is, the user will eventually experience the adverse effects of taking steroids. Steroid hormones and other performance enhancing drugs, such as erythropoietin, often act through changing levels of gene expression. Thus, there is a danger of eliciting an abnormal growth response, namely, cancer. Lyle Alzado, a former professional football player, attributed the brain tumor that eventually killed him to his rampant steroid use.

© Peter Read Miller/ASSOCIATED PRESS

Time & Life Pictures/Getty Images

9.6 Summary

- Eicosanoids are powerful signaling molecules derived from 20-carbon long polyunsaturated fatty acids. Their production can be blocked through the use of NSAIDs.

- Endocannabinoids are a second group of signaling molecules produced from arachidonic acid.

9.6 Concept Check

- Generally describe the steps involved in eicosanoid production.

- List the processes that eicosanoids mediate.

- Describe how NSAIDs block production of some eicosanoids.

The Bigger Picture

Lipids are a diverse and fascinating set of biological molecules. While often maligned in the media, lipids are critical molecules at all levels of biology. Phospholipids partition compartments in the cell and define the boundary of the cell itself. Neutral lipids such as triacylglycerols insulate and cushion organs, and provide energy in times of scarcity or disease. Cholesterol regulates the fluidity of membranes, and steroid hormones control gene expression and are critical to an organism's mineral balance. Bile salts, another cholesterol derivative, are detergents employed to assist in fat digestion and absorption. Finally, eicosanoids and endocannabinoids, a class of lipid signaling molecules derived from polyunsaturated fatty acids, regulate numerous biological responses, ranging from blood pressure to pain medication to appetite. Lipids are the focus of scrutiny of both researchers and pharmaceutical companies.

Bioinformatics Exercises

Exercise 1 Drawing and Naming Fatty Acids

Exercise 2 Introduction to Lipidomics

Exercise 3 Viewing and Analyzing Fatty Acid Synthase

Exercise 4 Lipid Metabolism and the KEGG Database

Problems

9.1 Properties, Nomenclature, and Biological Functions of Lipid Molecules

1. Examine the molecules in the figure.

    a. Classify or categorize them based on the classes of lipids discussed in this chapter.

    b. Are there any that you can chemically name?

    c. If any of these molecules are amphipathic, indicate which parts of the molecule are hydrophilic and which are hydrophobic.

    d. What is the precursor for each of these molecules?

    e. Saponification is the cleavage of an ester with a strong base. Lipids can also be classified as saponifiable (containing an ester) or nonsaponifiable (lacking an ester). Which of these lipids are saponifiable?

2. Put each of the following series in order of increasing melting point.

    a. stearate, palmitate, arachidate

    b. oleate, stearate, linoleate

    c. tripalmitin, tristearin, triolean

3. Examine the fatty acids in the figure used in problem 1 and:

    a. Describe each using the delta nomenclature, such as $18:1^{\Delta 9}$.

    b. Describe each using the omega nomenclature, such as ω-9.

    c. Give each an IUPAC name, such as octadecenoic acid, and a common name, for example, oleic acid.

4. As previously discussed, phospholipids are common components of membranes. Please indicate how these molecules would align themselves in a phospholipid bilayer, and provide reasons for your answer based on the structure and chemistry of these molecules.

5. Lyso-phospholipids are glycerophospholipids lacking one of the two acyl chains. Based on the shape of these molecules, would it be likely that a solution of lyso-PC would form a bilayer in solution or would it form some other structure?

6. What are the evolutionary advantages to storing energy in a reduced state?

7. Membrane phospholipids are often shown in cartoon form as a circle with two sticks coming out of it. Based on that model, propose cartoon stick figures for the following molecules:

    I. lyso-phosphatidylethanolamine

    II. cholesterol

    III. cholesteryl ester

    IV. 1-palmitoyl-2-linolyl-*sn*-glycero-3-phosphocholine

9.2 Fatty Acid Catabolism

8. When a molecule of steric acid (18:0) is catabolized through β-oxidation, how many molecules of acetyl-CoA are generated? How many $FADH_2$? How many molecules of $NADH/H^+$?

9. How have organisms evolved to ensure that β-oxidation and fatty acid biosynthesis do not occur at the same time? How is this similar to carbohydrate metabolism?

10. Carnitine was popular for a short time as a dietary supplement to help people "burn fat." Do you think this approach would work?

11. Describe the action of oral contraceptives or steroid hormones to a friend who is intelligent but not scientifically literate.

12. Both oral contraceptives and anabolic steroids are sex hormones. Would you anticipate that the effects of one could replace the other? In other words, could anabolic steroids block ovulation or could oral contraceptives cause increased muscle growth?

9.3 Fatty Acid Biosynthesis

13. What are the two sources of acetyl-CoA for fatty acid biosynthesis?

14. In the formation of acetoacetyl-ACP, the CO_2 used to synthesize malonyl-CoA is lost, as shown in Figure 9.18. Would this help make the reaction more or less energetically favorable? Why? What thermodynamic parameters would this influence?

15. AICAR (5-amino-4-carboxamide ribonucleotide) is an experimental compound used in the laboratory but banned in competitive athletic events. It has been called "exercise in a pill." AICAR has been shown in the laboratory to selectively activate AMP kinase (AMPK). Describe what effect this might have on lipid metabolism.

16. C75 is a synthetic molecule that acts in the brain to block the feeding response. It acts in part by inhibiting FAS and blocking the malonyl-CoA mediated inhibition of CPT I. C75 also decreases the phosphorylation, and hence the activity, of AMPK. Taking these three effects into account, how is lipid metabolism affected at the cellular level?

17. Significant effort over the past six decades has been spent on determining the structure of both ACC and FAS. Why have scientists and funding agencies spent so much time and resources on these enzymes?

9.4 Ketone Body Metabolism

18. Bovine ketosis (elevated plasma ketone bodies) is a common disease among cattle that have recently given birth. Why would these animals become ketotic?

19. Ketones, actually acetoacetate, are often tested for in urine rather than in blood. How does assaying urine rather than blood change the test? Can the same assay be used for blood, plasma, and urine? What compounds and interfering substances need to be considered? How would taking readings from urine versus blood change the information the assay provides?

20. Acetoacetate can spontaneously decarboxylate in blood.

    a. What are the products of this reaction?

    b. Would the reaction proceed more rapidly under acidic or basic conditions, and would this matter?

21. Once released from the liver, ketone bodies travel through the circulatory system to tissues that can metabolize them—most notably the brain, although heart and skeletal muscle also have the ability to use

ketone bodies. In these tissues, D-β-hydroxybutyrate is converted to acetoacetate by β-hydroxybutyrate dehydrogenase. What does this conversion tell us about the equilibrium and energetics of this reaction? Can heart and skeletal muscle synthesize ketone bodies? Why or why not?

22. What is the source of carbon atoms in ketone bodies?

23. Why is it unlikely that prokaryotes or plants would make ketone bodies?

9.5 Steroid Metabolism

24. Gallstones are small pebble-like aggregates of cholesterol and other bile components found in the gall bladder, the bile storage organ found below the liver. Although some small stones are comprised of bilirubin (a colored pigment), typical stones contain at least 80% cholesterol. The gall bladder can fill with these stones, creating a painful and dangerous situation that requires surgery. Two new therapies are being tested to remove gallstones. The first involves orally consuming bile salts, such as ursodeoxycholic acid and chenodeoxycholic acid; the second involves injecting methyl-tertbutyl ether into the gall bladder. Explain how each of these treatments would work.

25. One of the functions of cholesterol is regulating the fluidity of the plasma membrane of cells. Many species of cold water fish have low levels of cholesterol. How might such species maintain the fluidity of their membranes?

26. Bisphosphonates are a class of drugs used to treat osteoporosis. Specifically, nitrogen-containing oral bisphosphonates, such as Boniva and Fosamax, target the bone tissue and cause osteoclasts, the cells involved in bone reabsorption, to undergo apoptosis (programmed cell death). Bisphosphonates act by inhibiting farnesyl diphosphate synthase (the enzyme that forms farnesyl pyrophosphate and geranyl pyrophosphate). Examine the structure of a bisphosphonate (ibandronic acid, also known as Boniva).

Ibandronic acid
(Boniva)

What products of this pathway would be affected by the inhibition of farnesyl diphosphate synthase? Examine the substrates of farnesyl diphosphate synthase. How might this drug function with the enzyme? Could HMG-CoA reductase inhibitors be used to treat osteoporosis?

27. Pyrophosphomevalonate is synthesized by the sequential addition of phosphate groups to mevalonate. Draw the structures of mevalonate, 5-phosphomevalonate, and pyrophosphomevalonate. Where are the phosphate groups in pyrophosphomevalonate? Why are both groups not added simultaneously?

28. ADVAIR is an inhaled medication used to treat asthma. It is comprised of two compounds: fluticasone propionate and salmeterol. The structure of fluticasone is shown below. What type of molecule is this? How might it function?

Fluticasone
(ADVAIR)

9.6 Eicosanoid and Endocannabinoid Metabolism

29. Why is it a poor idea for a pregnant woman to take drugs such as ibuprofen in the third trimester of pregnancy?

30. Rimonabant is a reverse agonist for the cannabinoid receptor CB-1. Several studies suggest that the CB-1 receptor ligand binding site is buried in the plasma membrane. If this is the case, would this change the way we think of typical receptor–ligand or enzyme–substrate interactions? What types of weak forces would be involved in the binding of this drug to the receptor?

Rimonabant

31. There are many naturally occurring molecules related to THC, the active compound found in marijuana. If one of these molecules bound to the CB-1 receptor with a 10,000-fold higher affinity than anandamide (the native ligand), would the K_d value be higher or lower?

32. Capsaicin is the molecule that provides the heat in hot peppers.

Capsaicin

It binds to vanilloid receptors and mediates signals of heat and pain to the brain. Drinking water fails to quench the heat of spicy foods, but eating dairy foods, especially vanilla ice cream), works relatively well. Explain why.

33. Many people take aspirin to help prevent a heart attack. Provide a biochemical reason why aspirin may work in this regard.

34. C17 fatty acids are often included as internal standards in high performance liquid chromatography (HPLC) or gas chromatography mass spectrometry (GC-MS) experiments.

    a. What is the purpose of an internal standard?

    b. Why is C17 often included as the internal standard?

35. Thin layer chromatography (TLC) is a very old but widely used technique for separating different lipid classes. TLC plates are typically coated with silica gel, a polar chromatography medium. If you wanted to resolve cholesteryl stearate and lysophosphatidate, would you obtain better results using a nonpolar mobile phase, such as hexanes, or a polar one, perhaps methanol?

36. Ketone bodies in urine are frequently measured with a dipstick assay. A plastic stick is dipped in urine, and a purple color develops in proportion to the amount of ketone present.

    a. Typically, these assays detect acetone and acetoacetate but not β-hydroxybutyrate. Would this complicate the interpretation of the result? Would the assay still be a valid measure of ketone production?

    b. Ketones are detected on the breath of people who are ketotic. Would the loss of ketones through respiration markedly complicate the result?

    c. The reagent in many commercially available ketone test strips is sodium nitroprusside. Does the ability of the test to detect acetate or acetoacetate and not β-hydroxybutyrate provide information on how these compounds would react?

d. The ketone dipstick assay is used to detect levels of ketones in urine. What does it tell you about normal levels of these compounds in urine? What other types of compounds might interfere?

e. If this test was used to assay ketones in the urine of a diabetic animal, would you expect the glucose in the urine to interfere with the result?

f. Why does the complex turn purple in the presence of ketones?

Prussian blue

Data Interpretation

37. The questions below relate to a paper about CPT activity. You do not need to read the paper to interpret the figures. (*Journal of Biological Chemistry* by American Society for Biochemistry & Molecular Biol. Reproduced with permission of American Society for Biochemistry and Molecular Biol in the format Book via Copyright Clearance Center).

a. What is shown in panel A? Why were so many concentrations of drug used? Would using one concentration of inhibitor and looking at different time points provide the same information?

b. Based on panel B, how is the drug affecting CPT I activity?

c. Describe what is happening in panel C. Are these data consistent with the observations in panels A and B?

38. Use the following figure to answer the questions.

a. What is the effect of the drug on cellular cholesterol levels?

b. Why are the values on the y-axis not simply "cholesterol"?

c. Based on this experiment, can you tell how the drug is working?

d. Based on this experiment, can you hypothesize how the drug is working?

e. What is the vehicle, and why did it elevate cholesterol levels?

The next series of experiments were run with radiolabeled cholesterol precursors.

f. Based on these data, how would you propose the drug is functioning?

g. The graph shows no error bars or statistical analysis. Can you tell anything about the significance of the data without those analyses?

39. A collaborator has developed an assay in which she stimulates eicosanoid production in cultured cells by treating them with Indian cobra (*Naja naja atra*) venom. You attempt the assay but find that the cells have clearly begun to lyse. What is one potential conclusion that relates these two observations?

Experimental Design

40. Stearic acid has a pK_a of 4.33. What percentage of this fatty acid would be ionized in the stomach at pH 2.0? In the plasma at pH 7.2? In a lysosome at pH 4.5?

41. Using radiolabeled carnitine, design an experiment to show that fatty acids must be first esterified to carnitine before they are transferred into the mitochondrial matrix.

42. Malonyl-CoA regulates β-oxidation by regulating fatty acid transport into mitochondria. How could you determine which CPT enzyme is being blocked by malonyl-CoA?

43. Before degradation, fatty acids must be activated by coupling them to coenzyme A. How could you show that coupling to CoA is an ATP-dependent process?

44. Design an experiment to show that humans can synthesize oleate $(18:1^{\Delta 9})$ but not linolenate $(18:2^{\Delta 9,12})$. Design the experiment so that an institutional review board (the group overseeing medical and research ethics) would approve the study.

45. You are studying steroid metabolism in a species of plant. You hypothesize that some of the enzymes involved in squalene biosynthesis are in a single multi-enzyme complex, akin to fatty acid synthase. How would you test this hypothesis?

Ethics and Social Responsibility

46. Palm oil, also known as palm kernel oil, is a common ingredient in processed foods. Palm oil comes from tropical plantations and is typically raised in a manner that is not currently sustainable. Is it ethical to eat such foods?

47. It has been reported that, at any given moment in time, one-third of the world's population is in some form of pain. Pain can be debilitating, especially when chronic. While many advances have been made in terms of pain management, opiates, such as morphine, remain one of the most effective drugs for the treatment of severe pain, and others, such as codeine, are still commonly used to treat severe coughs. Despite the addictive nature of these drugs, and their potential for overdose and adverse reactions, they are still very popular and there is no vocal opposition to their clinical use. Given this background, why is there such strong opposition to the medical use of marijuana?

48. Several major cities in the United States have banned the use of *trans* fats in restaurant foods, on the grounds that these foods are a threat to public health. In your opinion, is this a valid reason to ban these foods? Can you think of other instances where foods have been banned or regulated for public health reasons? In your opinion, should the ban on *trans* fats be lifted, or should other substances be added to the list? Validate any scientific claims you make in your argument from a reputable source, such as a well-regarded peer-reviewed journal or scientific institute.

49. Several COX II inhibitors come with a black box warning. These drugs have been linked to an increased risk of heart attack. All drugs have some level of risk and some side effects, some of which are positive, some adverse. What is an acceptable level of risk for a COX II inhibitor compared to a drug used to treat (a) metastatic bone cancer and (b) erectile dysfunction? Is the acceptance of risk the same in all cases? Should it be the same in all cases?

50. Babies born prematurely often have significant problems in breathing because they have not produced sufficient surfactant (a detergent-like combination of phospholipids and amphipathic proteins) to break the surface tension of water on the surface of the alveoli in their lung. Should government agencies devote more funding toward developing new treatments for these babies?

51. Sex hormones are commonly used as pharmaceuticals, often as birth control pills or in hormone replacement therapy. These hormones are excreted from the body and end up in waste water. Based on what you know of the function of these molecules, would you anticipate that their presence in waste water presents an environmental concern? What are the scientific questions pertinent to this discussion?

Suggested Readings

9.1 Properties, Nomenclature, and Biological Functions of Lipid Molecules

Ehnholm, Christian, ed. *Cellular Lipid Metabolism.* New York, New York: Springer, 2009.

Fahy, E., S. Subramaniam, R. C. Murphy, M. Nishijima, C. R. Raetz, T. Shimizu, F. Spener, et al. "Update of the LIPID MAPS Comprehensive Classification System for Lipids." *Journal of Lipid Research* 50 (April 2009): S9–14.

Gurr, I. M., ed. *Lipid Biochemistry: An Introduction.* 3rd ed. New York, New York: Springer, 1980.

The AOCS Lipid Library. Retrieved from http://lipidlibrary.aocs. org/index.html

Vance, D. E., and J. E. Vance, eds. *Biochemistry of Lipids, Lipoproteins, and Membranes.* 5th ed., New York, New York: Elsevier, 2008.

9.2 Fatty Acid Catabolism

Frayn, K. N. "Fat as a Fuel: Emerging Understanding of the Adipose Tissue-Skeletal Muscle Axis." *Acta Physiological (Oxford)* 199, no. 4 (August 2010): 509–18.

Goepfert, S., and Y. Poirier. "Beta-Oxidation in Fatty Acid Degradation and Beyond." *Current Opinion in Plant Biology* 10, no. 3 (June 2007): 245–51.

Houten, S. M., and R. J. Wanders. "A General Introduction to the Biochemistry of Mitochondrial Fatty Acid β-Oxidation." *Journal of Inherited Metabolic Disease* 33, no. 5 (October 2010): 469–77.

Wanders, R. J., and H. R. Waterham. "Biochemistry of Mammalian Peroxisomes Revisited." *Annual Review of Biochemistry* 75 (2006): 295–332.

9.3 Fatty Acid Biosynthesis

Baron, A., T. Migita, D. Tang, and M. Loda. "Fatty Acid Synthase: A Metabolic Oncogene in Prostate Cancer?" *Journal of Cellular Biochemistry* 91, no. 1 (January 1, 2004): 47–53.

Burdge, G. C., and P. C. Calder. "Conversion of α-Linolenic Acid to Longer-Chain Polyunsaturated Fatty Acids in Human Adults." *Reproduction Nutrition Development* 45, no. 5 (September–October 2005): 581–97.

Girard, J., D. Perdereau, F. Foufelle, C. Prip-Buus, and P. Ferré. "Regulation of Lipogenic Enzyme Gene Expression by Nutrients and Hormones." *Federation of American Societies for Experimental Biology* 8, no. 1 (January 1994): 36–42.

Jakobsson, A., R. Westerberg, and A. Jacobsson. "Fatty Acid Elongases in Mammals: Their Regulation and Roles in Metabolism." *Progress in Lipid Research* 45, no. 3 (May 2006): 237–49.

Jitrapakdee, S., and J. C. Wallace. "The Biotin Enzyme Family: Conserved Structural Motifs and Domain Rearrangements." *Current Protein & Peptide Science* 4, no. 3 (June 2003): 217–29.

Kim, K. H. "Regulation of Mammalian Acetyl-Coenzyme A Carboxylase." *Annual Review of Nutrition* 17, (1997): 77–99.

Long, Y. C., and J. R. Zierath. "AMP-Activated Protein Kinase Signaling in Metabolic Regulation." *Journal of Clinical Investigation* 116, no. 7 (July 2006): 1776–83.

Ratledge, C. "Fatty Acid Biosynthesis in Microorganisms Being Used for Single Cell Oil Production." *Biochimie* 86, no. 11 (November 2004): 807–15.

Ruderman, N., and M. Prentki. "AMP Kinase and Malonyl-CoA: Targets for Therapy of the Metabolic Syndrome." *Nature Reviews Drug Discovery* 3, no. 4 (April 2004): 340–51.

Wakil, S. J., and L. A. Abu-Elheiga. "Fatty Acid Metabolism: Target for Metabolic Syndrome." *Journal of Lipid Research* 50 (April 2009): S138–43.

9.4 Ketone Body Metabolism

Baird, G. D. "Primary Ketosis in the High-Producing Dairy Cow: Clinical and Subclinical Disorders, Treatment, Prevention, and Outlook." *Journal of Dairy Science* 65, no. 1 (January 1982): 1–10.

Bergman, E. N. "Energy Contributions of Volatile Fatty Acids from the Gastrointestinal Tract in Various Species." *Physiological Review* 70, no. 2 (April 1990): 567–90.

Krebs, H. A. "The Regulation of the Release of Ketone Bodies by the Liver." *Advances on Enzyme Regulation* 4 (1966): 339–54.

McGarry, J. D., and D. W. Foster. "Regulation of Hepatic Fatty Acid Oxidation and Ketone Body Production." *Annual Review of Biochemistry* 49 (1980): 395–420.

Robinson, A. M., and D. H. Williamson. "Physiological Roles of Ketone Bodies as Substrates and Signals in Mammalian Tissues." *Physiological Reviews* 60, no. 1 (January 1980): 143–87.

9.5 Steroid Metabolism

Brown, M. S., and J. L. Goldstein. "Cholesterol Feedback: From Schoenheimer's Bottle to Scap's MELADL." *Journal of Lipid Research* 50 (April 2009): S15–27.

Goldstein, J. L., and M. S. Brown. "Regulation of the Mevalonate Pathway." *Nature* 343, no. 6257 (February 1, 1990): 425–30.

Russell, D. W., and K. D. Setchell. "Bile Acid Biosynthesis." *Biochemistry* 31, no. 20 (May 26, 1992): 4737–44.

9.6 Eicosanoid and Endocannabinoid Metabolism

Dennis, E. A., S. G. Rhee, M. M. Billah, and Y. A. Hannun. "Role of Phospholipase in Generating Lipid Second Messengers in Signal Transduction." *Federation of American Societies for Experimental Biology* 5, no. 7 (April 1991): 2068–77.

Funk, C. D. "Prostaglandins and Leukotrienes: Advances in Eicosanoid Biology." *Science* 294, no. 5548 (November 30, 2001): 1871–5.

Pertwee, R. G., A. C. Howlett, M. E. Abood, S. P. Alexander, V. Di Marzo, M. R. Elphick, P. J. Greasley, et al. "International Union of Basic and Clinical Pharmacology. LXXIX. Cannabinoid Receptors and Their ligands: Beyond CB$_1$ and CB$_2$." *Pharmacological Reviews* 62, no. 4 (December 2010): 588–631.

Shimizu, T., and L. S. Wolfe. "Arachidonic Acid Cascade and Signal Transduction." *Journal of Neurochemistry* 55, no. 1 (July 1990): 1–15.

Lipids I

1897 ———— Bayer Chemical begins selling aspirin

1905 ———— Franz Knoop feeds derivatized fatty acids to dogs to show that fatty acids are broken down into two carbon pieces (oxidized at the beta carbon)

1930s ———— Administering progesterone can inhibit ovulation

1939 ———— Synthesis of progesterone from saponins (Marker synthesis)

1960s ———— Initial discoveries and characterization of fatty acid synthase
1961 ———— Enovid, the first oral contraceptive, is marketed
1962 ———— Biotin determined to be active component of acetyl-CoA carboxylase
1970 ———— Mechanistic evidence of biotin in acetyl-CoA carboxylase
1971 ———— Aspirin inhibits prostaglandin biosynthesis (Vane et al.)

1979 ———— Platelet activating factor (a phospholipid) can cause acute anaphalaxis in rabbits

1982 ———— Sune Bergstrom, Bengt Samuelsson, and John Vane describe prostaglandins and their synthesis and won the Nobel Prize in Physiology or Medicine

1992 ———— Arachidonylethanolamine recognized as endogenous cannabinoid receptor ligand
1994 ———— Ceramide and sphingolipids linked to apoptosis

2011 ———— High-resolution structure of human ACC1 biotin carboxylase domain

CHAPTER 10

Lipids II

Metabolism and Transport of Complex Lipids

Avigator Thailand/Shutterstock

The strategic petroleum reserve is a store of oil and natural gas to be used in times of national emergency.

Complex Lipids in Context

The United States (U.S.) imports large quantities of oil for domestic use. If this supply were stopped, it could disrupt life across the country. To act as a buffer in the event of a disruption to supplies, the U.S. maintains a large reserve of crude oil, known as the Strategic Petroleum Reserve (SPR). The SPR currently holds over 725 million barrels of oil, which is enough to supply the total demands of the country for almost two months; however, not all of the supply is immediately accessible. Even at the maximum rate of pumping, it would take five months for the total amount of oil to be used. This is because the petroleum is stored as crude oil, rather than gasoline, heating oil, diesel, or jet fuel. The crude oil would need to be refined into those products before it could be used; it would also need to be transported from the SPR to a refinery and then to its final destination.

The SPR is in many ways a good analogy for the neutral lipid reserves of an organism. Animals store neutral lipids in specialized organelles in dedicated tissues that regulate the use of those lipids. Stored lipids provide energy for the organism in times of need and the starting materials for the synthesis of membranes. There are specific mechanisms for lipid mobilization—for example, for delivery to or release from tissues.

This chapter focuses on the synthesis and degradation of phospholipids and neutral lipids, and on the functions, regulation, transport, and trafficking of these molecules at the levels of both the cell and the organism. These interactions are illustrated in **Dynamic Figure 10.1**.

DYNAMIC FIGURE 10.1 Dietary lipids are digested in the gut and packaged into lipoproteins. Animals use lipoproteins to transport lipids in the bloodstream. Triacylglycerol and phospholipid metabolism are linked through phosphatidate.

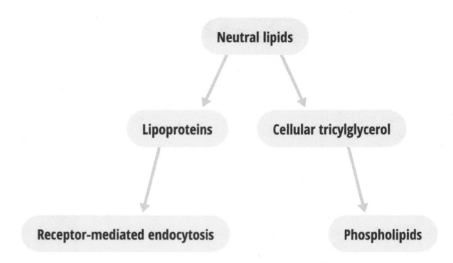

COMMON THEMES

Evolution's outcomes are conserved.	• As seen in other chapters, pathways for synthesis of molecules common to all of life, such as phospholipids, are conserved throughout evolution.
	• As animals evolved, they adapted to different environments and challenges. Analysis of genes from different animals reveals that genes coding for proteins involved in neutral lipid transport and storage evolved more recently, and thus may address needs that are lacking in more primitive species.
Structure determines function.	• Lipoproteins and lipid storage droplets have a similar structure: an amphipathic coating of phospholipids and proteins surrounding a nonpolar core.
	• The proteins that coat lipoproteins or lipid storage droplets adhere to the surface of these structures via amphipathic helices or hydrophobic patches on the surface of the protein.
	• Many of the enzymes involved in lipid metabolism require a protein cofactor for optimal activity.
	• In higher organisms, nonpolar molecules require some type of soluble carrier to move them through the circulation.
Biochemical information is transferred, exchanged, and stored.	• The storage and mobilization of neutral lipid stores is tightly regulated by the actions of several hormones.
	• The regulation of the biosynthesis of neutral lipids and glycerophospholipids is coordinated through phosphatidate (PA) and lysophosphatidate (lyso PA) via lipins and acyltransferases.
Biomolecules are altered through pathways involving transformations of energy and matter.	• The metabolism of both glycerophospholipids and neutral lipids converge at PA and lyso PA.
	• Lipoproteins provide an elegant and specific system for delivering both dietary and *de novo* lipids to different tissues.
	• Lipid storage droplets are analogous to lipoproteins both in form and function. Lipolysis (the regulated breakdown of triacylglycerols in the lipid droplet) results in the mobilization of energy through the release of free fatty acids and glycerol into the plasma.

Phospholipid Metabolism

Phospholipids are amphipathic lipid molecules containing a phosphate group and can be broadly categorized by their backbone alcohol. Glycerophospholipids use glycerol as their backbone, whereas sphingolipids employ sphingosine. Both have a single phosphate esterified to the backbone alcohol. A second, head group alcohol, also esterified to the phosphate, imparts many of the physical and chemical properties to the phospholipid. In addition to being characterized by their backbone, phospholipids are also categorized and named by their head group (**Figure 10.2**).

The most common glycerophospholipids, discussed here, are phosphatidylcholine (PC), phosphatidylethanolamine (PE), phosphatidylserine (PS), phosphatidylinositol (PI), phosphatidate (PA, also referred to as phosphatidic acid), phosphatidylglycerol (PG), and cardiolipin (CL). The sphingolipids discussed in this chapter are ceramide, sphingomyelin, sphingosine, and glycosphingolipids.

Biosynthesis of phospholipids in eukaryotes occurs mainly in the endoplasmic reticulum (ER). However, phospholipids can be modified or remodeled in the plasma membrane; the type of modification varies depending on the location of the enzymes that catalyze the modifications (**Figure 10.3**). In prokaryotes phospholipid biosynthesis occurs primarily in the inner leaflet of the plasma membrane.

The synthesis of phospholipids is an anabolic process which requires energy that can come in several forms but is typically in the form of an activated carrier (as seen with glycogen synthesis and fatty acid metabolism, for example). In the case of phospholipid synthesis, the carrier is the nucleotide **cytidine diphosphate (CDP)**.

This section and section 10.2 highlight how phospholipid metabolism and neutral lipid metabolism are inextricably linked at several points.

Cytidine diphosphate (CDP)

FIGURE 10.2 **The structure of some common phospholipids.** Shown are the glycerophospholipids phosphatidylserine, phosphatidylethanolamine, phosphatidylcholine, and phosphatidylinositol and the sphingolipid sphingomyelin.

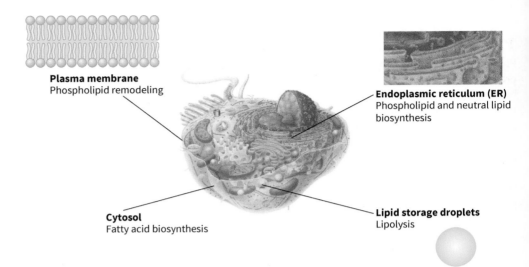

Plasma membrane
Phospholipid remodeling

Endoplasmic reticulum (ER)
Phospholipid and neutral lipid
biosynthesis

Cytosol
Fatty acid biosynthesis

Lipid storage droplets
Lipolysis

FIGURE 10.3 **Locations of lipid biosynthesis and degradation in the cell.** Lipids are made and degraded in different organelles in the cell.

10.1.1 Glycerophospholipids are derived from phosphatidate or diacylglycerol using activated carriers

Phosphatidate is central to both phospholipid and neutral lipid metabolism. Its synthesis begins with glycerol-3-phosphate (**Figure 10.4**). The glycerol-3-phosphate can be derived either from the phosphorylation of glycerol, as seen in the liver and some other tissues, or from the reduction of dihydroxyacetone phosphate (DHAP). Glycerol-3-phosphate is acylated to form lyso PA. Lysophospholipids, such as lyso PA, are lipids that lack one of the fatty acyl chains. Lyso PA can also be derived by first acylating dihydroxyacetone phosphate and then reducing the acylated form. PA is formed by the acylation of lyso PA. At this point, a branching occurs, in that PA can be used as a building block for triacylglycerol biosynthesis or can be shuttled into phospholipid biosynthesis.

Phosphatidate can undergo an exchange reaction with CTP, catalyzed by CDP-diacylglycerol (DG) synthase, to yield CDP-DG and pyrophosphate, PP_i, which is further hydrolyzed into two molecules of inorganic phosphate, P_i (**Figure 10.5**). Like other molecules joined to nucleotides, CDP-DG is an active carrier of DG, and it undergoes exchange reactions with other molecules, such as inositol, to give phosphatidylinositol and CDP, glycerol-3-phosphate to give phosphatidylglycerol and CDP, and phosphatidylglycerol to give cardiolipin and CDP. In each of these cases, CDP acts as a carrier of DG.

Phosphatidylcholine and phosphatidylethanolamine also employ CDP in their biosynthesis, but in each case, CDP activates a different group. Ethanolamine is phosphorylated by ethanolamine kinase, and choline by choline kinase with ATP serving as the source of the phosphate. The resulting product, either phosphoethanolamine or phosphocholine, undergoes an exchange reaction with CTP to give CDP-ethanolamine or CDP-choline, respectively, plus pyrophosphate (PP_i). The CDP-linked molecules can add the ethanolamine phosphate or choline phosphate moieties to DG, to produce PC or PE (**Figure 10.6**). PC can also be made by the methylation of PE. In these reactions S-adenosyl methionine serves as the methyl donor.

Phosphatidylethanolamine can also be used as a phospholipid precursor
Phosphatidylethanolamine is one of the most common phospholipids in all organisms; it also serves as a precursor for several other phospholipids. We have just seen how PE can contribute to PC biosynthesis, but PE can also undergo head group exchange with serine, to form phosphatidylserine and ethanolamine. This reaction is catalyzed by PE serine transferase (**Figure 10.7**).

Some other phospholipids can also change head groups. For example, PC can exchange with serine to yield phosphatidylserine and choline. Phosphatidylserine can be decarboxylated by phosphatidylserine decarboxylase to produce PE.

FIGURE 10.4 **Phosphatidate (phosphatidic acid) biosynthesis.** Phosphatidate is derived from either dihydroxyacetone phosphate or glycerol-3-phosphate.

Long-chain hydrocarbons can be attached through other linkages

While most often phospholipids have fatty acids attached via ester linkages to the glycerol backbone, other linkages are also observed. Ether lipids attach a long-chain fatty alcohol (analogous in structure to a fatty acid) to the glycerol backbone. In addition, ether lipids containing alcohols with double bonds between C-1 and C-2, termed plasmalogens, are also found in nature.

10.1.2 | Sphingolipids are synthesized from ceramide

Sphingolipid synthesis follows a somewhat different pathway than glycerophospholipid synthesis, but there are many similarities such as the building up of molecules in a modular fashion from activated carriers. The synthesis of sphingolipids begins with palmitoyl-CoA,

FIGURE 10.5 **Phosphatidy-linositol, phosphatidylglycerol and cardiolipin are built from activated diacylglycerol donors.** The alcohol groups in phosphatidylinositol and diacylglycerol are coupled to CDP-DG, which acts as an activated carrier of diglyceride to form the phosphodiester bond in those phospholipids. In the mammalian synthesis of cardi-olipin the alcohol is provided by phosphatidylglycerol.

which reacts with serine to form 3-ketosphinganine (**Figure 10.8**). In examining the backbone structure of the sphingolipids, it may be helpful to recall the structure of serine and that the carboxyl moiety of serine is lost as CO_2 in the formation of 3-ketosphinganine. The carbonyl of 3-ketosphinganine is reduced to a hydroxyl group forming sphinganine. This is

HO—CH$_2$—CH$_2$—NR$_3^+$

R = H   **Ethanolamine**
R = CH$_3$ **Choline**

ethanolamine kinase ⎰—ATP
or choline kinase ⎱—ADP

$$^-O-\overset{\overset{O}{\|}}{\underset{\underset{O^-}{|}}{P}}-O-CH_2-CH_2-NR_3^+$$

R = H   **Phosphoethanolamine**
R = CH$_3$ **Phosphocholine**

CCT ⎰—CTP
    ⎱—PP$_i$

Cytidine—$\overset{\overset{O}{\|}}{\underset{\underset{O^-}{|}}{P}}$—O—$\overset{\overset{O}{\|}}{\underset{\underset{O^-}{|}}{P}}$—O—CH$_2$—CH$_2$—NR$_3^+$

R = H   **CDP-ethanolamine**
R = CH$_3$ **CDP-choline**

C/EPT ⎰—1,2-diacylglycerol
     ⎱—CMP

R''—C—O—C—H ... CH$_2$—O—C—R'
CH$_2$—O—P—O—CH$_2$—CH$_2$—NR$_3^+$

R = H   **Phosphatidylethanolamine** (PE)
R = CH$_3$ **Phosphatidylcholine** (lecithin) (PC)

phosphatidylethanolamine ⎰—Ado-Met
methyltransferase ⎱—Ado-Hcy

CH$_2$—O—C—R'
R''—C—O—C—H
CH$_2$—O—P—O—CH$_2$—CH$_2$—N$^+$H$_2$CH$_3$

phosphatidylethanolamine ⎰—Ado-Met
methyltransferase ⎱—Ado-Hcy

CH$_2$—O—C—R'
R''—C—O—C—H
CH$_2$—O—P—O—CH$_2$—CH$_2$—N$^+$H(CH$_3$)$_2$

phosphatidylethanolamine ⎰—Ado-Met
methyltransferase ⎱—Ado-Hcy

CH$_2$—O—C—R'
R''—C—O—C—H
CH$_2$—O—P—O—CH$_2$—CH$_2$—N$^+$(CH$_3$)$_3$

Phosphatidylcholine (PC)

CCT=
CTP:phosphoethanolamine cytidyltransferase
or
CTP:phosphocholine cytdyltransferase

C/EPT=
CDP-ethanolamine:1,2-diacylglycerol phosphoethanolamine tranferase
or
CDP-choline:1,2-diacylglycerol phosphocholine transferase

Ado-Met=S-adenosylmethionine
Ado-Hcy=S-adenosylhomocysteine

FIGURE 10.6 **Phosphatidy-lethanolamine and phosphatidylcholine biosynthesis employs an activated alcohol.** Phosphatidylethanolamine is synthesized from diacylglycerol and an activated alcohol; in this case, the alcohol is activated by CTP resulting in CDP-ethanolamine or CDP-choline. Phosphatidylcholine can also be synthesized by the successive trimethylation of phosphatidylethanolamine. In this instance, *S*-adenosyl methionine serves as the methyl donor.

Palmitoyl-CoA   **Serine**

3-ketosphinganine synthase $\rightarrow CO_2^- + CoASH$

3-ketosphinganine

3-ketosphinganine reductase $\left\{ \begin{array}{l} NADPH + H^+ \\ NADP^+ \end{array} \right.$

Sphinganine

acyl-CoA transferase $\left\{ \begin{array}{l} R-\overset{O}{\overset{\|}{C}}-SCoA \\ CoASH \end{array} \right.$

Dihydroceramide

dihydroceramide dehydrogenase $\left\{ \begin{array}{l} FAD \\ FADH_2 \end{array} \right.$

Ceramide

FIGURE 10.8 **Sphingolipid biosynthesis.** Several common sphingolipids are intermediates in the biosynthesis of ceramide.

Phosphatidylethanolamine

+

Serine

phosphatidylethanolamine serine transferase $\rightarrow HO-CH_2-CH_2-NH_3^+$

phosphatidyl serine decarboxylase $\succ CO_2$

Phosphatidylserine

FIGURE 10.7 **Phosphatidylserine and phosphatidyletha- nolamine biosynthesis.** Phosphatidylserine can be derived through an exchange reaction of the amino acid serine and phosphatidylethanolamine. Likewise, phosphatidylserine can be decarboxylated to form phosphatidylethanolamine.

a biosynthetic pathway similar to the reactions of other anabolic pathways, such as fatty acid biosynthesis; hence, the electron donor for the reaction is NADPH. Dihydrosphingosine is acylated to form dihydroceramide, with the acyl donor being an acyl-CoA. As with many other biosynthetic pro- cesses, including phospholipid biosynthesis, an activated carrier is used to overcome an energetically unfavorable process. Dihydroceramide undergoes a second round of reduction to form ceramide. In this reaction, a double bond is formed between C-4 and C-5 in the acyl chain, with flavin adenine dinu- cleotide (FAD) as the cofactor. FAD is often used as a cofactor to introduce double bonds in several other biochemical pathways, for example, in the citric acid cycle and in some of the reactions of fatty acid biosynthesis.

Ceramide is the central sphingolipid (**Figure 10.9**). As with glycerophos- pholipids, it can undergo an exchange of head groups. For example, ceramide can react with phosphatidylcholine to yield sphingomyelin and diacylglycerol; it can also be glycosylated to form cerebrosides. In this instance, glucose is added to the ceramide using CDP-glucose as an active carrier. CDP-glucose is serving a similar role as CDP-DG does (discussed above).

10.1.3 Phospholipases and sphingolipases cleave at specific sites

The enzymes that cleave phospholipids are referred to as phospholipases (**Figure 10.10**). While some of these enzymes have specific names (such as lipin) related to their discovery, all enzymes can be categorized based on the substrates they cut and the point of cleavage. Phospholipases are categorized using a capital letter, or a letter and a number, to designate where the enzyme acts. Two of these enzymes play important roles in signal transduction and were previously mentioned.

Phosphatidylcholine

Ceramide

Diacylglycerol

Sphingomyelin

FIGURE 10.9 Sphingomyelin can undergo head group exchange to produce other sphingolipids. Ceramide can be generated by the action of sphingomyelinases on sphingomyelin. It can undergo exchange reactions with other glycerophospholipids to exchange phospho head groups (highlighted with a dashed line) and generate diacylglycerol. In this instance, ceramide exchanges with phosphatidylcholine to yield sphingomyelin and diacylglycerol.

Phospholipase A_2 cleaves the acyl chain in the second position of a phospholipid, typically freeing arachidonate as the fatty acid. The liberated arachidonate is used in eicosanoid biosynthesis. Low molecular weight phospholipases A_2 are common components of many venoms, such as those of some snakes and of bees (**Figure 10.11**). Part of the effect of the phospholipase in these venoms is due to the release of arachidonate, which leads to unabated eicosanoid biosynthesis; however, it is likely that the main function of the phospholipase is to destroy the plasma membrane of cells, resulting in rupture and cell death.

Phospholipase C cleaves phospholipids between the glycerol backbone and the phosphoalcohol head group. Phospholipase C is important in several signaling cascades, generating second messengers, such as DG and inositol-1,4,5-trisphosphate.

phospholipase A_2 (PLA$_2$)

phospholipase C (PLC)

FIGURE 10.10 **Phospholipase cut sites.** Phospholipases are named and categorized depending on where they cleave the phospholipid molecule. Phospholipases A_2 (PLA$_2$) cleaves the ester linkage in the 2 position of the glycerol backbone. Phospholipase C (PLC) cleaves on the backbone side of the phosphodiester linkage.

A.

Hinge

Membrane binding domain

Ca^{2+} ions

Catalytic domain

Human cytosolic phospholipase A_2

B.

Indian cobra (*Naja naja sagittifera*) **venom phospholipase A_2**

FIGURE 10.11 **Structure of two different phospholipases A_2.** **A.** Shown is the structure of a human cytosolic phospholipase A_2. The protein has two domains; the smaller of the two is a C2 domain and is important for binding Ca^{2+} and the lipid bilayer. This domain is primarily β sheet. The larger of the two domains is the catalytic domain. The C2 domain also acts as a lid to close down on the active site preventing substrate from binding in the active site before activation has occurred. Binding of Ca^{2+} by the C2 domain results in translocation of the enzyme from the cytosol to the membrane where liberation of arachidonate initiates prostaglandin production. (PDB ID 1CJY Dessen, A., Tang, J., Schmidt, H., Stahl, M., Clark, J.D., Seehra, J., Somers, W.S. (1999) Crystal structure of human cytosolic phospholipase A2 reveals a novel topology and catalytic mechanism. *Cell* 97: 349–360) **B.** The structure of a venom phospholipase from *Naja naja sagittifera* (Indian cobra) is shown. In contrast to the human cytosolic PLA$_2$, this is a much smaller molecule and is not as strictly regulated. Venom phospholipases lack the lid structure seen in other lipases. (PDB ID 1YXH Jabeen, T., Singh, N., Singh, R.K., Ethayathulla, A.S., Sharma, S., Srinivasan, A., Singh, T.P. (2005) Crystal structure of a novel phospholipase A(2) from Naja naja sagittifera with a strong anticoagulant activity *Toxicon* 46: 865–875)

Phosphocholine   **Ceramide**

FIGURE 10.12 **Sphingomyelinases.** Sphingomyelinases, like other phospholipases, are categorized by where they cut the substrate. Sphingomyelinase C cuts to yield phosphocholine and ceramide.

Sphingolipases Sphingolipids are cleaved by their own series of lipases. Sphingomyelinase cleaves sphingomyelin into ceramide and phosphocholine (**Figure 10.12**). This enzyme has several isoforms that are active at different pHs (neutral, acidic, or basic). The isoforms catalyze the same reaction but are found in different locations in the cell and provide different functions; for example, some modify structural sphingolipids, whereas others are involved in signal transduction.

The analysis of the different lipid molecules found in a cell, tissue, or organism is termed "lipodomics." This field is discussed in **Biochemistry: Lipidomics.**

Biochemistry

Lipidomics

Just as genomics is the study of the genome, and proteomics is the study of the proteome, lipidomics is the study of the lipidome, that is, the lipids of an organism, tissue, or cell.

As techniques and computational power increase and become more accessible, "–omics-based" approaches are another investigative tool for the researcher. Rather than asking a single specific question, such as "Do the levels of dioleoyl phosphatidylcholine in this cell increase when it is treated with drug X?," it is possible to ask a much broader question, such as "When cells are treated with drug X, what happens to the levels of each and every lipid in the cell?" The strength of this approach should be apparent. As with other bioinformatic studies, there is a plethora of potentially useful data, but sifting through that data continues to be challenging.

Lipid samples are, in many ways, simpler to manipulate than other types of biomolecules. Being small, largely hydrophobic, organic molecules, lipids can be isolated from tissues via simple liquid extraction with organic solvents. Care must be taken to avoid oxidation of sensitive species such as aldehydes. Likewise, the concentrations of some bioactive lipids may be at low levels. Analytical techniques, such as solid phase extraction, can be employed to concentrate these trace lipids.

One of the main workhorses of lipidomics is mass spectrometry. Although traditional mass spectrometry (GC-MS or FAB) has been used for decades to assist in the characterization of lipids, newer advances in ionization techniques have fewer drawbacks and can be used to detect whole molecules and

polar lipids; these techniques are commonly used in lipidomics. The two most common ionization techniques, electrospray ionization (ESI) and matrix assisted laser desorption ionization (MALDI), permit the ionization of samples isolated from high performance liquid chromatography (HPLC) or other chromatographic systems. Recent advances in MALDI techniques have permitted the direct desorption of lipids from a slice of tissue, so called *in situ* mass spectrometry. These ionization methods can be coupled with other ion separation and detection techniques for analysis.

It used to be difficult to identify a sample based on spectral data. The spectra of known molecules were contained in incredibly large tomes of data, and an investigator had to sift through this material to characterize a sample. In the case of mass spectrometry, analysis of fragmentation patterns gave indications as to the functional groups present. Advances in computational power and software have made it easier to translate the raw mass spectrometry data into candidate lipids from a database. Likewise, computers have facilitated the development of metabolic maps of lipidomic data. Thus, advances in techniques make these experiments possible, and computers and software have made it much easier to interpret data. An example of this is the lipidomics profile of tears. Thanks to lipidomic studies, it is now known that tears contain hundreds of different lipids and that the composition of tears changes in different disease states. The individual roles and functions of many of these lipids remain unknown.

Clearly the future of these techniques holds considerable promise for lipid profiling.

WORKED PROBLEM 10.1 | Along came a spider . . .

Many venoms contain phospholipases that are important in the mechanism of action of venom. Your research laboratory has been characterizing venom from a newly discovered species of spider of the family *Sicariidae*, a group that includes the brown recluse spider. One of the researchers treated an extract of cellular

lipids with the spider venom, performed thin layer chromatography (TLC) on the sample, and visualized them. The results of this experiment are shown below. Based on this information, propose one component of the venom.

Lane 1 = control lipid
Lane 2 = venom treated lipid

Abbreviations: Cer, ceramide; FFA, free fatty acids;
NL, neutral lipid; PC, phosphatidylcholine;
PE, phosphatidylethanolamine; SM, sphingomyelin.

Strategy Compare the lipid composition between the experimental venom-treated sample and the control. How have the lipids been affected by treatment with the venom? Based on the discussions in section 10.1, propose one or more enzymes that might be in the sample.

Solution Many venoms contain phospholipases. TLC is a simple and inexpensive way to separate and analyze phospholipids. In these samples, treatment of the cellular lipid extract with the venom led to the loss of sphingomyelin and the accumulation of ceramide. These results indicate that the enzyme is probably a sphingomyelinase acting as a phospholipase C (see Figure 10.12). To verify this finding, the venom would have to be separated into its component proteins to check that it does not contain combinations of other enzymes that yield similar results to those seen with a sphingomyelinase.

Follow-up question Describe the biological ramifications of this reaction in an organism bitten by this newly discovered species of spider.

10.1 Summary

- Glycerophospholipids have a glycerol backbone; sphingolipids have a sphingosine backbone.
- Phospholipases cleave glycerophospholipids at specific sites; sphingolipases do the same for sphingolipids.
- Glycerophospholipids and sphingolipids are built up and broken down in a modular fashion, using activated carriers.
- CDP is often used as the active carrier in biosynthesis of phospholipids. Glycerophospholipids are mainly derived from either DG or PA; sphingolipids are mainly derived from ceramide.

10.1 Concept Check

- Describe how the phospholipids are synthesized and interconverted.
- Identify common themes in phospholipid metabolism.

10.2 Digestion of Triacylglycerols

Triacylglycerols represent a particularly rich source of energy, providing 9 kcal/g of energy, which is twice that of carbohydrates and proteins. Triacylglycerols are therefore an excellent way for an organism to store energy. They are also hydrophobic and unlike proteins or carbohydrates are stored in the absence of water. This too is an advantage for an organism that is mobile because storing energy as triglycerides means the organism can store energy without having water to keep these molecules in solution. However, due to their hydrophobic nature, digestion and transport of triacylglycerols is not as simple as that of carbohydrates and proteins.

10.2.1 Triacylglycerol digestion begins in the gastrointestinal tract

There are two locations in the body where triacylglycerol breakdown occurs. Each has a different class of lipase associated with it.

In animals, minor amounts of lipid degradation occur in the mouth and stomach. These reactions are catalyzed by lingual lipase, produced on the surface of the tongue, and gastric lipase, produced in the stomach. These lipases degrade triacylglycerols into diacylglycerol and free fatty acid. They are most active at low pH values and are characterized as acidic lipases. While these lipases are clearly important in digestion, they are not as efficient or as important as pancreatic lipase. Neither lingual lipase nor gastric lipase requires other protein cofactors for maximal activity.

Lipid digestion begins in earnest in the upper small intestine, referred to as the duodenum (**Figure 10.13**). Bile, comprised of bile salts, cholesterol and apolipoproteins, is secreted from the gallbladder, through the common bile duct, and into the duodenum. Bile breaks up and solubilizes dietary triacylglycerols in the intestinal lumen. In effect, the components of bile act as detergents, breaking large globules of dietary lipid into smaller micelles of lipid coated with bile. This emulsification greatly increases the surface area of the lipid and thus provides pancreatic lipase greater access to the triacylglycerol in the micelles.

FIGURE 10.13 **Colipase and pancreatic lipase.**
A. Pancreatic lipase is made in the acinar cells of the pancreas. These cells form 90% of the mass of the pancreas and also secrete proteolytic enzymes. **B.** Acinar cells are different from the islet cells that produce the hormones insulin and glucagon. (A, B: Tortora; Derrickson, *Principles of Anatomy & Physiology*, 13e, copyright 2012, John Wiley & Sons. This material is reproduced with permission of John Wiley & Sons, Inc.) **C.** Pancreatic lipase consists of two domains, a larger, amino-terminal catalytic domain (right) and a smaller carboxy-terminal regulatory domain (left). The regulatory domain interacts with colipase, which is responsible for binding to lipid micelles. Colipase has three hydrophobic loops, termed "fingers" (two of which are visible), through which lipid binding occurs. (PDB ID 1N8S van Tilbeurgh, H., Sarda, L., Verger, R., Cambillau, C. (1992) Structure of the pancreatic lipase-procolipase complex. *Nature* 359: 159–162)

The main step in the degradation of dietary lipids is the hydrolysis of the ester linkage between the fatty acids of a triacylglycerol and the glycerol backbone. This reaction is catalyzed by pancreatic lipase, which is secreted from the acinar cells of the pancreas and delivered through the pancreatic duct to the common bile duct and the duodenum. While the pancreas may be best known for the pancreatic islets that produce the endocrine hormone insulin, the exocrine tissues of the pancreas, including the acinar cells, form 80% of the mass of the pancreas and are responsible for the production of hydrolytic enzymes.

There are three major differences in the two lipases of the upper gastrointestinal tract, referred to as acidic lipases, and the single lipase of the lower gastrointestinal tract, pancreatic lipase.

- Lingual and gastric lipases are active at acidic pH values (pH 3–6), whereas pancreatic lipase is active at alkaline pH. As partially digested food, referred to as chyme, leaves the stomach and moves into the duodenum and further down the digestive tract, the pH rises. As this happens, lingual and gastric lipases lose activity, and pancreatic lipase becomes more active.
- Lingual and gastric lipases are regulated differently. Acidic lipases do not require a protein cofactor for optimal activity, whereas pancreatic lipase requires a protein cofactor, known as colipase to achieve maximal catalysis.
- Lingual and gastric lipases have different substrates. In contrast to the acidic lipases, pancreatic lipase can act on either triacylglycerol (hydrolyzing it to diacylglycerol and a free fatty acid) or diacylglycerol itself (producing monoacylglycerol and a second molecule of free fatty acid). Therefore, pancreatic lipase can degrade one molecule of triacylglycerol into two molecules of free fatty acids and one molecule of 2-monoacylglycerol, all of which can be absorbed by the small intestine and metabolized.

Some lipases require protein cofactors for optimal activity   The cofactor colipase is a small protein that binds to both pancreatic lipase and the micelle. In effect, colipase helps to anchor pancreatic lipase to the micelle and increase the availability of substrate. It also binds pancreatic lipase via the enzyme's regulatory domain in the non-catalytic carboxy-terminus in an active conformation, helping to stabilize the active state of the enzyme. Other enzymes that have hydrophobic substrates, such as lipoxygenases, have domains that include structures similar to the carboxy-terminus of pancreatic lipase. These domains help the enzyme to bind to the micelle, lipoprotein, or membrane. It is unclear whether these enzymes also require protein cofactors for optimal activity. As discussed in sections 10.3 and 10.6, several lipases including lipoprotein lipase, hormone sensitive lipase, and adipocyte triacylglycerol lipase require protein cofactors for maximal activity.

10.2.2 | Dietary lipids are absorbed in the small intestine and pass into lymph before entering the circulation

Lipid micelles composed of monoacylglycerols, fatty acids, and cholesterol in the small intestine are absorbed by enterocytes. Within the enterocytes, the absorbance of these molecules is thought to occur predominantly by passive diffusion, although specific transporters may be involved in the absorbance of cholesterol and some fatty acids. Bile appears to be necessary for this process to occur; in the absence of bile, the diffusion of lipid to the enterocytes is so slow that it leads to lipid malabsorption or the inability to absorb dietary fat. The luminal side of these cells is the brush border, a surface covered in countless microvilli—tiny fingers of membrane that massively increase the surface area and facilitate absorption. Several properties help to drive diffusion of molecules into the enterocyte. For example, the fatty acids and 2-monoacylglycerols produced by the action of pancreatic lipase are rapidly absorbed by the enterocyte. Although it is unclear how these molecules cross the plasma membrane, it is generally accepted that, once they do, the two lipids are quickly reunited in the endoplasmic reticulum (ER). Likewise, the rapid formation of triacylglycerols and secretion into lymph all act to establish a concentration gradient of lipids across the enterocyte and thus facilitate diffusion.

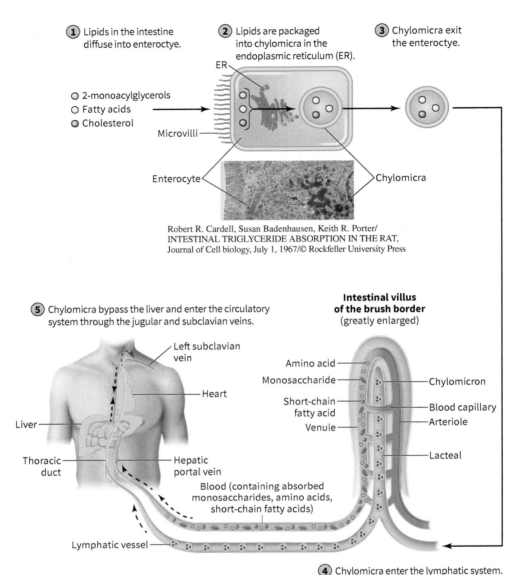

1 Lipids in the intestine diffuse into enteroctye.

2 Lipids are packaged into chylomicra in the endoplasmic reticulum (ER).

3 Chylomicra exit the enteroctye.

ER

○ 2-monoacylglycerols
○ Fatty acids
○ Cholesterol

Microvilli

Enterocyte

Chylomicra

Robert R. Cardell, Susan Badenhausen, Keith R. Porter/
INTESTINAL TRIGLYCERIDE ABSORPTION IN THE RAT,
Journal of Cell biology, July 1, 1967/© Rockfeller University Press

5 Chylomicra bypass the liver and enter the circulatory system through the jugular and subclavian veins.

Intestinal villus of the brush border (greatly enlarged)

Left subclavian vein

Heart

Liver

Thoracic duct

Hepatic portal vein

Amino acid
Monosaccharide
Short-chain fatty acid
Venule

Chylomicron
Blood capillary
Arteriole

Lacteal

Blood (containing absorbed monosaccharides, amino acids, short-chain fatty acids)

Lymphatic vessel

4 Chylomicra enter the lymphatic system.

FIGURE 10.14 **Assembly and secretion of chylomicra into lymph.** The microanatomy of the brush border helps explain the function of these cells. There is abundant surface area through which nutrients can be absorbed and secreted into the bloodstream (in the case of some nutrients) or the lymph, in the case of fats. Dietary lipids are reassembled into triacylglycerols in the endoplasmic reticulum (ER) of the brush border cells and packaged into chylomicra.

These are secreted into the lymph, which then enter the circulatory system via the subclavian vein, bypassing the liver. (ER: Alters, *Biology: Understanding Life*, 1e, copyright 2006, John Wiley & Sons. This material is reproduced with permission of John Wiley & Sons, Inc.; Steps 4, 5: Tortora; Derrickson, *Principles of Anatomy & Physiology*, 13e, copyright 2012, John Wiley & Sons. This material is reproduced with permission of John Wiley & Sons, Inc.)

In the enterocyte, the newly reassembled triacylglycerols from dietary lipids are packaged into a large particle called a **chylomicron** (plural **chylomicra**), which is used to transport dietary lipids in the circulation via the lymph. Chylomicra are a type of lipoprotein composed of a spherical assembly of amphipathic proteins and phospholipids surrounding a neutral lipid core. By entering the lymph first, lipids bypass the liver on their entry into the circulation (**Figure 10.14**).

Short-chain fatty acids (two to four carbons in length) are not re-esterified and are either directly metabolized by the enterocyte or enter the circulation through capillaries in the small intestine. Medium-chain fatty acids are re-esterified into triacylglycerols but are not packaged into chylomicra, and like short-chain fatty acids, enter the circulation directly through capillaries.

In enterocytes, triacylglycerols are formed by the 2-monoacylglycerol pathway. Although this pathway predominates in enterocytes, it is not how triacylglycerols are usually synthesized in other tissues, such as adipose or liver. In the 2-monoacylglycerol pathway, free fatty acids from the diet are first activated by coupling to coenzyme-A (forming an acyl-CoA). The energy required to form the acyl-CoA thioester linkage is provided by the hydrolysis of ATP, in a reaction catalyzed by acyl-CoA synthetase. The activated acyl chain is transferred

FIGURE 10.15 **Triacylglycerol synthesis in the small intestine occurs through the 2-monoacylglycerol pathway.** In the cells of the intestine, triacylglycerols are produced from 2-monoacylglycerol. This is different than in the other cells of the body.

to a molecule of 2-monoacylglycerol, in a reaction catalyzed by acyl-CoA:Monoacylglycerol acyltransferase (MGAT), forming a 1, 2-diacylglycerol. A third acyl chain is added by the action of acyl-CoA:DG acyltransferase (DGAT) (**Figure 10.15**). The acyl-CoA synthetase, MGAT, and DGAT are integral membrane proteins that are imbedded in the endoplasmic reticulum of the enterocyte where synthesis of triacylglycerol generally occurs.

As discussed later in this chapter, this is only one of the two major ways through which the organism can synthesize triacylglycerols, and 2-monoacylglycerol is only one of several substrates that can be used for triacylglycerol synthesis.

10.2.3 | Several molecules affect neutral lipid digestion

If triacylglycerols need to be broken down into fatty acids and monoglycerides for efficient absorption, then blocking their breakdown would also block their absorption. Lipase inhibitors are a class of dietary drugs that act as irreversible inhibitors of pancreatic (and to some extent gastric) lipases. The common trade name for this drug is orlistat, although it is marketed under the names Alli and Xenical. Orlistat is a synthetic analog of lipstatin, a naturally occurring molecule made by *Streptomyces toxytricini*. Examination of the structure reveals a long hydrophobic acyl chain, which may be important in substrate recognition, and a β-lactone ring. Beta-lactones are often employed as irreversible enzyme inhibitors. Once these molecules undergo nucleophilic attack, the strained β-lactone ring springs open and the nucleophile (often a serine in the active site of the enzyme) is irreversibly derivatized.

Orlistat is not a panacea for weight loss because it has an unpleasant side effect. When pancreatic lipase is inhibited and dietary fats remain undigested in the gastrointestinal tract, lipids leave the body as oily diarrhea (steatorreah).

Orlistat

WORKED PROBLEM 10.2 | Making use of dietary triacylglycerols

Describe in your own words how the carbons found in the fatty acyl chains of a triacylglycerol molecule move from your digestive system to your circulatory system.

Strategy You can answer this question on several different levels. At a basic level, describe the way that triacylglycerols are degraded, absorbed, synthesized into new triacylglycerols, and secreted into the lymph. At the chemical level, describe each of those steps in molecular detail, discussing the enzymes and cofactors involved, and the microenvironments of the individual triacylglycerol molecule.

Solution A molecule of dietary triacylglycerol could be solubilized in a micelle containing bile salts in the small intestine, then degraded into free fatty acids and a molecule of monoglyceride by pancreatic lipase and its cofactor, colipase. The lipids are then

absorbed by the enterocyte, where they are resynthesized into triacylglycerol in the ER. To accomplish this, fatty acids must be activated (by acyl-CoA transferase) into fatty acyl-CoAs, then incorporated into a molecule of monoacylglycerol (by MGAT). The final fatty acid is added by DGAT. The "rebuilt" molecule of triacylglycerol is packaged into a chylomicron and secreted into the lymph. The lymph empties directly into the circulation. By entering the circulation via this pathway, the lipids bypass the liver on the first pass through the circulation, unlike dietary proteins and carbohydrates, which enter through the hepatic vein.

Follow-up question Many nutritional supplements contain short-chain or medium-chain triglycerides for "quick energy." How would the digestion of those molecules, such as trihexanoate, differ from a "normal" dietary fat, such as glycerol trihexadecanoate, also known as tripalmitate?

Olestra: an artificial fat

More than 12 artificial sweeteners are approved for sale, but there is only one artificial fat on the market. Olestra is a synthetic product designed to mimic the effects of fats and oils in cooking and to retain the texture of fats when eaten (a property termed mouth feel), but without the caloric value associated with triacylglycerols.

Olestra is made from sucrose and fatty acids. Recall that sucrose (table sugar) is a disaccharide of glucose and fructose and it has eight free hydroxyl groups available for hydrogen bonding; hydrogen bonding in sucrose is responsible for its crystalline solid structure as well as its high boiling point and high solubility in water. Recall also that fatty acids are amphipathic molecules comprised of a carboxyl group attached to a long aliphatic hydrocarbon chain. They can aggregate into water-soluble micelles, but once esterified to glycerol, as is the case in triacylglycerols, fatty acids become highly insoluble, behaving more as fats or oils. In olestra, fatty acids are esterified to the hydroxyl groups of sucrose, creating a molecule that has the physical properties of a fat in terms of boiling point and melting point, hydrophobicity, and insolubility in water. However, the molecule does not have the structure of a triacylglycerol molecule; hence, lipases are unable to bind to this molecule, and it passes through the digestive tract unscathed (**Figure 10.16**).

Unfortunately, olestra's resistance to degradation has some unintended side effects. To taste and feel like fat in the mouth, olestra has to melt at near or just below body temperature. This means that when it leaves the digestive tract at the other end, it does so in the form of an oily liquid; like orlistat, olestra produces the unpleasant side effect of steatorreah.

Interestingly, olestra has found new applications outside food and nutritional science. Under the name Sefose, it is now being developed and marketed as a lubricant for small machines and as a hydrophobic solvent for some paints and stains. In both of these instances, it replaces petrochemicals and creates a potentially green alternative to traditional materials. Finally, olestra is being used as an experimental treatment to remove hydrophobic toxins, such as dioxin and other polychlorinated biphenyls (PCBs), from people exposed to these poisons.

A.

Sucrose core

Palmitate or other fatty acid

Olestra

B.

FIGURE 10.16 **Structure of olestra.** **A.** Olestra is synthesized from sucrose and oleic acid (or other fatty acids). Due to its complex structure, it is unable to be bound by esterases and degraded in the gut. **B.** While originally developed as a food ingredient, olestra is now being marketed as Sefose, a paint solvent.

10.2 Summary

- The degradation of dietary lipids begins in the mouth and stomach, but the process starts in earnest in the small intestine.
- Lingual, gastric, and pancreatic lipases all contribute to lipid digestion.
- Dietary lipids are re-esterified to neutral lipids, packaged into chylomicra and secreted into the lymph.
- Enterocytes employ a different pathway for triacylglycerol biosynthesis than elsewhere in the body.
- Several drugs block the intestinal breakdown of triacylglycerols.
- Artificial fats work because they cannot be broken down into fatty acids and absorbed.

10.2 Concept Check

- Name the proteins involved in these steps and where they function.
- Explain which of these steps require an input of energy (ATP hydrolysis) and, for each step, explain why an energy input is or is not required.
- Trace the path a molecule of triacylglycerol would follow to enter the lymph.

10.3 | Transport of Lipids in the Circulation

Lipids are hydrophobic molecules that are generally insoluble in water. This presents a challenge to a multicellular organism; how can lipids and other important hydrophobic molecules be transported in an aqueous environment? This section discusses two major means of transport: the transport of aggregates of lipid and protein known as **lipoproteins** and the transport of hydrophobic molecules bound to a hydrophilic protein.

10.3.1 | Lipoproteins have a defined structure and composition, and transport lipids in the circulation

Most lipoproteins have the same generic structure. With few exceptions, they are a spherical assembly consisting of a monolayer of phospholipid and cholesterol, surrounding a hydrophobic core of triacylglycerols and cholesteryl esters. Within the phospholipid–cholesterol monolayer, embedded proteins termed **apolipoproteins** act as ligands for receptors and as cofactors for lipases and other enzymes. Apolipoproteins help solubilize the lipoprotein's hydrophobic contents, and they are also important in the formation of lipoproteins (Table 10.1).

TABLE 10.1   Lipoproteins, Density, Composition, Origin, Fate

Lipoprotein	Density	Composition	Origin	Fate
Chylomicra	<1.006	B48, E, CII	Intestine	Loses TAG to muscle and adipose to become remnant
Chylo remnants	<1.006	B48, E	Blood	Binds to liver remnant receptor
VLDL	<1.006	B100, E, CII	Liver	Gets converted to IDL/LDL
IDL	1.006–1.019	B100, E	Blood	Gets converted to LDL
LDL	1.019–1.063	B100	Blood	Binds to tissues with LDLr, or oxidizes and forms plaques
HDL	1.063–1.31	AI, E, AIV, CII, CIII	Liver	Returns cholesterol to liver and steroidogenic tissues

Triglyceride and cholesteryl ester core

Phospholipid and cholesterol coat

Apolipoprotein

Helical axis

Rotated 90 degrees

Phospholipid

Triacylglycerol

Sterol

Hydrophilic face

Helical axis

Hydrophobic face

Helical wheel diagram

View down the helical axis

FIGURE 10.17 **Structure of lipoproteins and helical wheel diagrams.** All lipoproteins have a similar structure. A protein and phospholipid coat surrounds a hydrophobic core of triacylglycerol and cholesteryl esters. The coat proteins, such as apo AI, impart many of the properties of the particle by acting as ligands for receptors and as cofactors for enzymes. Along with apo AI, several other apolipoproteins use amphipathic α helixes to bind to the lipid bilayer. A segment of amino acid side chains are shown in a ball and stick depiction. These helices have a hydrophobic face and a hydrophilic face. This is best visualized by looking down the helical axis. A helical wheel diagram is an effective way to analyze helical structures and look for faces with properties such as hydrophobicity. In a helical wheel diagram the amino acids are plotted every 100 degrees of rotation around a central "wheel." In this view, hydrophobic residues are shown on one side of the helix, and hydrophilic ones are found on the other. (PDB ID 3R2P Mei, X., Atkinson, D. (2011) Crystal Structure of C-terminal Truncated Apolipoprotein A-I Reveals the Assembly of High Density Lipoprotein (HDL) by Dimerization. *J. Biol. Chem.* 286: 38570–38582)

While the structure has not been solved for all apolipoproteins, many use amphipathic α helices to interact with the lipid. These helices have a hydrophobic face embedded in the lipid bilayer and a hydrophilic face exposed to the aqueous surroundings. These structures can be predicted with the help of a helical wheel diagram. A helical wheel diagram depicts the amino acids of the helix while looking down the helical shaft. The side chains are positioned every 100 degrees around the outside of the wheel. Using this depiction, we can see if a helix has a face that is polar, nonpolar, or some other interesting property. In the case of the helices found in apolipoproteins, there is a nonpolar face that is embedded in the lipoprotein, while the remainder of the amino acids are either polar or charged. Even though the diagrams alone are insufficient to predict the secondary structure of a protein, helical wheel diagrams do show the topology and faces of a known or presumed helical part of the protein (**Figure 10.17**).

There are several major classes of lipoprotein including chylomicra, **high density lipoproteins** (HDL), **low density lipoproteins** (LDL), and **very low density lipoproteins** (VLDL); classes are categorized based on their ratio of protein to lipid.

10.3.2 | The trafficking of lipoproteins in the blood can be separated conceptually into three different paths

This section discusses individual lipoprotein species in the context of their metabolism. Although aspects of this metabolism happen concurrently, here the metabolism is split into three pathways to simplify and clarify the discussion.

Chylomicra deliver dietary lipids from the intestine to muscle and adipose
Section 10.2.2 discussed how lipids consumed in a fatty or mixed meal, comprised of fats, carbohydrates, and proteins, are broken down to the point where the lipids have been catabolized into free fatty acids and monoacylglycerols in the small intestine, absorbed by the intestinal enterocytes, and resynthesized into triacylglycerols in the endoplasmic reticulum (ER) of those cells. The triacylglycerols are then packaged into the largest of the

© Johannes M. M. Boots, Department of Internal Medicine, Maasstad Hospital, Rotterdam, The Netherlands

FIGURE 10.18 **Chylomicra in blood samples.** Shown are two blood samples, one from a normal patient (right) and one from a hyperlipidemic patient (left). Note the milky appearance of the plasma in the patient with hyperlipidemia.

lipoproteins, the chylomicra, processed in the Golgi apparatus, and secreted. Chylomicra are large (upwards of half a micron in diameter) and coated with apolipoproteins AI, CII, and B48. Their size is attributable to a massive core of neutral lipid formed from dietary fats. This makes the particles buoyant and the least dense of all of the lipoproteins. If blood is drawn following a fatty meal, the particles will float to the surface, forming a creamy layer of fat on top of the blood cells (**Figure 10.18**).

The blood supply from the intestine first passes through the liver via the hepatic portal vein. Chylomicra are spared this fate by draining into the lymph. Since lymph drains into the venous side of the circulatory system through the thoracic duct, chylomicra avoid the liver in their first pass through the circulation. This avoids giving the liver an initial lipid burden and instead delivers lipids straight to muscle and adipose tissues.

The chylomicra enter muscle and adipose tissues by passing through capillary beds in those tissues. The endothelial cells in these beds are studded with lipoprotein lipase (LPL), which degrades the triacylglycerol found in the chylomicra. The fatty acids and glycerides produced are absorbed by myocytes (cells in muscle) and adipocytes (cells in adipose tissue), and are then either burned for energy or stored for future use. Lipoprotein lipase is activated by apo CII on the surface of the chylomicra; this apolipoprotein acts as a cofactor for the enzyme.

As the lipid contents of the chylomicron are degraded and lost, the chylomicron shrinks in size and increases in density (because it loses more lipid than protein). The resulting particle is a **chylomicron remnant**, that is, a particle that has lost much of its dietary triacylglycerols but is still enriched in dietary cholesterol. As the particle is metabolized, it loses apo AI and CII from the surface, and gains apo E (apo B48 is unchanged and is thus found in both chylomicra and remnants). The apo E on the chylomicron remnant binds to a remnant receptor on the surface of the hepatocyte, and the remnant is removed from the circulation through receptor-mediated endocytosis. Once internalized in a lysosome, chylomicrons are degraded and the components (lipids and amino acids) are used for other cellular processes, such as synthesis of membranes or new proteins (**Figure 10.19**).

Postprandial *de novo* lipids are secreted from the liver to deliver lipids to adipose and muscle
If we presume that a meal includes some carbohydrates and proteins in addition to lipids, then after eating, or postprandially, other metabolic processes will happen at the same time as the chylomicra are delivering triacylglycerols to muscle and adipose. Some carbohydrates are absorbed by the organism and burned for energy, whereas others are used to build up stores of glycogen. Proteins are catabolized into amino acids, and the amino acids not needed for synthetic purposes are deaminated, and their carbon skeletons broken down into acetyl-CoA or substrates for gluconeogenesis. Because many organisms (humans included) can rapidly build up carbohydrate stores and are not typically deficient in amino acids, most of the diet is quickly converted into triacylglycerols. People may consume a low-fat diet, but 20 minutes after drinking a can of cola, the drink consumed has more in common chemically with a stick of butter than with a sugary soft drink.

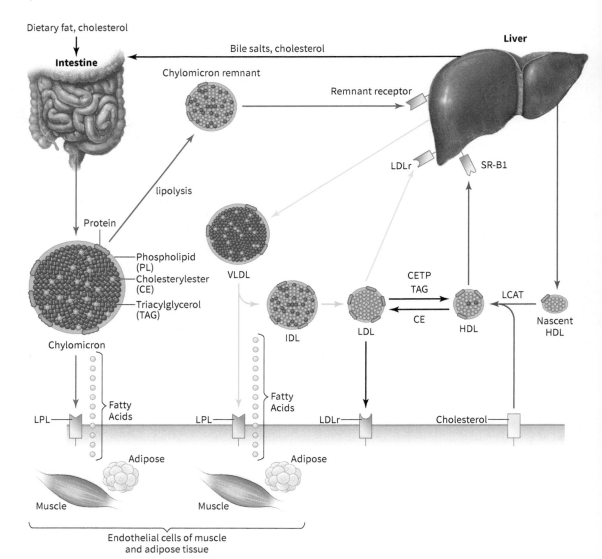

FIGURE 10.19 **Lipoprotein trafficking in the body.** Plasma lipoproteins have several origins and fates in the body. Chylomicra from the intestine transport dietary lipids to the endothelial lining of muscle and adipose tissue. Here LPLs is activated by its cofactor apo CII to hydrolyze triacylglycerols into free fatty acids and glycerol, which are absorbed by the tissues. VLDLs are released from the liver and transport fats made in the liver to muscle and adipose also using LPL to hydrolyze and deliver these molecules. As VLDLs lose triacylglycerols, they become smaller and denser, ultimately losing apo CII and forming LDL. HDLs emerge from the liver as discs of phospholipid surrounded by apo AI. Lecithin-cholesterol acyl-transferase (LCAT) forms cholesteryl esters, producing mature HDLs, which are removed from circulation. (Intestine, liver: Tortora; Derrickson, *Principles of Anatomy & Physiology*, 13e, copyright 2012, John Wiley & Sons. This material is reproduced with permission of John Wiley & Sons, Inc.)

Excess carbohydrates and amino acids are converted into triacylglycerols in the liver. These triacylglycerols are said to be synthesized *de novo* (from new) to differentiate them from dietary triacylglycerols and are packaged with dietary cholesterol into large lipoproteins. Due to their high lipid content, these particles are particularly buoyant and are therefore called VLDL; they are coated by apo B100, apo E, and apo CII. The function of VLDL is to deliver lipids synthesized in the liver to muscle for energy and to adipose tissue for storage. As the VLDLs travel through the circulation, they interact with lipoprotein lipase with apo C II acting as a cofactor. The triacylglycerols are hydrolyzed and absorbed by tissues similar to the way in which chylomicra deliver dietary fat.

Because triacylglycerols in VLDL are hydrolyzed and lost, the particle shrinks in size. Again, because the particle is losing lipid rather than protein, it increases in density,

FIGURE 10.20 **Development of atherosclerosis.** **A.** As we age, LDLs begin to accumulate in the subintimal space between the lining of the artery and the smooth muscle layer. Development of too much plaque can lead to tears and ruptures of the lining, resulting in a clotting response and heart attack or stroke. **B.** A micrograph of an artery showing plaque accumulation.

converting first to **intermediate density lipoprotein** (IDL) and finally to LDL, which has several different fates. First, LDLs are important in delivering cholesterol to tissues that need it, because the particles are enriched in cholesteryl esters (CEs), and can be bound by an LDL receptor (LDLr), which is expressed on the surface of tissues that are in need of cholesterol. The LDL particles are internalized by receptor-mediated endocytosis. Unfortunately, many people consume more cholesterol than their body needs. Over time, excess cholesterol accumulates in LDL particles, and the plasma concentration of these particles increases. The components of these particles are subject to oxidation. Both LDL and oxidized LDL are considered to be pro-atherogenic; that is, they contribute to the development of atherosclerosis, the hardening and narrowing of the arteries due to inflammation and accumulated cholesterol.

Because the vasculature of some arteries, especially the coronary arteries and carotids, is highly permeable to adjust for fluctuations in blood pressure, LDL particles pass from the lumen of the blood vessel into the subintimal space between the endothelial lining of the vessel and the structural layers of muscle and connective tissue (**Figure 10.20**). LDL can become trapped in this space and accumulation of these particles will elicit an inflammatory response, drawing macrophages to the site and forming a plaque. Gradually, over the course of years, this damage increases, with more LDL adding to the lesion and more cells attempting to contain the damage. As this occurs, the vessel becomes more occluded and less flexible. Eventually, the endothelial layer tears, exposing the plaque to the circulation system and initiating a clotting response. The clots formed can lead to reduced blood flow (ischemia), which in turn can lead to tissue damage, myocardial infarction (heart attack), or cerebral ischemia (stroke).

High density lipoproteins are secreted by the liver and return cholesterol to the liver from the circulation and peripheral tissues
There is a process to counter the buildup of cholesterol in the circulation or in oxidized LDL. **Reverse cholesterol transport** is the removal of cholesterol from the circulation and peripheral tissues to the liver. To accomplish this, the liver secretes a small, protein-rich lipoprotein: HDL. These lipoproteins are initially found as a phospholipid disc surrounded by an annulus or ring of apolipoproteins (typically apo AI and apo E). Due to the high ratio of protein to lipid in HDL, the density is higher than that of the other lipoproteins discussed.

TABLE 10.2 Lipases, Acyltransferases, and Cofactors

Enzyme	Protein cofactor
Pancreatic lipase	Colipase
Lipoprotein lipase	Apo CII
Hepatic lipase	Apo AI
LCAT	Apo AI
Hormone sensitive lipase	Perilipin 1A
ATGL	CGI-58

As the HDLs move through the circulation, they constantly collide with erythrocytes, other lipoproteins, and endothelial cells absorbing free cholesterol by diffusion. This is an effective means of absorbing free cholesterol, but the process would be limited if it were the only means of trapping cholesterol. The enzyme lecithin-cholesterol acyltransferase (LCAT) is found in plasma. It transesterifies an acyl chain from a molecule of PC (lecithin) in the HDL coat to free cholesterol, forming a molecule of cholesteryl ester (and lyso PC) (Table 10.2). Because the newly formed molecule of cholesteryl ester is more hydrophobic and less soluble in the lipid bilayer, large amounts of cholesteryl ester build up and form a core in the center of the HDL particles. As more cholesteryl ester is formed, the core of the particle grows, and the HDL changes from a disc to a sphere. Cholesteryl ester is trapped in the core of the HDL particle and is not free to exchange back with the surroundings.

When the HDL particle has increased in size and decreased in density, it has several fates. As shown in Figure 10.19, cholesteryl esters can be transferred to LDL by cholesteryl ester transfer protein (CETP). These LDLs can bind to receptors and be cleared from the circulation. Mature HDLs filled with cholesteryl ester binds to scavenger receptor B1 (SR-B1) on the surface of the liver, macrophages, and steroidogenic cells. The binding results in the delivery of cholesterol (but not HDL proteins) to these tissues. Likewise, HDL can bind to hepatic lipase. This lipase is highly homologous with lipoprotein lipase but, like SR-B1, is found in liver and steroidogenic tissues. Also, the uptake of HDL cholesteryl esters, like that of SR-B1, is independent of protein uptake and does not require the lipase to be catalytically active.

Because HDLs are involved in removing cholesterol from the circulation before it can accumulate in arteries, increased levels of plasma HDL cholesterol are thought to be anti-atherogenic; that is, the increased levels protect against the development of atherosclerosis. Numerous pharmaceutical approaches can be taken to try to modify or reduce plasma lipids. Table 10.3 lists examples of some of the more popular drugs used to treat high cholesterol.

Elevated plasma lipids (especially triacylglycerols and LDL cholesterol) are associated with heart disease, stroke, kidney failure, and atherosclerosis. Oftentimes, elevated plasma lipids are treated pharmacologically. A discussion of this is found in **Medical Biochemistry: The pharmacological treatment of atherosclerosis.**

10.3.3 | Brain lipids are transported on apo E-coated discs

The brain is separated from the rest of the circulation by the blood–brain barrier, a semipermeable membrane that selectively prevents entry of many molecules or assemblies, including lipoproteins, into the brain. As a result, brain tissue must synthesize its own cholesterol. Although neurons can synthesize cholesterol, they need to be able to export excess cholesterol; to do so

TABLE 10.3 Drugs That Affect Plasma Lipids and How They Function

Drug	Function
Statins	HMG-CoA reductase inhibitors, blocks endogenous cholesterol biosynthesis
Niacin	Increases HDL, mechanism unknown
Fibrates	Transcription factor (PPAR-α) agonists decrease VLDL and increase HDL levels
Colesevelam	Bile acid sequestrant (blocks bile acid reabsorbtion in intestine)
Ezetimibe	Cholesterol-binding resin (binds cholesterol in intestine)

Medical Biochemistry

The pharmacological treatment of atherosclerosis

Heart disease, stroke, and atherosclerosis combined are the leading cause of death in the Western world. Clearly, these are complex diseases in which multiple aspects of genetics, environment, diet, and physiology contribute to the occurrence and eventual outcome. Studies suggest that aberrant lipid transport and storage, especially cholesterol and cholesteryl esters, are the culprits in the etiology of these disorders.

Much effort has been devoted to the development of pharmacological interventions by modifying lipid metabolism in some way in order to stave off the development of these diseases. Approaches include blocking *de novo* cholesterol biosynthesis, blocking absorption of cholesterol in the gut, and modulating gene expression, for example, by elevating levels of anti-atherogenic proteins—proteins involved in the reversal of the disease process.

The statins have been one of the most successful classes of drugs over the past 25 years. Statins are the generic trade name for a group of molecules that block the production of new cholesterol in the body by competitively inhibiting the rate-determining and committed step in cholesterol biosynthesis: hydroxymethylglutaryl-CoA reductase (HMG-CoA reductase). These drugs are therefore known as HMG-CoA reductase inhibitors. Accompanying decreased cholesterol production is a simultaneous increase in liver LDL receptor levels and reverse cholesterol transport as the liver adjusts to compensate, helping to create a more favorable lipoprotein profile. In this case, statins cause changes seemingly independent of cholesterol levels. These pleotropic effects, that is, effects that stem from a single change affecting multiple targets, include decreased oxidative stress and inflammation, and improved endothelial tissue function. Clinically, statins act to lower total plasma cholesterol by lowering the production of new cholesterol; although not a panacea, statins are widely used and highly effective. Annual sales of these drugs are in the tens of billions of dollars.

A second class of compounds developed to regulate cholesterol is bile acid sequestrants or bile acid binding resins. Much of the body's cholesterol stores are used each day in the production of bile, and this bile is reabsorbed and recycled back through the circulation via bile acid transporters. Bile acid sequestrants help to lower cholesterol by binding bile in the small intestine and thus preventing its absorption.

Niacin (also known as vitamin B3 or nicotinic acid) is also used to treat high cholesterol levels. Ingestion of large doses of niacin elevates HDL levels. The mechanism by which this works is still under investigation. Consumption of large doses of niacin can lead to skin flushing. Research is underway into niacin analogs that could achieve the positive HDL-elevating effects without this side effect.

The final class of compounds is the fibrates, lipid-lowering drugs that work predominantly to lower triglyceride levels and elevate HDL concentrations. PPAR-α is a transcription factor that effects the expression of many genes, including genes coding for the HDL proteins apo AI and apo AII, and the enzyme lipoprotein lipase. Fibrates are PPAR-α agonists, and they increase fatty acid uptake; they also increase the activation of those fatty acids to fatty acyl-CoA and their β-oxidation. Overall, the picture is one of elevated levels of HDL (via increased levels of HDL proteins), increased catabolism of triacylglycerols, and lower levels of VLDL.

Often, statins, fibrates, niacin, and resins are used in combination to achieve the desired pharmacological effect. However, many of these drugs are metabolized using the same enzymes and pathways in the liver; therefore, clinicians and pharmacists need to be aware of drug interactions.

Other drug treatments for high plasma cholesterol are under development. Compounds which block the degradation of the LDL receptor hold significant promise as future treatments for hypercholesterolemia.

WORKED PROBLEM 10.3 | It runs in the family

Familial hypercholesterolemia (FH) is a genetic disorder in which affected individuals have extremely high LDL levels. Normal levels in a healthy person are 50 to 80 mg of LDL cholesterol/deciliter, but patients with FH have levels of more than 1,000 mg/dl. Based on your knowledge of lipoprotein metabolism, propose a defect that could result in these high levels.

Strategy At the core of FH are highly elevated plasma cholesterol levels. These could be caused by increased levels of cholesterol entering the circulation (either via increased synthesis or by increased secretion) or less cholesterol leaving the circulation. What

types of mutations could lead to these effects? Which of these is more likely to happen?

Solution Several mutations can cause FH, but all result from a loss of function, in this case, the ability to remove LDL from circulation. This can result from mutation of either the genes coding for the LDL receptor or the ligand of that receptor (apo B100).

Follow-up question Would you anticipate that HDL levels would be changed in a patient affected by FH? Make a defendable hypothesis regarding how the conditions found in FH might affect HDL levels.

---

they secrete small disk-shaped HDL-like particles coated with apo E. There are three different genotypes of the apo E allele, apo E2, 3, and 4, coding for the three different variants of apo E. These isoforms differ at positions 112 and 158 in the human protein. The E2 isoform has cysteine in both positions, the E4 isoform has arginine in both positions, and the E3 isoform has a cysteine in position 112 and an arginine in position 158. Although these variants have

A.

Phospholipid bilayer

Apo E

Cholesterol

B.

Isoform	Isoform-specific amino acid difference	
	112	158
Apo-E2	Cys	Cys
Apo-E3	Cys	Arg
Apo-E4	Arg	Arg

FIGURE 10.21 **Brain lipids are transported in phospholipid discs.** **A.** Lipids in the central nervous system are shuttled on apo E-coated discs. These lipoproteins are similar to nascent HDL secreted by the liver but lack a neutral lipid core. **B.** Polymorphisms at positions 112 and 158 in apo E are linked to an increased risk of Alzheimer's disease.

not been correlated with any type of cardiovascular disease or changes in lipoprotein metabolism, apo E4 has been correlated with an earlier age of onset of Alzheimer's disease. Having one copy of the apo E4 allele lowers the average age from 84 to 77 years for onset of Alzheimer's disease; having two copies lowers it to 69 years. Exactly how apo E4 is implicated in the etiology of this disease is unclear; however, it may be that apo E interacts with and assists in the clearance of A-β, one of the misfolded proteins found in β-amyloid plaques in the brains of patients with Alzheimer's disease. It could be that the apo E4 isoform of the protein is unable to clear these misfolded proteins and as such contributes to disease (**Figure 10.21**).

10.3.4 Fatty acids and hydrophobic hormones are transported by binding to carrier proteins

Free fatty acids released from adipose tissue are transported through the blood to the heart, liver, and muscle to be catabolized for energy. Because of their detergent-like nature, unesterified fatty acids could be harmful to the organism, denaturing proteins and solubilizing membranes. To render them harmless, fatty acids are transported bound to serum albumin.

A globular protein, serum albumin is made in and secreted by the liver. It binds nonspecifically to fatty acids and other molecules, including some drugs through its many hydrophobic pockets. Crystallographic data suggest that as many as 12 binding sites may exist, although it is likely that only one or two sites are occupied at any time. Albumin is conserved in higher organisms and is mostly α helical with a molecular weight of 60 to 68 kDa, depending on the species. Plasma concentrations of serum albumin may be as high as 5%, making it one of the more concentrated proteins in the body. Its high concentration is thought to help albumin maintain the osmotic pressure of the blood. Albumin is acidic, with negatively charged amino acids outnumbering positively charged ones. The isoelectric point (pI) of bovine serum albumin (BSA) is 4.7.

Drug molecules undergo complex interactions in the body. Many drugs bind to albumin in the blood and are thus rendered ineffective because they are sequestered away from their site of action. Although tight binding to albumin effectively lowers the concentration of a free drug, it may also increase the half-life of the drug in the body. Also, competition among different drug molecules (or between drug molecules and other hydrophobic molecules) to bind to albumin may lead to drug interactions by affecting a drug's free or functional concentration.

In the laboratory, albumin is often included in buffers, where it acts as a fatty acid acceptor or as an extra source of protein that can protect purified proteins from degradation due to contaminating proteases. Albumin provides a source of protein for enzymes to degrade, outcompeting any contaminating proteases that may remain. Albumin is also often used to coat plastics or hybridization membranes to decrease nonspecific binding of other proteins or nucleic acids (**Figure 10.22**).

A.

Albumin ribbon diagram
with space-filling warfarin

Warfarin

Surface of hydrophobic pocket

B.

Hydrophobic pocket of albumin
in absence of drug

Warfarin bound in hydrophobic pocket

FIGURE 10.22 **Albumin bound to the anticoagulant drug warfarin.** **A.** Serum albumin is a largely globular protein and is lacking in β sheet structures. It has several hydrophobic pockets, one of which is shown in a molecular surface. **B.** A close-up view of one of these hydrophobic pockets is shown in the absence and presence of the hydrophobic drug warfarin. These pockets can also bind to unesterified (free) fatty acids. Binding of drug molecules can decrease their efficacy, increase their half-life, and generally change their pharmacological properties (their pharmacokinetics). (PDB ID 2BXD Ghuman, J., Zunszain, P.A., Petitpas, I., Bhattacharya, A.A., Otagiri, M., Curry, S. (2005) Structural Basis of the Drug-Binding Specificity of Human Serum Albumin. *J. Mol. Biol.* 353: 38)

Albumin is only one of several proteins that bind, sequester, and transport hydrophobic molecules; others include sex hormone–binding globulin, transcortin, thyroxine-binding globulin, and transthyretin. Each of these proteins is globular and contains a pocket that is responsible for binding the hydrophobic molecule it carries. The interactions of these proteins with the molecules they carry are analogous to the interactions between enzymes and substrates. In some cases, the interaction is highly specific, such as sex hormone–binding globulin interacting tightly and specifically with testosterone and estrogens but weakly, if at all, with corticosteroids. In other cases, the interaction is less specific; for example, transcortin binds to cortisone but also to aldosterone and progesterone. **Table 10.4** summarizes the molecules these proteins have been found to transport.

Carrier proteins have important functions. As alluded to with albumin, they bind and facilitate the transport of their hydrophobic cargo, and they bind to and thus block the effect of signaling molecules, as illustrated below for thyroid hormones and oral contraceptives.

Thyroid hormones, including thyroxine (T3) and triiodothironine (T4), are key chronic regulators of metabolism and energetic balance, that is, the balance between energy storage (as fat) and energy burning. When diagnosing a metabolic disease in a patient, a clinician will

TABLE 10.4 Shuttle Proteins and Their Cargoes

Protein	Cargo
Sex hormone–binding globulin (SHBG)	Estrogen and testosterone
Transcortin (cortisol-binding globulin)	Glucocorticoids, progesterone, corticosteroids
Thyroxine-binding globulin	Triiodothironine (T3) and thyroxine (T4)
Transthyretin	Thyroxine (T4) and retinol
Serpin (thyroid-binding globulin)	Thyroxine and cortisol

often ask the laboratory to assay for free T3 or free T4 (i.e., the fraction of each hormone that is free or unbound, which represents the amount of hormone that is functional in the bloodstream). Various conditions can affect the levels of thyroxine-binding globulin and hence indirectly influence the levels of T3 and T4 in the blood.

Like many drugs, oral contraceptives are also transported in part by carrier proteins. A desirable side effect of some oral contraceptives is decreased incidence of acne. This condition is caused by a complex interplay of many factors, but one molecule implicated in the development of acne is testosterone. People with elevated testosterone levels, due either to natural biology or abuse of a synthetic testosterone, often experience increased acne. Various oral contraceptives, including drospirenone and ethinyl estradiol (marketed under the names Beyaz or Yaz), and norgestimate and ethinyl estradiol (marketed as Ortho tri-cyclen) elevate serum levels of sex hormone–binding globulin. This protein preferentially binds to testosterone and thus lowers testosterone levels, making these drugs anti-androgenic. The exact way in which this influences acne is still under investigation.

10.3 Summary

- Hydrophobic molecules, including lipids, and hydrophobic hormones and vitamins are transported in the circulation bound to either lipoproteins or a soluble globular protein.
- Lipoproteins are spherical assemblies of neutral lipid (triacylglycerol and cholesteryl ester), surrounded by phospholipid and apolipoproteins.
- Lipoproteins have distinct fates in the circulation, based on the types of apolipoproteins found on their surface.
- Chylomicra deliver dietary lipids from intestine to muscle and adipose. Chylomicron remnants deliver dietary cholesterol to the liver.
- The liver secretes VLDL to transport fats made in the liver to other tissues. LDLs deliver cholesterol to tissues that need it, but it can accumulate and become oxidized, increasing risks of heart attack and stroke.
- HDLs bind cholesterol in the circulation and returns it to the liver or tissues involved in steroid hormone production.
- Brain lipids are bound to discs coated with apo E.
- Many hormones, including many ligands for nuclear hormone receptors (steroids), are transported inside specific globular proteins.

10.3 Concept Check

- Describe how and where lipoproteins function.
- Cite examples of enzymes and coactivators in lipoprotein metabolism.
- Explain why some lipoprotein profiles are considered beneficial to human health, whereas others are not.
- Molecules such as albumin and binding globulins transport only a few molecules at a time, and they vary in term of their specificity. Provide examples of each of these molecules and how they function. Also, explain how levels of these transport molecules influence the effectiveness of the molecules they bind.

10.4 | Entry of Lipids into the Cell

Lipids gain entry into the cell in several ways. The process by which free fatty acids are absorbed is still debated, but other processes, such as receptor-mediated endocytosis of LDL, are well established.

10.4.1 | Fatty acids can enter the cell via diffusion or by protein-mediated transport

As mentioned in section 10.3, lipoproteins are degraded by the lipases, lipoprotein lipase and hepatic lipase. The breakdown products of these lipases—free fatty acids and monoacylglyc- erols and diacylglycerols—are rapidly absorbed by cells. This poses an interesting question: How can the charged carboxyl head group of the fatty acid diffuse across the nonpolar lipid bilayer? One hypothesis proposes that microenvironments may exist in which the pH is low enough to protonate the fatty acid head group (fatty acids have a pK_a of 4 to 5, so they can be protonated at near physiological pH), thus reducing its polarity and allowing the molecule to diffuse across the membrane. In the cytosolic leaflet of the membrane, fatty acids are rapidly esterified to other lipids; again, this prevents them from acting as detergents and disrupting cellular functions (**Figure 10.23**).

An alternative hypothesis is that single molecules of long-chain fatty acids enter the cell via fatty acid transport proteins (FATPs), a family of six transmembrane proteins. Although the structure of these proteins and the mechanism they use to facilitate fatty acid movement is unknown, it is clear that FATPs increase fatty acid transport in a concentration-dependent manner; that is, more protein leads to increased transport. Additionally, the transport can be saturated and is specific for both long-chain and very-long-chain fatty acids (as opposed to shorter fatty acids or other hydrophobic molecules). The expression of these proteins is also tissue specific and responsive to cellular signals, such as insulin.

It is highly likely that FATPs work in conjunction with other proteins. They co-localize on the plasma membrane with CD-36, a protein hypothesized to bind fatty acids from plasma, and pass them to FATP. In some FATP family members, fatty acid transport and activation to a fatty acyl-CoA are coupled on the same protein, although mutation of the acyl-CoA ligase activity does not seem to impede lipid transport. As more is learned about this mechanism, it is likely that other proteins implicated in lipid transport, such as fatty acid binding protein (FABP) or the caveolins, may also play a role. Hence, it appears that more than one mechanism for fatty acid internalization may be at work.

Not all lipids are assimilated one molecule at a time. For example, LDLs bind to a receptor on a hepatocyte or other cell in need of cholesterol. The cell internalizes these particles and uses the cholesterol contents of the LDL. The process is termed receptor-mediated endocytosis and is the focus of section 10.4.2.

10.4.2 | Lipoprotein particles and many other complexes enter the cell via receptor-mediated endocytosis

In receptor-mediated endocytosis, a ligand such as the apolipoprotein apo B100 binds to its receptor, in this case the LDL receptor. Binding of multiple ligands to receptors initiates a response on the cytosolic side of the membrane

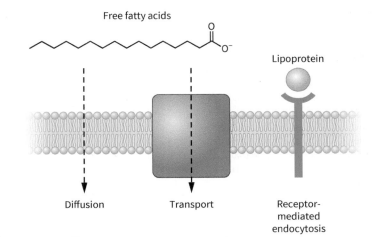

FIGURE 10.23 **Lipids gain access to the cell via at least three different mechanisms.** Single fatty acid molecules can gain entry to the cell either by diffusing through the plasma membrane or via a transport protein. Bulk lipids (lipoproteins) enter the cell through receptor-mediated endocytosis.

(Figure 10.24). The cytoplasmic tail of the LDL receptor interacts with adaptor proteins, such as AP2. As the name suggests, these proteins are adaptors between the receptor and its ligand, **clathrin**, a structural protein and key component of receptor-mediated endocytosis. The receptors begin to cluster in groups called **patches**, which then invaginate, forming a structure known as a **coated pit**. The cytosolic coating on this pit is largely comprised of clathrin.

As the clathrin network forms, additional proteins become involved, including motor proteins such as dynamin. The patch gradually invaginates into a coated pit; the pits are visible using electron microscopy, and the coating comes from the clathrin skeleton. Finally, the coated pit

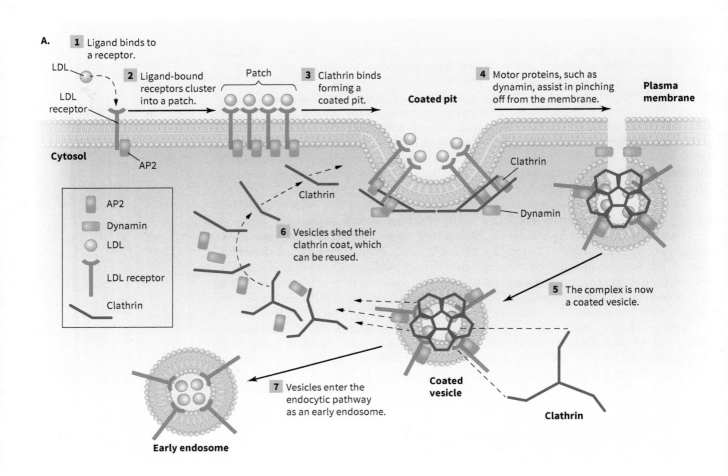

FIGURE 10.24 **Receptor-mediated endocytosis is one of several trafficking pathways in the cell.**

A. In receptor-mediated endocytosis, vesicles coated by the protein clathrin are pinched off the plasma membrane and processed into endosomes. **B.** A space-filling structure of a clathrin triskelion shows it is comprised of three heavy chains and three light chains. These chains are pitched at an angle such that the entire structure is slightly puckered forming a tripod. (PDB ID 3LVH Wilbur, J.D., Hwang, P.K., Ybe, J.A., Lane, M., Sellers, B.D., Jacobson, M.P., Fletterick, R.J., Brodsky, F.M. (2010) Conformation switching of clathrin light chain regulates clathrin lattice assembly. *Dev. Cell* 18: 841–848) **C.** A clathrin-coated vesicle is made up of 108 heavy and 108 light chains. A single triskelion of three heavy and three light chains is highlighted. (PDB ID 1XI4 Fotin, A., Cheng, Y., Sliz, P., Grigorieff, N., Harrison, S.C., Kirchhausen, T., Walz, T. (2004) Molecular model for a complete clathrin lattice from electron cryomicroscopy *Nature* 432: 573–579)

pinches off from the membrane and becomes a **coated vesicle**. The vesicle is trafficked inside the cell, where its clathrin and adaptor proteins are removed and recycled to form new coated pits. The uncoated vesicle fuses with other vesicles, including those containing proton pumps. These pumps are ATPases that use ATP hydrolysis to pump protons from the cytosol to the lumen of the vesicle. This acidifies the vesicle, resulting in protonation of key amino acids, conformational changes to proteins and ultimately the release of LDL from the LDL receptor.

LDL receptors are sorted away from the rest of the vesicular proteins and pinched off to be recycled back to the plasma membrane in an endosome, a vesicular trafficking organelle. Acidification of the vesicle also activates acidic lipases and proteases that break LDL into the constituent components.

AP2, the adaptor protein complex found in receptor-mediated endocytosis, is not related to the adipocyte fatty acid binding protein (AFABP), formerly known as AP2, or to the transcription factor ap2. These similar names highlight a problem that is often encountered when studying proteins with different or redundant names. Often, proteins, genes, or diseases are renamed when more information becomes available.

In addition to the adaptor proteins, other associated proteins are also found in coated pits. Many of these other proteins have domains or catalytic activities that modify the plasma membrane, facilitating the curvature of the plasma membrane, and formation of the coated pit.

Clathrin is found in the cell as a trimer of dimers. Each dimer is comprised of a rod-like light chain and a thicker, L-shaped heavy chain. The heavy and light subunits associate together, then three of these dimers bind through their light chains to form a shape termed a triskelion, as shown in Figure 10.24. The triskelion is not planar; rather, the arms extending from the central vertex are slightly bent toward each other, creating a gently sloping pyramidal shape overall. This shape helps the polymerized clathrin to form a basket-like structure. The clathrin triskelions join together to form a cage of repeating hexagons and pentagons that is similar to the pattern on a soccer ball. The arms of the triskelion are flexible and have polyvalent interactions with all other proteins; thus, each protein contributes to the structure giving the coated pit the ability to assemble or disassemble in a rapid and cooperative fashion.

The architecture of these proteins and their chemistry contribute to the overall strength and dynamics of the interaction. The proteins are polyvalent, containing multiple receptors and clathrin-binding sites. Like antibodies, these proteins increase the likelihood of a second binding event and increase the overall strength of the interaction. This can be compared to the scene in many action films where someone is clinging to the edge of a cliff or ledge for dear life. If holding on with only one arm, people fall if they lose their grip; however, if holding on with two arms, they will still be able to hang on with one arm, even if the other slips. For both movie stars and proteins, having two arms of similar length makes it easier to create two points of contact.

After assembly of the coated pit, the vesicle needs to pinch off and split away from the membrane. The associated protein amphiphysin dimerizes around the neck of the vesicle and recruits dynamin to the complex. Dynamin is a GTPase that coils around the neck of the budding vesicle and extends as GTP is hydrolyzed, as shown in Figure 10.24.

Following the separation of the vesicle from the membrane, clathrin and the adaptor proteins are rapidly removed. Enzymes that modify phospholipids weaken the interactions between the coat components and the membrane coating via modification of head groups.

This section discussed receptor-mediated endocytosis in the context of the LDL receptor; however, there are more than 900 different receptors coupled to 7-transmembrane G proteins, and many of these other receptors are also internalized via clathrin-coated pits. Examples include the aquaporins, receptors involved in heavy metal transport, and opioid receptors in the brain.

WORKED PROBLEM 10.4 | Need for GTP

How could you demonstrate that GTP hydrolysis is required for receptor-mediated endocytosis to proceed?

Strategy To demonstrate that receptor-mediated endocytosis depends on GTP hydrolysis, we would need a model system for studying the process and an experimental way to test the hypothesis.

Solution We could use a cultured cell system for the study. Many such cell lines are commonly used in thousands of laboratories worldwide. Some means of measuring receptor-mediated endocytosis would also be needed. Since it has already been demonstrated that LDL particles are internalized by receptor-mediated endocytosis, LDL particles that have been labeled with a fluorescent or radioactive lipid could be used, and their accumulation in an endosomal compartment could be followed as a way to quantitate the process. Several compounds act as GTPase inhibitors and are commercially available. Thus, control cells could be compared with cells treated with a GTPase inhibitor to look at whether inhibiting a GTPase activity blocks or dampens the endocytic response.

Follow-up question   What type of phenotype would you predict for a clathrin knockout mouse?

10.4 Summary

- Lipids can enter the cell through either diffusion or endocytosis.
- Cells use receptor-mediated endocytosis to engulf LDL particles.
- Specific adaptor protein complexes bind to receptors and to the structural protein clathrin.
- The GTPase dynamin is important in the pinching off of the clathrin-coated vesicle.
- Following endocytosis, the vesicle is uncoated and most proteins are recycled.
- The new endosome is acidified and trafficked to a lysosome, where the cholesterol contents are liberated for other cellular processes.

10.4 Concept Check

- Name the types of lipids that are absorbed by diffusion, and explain what helps to make that process favorable.
- Describe the arguments supporting the hypothesis that specific proteins are involved in lipid absorption.
- Receptor-mediated endocytosis is used to internalize many receptors and their ligands, including LDL bound to the LDL receptor. Outline the steps of receptor-mediated endocytosis and the proteins involved, and explain how the structure of these proteins contributes to their function.

10.5 Neutral Lipid Biosynthesis

High levels of free fatty acids are harmful to the cell. Although highly reduced and energetically rich, free fatty acids are amphipathic and are therefore not the best way to store energy. Instead, fatty acids are esterified to a glycerol backbone for storage; however, this pathway (*de novo* triglyceride biosynthesis) differs from that of dietary lipids (the 2-monacylglycerol pathway).

10.5.1 Triacylglycerols are synthesized by different pathways depending on the tissue

Triacylglycerol biosynthesis occurs predominantly in two tissues: liver and adipose. Liver tissue makes new fatty acids via *de novo* synthesis from acetyl-CoA, which is derived from glucose through glycolysis and decarboxylation of pyruvate. These new fatty acids are esterified into triacylglycerols and exported as VLDL. Adipose tissue absorbs free fatty acids generated by the action of lipoprotein lipase on the triacylglycerol-rich lipoprotein particles, chylomicra and VLDL; adipose tissue then re-esterifies these fatty acids into new triacylglycerols for storage. In both liver and adipose tissue, the enzymes required for triacylglycerol biosynthesis are found in the ER.

In the enterocyte, 2-monoacylglcerol is used as the source of the glycerol backbone in triacylglycerol biosynthesis; however, this is not the pathway used by other tissues. In liver and adipose tissue, the starting material is glycerol-3-phosphate.

There are several different pathways by which liver and adipose tissue can obtain glycerol-3-phosphate, the most common being glycolysis. We previously saw in Figure 10.4 how dihydroxyacetone phosphate (DHAP) can be reduced by glycerol-3-phosphate dehydrogenase to form glycerol-3 phosphate. Liver also contains a glycerol kinase that can directly phosphorylate glycerol into glycerol-3-phosphate. Because adipose tissue lacks significant levels of glycerol kinase, glycerol cannot be recycled in the adipocyte; this ensures that glycerol is exported when the cells are undergoing lipolysis (triacylglycerol breakdown).

The enzyme glycerol-3-phosphate acyltransferase acts on glycerol-3-phosphate to yield lysophosphatidate (lyso PA). The fatty acid is esterified to C-1 of the glycerol backbone. Fatty acids are not esterified directly; instead, they are first activated by coupling them to coenzyme A (producing fatty acyl-CoA), a process that requires the hydrolysis of ATP and provides the energy for the subsequent acyl transfers (**Figure 10.25**).

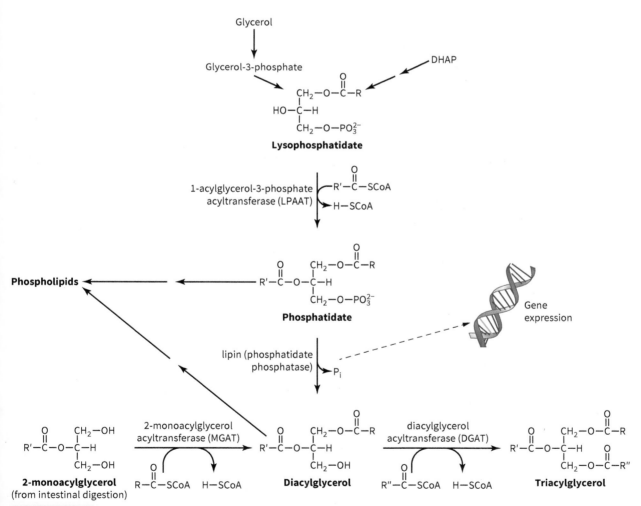

FIGURE 10.25 **Glycerol-3-phosphate pathway of triacylglycerol biosynthesis.** Triacylglycerols in liver and adipose tissue are predominantly made through the glycerol-3-phosphate pathway. Adipocytes lack glycerol kinase and thus are unable to produce *de novo* TAG via this pathway.

A second acyl chain is esterified to C-2 of glycerol by the action of lysophosphatidic acid acyltransferase (LPAT). This generates phosphatidate (PA). PA is then dephosphorylated to diacylglycerol (DG) by phosphatidic acid phosphatase (a phospholipase C). Finally, the remaining free hydroxyl group in DG is esterified to the third acyl chain via the action of diacylglycerol acyltransferase (DGAT).

Excess free cholesterol in the cell is stored as cholesteryl ester. In the ER, the enzyme responsible for this action is acyl-CoA: cholesterol acyltransferase (ACAT). Although this reaction produces cholesteryl ester, it differs from the synthesis of cholesteryl esters in the plasma. In plasma, the reaction is catalyzed by lecithin: cholesterol acyltransferase (LCAT), using phosphatidylcholine (PC or lecithin) as the acyl donor.

10.5.2 | Triacylglycerol metabolism and phosphatidate metabolism are enzymatically linked

Phosphatidate and diacylglycerol, two intermediates in triacylglycerol biosynthesis, are also important intermediates in phospholipid biosynthesis (Table 10.5). The branch point in these pathways is the dephosphorylation of phosphatidate to diacylglycerol. This reaction is catalyzed by a phosphatidate phosphatase known as lipin, which helps coordinate cross talk between these two pathways.

Lipins are a family of related proteins, coded for by different genes. Each protein functions as a phosphatidate phosphatase, generating diacylglycerol from phosphatidate. Therefore, the lipins help to coordinate neutral lipid biosynthesis with the biosynthesis of phosphatidylcholine and phosphatidylethanolamine. Lipins also possess an amino acid sequence, termed a nuclear localization sequence, which allows them to traffic to the nucleus. Once

TABLE 10.5	**Enzymes in This Chapter That Use Phosphatidate or Lysophosphatidate as a Substrate or Product: A Metabolic Crossroads**	
Protein	**Enzymatic Activity**	**Other Ascribed Functions**
Lipin	PA phosphatase/transcriptional co-activator	Regulates switch between glycerophospholipid and neutral lipid metabolism; also, functions in transcription in a complex with PPARs
DAG kinase	Phosphorylates DAG into PA	Functions prominently in signaling
MAG kinase	Phosphorylates MAG into lyso PA	Unknown
Endophilin-1	Lyso PA acyltransferase	Vesicular budding and fusion; plays role in membrane remodeling during receptor-mediated endocytosis

WORKED PROBLEM 10.5 | Different paths

Triacylglycerol biosynthesis occurs through different pathways in the enterocyte (section 10.2) and the adipocyte (section 10.5). Why might the organism use two different means of synthesizing triacylglycerols?

Strategy Compare the biosynthetic pathways and the functions of the two tissues. How might these give clues as to why the pathways are different?

Solution While it is not possible to definitively state why there are two different means of triacylglycerol biosynthesis, we can identify two areas that provide clues. The first is the substrate available to each tissue. In the enterocyte, triacylglycerol is synthesized from 2-monoacylglycerol, whereas in the adipocyte or liver, the glycerol-3-phosphate is available through carbohydrate metabolism.

Follow-up question In performing triacylglycerol breakdown (lipolysis) assays on isolated adipocytes in the laboratory, would it make a difference if glycerol or fatty acids were being measured?

inside, lipins can form a complex with several transcription factors. This complex helps to regulate the genes involved in fatty acid biosynthesis and β-oxidation. Thus, lipin is not only a key enzyme in lipid metabolism, it also acts to help regulate gene expression of proteins involved in lipid metabolic pathways. Mutation or deletion of the lipin genes results in several clinical syndromes, or lipodystrophies, in which irregular lipid metabolism leads to fatty liver, muscle damage and myoglobin accumulation in the blood, peripheral nerve damage or neuropathy, insulin resistance, inflammation, and anemia. A discussion of other diseases that result from problems with lipid metabolism can be found in **Societal and Ethical Biochemistry: Lipid storage disorders.**

Societal and Ethical Biochemistry

Lipid storage disorders

The inability to properly metabolize molecules frequently results in disease. When the molecule in question is common to all of biochemistry, such as a fatty acid, the mutation is rarely seen in nature because the organism would fail to develop. However, there are instances where the mutation results in disease. The lipid storage disorders are a group of diseases resulting from the inability to properly synthesize or catabolize several complex lipids. Often, in these disorders, lipids accumulate in lysosomes and are part of a broader category of diseases, referred to as lysosomal storage disorders. Depending on the mutation, different tissues are affected and different pathologies are observed. Many of these disorders are severe, and several are fatal.

Lipid storage disorders arise from the inability to properly metabolize a specific lipid molecule. This happens due to the loss of function of a specific enzyme in that metabolic pathway. These are recessive disorders because possessing a single functional copy of the gene is all that is needed to synthesize functional enzymes. Often these diseases are autosomal; that is, the genes implicated are found on an autosome, although some are sex-linked with the genes found on a sex chromosome. Several of the more common lipid storage disorders are described in **Table 10.6.**

Although some of these diseases are rare, they are clearly worth studying. Not only do advances in understanding the causes and effects of these diseases help those affected and their families, but the basic knowledge obtained contributes to our understanding of metabolic pathways, genetics, and biochemistry as a whole, helping to advance science and medicine in ways we cannot always predict.

TABLE 10.6 **Lipid Storage Disorders**

Disorder	Proteins Implicated	Location in the Cell	Pathophysiology	Manifestation
Niemann Pick disease (types A and B)	Acid sphingomyelinase	Lysosome	Accumulation of sphingomyelin in lysosomes	Accumulation of lipid in greatly enlarged lysosomes of many tissues. Type A fatal by 18 months; type B fatal by early adulthood.
Niemann Pick type C	NPC1 or NPC2	Lysosome	Accumulation of free cholesterol in lysosomes	Fatal by early adulthood
Cholesteryl ester storage disease (CESD) or Wolman's disease	Lysosomal acid lipase	Lysosome	Accumulation of cholesteryl esters in lysosomes	Enlarged liver (hepatomegaly), elevated plasma lipids (hyperlipidemia)
Gaucher's disease	Glucocerebrosidase	Lysosome	Accumulation of glucocerebrosides in lysosomes	Hepatomegaly, enlarged spleen, monocyte dysfunction
Tay-Sach's disease	Hexosaminidase A	Lysosome	Accumulation of gangliosides in neurons	Physical and mental deterioration, death by age 4
Fabry's disease	α galactosidase A	Lysosome	Accumulation of ceramide trihexoside	Pain, fatigue, kidney, heart, and skin complications
Chanarin-Dorfman syndrome	CGI-58	Lipid storage droplet	Increased storage of triacylglycerols in multiple tissues	Hepatomegaly, ichthyosis (scaly skin), cataracts, mild cognitive impairment

10.5 Summary

- Triacylglycerol is synthesized by different pathways in different tissues.
- Triacylglycerol biosynthesis occurs in the endoplasmic reticulum.
- Phosphatidate (synthesized from glycerol-3-phosphate) is a key intermediate in the synthesis of triacylglycerol.
- Cross talk between phosphatidate and triacylglycerols occurs at several places in metabolism. The lipins may be involved in this cross talk.

10.5 Concept Check

- Describe the synthesis of triacylglycerols in all three tissues, and explain how they differ.
- Describe the cross talk between phospholipid metabolism and triacylglycerol metabolism.

10.6 Lipid Storage Droplets, Fat Storage, and Mobilization

Neutral lipid molecules, such as triacylglycerols and cholesteryl esters, are too hydrophobic to be soluble in the cytosol. These molecules can be found in the lipid bilayer, but they will disrupt the bilayer at relatively low concentrations. Instead, neutral lipids are found in lipid storage droplets.

10.6.1 Bulk neutral lipids in the cell are stored in a specific organelle, the lipid storage droplet

Although triacylglycerol synthesis occurs in the endoplasmic reticulum (ER), storage of fats occurs in specialized organelles termed **lipid storage droplets**. These organelles are distinct from all others in the cell in that, instead of being bound by a phospholipid bilayer and an aqueous core, they have a phospholipid monolayer coating a core of hydrophobic triacylglycerols or cholesteryl esters.

Several mechanisms have been postulated for formation of lipid droplets. In this mechanism, triacylglycerols synthesized in the endoplasmic reticulum (ER) begin to form an inclusion, termed a "lens," between the leaflets of the ER membrane. These inclusions then either bud and are pinched off or are cleaved from both leaflets of the membrane to form new lipid storage droplets. Small lipid droplets could then fuse into larger ones through an unknown process. In the adipocyte, these droplets can comprise 95% of the volume of the cell and may exceed 100 microns in diameter.

All lipid storage droplets are coated with a variety of proteins involved in the trafficking and metabolism of the fatty contents. Chief among these are the perilipins, a family of proteins arising from five related genes that are important regulators of lipid metabolism. The best characterized of these proteins is perilipin 1A, which is found in adipose tissue (**Figure 10.26**).

10.6.2 Specific phosphorylation of lipases and lipid droplet proteins regulate lipolysis (triacylglycerol breakdown)

Lipolysis, the regulated mobilization and breakdown of triacylglycerols (TAG), is triggered by hormonal signals. In the basal or unstimulated state, perilipin is found on the lipid droplet surface, bound together with another regulator, the colipase CGI-58. Adipocyte triacylglycerol

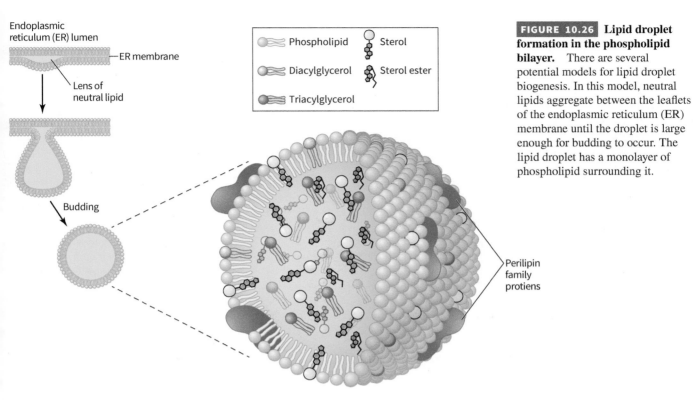

Endoplasmic
reticulasmic (ER) lumen

ER membrane

Lens of
neutral lipid

Budding

Phospholipid	Sterol
Diacylglycerol	Sterol ester
Triacylglycerol	

Perilipin
family
protiens

FIGURE 10.26 **Lipid droplet formation in the phospholipid bilayer.** There are several potential models for lipid droplet biogenesis. In this model, neutral lipids aggregate between the leaflets of the endoplasmic reticulum (ER) membrane until the droplet is large enough for budding to occur. The lipid droplet has a monolayer of phospholipid surrounding it.

lipase (ATGL), the enzyme that catalyzes the first step of lipolysis, is distributed on the lipid storage droplet and in the cytosol. Hormone sensitive lipase (HSL) and monoacylglycerol lipase (MGL), the enzymes that catalyze the remaining two reactions, are found in the cytosol. Lipolysis is quiescent, occurring at low background levels.

Lipolytic stimuli to the adipocyte usually come in the form of a catecholamine signal. A hormone signal, often one of the catecholamines (epinephrine, norepinephrine, and dopamine) or glucagon, binds to a β-adrenergic receptor on the surface of the adipocyte. These receptors are coupled to a heterotrimeric G protein, and binding initiates the signaling cascade that activates the cAMP-dependent protein kinase, protein kinase A (PKA). We saw previously PKA function in a variety of metabolic pathways, including glycogen metabolism. PKA has two major substrates in the lipolytic cascade: HSL and perilipin A. Phosphorylation of these targets causes translocation of HSL to the surface of the lipid droplet and structural changes in perilipin proteins at the droplet surface, leading to a marked increase in lipolysis.

The distinct regulatory and catalytic cascade in lipolysis is still being elucidated; however, it is clear that three lipases are involved.

- Adipose triacylglycerol lipase (ATGL) is the enzyme which removes the first fatty acid from triacylglycerol resulting in diacylglycerol (DAG) and a free fatty acid. ATGL is stimulated through binding to its cofactor CGI-58. Release of CGI-58 from perilipin initiates this reaction and also starts triacylglycerol breakdown.

- The removal of the second fatty acid is catalyzed by HSL, resulting in monoacylglycerol (MAG) and a second free fatty acid. HSL is activated through interactions with perilipin, and both proteins must be phosphorylated by PKA for optimal activity.

- The third reaction is catalyzed by monoacylglycerol lipase (MGL), which cleaves the remaining ester resulting in free glycerol and a third molecule of fatty acid. This enzyme is cytosolic and is not thought to be regulated by other proteins.

Free fatty acids and glycerol generated in lipolysis are released into the circulation, where they are transported to the liver, muscle, and the heart for use. This is typically β-oxidation for fatty acids and gluconeogenesis for glycerol.

The proteins coating triacylglycerol-filled lipid storage droplets in adipose tissue are also found in cells active in steroid hormone production. In the Leydig cells of the testis, or in the cells of the adrenal cortex, perilipins coat cholesteryl ester-rich lipid droplets and, presumably,

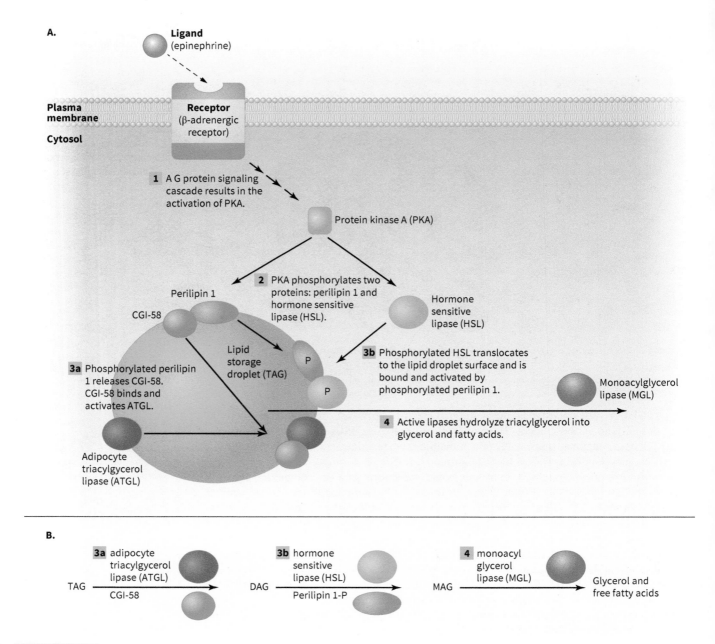

FIGURE 10.27 **Signaling cascades implicated in lipolysis.**
Lipolysis is acutely regulated via the action of PKA on lipases
and perilipin 1. **A.** Binding of a catecholamine or glucagon signal
activates PKA, which has several targets in the adipocyte. Phosphorylation of perilipin 1 causes release of CGI-58, which can then bind
and activate ATGL, catalyzing the release of the first fatty acid from
triacylglycerol. Phosphorylation of HSL results in translocation to
the lipid droplet surface. There, interaction of HSL with phosphorylated perilipin 1 results in cleavage of the second fatty acid from
diacylglycerol. Hydrolysis of the third fatty acid is catalyzed by the
cytosolic enzyme monoglyceride lipase. **B.** The summary of reactions and cofactors in triglyceride breakdown.

regulate interaction of their contents with lipases through a similar mechanism to triacylglycerol lipolysis (**Figure 10.27**).

Neutral lipids in plants have evolved some different, and in some cases highly specialized,
functions. Plants with seeds that dry out as part of the maturation process (dessicatable seeds)
contain oil droplets coated with a layer of structural proteins called the oleosins. Like the perilipins, oleosins are thought to provide anchorage sites for enzymes and cofactors involved in
metabolism of the oil body, a seed organelle analogous to the lipid storage droplet. Oleosins
are thought to prevent oil droplets from coalescing in the dried seed. Because plant oils such
as canola, corn, palm, and soy are potential sources of food, energy (biodiesel), and chemical
feedstocks, there is considerable interest in the function of oleosins and their potential as a
target for genetic modification.

10.6.3 | Triacylglycerol metabolism is regulated at several levels

Triacylglycerols are one of the most prized energy stores of an organism, which devotes significant resources to the regulation of those stores. As is clear to anyone trying to either lose or gain weight, biology sometimes has other plans. This section briefly reviews how the organism regulates levels of triacylglycerols.

Triacylglycerol storage happens in two different time frames: acute storage and mobilization occurring over minutes to hours, and chronic storage occurring over weeks or longer.

Acute storage and mobilization of triacylglycerol occurs via the manipulation of levels of cAMP. When the organism needs to mobilize energy, it releases lipolytic hormones, such as the catecholamines epinephrine, norepinephrine, and dopamine, or the peptide hormone glucagon. These hormones act through receptors to activate adenylate cyclase, elevating levels of the second messenger cAMP. This second messenger activates protein kinase A, which then activates a lipolytic response through the phosphorylation of the perilipins and HSL. Lowering levels of cAMP by the action of phosphodiesterases inactivates PKA.

Insulin acts acutely on triacylglycerol metabolism by increasing protein phosphatase 1 activity, which in turn dephosphorylates HSL and perilipin 1A.

AMP kinase (AMPK) also plays a role in the regulation of lipolysis. HSL is also a substrate of AMPK; however, phosphorylation of HSL by AMPK inactivates the protein. Given that AMPK is active when cellular concentrations of AMP are high, and the energetic state of the cell is low, this may seem paradoxical; however, this may be a means by which the cell mediates lipolysis. Excess fatty acids require ATP for activation and reincorporation into complex lipids. AMPK is thought to help prevent lipolysis from proceeding unabated.

Chronic lipid storage levels are partially affected by both levels of gene expression and diet. Several transcription factors are important in the expression of genes coding for many of the proteins discussed here.

WORKED PROBLEM 10.6 | Coffee for weight loss?

Many weight-loss products contain caffeine (3,5,7-trimethyl xanthine), the world's most common phosphodiesterase inhibitor. Based on your knowledge of lipolysis, would caffeine affect this process, and if so, how?

Strategy Caffeine is a phosphodiesterase inhibitor. What is the role of phosphodiesterase, and how might this affect lipolysis?

Solution As the name suggests, phosphodiesterases cleave phosphodiesters. Here, the phosphodiester in question is cAMP. Phosphodiesterases act on cAMP to form AMP, which cannot activate PKA. Hence, by inhibiting the enzyme that breaks down the cAMP, levels of cAMP will be elevated and will activate PKA.

Anyone who has used strong coffee or energy drinks to help them stay awake all night knows that caffeine has many physiological functions. In theory it leads to increased lipolysis, although it is more likely that in weight loss products it serves as a general stimulant.

Follow-up question Name and describe two techniques by which you could determine whether two of the proteins involved in lipolysis interact with one another. The techniques appendix may help you.

10.6 Summary

- Neutral lipids are stored in specific organelles termed lipid storage droplets.
- The surface of lipid storage droplets is coated with proteins, among them the perilipins.
- Phosphorylation of lipases and perilipins regulate lipolysis, the controlled breakdown of triacylglycerols.
- Triglyceride stores are regulated acutely by catecholamines and insulin through the modulation of cAMP levels, which affects PKA phosphorylation of lipases and perilipin. AMPK may also play a role.
- Long-term triglyceride stores are regulated by several transcription factors.

10.6 Concept Check

- Describe the signaling pathways implicated in lipolysis.
- Describe the interplay of lipases, perilipins, and other proteins in lipolysis.

10.7 | Lipid Rafts as a Biochemical Entity

The term "raft" probably conjures up an image of a loose bundle of logs, crudely tied together to provide adventure when sailing down a river or as a method for castaways to escape from a desert island. Rafts may keep people afloat, but the strength of the structures and just how long they last are debatable. **Lipid rafts** are in many ways similar to these makeshift structures.

10.7.1 | Lipid rafts are loosely associated groups of sphingolipids and cholesterol found in the plasma membrane

Lipid bilayers are comprised of different types of phospholipids, cholesterol, and multiple proteins, as discussed earlier, but this is only part of the picture. The lipids found in the lipid bilayer are not homogenously mixed. Lipid rafts are organized microdomains of the lipid bilayer. They are small (10 to 200 nm), loose aggregates of lipid, enriched in sphingomyelin and cholesterol, floating in the outer (exoplasmic) face of the lipid bilayer. Cholesterol appears to be a critical component of the raft, and depletion or manipulation of membrane cholesterol disrupts the raft. The acyl chain content of a raft is more saturated than the rest of the membrane; therefore, the raft is assumed to be less fluid than the surrounding phospholipid sea. Also, the increase in saturated lipids in the raft is thought to result in closer packing of the lipids, leading to stronger interactions of head groups through hydrogen bonding or coulombic interactions in the polar regions of the lipid head groups. The overall shape of the molecules involved in raft formation may also be important. Sphingomyelin and cholesterol form cone-shaped structures that complement each other to facilitate close molecular packing. The nature of the forces involved in raft formation and stabilization are still being elucidated.

Lipid rafts were originally identified as detergent-resistant extracts of membranes. When membranes were extracted at low temperatures (around 4°C) with non-ionic detergents such as Triton-X-100, these small structures remained. This led to some controversy in the field, with some researchers suggesting that these structures were artifacts of the experiment. More recently, numerous fluorescent techniques have been used to investigate rafts; for example, fluorescence resonance energy transfer microscopy (FRET) and fluorescence correlation/cross correlation spectroscopy (FCS/FCCS). These techniques, coupled with newly developed fluorescent probes and compounds that can alter the chemical composition of the lipid bilayer, are being used to study lipid rafts in terms of structure and lifetime, that is, how long the structure stays together (currently thought to be in the millisecond-to-second time scale) (**Figure 10.28**).

10.7.2 | Lipid rafts have been broadly grouped into two categories: caveolae and non-caveolar rafts

Caveolae are flask-shaped invaginations of the plasma membrane. They were originally identified in the 1950s from electron microscopy as cave-like invaginations of the plasma

FIGURE 10.28 **Lipid rafts and microdomains form in the plasma membrane.** Lipid rafts are microdomains enriched in cholesterol and sphingolipids or glycosphingolipids. The geometry of cholesterol and sphingolipids allows them to pack more tightly together resulting in a patch of membrane that is less fluid than the surroundings.

membrane. The caveolins, which are groups of three cholesterol-binding proteins, associate with these invaginations and form coated vesicles that are pinched off from the plasma membrane. Caveolae and caveolins are the best characterized raft-associated proteins, and they have been implicated in membrane trafficking. The rafts found in caveolae are enriched in cholesterol and sphingomyelin.

Non-caveolar rafts are flat structures found in the plane of the plasma membrane. In addition to sphingomyelin and cholesterol, these rafts are enriched in glycolipids, which may provide points at which cellular proteins or pathogens may attach.

Numerous proteins associate with lipid rafts. Palmitoylated proteins, such as those found in hedgehog, a key developmental regulator in *Drosophila* and humans, are common in rafts, as are GPI-anchored proteins and proteins that bind to the membrane through glycolipids. This may be due to the saturated hydrocarbon tails of these lipids associating with the raft, although

A.

Caveola

Caveola

500 nm

Asier Echarri, Miguel A. Del Pozo/ Caveolae – mechanosensitive membrane invaginations linked to actin filaments/J Cell Sci 2015 128: 2747-2758

B.

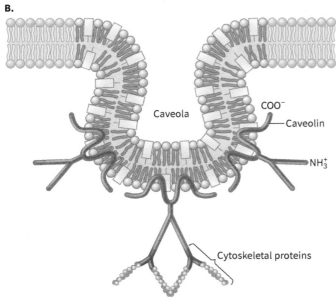

Caveola

COO⁻

Caveolin

NH_3^+

Cytoskeletal proteins

FIGURE 10.29 **Caveolae and caveolins** **A.** Caveolae are flask-shaped invaginations of membrane coated with the caveolins. These structures differ from clathrin-coated pits, partially in their protein composition. **B.** Caveolins are integral membrane proteins associated with caveolae. These are dimeric proteins that bind to sphingomyelin and cholesterol-rich rafts through their carboxy-terminus and interact with the cytoskeleton through their amino-terminus.

it is likely that protein factors are also important. Mutations of key residues at the lipid–protein interface will displace many proteins from rafts.

The importance of lipid rafts has now been demonstrated in many biological processes, and they are now part a rapidly expanding field of research. Two examples of these processes are cell signaling and the biology of pathogenic agents (**Figure 10.29**).

Cell signaling

Multiple signaling pathways are associated with lipid rafts. In each of these instances, the proteins of the pathway interact with the raft through glycolipid or GPI anchors, or through the raft itself via a membrane-spanning helix. Rafts may be involved in the clustering of these proteins and in assembly of macromolecular signaling complexes. Insulin signaling is one example of a pathway that employs lipid rafts.

Pathogenicity

Lipid rafts are important in the pathogenicity of various infectious agents, including some bacteria, viruses, prions, and protozoa. In these cases, the carbohydrate moieties of glycolipids are often the sites of attachment or budding for viruses, including human immunodeficiency virus-1 or HIV-1. They are also sites of action for bacterial toxins, such as anthrax; they may also be important for pathogen entry into the cell and survival such as *Plasmodium falciparum*, the causal agent in malaria.

A better understanding of rafts and their biological roles may make it possible to improve treatments for certain diseases by exploiting the pathogen's dependence on these structures.

WORKED PROBLEM 10.7 | The trouble with rafts

You are investigating a protein complex that may be associated with lipid rafts. What complications might arise in investigating lipid rafts?

Strategy What techniques have been used previously to examine lipid rafts? What are the strengths and limitations of these techniques?

Solution Lipid rafts are relatively small and transient. Thus, the raft itself may contain relatively few molecules of cholesterol or sphingolipid (50 to several hundred) and only a few protein molecules. Rafts were originally identified using electron microscopy.

This technique can be used because of the size of rafts, but it fails to capture their transient and dynamic nature, since it requires the examination of dead, fixed material in a vacuum. Newer techniques employ fluorescent imaging of cells or cell membranes. These techniques (FRET and FCS/FCCS) can capture interactions in live cells occurring over microseconds.

Follow-up question Methyl-β-cyclodextrins are a class of carbohydrate molecules that can be used to deplete the cell of cholesterol. How might these compounds be useful in a study of lipid rafts?

10.7 Summary

- Lipid rafts are microdomains of the plasma membrane enriched in cholesterol and sphingolipids.
- Lipid rafts have been implicated in membrane trafficking, protein interaction with the plasma membrane, and organization of signaling complexes.

10.7 Concept Check

- Describe the forces involved in tethering raft lipids together.
- Describe one process in which rafts have been implicated.

The Bigger Picture

Lipids are as essential to life as proteins, carbohydrates, or nucleic acids. Although often maligned in the popular media, lipids form the boundaries of cells, and they are vital for energy storage and cellular homeostasis. Errors in lipid metabolism (either inborn or induced through overnutrition) can have grave consequences (Table 10.6).

Lipids are transported in the circulation bound to globular proteins, or in large protein lipid complexes known as lipoproteins. The significance of these functions in biology and medicine is evidenced by the fact that many people have heard of HDL and LDL. Although this chapter focuses on the transport of bulk lipids and certain hormones, fat soluble vitamins and many drugs are also transported by these systems.

Phospholipid metabolism and neutral lipid metabolism reach a crossroads at phosphatidate. The regulation of lipid stores is a much more complicated process than was envisioned even a decade ago. We now appreciate that the regulated breakdown of neutral lipids involves phosphorylation of both enzymes and coat proteins on the surface of the lipid storage droplet. Some of these same proteins interact with trafficking proteins and may have a role in lipid droplet assembly. Furthermore, at least one protein, lipin, serves double duty as both a phosphatidate phosphatase and a transcriptional regulator.

Finally, microdomains of cholesterol and sphingolipids, termed lipid rafts, are emerging as important anchor points for signaling complexes, cytoskeletal proteins, receptor trafficking, and neurotransmission.

Problems

10.1 Phospholipid Metabolism

1. What is meant by *de novo* phospholipid biosynthesis?

2. Phospholipases cut phospholipids.

    a. Draw the structure of palmitoyl oleoyl phosphatidylcholine.

    b. What would the products be if that lipid were cut with phospholipase A_2?

    c. What would the products be if that lipid were cut with phospholipase C?

3. Choose a phospholipid and examine the thermodynamics of the steps in its biosynthesis. Based on your knowledge of the reactions involved, would the ΔG values for these reactions be positive, negative, or near zero? What is your reasoning for the values you generated?

10.2 Digestion of Triacylglycerols

4. Shown is the structure of pancreatic lipase. Describe the topology of this molecule in your own words. Is it mostly α helix, β sheet, or some combination of the two? Can you see any potential domains to the protein? Are there any particularly striking features that you have not seen in other proteins? Can you propose a function for any of those features? (PDB ID 1N8S van Tilbeurgh, H., Sarda, L., Verger, R., Cambillau, C. (1992) Structure of the pancreatic lipase-procolipase complex. *Nature* 359: 159–162)

Pancreatic lipase

5. The U.S. government has stipulated that foods made with olestra must be supplemented with vitamin K. What is the basis for this stipulation?

6. Many lipases employ a catalytic triad (asp-his-ser), similar to the protease chymotrypsin, in their mechanism. Propose a mechanism for a lipase that cleaves an ester linkage.

7. Why does carbohydrate digestion begin in the mouth, protein digestion in the stomach, but lipid digestion in the intestine?

8. Examine the structure of orlistat. Based on the structure, what weak forces may be involved in binding to pancreatic lipase? Which amino acids in pancreatic lipase would be involved in binding?

Orlistat

9. Orlistat and penicillin both contain β-lactam or lactone functional groups.

   a. What is a β-lactam or lactone?

   b. Can orlistat be used as an antibiotic? Can penicillin be used as a weight loss agent? Why or why not?

   c. Does the common β-lactam or lactone structure tell you anything about the mechanism of action of these drugs? What does it tell you about the enzymes they inhibit?

10. Olestra is being used as a treatment for people who have been exposed to toxins such as dioxin. Examine the structure and properties of these molecules. Propose how this treatment might work.

Dioxin

11. Methyl *tert*-butyl ether (MTBE) is being used experimentally as a treatment for gallstones. Examine the structure and properties of these molecules. Describe how this would work.

10.3 Transport of Lipids in the Circulation

12. Concept maps are tools used to link together ideas and objects to help organize, represent, and structure knowledge. One way of constructing a concept map is to assemble a list of nouns on index cards or scraps of paper and connect these using arrows labeled with verbs. Identify the words you think are key terms in this section. Create a concept map showing which proteins interact with each other, and what roles they play in lipoprotein metabolism.

13. Several enzymes, for example, hepatic lipase and lipoprotein lipase, can bind to lipoproteins. There are mutant variants of these enzymes that bind lipoproteins but are not catalytically active. Cells expressing these mutants can still absorb cholesterol. What does that tell us about the functions of these proteins in cholesterol absorption?

14. Why is fatty acid free bovine serum albumin (BSA) often included in lipase assays?

15. Heart disease is the cause of death of nearly one in three Americans. Why would such a flawed system of transport evolve? What are the environmental factors at work in the selection of genes coding for the proteins discussed in lipoprotein metabolism?

10.4 Entry of Lipids in to the Cell

16. How could you show that the adaptor protein AP2 has a phosphatidylinositol 4,5 bisphosphate (PIP2) binding domain?

17. Antisense is a technique used to silence genes and decrease protein expression in a cell or organism. It is described in the techniques index. Using antisense, if you knocked down each of these proteins, what would you expect to happen? Where would molecules pile up or the pathway arrest?

   a. LDLr

   b. AP2

   c. clathrin

   d. dynamin

18. How could you show that clathrin is a trimer of dimers; that is, what is the ratio of clathrin subunits in the holoprotein?

19. How could you calculate the total number of clathrin molecules on the surface of an endosome?

10.5 Neutral Lipid Biosynthesis

20. Describe how triacylglycerol biosynthesis differs between an adipocyte and an enterocyte.

21. A low-carbohydrate diet proclaims that, without glucose, adipose tissue is unable to store triacylglycerol. Is this true?

22. Is energy required for triacylglycerol biosynthesis? When, where, and how (in what form) is this energy provided?

23. What is the role of PA in neutral lipid metabolism?

24. Cholesteryl ester is the storage form of cholesterol. Based on your knowledge of lipid metabolism, does the synthesis of cholesteryl ester cost or provide energy? What might be the source of that energy in this reaction?

10.6 Lipid Storage Droplets, Fat Storage, and Mobilization

25. Which tissues of the body are largely responsible for β-oxidation and which for gluconeogenesis? Why run both catabolic (β-oxidation) and anabolic (gluconeogenesis) pathways at the same time?

26. Why are at least three different lipases involved in the mobilization of lipid stores?

27. The perilipins are neither acylated nor farnesylated. Propose a mechanism by which they tether to lipid storage droplets.

28. Lipid storage droplets are the only organelle known that is bound by a phospholipid monolayer. Why is there only a monolayer?

10.7 Lipid Rafts as a Biochemical Entity

29. In your own words, describe a lipid raft. How large are these rafts, and what are their proposed components?

30. One of the complicating factors encountered when studying lipid rafts is their transient nature. If a structure lasts for only a short time (seconds or less), what techniques could be used to study its formation?

31. Examine the structures of lipids that are suspected to be found in a lipid raft. What types of interactions (weak forces) would you expect to help stabilize this structure? Characterize the strengths of those interactions.

32. Examine the overall shape of cholesterol and sphingomyelin shown in Figure 10.28. The shapes of these structures can be described as a cone or inverse cone. In your own words, describe how the packing of these molecules could occur in raft formation. If that section of membrane needed to form an invagination, that is, if a caveolae or coated pit were forming, how would the composition of that membrane have to change? What changes would need to be made to the lipid composition to achieve that conformation?

Data Interpretation

33. A paper you are reading contains this figure of a micrograph and western blots. Please use the figure and caption to answer the questions below.

A.

Tomasz Szul/Medical Images

B.

C.

D.

E.

F.

A. Immunofluorescence image of POI (protein of interest) immunostained with Oregon Green 488 (green) and nuclei stained with DAPI (blue). **B.–F.** Western blots of sucrose ultracentrifugation gradients stained for the following proteins: **B.,** POI; **C.,** oxidative phosphorylation complex IV (mitochondria); **D.,** GAPDH (cytosol); **E.,** Golgin-97 (golgi); **F.,** disulfide isomerase (endoplasmic reticulum).

   a. Where is the POI found in the cell? Which organelle?

   b. What is the point of having two methods of determining the location of the protein?

   c. Why were these proteins chosen?

34. A paper hypothesizes that a specific protein cofactor is needed for optimal lipase activity. Both proteins are expressed in adipose tissue. Several knockdown constructs (RNAi) were prepared to silence expression of the cofactor and the following data were obtained, as shown in the table below. Check the appendix for descriptions of experimental techniques you may not have encountered before.

Values are standard error of the mean (S.E.M.) for $n = 6$ samples.

   a. Why were five constructs used?

   b. What is the purpose of the scrambled construct?

   c. Why were western blots run for both cofactor and lipase if the RNAi construct was only designed to silence the cofactor?

   d. Why were western blots performed rather than reverse transcriptase polymerase chain reaction (RT-PCR), northern blots, or some other technique?

   e. Which RNAi construct was most effective at silencing the expression of the cofactor?

   f. Why are glycerol and fatty acid release different?

   g. What does the statistical analysis of this data tell you?

   h. What are your conclusions from this figure?

35. You are investigating some of the enzymatic properties of a novel cobra venom. Samples of cellular lipids were treated with venom or a mixture of venom and EGTA. The resulting lipids were subjected to analysis by thin-layer chromatography.

Lane 1 = control lipids (no treatment)
Lane 2 = lipids + venom + EGTA
Lane 3 = lipids + venom

   a. What enzymatic activity does the enzyme apparently have?

   b. What are the products of the reaction?

   c. What does the EGTA data tell you about the reaction?

Experimental Design

36. PE can be synthesized by several different pathways. How could you demonstrate that a cellular pool of PE was derived from phosphatidylserine rather than from some other source?

Construct	WB: cofactor	WB: lipase	Glycerol release (mmol/min/10–6 cells)	Fatty acid release (mmol/min/10–6 cells)
Scrambled	⬛	⬛	4.8±0.2	0.7±0.3
1	⬬	⬛	5.0±0.3	1.2±0.3
2	⬬	⬛	4.6±0.1	0.9±0.1
3	⬬	⬛	4.9±0.4	0.8±0.2
4	⬛	⬛	5.1±0.2	1.2±0.3

WB, western blot

37. The laboratory you are working in is investigating a family with very low levels of HDL and increased plasma triacylglycerols, but unexpectedly low risk of heart disease. What questions could you ask to start to investigate this paradox?

38. There are several points at which phospholipid metabolism and neutral lipid metabolism cross paths. Several proteins have recently been identified that have catalytic activity. Design an experiment to test whether a novel protein you have discovered has phosphatidate phosphatase activity.

39. The laboratory you are working in is studying how a newly discovered peptide hormone is absorbed by the cell. How could you test to see whether the receptor hormone complex is removed from the membrane via receptor-mediated endocytosis?

40. Design an experiment to test the hypothesis that the phosphorylation of perilipin A is required for maximal lipolysis.

Ethics and Social Responsibility

41. Many aspects of science that we now accept as dogma were once controversial or even heretical. The existence of lipid rafts was long considered a controversial topic. Can you think of other scientific topics in the current media that are considered controversial? What is your opinion on these topics? How have you formed these opinions? In other words, are your opinions based on science or punditry?

42. In the West of Scotland Study, statins were given to a hypercholesterolemic but otherwise healthy population. One of the conclusions at the end of the study was that taking statins gave this population added protection against myocardial infarction. Hence, one possible further conclusion was that everyone should be taking statins, although many consider this an extreme conclusion. Food and water supplies in the United States have been supplemented or treated with several vitamins, minerals, and small inorganics (chlorine and fluoride). Given the prevalence of some diseases, does it make sense to put prophylactic pharmaceuticals in the food or water supply?

43. Olestra was developed in 1968 but did not gain approval from the Food and Drug Administration (FDA) until 1996, some 28 years later, as concerns over its use were reviewed and tested. Based on what you know about olestra and lipid metabolism, write arguments from the perspective of the company (Procter & Gamble) in support of approving olestra for public consumption, and from the perspective of a consumer watchdog group citing concerns about the approval.

44. One fear the FDA had about the widespread approval of olestra was that people would consume more olestra-rich foods in the belief that they were "healthy" food items. Do you think development of molecules such as olestra make people more lax with regard to their dietary habits?

45. Is it ethical to work on a project to develop a molecule like orlistat when millions of people around the world (including many in the United States) do not have enough to eat each day?

Suggested Readings

10.1 General and Phospholipid Metabolism

Ehnholm, Christian, ed. *Cellular Lipid Metabolism.* New York, New York: Springer, 2009.

Fahy, E., S. Subramaniam, R. C. Murphy, M. Nishijima, C. R. Raetz, T. Shimizu, F. Spener, et al. "Update of the LIPID MAPS Comprehensive Classification System for Lipids." *Journal of Lipid Research* 50 (April 2009): S9–14.

Gurr, I. M., ed. *Lipid Biochemistry: An Introduction.* 3rd ed. New York, New York: Springer, 1980.

Gurr, I. M., J. L. Harwood, and K. N. Frayne. *Lipid Biochemistry: An Introduction.* 5th ed. New York, New York: Wiley-Blackwell, 2002.

Kent, C. "Eukaryotic Phospholipid Biosynthesis." *Annual Review of Biochemistry* 64 (1995): 315–43.

Simmons, K., ed. *The Biology of Lipids: Trafficking, Regulation and Function.* Woodbury, New York: Cold Spring Harbor Laboratory Press, 2011.

The AOCS Lipid Library. Retrieved from http://lipidlibrary.aocs.org/index.html

Vance, D. E., and J. E. Vance, eds. *Biochemistry of Lipids, Lipoproteins, and Membranes.* 5th ed. New York, New York: Elsevier, 2008.

Wenk, Markus. "The Emerging Field of Lipidomics." *Nature Reviews Drug Discovery* 4 (2005).

10.2 Digestion of Triacylglycerols

Chapus, C., M. Rovery, L. Sarda, and R. Verger. "Minireview on Pancreatic Lipase and Colipase." *Biochimie* 70 (1988): 1223–34.

Cheng, D., T. C. Nelson, J. Chen, S. G. Walker, J. Wardwell-Swanson, R. Meegalla, R. Taub, et al. "Identification of Acyl Coenzyme A: Monoacylglycerol Acyltransferase 3, an Intestinal Specific Enzyme Implicated in Dietary Fat Absorption." *Journal of Biological Chemistry* 278, no. 16 (2003): 13611–4.

Hibuse, T., N. Maeda, T. Funahashi, K. Yamamoto, A. Nagasawa, W. Mizunoya, K. Kishida, et al. "Aquaporin 7 Deficiency Is Associated with Development of Obesity Through Activation of Adipose Glycerol Kinase." *Proceedings of the National Academy of Sciences of the United States of America* 102, no. 31 (August 2, 2005): 10993–8.

Li, C., T. Tan, H. Zhang, and W. Feng. "Analysis of the Conformational Stability and Activity of *Candida antarctica* Lipase B in Organic Solvents: Insight from Molecular Dynamics and Quantum Mechanics/Simulations." *Journal of Biological Chemistry* 285, no. 37 (2010): 28434–41.

Lowe, M. E. "Structure and Function of Pancreatic Lipase and Colipase." *Annual Review of Nutrition* 17 (1997): 141–58.

Lowe, M. E., J. L. Rosenblum, and A. W. Strauss. "Cloning and Characterization of Human Pancreatic Lipase cDNA." *Journal of Biological Chemistry* 264 (1989): 20042–8.

Persson, B., G. Bengtsson-Olivecrona, S. Enerback, T. Olivecrona, and H. Jornvall. "Structural Features of Lipoprotein Lipase. Lipase Family Relationships, Binding Interactions, Non-Equivalence of Lipase Cofactors, Vitellogenin Similarities and Functional Subdivision of Lipoprotein Lipase." *European Journal of Biochemistry* 179 (1989): 39–45.

van Tilbeurgh, H., S. Bezzine, C. Cambillau, R. Verger, and F. Carriere. "Colipase: Structure and Interaction with Pancreatic Lipase." *Biochimica et Biophysica Acta* 1441, no. 2–3 (1999): 173–84.

Weibel, E. K., P. Hadvary, E. Hochuli, E. Kupfer, and H. Lengsfeld. "Lipstatin, an Inhibitor of Pancreatic Lipase, Produced by *Streptomyces toxytricini*. I. Producing Organism, Fermentation, Isolation and Biological Activity." *Journal of Antibioics (Tokyo)* 40, no. 8 (August 1987): 1081–5.

Winkler, F. K., A. D'Arcy, and W. Hunziker. "Structure of Human Pancreatic Lipase." *Nature* 343 (1990): 771–4.

10.3 Transport of Lipids in the Circulation

Hamilton, R. L., M. C. Williams, C. J. Fielding, and R. J. Havel. "Discoidal Bilayer Structure of Nascent High Density Lipoproteins from Perfused Rat Liver." *Journal of Clinical Investigation* 58, no. 3 (September 1976): 667–680.

Mahley, R. W., T. L. Innerarity, S. C. Rall, Jr., and K. H. Weisgraber. "Plasma Lipoproteins: Apolipoprotein Structure and Function." *Journal of Lipid Research*, 25, (1984): 1277–1294.

Panáková, D., H. Sprong, E. Marois, C. Thiele, and S. Eaton. "Lipoprotein Particles Are Required for Hedgehog and Wingless Signaling." *Nature* 435, (2005): 58–65.

Vance, J. E., and H. Hayashi. "Formation and Function of Apolipoprotein E-Containing Lipoproteins in the Nervous System." *Biochimica et Biophysica Acta* 1801, no. 8 (August 2010): 806–18.

10.4 Entry of Lipids into the Cell

Fernandes, John. *Inborn Metabolic Diseases: Diagnosis and Treatment.* 4th ed. Berlin, Germany: Springer, 2006.

Goldstein, J. L., and M. S. Brown. "The LDL Receptor." *Arteriosclerosis, Thrombosis, and Vascular Biology* 29, no. 4 (April 29, 2009): 431–8.

Kikuchi, A., H. Yamamoto, and A. Sato. "Selective Activation Mechanisms of Wnt Signaling Pathways." *Trends in Cell Biology* 19, no. 3 (March 19, 2009): 119–29.

McMahon, H. T., and E. Boucrot. "Molecular Mechanism and Physiological Functions of Clathrin-Mediated Endocytosis." *Nature Reviews Molecular Cell Biology* 12, no. 8 (July 22, 2011): 517–33.

Reider, A., and B. Wendland. "Endocytic Adaptors—Social Networking at the Plasma Membrane." *Journal of Cell Science* 124, Pt. 10 (May 15, 2011): 1613–22.

Sorkin, A. "Cargo Recognition During Clathrin-Mediated Endocytosis: A Team Effort." *Current Opinion in Cell Biology* 16, no. 4 (2004): 392–9.

Tien, A. C., A. Rajan, and H. J. Bellen. "A Notch Updated." *Journal of Cell Biology* 184, no. 5 (March 9, 2009): 621–9.

Zwang, Y., and Y. Yarden. "Systems Biology of Growth Factor-Induced Receptor Endocytosis." *Traffic* 10, no. 4 (April 10, 2009): 349–63.

10.5 Neutral Lipid Biosynthesis

Athenstaedt, K., and G. Daum. "The Life Cycle of Neutral Lipids: Synthesis, Storage and Degradation." *Cellular and Molecular Life Sciences* 63, no. 12 (2006): 1355–1369.

Buhman, K. K., H. C. Chen, and R. V. Farese, Jr. "The Enzymes of Neutral Lipid Synthesis." *Journal of Biological Chemistry* 276, no. 44 (November 2, 2001): 40369–72.

Csaki, L. S., and K. Reue. "Lipins: Multifunctional Lipid Metabolism Proteins." *Annual Review of Nutrition* 30 (August 21, 2010): 257–72.

Reue, K., and D. N. Brindley. "Thematic Review Series: Glycerolipids. Multiple Roles for Lipins/Phosphatidate Phosphatase Enzymes in Lipid Metabolism." *Journal of Lipid Research* 49, no. 12 (December 2008): 2493–503.

Yen, C. L., S. J. Stone, S. Koliwad, C. Harris, and R. V. Farese, Jr. "Thematic Review Series: Glycerolipids. DGAT Enzymes and Triacylglycerol Biosynthesis." *Journal of Lipid Research* 49, no. 11 (November 2008): 2283–2301.

10.6 Lipid Storage Droplets, Fat Storage, and Mobilization

Bickel, P. E., J. T. Tansey, and M. A. Welte. "PAT Proteins, an Ancient Family of Lipid Droplet Proteins That Regulate Cellular Lipid Stores." *Biochimica et Biophysica Acta* 1791, no. 6 (June 2009): 419–40.

Brasaemle, D. L. "Thematic Review Series: Adipocyte Biology. The Perilipin Family of Structural Lipid Droplet Proteins: Stabilization of Lipid Droplets and Control of Lipolysis." *Journal of Lipid Research* 48, no. 12 (December 2007): 2547–59.

Olofsson, S. O, P. Boström, L. Andersson, M. Rutberg, M. Levin, J. Perman, and J. Borén. "Triglyceride Containing Lipid Droplets and Lipid Droplet-Associated Proteins." *Current Opinion in Lipidology* 19, no. 5 (October 2008): 441–7.

Walther, T. C., and R. V. Farese, Jr. "The Life of Lipid Droplets." *Biochimica et Biophysica Acta* 1791, no. 6 (June 2009): 459–66.

10.7 Lipid Rafts as a Biochemical Entity

Anderson, Richard G. W. "The Caeolae Membrane System." *Annual Review of Biochemistry* 67 (1998): 199–225.

Calder, P. C., and P. J. Yaqoob. "Lipid Rafts—Composition, Characterization, and Controversies." *Nutrition* 137, no. 3 (March 2007): 545–7.

Fielding, C. J., ed. *Lipid Rafts and Caveolae: From Membrane Biophysics to Cell Biology.* New York, New York: Wiley-VCH, 2006.

Glebov, Oleg O., Nicholas A. Bright, and Benjamin J. Nichols. Flotillin-1 defines a clathrin-independent endocytic pathway in mammalian cells *Nature Cell Biology* 8 (2006): 46–54.

Morrow, I. C., and R. G. Parton. "Flotillins and the PHB Domain Protein Family: Rafts, Worms and Anaesthetics." *Traffic* 6, no. 9 (September 2005): 725–40.

Lipids II

1950s	Caveolae is first described in electron micrographs
1953	Fibrates are first synthesized
1967	Fibrates first used to treat high levels of plasma lipids
1968	Olestra is developed
1971	First HMG-CoA reductase inhibitor (statin) is isolated from *Penicillium* fungus
1984	Brown and Goldstein win the Nobel Prize for regulation of cholesterol metabolism
1987	Mercor, the first statin approved for clinical use
1991	Perilipin is identified
1994	Sirtuins are first described in the literature
1996	Olestra is approved for sale to the public
1997	Lipid rafts are first characterized
1999	Pancreatic lipase inhibitor (orlistat) is approved for clinical use
2003	Earliest mention of the term "lipidomics" in the biomedical literature
2005	Statin sales exceed $19.7 billion in the United States alone
2012	Statin sales exceed $29 billion worldwide
2014	Total number of papers in medical publishing mentioning sirtuins breaks 3,500

CHAPTER **11**

Amino Acid and Amine Metabolism

James Leynse/Corbis Historical/Getty Images

The Fresh Kills Landfill was the principal waste disposal facility for New York City for over 50 years, handling at its peak 13,000 tons of garbage daily. The landfill is currently being converted into a park and solar energy generating station.

Amine Metabolism in Context

Most human endeavors involve waste. In almost all we do, we create some by-product that is unusable or needs to be directed toward some other function. A simple example is building a house. Whether we build it out of wood or stone, inevitably, there is scrap left behind. This scrap material may be wasted (put into a landfill), or it may be directed toward a different function, such as building a tree house or being processed into other products.

Biological systems are in many ways analogous to these examples. Chemotrophs are organisms that take in all the nutrients and energy they need in chemical form from their environment. The metabolism of some of these molecules produces toxic by-products that must be neutralized, recycled, or eliminated from the system.

Amino acids and xenobiotics are two types of molecules that pose challenges when metabolized. We do not typically store amino acids in the same way that we store carbohydrates or lipids, but we can catabolize the carbon skeleton of amino acids into other metabolites. This requires detoxifying the amino acid by removing the amino group, but direct removal of an amino group would generate ammonia, a highly toxic by-product. Animals have evolved different means of coping with this load; for example, many higher animals synthesize urea from the ammonia through a process called the urea cycle. Xenobiotics include molecules that are strange or foreign to the organism, including the compounds that give food and drink their characteristic flavors. Xenobiotics also include most drug molecules. Metabolism of xenobiotics is critical to modern medicine and pharmaceutical science. The different aspects of this chapter are described in **Dynamic Figure 11.1**.

CHAPTER OUTLINE

11.1 Digestion of Proteins

11.2 Transamination and Oxidative Deamination

11.3 The Urea Cycle

11.4 Pathways of Amino Acid Carbon Skeleton Scavenging

11.5 The Detoxification of Other Amines and Xenobiotics

11.6 The Biochemistry of Renal Function

DYNAMIC FIGURE 11.1 Prior to being catabolized for breakdown, the amino group of amino acids needs to be removed from the molecule and detoxified prior to excretion by the kidney. Xenobiotics are modified by the liver and secreted by the kidney.

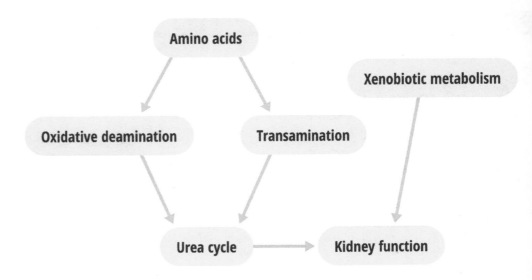

COMMON THEMES

Evolution's outcomes are conserved.	• Both the pathways and structures found in amino acid catabolism are conserved throughout evolution. • Specific proteins (cytochromes) encountered in this chapter are coded for by genes that can be used to track evolutionary change. • Organisms evolved specialized pathways to detoxify ammonia and spare water when excreting nitrogenous wastes. • Carnivorous organisms upregulated certain metabolic pathways to compensate for a diet rich in protein. • Pathways and whole-organ systems evolved to help organisms detoxify potentially harmful molecules.
Structure determines function.	• Many of the enzymes involved in amino acid metabolism are allosterically regulated. • Many xenobiotics are detoxified by making them more water soluble, which decreases their ability to enter the cell and increases the likelihood that they will be eliminated in the urine.
Biochemical information is transferred, exchanged, and stored.	• Allosteric regulators generated in other parts of metabolism regulate many aspects of amino acid catabolism. • Covalent modification (phosphorylation or adenylation) is used to regulate some pathways.
Biomolecules are altered through pathways involving transformations of energy and matter.	• The pathways of amino acid catabolism are coordinated with one another and with whole-body metabolism. • Reactions where one functional group is exchanged for another, such as a transamination, have little to no associated energetic cost. • Catabolic pathways are generally oxidative; that is, the products are more oxidized than the substrates, and yield energy, often as NADH, $FADH_2$, or NADPH. • The synthesis of urea is a biosynthetic pathway and a reduction of the carbon atom of urea. As a result, urea biosynthesis requires the hydrolysis of several molecules of ATP to make the reaction proceed in the forward direction. • Most amino acids use similar chemistry (transamination) to eliminate the amino group before catabolism of the carbon skeleton. • Similar types of reactions are seen in the citric acid cycle, β-oxidation, and catabolism of several amino acids.

11.1 | Digestion of Proteins

All animals must consume proteins in their diet to provide a source of amino acids. Under most circumstances, the organism does not absorb whole proteins but breaks these larger molecules or protein polymers down into smaller subunits—di- and tripeptides and amino acid monomers. As with lipid and carbohydrate digestion, enzymes begin to break down protein molecules in the stomach, but most of the digestion and all of the absorption occurs in the small intestine.

11.1.1 | Protein digestion begins in the stomach

The stomach is highly acidic with a pH of approximately 1. The acid-producing parietal cells lining the stomach employ ATPases in the plasma membrane to pump H^+ into the stomach lumen (**Figure 11.2**). Chief cells secrete proteases and peptidases, which begin to degrade proteins. These enzymes are synthesized in an inactive state, as **zymogens**, also known as **proenzymes**; in this way, enzymes are prevented from degrading the cell's proteins and hence from damaging the cell itself. Zymogens require some type of modification for activation. In this instance, proteolytic enzymes are activated by the acidic environment of the stomach. Consequently, the zymogen pepsinogen is converted to pepsin while still in the stomach.

Zymogens are not the only way in which the organism protects itself from its own digestive enzymes. Mucus, which is a viscous combination of glycoproteins, provides a barrier to help keep proteolytic enzymes away from the cells lining the stomach. Cells that secrete mucus also secrete bicarbonate ions, which prevent acidic damage. Depletion of this barrier, due to infection or injury, can lead to damage of the stomach lining causing an ulcer.

Stomach acid is controlled pharmacologically in different ways
Whether due to one's diet or stress, excess stomach acid is a common complaint. In response, science and medicine developed some simple treatments, and others more strategic, for excess stomach acid.

The oldest and still the most common treatment for excess stomach acid is to neutralize it with a weak base using antacid tablets. These tablets often contain calcium carbonate ($CaCO_3$) or magnesium carbonate ($MgCO_3$). Because they are weak bases, they work instantly by neutralizing stomach acid. In addition, these preparations provide Ca^{2+} or Mg^{2+}, necessary nutrients in the diet. Although antacids are generally effective, they have a chalky taste that some people find displeasing. In addition, stoichiometric amounts of base need to be consumed to neutralize the excess stomach acid.

Two newer approaches work at the level of acid production. Omeprazole (Prilosec) and lansoprazole (Prevacid) are examples of proton-pump inhibitors (PPIs). These drugs block the production of acid in the stomach by irreversibly inhibiting the action of the ATPase found on the surface of parietal cells in the gastric mucosa. This ATPase uses the energy of ATP hydrolysis to pump one proton into the stomach in exchange for a potassium ion. Prevacid and Nexium (the next-generation of Prilosec) are some of the best-selling drugs and are widely used; however, no matter how benign they may appear, these inhibitors are pharmaceuticals and taking them is not without risk. Although these drugs are well-tolerated and side effects are minor, they may increase susceptibility to disease, such as infection with *Clostridium difficile* (*C. diff*), block absorbance of some micronutrients, and interact with other medications. The United States Food and Drug Administration (FDA) recommends that patients consume a two-week course of proton-pump inhibitors no more than three times per year.

Omeprazole   **Lansoprazole**

A third means by which gastric acid can be controlled is through blocking the biochemical signals that cause the parietal cell to secrete acid. Histamine is the chemical signal used by the body to trigger these cells. Histamine is also the molecule that causes swelling and stuffy

A. Pepsinogen → Pepsin

HCl

H⁺
Cl⁻

Stomach

Chief cell
Parietal cell

Active site aspartate residues

Pepsin

B. Trypsinogen ⟶ Trypsin
Chymotrysinogen ⟶ Chymotrypsin

Liver

Pancreas

Gallbladder

Bile duct

Pancreatic duct

Islet cells (hormones)
Acinar cells (enzymes)

Catalyric triad (Asp, His, Ser)

Trypsin

C. proteolytic activation

Change in secondary structure

Chymotrypsinogen (zymogen)

Chymotrypsin (active)

FIGURE 11.2 **Overview of protein digestion.** **A.** Protein digestion begins with the enzyme pepsin in the acidic environment of the stomach. (Tortora; Derrickson, *Principles of Anatomy & Physiology*, 13e, copyright 2012, John Wiley & Sons. This material is reproduced with permission of John Wiley & Sons, Inc.; PDB ID 1PSN Fujinaga, M., Chernaia, M.M., Tarasova, N.I., Mosimann, S.C., James, M.N. (1995) Crystal structure of human pepsin and its complex with pepstatin. *Protein Sci.* 4: 960–972) **B.** The pancreatic enzymes trypsin and chymotrypsin continue protein degradation in the small intestine. (Tortora; Derrickson, *Principles of Anatomy & Physiology*, 13e, copyright 2012, John Wiley & Sons. This material is reproduced with permission of

John Wiley & Sons, Inc.; PDB ID 1S81 Transue, T.R., Krahn, J.M., Gabel, S.A., DeRose, E.F., London, R.E. (2004) X-ray and NMR characterization of covalent complexes of trypsin, borate, and alcohols. *Biochemistry* 43: 2829–2839) **C.** Proteolytic activation of enzymes in the stomach leads to changes in protein structure. (Left: PDB ID 2CGA Wang, D., Bode, W., Huber, R. (1985) Bovine chymotrypsinogen A X-ray crystal structure analysis and refinement of a new crystal form at 1.8 A resolution. *J. Mol. Biol.* 185: 595–624; Right: PDB ID 4Q2K Chua, K.C.H., Pietsch, M., Zhang, X., Hautmann, S., Chan, H.Y., Bruning, J.B., Gutschow, M., Abell, A.D. (2014) Macrocyclic Protease Inhibitors with Reduced Peptide Character. *Angew. Chem. Int. Ed. Engl.*)

1. Substrate binds. Aspartyl residues in active site polarize water molecule that attacks peptide carbonyl carbon.	2. A tetrahedral intermediate forms. This intermediate collapses, resulting in cleavage of the peptide bond.	3. Products are released.

FIGURE 11.3 **Pepsin is an aspartyl protease.** Pepsin is an aspartyl protease using a pair of aspartate residues in the active site to polarize a water molecule, increasing its nucleophilic character and enabling attack on the carbonyl carbon of the peptide (amide) bond. The resulting tetrahedral intermediate collapses, resulting in bond cleavage.

noses during allergy season, but its effect here is different. There are at least three classes of histamine receptors: H_1, which is ubiquitously expressed; H_2, which is most strongly expressed in the gastric mucosa; and H_3, which is found at the highest concentration in nervous tissue. All are examples of G protein coupled receptors. Inhibitors of the H_2 receptor, such as cimetidine (Tagamet) and ranitidine (Zantac) are H_2 receptor antagonists; they act by blocking the signals that stimulate the parietal cell to secrete acid.

11.1.2 Protein digestion continues in the small intestine, aided by proteases

Additional degradation of proteins takes place in the small intestine. Pancreatic enzymes such as trypsin and chymotrypsin further break down proteins into short peptides or free amino acids. The mechanism of action for these enzymes was discussed in section 4.3. The pancreatic enzymes are proteases; that is, they cleave peptide (amide) linkages between amino acids. Trypsin and chymotrypsin are serine proteases; they employ a classic catalytic triad (Asp-His-Ser) with the deprotonated serine acting as the nucleophile. Both trypsin and chymotrypsin are secreted as the zymogens trypsinogen and chymotrypsinogen, which are both activated by proteolytic cleavage. This cleavage can come from active trypsin itself or from enteropeptidase, another serine protease secreted from the intestinal mucosa. Pepsin is an aspartyl protease; it uses a pair of aspartate residues to coordinate a water molecule to attack the carbonyl carbon of the peptide bond (**Figure 11.3**).

Following cleavage by proteases, peptidases cleave the smaller units into individual amino acids, dipeptides, or tripeptides. The peptidases include aminopeptidase and carboxypeptidase, which cleave amino acids from the amino or carboxyl side of short oligopeptides (**Table 11.1**).

11.1.3 Amino acids are absorbed in the small intestine

The small intestine is also where absorption of amino acids occurs. The brush border of the small intestine is lined with epithelial enterocytes and embedded in their plasma

TABLE 11.1 **Digestive Enzymes of the Gastrointestinal Tract**

Zymogen	Enzyme	Location	Mechanism	Substrate
Pepsinogen	Pepsin	Stomach	Aspartyl protease	C side of phe, trp, tyr
Trypsinogen	Trypsin	Small intestine	Serine protease	C side of lys, arg
Chymotrypsinogen	Chymotrypsin	Pancreas/small intestine	Serine protease	C side of phe, tyr, trp

FIGURE 11.4 **Amino acid absorption.** **A.** Amino acids are transported into enterocytes via transporters. Each of these transporters uses the potential energy of chemical gradients, such as sodium, to drive amino acid transport. The amino acids are transported out of the enterocyte and into the bloodstream down their concentration gradient. **B.** Whole proteins are endocytosed into the enterocyte and then either degraded into amino acids in a lysosome or passed through the enterocyte and secreted into the circulation.

membranes are transporters and peptidases (**Figure 11.4**). Transmembrane peptidases are integral membrane proteins that break dipeptides and tripeptides into free amino acids; most peptides longer than three amino acids are not absorbed. The epithelial enterocytes also have transporters that move the amino acids from the intestinal lumen to the bloodstream. These transporters are symporters that rely on the cotransport of sodium ions to drive amino acid absorption. Dipeptides and tripeptides are transported using the peptide transporter—a symporter that uses a proton gradient rather than a sodium ion gradient to drive peptide transport into the cell. Once inside the cell, peptides are cleaved into amino acids by cytosolic peptidases.

There is one exception to the rule that proteins are degraded to amino acids before entering the circulation. In neonatal mammals, whole milk proteins are either endocytosed by the enterocyte and degraded in lysosomes, or the proteins pass unscathed through the enterocyte and enter the circulation in their native conformation. This mechanism is thought to grant neonates the ability to absorb antibodies from their mother's milk (an example of passive immunity) and protect them from infection in their first weeks of life. It is unclear at what point enterocytes stop importing whole proteins, known as the process of closure. In some animals, such as rats, closure can be as late as weaning, although it is likely that the switch is a combination of genetic and environmental factors.

Amino acids are secreted from enterocytes and transported in blood. Cells express amino-acid transporters on their surface and thus take up amino acids from the circulation. The transporters involved in this process are still being investigated, but several tissues deserve special mention. The kidney filters all amino acids out of blood and then reabsorbs them from

TABLE 11.2   Examples of the Inborn Errors of Amino Acid Metabolism

Disorder	Pathway	Effect or Symptoms
Urea cycle disorders	Urea cycle	Six disorders related to deficiencies of the enzymes of the urea cycle. Patients experience hyperammonemia and nerve damage. Often severe to fatal.
Maple-syrup urine disease	Branched-chain amino acid metabolism (α-keto acid dehydrogenase)	Deficiency of branched-chain α-keto acid dehydrogenase leads to elevated levels of branched-chain amino acids and branched-chain α-keto acids, causing neurological damage and death. The disease is named for the sweet maple odor produced by the catabolite sotolon found in the urine of affected subjects.
Phenylketonuria (PKU)	Tyrosine metabolism (phenylalanine hydroxylase)	A deficiency in phenylalanine hydroxylase leads to elevated levels of phenylpyruvate, which is found in the urine of affected subjects. If left untreated, the disease can lead to mental retardation and neurological damage, but the disease is currently diagnosed in infants and successfully treated with a low phenylalanine diet.
Albinism	Tryosine metabolism (tyrosinase)	Tyrosinase deficiency results in the inability to convert tyrosine into the pigment melanin. Subjects lack pigmentation in skin, hair, and eyes.
Hyperprolinemia	Proline catabolism	A deficiency in one of the enzymes that catabolize protein leads to proline levels 3 to 10 times normal, resulting in neurological problems.

the filtrate. As with the intestine, sodium ions drive this process, and many of the amino acid transporters expressed in enterocytes are also expressed in the kidney. The brain is protected from the circulation by the blood-brain barrier, a semipermeable membrane that permits the exchange of only some metabolites. This barrier is not freely permeable to amino acids. The adverse effects of a breakdown in parts of the blood-brain barrier can be seen in diseases such as brain cancer or stroke, or in physical trauma such as head injury. Failure to properly absorb amino acids is seen in several inborn errors of metabolism (Table 11.2).

11.1.4 | Amino acids serve many biological roles in the organism

Although we generally think of amino acids as the building blocks of proteins, they also serve many other important roles. Half of the amino acids can act as neurotransmitters, such as glutamate, or the precursors of neurotransmitters; for example, histidine is the precursor of histamine. Amino acids serve as metabolic intermediates that feed into other pathways, act as allosteric regulators, and are involved in the metabolism of other amino acids. Like most biological molecules, the function of amino acids is often not as simple as first appears.

WORKED PROBLEM 11.1 | Acid reflux

If someone has heartburn and takes two over-the-counter calcium-based antacid tablets, how much acid will be neutralized? What will be the final pH of the stomach?

Strategy   This question has several parts and requires several assumptions to be made. What is the initial pH of the stomach, the volume of the stomach (this can range from less than 100 milliliters to over 4 liters), and the dose and type of antacid? Also, are the stomach contents buffering any reaction that may take place?

Solution   We can simplify the calculations by assuming that, for this example, the volume of the stomach is about 1 liter, pH is 1.0, and the stomach is currently not buffered by any contents (few biological buffers are active at such a low pH value).

Over-the-counter antacids typically contain 500 mg of calcium carbonate ($CaCO_3$) per tablet. Thus, two tablets of antacid

contain 1 g of $CaCO_3$. Using the molecular mass of the compound (100 g/mol), we can calculate the number of moles in one gram:

$$1.00 \text{ g } CaCO_3/(100 \text{ g/mol}) = (0.01 \text{ mol})$$

The $CaCO_3$ will dissociate into Ca^{2+} and CO_3^{-2} ions in solution. The carbonate ion is the conjugate base of carbonic acid (H_2CO_3), which is a diprotic acid; hence, 1 mole of carbonate can react with 2 moles of protons. Therefore, two tablets of antacid can neutralize 0.02 mol of acid.

To calculate the pH change to the stomach, we will use an approach similar to that used for solving a titration problem. To find the molarity of acid in the stomach, we will take the negative antilog (10^{-x}) of the pH value:

$$10^{-1} = 0.1$$

At pH = 1, the concentration of acid in the stomach is 0.1 M. If the volume of the stomach is 1 liter, the stomach will contain 0.1 mol of acid:

$$0.1 \text{ M} = 0.1 \text{ mol/L}$$

$$0.1 \text{ mol/L } (1 \text{ L}) = 0.1 \text{ mol}$$

We neutralized 0.02 mol of this acid and therefore have 0.08 mol of acid remaining:

$$0.1 \text{ mol acid} - 0.02 \text{ mol} = 0.08 \text{ mol}$$

To determine the new pH of the stomach, we must first convert this number of moles to a concentration. The negative log of this value will be the new pH:

$$(0.08 \text{ mol acid/1 L}) = 0.08 \text{ M acid}$$

$$-\log(0.08) = 1.1$$

Thus, consumption of the two tablets raises the stomach pH by 0.1 pH units (although they are still useful clinically).

Carbonic acid and bicarbonate (HCO_3^-) are weak bases, with pK_a values of 3.6 and 10.3, respectively. Why are these compounds not acting as buffers? The low pH of the stomach (more than 1 pH unit away from a pK_a value) prevents the buffers from working. Clearly, in other organs, including blood, bicarbonate is a critical buffer.

Follow-up question   The parietal cells of the stomach produce acid to maintain stomach pH at or near 1.0. Proton-pump inhibitors act to block these proteins and limit acid production. If we model the activity of proton pumps in the stomach using classical Michaelis-Menten kinetics, how might proton-pump inhibitors affect this process? What would be the final effect on pH?

11.1 Summary

- Proteins are degraded into short peptides and free amino acids by proteases and peptidases in the stomach and small intestine.
- Parietal cells in the stomach secrete acid to provide a low pH for optimal proteolytic activity in the stomach. Several classes of acid-lowering drugs target these cells.
- Enterocytes in the lining of the small intestine absorb amino acids, dipeptides, and tripeptides. Specific transporters facilitate this process.
- Amino acids are secreted into the bloodstream and absorbed by cells.

11.1 Concept Check

- Explain how proteins are degraded and how amino acids are assimilated by the organism.
- Compare the process of protein digestion and absorption to the breakdown and absorption of other molecules such as lipids and carbohydrates.
- Provide some of the ways in which acid production can be affected.

11.2 Transamination and Oxidative Deamination

Following a meal, excess carbohydrates can either be used to build up glycogen stores or be catabolized through glycolysis, converted into fatty acids, and stored as triacylglycerols. The energy found in excess dietary amino acids is also stored as fat. In times of extreme need, the organism can catabolize proteins found in muscle. In both storage and breakdown, excess amino acids offer a distinct metabolic challenge to the organism.

The amine moiety central to all amino acids is not found in carbohydrates and lipids and must be removed from the amino acids in order to convert them to fatty acids for storage or catabolized through the citric acid cycle.

To complicate the matter further, ammonia (NH_4^+) formed by the removal of a primary amine is somewhat toxic to the organism and must either be metabolized further or quickly eliminated. Rather than deaminate amino acids in peripheral tissues, amine groups are transported on amino acids, and the amines are detoxified in the kidney or the liver.

A.

α-keto acid

+

Amino acid

transaminase

Amino acid

+

α-keto acid

B.

Amino acid
(glutamate)

$H_2O + NAD^+$ $NADH/H^+$

α-keto acid
(α-ketoglutarate)

$+ NH_4^+$

FIGURE 11.5 **Transamination and oxidative deamination reactions.** **A.** Most amino acids are transaminated with α-keto acid to form a new amino acid and a new α-keto acid. Often the transamination occurs with α-ketoglutarate, generating the amino acid glutamate. **B.** Amino acids can also be oxidatively deaminated, regenerating the α-keto acid, liberating ammonia, and producing a molecule of NADH.

11.2.1 Ammonia can be removed from an amino acid in two different ways

Alpha-keto acids such as pyruvate or α-ketoglutarate are commonly found in biochemistry and play key roles in amine metabolism. Ammonia can be removed from an amino acid through **transamination**, in which the amine is transferred to an α-keto acid, or **oxidative deamination**, in which the amine is removed as ammonia. Both reactions involve an α-keto acid, which is characterized by having a carbonyl adjacent to a carboxylic acid moiety (**Figure 11.5**). Alpha-keto acids may contain other functional groups, such as other carboxylic acids or hydroxyl groups; they also vary in the number of carbons they contain.

Transamination generates a new amino acid and a new α-keto acid. Most amino acids have corresponding transaminases, but none has been identified for lysine and threonine. The α-keto acid employed by many of these enzymes is either α-ketoglutarate or pyruvate, and they generate the amino acids glutamate and alanine, respectively, when transaminated. Therefore, the cell also uses this mechanism as a simple means of synthesizing amino acids from their corresponding α-keto acids.

In oxidative deamination, the source of the oxygen is water and a molecule of NADH/H^+ is generated. The most common amino acid used is glutamate, which is interconverted to α-ketoglutarate. The resulting free ammonia is converted to other less-toxic nitrogenous compounds such as uric acid (in birds and reptiles) or **urea** (in mammals).

11.2.2 The glucose–alanine shuttle moves nitrogen to the liver and delivers glucose to tissues that need it

Transamination reactions provide the organism with an elegant means of shuttling carbon and nitrogen metabolites to and from tissues that need them (**Figure 11.6**). There are several metabolic states in which muscle will catabolize protein in order to provide glycolytic intermediates and glucose. These include starvation and uncontrolled diabetes mellitus, both instances of where amino acids are burned for energy. In muscle, alanine is generated by the transamination

FIGURE 11.6 **Glucose–alanine shuttle.** The glucose–alanine shuttle allows amines and pyruvate from muscle tissue to be shuttled to the liver to provide substrates for gluconeogenesis and the urea cycle. In turn, muscle tissue is provided with glucose, and muscle glycolysis proceeds.

Glutamine

glutamine synthetase — ADP, ATP + NH$_4^+$ — H$_2$O, NH$_4^+$ — glutaminase

Glutamate

glutamate dehydrogenase — H$_2$O, NH$_4^+$ — H$_2$O, NH$_4^+$

α-ketoglutarate ⟶ **Citric acid cycle**

FIGURE 11.7 **Overview of glutamine metabolism.** Glutamine and glutamate are important molecules in amine metabolism. Several enzymes are involved in the synthesis and breakdown of these metabolites.

of pyruvate, a reaction catalyzed by alanine transaminase (ALT). The alanine is released from muscle cells and then travels through the circulation to the liver, where it undergoes another transamination reaction to generate glutamate from α-ketoglutarate. The glutamate is oxidatively deaminated by **glutamate dehydrogenase** and the α-ketoglutarate is regenerated. The pyruvate that results from the deamination of alanine is used by the liver to generate glucose through gluconeogenesis. Glucose is released from the liver and travels to muscle where it goes through glycolysis to generate pyruvate. Depending on the energetic needs of individual tissues, this cycle, referred to as the **glucose-alanine shuttle**, can deliver glucose to tissues that need it or amines to the liver for detoxification. The metabolic burden of gluconeogenesis and urea synthesis occurs in the liver, freeing muscle to perform physical work.

11.2.3 Glutamine is also important in nitrogen transport

Although alanine is used to shuttle amines to the liver, it is not the only mechanism in the body for moving amino groups (**Figure 11.7**). Glutamine is the amino acid found in the highest concentration in the blood; it also serves to detoxify and transport ammonia. The enzyme responsible for the synthesis of glutamine from glutamate and ammonium ion in the liver is glutamine synthetase.

Glutamine synthetase regulates glutamine levels

Glutamine synthetase is a dodecamer (12 subunits) of identical subunits arranged in two hexagonal rings stacked on top of one another. Each subunit has an active site that is accessible from both the top and the bottom. ATP enters from the top, and glutamate and ammonia enter from the interface between the two hexameric rings. Each active site contains two divalent metal ions (either Mg^{2+} or Mn^{2+}), located in the center of the active site; these ions are important in glutamate binding and catalysis (**Figure 11.8**).

Glutamine synthetase is acutely regulated by covalent modification and numerous allosteric regulators. We often think of phosphorylation as a covalent modification that can alter the activity or localization of an enzyme; glutamine synthetase is not phosphorylated and is instead adenylated on a specific tyrosine residue. In adenylation, an adenosine monophosphate (AMP) group is added through a phosphodiester linkage to a tyrosine residue. Addition of the bulky adenylate group blocks the activity of that subunit of the enzyme. However, because there are 12 subunits, regulation can be fine-tuned by adjusting the level of adenylation.

Glutamine synthetase is also controlled by allosteric regulators. These small molecules coordinate glutamine metabolism with other pathways, and they offer a regulatory checkpoint for the synthesis of glutamine. Nine different regulators bind to glutamine synthetase, and all of them inhibit its action. The regulators are AMP, amino acids that figure prominently

FIGURE 11.8 **Structure of glutamine synthetase.** Glutamine synthetase is a homododecamer, 12 subunits composed of two 6-membered rings. (PDB ID 1LGR Liaw, S.H., Jun, G., Eisenberg, D. (1994) Interactions of nucleotides with fully unadenylylated glutamine synthetase from Salmonella typhimurium. *Biochemistry* 33: 11184–11188)

Side view   **Top view**

in cellular amino acid metabolism (alanine, glycine, and serine), carbamoyl phosphate, and downstream products of glutamine (cytidine triphosphate [CTP], glucosamine-6-phosphate, histidine, and tryptophan). While this might seem like a curious list, examination of the molecules in question reveals that each of these molecules either provides a readout on the metabolic state of the cell or is a product made from glutamine.

Glutamine has several advantages as a nitrogen carrier. First, it carries two equivalents of nitrogen: one as an amine in the common portion of the amino acid and one as a carboxamide group in the side chain. Because the amide side chain of glutamine is not charged, glutamine can transport at least one of these moles of nitrogen in an uncharged and detoxified state.

Glutaminase generates glutamate and ammonia

Glutamine serves as a starting material for several important intermediates; thus, it can be metabolized to eliminate ammonia in several different ways. In the kidney and liver, glutamine can be deamidated to yield glutamate and free ammonia; **glutaminase** is the main enzyme responsible for this reaction. In the liver, ammonia generated in this way is consumed in urea synthesis, whereas in the kidney it is directly eliminated in the urine. The liver also contains glutamine synthetase; however, glutamine synthetase and glutaminase are found in different cells within the liver. The presence of glutamine synthetase allows the liver to sequester excess ammonia as glutamine if urea biosynthesis becomes overwhelmed. In addition, having these two distinct pathways provides the liver with a way to detoxify amines in situ via hepatic formation of urea or to shift the metabolic burden of disposal to the kidney, where glutamine is deamidated and disposed of as ammonia.

Under conditions of starvation or a high-protein diet, glutaminase gene expression is upregulated, as might be expected. Other factors that regulate the kidney and liver isoforms of this protein are not clearly understood, although kinases involved in cell growth and differentiation (MAP kinases) have been implicated in the regulation of both isoforms.

As discussed in the next section, glutamine serves several important roles in the central nervous system. Glutamate is an important neurotransmitter but can be deactivated by adding an amino group to form glutamine. Neurons are highly sensitive to ammonia. Glutamate can act as a buffer for ammonia or can be used to alter levels of glutamine in these cells.

Glutamate dehydrogenase liberates a second mole of ammonia

Glutamine carries two amine moieties, one on the side chain and the other in the α-amino group common to all amino acids. After deamination to glutamate, the second amine can still be liberated. Glutamate dehydrogenase catalyzes the oxidation of the amine of glutamate to an imine, which quickly hydrolyzes in water to liberate a second ammonia group and produce α-ketoglutarate, shown in Figure 11.7. Glutamate dehydrogenase is found in the mitochondrial matrix of the kidney, the liver, and nervous tissue.

Glutamate dehydrogenase is regulated by numerous allosteric regulators, which can bind at several sites on each monomer. For example, ADP and NAD^+ bind in the second coenzyme-binding site, adjacent to the hinge. Binding stabilizes the enzyme in the active conformation, in which the active site is accessible to substrate. In contrast, ATP, GTP, leucine, and NADH stabilize the closed conformation by binding either in the substrate site or in the second coenzyme-binding site. Some data indicate that there may be a third binding site, which could explain some of the more complex effects observed. These regulators should make metabolic sense. Those that signal the cell is in a low energy state (NAD^+ and ADP) activate the enzyme to produce more α-ketoglutarate, a key citric acid cycle intermediate. Conversely, regulators that indicate the cell has sufficient energy (ATP, GTP, and NADH) inhibit the enzyme. As with glutamine synthetase, the regulators of this enzyme balance the need for biochemical building blocks with the energetic demands of the cell.

Ammonia toxicity arises as a result of glutamate dehydrogenase. This enzyme generates free ammonia and α-ketoglutarate from glutamate, but it can also perform the reverse reaction. If ammonia levels are high, this can lead to depletion of mitochondrial α-ketoglutarate and disturbances of the citric acid cycle and ATP production. In addition, this reaction requires NADPH, which will potentially deplete if the reaction proceeds unabated. This reaction happens at ammonia concentrations as low as $100\ \mu M$, too low to substantially influence plasma pH but high enough to cause cell or organismal death.

The causal parasite in malaria (*Plasmodium falciparum*) infects erythrocytes and employs glutamate dehydrogenase to synthesize NADPH, which is used as an electron source for antioxidative enzymes (glutathione reductase and thioredoxin reductase). Because the erythrocyte lacks glutamate dehydrogenase, small molecules that target this enzyme are potential candidate molecules for antimalarial drug development.

Why are there two different mechanisms (transamination and oxidative deamination) for the metabolism of amines? First, having two mechanisms instead of just one provides a safe way of shuttling potentially toxic metabolites around the organism. Second, transamination provides a pathway for synthesis of amino acids and α-keto acids by exchanging amino groups with α-keto acids. Third, transamination and the glucose–alanine shuttle help to concentrate metabolic tasks to specific organs, such as urea production in the liver, allowing for more specific organ function. Muscle does not make urea and does not need to because muscle and the liver have evolved specialized functions. Nitrogen from amino acid catabolism in muscle is sent to the liver for detoxification. In addition, muscle gains glucose that is made by the liver.

The question of which of these two pathways is used on a particular amino acid at a particular time is more complex. The interplay of the energetic state of the organism, the need for specific amino or α-keto acids, and the availability of those and other metabolites in a given tissue shift the balance between transamination and oxidative deamination.

We may also ask why alanine and glutamine are the most common nitrogen carriers in the blood. Again, the answers are imbedded in the multiple functions these compounds play in metabolism. Alanine generated in muscle, either by protein breakdown or by transamination of pyruvate obtained through glycolysis, moves toxic nitrogenous wastes to the liver for detoxification. In addition, the pyruvate that results from transamination provides a source of carbons for gluconeogenesis. Glutamine can transport two amines, one in the side chain as an amide and the other as the amino group common to all amino acids. The amide is not protonated and bears no charge; hence, this is another way of transporting nitrogenous wastes safely, with no risk of affecting plasma pH. The deamidation of glutamine in either the liver or kidney yields glutamate, which can be used as an amino acid, or can be further transaminated or oxidatively deaminated to give α-ketoglutarate. This intermediate provides another link between the citric acid cycle and the rest of metabolism. In addition, this process can keep glycolysis moving forward under anaerobic conditions for a limited time.

WORKED PROBLEM 11.2 | Oxidative deamination

Draw the α-keto acid that would result from the oxidative deamination of each of these amino acids.

Alanine   **Glutamate**   **Isoleucine**

Strategy Examine the structures of each amino acid. Which amine will be oxidized? What will be found in its place in an α-keto acid?

Solution

Follow-up question What are the products of these transamination reactions? Would energy be consumed in these reactions?

11.2 Summary

- Amino acids all contain a potentially toxic amino group that must be removed and detoxified.
- Amino groups can be shuttled between amino acids and α-keto acids, resulting in a new α-keto acid and a new amino acid.
- The glucose–alanine shuttle is a means of delivering ammonia to the liver for detoxification while delivering glucose back to tissues that need them.
- Amines can also be removed as ammonia, in a process known as oxidative deamination; one molecule of NADH/H$^+$ is produced in the process.
- Glutamine is one of the main carriers of ammonia in the blood.

- Describe how and where the first steps in amino acid catabolism occur and give the products of these reactions.
- Explain which of the reactions in the first steps of amino acid catabolism are energetically "free," that is, neither costing nor producing energy, and which produce energy.

11.3 The Urea Cycle

Ammonia is a toxic substance. Normal blood levels range from 10 to 40 micromoles/L. High levels of ammonia elevate blood pH, making it more difficult for hemoglobin to deliver oxygen to metabolically active tissues, and more difficult to transport carbon dioxide (CO_2) in the blood. Many organisms are slightly tolerant of a small drop in plasma pH, for example, from pH 7.4 to 7.2, but less tolerant of a similar rise in plasma pH, for instance, from pH 7.4 to 7.6. Furthermore, ammonia is a neurotoxin and can permeate the blood-brain barrier. Once it enters the brain, ammonia can undergo an amination reaction with α-ketoglutarate to form glutamate. This depletes the neurons of citric acid cycle intermediates, effectively blocking a major pathway of energy production in the cells and thus leading to cell death. Elevated levels of glutamate, itself a neurotransmitter, lead to increased glutamine production. This depletes the cells of glutamate by shunting the molecule toward glutamine production and away from the production of γ amino butyric acid (GABA), a protective neurotransmitter. Also, high levels of ammonia may help to break down the H^+ gradient in mitochondria, another potentially toxic effect. An organism that lacks a means of coping with ammonia will not survive for long.

11.3.1 Ammonia detoxification begins with the synthesis of carbamoyl phosphate

The first step in the detoxification of ammonia is the condensation of ammonia with CO_2 to from carbamoyl phosphate. This is a reaction catalyzed by carbamoyl phosphate synthetase and requiring ATP (**Figure 11.9**). The reaction occurs in three distinct stages:

- CO_2 reacts with ATP to form a carboxyl phosphate.
- The phosphate is exchanged for a molecule of ammonia, creating a carbamate.
- The carbamate is phosphorylated by a second molecule of ATP to produce carbamoyl phosphate.

There are different isoforms of carbamoyl phosphate synthetase. This section focuses on the mitochondrial form of the enzyme: carbamoyl phosphate synthetase I. This isoform is involved in the production of carbamoyl phosphate for the urea cycle. Carbamoyl phosphate synthetase II, the cytosolic form of the enzyme, is responsible for the production of building blocks for pyrimidine biosynthesis.

11.3.2 The urea cycle synthesizes urea and other metabolic intermediates

Carbamoyl phosphate is not the terminal destination for nitrogenous waste. Mammals convert carbamoyl phosphate into the far less toxic urea using a pathway termed the **urea cycle**. This cycle employs several amino acids, such as ornithine and citrulline, which have not been mentioned previously. They are not included in the 20 amino acids commonly found in proteins; nevertheless, they are amino acids and are important in amine metabolism.

FIGURE 11.9 **Carbamoyl phosphate synthesis.** Bicarbonate anion attacks the phosphorous center of the γ-phosphate of ATP, generating an ATP-carboxyl phosphate. ADP departs, and ammonia binds. The lone pair of electrons on ammonia attacks the carbonyl carbon, generating a carbamate. ATP binds and, as before, the negatively charged oxygen attacks the γ-phosphate of ATP. ADP leaves, and carbamoyl phosphate is generated.

The reactions of the urea cycle

The urea cycle begins with carbamoyl phosphate condensing with ornithine to form citrulline. The phosphate on carbamoyl phosphate is the leaving group in this reaction, and it provides the driving energy for the reaction to proceed. Examining the structures of ornithine and carbamoyl phosphate can help in determining the rest of the steps in urea production. As we have seen in other pathways, comparing structures and functional groups of molecules in a pathway helps connect a chemical logic to the steps in the urea cycle. The structure of ornithine might look familiar: ornithine is effectively lysine minus a methylene group. Coupling carbamoyl phosphate to ornithine could be achieved in several ways, but the one employed by nature is to couple the carbamoyl carbon to the primary amine on the side chain of ornithine. This reaction is analogous to the second step of carbamoyl phosphate synthesis in which the attack of ammonia on carboxyl phosphate forms the initial carbamate. In both reactions, the phosphate is the leaving group (**Figure 11.10**).

In the next step of the pathway, citrulline links with aspartate to form argininosuccinate, a reaction that is catalyzed by argininosuccinate synthase. Again, the carbon involved in the chemistry of the reaction is the carbamoyl carbon, and the nitrogen comes from the amine of

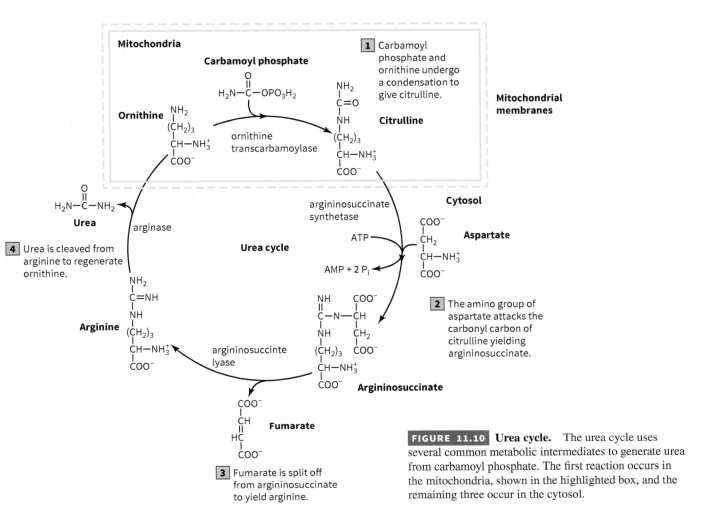

FIGURE 11.10 **Urea cycle.** The urea cycle uses several common metabolic intermediates to generate urea from carbamoyl phosphate. The first reaction occurs in the mitochondria, shown in the highlighted box, and the remaining three occur in the cytosol.

aspartate. A molecule of ATP is hydrolyzed into AMP and PPi in the reaction (providing the energetic equivalent of two molecules of ATP being hydrolyzed).

Argininosuccinate is cleaved by argininosuccinase (also known as argininosuccinate lyase) to give two molecules, both of which should be familiar at this point: the amino acid arginine and the citric acid cycle intermediate fumarate (a *trans* unsaturated dioic acid, four carbons in length). Tracking the structures of molecules throughout the pathway or considering the structure of arginine can help in recalling the intermediates in these pathways. The final step of the urea cycle is the formation of urea from arginine, in a reaction catalyzed by arginase. Water serves as the source of oxygen for the new carbamate, and ornithine is regenerated.

The urea cycle occurs in two subcellular compartments. The first two reactions (formation of carbamoyl phosphate and condensation of carbamoyl phosphate with ornithine to form citrulline) occur in the mitochondrial matrix. This location takes advantage of free ammonia generated by the oxidative deamination of amino acids in the mitochondria without releasing ammonia into the cytosol, where it may be able to enter the bloodstream. Citrulline is exported from the matrix to the cytosol via the ornithine transporter, which has two isoforms (ORC 1 and ORC 2), and also transports arginine, citrulline, and lysine. The remaining steps of the urea cycle occur in the cytosol. Ornithine regenerated following the cleavage of urea is imported back into the mitochondrial matrix to propagate the cycle.

The urea cycle can be studied as a separate and discrete entity, but in reality it always occurs in a sea of metabolites. The aspartate employed in the urea cycle is the same as the aspartate discussed in other chapters. However, partitioning of metabolites can direct them to different metabolic fates and proscribe different metabolic functions. For example, fumarate generated in the urea cycle (in the cytosol) is chemically the same as fumarate generated in the citric acid cycle (in the mitochondrial matrix), but partitioning by the mitochondrial membranes leads to different metabolic fates. In both pools, fumarate is converted to malate and then, via fumarase (a hydratase), to oxaloacetate. However, in the citric acid cycle, oxaloacetate serves as a substrate for citrate production, whereas in the cytosol it can either be transaminated into aspartate (to provide intermediates for the urea cycle) or decarboxylated into phosphoenolpyruvate for gluconeogenesis. Likewise, the intermediates in the urea cycle can serve as precursors for other molecules. Thus, arginine can serve as a source for the signaling hormone nitric oxide (NO), being converted to citrulline in the process, and ornithine can be decarboxylated to form polyamines, such as putrescene.

11.3.3 Nitrogen metabolism is regulated at different levels

The urea cycle is primarily responsible for the detoxification and disposal of ammonia. Levels of ammonia rise in response to the oxidative deamination of amino acids, particularly glutamate.

The regulation of the urea cycle occurs at two different levels, through either carbamoyl phosphate synthetase I (CPS I) or the other enzymes of the pathway. CPS I is regulated allosterically, whereas the other enzymes of the pathway are primarily regulated by levels of substrate, as discussed below.

Carbamoyl phosphate synthetase I is responsible for the first step in urea synthesis, in which carbamoyl phosphate is synthesized from ammonia, CO_2, and ATP. CPS I is allosterically activated by *N*-Acetylglutamate (NAG). This regulator is synthesized by *N*-Acetylglutamate synthase, which employs glutamate and acetyl-CoA as substrates. The synthesis of *N*-Acetylglutamate is positively regulated by levels of substrate, glutamate, and the allosteric regulator arginine. Concentrations of both glutamate and arginine are elevated when there are excess amino acids, thus increasing urea production via *N*-Acetylglutamate.

N-**Acetylglutamate** (NAG)

The other enzymes of the urea cycle are acutely regulated by the levels of substrate available to them. Other means of control, such as phosphorylation or allosteric mechanisms, have not been observed for these enzymes; however, they are also regulated at transcriptional level. For example, consumption of a diet rich in protein leads to upregulation of the genes coding for these enzymes.

11.3.4 Mechanisms for elimination of nitrogenous wastes differ between mammals and non-mammals

So far, this section has focused on human nitrogen metabolism. Several factors must be taken into consideration when thinking about nitrogen metabolism in other organisms. Urea biosynthesis is energetically expensive; neutralizing a single molecule of ammonia requires the energetic equivalent of the hydrolysis of three ATP molecules and sufficient water for excretion via the kidneys. Hence, not all organisms use this method to dispose of nitrogenous wastes.

Ammonotelic organisms such as insects, crustaceans, aquatic invertebrates, and some fish and amphibians typically eliminate wastes as ammonia secreted through the skin. These species adapted to the ample water in their environment and have no need to expend energy on urea biosynthesis. This indicates that evolution of the genes encoding proteins found in the urea cycle have evolved more recently than the appearance of these organisms.

Birds and reptiles employ a different means of eliminating nitrogenous wastes. Termed **uricotelic** organisms, they synthesize uric acid and eliminate it in their waste, which is technically not urine (**Figure 11.11**). Birds and reptiles have evolved adaptations to different environmental challenges. For example, to facilitate their ability to fly, birds have evolved ways to conserve weight. Using urea to eliminate nitrogenous wastes would necessitate a

FIGURE 11.11 **Nitrogenous wastes.** Different organisms produce different types of nitrogenous wastes. Aquatic organisms such as sponges, corals, jellyfish, and crustaceans secrete ammonia. Mammals produce urea, which is secreted in the urine, whereas birds and some reptiles secrete uric acid in their waste.

urinary bladder to store the urine; there would be also a need to carry the water weight of the urine itself. By producing uric acid, birds avoid this necessity. Reptiles face a different challenge. Many reptiles, in particular the diapsids, such as crocodiles, lizards, and snakes, come from arid or saltwater environments where fresh water is in short supply. These animals expel nitrogenous waste as uric acid to spare water rather than weight.

11.3.5 Some mammals have adapted to high- or low-protein diets

Up until now, our discussion of urea biosynthesis presumed that the organism in question was human and consumed a relatively protein-rich diet, consuming about 15% of calories from animal or plant protein. However, not all mammals fall into this category; some consume a carnivorous diet with exceedingly high amounts of protein, whereas others (most herbivores) consume far less. Both groups of animals have evolved adaptations to assist in their management of nitrogen.

Humans and all higher animals are unable to "fix" nitrogen, that is, to use N_2 gas in the air to produce reduced forms of nitrogen, such as the nitrogen of amino acids. In order to synthesize the nonessential amino acids, we must have a source of reduced nitrogen, such as an amine, to begin the process.

Carnivores Obligate carnivores consume all their calories from animal sources. In the wild, this means a diet with a high concentration of protein and little carbohydrate and fat. Zebras and antelopes, the prey of large carnivores, are generally lean animals that do not exhibit the marbling seen in a good beef steak, and are far lower in fat than the meat that humans would typically eat. The domestic cat is an example of an obligate carnivore, as are all felids (the cat family), pinnepeds (walruses and seals), and weasels. The diet of the cat has led to some important and interesting traits in nitrogen metabolism. For example, the urea cycle in cats is always functioning at a high level, and the control mechanisms discussed previously do not apply in this case. Thus, cats are always at the ready to catabolize a high-protein diet, but they cannot shut down the urea cycle and cannot spare their own protein when food is scarce.

This difference in diet and metabolism leads to some interesting complexities in carnivore metabolism. Cats are unable to synthesize the amino acid arginine. If cats consume a diet that contains enough arginine to fuel the urea cycle, this does not present a problem; however, a single meal devoid of arginine can make a cat hyperamonemic (high plasma ammonia levels, which affect respiration and the nervous system). This condition can be fatal. To combat this, many commercial cat foods are supplemented with arginine.

Herbivores Herbivores face a different problem; in the wild these organisms consume a low-protein diet that consists mainly of carbohydrates. Dietary proteins are at a premium for these organisms, and they have evolved mechanisms to help conserve the nitrogen found in such proteins. In herbivorous mammals, urea is shunted back to the intestine in a similar fashion as uric acid in some herbivorous birds. There, intestinal bacteria can reduce the urea or uric acid back to amino acids, which can be absorbed by the animal and used for protein biosynthesis. This ancient, highly evolved, and efficient system can cause problems when animals become domesticated. For example, cattle or horses fed large quantities of high-protein grain that they would not encounter in the wild can develop health problems related to an elevated nitrogen burden.

WORKED PROBLEM 11.3 | Follow that nitrogen

Parts of the urea cycle occur in the mitochondria and parts in the cytosol. How could you demonstrate that this is the case? Design an experiment to show which aspects of the urea cycle happen in the mitochondria and which happen in the cytosol.

Strategy We will need a source of tissue or cells capable of undergoing the urea cycle and some means of tracking the intermediates. We will also need some means of separating the mitochondrial and cytosolic fractions of the cell. Radiolabeled tracers have been helpful in deducing metabolic pathways in the past, but another approach would be to use stable isotopes (such as N^{15} labeled ammonia) and follow those using mass spectrometry.

Solution First, we would fractionate the cells into a mitochondrial and a cytosolic fraction. To each fraction we would add labeled ammonia ($N^{15}H_4^+$). If necessary, we could supplement these fractions with exogenous levels of the required cofactors or precursors (ATP, citrulline, or aspartate). Samples would be incubated for different times, and the products examined by mass spectrometry to see what new molecules the labeled ammonia has been converted into. If the urea cycle in the sample is functioning as described in this chapter (highly likely), then we should see no product from the cytosolic fraction; that is, the ammonia would not be metabolized. However, in the mitochondrial fraction, some of the N^{15} ammonia would be converted to N^{15} carbamoyl phosphate. Both fractions would have to be combined to obtain N^{15} urea as a final product.

Follow-up question Zinc is an important cofactor in some enzymes. How could you demonstrate which steps in nitrogen metabolism are zinc dependent?

11.3 Summary

- Mammals detoxify ammonia to urea through a process termed the urea cycle.
- Ammonia is bound to CO_2 to form carbamoyl phosphate; the equivalent of two molecules of ATP is consumed in this reaction.
- The intermediates of the urea cycle include ornithine and citrulline, two amino acids not found in proteins. The urea cycle also contains amino acids commonly found in proteins, such as arginine and aspartate, and citric acid cycle intermediates such as fumarate.
- The urea cycle synthesizes urea, helps to metabolize amino acids, and provides citric acid cycle intermediates.
- Animals other than humans have evolved different mechanisms to help them adapt to their diet. These adaptations include elevated levels of urea cycle enzymes in obligate carnivores or the means to recycle nitrogen back through the gut in some herbivores.

11.3 Concept Check

- Describe how nitrogenous wastes are detoxified in the organism.
- Explain where urea biosynthesis overlaps with other metabolic pathways and why it does so.
- Explain how animals other than humans metabolize nitrogen.

11.4 Pathways of Amino Acid Carbon Skeleton Scavenging

Following removal of the amino group from an amino acid, several different fates can befall the remaining carbon skeleton. This section describes how different amino acid skeletons are broken down for energy or long-term storage as fat. Many amino acid derivatives are

3 carbon skeletons
Alanine
Cysteine
Glycine
Serine
Threonine
Tryptophan

2 carbon skeletons
Isoleucine
Leucine
Lysine
Threonine

Fatty acid biosynthesis

Pyruvate

CO_2

Acetyl-CoA

Acetoacetate (ketone bodies)

Glucose (Gluconeogenesis)

2 carbon skeletons
Leucine
Lysine
Phenylalanine
Tyrosine

4 carbon skeletons
Asparagine
Aspartate

Oxaloacetate

Citrate

Glucogenic
Ketogenic
Both glucogenic and ketogenic

Gluconeogenesis

Ketone body and fatty acid biosynthesis

4 carbon skeletons
Phenylalanine
Tyrosine

Fumarate

Citric acid cycle

Isocitrate

CO_2

Succinyl-CoA

α-ketoglutarate

4 carbon skeletons
Isoleucine
Methionine
Threonine
Valine

CO_2

5 carbon skeletons
Arginine
Glutamate
Glutamine
Histidine
Proline

FIGURE 11.12 **Amino acid carbon skeletons enter the citric acid cycle.** All amino acid breakdown products yield metabolites that are consumed in the citric acid cycle.

important signaling molecules, cofactors, or metabolic intermediates. Those pathways are not discussed here, except in terms of where these metabolites lead.

Amino acids can be categorized as **glucogenic**, producing breakdown products which undergo gluconeogenesis, or **ketogenic**, producing breakdown products which can only produce ketone bodies (**Figure 11.12**). There are only two solely ketogenic amino acids: leucine and lysine. Some amino acid skeletons, such as threonine, have their carbons catabolized into both glucogenic and ketogenic substrates but are considered glucogenic amino acids because they contribute to glucose production. In addition, any amino acid can be broken down and stored as fat; when consumed in excess, this is the fate of many amino acids.

Although numerous reactions are involved in amino acid catabolism, most of them can be ordered into a few categories. The first reaction is generally the removal of the amino group, often through a transamination to an α-keto acid as discussed in section 11.2. The reactions of amino acid catabolism are often similar to those seen in β-oxidation, in that carbon skeletons are desaturated (an FAD-dependent process), hydrated to an alcohol, and then oxidized to a carbonyl (an NAD^+-dependent process). Hydroxylation of rings or ring opening often involves molecular oxygen and the dioxygenase class of enzymes. Finally, carbon groups can be added or lost as CO_2, or removed by tetrahydrofolate-dependent reactions (**Figure 11.13**).

Like fatty acids and carbohydrates, the carbon skeleton of an amino acid is catabolized via the citric acid cycle; however, in contrast to fatty acids and carbohydrates, there are multiple places where the carbon skeletons of amino acids can contribute. For example, amino acids can contribute to seven different metabolites that either lead into the citric acid cycle or are part of the cycle itself (α-ketoglutarate, succinate, fumarate, oxaloacetate, pyruvate, acetyl-CoA, and acetoacetate). The last two metabolites on this list, acetyl-CoA and acetoacetate, cannot be converted into glucose. Skeletons metabolized through these two can only lead to ketone body production, not glucose. The remaining metabolites, pyruvate, α-ketoglutarate, succinyl-CoA, fumarate, and oxaloacetate can all contribute to gluconeogenesis. A summary

FIGURE 11.13 **Types of reactions used in carbon skeleton metabolism.** **A.** As we have seen in the citric acid cycle and β-oxidation, alkanes can be oxidized to an alkene, then hydrated to form an alcohol, and oxidized again to form a carbonyl group. **B.** Mono- and dioxygenases either perform substitution reactions or ring opening reactions on aromatic systems. **C.** Tetrahydrobiopterin is an important cofactor in substitution reactions occurring in an aromatic system. **D.** The donor of single carbons in this reaction is $5',10'$-methylenetetrahydrofolate. **E.** Transamination reactions employ pyridoxal phosphate as the cofactor but oxidative deaminations use NAD^+ or $NADP^+$ mediated mechanisms or nucleophilic attack by a threonine side chain.

is given in **Table 11.3**. This section discusses the catabolism of amino acids in terms of their end product, starting with three-carbon amino acids.

11.4.1 Three-carbon skeletons produce pyruvate

The metabolism of three-carbon animo acid skeletons is shown in **Figure 11.14**.

- *Threonine* is cleaved into acetaldehyde and then converted into acetyl-CoA, a ketogenic product. Threonine can also undergo cleavage to form glycine, which leads to pyruvate.

- *Glycine* undergoes addition of a hydroxymethyl group to form serine. N^5, N^{10}–Methylenetetrahydrofolate (N^5, N^{10}–Methylene-THF) serves as the donor of the hydroxymethyl group.

- *Alanine* can be transaminated with α-ketoglutarate to give pyruvate and glutamate. This is a pyridoxal phosphate (PLP)-dependent reaction.

- *Serine* is dehydrated by serine dehydratase, also a PLP-dependent enzyme. The resulting product spontaneously hydrolyzes into ammonia and pyruvate.

- *Cysteine* can be acted on by various pathways to eliminate the sulfur as H_2S, SO_3^{2-}, or SCN^-. Oxidative deamination of the product yields pyruvate.

TABLE 11.3   **Amino Acid Catabolism**

Amino Acid	Catabolized Through	Glucogenic or Ketogenic	Amino Acid	Catabolized Through	Glucogenic or Ketogenic
Alanine Serine Cysteine Glycine Threonine Tryptophan	Pyruvate (3 carbon)	Glucogenic	Phenylalanine Tyrosine Aspartate	Fumarate	Glucogenic
Aspartate Asparagine	Oxaloacetate (4 carbon)	Glucogenic	Leucine Isoleucine Threonine	Acetyl-CoA	Ketogenic Both Both
Glutamate Glutamine Proline Arginine Histidine	α-keto glutarate (5 carbon)	Glucogenic	Leucine Lysine Phenylalanine Tyrosine Tryptophan	Acetoacetate	Ketogenic Ketogenic Both Both Both
Valine Isoleucine Methionine	Succinyl-CoA	Glucogenic			

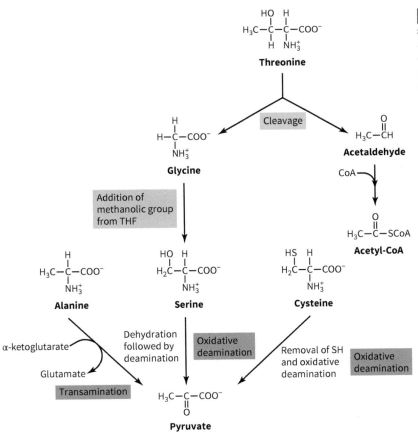

FIGURE 11.14 **Metabolism of three-carbon skeletons.**   The three-carbon amino acids cysteine, alanine, and serine all feed into pyruvate through oxidative loss of ammonia. Threonine is cleaved into acetaldehyde or acetyl-CoA and glycine. Glycine is carboxylated into serine.

11.4.2   Four-carbon skeletons produce oxaloacetate

The metabolism of four-carbon amino acid skeletons is shown in **Figure 11.15**.

- *Aspartate* undergoes a transamination reaction with α-ketoglutarate to give oxaloacetate and glutamate.

Asparagine

Aspartate

Oxaloacetate

FIGURE 11.15 **Metabolism of four-carbon skeletons.** Asparagine is deaminated into aspartate. The amino group that is removed is highlighted with a dashed box. Aspartate is transaminated into oxaloacetate.

- *Asparagine* can be hydrolyzed by asparaginase to ammonia and aspartate. As discussed in section 11.3, asparagine also participates in the urea cycle, in which case the carbons end up as fumarate, another citric acid cycle intermediate.

11.4.3 Five-carbon skeletons produce α-ketoglutarate

The metabolism of five-carbon amino acid skeletons is shown in **Figure 11.16**.

- *Histidine* is deaminated to urocanate. Urocanate undergoes two successive reactions involving water. First, a hydratase generates 4-imidazolone-5-propionate, and then a second molecule of water is added to form *N*-Formaminoglutamate. The terminal formamino group is transferred to **tetrahydrofolate** to yield glutamate.
- *Arginine* is hydrolyzed to urea and ornithine. Ornithine undergoes a transamination with α-ketoglutarate to yield glutamate and glutamate-γ-semialdehyde, which is oxidized to glutamate.
- *Proline* is oxidized to form pyrroline-5-carboxylate. This spontaneously decomposes in a ring-opening reaction to form glutamate-5-semialdehyde; from there it is metabolized to glutamate.
- *Glutamine* undergoes oxidative deamination to give ammonia and glutamate.
- *Glutamate* can undergo a number of different transamination reactions to form α-ketoglutarate. The other amino acids in this category are also catabolized into glutamate and thus enter the citric acid cycle.

11.4.4 Methionine, valine, and isoleucine produce succinyl-CoA

The metabolism of methionine, valine, and isoleucine is shown in **Figure 11.17**:

- *Methionine* is demethylated via **S-Adenosylmethionine** to form homocysteine. Homocysteine undergoes a condensation reaction with serine to form cystathione. Cystathione is cleaved into cysteine and deaminated to α-ketobutyrate, which is then decarboxylated to form propionyl-CoA, which is metabolized as above.
- *Valine* loses its amine moiety via transamination and is decarboxylated to generate a short branched-chain acyl-CoA. It is desaturated in an FAD-dependent reaction to generate an α–β double bond, and then hydrated to yield β-hydroxybutyryl-CoA. Coenzyme-A is lost, and the hydroxyl group is oxidized to a ketone (methylmalonate semialdehyde). These reactions are similar to the steps of β-oxidation. Loss of CO_2 and oxidation yields propionyl-CoA, which is converted to succinyl-CoA by successive carboxylation and isomerization. These final few steps of the pathway are the same ones used in the catabolism of odd-chain fatty acids in β-oxidation. Beta oxidation cleaves the odd-chain fatty acid to a three-carbon propionyl-CoA, which is carboxylated to methylmalonyl-CoA and then isomerized to succinyl-CoA.
- *Isoleucine* is metabolized in an analogous fashion to valine. It is deaminated, desaturated, hydrated, and oxidized, but in this case the product of the reactions is α-methylacetoacetyl-CoA. Loss of acetyl-CoA yields propionyl-CoA, which is converted to succinyl-CoA.

11.4.5 Other amino acids produce acetyl-CoA, acetoacetate, or fumarate

The metabolism of amino acids that yield acetyl-CoA, acetoacetate, or fumarate is shown in **Figure 11.18**.

- *Leucine* is metabolized like the other branched-chain amino acids, isoleucine and valine. It is deaminated and desaturated but then carboxylated to form β-methylglutaconyl-CoA.

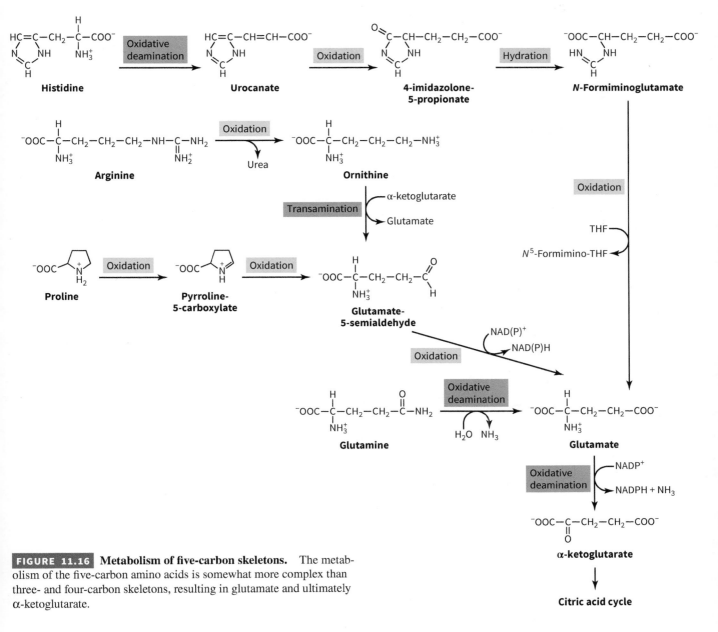

FIGURE 11.16 **Metabolism of five-carbon skeletons.** The metabolism of the five-carbon amino acids is somewhat more complex than three- and four-carbon skeletons, resulting in glutamate and ultimately α-ketoglutarate.

This molecule is then hydrated to form β-hydroxy-β-methylglutaryl-CoA or HMG-CoA, discussed in section 9.5. HMG-CoA is acted on by HMG-CoA lyase to generate acetyl-CoA and acetoacetate.

- *Phenylalanine* is hydroxylated to tyrosine in a reaction that is **tetrahydrobiopterin** dependent.
- *Tyrosine* is transaminated to yield *p*-hydroxyphenylpyruvate. Parahydroxyphenylpyruvate dioxygenase catalyzes a reaction resulting in the loss of CO_2, hydroxylation of the phenyl ring, and rearrangement of the product to give homogentisate. A second dioxygenase causes ring opening and formation of 4-maleylacetoacetate. An isomerization yields 4-fumarylacetoacetate, which is hydrolyzed to fumarate and acetoacetate.
- *Lysine* undergoes a condensation reaction with α-ketoglutarate to form saccharopine. Glutamate is cleaved from saccharopine in an oxidation reaction to form α-aminoadipate-6-semialdehyde. A second oxidation gives α-aminoadipate, and a transamination results in α-ketoadipate. Carbon dioxide (CO_2) is lost to yield glutaryl-CoA. At this point in the pathway, similarities are seen with both branched-chain amino acid catabolism and β-oxidation. A double bond is incorporated to yield glutaconyl-CoA, another

FIGURE 11.17 **Methionine, valine, and isoleucine catabolism.** Methionine is catabolized into cysteine and α-ketobutyrate, the latter of which is decarboxylated into propionyl-CoA, eventually entering the citric acid cycle as succinyl-CoA. The branched-chain amino acids valine and isoleucine are deaminated and then catabolized using reactions similar to those seen in β-oxidation.

molecule of CO_2 is lost to yield crotonyl-CoA, and the double bond is hydrated to yield β-hydroxybutyryl-CoA. One final oxidation gives acetoacetyl-CoA, which can be converted to acetoacetate as discussed previously.

- *Tryptophan* requires the most steps to catabolize. The first step is the opening of the five-membered nitrogen-containing indole ring, catalyzed by a dioxygenase. This is decarboxylated to yield kynurenine, which is hydroxylated on the C-3 of the aromatic ring that is ortho to the amino group. The next reaction cleaves this molecule in

FIGURE 11.18 **Catabolism of leucine, tyrosine, phenylalanine, lysine, and tryptophan.** These amino acids are catabolized through multistep pathways resulting in the production of acetyl-CoA, fumarate, and acetoacetate.

two, leaving alanine and 3-hydroxyanthranilate. From here, the molecule undergoes a series of oxidations and rearrangements culminating in the loss of ammonia and generation of α-ketoadipate. From this point, the reactions proceed as they would for lysine.

A common motif in amino acid metabolism is the use of **pyridoxal phosphate**-dependent mechanisms. The chemistry of these mechanisms is discussed in **Biochemistry: Pyridoxal phosphate-dependent mechanisms**.

Biochemistry

Pyridoxal phosphate-dependent mechanisms

Many reactions in metabolism occur adjacent to a carboxyl carbon. For example, this chapter highlights transamination and oxidative deamination reactions, both of which occur on the α carbon. Likewise, we can deprotonate and reprotonate an α carbon to generate a stereoisomer of an amino acid, or decarboxylate an amino acid to generate a bioactive amine, often found as neurotransmitters and hormones. The chemistry surrounding these diverse reactions is governed by a single cofactor: pyridoxal phosphate (PLP).

Pyridoxal, also known as vitamin B$_6$, is absorbed in the body as an aldehyde and phosphorylated in the liver to the active form (PLP). Although many different enzymes and mechanisms are associated with PLP, several underlying principles unify these reactions and mechanisms. PLP reacts through a mechanism mediated by a Schiff base. Before substrate binding, PLP is bound through a Schiff base to the ε-amino group of a lysine side chain and the aldehyde moiety of PLP. The Schiff base here forms between the aldehyde moiety of the pyridoxal and the amino group of a lysine side chain forming an internal aldimine through the following mechanism:

| 1. Amino group of lysine in active site attacks carbonyl of PLP. | 2. PLP dehydrates forming Schiff base, an internal aldamine. | 3. Substrate binds. Amino group attacks Schiff base generating an external aldamine with substrate. | 4. Loss of proton leads to electron flow to amine. |

| 5. Eliminating lysine. | 6. Electrons flow into ring system of PLP, resulting in deprotonation. | 7. Electron flow reverses through quinoid form of PLP. | 8. Reprotonating the Schiff base carbon. |

| 9. The α-keto product is produced. |

When the substrate binds (in this example, the enzyme is aspartate transaminase and the substrate is aspartate), the Schiff base is exchanged from the internal aldimine to an external aldimine with the substrate. In this transition, the tetrahedral intermediate is stabilized by weak interactions with the oxyanion on the PLP ring or amino acid side chains in the enzyme (interactions with arginine side chains are shown).

Electrons flow from the substrate down through the Schiff base and into the ring nitrogen, which acts as an electron sink, drawing the electrons through the complex, forming a quinonoid intermediate.

Electrons flow back up through the ring and abstract a proton from an adjacent amino acid, forming a ketamine intermediate. Finally, water enters, displacing the Schiff base and forming the α-keto acid and pyridoxamine phosphate. Next, a new α-keto acid (typically α-keto glutarate) binds, and the reverse reaction proceeds.

Not all PLP-mediated mechanisms employ the Schiff base aspect of the molecule. Glycogen phosphorylase uses the phosphate group of PLP in catalyzing the breakdown of glycogen.

WORKED PROBLEM 11.4 | Complete proteins

Shown below is the typical amino acid breakdown of a soy protein sample. Based on the amino acid metabolism discussed so far and presuming one could eat enough, could a person survive on soy protein alone?

Amino Acid	% Mass of Dry Weight Protein	Amino Acid	% Mass of Dry Weight Protein
Arginine	1.12	Lysine	1.04
Alanine	0.71	Methionine	0.23
Aspartate	1.91	Phenylalanine	0.81
Cysteine	0.14	Proline	0.81
Histidine	0.45	Serine	0.84
Glutamate	2.96	Threonine	0.64
Glycine	0.70	Tyrosine	0.41
Isoleucine	0.72	Valine	0.63
Leucine	1.28		

Strategy Plant proteins are often considered an incomplete source of protein because they lack specific amino acids sufficient in quantity to prevent malnutrition. Therefore, combinations of proteins are often consumed to preserve health. To simplify the problem, we can ignore for a moment the fact that humans are unable to synthesize ten of the amino acids, and we will focus solely on the carbon skeletons.

Solution Could a diet of soy protein provide enough glucose through gluconeogenesis to keep someone alive? Examining the ratios of glucogenic to ketogenic amino acids, it is clear that all of the glucogenic amino acids are present. Thus, if soy were the sole source of food, and carbohydrate and lipid metabolism were the only concern, a person could apparently survive for some time before other dietary deficiencies would appear. Soy protein differs somewhat from other plant proteins in being a complete protein, containing all of the essential amino acids in sufficient quantity.

Follow-up question Would supplementing the above diet with lysine from corn be helpful to the situation?

11.4 Summary

- Following deamination, the side chains of amino acids are catabolized into either glucogenic or ketogenic substrates.
- Glucogenic amino acids can be converted into glucose via gluconeogenesis.
- Ketogenic amino acids can only be converted into lipids (fatty acids or ketone bodies).
- Amino acids with three, four, or five carbons enter into metabolism as pyruvate, oxaloacetate, and α-ketoglutarate, respectively.
- Other amino acids yield fumarate, succinyl-CoA, acetoacetate, or acetyl-CoA.

11.4 Concept Check

- Describe how the side chains of amino acids are catabolized.
- Explain which amino acids contribute to gluconeogenesis, which to fatty acid biosynthesis, and which to both.

11.5 | The Detoxification of Other Amines and Xenobiotics

Not all molecules we consume fall into the simple categories of carbohydrate, fat, protein, or nucleic acids. All foods contain compounds that provide color, flavor, and aroma. These molecules are broadly categorized as **xenobiotics**. These compounds may have evolved to attract insects or to repel predators, but they are not molecules found in human metabolism. Hence, they need to be eliminated from the body.

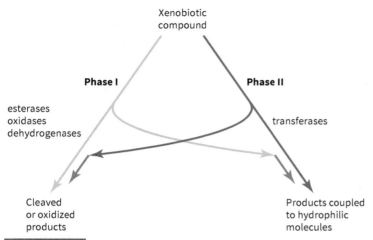

FIGURE 11.19 **Phase I and phase II metabolism.** Xenobiotic metabolism can be classified as either phase I or phase II. In phase I, oxidative reactions make molecules smaller and more water soluble. In phase II, molecules are coupled to soluble groups to increase their likelihood of being excreted in the urine. Molecules also may be metabolized through both processes.

In addition, other organisms produce toxins that we may consume, either intentionally or unintentionally. For example, while molds and fungi produce molecules that are toxic in high concentrations, many people enjoy the strong flavor of blue cheese or the savory flavor of some mushrooms, flavors caused by these same molds and fungi. Small amounts of these molecules in the diet may not be harmful, but these also need to be eliminated from the body.

In the course of our metabolism, some alkenes or alcohols become oxidatively degraded to form aldehydes or carboxylic acids. These molecules may be toxic if allowed to accumulate, so they too require some form of detoxification and removal.

Finally, modern medicine has provided us with a wide array of compounds that can relieve problems as minor as headaches or as significant as cancer. The metabolism and elimination of these drugs is critical to their function.

The metabolism of foreign molecules consumed in the diet, toxins, and drugs is collectively known as **xenobiotic metabolism**, the process by which the body detoxifies and eliminates these foreign molecules. The overall scheme of xenobiotic metabolism is to create more water-soluble molecules. This decreases the likelihood of xenobiotics entering a cell through the plasma membrane and increases the likelihood of their being eliminated in the urine. Xenobiotics may also be cleaved into smaller fragments and then modified with small molecules that are recognized by receptors, which remove these molecules from the cell. Many cancers that are multidrug resistant (MDR) owe that resistance to the ability of the patient to detoxify or export anticancer drugs from their site of action.

Xenobiotic metabolism can be divided into two phases: phase I, oxidation, and phase II, conjugation to larger molecules such as glutathione or glucuronic acid (**Figure 11.19**).

11.5.1 Phase I metabolism makes molecules more hydrophilic through oxidative modification

In phase I, xenobiotics undergo reactions that make them more hydrophilic, either through oxidation or cleavage reactions, such as an ester cleavage that unmasks more polar moieties (**Figure 11.20**). These reactions are carried out by several families of enzymes, including dehydrogenases, hydrolases, flavin monooxidases (FMO), cytochrome P450 enzymes, and **monoamine oxidases (MAOs)**. The latter two are discussed below.

FIGURE 11.20 **Examples of phase I metabolism.** Nicotine is acted on by several enzymes to give a range of metabolites. Note that the final products may appear quite different from the starting metabolite.

Cytochrome P450 enzymes **Cytochrome P450 mixed function oxidases** are a broad family of enzymes that employ NADPH and molecular oxygen (O_2) to oxidatively modify substrate molecules. These oxidases are membrane-associated enzymes commonly found in either the inner mitochondrial membrane or the endoplasmic reticulum (ER), and they are most strongly expressed in the liver. There are many cytochrome P450 enzymes: humans have nearly 60 genes, and over 11,000 genes are known in other species. Each enzyme has a broad range of substrate specificities; however, individual drug molecules may be acted on by specific cytochromes. The enzymes implicated in the metabolism of a drug provide important information used in developing the dosages of that compound.

The functions of these enzymes can be broadly divided into those involved in detoxifying xenobiotics and those involved in lipid metabolism.

There is a standard nomenclature system for cytochrome P450 genes. All are abbreviated as CYP, followed by a numeral indicating the gene family, a capital letter indicating the subfamily, and a second number indicating the gene, for example, CYP3A4. Some genes have retained other names, such as thromboxane A2 synthase or aromatase, in addition to the standard nomenclature.

Previously we discussed cytochrome proteins in terms of the electron transport chain. The cytochromes of the electron transport chain are small, low molecular weight cytochromes. Both low molecular weight cytochromes and cytochrome P450 enzymes are heme proteins. While both catalyze redox chemistry, cytochrome c and cytochrome P450 enzymes serve very different functions in biology.

Cytochrome P450 enzymes are globular, predominantly α helical proteins found in the ER or mitochondria. They all have a heme prosthetic group bound by coordination of the central heme iron to a cysteine on the distal side of the ring. The active site of the enzyme (CYP3A4 in this example) is remarkably small, and the structure undergoes relatively little conformational change upon substrate binding. It is likely that this contributes to the broad substrate specificity of this enzyme. Key hydrophobic residues line the active site and play a role in controlling the steric interactions of the enzyme with its many substrates. CYP3A4 is one of the most highly expressed cytochromes and is involved in the detoxification of more than 200 common pharmaceuticals.

NADPH supplies the electrons used to reduce CYP, although numerous mechanisms and proteins are involved in the transfer of these electrons. Typically, these involve flavoproteins or small cytochromes such as cyt b5. The mechanisms involved for other cytochromes vary depending on the substrates and electron donor pairs, although all employ a heme group to bind the reactive oxygen species.

Phase I metabolism often results in products that are still metabolically active. Several drugs are supplied in a biologically inactive form that only become active after undergoing phase I metabolism. For example, the HMG-CoA reductase inhibitor Mevacor (lovastatin), used to treat overactive high plasma cholesterol, must be cleaved by esterases to generate the active form of the molecule.

Monoamine oxidases MAOs employ a covalently fixed molecule of FAD to catalyze the conversion of a primary amine to an aldehyde (**Figure 11.21**). There are two isoforms, MAO-A and MAO-B, of this enzyme, both of which figure prominently in the deactivation of neurotransmitters and hormones, also known as bioactive amines.

Because MAOs deactivate these signaling molecules, inhibition of MAOs should result in elevation of the signaling molecules. This is the case, and MAO inhibitors (MAOIs) are an important class of antidepressant molecules. However, the extensive substrate range for these enzymes means that the inhibition results in a wide range of side effects. Likewise, because the MAOs are important in detoxifying molecules found in the diet, patients taking MAOIs need to pay close attention to what they eat. For example, consumption of red wine, yeast extracts, sharp cheeses, or certain cured meats can elevate concentrations of tyramine in the blood. Without MAOs to degrade it, the usually harmless tyramine can build up, resulting in greatly increased blood pressure and creating a potentially fatal condition known as hypertensive crisis.

Tyramine

MAOIs also illustrate a mechanism of drug–drug interactions. Over-the-counter cold medications often include molecules that elicit similar effects to MAOIs. One example is the

FIGURE 11.21 **Monoamine oxidases are FAD-dependent monoxidases.** **A.** Monoamine oxidases are responsible for inactivating many neurotransmitters and other bioactive amines. **B.** MAO-A and B employ a similar mechanism but differ in the access to the active site. MAO-A contains an isoleucine guarding the passage while MAO-B has the active site blocked by a much bulkier tyrosine residue. This regulates substrate specificity. (Left: PDB ID 2Z5X Son, S.Y., Ma, J., Kondou, Y., Yoshimura, M., Yamashita,

E., Tsukihara, T. (2008) Structure of human monoamine oxidase A at 2.2-A resolution: The control of opening the entry for substrates/inhibitors. *Proc. Natl. Acad. Sci. Usa* 105: 5739–5744; Right: PDB ID 4CRT Esteban, G., Allan, J., Samadi, A., Mattevi, A., Unzeta, M., Marco-Contelles, J., Binda, C., Ramsay, R.R. (2014) Kinetic and Structural Analysis of the Irreversible Inhibition of Human Monoamine Oxidases by Ass234, a Multi-Target Compound Designed for Use in Alzheimer'S Disease. *Biochim. Biophys. Acta* 1844:1104)

combination of the MAOI phenelzine (Nardil) and the expectorant dextromethorphan. Both of these medications elevate levels of serotonin, so if taken together they can result in dangerously high levels of serotonin, referred to as serotonin syndrome. Although cases of this interaction are rare, serotonin syndrome can also be fatal. Patients exhibit restlessness, hallucination, increased body temperature, tachycardia (increased heart rate), nausea, and rapid changes in blood pressure. Similar effects can be seen in subjects who abuse cough syrups that contain dextromethorphan. As a result of these and other similar interactions, patients taking MAOIs are told not to take any over-the-counter cold medicines.

The isoforms MAO-A and MAO-B differ in their overall topology. Both have a covalently linked FAD cofactor and are anchored in the outer mitochondrial membrane by a C-terminal hydrophobic α helix; however, the shape of the substrate-binding pocket differs. MAO-A has a single large hydrophobic cavity for substrate binding, whereas MAO-B has two smaller funnel-shaped cavities separated by an isoleucine residue, a molecular gatekeeper. Rotation of this isoleucine side chain moves it out of the way, enabling the two chambers to accommodate substrates of varying size. Another difference is that MAO-B contains a tyrosine residue at position 326, whereas MAO-A contains an isoleucine at an analogous position in the active site (335). This simple difference changes the inhibitor specificity for the isoforms.

Most of the chemistry that occurs in MAOs happens in the flavin ring, but three amino acid side chains also figure prominently in the reaction. A conserved lysine residue binds to both a water molecule and the N-5 position of the flavin ring, and two conserved tyrosine residues sandwich substrates, potentially helping with substrate binding and increasing the nucleophilicity of the substrate amine. Mutation of any of these residues alters enzymatic activity.

11.5.2 Phase II metabolism couples molecules to bulky hydrophilic groups

In phase II metabolism, molecules are conjugated to other chemical groups, the most common of which are glucuronic acid, glutathione, glycine, methyl groups, and sulfate. Glycine, methyl groups, and sulfate should need little explanation, but glucuronic acid and glutathione may be less familiar.

Glucuronic acid   **Glutathione**

Glucuronic acid is an oxidized form of glucose in which the C-6 has been enzymatically oxidized from an alcohol to a carboxylic acid. Conjugation to an oxidized xenobiotic occurs between the C-1 of the glucuronic acid and a hydroxyl or amino group in the xenobiotic, with UDP-glucuronic acid acting as the active donor.

Biphenylamine   **Glucuronic acid derivative**

Glutathione (GSH) is a tripeptide of glycine, cysteine, and glutamate; however, the glutamic acid is attached via an unusual peptide bond formed between the side chain of the glutamate (the γ-carboxyl group) and the free amine of the cysteine. Glutathione helps to provide a reducing environment in the cell and is found in its oxidized state as a glutathione dimer. In some cell types, such as liver cells, the concentration of glutathione can be quite high, upwards of 5 mM in a 90:10 ratio of reduced monomer:oxidized dimer. When used in phase II metabolism, the thiol moiety is the active group, undergoing conjugation to electrophilic centers in the target xenobiotic. Attaching this bulky, highly soluble, anionic group to xenobiotics helps to make the xenobiotics less able to permeate into cells and more water soluble; hence, they are more easily passed through the kidney and into the urine.

A group of transferases are responsible for covalently modifying molecules in phase II. The best characterized of these are the **glutathione-*S*-transferases (GSTs)**.

Glutathione-*S*-transferases

GSTs are the enzymes that conjugate glutathione to an electrophilic center of a substrate molecule. They are expressed differentially in all tissues of the body, with expression levels of the different isoforms varying in response to factors such as tissue, environmental challenge, disease states (for example, some cancers), sex, and age.

This section focuses on the role that GSTs play in phase II metabolism, but other enzymes serve similar purposes. For example, *N*-Acetyltransferases, methyltransferases, UDP-glucuronosyl transferases and sulfotransferases are all used by the liver to derivatize xenobiotics. The result of these modifications is to render the xenobiotic inactive through the addition of more polar or charged groups. This prevents the molecule from crossing membranes and makes it more likely to be eliminated in the urine. Although this part of xenobiotic metabolism is termed phase II, some molecules undergo these reactions without first being modified in phase I.

Some examples of how phase I and II metabolism are used in the analysis of many drugs are discussed in **Societal and Ethical Biochemistry: Drug testing.**

Societal and Ethical Biochemistry

Drug testing

Throughout history, people have used or abused molecules for a variety of reasons. Examples include molecules that allow one to wake up or to be more alert (caffeine or amphetamines), to relax (alcohol or tetrahydrocannabinol, THC), to relieve pain (ibuprofen or morphine), to have spiritual experiences (nicotine or hallucinogens), to escape reality, or to fit in socially (all of the above). Some of these molecules (caffeine, nicotine, ibuprofen) are deemed relatively safe, and their use is legal. Others (alcohol, THC, narcotics, opioids, hallucinogens) are either highly regulated or illegal.

Governments have a strong mandate to create and enforce laws prohibiting the use of many recreational drugs, and to keep people who use such drugs from working in positions where they may cause harm if they are in an impaired or drug-dependent state. Hence, scientists have developed tests for illegal compounds.

Drug testing offers an interesting window into both drug metabolism and pharmacology. Often the substance assayed is urine, although in some instances blood or even breath (in the case of ethanol use) can be assayed. Each of these tests has different strengths and weaknesses. Breath can be assayed easily and gives an indication of the amount of alcohol in blood. Urine testing can provide an average of the metabolites excreted over the past several hours, but the substances assayed may be metabolic breakdown products and also may be dilute. Blood gives perhaps the most "accurate" picture, but the amounts that can be assayed are limited.

As small organic molecules, drugs can generally be identified using the methods found in analytical laboratories. Often, the substances being tested for in urine or blood need to be concentrated using solid-phase extraction. Molecules are extracted from the sample by passing them over a hydrophobic interaction column—a column coated with hydrophobic molecules like phenyl groups or chains of carbons of varying length. The drugs and their derivatives are more nonpolar than water and adhere to the column matrix. The column is eluted with a nonpolar solvent, such as hexane, and analyzed using either high performance liquid chromatography (HPLC) or mass spectrometry. These techniques can be highly sensitive, detecting nanogram-to-picogram quantities of material. The molecules found can be either positively identified by mass or by comparison to known standards.

It is helpful to look at the metabolism of a single drug as an example of what can happen in metabolism and excretion. Caffeine (1,3,7-trimethylxanthine) is a common molecule that many people use to help start their day. It is found naturally in many plants, including coffee, tea, and cocoa. A typical dose of caffeine in an 8-ounce cup of drip coffee is about 100 to 175 mg, but some energy drinks contain more than twice that concentration. In the body, the liver works to detoxify caffeine and make it more water soluble so that it can be eliminated in the urine by the kidney.

The first step in caffeine metabolism is the removal of one of the methyl groups, resulting in paraxanthine (1,7-dimethylxanthine, the major metabolite), theobromine (3,7-dimethylxanthine), or theophylline (1,3-dimethylxanthine), all of which are examples of phase I metabolism.

Metabolites

Caffeine

Theobromine

1,3,7-trimethyluric acid

Theophylline

Paraxanthine

Each of these molecules can be detected in urine, but each can also be further metabolized. Theobromine, for example, can be further demethylated into methyl xanthines and methyl uric acid. Hence, there can be multiple breakdown products for a single drug, any one of which can be telling when it comes to drug testing. Although testing for caffeine and its metabolites is relatively innocuous, testing for metabolites or derivatives of other substances (for example, morphine) is important in medicine, society, and law.

WORKED PROBLEM 11.5 | Metabolism of an anticancer drug

The anticancer drug tamoxifen is often used to treat some types of breast cancer. Its structure is shown along with the structure of one of its metabolites. Based on these structures, propose a pathway through which tamoxifen is metabolized by the liver.

Strategy Examine the structure of tamoxifen and the structure of the metabolite. What chemical changes have been made to these structures? Of the reactions discussed in this section, which reactions could lead to these changes and which could not?

Tamoxifen

4-hydroxytamoxifen

Solution Tamoxifen is hydroxylated by a cytochrome P450 enzyme. We can eliminate phase II metabolism as a potential pathway because the molecule is not coupled to a larger hydrophilic molecule, such as glucuronic acid or glutathione. Likewise, we can rule out some of the reactions of phase I metabolism because there are no esters to be cleaved or monoamines to be oxidized. This leaves the cytochromes as likely candidates for metabolizing these molecules. In the case of tamoxifen, the specific isoform implicated is CYP2D6, although others are involved in producing other metabolites. In the course of designing new drugs, structure–activity relationships provide some guidance as to how a drug may be metabolized, but the specific route used to detoxify a drug must be experimentally observed.

Follow-up question One of the metabolites is *N*-Desmethyl tamoxifen. What reactions and enzymes might be responsible for this metabolite of tamoxifen?

11.5 Summary

- There are many foreign molecules, or xenobiotics, in the body that need to be eliminated.
- Xenobiotics are typically cleaved into smaller pieces, made more hydrophilic, or coupled to larger hydrophilic molecules to decrease their ability to cross the plasma membrane and increase their ability to be excreted in urine.
- Phase I metabolism involves cleaving the xenobiotic or oxidatively damaging it to make it more water soluble.
- The cytochrome p 450 enzymes employ a heme functional group to generate reactive oxygen species that react with substrate molecules.
- MAOs are flavoproteins that use a covalently bound flavin group to oxidize amines. These enzymes act in neurotransmitter and hormone metabolism and in detoxifying reactions.
- Phase II metabolism involves coupling molecules to larger, water-soluble molecules such as glucuronic acid and the tripeptide glutathione.
- GSTs are enzymes that couple glutathione to substrate molecules to be excreted.

11.5 Concept Check

- Describe where xenobiotics come from and how they enter the body.
- Describe how xenobiotics are metabolized and eliminated, including the two main pathways that are used.
- Describe the chemistry of the three major enzymatic systems involved in the detoxification of xenobiotics discussed in this section (CYP, MAO, and GST).
- Explain why understanding how a drug is metabolized is crucial to understanding how it functions.

11.6 | The Biochemistry of Renal Function

Nitrogenous wastes, drugs, and xenobiotic metabolites need to be secreted from organisms. In fish and higher organisms, kidneys filter this waste and remove it from the circulation. In addition to filtering out wastes, the kidneys also need to be able to retain metabolites such as amino acids and glucose that the organism needs. This section discusses renal or kidney function, the filtration of wastes and retention of metabolites, as well as three other related renal functions: acid–base balance, CO_2 synthesis, and regulation of plasma osmolarity. These functions collectively allow the kidney to eliminate wastes as well as regulate fluid retention, pH, and concentrations of electrolytes in the body. The role of hormones on the kidney and the associated adrenal gland is also discussed.

There are many different xenobiotics, and an organism may be exposed to different molecules depending on its diet. The exposure can change through seasonal fluctuations, location, or progression through the life cycle. Likewise, as xenobiotics are detoxified, multiple products can be formed, meaning that many different molecules need to be expelled from the organism.

Using specific pumps or channels for each molecule would be inefficient and complicated, yet these molecules must be removed to avoid their rapid buildup in the circulation. Organisms have evolved such that *all* small molecules are filtered out of the blood; an elegant mechanism of molecular pumps and diffusion is then used to recover and retain needed metabolites and water.

Kidney function is critical to health. One means of ascertaining kidney function is an analysis of the chemicals found in blood. This is discussed in **Medical Biochemistry: Clinical chemistry**.

Medical Biochemistry

Clinical chemistry

Biochemistry provides a wealth of tools used by clinicians and investigators to examine the metabolism of a patient or test subject. One of the simplest and most widely used assays is a CHEM 7 or CHEM 20, also known as blood work. In this assay, a sample of blood is drawn, usually in the fasted state, and tested for about 7 to 20 different parameters. A common panel of assays is shown in **Table 11.4**. Collectively, the results give the physician or investigator clues (some of them strong clues) as to what is happening at the chemical level and possibly causing disease or a disorder. Several of the compounds were mentioned in this chapter and merit further discussion.

LDH is lactate dehydrogenase, encountered in section 6.5 (fates of pyruvate). In general, LDH is localized to specific tissues: heart, kidney, liver, muscle. If LDH is released from those tissues, it will not be excreted by the kidney and will accumulate. LDH is therefore a marker for general tissue damage.

This chapter discusses alanine transaminase (ALT) and aspartate aminotransferase (AST) and their role in amine and amino acid metabolism. Both of these enzymes are localized to the liver. Therefore, like LDH, elevated levels of these enzymes in blood are a marker of liver damage. Similarly, gamma-glutamyl transpeptidase (gamma-GT) is another liver enzyme that is a marker for liver damage. Among its multiple functions, gamma-GT catalyzes the transfer of the gamma-linked glutamate from glutathione to an acceptor molecule.

BUN is a measure of the urea level in blood. Elevated BUN levels typically indicate problems with renal function and decreased urea clearance rates in the kidney. Creatinine, an important breakdown product of creatine in muscle, is discussed in chapter 12. Like urea, creatinine is typically cleared from circulation by the kidney, and elevated levels indicate renal damage.

One final molecule that is often included on chemistry panels is creatine phosphokinase (CPK). This enzyme is specifically found in liver and muscle tissue, where it functions in creatine metabolism. Elevated levels of CPK indicate muscle damage or, more frequently, heart attack.

TABLE 11.4 Clinical chemistry panel

Metabolite	Normal Concentration	Metabolite	Normal Concentration
Normal results		**Normal results**	
Albumin	3.9–5.0 g/dL	Gamma-GT	0–51 IU/L
Alkaline phosphatase	44–147 IU/L	Glucose test	64–128 mg/dL
ALT	8–37 IU/L	LDH	105–333 IU/L
AST	10–34 IU/L	Phosphorus—serum	2.4–4.1 mg/dL
BUN	7–20 mg/dL	Potassium	3.7–5.2 mEq/L
Calcium—serum	8.5–10.9 mg/dL	Serum sodium	136–144 mEq/L
Serum chloride	101–111 mmol/L	Total bilirubin	0.2–1.9 mg/dL
CO_2	20–29 mmol/L	Total cholesterol	100–240 mg/dL
Creatinine	0.8–1.4 mg/dL	Total protein	6.3–7.9 g/dL
Direct bilirubin	0.0–0.3 mg/dL	Uric acid	4.1–8.8 mg/dl

11.6.1 Molecules smaller than proteins are filtered out of the blood by the glomerulus

The basic filtration unit of the kidney is the **nephron**. Each human kidney contains 1 to 1.5 million nephrons. In other animals, kidneys operate similarly, but particular functions depend on the species and the environment for which they have adapted. The kidney can broadly be divided into two parts: the cortex or outer coating and the medulla or core. The nephron bridges these two parts. Each nephron can be subdivided into two structures: one that filters the blood and another to reabsorb water and other essential molecules. The remaining liquid, the urine, flows through the ureter and is collected in the urinary bladder.

The glomerulus and Bowman's capsule

The filtration aspect of kidney function is carried out in the **glomerulus**, a network of highly porous capillaries. Large objects, such as cells, are retained in the capillaries, while small molecules are filtered out. The filtration unit consists of fenestrated endothelial cells; these are cells with small pores that form the capillary and associated basement membrane. The spaces are small enough to allow molecules with a Stokes radius of less than 2 nm (an approximate molecular weight of 7 kDa) to be filtered out. Anything with a Stokes radius greater than 3.5 nm is almost completely retained (serum albumin, with a molecular weight of 64 kDa and a Stokes radius of 3.5 nm, is retained). To keep the blood liquid, about 20% of plasma is also retained, but everything else is lost to the filtrate.

In certain cases of kidney damage or persistent high blood pressure, proteins can leak from the glomerulus into the filtrate and eventually into the urine, a condition known as **proteinuria**.

The filtrate lost from the capillary network in the glomerulus enters the **Bowman's capsule**—a glove that envelops the glomerulus and collects the filtrate. At this point, the filtrate contains water, electrolytes, amino acids, and glucose in about the same concentration as found in blood, but it lacks cells and proteins. If the filtrate itself were to be excreted in humans, the organism would lose these essential molecules and would excrete nearly 200 liters of fluid a day. Water and metabolites are reabsorbed in the second phase of renal function.

11.6.2 | Water, glucose, and electrolytes are reabsorbed in the proximal convoluted tubule, loop of Henle, and distal convoluted tubule

The initial stages of reabsorption occur in the **proximal convoluted tubule**. The proximal convoluted tubule reabsorbs glucose and amino acids using a sodium ion coupled symporter (**Figure 11.22**). The gradient of sodium ions, which helps to drive the absorption of glucose and amino acids, is created by a sodium/potassium antiporter on the plasma side of the cell. The energy to drive this process is substantial; 10%–15% of the organism's resting energy demands go to maintaining these gradients and to reabsorbing nutrients and electrolytes from the filtrate. The energy comes from the hydrolysis of ATP and is thus considered active transport.

The gradient created by reabsorbing sodium ions, glucose, and amino acids also draws water back from the filtrate into the blood. Water moves through an aquaporin, its own protein channel. This system normally absorbs most of the glucose and amino acids as well as 70% of the water lost in the initial filtration step. If plasma glucose is high, as is the case in diabetes, the glucose transporters are unable to reabsorb all the glucose, and some of it appears in the urine. The remaining glucose in the filtrate also shifts the osmotic gradient across the cells of the proximal convoluted tubule, so that water is also retained in the filtrate. This results in increased urinary volume and the increased frequency of urination seen in people with diabetes.

The proximal convoluted tubule absorbs glucose and amino acids; the filtrate that remains is still relatively high in electrolytes and contains a considerable volume of water. If this were urine, the total volume in humans would be over 20 liters a day and be nearly as concentrated in electrolytes as seen in plasma. This difficulty is overcome in two ways. The first lies in the anatomy of the nephron. As the filtrate is concentrated during its passage through the proximal convoluted tubule, it descends into a structure called the

FIGURE 11.22 Ion pumps and aquaporins in the proximal tubule. Small organic molecules such as glucose, amino acids, and some metabolites are transported back into the cells lining the proximal tubule using specific Na^+ symporters. The sodium gradient used to drive this transport is created by Na^+/K^+ ATPases. Water diffuses back into the cell from the filtrate and out of the cell into the blood through aquaporins.

FIGURE 11.23 **Ion balance and water reabsorption.** The proximal tubule, loop of Henle, and distal tubule are wrapped by the vasa recta. The proximal tubule and descending loop of Henle are permeable to water, increasing the concentration of the filtrate. In the distal tubule, sodium and chloride ions are pumped out generating dilute filtrate. Values are measured in milliOsmoles (mOsm), the millimoles of solute per liter that contribute to the osmotic pressure of a solution. In the collecting duct, more ions and metabolites (Na^+, Cl^-, bicarbonate, and urea) are reabsorbed or diffused into the vasa recta, bringing water with them. This results in concentrated urine. (Tortora; Derrickson, *Principles of Anatomy & Physiology*, 13e, copyright 2012, John Wiley & Sons. This material is reproduced with permission of John Wiley & Sons, Inc.)

loop of Henle (**Figure 11.23**). The descending arm of this loop is permeable to water, whereas the ascending arm is impermeable to water. The loop also contains sodium pumps capable of setting up a 200 mOsM gradient between the filtrate and the extracellular fluid surrounding the loop. However, because the descending arm is water permeable, water diffuses out to maintain a small gradient between the fluid in the lumen of the loop and the interstitial fluid. The net result of this is a large gradient between the interstitial fluid at the entry point of the loop and the bottom of the loop (from 300 to 1200 mOsM).

Intertwined with the loop of Henle is a network of capillaries known as the **vasa recta**. In the capillaries surrounding the descending limb of the loop of Henle, Na^+ and Cl^- ions are absorbed, and water leaves due to the high concentration at the bend of the loop. However, in the vessels surrounding the ascending loop, the reverse occurs because the plasma is now hypertonic compared to the extracellular fluid; thus, electrolytes are lost from the plasma, and water is reabsorbed until an isotonic concentration is reached.

The story is not complete, however. The urine that leaves the proximal convoluted tubule is still quite dilute. In the final stage of reabsorption, water is removed from the collecting duct to yield urine. There are no pumps for water molecules; rather, water is removed as it is in the other steps of reabsorption, by passive diffusion. This is regulated in several different ways. First, as the dilute urine passes down the collecting duct, it passes through the intracellular region by the loop of Henle. Pores in the cells of the collecting duct allow water to diffuse out of the duct in response to the high salt concentration around the loop of Henle. This porosity is acutely regulated by antidiuretic hormone. High levels of antidiuretic hormone make this duct more porous. Significant quantities of water escape the duct, resulting in the

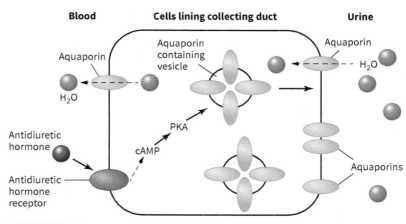

FIGURE 11.24 **Antidiuretic hormone.** The peptide antidiuretic hormone signals through a heterotrimeric G protein coupled receptor to activate protein kinase A. PKA phosphorylation of vesicle proteins causes fusion with the luminal side of the plasma membrane. This presents more aquaporins to the membrane and results in the reabsorption of more water.

production of concentrated urine. In the absence of the hormone, the pores are closed and large quantities of dilute urine are produced. On a molecular level, antidiuretic hormone is a peptide hormone that acts via a 7-transmembrane helix spanning receptor to elevate cytosolic levels of cAMP. Elevated cAMP concentrations activate protein kinase A (PKA), which phosphorylates proteins on the surface of vesicles containing aquaporins, causing them to migrate to the plasma membrane of endothelial cells lining this duct and facilitate water transport (**Figure 11.24**).

The other major hormone system that regulates water reabsorption is the renin–angiotensin system. Aldosterone is a steroid hormone made in the adrenal gland. It acts in the distal convoluted tubule to increase expression of sodium pumps, thereby increasing retention of sodium and water. The renin–angiotensin system signals to the adrenal gland to release aldosterone.

Not all molecules leave the kidney by diffusion. Some are pumped out via generic anion or cation pumps (**Table 11.5**). These molecules recognize small organic ions and pump them into the cells lining the proximal convoluted tubule. This process is driven by gradients of Na^+ diffusing into and dicarboxylic acids diffusing out of the cell.

Bicarbonate is reabsorbed in the proximal convoluted tubule through a multistep mechanism. Carbonic anhydrase is found in two locations: the cytosol and the membrane lining the distal convoluted tubule. In the filtrate, carbonic anhydrase acts to form CO_2 and water. The CO_2 diffuses into the cells lining the tubule, where a second molecule of carbonic anhydrase reforms carbonic acid (**Figure 11.25**). The acid dissociates and the resulting HCO_3^- is pumped from the endothelial cell into the bloodstream. To maintain cellular pH and keep the process going, protons are pumped back into the filtrate using a sodium-dependent antiporter.

TABLE 11.5   **Transport of Metabolites in the Kidney**

Metabolite	Where Reabsorbed	How Reabsorbed
H_2O	Proximal convoluted tubule	Osmotic gradient, via aquaporins
Na^+	Distal convoluted tubule/collecting duct	Na^+/K^+ ATPase
K^+	Distal convoluted tubule/collecting duct	Na^+/K^+ ATPase
Cl^-	Distal convoluted tubule/collecting duct	Cl^- channels (passive) and $Na^+/K^+/Cl^-$ cotransporters
CO_2	Collecting duct	Passive diffusion
HPO_4^{-2}	Proximal convoluted tubule	Na^+ symporter
Glucose	Proximal convoluted tubule	Na^+ symporter
Amino acids	Proximal convoluted tubule	Na^+ or H^+ symporter
Organics	Proximal convoluted tubule	Na^+ or H^+ symporter
Urea	Collecting duct	Passive diffusion

FIGURE 11.25 **Acid–base balance and CO_2 balance in the kidney.** Protons are pumped from cells lining the distal tubule into the filtrate. This pushes the equilibrium to the right, favoring CO_2 and H_2O. CO_2 diffuses into the cells where the reverse reaction (also catalyzed by carbonic anhydrase) occurs. This generates carbonic acid (H_2CO_3), which ionizes into bicarbonate and a proton. Bicarbonate (HCO_3^-) diffuses out of the cell into the blood side of the cell. Finally, Na^+ ions are pumped from the cell by a Na^+/K^+ ATPase. This mechanism helps the body conserve sodium ions as well as provide the gradient that helps keep bicarbonate retention possible.

Surprisingly, perhaps not all the urea is eliminated in the filtrate. In addition to allowing water to pass, the aquaporins found in the collecting duct are permeable to urea. Increased urea absorption results in increased water retention and decreased urinary volume.

Kidney function is ascertained clinically using several different tests. The total amount of urea found in blood (blood urea nitrogen, BUN) and creatinine (a muscle catabolite) are typically used as indirect measures of kidney function. If these molecules are not cleared from the circulation by the kidney, they will accumulate, leading to elevated levels. Accumulation of proteins in the urine, particularly albumin, is also indicative of kidney damage. An injection of the polysaccharide inulin is sometimes administered as a final test of renal function. This molecule is neither retained in the circulation nor reabsorbed; as such, it can be used as a measure of how well filtration is occurring, such as the glomerular filtration rate.

WORKED PROBLEM 11.6 | Active or passive?

The kidney offers an interesting example of the interdependence of many biological systems. Which molecules are dependent on sodium gradients for transport?

Strategy Think about the processes that go on in the kidney. Which of these require some investment of energy or a gradient for transport to occur?

Solution Glucose, amino acids, urea, and protons are either directly or indirectly dependent on sodium ions for transport.

Follow-up question Glucose is reabsorbed in the kidney by a glucose transporter. How could you show that this process can be saturated?

11.6 Summary

- Kidneys serve several functions, including filtration of wastes from plasma, hormone secretion, acid–base balance, secretion of ammonia, and maintenance of osmolarity.
- Filtration of the blood occurs in the glomerulus and Bowman's capsule.
- All cells and all molecules or complexes larger than a medium-sized protein are retained in the glomerulus.
- Key molecules, water, electrolytes, and amino acids are reabsorbed in the proximal convoluted tubule, loop of Henle, and distal convoluted tubule.
- The kidney uses a combination of active and passive transport to reabsorb these molecules.
- By balancing water and sodium reabsorption, the kidney is able to regulate the osmolarity of the plasma.
- By balancing ammonia biosynthesis and carbonate reabsorption, the kidney regulates acid–base balance.

11.6 Concept Check

- Explain the process by which the kidney filters out wastes from blood.
- Describe how different molecules are reabsorbed into the bloodstream and where in the kidney these processes occur.
- Describe the function of the hormones involved in the regulation of reabsorption of electrolytes and water from the filtrate.
- Describe other functions performed by the kidney such as acid–base balance.
- Explain how kidney function is tested or determined in the clinic.

The Bigger Picture

Both the amino group of amino acids and any molecules that suffer oxidative damage are considered waste products and need to be removed from an organism. In addition, in the course of day-to-day living, we are exposed to environmental toxins, drugs, and other xenobiotic molecules that have to be removed from the body. This chapter describes how amines and xenobiotics are detoxified and eliminated.

Bioinformatics Exercises

Exercise 1 Viewing and Analyzing Pyridoxal Phosphate Enzymes

Exercise 2 Amino Acid Metabolism and the KEGG Database

Problems

11.1 Digestion of Proteins

1. What is the difference between a protease and a peptidase? Between an aminopeptidase and a carboxypeptidase?

2. Pepsin is an aspartyl protease. How might mutation of the active site aspartate residue to a glutamate residue affect the enzyme? What kinetic parameters (e.g., V_{max}, k_{cat}, K_m) would be affected, and how? What would the mechanism of the new mutant look like? If one of the active site aspartates were mutated to asparagine, how would that affect the enzyme?

3. Trypsin is a serine protease with a classic catalytic triad. How would mutation of the active site serine to each of the following amino acids affect catalysis and kinetic parameters of the enzyme?

    a. serine to alanine

    b. serine to aspartate

    c. serine to threonine

4. In the course of a hypothetical meal, the stomach expands from 0.25 liters to 1.25 liters. If we assume that no buffering occurs and no acid is produced from the stomach contents, how much acid must be secreted to maintain pH = 1.0? How many grams of ATP would be consumed in the production of that acid?

5. The digestive enzyme renin is found in juvenile goats, cows, camels, and sheep. Renin, which is used in cheese-making, is a protease. Following heating and renin treatment, the curds coagulate and separate away from the whey. Why would treating a protein with a protease make it coagulate, when it might be expected that smaller pieces would be more soluble?

6. The pK_a of the amino and carboxyl groups on alanine are 9.9 and 2.4, respectively. Under physiological conditions (pH 7.4), what percentage of alanine is ionized?

11.2 Transamination and Oxidative Deamination

7. Alanine has a hydrophobic side chain. Would you anticipate solubility of this amino acid in plasma to be a problem?

8. Draw the structure resulting from the transamination of these amino acids. Have you seen any of these previously and if so where?

    I. alanine

    II. aspartate

    III. glutamate

    IV. phenylalanine

9. What difficulties would any organism encounter if it were unable to perform transamination reactions?

10. We have not discussed the energetics of the transaminase reaction. What would you predict for a ΔG value for a transaminase? Strongly positive, strongly negative, or close to zero? Explain your reasoning.

11. Can you explain why alanine is used to shuttle amino groups between muscle and liver, rather than some other amino acid such as glycine?

11.3 The Urea Cycle

12. What is the source of the carbons in fumarate when they arise from the urea cycle? What is the source of the carbons in arginine? What is the source of the nitrogen atoms in arginine?

13. Ornithine can be decarboxylated to form polyamines such as putrescene (1,4-diaminobutane). What would the structure look like if ornithine was decarboxylated? Give a general description of the chemistry of the decarboxylation. What cofactors, electron donors, electron acceptors, or nucleophiles may be involved in this chemistry? What would you predict for a value of the free energy of reaction (positive, negative, near zero)? Explain your reasoning.

14. Citrulline, ornithine, and other metabolites are now commonly found in energy or sports recovery drinks. What is the reason for adding these metabolites to energy drinks? What might they be doing, and does it work? What drawbacks would these molecules have to overcome to do what they are described as being able to do?

15. Some farmers give their cattle low-quality feeds supplemented with urea. What is the reason for the urea supplement? How would this help the animal?

16. Cats require arginine for the urea cycle but cannot synthesize it. If cat food included high levels of other urea cycle intermediates, could any of them compensate for low arginine levels and keep the cycle going?

17. Ornithine is not found in proteins. One reason for this is that ornithine can spontaneously form a lactam. Draw the structure of this lactam. Describe why it would be evolutionarily selected against. Lysine is similar to ornithine. Why does lysine not form a lactam?

11.4 Pathways of Amino Acid Carbon Skeleton Scavenging

18. We tend to focus on the fates of the carbon atoms in amino acid carbon skeleton scavenging. Where in these pathways is energy required or released? What other thermodynamic principles allow these reactions to proceed in the forward direction?

19. The catabolism of carbon skeletons of amino acids is organized by how they enter the common catabolic pathways (acetyl-CoA and the citric acid cycle), but they could also be organized by type of reactions. If you were to reorganize these pathways, what other means could you use to organize them?

20. In obligate carnivores, are carbon skeletons truly scavenged? What is the fate of these carbons?

21. Many humans are vegetarians or vegans whereas others eat large quantities of meat or fish. Can those people adapt their nitrogen metabolism to their specific diet, as other species discussed in this chapter have?

11.5 The Detoxification of Other Amines and Xenobiotics

22. Agonists are drugs that bind to receptors and activate them. The β-adrenergic receptor agonist propranolol is metabolized in the liver to 4-hydroxypropranolol. Would you expect this to be phase I or phase II metabolism? Based on the structure of propranolol, propose a structure of 4-hydroxypropranolol. Of the other metabolites shown in the figure, which pathways would you categorize as phase I and which as phase II?

23. Homeless shelters rarely if ever offer grapefruit juice to drink because of the potential for interactions with medications the residents may be taking. If a compound that was naturally occurring in grapefruit juice were metabolized through a MAO or CYP pathway, how could a drug interaction occur?

24. Which reactions of phase I and phase II metabolism require energy, and where does this energy come from (in what molecular form)?

25. MAOIs have a two-week washout period, that is, the time over which the effect of the drug goes away once someone has stopped taking it. Why does this occur, and what happens over the two weeks?

11.6 The Biochemistry of Renal Function

26. Cells with large numbers of Na^+ pumps often have more mitochondria. Why might this be the case?

27. About 70% of a small molecule is cleared in one pass of the kidney. What does this tell us about how this molecule is being treated in the kidney?

28. How many passes would it take to clear 90% of inulin from the circulation?

29. If 1.5 kg of NaCl is filtered each day by the kidney, how many sodium ions are there? What is the energetic potential of separating that number of sodium ions across a plasma membrane?

30. On average, 180 liters of plasma are filtered each day. If humans had to expend one molecule of ATP for every molecule of water retained, approximately how many molecules of ATP would be required? If 36 molecules of ATP are produced by the aerobic catabolism of one molecule of glucose, how many grams of glucose would be required?

31. Crush syndrome (traumatic rhabdomyolysis) is a phenomenon frequently observed after earthquakes or building collapses. In this syndrome, people who have had a body part, such as a leg trapped or crushed, enter acute kidney failure following release of the trapped body part. Based on your knowledge of kidney function and general biochemistry, what might be some of the agents released from the damaged tissues that could contribute to this organ failure?

Data Interpretation

32. A protease you are studying cleaves between basic residues. It is insensitive to metal chelating agents such as EDTA and EGTA and to thiol-derivitizing agents, such as *N*-Ethylmaleamide, but is inhibited by organic phosphonates, such as phenylmethyl sulfonyl fluoride. Two residues appear to be critical for catalysis: a serine and a glutamate. Based on this collective data, which of the proteases noted in this text would be similar, and how might this protein function?

33. Given the following data, what is the sequence of this peptide?

Treatment with	Yields (No Stoichiometry or Sequence Implied)
Carboxypeptidase A	No products
Trypsin	No products
Chymotrypsin	(Met, Ile, Ser, Tyr) Trp (Ala, Lys)
Thrombin	No products
Dabsyl Cl/HCl	Lys, Ser
O-iodosobenzoate	Trp, (Ala, Lys) (Trp, Tyr, Ile, Met, Ser)
CNBr	(Met, Ser) (Trp, Tyr, Ile, Lys, Ala)

If you need help with how these reagents work, consult the techniques appendix.

34. Melamine is a component of some plastics. Because of its high nitrogen content and low price, it has been illegally used in the past to make samples of protein look as though they have higher levels of protein. Why would melamine give a positive test for protein when tested with a Kjeldahl assay but not with a BCA or Bradford assay?

Melamine

35. A newborn presents in the clinic with vomiting, poor feeding, lethargy, and seizures. The child smells faintly of dirty socks. Urinalysis reveals elevated levels of isovaleryl glycine. Plasma chemistry indicates elevated levels of isovaleryl carnitine. What is the disorder, and where is the odor, isovaleryl glycine, and isovaleryl carnitine originating?

Experimental Design

36. You discover a novel protease in a species of fungi. How would you go about determining where the protease cuts substrate proteins?

37. Some reactions of the urea cycle occur in the mitochondria and others in the cytosol. How would you design an assay to test where in the cell a process is occurring, especially if the process occurs partly in one organelle and partly in another?

38. In an organism that does not have a liver, how could you test to see where in that organism urea biosynthesis is occurring? What controls would you need to use? What type of assay would you need to perform, and what would need to be included in that assay?

39. You discover a novel inhibitor of glucose transport in the kidney. As part of applying for Food and Drug Administration (FDA) approval for your new drug, you need to show how it is metabolized and cleared from the body. How would you test to see how your drug is metabolized and excreted?

40. If the drug referred to in the previous question inhibits glucose transport, how might it affect other aspects of renal function? How would you test your hypothesis?

Ethics and Social Responsibility

41. Phenylketonuria (PKU) affects 1 in every 15,000 live births in the United States. Treating someone with PKU means about 18 years on an expensive and highly restrictive diet, but not treating the disease leads to significant cognitive impairment. What rights do individuals and the government have to test and treat people with this disease?

42. Affirm, deny, or qualify this statement: "Like many over-the-counter drugs, proton pump inhibitors are overused to the point of abuse."

43. Raising beef cattle consumes vast amounts of energy and natural resources compared to other sources of protein. If we examine solely the economic impact of beef consumption, does it make sense to eat beef and, if so, how often?

44. A friend decides to consume a vegetarian diet but only wants to eat French fries. How would you use your biochemical knowledge to explain to her that this is probably not the healthiest course of action? A few weeks later your friend has decided she will supplement her diet with lentils, which she explains are high in protein. What might you recommend to her at this point?

45. Over 15,000 kidney transplants are performed each year in the United States. Many of the people who require such operations also have other health problems, such as diabetes, hypertension, heart disease, or obesity. In addition, kidney transplants and the immunosuppressive drugs patients need to take after the operation are expensive, in some cases costing over $1,000 a month. What criteria do you think should be in place for people to be eligible for kidney transplants?

Suggested Readings

11.1 Digestion of Proteins

Barrett, G. C., and D. T. Elmore. *Amino Acids and Peptides*. Cambridge, United Kingdom: Cambridge University Press, 1998.

Benos, Dale J. "Developmental Biology of Membrane Transport Systems." Retrieved from http://books.google.com/books/about/Developmental_biology_of_membrane_transp.html?id=GVjnebaPMMgCAcademic Press

Brix, Klaudia, and Walter Stöcker, eds. *Proteases: Structure and Function*. New York, New York: Springer, 2013.

Bröer, S. "Amino Acid Transport Across Mammalian Intestinal and Renal Epithelia." *Physiological Reviews* 88, no. (January 2008): 49–86.

Chiba, Isamu, and Takao Kami, eds. *Serine Proteases: Mechanism, Structure and Evolution*. Hauppauge, New York: Nova Science Publishers, 2012.

Lendeckel, Uwe, and Nigel M. Hooper, eds. *Proteases in Gastrointestinal Tissues (Proteases in Biology and Disease)*. New York, New York: Springer, 2010.

11.2 Transamination and Oxidative Deamination

Brosnan, M. E., and J. T. Brosnan. "Hepatic Glutamate Metabolism: A Tale of 2 Hepatocytes." *The American Journal of Clinical Nutrition* 90, no. 3 (September 2009): 857S–861S.

Curthoys, Norman P., and Malcolm Watford. "Regulation of Glutaminase Activity and Glutamine Metabolism." *Annual Review of Nutrition* 15 (1995): 133–159.

Eisenberg, David S., Harindarpal S. Gill, Gaston M. U. Pfluegl, and Sergio H. Rothstein. "Structure-Function Relationships of Glutamine Synthetases." *Biochimica et Biophysica Acta* 1477 (2000): 122–145.

Gill, H. S., and D. Eisenberg. "The Crystal Structure of Phosphinothricin in the Active Site of Glutamine Synthetase Illuminates the Mechanism of Enzymatic Inhibition." *Biochemistry* 40 (2001): 1903–1912.

Haussinger, D., and W. Gerok. "Hepatocyte Heterogeneity in Glutamate Uptake by Isolated Perfused Rat Liver." *European Journal of Biochemistry* 136 (1983): 421–5.

Liaw, Shwu-Huey, I. Kuo, and D. Eisenberg. "Discovery of the Ammonium Substrate Site on Glutamine Synthetase, a Third Cation Binding Site." *Protein Science* 4 (1995): 2358–65.

Peterson, P. E., and T. J. Smith. "The Structure of Bovine Glutamate Dehydrogenase Provides Insights into the Mechanism of Allostery." (1999) *Structure* 7 (1999): 769–82.

Smith, T. J., P. E. Peterson, T. Schmidt, J. Fang, C. A. Stanley. "Structures of Bovine Glutamate Dehydrogenase Complexes Elucidate the Mechanism of Purine Regulation." *Journal of Molecular Biology* 307 (2001): 707.

Thangavelu, K., Catherine Qiurong Pan, Tobias Karlberg, Ganapathy Balaji, Mahesh Uttamchandani, Valiyaveettil Suresh, Herwig Schüler, Boon Chuan Low, and J. Sivaramana. "Structural Basis for the Allosteric Inhibitory Mechanism of Human Kidney-Type Glutaminase (KGA) and Its Regulation by Raf-Mek-Erk Signaling in Cancer Cell Metabolism." *Proceedings of the National Academy of Sciences of the United States of America* 109, no. 20 (May 15, 2012): 7705–7710.

Werner, C., M. T. Stubbs, R. L. Krauth-Siege, G. Klebe. "The Crystal Structure of *Plasmodium Falciparum* Glutamate Dehydrogenase, a Putative Target for Novel Antimalarial Drugs." *Journal of Molecular Biology* 349 (2005): 597.

11.3 The Urea Cycle

Hoar, William Stewart, Anthony P. Farrell, David J. Randall, Patricia A. Wright, and Paul M. Anderson. *Fish Physiology: Nitrogen Excretion.* Vol. 20. Cambridge, MA: Academic Press, 2001.

Kaneko, Jiro J., John W. Harvey, and Michael Bruss. *Clinical Biochemistry of Domestic Animals.* Retrieved from http://books.google.com/books/about/Clinical_Biochemistry_of_Domestic_Animal.html?id=spsD4WQbL0QC

Prosser, C. Ladd. *Comparative Animal Physiology, Part 2.* Hoboken, New Jersey: John Wiley and Sons, 1991.

Singer, M. A. "Do Mammals, Birds, Reptiles and Fish Have Similar Nitrogen Conserving Systems?" *Comparative Biochemistry and Physiology—Part B: Biochemistry & Molecular Biology* 134, no. 4 (April 2003): 543–58.

Walsh, Patrick J., and Patricia A. Wright. "Nitrogen Metabolism and Excretion." Boca Raton, Florida: CRC Press, 1995.

11.4 Pathways of Amino Acid Carbon Skeleton Scavenging

Abelson, John N., Melvin I. Simon, John R. Sokatch, and Robert Adron Harris. *Branched-Chain Amino Acids, Part B, Volume 324 (Methods in Enzymology).* Amsterdam, Netherlands: 2000.

Bender, David A. *Amino Acid Metabolism.* 3rd ed. Hoboken, New Jersey: John Wiley & Sons, 2012.

Jorgensen, H., W. C. Sauer, and P. A. Thacker. "Amino Acid Availabilities in Soybean Meal, Sunflower Meal, Fish Meal and Meat and Bone Meal Fed to Growing Pigs." *Journal of Animal Science* 58, no. 4 (1984).

Kaplan, Nathan P., Nathan P. Colowick, Herbert Tabor, and Celia White Tabor, eds. *Metabolism of Amino Acids and Amines, Part B, Volume 17B.* Amsterdam, Netherlands: 1971.

Sharma, Virender K., and Steven E. Rokit. *Reactive Intermediates in the Oxidation of Amino Acids, Peptides, and Proteins.* Hoboken, New Jersey: Wiley, 2013.

11.5 The Detoxification of Other Amines and Xenobiotics

Angelucci, Francesco, Paola Baiocco, Maurizio Brunori, Louise Gourlay, Veronica Morea, and Andrea Bellelli. "Insights into the Catalytic Mechanism of Glutathione S-Transferase: The Lesson from *Schistosoma haematobium.*" *Structure* 13, no. 9 (September 1, 2005): 1241–6.

Cornish, H., and A. A. Christman. "A Study of the Metabolism of Theobromine, Theophylline, and Caffeine in Man." *Journal of Biological Chemistry* 228 (1957): 315–24.

De Montellano, P. R. O. *Cytochrome P450: Structure, Mechanism, and Biochemistry.* New York, New York: Springer, 2005.

Dick, C. W., and R. J. Baker. "Phylogenetic Relationships Among Megabats, Microbats, and Primates." *Proceedings of the National Academy of Sciences of the United States of America* 88 (1991): 10322–26.

Finberg, J. P., and M. B. Youdim. "Selective MAO A and B Inhibitors: Their Mechanism of Action and Pharmacology." *Neuropharmacology* 22, spec. no. 3 (Mar 1983): 441–6.

Guengerich, F. P. "Mechanisms of Cytochrome P450 Substrate Oxidation: Minireview." *Journal of Biochemical and Molecular Toxicology.* 21 (2007):163–168.

Hayes, J. D., and D. J. Pulford. "The Glutathione S-transferase Supergene Family: Regulation of GST and the Contribution of the Isoenzymes to Cancer Chemoprotection and Drug Resistance." *Critical Reviews in Biochemistry and Molecular Biology* 30, no. 6 (1995): 445–600.

Kot, M., and W. A. Daniel. "The Relative Contribution of Human Cytochrome P450 Isoforms to the Four Caffeine Oxidation Pathways: An in Vitro Comparative Study with cDNA-expressed P450s Including CYP2C Isoforms." *Biochemical Pharmacology* 76, no. 4 (August 15, 2008): 543–51.

Szklarz, G., and J. R. Halpert. "Molecular Basis of p450 Inhibition and Activation: Implications for Drug Development and Drug Therapy." *Drug Metabolism and Disposition* 26, no. 12 (1998).

11.6 The Biochemistry of Renal Function

Boron, W., and E. Boulpaep. *Medical Physiology.* 3rd ed. Philadelphia, Pennsylvania: Elsevier, 2016.

Hamburger, Jean. *Structure and Function of the Kidney.* Philadelphia, PA: W. B. Saunders Co., 1971.

Lote, C. J. *Principles of Renal Physiology.* 4th ed. New York, New York: Springer, 2000.

More, Ed. *Biochemistry Kidney Functions* (INSERM Symposium). Amsterdam, Netherlands: Elsevier, 1982.

Valtin, Heinz, and James A. Schafer. *Renal Function.* 3rd. ed. Philadelphia, Pennsylvania: Lippincott Williams & Wilkins, 1995.

Amino acid and amine metabolism

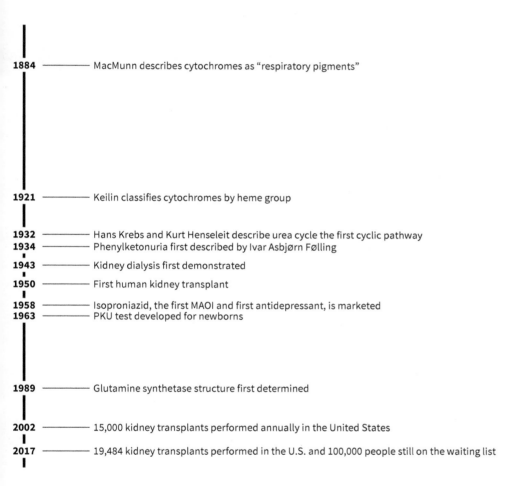

| 1884 | MacMunn describes cytochromes as "respiratory pigments" |

| 1921 | Keilin classifies cytochromes by heme group |

1932	Hans Krebs and Kurt Henseleit describe urea cycle the first cyclic pathway
1934	Phenylketonuria first described by Ivar Asbjørn Følling
1943	Kidney dialysis first demonstrated
1950	First human kidney transplant
1958	Isoproniazid, the first MAOI and first antidepressant, is marketed
1963	PKU test developed for newborns

| 1989 | Glutamine synthetase structure first determined |

| 2002 | 15,000 kidney transplants performed annually in the United States |
| 2017 | 19,484 kidney transplants performed in the U.S. and 100,000 people still on the waiting list |

CHAPTER **12**

Regulation and Integration of Metabolism

Dong Wenjie/Getty Images

The integration of biochemical pathways and how they influence each other is in many ways analogous to how multiple businesses function in the economy.

Metabolism in Context

Running any business, even a small one, is a very complicated proposition. Will the business be able to keep enough inventory to meet customers' demands? How will it store that inventory, and how can the business coordinate between manufacturers, warehouses, and retail outlets? The small business in this analogy can represent any biochemical pathway. Studied on its own in terms of its steps, how it is regulated, and where it occurs, any biochemical pathway can be simply viewed as stand-alone, unconnected, and isolated. This chapter unites and explores the complex interplay of these different pathways. To return to the small business analogy, this chapter is less about a single business and more about economics; how all the small businesses, or pathways, interact with one another to form the economy or a biochemical network. A perturbation in one area will affect another area and when one sector, such as energy or housing, is faring poorly, the entire economy suffers.

First, we look at the different players in the metabolic economy, that is, the molecules commonly found at the intersection of different pathways and the organs and tissues that metabolize these molecules. Next, we discuss how the organs communicate with each other, and the vital role of the brain in overall regulation of metabolism. Finally, the chapter examines the role of metabolism in disease, explaining how aberrant metabolism can cause disease and conversely how disease can turn metabolism against the organism. The different aspects of this chapter are illustrated in **Dynamic Figure 12.1**.

CHAPTER OUTLINE

12.1 A Review of the Pathways and Crossroads of Metabolism

12.2 Organ Specialization and Metabolic States

12.3 Communication between Organs

12.4 Metabolic Disease

DYNAMIC FIGURE 12.1 This chapter reviews individual metabolic pathways, how organ specialization helps the organism better manage energy stores, and how these organs communicate using hormones. Finally, the chapter discusses how metabolism shifts during metabolic disease.

COMMON THEMES

Evolution's outcomes are conserved.	• Many of the pathways we will see in this chapter are conserved throughout evolution.
	• Organs have evolved specific functions to help cope with metabolic challenges. A comparison of humans with other organisms illustrates some of these differences.
	• Specific mechanisms have evolved for organisms to cope with the ebb and flow of energy throughout the day, the year, the seasons, and the life span.
	• The explosion of diseases related to metabolic syndromes reflects how humans as a species have been unable to adapt to recent changes in diet and lifestyle, compared to the conditions adapted to over the past 40,000 years.
Structure determines function.	• The structure of simple organic molecules, such as catecholamines, steroids, and peptides, are critical in their interaction with receptors.
	• The chemical bonds in triacylglycerols are highly reduced, increasing the amount of energy that can be obtained through oxidation.
	• Triacylglycerols are hydrophobic molecules and are stored without water. This is not the case with carbohydrates or proteins.
	• The structure and chemistry of some metabolites—ketone bodies, acetate, glucose—can directly or indirectly cause damage to molecules, cells, and tissues when concentrations are elevated, as happens in some disease states.
Biochemical information is transferred, exchanged, and stored.	• Metabolism is regulated hormonally through endocrine hormones and neuronally through direct innervation of some tissues from the brain.
	• The hypothalamus is important to the integration of metabolism resulting in cravings, such as appetite, and complex behaviors, like eating.
	• Hormonal signals that regulate metabolism are constantly in flux.
Biomolecules are altered through pathways involving transformations of energy and matter.	• Under different metabolic states, a metabolite may be transformed for specific purposes. For example, alanine formed from pyruvate in muscle can be shuttled to the liver for detoxification of the amine moiety and generation of glucose from the carbon backbone. Similarly, the liver uses acetyl-CoA to form ketone bodies that can provide fuel for the brain.
	• The fundamental laws of thermodynamics, such as the conservation of energy, underlie and apply to all of metabolism.

12.1 A Review of the Pathways and Crossroads of Metabolism

An important distinction between metabolism as a whole and the organic reactions of metabolism is the context under which these reactions occur. For instance, if the metabolites and enzymes that participate in metabolic pathways were isolated and recombined in a beaker, the end products might be the same, but many of the important levels of control would be lost since metabolic pathways are interdependent. This section briefly reviews the major catabolic and anabolic pathways covered in previous chapters, identifies key metabolites that help to shuttle metabolites between pathways, and provides a more integrated discussion of the roles of these metabolites.

12.1.1 The pathways of metabolism are interconnected

As we have discussed, different metabolic pathways build up or break down different metabolites reviewed in **Figure 12.2**. These pathways are highly conserved throughout biology.

All of the major metabolic reactions for lipids, carbohydrates, and proteins take place within the cell and are almost evenly divided between the cytosol and the mitochondria (**Figure 12.3**). Two pathways, the urea cycle and gluconeogenesis, take place in both locations. With the exception of the electron transport chain, none of these pathways require molecular oxygen, and each of these pathways can operate either in the aerobic or anaerobic state.

Beta oxidation catabolizes fatty acids Fatty acids are broken down to acetyl-CoA through β-oxidation. This pathway occurs in the mitochondria in most cells of the body. The brain is an exception in that it can undergo low levels of β-oxidation, but it cannot obtain fatty acids from the blood for this process due to the blood-brain barrier. Most of the acetyl-CoA produced by β-oxidation is further oxidized in the citric acid cycle; however, if concentrations elevate, some is diverted to ketone body production in the liver.

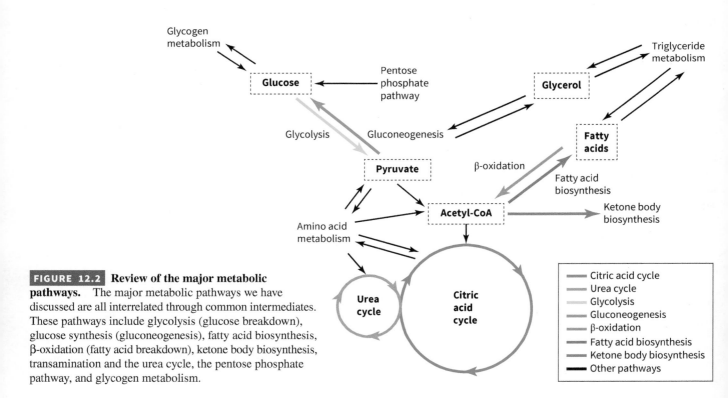

FIGURE 12.2 **Review of the major metabolic pathways.** The major metabolic pathways we have discussed are all interrelated through common intermediates. These pathways include glycolysis (glucose breakdown), glucose synthesis (gluconeogenesis), fatty acid biosynthesis, β-oxidation (fatty acid breakdown), ketone body biosynthesis, transamination and the urea cycle, the pentose phosphate pathway, and glycogen metabolism.

Fatty acid biosynthesis generates fatty acid from acetyl-CoA
Fatty acid biosynthesis occurs in the cytosol, producing fatty acids from reduced building blocks (acetyl-CoA). Fatty acyl-CoAs can be esterified to glycerol-3-phosphate to form lysophosphatidate, the branching point between phospholipid and triacylglycerol metabolism.

Glycolysis catabolizes glucose to pyruvate
Glucose is degraded through glycolysis into pyruvate. This process occurs in the cytosol of all known cell types. In the absence of sufficient oxygen for the electron transport chain, pyruvate is reduced to lactate by NADH, to regenerate NAD^+, permitting the continuation of glycolysis and the generation of ATP.

Gluconeogenesis is the synthesis of glucose from three-carbon precursors
In gluconeogenesis, glucose is generated from precursor molecules such as pyruvate, glucogenic amino acids, and glycerol. Many of the reactions in gluconeogenesis are the reverse of glycolysis; however, there are four reactions that occur only in gluconeogenesis. Not all molecules can contribute to gluconeogenesis. Acetyl-CoA cannot be used to synthesize glucose and is therefore trapped as lipidic molecules (fatty acids or ketone bodies).

Amino acids are transaminated or deaminated to generate α-keto acids
Transamination of amino acids also occurs in most cells. The α amino group of an amino acid is passed to an α-keto acid, generating a new amino acid and a new α-keto acid. In muscle tissue, this reaction often occurs when amino acids are being catabolized. Amino groups are transaminated to pyruvate and generate the amino acid alanine; the new α-keto acid is catabolized via other reactions, culminating in the citric acid cycle, ketone body formation, or gluconeogenesis.

Oxidative deamination occurs in the liver and the kidney. The amino group of an amino acid is removed and secreted, in the case of the kidney, or detoxified to urea, in the case of the liver.

Ketone bodies are generated from acetyl-CoA
Ketone body formation occurs predominantly in the liver, when levels of carbohydrates are low and acetyl-CoA is high. The liver generates acetoacetate and α-ketobutyrate from acetyl-CoA to provide a small, water-soluble energy carrier that can cross the blood-brain barrier; other tissues such as heart, muscle, and liver can subsist on fatty acids and minimal amounts of glucose for energy.

Cytosol
- Glycolysis
- Fatty acid biosynthesis
- Glycogen metabolism
- Pentose phosphate pathway
- Subsequent steps of urea cycle
- Subsequent steps of gluconeogenesis

Mitochondrion
- β-oxidation
- Citric acid cycle
- First steps of urea cycle
- First steps of gluconeogenesis
- Ketone body biosynthesis
- Electron transport chain

Endoplasmic reticulum
- Fatty acid elongation
- Fatty acid desaturation

FIGURE 12.3 **Overview of where metabolism occurs in the cell.** The major metabolic reactions we have discussed all take place within the cell. These reactions are almost evenly divided between the cytosol and the mitochondria. Two pathways (the urea cycle and gluconeogenesis) take place in both locations. Fatty acid biosynthesis occurs in the cytosol, while elongation and desaturation happen in the endoplasmic reticulum.

12.1.2 Several metabolites are at the intersection of multiple pathways

By this stage, many metabolites will be familiar. At the mention of fatty acids or glucose, you should have a mental picture of the structure of the molecules, their biological functions, and how they are built up and broken down. Hopefully, you can also place these molecules in some sort of metabolic context, although this is harder to do because the role of metabolites is often unclear. Scientific opinion about the function of these molecules evolves as research generates new findings. This section reviews and examines the role of many of the major metabolites in the context of metabolism in the body (**Table 12.1**).

- Glucose is blood sugar, the main carbohydrate source of fuel in the body. It is stored in and mobilized from glycogen. Glucose is the main fuel source for some tissues such as the brain and the kidney and the sole fuel source for some others, including erythrocytes and sperm. It is catabolized in all tissues via glycolysis and can be produced from non-carbohydrate sources through gluconeogenesis in the liver.

- Fatty acids in the blood come from **adipose tissue** (fat tissue) and are transported bound to albumin. They are stored in limited amounts in the liver and muscle, and can fuel these tissues and the heart but not the brain. Due to their reduced state, fatty acids are a committed fuel—once reduced to a fatty acid, the carbons can be burned through β-oxidation, the citric acid cycle and oxidative phosphorylation, or converted to ketone bodies.

- Pyruvate is found at the intersection of four pathways in mammals. It can be used in muscle tissue to generate lactate under anaerobic conditions, to keep glycolysis proceeding. In transamination reactions, pyruvate can accept an amino group from other

TABLE 12.1 **Metabolites at a Crossroads**

Metabolite	Structure	Made in	Stored in	Metabolized by
Glucose		Liver (gluconeogenesis)	Liver and muscle (glycogen)	All tissues (glycolysis)
Fatty acids		Liver (fatty acid biosynthesis)	Adipose tissue (triacyglycerol)	Liver and muscle (β-oxidation)
Pyruvate		All tissues, product of glycolysis	Transient	All tissues (citric acid cycle)
Lactate		Muscle, anaerobic product of glycolysis	Transient	Muscle (pyruvate) Liver (gluconeogenesis)
Alanine		Muscle, transamination	Transient	Liver (transamination and gluconeogenesis)
Glutamine		Muscle, transamination	Transient	Liver and kidney (transamination, oxidative deamination, urea cycle)
Ketone bodies		Liver, ketone body biosynthesis	Transient	Brain (used as fuel for citric acid cycle)
Glycerol		Liver, by-product of glycolysis	Adipose tissue (triacylglycerol)	Liver (gluconeogenesis)

amino acids, producing alanine. Pyruvate can be oxidized into acetyl-CoA for the citric acid cycle and oxidized to generate reducing equivalents for the electron transport chain. Finally, pyruvate can be carboxylated to provide oxaloacetate. Although this reaction can be anaplerotic (it replenishes the oxaloacetate of the citric acid cycle), it is often used instead in gluconeogenesis to provide glucose for other tissues.

- Lactate is generated in anaerobically exercising muscle as a way to oxidize NADH to NAD^+. It can accumulate in muscle, causing other physiological effects, such as a drop in pH and an associated increase in oxygen delivery by hemoglobin; alternatively, it can be transported through the blood to the liver, where it is converted to pyruvate and used in gluconeogenesis.

- Alanine is made in muscle from pyruvate. It serves a dual role in metabolism, shuttling what would otherwise be a toxic ammonia molecule to the liver for detoxification by the urea cycle and, at the same time, transferring carbon atoms to the liver for use in gluconeogenesis.

- Glutamine is another amino acid from muscle that transports amines from muscle to the liver for urea biosynthesis. If the liver cannot keep up, as is seen in some disease states such as hepatitis and cirrhosis, the kidney can deaminate glutamine into first glutamic acid, then α-ketoglutarate. The ammonia is released into the urine, and the α-ketoglutarate can participate in renal gluconeogenesis.

- Ketone bodies are formed from acetyl-CoA in times of low glucose availability. These molecules are made by the liver, and they provide an alternative energy source for the brain.

- Glycerol forms the backbone of triacylglycerol molecules. It is released from adipose tissue and transported to the liver, where it participates in synthesis of liver triacylglycerols or gluconeogenesis.

As we can see, several metabolites converge on multiple pathways, and measuring the rate of flux through these pathways may not be as simple as once envisioned. The study of flux through a pathway is considered in **Biochemistry: Flux through a pathway**.

Biochemistry

Flux through a pathway

Flux is the rate of flow or passage through a pathway. When we think of pathways as being analogous to an assembly line, we can model flux simply as the rate of production over time. This is typically given the term J:

$$J = \frac{dq}{dt}$$

where q is the quantity of product made.

If a metabolic pathway such as glycolysis were simply analogous to an assembly line, this approximation might fit, but as we have seen, metabolism is a complex interplay of many factors transpiring in the compartments of the cell. There are numerous places that metabolic intermediates can enter or exit from a metabolic pathway, the pathways themselves are complex, and there are sometimes competing reactions or other enzymes that can catalyze the same reaction (e.g., glucokinase and hexokinase in glycolysis).

Modern approaches to metabolic flux use computational models that take some of these factors into account. There are several mathematical models including metabolic control analysis, flux balance analysis, choke point analysis, and dynamic metabolic simulation that are used in these studies. Each of these models examines the concentration of metabolites and rates of enzymatic reactions under different conditions and assumptions, such as steady state or a single enzyme as the rate determining step, to calculate flux through the pathway. Disruptions are introduced into the system to see how flux changes. Why might it be important to measure, calculate, or understand flux through a pathway? When we consider that pathways are not isolated but are rather interconnected, we begin to see how flux through a pathway can influence all of metabolism. This may have important implications in allosteric regulation of individual enzymes in a pathway, athletic performance, or progression of disease. Likewise, if we are engineering a biological system to produce a specific product—an intermediate in a pathway, an engineered protein, or the organism itself—we might be concerned as to what conditions are optimal for growth. All of these parameters can be considered using flux analysis.

WORKED PROBLEM 12.1 | Follow that nitrogen...again!

A mouse previously fed a diet containing amino acids labeled with the stable isotope ^{15}N was moved to the fasted state. Based on your current knowledge of metabolism, which labeled compounds would you expect to find in the blood and urine of the mouse in the fasted state?

Strategy Levels of amino acids increase following a meal but drop relatively soon thereafter. If an animal has been fasted, it has received no food for enough time to ensure that there are no dietary amino acids in the bloodstream; in addition, levels of stored carbohydrates will have dropped. If we presume the fast has gone on long enough to catabolize some protein (most likely from muscle, the largest store of amino acids in the body), what will be the result of muscle protein catabolism?

Solution We may expect to see three pools of ^{15}N in the blood, corresponding to alanine, glutamine, and urea. The alanine and glutamine act as transporters of nitrogen from muscle to the liver, where the amine moiety of the amino acids is detoxified through urea synthesis. The liver secretes urea for elimination by the kidney. In the urine, we may expect to see one or two pools of ^{15}N. We would definitely expect to see urea, but we might also expect to see some levels of ammonia synthesized by oxidative deamination of amino acids (glutamine) by the kidney.

Follow-up question Name and describe two methods for detecting ^{15}N.

12.1 Summary

- The major anabolic and catabolic pathways are all intertwined.
- Many metabolites serve to link different metabolic pathways or organ systems. This has arisen as specialized tissues have evolved that can shift the metabolic burden from one tissue to another.
- Pyruvate, alanine, glutamine, glycerol, and lactate all serve to shift the metabolic burden from one tissue to another.

12.1 Concept Check

- Describe what happens in each of the metabolic pathways, and the major products in each case.
- Describe other ways molecules can enter or leave these pathways.
- Explain which molecules are involved in more than one pathway or facilitate more complex levels of metabolic organization, such as between organ systems, and explain how these molecules function in these roles.

12.2 | Organ Specialization and Metabolic States

Organisms struggle throughout their lifespan to maintain **homeostasis** or the balance between energy-poor and energy-rich states. Considering only the pathways studied in previous chapters, as many as 100 different enzymes catalyze the reactions involved. A similar number of regulatory proteins, hormones, receptors, kinases, phosphatases, and other proteins are also involved in the regulation of metabolism. Thus, biochemistry is not just a study of catalysis but also a study of regulation.

In a complex organism, the situation is even more complicated because distinct cell types have evolved with differing metabolic functions. Although the core processes of metabolism (glycolysis, β-oxidation, the citric acid cycle, and the electron transport chain) are clearly conserved, cells have evolved elegant mechanisms of control and levels of specialization. For example, muscle cells, adipocytes, and neurons are all capable of conducting glycolysis, but the conditions under which the glycolysis will occur are regulated differently in the three cell types, with each having evolved a distinct function to fill a distinct need. The specialization of different cell types has further evolved into discrete organ systems with specific metabolic functions. This section first examines the function of some of the major organs of the body in the context of metabolism, then focuses on the distinct metabolic states that the organism may pass through in its lifecycle and the demands these states put on each system.

12.2.1   Different organs play distinct roles in metabolism

Organs play distinct roles in metabolism. Some, such as the liver and adipose tissue, generate energy for other tissues, whereas others, such as the brain, cannot respond to an energy demand from any other tissues. This section discusses and reviews the functions of these tissues in metabolism as a whole and how they work in conjunction with one another.

The liver is central to the metabolism of proteins, carbohydrates, and lipids
Whereas the brain is the master regulator of metabolism, the liver is the caretaker (**Figure 12.4**). Although the liver is indeed involved in the detoxification of various metabolites, it is even more important in the balance of carbohydrate, lipid, and amino acid metabolism.

The liver can conduct all of the major metabolic pathways. The rest of this section discusses the metabolism of three major metabolites: amino acids, lipids, and carbohydrates.

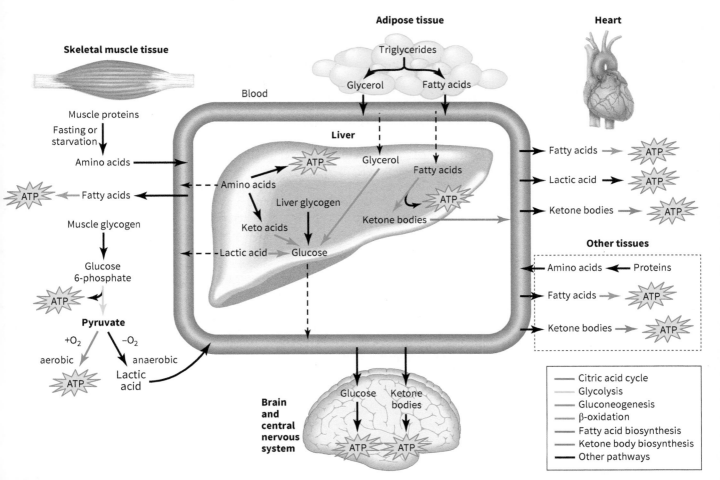

FIGURE 12.4 **Overview of where metabolism occurs in the body.** Specific organs evolved to fulfill different metabolic jobs. The heart and the brain do not store any energy but rather depend on other organs for fuel. The liver and muscle store carbohydrate as glycogen. Adipose is the predominant triacylglycerol store, although muscle and the liver can store triacylglycerol as well. The liver is responsible for the urea cycle, gluconeogenesis, and ketone body biosynthesis. (Tortora; Derrickson, *Principles of Anatomy & Physiology*, 13e, copyright 2012, John Wiley & Sons. This material is reproduced with permission of John Wiley & Sons, Inc.)

Most urea production occurs in the liver. Amino acids from the diet or from the breakdown of muscle tissue are shuttled to the liver for oxidative deamination, or for transamination with α-keto acids into other amino acids. The liver also receives alanine from muscle, created by the transamination of other amino acids to pyruvate. In the liver, these amino acids are detoxified; the amino group is oxidatively removed and used in urea biosynthesis. From here, urea is released into the bloodstream and excreted by the kidney. The carbon skeletons of amino acids are used to make new glucose via gluconeogenesis, fatty acids, or ketone bodies.

The liver also receives fats from chylomicron remnants. These lipids are repackaged with other lipids made from glucose and fatty acids, and they are secreted into the bloodstream as very-low-density lipoprotein (VLDL), which delivers triacylglycerols to muscle and adipose tissue. The liver can also accept free or (unesterified) fatty acids and glycerol from adipose tissue. These fatty acids are used to make ketone bodies to fuel the brain, while the glycerol fraction is used for gluconeogenesis. As with ketone bodies, the glucose produced in the liver is not retained but rather is secreted to the blood for other tissues to use.

The liver and muscle are the two major stores of glycogen in the body. About 25% of the body's glycogen stores are found in the liver, and the remaining 75% are found in muscle tissue. Because the liver expresses the enzyme glucose-1-phosphatase, it can produce glucose from the glucose-1-phosphate liberated in glycogenolysis and hence can release this glucose to the bloodstream for use by other tissues. Any glucose made in **hepatocytes (liver cells)** via gluconeogenesis will also be released.

Muscle catabolizes molecules for energy   Muscles allow organisms to move to either obtain energy or get out of harm's way. Unlike the liver, muscle does not normally contribute to the metabolic needs of other organs; instead, it makes demands on other organs such as the liver and adipose tissue. In rare worst-case scenarios, muscle can catabolize amino acids for fuel.

While all tissues can use amino acids to synthesize proteins, excess amino acids are catabolized. Amino acids that are catabolized in muscle are often transaminated to pyruvate, generating alanine. Alanine travels through the blood to the liver, where it is transaminated to another α-keto acid or oxidatively deaminated to regenerate pyruvate. In the liver, pyruvate is used for gluconeogenesis, producing new glucose that is returned to muscle and burned as fuel. This is the **glucose–alanine cycle**.

Muscle can use fatty acids from chylomicra, VLDLs, or free fatty acids released from adipose tissue and transported in the blood by albumin. Muscle has the ability to store small quantities of these molecules in lipid storage droplets, although most of the lipid used by muscle is burned for energy. Muscle does not generate appreciable quantities of ketone bodies.

The other primary muscle fuel is carbohydrate. Muscle readily undergoes glycolysis, and it contains three-fourths of the body's glycogen reserves. Unlike the liver, muscle lacks glucose-1-phosphatase. As a result, any glucose released from glycogen is retained by muscle and burned in that cell.

Muscle can broadly be categorized as red or white. Red muscle, characterized metabolically as oxidative muscle, is slow-twitch muscle. Its cells are enriched in myoglobin and mitochondria and are therefore redder in color. White muscle, characterized metabolically as glycolytic muscle, is fast-twitch muscle; its primary fuel is glucose. White muscle cells contain less myoglobin and fewer mitochondria, and it has a higher amount of collagen. Section 12.4 discusses the roles of these different types of muscle and the use of an alternative fuel.

We might think that a well-trained athlete has lean muscle devoid of fat, but depending on the type of athlete, the opposite may be found. This is discussed in **Medical Biochemistry: The athlete's paradox**.

Medical Biochemistry

The athlete's paradox

Well-conditioned endurance athletes have low percentages of body fat. The muscles of these athletes have an increased capacity to burn fatty acids; that is, these muscles are oxidative and have a greater sensitivity to insulin. We might anticipate these states in a trained athlete, but what is surprising is that the muscles of these athletes have elevated levels of stored triacylglycerols. This is known as the athlete's paradox.

Normally, levels of muscle triacylglycerols correlate directly with insulin resistance. Overweight subjects have more triacylglycerol deposition and more insulin resistance than lean individuals; obese individuals have even more stored triacylglycerols and increased insulin resistance. In conditioned athletes, there is elevated triacylglycerol storage, but this fails to correlate with insulin resistance. Obese and insulin-resistant patients who undertake a chronic exercise program also see selective partitioning of triacylglycerol into muscle, coupled with improved insulin sensitivity. Because of this disconnect, and the implications for type 2 diabetes, the athlete's paradox is a fascinating question that has ramifications for health.

There are several theories about what causes the athlete's paradox. One of the more promising explanations is that in athletes the muscle triacylglycerol turns over more rapidly than normal. This theory is supported by findings that levels of diacylglycerol and ceramide are also elevated in athletes, as are levels of several enzymes and regulatory proteins.

Adipose tissue stores fat for future use

Like the liver, adipose tissue takes care of the rest of the body. Adipose tissue was once thought of as an inert warehouse where energy was stored as triacylglycerol. However, more recent studies have shown that adipose tissue is both a thriving, metabolically active tissue and an endocrine tissue, secreting several molecules that regulate appetite and metabolism. Thus, there are two tissues that help to take care of the energetic needs of the other organs of the body: the liver, which provides in the short term, and adipose tissue, which functions in both long-term storage and the near future.

Adipose tissue does little in terms of amino acid metabolism. While it uses some glucose to produce glycerol for triacylglycerol metabolism and uses glycolysis and oxidative phosphorylation to make ATP, it cannot store carbohydrates as glycogen. Instead, adipose tissue tends to store and regulate the release of free fatty acids and glycerol from triacylglycerols.

Adipocytes, the fat-storing cells of adipose tissue, acquire fatty acids from either chylomicrons or VLDL, storing these lipids in triacylglycerols in a single large lipid storage droplet. When stimulated, the adipocyte will release free fatty acids and glycerol. Due to the absence of glycerol kinase, the adipocyte cannot recycle glycerol once all three fatty acyl chains have been hydrolyzed. Instead, glycerol is released from the adipocyte and travels to the liver where it is used in gluconeogenesis to make glucose. Fatty acids are transported in the blood by serum albumin to muscle and liver tissue. Muscle will burn these fatty acids for fuel, whereas the liver will convert them to ketone bodies.

Adipose tissue is organized into discreet deposits, effectively organs or parts of organs, termed fat pads. There are eight major fat deposits in the body. As anyone who has tried to gain or lose weight knows, not all fat pads are metabolically equivalent; they burn or store fat at different rates. It may be easier, for example, to lose weight in your arms and legs compared to the abdomen. Studies of how individual fat pads respond to metabolic stimuli are the focus of research.

The blood transports metabolites

The blood serves as a transport system for many of the metabolites discussed, including glucose, free fatty acids, pyruvate, lactate, alanine, glycerol, and ketone bodies. Although many molecules are transported in the blood, others cannot be transported in this way. For example, ATP and glycogen are isolated in the cell; also, once formed inside an adipocyte or **myocyte**, triacylglycerol is not secreted back into blood; the liver secretes triacylglycerols in lipoprotein complexes.

Blood cells use glucose as their main fuel. The phagocytic cells of the immune system, such as macrophages, require additional NADPH formed in the pentose phosphate pathway to generate reactive oxygen species.

The kidney secretes toxic metabolites but can also carry out gluconeogenesis

The kidney is important for the excretion of toxic metabolites from the body. In the context of metabolism, the main focus is on the metabolite urea. Although the kidney can make some urea and eliminate some nitrogen directly, most urea is made in the liver and transported to the kidney via the blood. Due to the large chemical gradients used in filtering the plasma, the kidney has a high need for energy; in the resting state, it consumes 10% of the body's energetic need.

During liver failure or in extreme states of starvation, the liver has a limited ability to produce glucose via gluconeogenesis. In such situations, the kidney may be able to provide as much as half of the gluconeogenesis needed. Glutamine from muscle tissue is transported to the kidney, where it can undergo oxidative deamination, first to glutamate and then to α-ketoglutarate. The ammonia groups released in these reactions are not recaptured as urea but rather are directly secreted into the urine as ammonia. The α-ketoglutarate formed is anaplerotic and enters the citric acid cycle; from there it can participate in gluconeogenesis via oxaloacetate.

The brain is unable to store energy   The brain plays two roles in metabolism: Like all tissues, it has a metabolic need; it also regulates both appetite and metabolism (discussed in section 12.3).

The brain is the least self-sufficient of any of the organs; it requires a constant supply of energy and cannot survive for more than a few minutes without it. Two other factors work against the brain. First, almost the entire brain is important and cannot be scavenged for energy. Whereas we can lose 50% or more of our muscle mass and still move around unhindered, the same is not true of neurological function; any loss of brain or nervous tissue has significant consequences. Second, the brain is protected and separated from the rest of the body by the blood-brain barrier, a semipermeable membrane that protects the central nervous system. This barrier is permeable to glucose and many amino acids but not to free fatty acids. One further metabolic complication is that the brain uses several amino acids as signaling molecules. As discussed in section 11.3, accumulation of ammonia in the brain can lead to depletion of α-ketoglutarate, blocking energy production in the neuron and leading to the death of the cell. For all of these reasons, glucose is the brain's fuel of choice. In the resting state, the brain needs about 120 g of glucose a day, roughly 20% of the body's resting energetic needs.

The brain's dependency on glucose could pose a significant problem for the organism. If the brain were dependent on glucose alone for fuel, the consequences for the organism would be severe if glycogen supplies were depleted, unless there was a proteinaceous tissue that could be catabolized to generate new glucose via gluconeogenesis. Nature has evolved a relatively simple and ingenious means for solving this problem. Instead of importing fatty acids, the liver converts fatty acids to ketone bodies. Once ketone bodies enter the cell, the reactions that were used to synthesize β-hydroxybutyrate are reversed, producing two molecules of acetyl-CoA that can be metabolized for energy by the brain.

12.2.2 | The organism shifts between different metabolic states depending on access to food

Having discussed the various roles that organs play in metabolism, the next point to consider is the different metabolic states the organism is likely to encounter over its life span, such as when the organism is fed, when it is fasted, or when it may be starved (**Figure 12.5**). Some of these states are encountered several times a day, whereas others may never be experienced. The states discussed in this section are time dependent; that is, it takes time to eat food, digest it, and then become hungry again. They are discussed also in terms of both human and mouse metabolism because the mouse is the most commonly used model organism in metabolic studies. Other organisms may eat far less frequently or have other adaptations that help to compensate for dietary excess or need. For example, reptiles may eat as infrequently as once a month, whereas hibernating animals store large amounts of energy between spring and fall, then burn those calories off during their winter hibernation.

FIGURE 12.5   States of metabolism.   As starvation progresses, plasma glucose levels drop and plateau as protein is spared. When this happens, levels of ketone bodies rise and replace some of the need generated by the absence of glucose. All concentrations are measured using the left-hand axis, with the exception of insulin, which uses the right-hand axis.

Mixed meal

~20% ~20%
~60%

Cafeteria diet

~40%
~5%
~55%

Snack foods

~50%
~1%
~49%

☐ Protein   ☐ Fat   ☐ Carbohydrate

FIGURE 12.6 **Compositions of different diets.** An average diet in a mixed meal may consist of 60% calories from carbohydrate, 20% of calories from protein, and 20% of calories from fat. A cafeteria diet may consist of 55% calories from carbohydrates, 5% of calories from protein, and 40% calories from fat. Some snack foods have less than 1% calories from protein, 50% of calories from fat, and the remainder from carbohydrates. In many instances these carbohydrates come from simple sugars.

In each of the states considered, we will assume that the organism has consumed in the diet a combination of proteins, carbohydrates, and lipids. In metabolic studies, this is known as a **mixed meal**, which typically consists of some defined mixture; for example, 20% of calories from fats, 20% from proteins, and 60% from carbohydrates (**Figure 12.6**). In what is known as the **cafeteria diet**, there is a high concentration of saturated fats and simple sugars, as one might expect to find in a cafeteria; in this case, the figures are 40% of calories from fat, 5% from protein, and 55% from simple sugars. Variants of the cafeteria diet are used to study obesity and heart disease. In a diet filled with snack foods, people consume large quantities of lipids and carbohydrates with minimal protein.

People often undertake diets to lose weight or for other health reasons. These can range from moderate caloric restriction plans to severe limitations on some nutrients, such as diets low in sodium or cholesterol, to the absolutely bizarre diet regimens. People may lose a few pounds consuming nothing but cabbage soup, grapefruit, or boiled kelp for a few weeks, but such diets are certainly not healthy. Moreover, restriction plans rarely produce meaningful weight loss one year after they cease. The only weight loss systems that have proven efficacious are those that teach people to consume healthy food in moderation and to combine that plan with a reasonable daily exercise program.

In recent years, high protein–low carbohydrate diets have become popular. These diets allow consumption of high amounts of fat and protein but without carbohydrate. Part of the notion behind these diets is that consuming protein and fat provides a feeling of fullness, so the person then eats less. Biochemically, a diet low in carbohydrates forces the body to burn glycogen quickly, resulting in rapid weight loss; this is followed by a period of **ketosis**, presumably to mobilize the body's fat stores. Undoubtedly, some of these diets help people to lose weight, but it is unclear how the weight loss is achieved. Most studies find that people tire of eating steak with butter at every meal, and simply eat less. The long-term health ramifications of eating a high-fat, high-protein diet with the elevated dietary cholesterol and sodium levels such a diet typically entails is still being debated.

Fed and postprandial states occur immediately after eating

As its name suggests, the **fed state** is one in which the organism has just finished feeding and has food in its stomach. An overlapping state is the **postprandial state**, that is, the periods during which metabolites are absorbed from the small intestine. These terms are often used interchangeably; clearly, they have a high degree of similarity and can be difficult to delineate outside a laboratory setting.

In the fed and postprandial states, amylases have begun to break dietary polysaccharides (starches, amylose, amylopectin) into monosaccharides. Proteases have begun to cleave proteins into amino acids or dipeptides and tripeptides. As the partially digested material (known as chyme) leaves the stomach, it encounters other proteases and lipases. These molecules are absorbed by the body and enter the circulation. Glucose and amino acids enter the blood, while dietary lipids are processed into chylomicrons and secreted first into the lymph and then from there into the bloodstream. This allows lipids to bypass exposure to the liver on their first pass through the circulation.

In the fed and postprandial states, elevated levels of glucose stimulate the pancreas to secrete the peptide hormone **insulin**. In the healthy organism, increased insulin elicits

TABLE 12.2   **Metabolic States**

State	Fuel
Fed	Mixed from diet
Postprandial	Fatty acids made from dietary sources in the liver; glucose
Postabsorptive	Fatty acids from adipose tissue; glucose from glycogen stores
Re-fed	Mixed from diet; use of liver gluconeogenesis to replenish glycogen
Fasted	Carbohydrates depleted, fatty acids, ketone bodies, gluconeogenesis
Starved	Ketone bodies and fatty acids, limited gluconeogenesis

a signaling response in cells, causing more glucose transporters to move to the cell surface. This allows cells to absorb more glucose and either burn it or store it for future use (**Table 12.2**).

In the fed state, lipids are transported through the circulation on chylomicrons. Lipids are exposed to lipoprotein lipase in the capillary beds in adipose tissue and muscle tissue. Apolipoprotein CII is found on the surface of the chylomicrons and acts as a cofactor, stimulating the lipase to degrade triacylglycerols in the chylomicrons and absorb the released fatty acids and monoglycerides. The remaining particle, a chylomicron remnant, is enriched in dietary cholesterol; it binds to a chylomicron-remnant receptor on the surface of the hepatocyte and is internalized by receptor-mediated endocytosis.

As cells absorb and become satiated with glucose, there are two ways to store the carbon atoms from the glucose: as glycogen or as fatty acids (after oxidation to acetyl-CoA). Dietary amino acids also cannot be stored in large quantities. Most dietary protein, over 90% in some diets, is catabolized into carbon skeletons and stored as fat, with the liver being the location for both of these pathways. Yet the liver is not adapted to storing large quantities of fat and will malfunction if it is forced to do so. Instead, the liver synthesizes triacylglycerols de novo from carbohydrates and amino acid skeletons, packages these triacylglycerols plus cholesterol esters into VLDL, and secretes these into the circulation. In the circulation, VLDL delivers triacylglycerols to adipose tissue and muscle tissue for storage or energy. The VLDL loses some of its triacylglycerol core, shrinks in size and increases in relative density, becoming an LDL particle. LDL can deliver cholesterol to tissues as needed by binding an LDL receptor and being internalized through receptor-mediated endocytosis.

Collectively, the fed and postprandial states constitute the **absorptive state**, that is, the state in which nutrients are absorbed by the body. The act of eating can take anything from a few minutes to several hours. In humans, the postprandial state is often defined as from 0 to 5 hours after eating a mixed meal, although the actual time depends on factors such as the composition of the diet. In other animals, these numbers may vary considerably, depending on the organism's biology. For example, an owl or a snake that swallows prey whole may have that meal in the stomach for much longer than is the case with someone eating a pizza. It is more difficult to determine when rodents, such as rats and mice, have recently eaten and are therefore in the postprandial state. In some studies, experiments with small rodents are carried out early in the morning, based on the assumption that these nocturnal animals have recently eaten. It is common practice in the laboratory to develop a feeding protocol in an attempt to dictate the feeding time for animals on a study.

The postabsorptive state follows digestion but precedes hunger   The postabsorptive state follows the postprandial one. In the former, there is a fall in glucose from dietary sources and postprandial lipids because these molecules become sequestered in tissues that will burn or store them. As plasma glucose is depleted, the pancreatic hormone **glucagon** signals for glycogen to be mobilized from the liver to help maintain euglycemia, that is, the normal concentration of plasma glucose of 70–120 mg/dl. In addition, epinephrine and other

catecholamines signal adipose tissue to mobilize fatty acids from triacylglycerols for fuel. As the postabsorptive state continues, the liver begins to use glycerol from adipose tissue, and alanine and lactate from muscle, to produce new glucose by gluconeogenesis. Glucose produced via gluconeogenesis and glucose liberated from glucose-1-phosphate via glycogenolysis are released from the liver and used by other tissues, predominantly the brain. In this state, insulin levels are low, and glucagon and epinephrine levels are high. This promotes gluconeogenesis in the liver, and the breakdown of glycogen and use of fatty acids as fuel by the liver and muscle.

As the postabsorptive state continues, the liver begins to use acetyl-CoA from fatty acids to produce ketone bodies. Elevated ketone levels are associated with disease states or weight loss, but ketone bodies are a normal part of metabolism and are found at low levels in plasma at all times. Ketone bodies increase each night as we sleep and fall when we eat breakfast.

Many humans in the developed world eat several meals each day and have snacks in between. Some researchers argue that this situation means that many people never fully enter a postabsorptive or fasted state.

The re-fed state describes a re-fueling state
When someone in the postabsorptive state has consumed a meal, the metabolism does not immediately return to the fed or postprandial state. As levels of glucose, amino acids, and dietary fats in chylomicrons increase, the liver remains refractory or resistant to the effects of glucose and insulin, allowing other tissues to "feed" first, replenish glycogen levels, and return to a glycolytic state. Indeed, the liver continues to undergo gluconeogenesis but uses this glucose for liver glycogenesis. As glucose levels increase, the liver again begins to respond and returns to a postprandial state, absorbing glucose and synthesizing fatty acids and triglycerides for VLDL.

In the fasted state, energy conservation begins
Somewhere between 12 and 48 hours after consuming a meal the body is in the **fasted state**, which is marked by a lack of dietary lipids in the circulation. Chylomicrons and their remnants are absent, VLDL concentration is low, and LDL and HDL predominate. Levels of free fatty acids from adipose tissue increase in the blood, while levels of fatty acids and triacylglycerols increase in the liver. Liver glycogen stores have been largely depleted, and the liver undergoes high levels of gluconeogenesis and ketone body production. In this state, the body begins to shift into a metabolic state where it can preserve itself for the longer term in the absence of other food sources. Liver, muscle, and heart tissues can all use fatty acids to meet their energetic needs; however, the brain also needs glucose due to the blood-brain barrier. The liver can use glycerol from adipose tissue or most amino acid skeletons as a source of carbon for gluconeogenesis, but using these fuels is not without consequence. Amino acids cannot be stored; therefore, any use of amino acids for fuel is observed as a loss of protein mass, and wasting begins.

The starved state attempts to preserve life
Somewhere between 24 and 48 hours after a meal, the body moves from the fasted to the **starved state**, altering metabolism to spare protein in muscle and use ketone bodies as the predominant fuel for the brain. This happens in part through upregulation of mitochondrial hydroxymethylglutaryl-CoA synthase (mitochondrial HMG-CoA synthase), the rate-determining step in ketone body biosynthesis. As the starved state progresses, the brain also switches from using glucose to using ketone bodies as its main source of fuel. This too helps spare muscle tissue because the metabolic demand of the brain drops from its normal requirement of 120 g of glucose a day to only 40 g in the starved state. The details of this metabolic switch are still under investigation (Table 12.3).

Theoretically, the starved state can last for some time. For example, a 100 kilogram individual with 28% body fat has about 28 kilos of triacylglycerol available to burn. In the absence of other food, this fuel

TABLE 12.3 **Fuel Metabolism in Starvation**

Fuel	Fuel consumption, g/24 h	
	Day 3	Day 40
Fuel use by brain		
Glucose	120	40
Ketone bodies	50	100
Glucose use by other tissues	50	40
Fuel mobilization		
Adipose tissue lipolysis	180	180
Muscle protein degradation	75	20
Fuel output by the liver		
Glucose	150	80
Ketone bodies	150	150

FIGURE 12.7 **Energy reserves in normal and obese states.** Shown are the energetic reserves of a 155 and a 310 pound man. In the obese state, more than four times as many calories are stored, and the majority of them are stored as triacylgycerols.

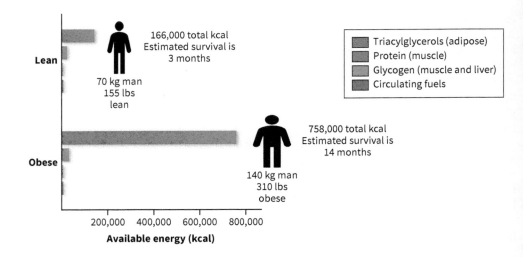

could last for 155 days, or slightly over 5 months, presuming the burning of 180 g a day. When triacylglycerol stores are fully depleted, the individual begins to burn whatever fuels remain, demyelinating nerves and damaging organs as protein is catabolized from the heart, liver, and kidneys. By this point, even if the individual returns to a normal diet, damage can persist, sometimes permanently. However, this situation rarely occurs because someone undergoing prolonged starvation usually succumbs to an opportunistic infection due to a weakened immune system, or to heart failure precipitated by a lack of potassium in the diet (**Figure 12.7**).

WORKED PROBLEM 12.2 | I could eat …

Think about the last thing you had to eat and when you ate it. What metabolic state are you currently in? Are your levels of amino acids, glucose, dietary fats, fatty acids, and ketone bodies likely to be elevated or depressed?

Strategy Examine what you have eaten over the past 12 hours and at what times. How does your food intake compare with the metabolic states discussed?

Solution Derek, a student taking biochemistry, skipped his breakfast this morning due to an early class. For lunch, about two hours ago he ate an apple and two granola bars. This meal was relatively low in protein but mixed in terms of carbohydrate and fat content. Given that he was coming off what amounts to a short (approximately 14 hour) fast, the carbohydrates that entered his circulation probably went first to replenishing muscle glycogen. However, since it has been two hours since he last ate, any remaining carbohydrates have probably been taken up by his liver and either stored as glycogen or transformed into triacylglycerols. So at this point, he probably has low levels of ketone bodies and fatty acids in his blood and moderate levels of glucose, amino acids, and VLDL.

Follow-up question Presuming you eat nothing more for the next 24 hours, how will the levels of metabolites change?

12.2 Summary

- Different organs have evolved specialized functions and roles in metabolism.
- Some organs store metabolites: Liver and muscle tissues store glycogen, and adipose tissue stores triglycerides; muscle can serve as a source of amino acids in times of energetic need.
- Some organs have specialized metabolic needs and cannot store energy. The brain requires a constant supply of energy in the form of glucose or ketone bodies.
- The organism passes through multiple metabolic states as it goes through a day, year, or lifetime.
- Specific biochemical adaptations have evolved to help the organism survive in the absence of a constant flow of nutrients.

12.2 Concept Check

- Describe the roles each organ plays: explain which organs act as energy storehouses and for which molecules, and which molecules are released and where they go.

- Explain what metabolic process occurs in each state from a biochemical perspective, when these switches in metabolism occur, and how the alterations in metabolism help the organism survive in the absence of food.

12.3 | Communication between Organs

As we have seen recurrently throughout metabolism, signaling molecules or hormones and signaling cascades, especially ones involving kinases, are prevalent in biochemistry. These types of regulatory mechanisms are well-adapted to balance metabolism in the short term. Signaling molecules do not offer the acute regulation of allosterism, nor do they take as long to effect change as alterations in gene expression, although both allosterism and gene expression are necessary means of regulation of metabolism and some are hormonally dependent. Sections 12.1 and 12.2 discussed the role of metabolic pathways and metabolites, and of organs and metabolic states. This section discusses hormones and the organs that produce them in the wider context of metabolism; it also looks at the effects of hormonal signaling on brain tissue and how the brain, in turn, affects both appetite and metabolism.

12.3.1 | Organs communicate using hormones

Endocrinology is the study of chemical signaling and its effects in the body. The signaling molecules are **hormones**, which are produced by endocrine organs and secreted into the bloodstream (**Table 12.4**). These hormones are then carried through the body until they meet with the receptor on or in cells of the target organ. Binding of the hormone to its receptor triggers metabolic changes in the target organ such as activating enzymes or changing gene transcription. Hormones can be categorized in several ways; the most common, and the one used here, is by structure. These include peptide hormones, hormones derived from tyrosine, and steroid hormones. (PDB ID 1GCN Sasaki, K., Dockerill, S., Adamiak, D.A., Tickle, I.J., Blundell, T. (1975) X-ray analysis of glucagon and its relationship to receptor binding. *Nature* 257: 751–757)

Glucagon
(peptide hormone)

Thyroxine
(derived from tyrosine)

Epinephrine
(derived from tyrosine)

Estrogen
(steroid hormone)

TABLE 12.4 Hormones: Where They Are Made and How They Elicit Responses

Hormone	Source	Released by	Target tissue	Receptor type	Effect
T3 and T4	Thyroid	Thyroid stimulating hormone (TSH)	All	Nuclear receptor (transcription factor)	Gene expression (increase metabolic rate)
Insulin	Pancreas	High glucose	All	Receptor tyrosine kinase	Glucose uptake, gene expression
Glucagon		Low glucose	Liver	7 TM GPCR	Energy mobilization from stores
Catecholamines (dopamine, epinephrine, norepinephrine)	Adrenals	Nervous inputs to adrenal, stress	All	7 TM GPCR	Energy mobilization from stores
Corticosteroids (minerals and glucocorticoids)		Adrenocorticotropic hormone, stress	All	Nuclear receptor (transcription factor)	Energy mobilization (gluconeogenesis) Water reabsorption from the kidney
Leptin	Adipose tissue	Under investigation	Hypothalamus/arcuate	Receptor tyrosine kinase	Satiety
Adiponectin				7 TM GPCR	
Ghrelin	Gut				Appetite
GLP-1					Satiety
PYY(3-36)					Appetite
Cholecystokinin			Pancreas, gut, brain		Stomach emptying, appetite
Vasopressin	Posterior pituitary	Plasma osmolarity	Kidney		Water reabsorbtion in the kidney
Oxytocin		Innervation of pituitary	Brain		Human bonding

Peptide hormones

Peptide hormones can be as few as eight amino acid residues in length, but others are on the order of small proteins. For example, human insulin is 51 amino acids long. Peptide hormones are often synthesized from an mRNA message as part of a larger protein, known as a prohormone. The prohormone is cleaved in the endoplasmic reticulum to generate the active peptide, which is then secreted. Peptide hormones are important in the regulation of most physiology, and they are among the most powerful signaling molecules. Insulin and glucagon are examples of peptide hormones discussed in previous chapters, but other peptide hormones important in metabolism include **adiponectin**, cholecystokinin (also known as CCK-PZ), gastrin, **ghrelin**, **leptin**, and **PYY(3-36)**. Neuropeptides (short peptides that act as neurotransmitters, signaling between neurons) are synthesized and function in a similar manner. The list of peptide hormones continues to grow.

Catecholamines and thyroid hormones are derived from tyrosine

The second class of hormones can be broadly categorized as tyrosine derivatives; they include the catecholamines and thyroid hormones.

The catecholamines **epinephrine**, dopamine, and **norepinephrine** are small organic molecules that are named because of their structural similarity to catechol (1,2 dihydroxybenzene). The catecholamines are synthesized in a multistep pathway (**Figure 12.8**).

First, tyrosine is hydroxylated to L-Dihydroxyphenylalanine (L-DOPA) in a reaction catalyzed by tyrosine hydroxylase. This is the rate-limiting step in catecholamine biosynthesis and is dependent on a tetrahydrobiopterin cofactor for activity. Molecular oxygen is the source of the oxygen in the hydroxyl group. The L-DOPA is decarboxylated by L-DOPA decarboxylase, leaving dopamine. As with many enzymes that catalyze reactions centered on the α carbon of amino acids, this enzyme is dependent on pyridoxal phosphate (PLP).

In the next step, dopamine is hydroxylated to yield norepinephrine. While the hydroxylations discussed in previous chapters were the product of the hydration of a double bond, here, the benzylic position from the aromatic ring forms a more stable carbocation and is directly hydroxylated by dopamine β-hydroxylase. Again, molecular oxygen is required. In addition, this enzyme uses ascorbic acid and employs a similar mechanism to proline hydroxylase, although dopamine hydroxylase employs an active-site copper ion instead of iron and succinate.

Norepinephrine undergoes *N*-Methylation to form epinephrine, in a reaction catalyzed by phenylethanolamine *N*-Methyltransferase, with *S*-Adenosylmethionine as the source of the methyl group.

The **thyroid hormones**, including triiodothyronine (T3) and thyroxine (T4), are also derived from tyrosine, although their pathways differ markedly from that of catecholamine formation. Thyroid hormone biosynthesis begins with the synthesis of the protein thyroglobulin, a large (669 kDa) protein, in the endoplasmic reticulum. Thyroglobulin is processed in the thyroid and undergoes substitution reactions on the aromatic tyrosine rings of thyroglobulin, resulting in monoiodotyrosine or diiodotyrosine.

Monoiodotyrosine (MIT)

Diiodotyrosine (DIT)

3,5,3',5'-tetraiodothyronine (L-Thyroxine; T4)

3,5,3'-triiodothyronine (T3)

Once derivatized, the iodinated tyrosyl side chains undergo a conjugation reaction, forming dimers that are still attached to thyroglobulin. The modified thyroglobulin is endocytosed by follicular cells in the thyroid. In the lysosome, it undergoes proteolytic cleavage to release T4 and some T3. After release from the follicular cell, these hormones travel to other tissues, where they are further modified, either by decarboxylation or by deiodination catalyzed by deiodinases, a family of selenium-dependent enzymes. These other forms of thyroid hormone may be more active or have more distinct effects in different cells and tissues of the body.

Thyroid hormones act through nuclear hormone receptors, a family of proteins that includes steroid receptors. These proteins are found inside the cell where they bind to the hormone and translocate to the nucleus to change gene expression.

Steroid hormones are derived from cholesterol
Steroid hormones, such as **cortisol** and the sex hormones, are hydrophobic hormones that are derived from cholesterol and made in gonadal tissue or the adrenal glands. Like thyroid hormones, steroids act through nuclear hormone receptors, proteins that bind to the hormone and act as transcription factors, to alter gene expression. Because this process is lengthier, involving RNA and protein synthesis, steroid hormones typically function over longer periods of time—hours to days rather than seconds to minutes (**Figure 12.9**).

Hormones have distinct mechanisms of action
Both the catecholamines and the thyroid hormones affect almost every cell of the body. The catecholamines act primarily through transmembrane receptors. Despite being mainly hydrophobic, thyroid hormones are not membrane permeable because the iodo groups on the aromatic rings are sufficiently electron-withdrawing to lower the pK_a of the phenolic proton, leaving the hormone with two negative charges at physiological pH. Instead, there are hormone transporters that usher T3 and T4 into the cytosol. Thyroid hormones bind to specific receptors in the cytosol that translocate to the nucleus and act as transcription factors, influencing gene expression. Steroid hormones and other hydrophobic signaling molecules also act via nuclear hormone receptors.

L-Tyrosine

tyrosine hydroxylase
O$_2$, tetrahydro-biopterin
H$_2$O, dihydro-biopterin

L-Dihydroxyphenylalanine (L-DOPA)

DOPA decarboxylase aromatic L-Amino acid decarboxylase
CO$_2$

Dopamine

dopamine β-hydroxylase
O$_2$, ascorbic acid
H$_2$O, dehydro-ascorbic acid

Norepinephrine

phenylethanolamine *N*-Methyltransferase
S-Adenosyl-methionine
Homocysteine

Epinephrine

FIGURE 12.8 Biosynthesis of catecholamines. Catecholamines are synthesized in a cascade. First, tyrosine is hydroxylated into L-DOPA. DOPA is decarboxylated into dopamine. Hydroxylation of dopamine yields norepinephrine. *N*-Methylation of norepinephrine gives the final product of the pathway, epinephrine.

FIGURE 12.9 **Action of thyroid and steroid hormones.** Thyroid and steroid hormones work by binding to a nuclear hormone receptor in the cytosol. Binding of the hormone to the receptor activates the receptor, facilitating translocation to the nucleus, binding of DNA, and activation of specific genes.

Organs produce and respond to specific hormonal signals

Endocrinology focuses on the endocrine organs, including the pancreas, thyroid, adrenals, gonads, and pituitary; however, it is now generally accepted that most, if not all, organs have endocrine function and can secrete hormonal signals. The brain, pancreas, adrenal glands, thyroid, gut, and adipose tissue are all important in the regulation of metabolism. The function of these organs and the hormones that they secrete are found in **Table 12.5**.

12.3.2 | Hormonal signals to the brain regulate appetite and metabolism

Advances in neuroscience and biochemistry have shown that a few select regions of the hypothalamus regulate the intersection of metabolism, appetite, and complex behaviors such as feeding.

The hypothalamus coordinates hormonal signals and neuronal responses

The **hypothalamus** is a roughly spherical organ, about 1 cm in diameter, with a notch on the bottom side that divides the organ into two symmetric halves. The notch is the third ventricle, a fluid-filled cavity that runs through the midline of the brain. The regions of the hypothalamus lining the third ventricle are the sites of action of many of the hormones discussed here, and the blood-brain barrier is more porous in this region, permitting passage of these hormones. This section focuses on two regions of the hypothalamus: the arcuate nucleus and the paraventricular nucleus.

The **arcuate nucleus** is a cluster of cells less than a millimeter across. In the 1950s it was discovered that lesions of the brain in the region of the arcuate nucleus led to voracious appetite; hence, it was hypothesized that this tiny region of the brain integrated or controlled appetite. It contains two types of neurons pertinent to this discussion. These neurons are broadly classified by the types of signals they release: one class of neuron releases **neuropeptide Y (NPY)**, agouti-related peptide (AgRP), and γ-amino butyric acid (GABA); the other neuron releases the neuropeptides pro-opiomelanocortin (POMC) and cocaine-amphetamine related transcript (CART). The NPY/AgRP/GABA neurons are **orexigenic**; that is, they promote appetite. The POMC/CART neurons are **anorexigenic**; they blunt appetite. These different classes of neuron have different receptors to receive communications from the rest of the body. Both classes receive signals from leptin and insulin, which blunt appetite. These signals activate anorexigenic neurons and pathways (POMC/CART neurons) and dampen down

TABLE 12.5	Hormonal Disorders	
Disease	**Hormone affected**	**Symptoms**
Diabetes insipidus	Vasopressin	Mutation of vasopressin receptor leads to less sodium reabsorbtion in the kidney and excessive urination.
Diabetes mellitus	Insulin	Signaling defect results in inability to properly take glucose into cells.
Addison's disease	Corticosteroids	Low levels of corticosteroids leads to mineral imbalance and hypoglycemia.
Cushing's disease	Adrenocorticotropic hormone (ACTH)	Increased levels of ACTH leads to elevated corticosteroids and weight gain.
Hashimoto's disease	Thyroid hormones	Autoimmune attack on thyroid protein(s) results in depressed thyroid hormone levels and weight gain.
Graves' disease	Thyroid hormones	Elevated thyroid hormones result in weight loss and increase in metabolic rate.

A.

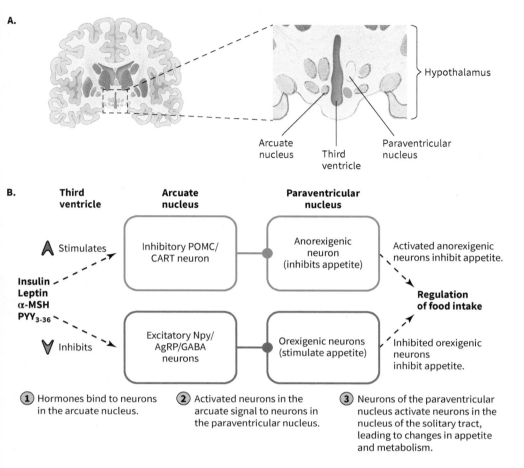

FIGURE 12.10 **Innervation of the arcuate nucleus.**
A. A detailed representation of the communications between the third ventricle, arcuate, and the periventricular nucleus is shown. (Tortora; Derrickson, *Principles of Anatomy & Physiology*, 13e, copyright 2012, John Wiley & Sons. This material is reproduced with permission of John Wiley & Sons, Inc.) **B.** The neurons of the arcuate respond to leptin and insulin and produce either the neurotransmitters NPY/AgRP/GABA or POMC and CART. NPY/AgRP/GABA neurons are orexigenic and signal to eat more. POMC/CART neurons are anorexigenic and blunt appetite.

orexigenic neurons and pathways (NPY/AgRP/GABA neurons). The gut hormone PYY(3-36) is an anorexigenic hormone; it binds and inhibits NPY/AgRP/GABA neurons.

The neurons of the arcuate nucleus bind and integrate hormonal signals and convert this information into neuronal signals. These neurons interact with one another, modulating signals; they also interact with other neurons in the paraventricular nucleus (**Figure 12.10**).

The neurotransmitters of the NPY family are named for their high proportion of tyrosine residues, as many as five in a 36-amino-acid-long peptide. NPY neurons in the arcuate secrete NPY, which signals to neurons in a variety of regions, including the paraventricular nucleus.

Alpha-melanocyte stimulating hormone (α-MSH) is a molecule that was discovered for its role in the stimulation of melanin in pigmented cells, called melanocytes. It is one of eight different signaling molecules derived from proteolytic cleavage of pro-opiomelanocortin (POMC). Other molecules derived from POMC include endorphins and adrenocorticotropic hormone (ACTH). The products of pro-opiomelanocortin play diverse roles, such as the regulation of pain and blood pressure.

The receptor for α-MSH in the paraventricular nucleus is the melanocortin-4 receptor (MC4R). This receptor is interesting due to its involvement in appetite and energy balance, as well as in reproductive physiology. Male knockout mice for the melanocortin-4 receptor experience sexual dysfunction (decreased motivation and decreased copulatory performance) compared to wild-type siblings. Melanocortin-4 receptor agonists, either drugs or hormones, cause the opposite effect and have been tested with favorable results in both men and women with sexual dysfunction. Therefore, any drug developed to regulate appetite via melanocortin-4 receptor may also affect sexual behavior, and vice versa.

Neurons in other areas of the hypothalamus also are innervated by the arcuate nucleus. Signals from these are thought to regulate appetite and energy balance.

Although this section focuses on the hormonal basis of feeding and energy balance, it is only one part of a complex story. Humans eat for a variety of reasons. It is probably fair to say that many people often eat even though they are not hungry. Eating is usually pleasurable and, as such, has a large hedonic component. For example, we eat hot dogs at sporting events and popcorn at the movies, and we feast on holidays, often simply because of culture and habit. The mere mention of a plate of warm chocolate chip cookies or pizza can stimulate the appetite of someone who would not otherwise be hungry. Clearly, there are other signals that collectively weigh in to alter the decision to eat or not, for example, visual signals, olfactory signals, memories of pleasurable meals past and emotional states. Interestingly, the opposite is also true. Someone who becomes violently ill or suffers with a bout of food poisoning carries an aversion to those foods in her or his memory. The sight, smell, or even the mere mention of them can cause a physiological response, making someone feel ill at the thought of consuming them again.

12.3.3 | Transcription factors and histone acetylases and deacetylases regulate metabolism in the longer term

We have discussed acute regulation of metabolism via allosteric control and modifications of enzymes, but alterations in gene expression are also important in the regulation of metabolism. The sirtuins, a group of seven proteins that can act as deacetylases, regulate genes by modifying histones and may directly affect metabolic pathways by deacetylating enzymes.

Hormones regulate expression of genes controlling metabolism Hormones regulate gene expression through several different mechanisms. This section discusses two of these mechanisms, nuclear hormone receptors and resident nuclear transcription factors, and how they respond to hormonal signals.

Nuclear hormone receptors are small proteins found in the cytosol or nucleus of the cell. Upon binding to a ligand, they become active and translocate to specific DNA sequences, where they bind and activate gene transcription. These ligands are largely hydrophobic: steroid and thyroid hormones. Often, the hormone–receptor complexes dimerize with other nuclear hormone receptors to fine-tune gene activation. Therefore, binding of the hormone to the receptor causes activation, resulting in a receptor that can bind to specific DNA sequences and activate specific genes.

The cyclic AMP response element binding protein (CREB) is an example of a resident nuclear transcription factor (**Figure 12.11**). This transcription factor resides permanently in the nucleus but is activated by phosphorylation. The phosphorylation of CREB may be catalyzed by several different enzymes, but protein kinase A (PKA) was one of the first enzymes identified. Catecholamines or glucagon act through a 7-transmembrane helix receptor coupled to a heterotrimeric G protein to activate PKA resulting in phosphorylation of CREB. Once phosphorylated, CREB dimerizes with either another copy of itself or with a related transcription factor; it then binds to the cyclic AMP response element, a short stretch of DNA that is found in the promoter region of cAMP responsive genes. Binding of the transcription factor complex initiates binding of other proteins, including coactivators and histone-modifying enzymes, all of which act to alter the levels of gene expression.

Sirtuins broadly regulate gene expression through histone modification Sirtuins are found in organisms ranging from bacteria to humans and may regulate the expression of genes involved in metabolism and aging. Originally identified in yeast, these proteins have an NAD^+-dependent histone deacetylase activity, removing acetyl groups from lysine and increasing the interaction of histone proteins with DNA (**Figure 12.12**). This activity results in the breakdown of NAD^+ into nicotinamide and O-Acetyl-ADP ribose. Nicotinamide is an inhibitor of sirtuin activity.

The sirtuin story is not a typical one from a scientific perspective. It has been known for decades that, in many organisms, severe caloric restriction results in dramatically increased life span, but for many years the causal factor was unknown. At the same time scientists

FIGURE 12.11 **Action of CREB.**   CREB is the cyclic AMP response element binding protein. This resident nuclear transcription factor responds to PKA phosphorylation to bind a cyclic AMP response element in promoter regions of some genes, activating transcription.

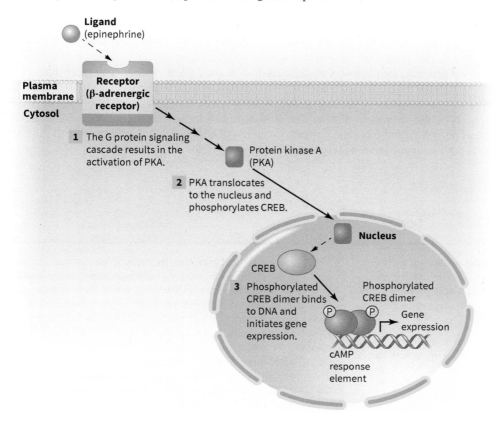

were fascinated with the French paradox; that is, the observation that people in some parts of France live longer in spite of having greater risk factors for premature mortality. It was unclear what aspect of the French diet or lifestyle was responsible for this increased longevity. The answer in both cases has been linked to the sirtuins, but the results of many of these studies are controversial. Overexpression of sirtuins results in increased life span in several model organisms. In addition, resveratrol, a component of red wine, seems to activate sirtuins. The apparent benefits of sirtuins in relation to longevity made them desirable targets for the treatment of several diseases found in aging, such as type 2 diabetes, cancer,

FIGURE 12.12 **Sirtuins reactions.**   The sirtuins are a family of NAD^+-dependent deacetylases. These proteins have been implicated in many cellular processes including the regulation of metabolism and aging. Sirtuins deacetylate lysines generating nicotinamide, and 2′-O-Acetyl-ADP-ribose (OAADPr). This reaction begins with binding of acetyllysine, then NAD^+. Nicotinamide is released followed by deacetylated lysine and OAADPr.

and neurodegenerative disorders. Again controversies arose. The effects of the sirtuins are not the same in all organisms and, more important, when transgenic organisms with increased life span were bred into a common background, in some instances the observed benefit was lost; that is, life spans returned to normal.

The sirtuin story is still unfolding. Clearly sirtuins have a role in the cell. One of the more interesting observations is that the sirtuins deacetylate many proteins, potentially preserving function in the event that a protein has been acetylated accidentally. This includes several enzymes in metabolic pathways we have studied including acetyl-CoA synthetase, long-chain acyl-CoA dehydrogenase, and 3-hydroxy-3-methylglutaryl-CoA synthase 2. Given that several of the sirtuins are found in the mitochondrial matrix, where there are high levels of acetyl-CoA (an acetyl group donor), it may be that at least one of these proteins serves to maintain and protect mitochondrial proteins. Further research will be needed to clarify the role of the sirtuins (if any) in aging and longevity.

WORKED PROBLEM 12.3 | Obese mice

There are six different naturally occurring obese mouse models. Two of these are the obese (ob/ob) and diabetic (db/db) phenotypes. One of these mice has a defect in leptin production; the other has a defect in the leptin receptor. Propose a simple experiment to determine which mouse is which.

Strategy Leptin is a soluble proteinaceous signaling molecule synthesized in adipose tissue. It acts in the brain to regulate satiety and metabolism. If you had access to a supply of leptin or you were able to synthesize this hormone, how might this factor into your experiment? What would be valid controls for the experiment?

Solution One simple means of testing this hypothesis would be to inject both animals with leptin. The mice that were defective in leptin production should show a decrease in appetite and in weight because the leptin would replace the hormone that was naturally absent. On the other hand, mice deficient in the leptin receptor would be unaffected by injections of leptin.

There are several problems that can be encountered in an experiment such as this. Extensive preliminary experiments would be needed to determine the time it takes for the hormone to act, what level of hormone to inject, and the time taken for the body to eliminate the hormone. When it was first proposed that there was a hormone that regulated satiety in these mice, the factor itself was unknown. A clever, but somewhat disturbing, experiment used to check this was a parabiosis study: two mice, one lacking the hormone and one lacking the receptor, were surgically conjoined so that they had a common circulation. The mouse lacking the ability to make leptin lost weight while the other remained unchanged.

Follow-up question It has been proposed that in some people leptin injections could help with weight loss. Based on what you know of other metabolic diseases and how other hormones signal, discuss this proposal. Does it have merit? What are the strengths and weaknesses of this therapy? Are there ethical ramifications of such a treatment?

12.3 Summary

- The hormones discussed in this chapter can broadly be divided structurally into peptides, tyrosine derivatives, and steroids.
- Specific organs synthesize, secrete, and respond to these hormonal signals.
- Some organs such as the pancreas, thyroid, and adrenals are classically thought of as endocrine organs, but more recently it has been found that most tissues secrete some type of signaling molecule; these molecules include adiponectin and leptin from adipose tissue, and others from the gut.
- Many hormones signal to the brain to regulate appetite and metabolism. These hormones act through the hypothalamus.
- Hormones from the circulation act in the arcuate nucleus, a region of the brain that receives hormonal signals, that is, ghrelin, insulin, leptin, and PYY(3-36), and transmits signals to other parts of the hypothalamus, specifically, the paraventricular nucleus. From the paraventricular nucleus, the arcuate nucleus signals are processed in other parts of the brain to regulate complex behaviors such as appetite and satiety.
- Metabolism is regulated in the longer term by transcription factors and histone-modifying proteins such as the sirtuins.

12.3 Concept Check

- Describe differences among the chemical signals discussed and the ways in which they are synthesized.
- Describe where signals such as catecholamines and peptide hormones are made and where they act in the body.
- Explain how the hypothalamus functions in the regulation of metabolism, how transcription factors assist in the regulation of metabolism, and the role of sirtuins.

12.4 | Metabolic Disease

Homeostasis represents a metabolic ideal. By its very nature, metabolism is a study in energy balance. Concentrations of nutrients and signaling molecules are not fixed; they vary from hour to hour, day to day, season to season, and year to year. To prosper, the organism has to be able to cope and change with these fluctuations. Unfortunately, organisms cannot always cope with changing conditions. Hunger and famine have always plagued humankind and were one of the leading killers in the twentieth century. Curiously, in Western society, famine has now been replaced by diseases stemming from nutritional excess. Many modern practices result in people living in a state outside homeostasis.

This section starts with a discussion of overnutrition (consumption of too many calories), obesity, diabetes, and metabolic syndrome. It also explores diseases that stem from a lack of nutrition or an inability to properly regulate metabolic pathways, conditions seen in acquired immunodeficiency syndrome (AIDS) and some cancers. The section then discusses metabolic changes resulting from alcohol consumption and concludes by considering several metabolic states that are important in biochemistry but are not truly disease states, such as the metabolic alterations that occur during exercise and hibernation.

12.4.1 | Diseases of excess: obesity, diabetes, and metabolic syndrome

If food cost is represented as a percentage of personal income, the United States has the cheapest food supply of any country on Earth, and the easiest access (**Figure 12.13**). Consequently, a high percentage of people eat too much, although even in the United States, 5.4% of households, including 9.8% of households with children, suffer from hunger and do not get enough to eat each day. Unfortunately, access to an almost unlimited food supply, coupled with minimal physical effort in everyday life, differs greatly from the conditions that prevailed as we evolved, resulting in considerable health risks for people today.

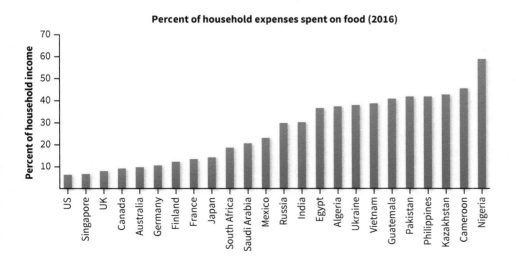

Percent of household expenses spent on food (2016)

FIGURE 12.13 **Percent of household income spent on food.** In 2016, Americans spent less on food as a percentage of household income than any other country in the world. (U.S. Department of Agriculture.)

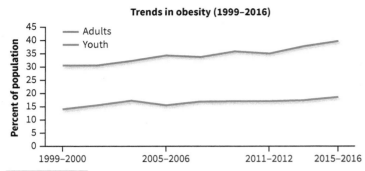

Trends in obesity (1999–2016)

FIGURE 12.14 **Obesity is epidemic in the United States.** Over the past 30 years the number of people who are overweight or obese has exceeded 65% in the United States. The NHANES study is the National Health and Nutrition Examination Study, a national study sponsored by the Centers for Disease Control and Prevention.

Obesity is the most common disease in America

Body mass index (BMI) is an indicator of how overweight an individual is. It is calculated by dividing mass in kilograms by height in meters squared. An optimal BMI is in the range of 18.5 to 24.9. Currently, 32.3% of Americans are overweight, having a BMI of over 25 kg/m^2. A further 36.5% of Americans are considered obese (BMI > 30 kg/m^2). Collectively, this means that 68.8% of Americans are in an unhealthy weight range.

BMI is not a perfect measure of how overweight someone is. It fails to take into consideration people of different builds or ethnicities and fails to consider the distribution of fat in the body (abdominal fat versus whole body fat). Nevertheless, BMI positively correlates with weight and is one measure that is used to determine obesity (**Figure 12.14**).

Fat storage is an important evolutionary adaptation that allows us to survive in times when food is not available; however, an excess of fat storage can be problematic. Although obesity is not in itself a terminal disease, it is a major contributor to type 2 diabetes, heart disease, and some cancers.

Obesity can have hormonal causes, but it is generally the result of overnutrition and lack of exercise. The effect of obesity is significant. In the obese state, adipose tissue becomes leaky, releasing free fatty acids into the plasma in the absence of lipolytic stimuli. These elevated plasma fatty acids have been implicated in the development of type 2 diabetes. The influx of fatty acids to muscle cells shifts metabolism in that tissue toward β-oxidation and away from glycolysis. At the same time, the liver is also undergoing greater levels of β-oxidation and of gluconeogenesis due to elevated fatty acids. Collectively, this contributes to **hyperglycemia**, that is, elevated plasma glucose.

Obesity also leads to hormonal changes. In the obese state there are elevated levels of stress hormones, such as cortisol and epinephrine, as well as several pro-inflammatory cytokines, which are signaling molecules secreted by the immune system. At the same time, insulin levels are often elevated, but tissues are less responsive to these elevated levels, a prediabetic condition known as insulin resistance. Leptin levels are elevated, and adiponectin levels are decreased. For reasons that are not fully clear, hormones regulated by the hypothalamus are also aberrant. For example, thyroid releasing hormone (TRH) is often elevated. Paradoxically, levels of thyroid hormones may or may not be elevated, although hypothyroidism (low levels of thyroid hormones) is associated with obesity. Growth hormone levels are low because its release is blunted, whereas levels of both androgens and estrogens are elevated. Overall, this presents a rich and complex regulatory issue that underlies many of the problems and complications of obesity.

Obesity can be treated pharmacologically in several ways (**Figure 12.15**). These include the fat absorption inhibitor Orlistat and several antidepressants that act to blunt appetite. The drug metformin, an insulin sensitizer, increases the sensitivity and responsiveness of cells to insulin; it has been used in some instances to treat obesity, although it is more commonly used to treat diabetes. Newer experimental treatments include PYY(3-36), growth hormone, leptin, and various drugs that target the hypothalamus. These drugs may have the advantage of truly targeting metabolism rather than simply appetite, although there is always the potential for adverse effects.

Sibutramine
(Meridia)

Rimonabant

Lorcaserin

Orlistat
(Xenical, Alli)

FIGURE 12.15 **Drugs that target obesity.** Drugs that target obesity can be categorized into those that block lipid absorption and those that suppress appetite. Several of these drugs have been withdrawn due to undesirable side effects. Sibutramine (Meridia) is an SSRI and appetite suppressant and was withdrawn in 2010. Rimonabant is a reverse agonist of the cannabinoid receptor CB1, an appetite suppressant, and was withdrawn in 2009. Lorcaserin is a 5-HT 2c receptor agonist and an appetite suppressant. Orlistat (Xenical, Alli) is a pancreatic lipase inhibitor and blocks fat absorption.

Diabetes is a disease of insulin signaling

Diabetes has been recognized as a disease since 1500 BCE. There are several different types of diabetes. These diseases as well as other hormonal disorders are discussed in Table 12.5. Diabetes insipidus results from an imbalance of vasopressin and thus the inability to reabsorb sodium from urine, which in turn causes a loss of sodium and water. The outcome causes copious urination and loss of electrolytes. Diabetes insipidus is unrelated to the other three forms of diabetes, which are types of **diabetes mellitus** that arise from complications in insulin signaling. It is diabetes mellitus that people typically think of when they hear the term diabetes. Diabetes mellitus can be broadly divided into two categories: **type 1 diabetes mellitus**, previously known as juvenile diabetes, and **type 2 diabetes mellitus**, previously known as adult onset diabetes. A third form of the disease, gestational diabetes, occurs in pregnant mothers.

Type 1 diabetes mellitus is an autoimmune disease that typically strikes children and young adults between the ages of 12 and 21. The immune system of the patient recognizes the pancreatic β cells as foreign and destroys them, resulting in the loss of insulin. The causes of type 1 diabetes are not totally clear, with both genetic and environmental factors apparently affecting the development of the disease. Currently, 5% of people with diabetes in the United States have type 1 disease.

In type 2 diabetes, the problem arises not from a lack of insulin but an inability of cells to properly respond to this signal. The defect usually lies not at the level of the insulin receptor but is a post-receptor defect in signaling. The disease begins to manifest itself as a prediabetic condition termed **insulin resistance**. In the case of insulin resistance, plasma insulin concentrations become higher and higher, until the pancreas can no longer keep up and the subject goes into β cell failure, resulting in type 2 diabetes. The causes of type 2 diabetes are also unknown, but several risk factors have been identified. Although there is a genetic component to the disease, environmental factors seem to be more important, including dietary excess, obesity, and sedentary lifestyles.

Gestational diabetes is similar to type 2 diabetes and is thought to arise from elevated levels of pregnancy hormones influencing insulin signaling. The disease often reverts after delivery, but women who have experienced gestational diabetes are at increased risk for developing type 2 diabetes later in life.

At the root of all types of diabetes is the body's inability to use glucose. Without insulin or insulin signaling, glucose transporters are not mobilized to the cell surface, so glucose cannot enter the cell. Sensing that glucose is low or unavailable, the body shifts its metabolism to the starved state. Fatty acids are mobilized from adipose tissue, the liver produces both ketone bodies and glucose through gluconeogenesis, and muscle begins to waste as amino acids are catabolized to provide glucogenic precursors.

Multiple drugs are available for treatment of diabetes

Several pharmacological interventions are available for treatment of diabetes. Arguably one of the greatest discoveries in the history of endocrinology, and a turning point in the history of medicine, was the discovery and isolation of insulin. Today, numerous formulations of insulin are available. They include slow- or fast-acting insulin, in which single amino acid mutations have been made to recombinant human insulin, to promote or discourage crystallization. As the crystals dissolve in the bloodstream, the concentration of active insulin increases.

Biguanides
(Metformin)

Sulfonylureas
(Glyburide)

Thiazoladinediones
(Avandia)

All types of diabetes can be treated with insulin, but type 2 diabetes is also treated with oral antidiabetic agents. Metformin is an insulin sensitizing agent; it acts on the liver and suppresses gluconeogenesis. In diabetes, gluconeogenesis can be elevated by as much as threefold, but metformin can reduce this to twofold. The exact mechanism by which metformin works is still being elucidated; however, it is known that **AMP-activated protein kinase (AMPK)** is required for activity, and that metformin activates AMPK, which has additional benefits. AMPK promotes catabolic pathways, and activating AMPK stimulates glycolysis through glucose transport, β-oxidation and ketone body biosynthesis; at the same time, it inhibits glycogen synthesis and triglyceride biosynthesis.

Sulfonylureas, such as glyburide, are drugs that act as insulin secretagogues; that is, they promote the secretion of insulin. Sulfonylureas work by inhibiting the ATP-dependent K^+ pump required for insulin secretion. This causes a depolarization of the β cell membrane resulting in the opening of Ca^{2+} channels. The increase in cellular Ca^{2+} causes fusion of vesicles of insulin with the plasma membrane.

A final class of oral antidiabetic drugs is the **thiazoladinediones (TZDs)**, such as rosiglitizone. TZDs are **peroxisome proliferator-activated receptor (PPAR)** agonists. These drugs bind to the PPAR class of transcription factor, activating them. The transcription factor PPAR-γ regulates many genes involved in lipid metabolism and fat storage. Therefore, by activating these genes, cells are more able to store lipid. This may seem like a paradox: why give a drug that makes people store more fat to treat a disease with obesity as a risk factor? However, TZDs apparently help to store fatty acids and make adipose tissue less "leaky," lowering levels of plasma fatty acids.

Although there are many treatments for diabetes, it is still a highly prevalent disease. In 2016 it was estimated that 9.3% of the population of the United States is directly affected by diabetes: over 29 million Americans are diagnosed with the disease, and an additional 8.1 million are undiagnosed. The American Diabetes Association reports that diabetes is the leading cause of blindness and kidney failure and accounts for over 65,000 amputations each year. Diabetes also contributes to cardiovascular disease and stroke. The total cost of diabetes in 2014 was more than $245 billion, nearly 1 in every 5 dollars spent in health care in the United States. In addition to being a risk factor in other disorders, diabetes was the seventh leading cause of death in the United States in 2016.

Metabolic syndrome is an amalgam of diverse symptoms underlying many diseases

It has long been known that there are significant links between diabetes, obesity, heart disease, stroke, high blood pressure (hypertension), elevated plasma lipids (hyperlipidemia), and elevated plasma glucose (hyperglycemia). Collectively, these conditions have been named "syndrome X" or **metabolic syndrome**. Although these conditions had a relatively minor role in human health before the industrial revolution, in modern times, metabolic syndrome is a major part of the etiology (the study of causation of disease) of five of the top ten causes of death in the United States: heart disease, cancer, stroke, diabetes, and kidney disease (**Figure 12.16**). In most people, the root cause of metabolic syndrome is

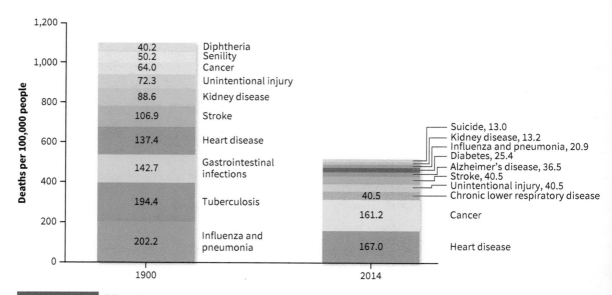

FIGURE 12.16 **Mortality rates in 1900 and 2014.** Five of the top ten leading causes of mortality in the United States are affected by the metabolic syndrome. These causes include heart disease, diabetes, cerebrovascular disease, kidney disease, and some cancers. (CDC data.)

simple: overnutrition compounded by a sedentary lifestyle. If those two circumstances were reversed, most cases of metabolic disease could be ameliorated or remedied. Despite research and advances in understanding, the reality is that changes to diet and lifestyle would help more than most pharmaceutical intervention ever aspires to achieve.

12.4.2 | Diseases of absence: starvation, cachexia, and cancer

Although obesity and diabetes are clearly epidemic health problems, at the opposite extreme, metabolic wasting diseases and starvation are also a cause for concern. Despite increased caloric consumption, there are many disease states in which patients waste away, a condition known as **cachexia**; these diseases include AIDS, cancer, and tuberculosis. Although a secondary effect of these diseases and not in and of itself terminal, cachexia is a risk factor and does contribute to the mortality in these diseases.

Two possible causes have been suggested for cachexia, and both may contribute to the disease state. The first possible cause relates to the fact that anorexia is observed in some but not all instances of cachexia, which suggests that there may be an alteration of metabolic rate independent of food intake. The hypothesis is that there may be a disconnect in a metabolic feedback loop, possibly involving adiponectin, ghrelin, leptin, or PYY(3-36), and leading to a decrease in appetite but an increase in metabolic rate.

The second plausible cause states that elevated levels of cytokines (the signaling molecules of the immune system), either coming from a tumor or secreted in response to a tumor, alter gene expression, resulting in wasting. The cytokines implicated in this mechanism include tumor necrosis factor-α (TNF-α), interleukin-6 (IL-6), interferon-γ (INF-γ), and the hormones angiotensin II and the glucocorticoids. Secretion of these factors contributes to the loss of skeletal muscle mass due to both decreased muscle protein synthesis and increased degradation. Additionally, these muscles burn more energy through increased thermogenesis due in part to increased expression of uncoupling proteins.

Cancer cells exhibit rampant glycolysis

The Warburg effect is the observation that cancer cells in many tumors exist in a highly glycolytic state, using glucose as their sole energy source. In addition, these cells do not produce acetyl-CoA from pyruvate; instead, they ferment pyruvate to lactate in the cytosol, even in the presence of oxygen. In terms of *why* this adaptation occurs, one hypothesis is that it may allow cells to grow at low oxygen concentrations inside the tumor; another hypothesis is that cancer cell proliferation occurs because the cells need to use the products of the glycolysis to synthesize the molecules necessary for cell growth. In terms of *how* it occurs, the tumor cell may produce proteins or silence genes to somehow disable mitochondria and thus prevent them from initiating **apoptosis**.

The Warburg effect may also have a direct impact on gene expression. For example, in colon cancer cells, research has shown that by switching from other fuels, such as fatty acids to glucose, butyrate will accumulate, inhibiting histone deacetylases and affecting gene expression through epigenetic changes. Sirtuins also may be important in the regulation of the Warburg effect. Sirtuins have been shown to regulate the stability of transcription factor HIF-1, which regulates the expression of several key proteins in glycolysis.

Kwashiorkor and marasmus result from starvation and malnutrition

Two other states related to starvation merit discussion: kwashiorkor and marasmus.

Kwashiorkor is a type of starvation marked by severe protein deficiency. It is most commonly seen in small children and infants who are abruptly weaned from milk or formula onto a high-carbohydrate diet, as is often seen during a famine. Because of the lack of protein in the diet, there is fatty liver, edema, and distention of the abdomen (**Figure 12.17**).

FIGURE 12.17 **Kwashiorkor and marasmus.** **A.** Kwashiorkor results from severe protein deficiency. The abdomens of affected children are distended from fluid retention and edema. **B.** Marasmus results from overall caloric insufficiency leaving the victim emaciated.

Max McClure/Alamy Stock Photo

Mike Goldwater/Alamy Stock Photo

FIGURE 12.18 **Ethanol metabolism.** Most ethanol is oxidized to acetaldehyde by alcohol dehydrogenase. Acetaldehyde has a short half-life and is quickly converted into the less reactive acetate by aldehyde dehydrogenase.

Marasmus is the general starvation that comes from lack of sufficient calories. Victims of marasmus often obtain calories but at levels below those needed for basic survival. Likewise, meals may come at irregular intervals, complicating the metabolic picture. The result is general wasting, dehydration, and malnutrition.

12.4.3 Diseases of indulgence: alcohol overconsumption

Ethanol is a naturally occurring molecule and a small part of the diet in all cultures of the world. Although some cultures abstain from consuming alcoholic beverages, many foods contain small amounts of naturally occurring ethanol; for example, ordinary orange juice is typically 0.5% ethanol by volume. Other cultures have used ethanol historically to preserve foods and beverages; for example, in grape-growing countries, wine is a means of preserving grape juice. Likewise, beer and other fermented drinks were thought to rise in popularity, partially from the need for a beverage that was not contaminated with pathogenic microbes. The hops and other herbs in fermented drinks contain microbial growth inhibitors. Of course, ethanol is consumed today for numerous reasons. The National Institutes of Health (NIH) estimates that in the United States one out of every three people abstain from all alcoholic beverages, or drink in very limited amounts (a few drinks per year), and that one person in six has a drinking problem. Even if people abstain from alcoholic beverages, they still need to metabolize the ethanol found in some foods.

Ethanol is largely metabolized by the liver. Alcohol dehydrogenase catalyzes the oxidation of ethanol to acetaldehyde, a process that is NAD^+ dependent (**Figure 12.18**). Acetaldehyde is oxidized to acetate in the mitochondria by aldehyde dehydrogenase, generating a second molecule of NADH. Acetate generated in the mitochondria is typically coupled to coenzyme A and oxidized through the citric acid cycle, although this is not a committed fate. Free acetate can be detected in the cytosol as well as the plasma. Acetate contributes to both fatty acid and cholesterol biosynthesis and may serve as a fuel for the brain when consumed chronically in excess.

The biochemistry of hangovers
Many people overconsume ethanol on occasion; the ethanol permeates most tissues of the body and rapidly increases in concentration as consumption continues. Ethanol is generally categorized as a depressant because it decreases respiration and slows reflexes, which alters perceptions and affects judgment. The legal blood alcohol concentration in most states is 0.08% v/v. A concentration above 0.25% typically results in unconsciousness, whereas one above 0.4% can result in coma or death. Even if these excessive levels are not reached, there can still be aftereffects. In the drunken state (blood alcohol of 0.08% to 0.2%) ethanol concentrations are in the millimolar level, but the K_m for most of the isozymes of alcohol dehydrogenase are also in the low millimolar to micromolar level, so ethanol is eliminated relatively rapidly.

Acetaldehyde, the first product of ethanol consumption is toxic, but levels rarely elevate to the point of toxicity. The toxicity of acetaldehyde is perhaps best illustrated by populations sensitive to alcohol consumption. In many Asian populations, a point mutation in aldehyde dehydrogenase renders the enzyme inactive. In people with this mutation, consumption of even small amounts of ethanol rapidly leads to flushing and hangover-like symptoms, including headaches and nausea. Pharmacological inhibition of aldehyde dehydrogenase can produce similar results. Disulfiram, the active ingredient in the drug Antabuse, used to treat chronic alcoholism, or any one of several related toxins derived from fungi, result in inhibition of aldehyde dehydrogenase. Consumption of small amounts of ethanol while taking Antabuse results in acute hangover-like symptoms.

Disulfiram
(Antabuse)

People suffering from a hangover often feel weak. As ethanol is metabolized, the ratio of $NADH/NAD^+$ is increased; that is, more NADH is produced in the oxidation of ethanol to acetate. Changes in this ratio result in decreased gluconeogenesis in the liver. As a result, plasma glucose levels drop (hypoglycemia) and lactate levels from muscle increase. Elevated lactate in conjunction with increased acetate can result in **acidosis**, or decreased plasma pH.

Other hangover symptoms result from dehydration. Ethanol blocks the release of vasopressin from the **posterior pituitary**, resulting in decreased sodium reabsorption in the kidney and increased urination. This effect, compounded by nausea and vomiting from stomach irritation, can account for some of the dizziness and thirst felt in a hangover.

Chronic alcohol consumption causes other health effects
Chronic alcohol consumption carries with it other significant health effects. Alcoholism often results in malnutrition due to the general failure to consume a nutritious diet, the loss of water-soluble electrolytes and vitamins through increased urination, and the inability to absorb certain B vitamins in the intestine.

The chronic consumption of ethanol provides a higher than normal ratio of NADH/NAD$^+$. As mentioned, this decreases gluconeogenesis and shifts metabolism to ethanol and its final product acetate; it also contributes to increased fatty acid biosynthesis and hypoglycemia. Because the brain and body tissues are starved of glucose, lipolytic signals trigger mobilization of fatty acids out of adipose tissue for ketone body production. This results in increased fat accumulation in the liver, referred to as fatty liver, and in the blood, referred to as hyperlipidemia. Fatty liver is a reversible process but is the beginning of the scarring of the liver and the development of cirrhosis and hepatocarcinoma, or liver cancer. The result of this is a decrease of plasma glucose and a significant elevation of ketone bodies, lactate, amino acids, and lipids, both free fatty acids and VLDL/LDL. Perhaps the only metabolic benefit in those addicted to alcohol is an elevated HDL level.

Another complication of ethanol metabolism is the formation of adducts between ethanol, acetaldehyde, or acetate and different molecules of the body. Acetaldehyde in particular is quite reactive; it can randomly add to molecules, altering their structure, function, or activity. The molecules of the cell also can be altered through reactive oxygen species, that is, reactive by-products of oxidative metabolism that randomly modify and damage proteins, membranes, and DNA. These species are clearly causal factors in hepatic cell death and liver scarring. Over time, oxidative damage to DNA is responsible for hepatocarcinoma. Increased risk of developing several cancers, including liver and breast cancer, has been linked to alcohol consumption.

A final complication of chronic ethanol consumption is hypoxia or low oxygen concentration. Ethanol puts a metabolic burden on the liver, increasing flux through several pathways that require molecular oxygen. This creates a need for more oxygen in the liver and can create such a demand that regions of the liver distant from arteries face hypoxic conditions. In this state, the cells generate signaling molecules that leave them further depleted of oxygen. In addition, decreased plasma pH decreases the ability of the hemoglobin to carry oxygen; this in combination with a malnourished state can lead to anemia in the person with alcoholism. Collectively, these effects contribute to the hypoxic state, which is another source of damage to the tissues. Ethanol can also result in changes in gene expression, although it is unclear whether this is directly due to the ethanol itself or to downstream effects of cell signaling.

As damage to the liver continues, levels of proinflammatory cytokines, such as TNF-α, increase. In cirrhosis, cells apoptose, or in some instances become necrotic, and are replaced by connective tissue. Over time, this combination can be so severe as to drive people with alcoholism into liver failure.

12.4.4 | Other metabolic states

Several other metabolic states warrant commentary. First are those found in trained athletes. Metabolic states in exercise physiology can be categorized by the type of exercise performed: these are sprinting exercise, when running at full speed for less than 400 meters, and distance exercise, any exercise greater than sprinting (Table 12.6). Sports

TABLE 12.6 Speed of Track and Field Events

Distance, meters	Time, sec	Velocity, m/s
100	9.58	10.438
150	14.35	10.453
200	19.19	10.422
300	30.85	9.724
400	43.03	9.296
600	72.81	8.241
800	100.91	7.928

that require short bursts of energy, from table tennis to powerlifting, fall into the sprinting category, while anything longer is a distance activity.

The delineation between these two types of exercise can be clearly seen if one examines elite athletes' biochemistry. Runners covering short distances (up to 200 meters) have a similar speed. The runner needs to cover a short distance to gain the momentum to achieve that speed; however, once the speed is attained, runners can continue at that speed for about 200 meters or a little less than 20 seconds. Thus, the world record in the 100 meters is a bit more than double the speed of a top football recruit running the 40 meters, and about half of the world record in the 200 meters. At greater distances, such as 400 and 800 meters, the speed does not simply double again but drops significantly. Biochemistry explains the basis of this difference.

The biochemistry of the sprint

A sprint happens almost instantaneously. There is only one fuel that can be used so quickly: ATP. The initial stages of a sprint use the muscle cell's ATP store to rapidly generate explosive muscle movement, but the ATP store lasts only a few seconds. Glycolysis will rapidly take over, producing more ATP and generating lactate from the pyruvate product; therefore, sprinting is largely considered an anaerobic activity. A mechanism is needed to restore these ATP levels. There is a buffer for ATP, that is, a means of rapidly regenerating ATP in the absence of other energy production. Creatine kinase can transfer a phosphate group from creatine phosphate to ADP, or vice versa; under states where ATP is depleted, creatine phosphate can help rapidly replenish levels, but levels of creatine phosphate are also limited: there is only enough to use for a few seconds. Athletes attempt to elevate levels of creatine phosphate by taking creatine supplements, but the value of this practice is questionable.

Creatine that escapes from muscle is catabolized in the liver to creatinine and secreted by the kidneys.

Distance events require a different metabolic approach

In marathon running, we see the opposite extreme of exercise physiology. Marathon runners who are trained to run at this distance (26.2 miles or 42.2 km) also largely burn carbohydrates through glycolysis and oxidative phosphorylation, mostly from stored glycogen. Most distance athletes consume some carbohydrate drink or gel while running. In some cycling events, for example, the Tour de France, half of the total calories consumed in the course of the day are taken in on the bike. If athletes do not replenish these carbohydrates in some way during a race, they risk total depletion of carbohydrate reserves and resulting muscle exhaustion. When this occurs, muscles shut down and the athlete cannot use them. This is referred to as "hitting the wall," and stops runners in their tracks until they replenish some carbohydrates, either by consuming carbohydrates or through gluconeogenesis from protein or glycerol sources.

Many animals undergo periods of metabolic dormancy

Another interesting metabolic state is **hibernation**, the winter period when some mammals sleep and enter torpor, in which metabolic rate, respiration rate, and body temperature all drop. Most animals have evolved mechanisms to downregulate their metabolism in times of energy scarcity or depleted resources. Torpor may refer to the metabolic state seen in hibernation, but in some organisms it can occur daily or due to environmental conditions, such as low temperature or lack of food. Torpor is thought to preserve the organism and let it conserve energy. Another, similar process to hibernation is aestivation. **Aestivation** is a process undergone by organisms, such as mollusks and arthropods, in which they become dormant and slow their metabolism in warm or dry months. Physiological changes also help these organisms to conserve water. A third state is **brumation**, in which animals are still awake but have slowed their metabolic rate. Ectotherms, such as fish and reptiles, undergo brumation; they are unable to regulate their body temperature and therefore do not alter it as is done in hibernation. Thus, brumation differs from hibernation and aestivation. Other than these gross observations, metabolic links between brumation and hibernation have not been clearly established.

Studies of animal dormancy have direct implications for human health. In preparation for hibernation, many animals model obesity by eating excessively and storing calories as fat. In addition, some animals become insulin resistant before hibernation, similar to type 2 diabetes.

With changes in feeding in the periods proceeding dormancy, many birds will overeat prior to migration. Humans have noticed this since antiquity and have also noted how this changes the different aspects of birds as a human food source, most notably the amount of fat that accumulates in the liver. One particular example of this is discussed in **Societal and Ethical Biochemistry: Foie gras.**

Societal and Ethical Biochemistry

Foie gras

Few foods are as curious or controversial as foie gras, a delicacy famed in French cuisine for its unusual rich buttery flavor and texture. Foie gras is often lightly seared or grilled, or is blended into a spread or pate. However, the production of foie gras has raised ethical concerns.

Foie gras is the liver of a duck or goose that has been specifically fattened. In fact, ducks and geese are gavaged or force fed as much grain as they can hold, through a special funnel inserted into the esophagus of the bird. This process is repeated several times a day for two to three weeks. As this happens, the bird's liver engorges and becomes fatty, enlarging up to ten times its normal size, and producing the buttery texture sought after in foie gras.

In the biochemical sense, the liver of these animals is storing fat produced predominantly from carbohydrates found in grain. Although this is a metabolic extreme, it is not totally unnatural. In the wild, migratory birds will engorge themselves before starting their migration, and their livers will swell with fat.

Because of the process by which foie gras is produced, many localities now consider serving the product unethical. For example, the state of California, the city of Chicago, and several countries in Europe, have sought to ban foie gras. Nevertheless, gavage of animals has gone on since the time of 2500 BCE, and France recognizes foie gras as part of its cultural heritage.

Alternative production methods are under investigation. Appetite is controlled in part through the hypothalamus, so one approach has been to surgically damage the regions of the hypothalamus involved in the regulation of appetite. Geese that have undergone this process consume three or four times more food, and they grow fatty livers that are similar to those of gavaged birds, but this technique has not grown in popularity, perhaps due to the resources needed to perform it. A second technique capitalizes on the natural behavior of geese and ducks. While preparing to migrate, the geese and ducks are given free access to a diet rich in acorns and olives. This results in a smaller liver, but one that still has the flavors, textures, and levels of fat that chefs and diners prefer. It is not yet clear whether this product will be as popular with consumers as foie gras.

WORKED PROBLEM 12.4 | Characterizing a knockout mouse

You are asked to help characterize a knockout mouse made in your laboratory. A gene coding for a fat storage protein was deleted in this mouse, which is lean and has normal food consumption and activity, but has elevated plasma insulin and an impaired **glucose tolerance test (GTT)**.

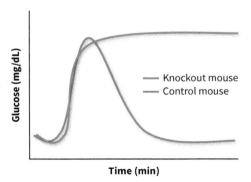

How would you characterize these results?

Strategy Examine the data at hand. What does a GTT determine, and how does it work? What is the significance of the elevated insulin level?

Solution This mouse is a lean model for type 2 diabetes mellitus. It needs elevated insulin levels to maintain normal metabolism because its cells respond poorly to the insulin signal. The GTT is a way to ascertain how well the organism can respond to a glucose challenge. Glucose levels rise in both animals, but glucose clearance is delayed in the knockout mouse; the explanation for diabetes is not as apparent, but it may be due to an impairment in triacylglycerol storage, which can result in elevated plasma fatty acids and contribute to an insulin resistant phenotype.

Follow-up question Given that the mouse has reduced adipose tissue mass, elevated insulin levels, and normal activity and food consumption, predict the levels of other hormones in this organism. In other words, how has this mutation affected hormone levels, based on the phenotype observed?

12.4 Summary

- Obesity resulting from overnutrition and lack of exercise is at epidemic proportions in Western society. It is a significant risk factor for the development of type 2 diabetes mellitus.
- Type 2 diabetes mellitus arises from cells of the body failing to appropriately respond to insulin secreted from the pancreas. The cause is still unknown, but it is likely that the disease is polygenic, resulting from the interplay of multiple proteins.
- Metabolic syndrome or syndrome X is a group of related pathophysiologies that contribute to many of the most common and debilitating diseases, including heart disease, stroke, diabetes, and some cancers.
- Cancer, AIDS, and other diseases can lead to cachexia, a wasting of the body. This may be due to damaged feedback loops in hormonal signaling, elevated cytokines, or other unknown causes.
- The Warburg effect is the observation that tumors are highly glycolytic and undergo anaerobic metabolism in the presence of oxygen. Sirtuins, HIF-1, and epigenetic modifications may play a role in this syndrome.
- Starvation can be exhibited as kwashiorkor or marasmus.
- Excessive ethanol consumption results in decreased hepatic gluconeogenesis and elevated fatty acid metabolism. Chronic ethanol consumption results in a hypoxic state in the liver, causing liver damage or cirrhosis, and eventual liver failure.
- Other metabolic states resulting from diet, ethanol consumption, and exercise or hibernation alteration in metabolism have been extensively studied.

12.4 Concept Check

- Describe what is happening in obesity, metabolic syndrome, starvation, cancer, and alcoholism at the molecular level.
- Explain what treatments are available for these diseases and how they act on the molecular level.
- Describe the complications or symptoms of these conditions and how they can be explained biochemically.

The Bigger Picture

This chapter showed that metabolism is far from a solved question or a simple series of organic reactions. Despite significant advances in our knowledge of how nutrients are metabolized, there is still a long way to go. It is important to understand the pathways by which molecules are built up and broken down, the energetics and kinetics of these reactions, and, where applicable, the mechanism through which the reactions occur. However, metabolism is also a complex interplay of signaling and regulation, allostery and post-translational modification, and regulation of gene expression. Holistically, metabolism relies heavily on organ specialization and on communication between organs. Recent advances have begun to reveal the brain's role in both metabolism and the regulation of behaviors related to metabolism. The organism can, to some extent, compensate for alterations to caloric need or nutritional excess or scarcity. Disease can result from either overnutrition or undernutrition. Both of these processes can be explained on the biochemical level. Given the discoveries made in the past 50 years, our current understanding of metabolism may have barely scratched the surface.

Bioinformatics Exercises

Exercise 1 Insulin Secretion and the KEGG Database

Exercise 2 Insulin Control of Glucose Metabolism and the KEGG Database

Problems

12.1 A Review of the Pathways and Crossroads of Metabolism

1. The brain use ketone bodies for fuel in times of fasting. What does muscle use in place of ketone bodies?

2. Glycerol kinase and glucose-6-phosphatase are two enzymes that tailor metabolic responses to specific tissues. How do these two enzymes provide specialized metabolic responses? What do these two enzymes do to specialize the metabolic response? What other enzymes act this way?

3. The urea cycle is an example of a pathway that occurs in a specific tissue that requires a specialized metabolic response. What does the urea cycle do, and where does it do it? What are other examples of specific pathways, and where are they found?

12.2 Organ Specialization and Metabolic States

4. Why does the liver undergo gluconeogenesis when in the re-fed state?

5. There are two hydroxymethylglutaryl-CoA (HMG-CoA) synthases in the cell. Where are they found? In which pathways do they function? One of these synthases is under control of SREBP and the other of a PPRE. Hypothesize as to which molecule controls which synthase.

12.3 Communication between Organs

6. Propose a mechanism for the decarboxylation of L-DOPA to dopamine. This is a pyridoxal phosphate-dependent mechanism.

7. Examine the synthesis of epinephrine from L-DOPA. Why not insert a double bond in dopamine and then hydrate it to form the alcohol?

8. Examine the name phenylethanolamine *N*-Methyltransferase. What is the substrate for this enzyme? What does this enzyme do? What is the source of the methyl group, and where does it end up in the final molecule? Draw the structure of the final compound.

9. Thyroid follicular cells use a sodium transporter to bring iodide ions into the cell. What type of transport mechanism is this?

10. Thyroglobulin is endocytosed from the follicular granule. Review endocytosis from Chapter 10, then draw an illustration to show how that process occurs.

11. Propose a mechanism for the proteolytic cleavage of T3 and T4 from thyroglobulin.

12. Glucagon is a short helical peptide.

   a. How could you determine the tertiary structure of glucagon?

   b. In what ways would it be easier to determine the structure of glucagon than of a larger protein?

   c. In what ways would it be harder to determine the structure?

13. Endocrinology has existed as a field for over 100 years. Why are we only now discovering some hormones?

14. How has completion of the human genome assisted in the discovery of new hormones?

15. Many hormones are peptides and are degraded in the stomach; hence, they are not orally available. Why is this an evolutionary advantage?

16. Based on the discussion in the chapter, what are the symptoms of hypothyroidism?

17. Hyperthyroidism and Graves' disease are treated with radioactive iodine, most notably ^{131}I.

   a. How does this treatment work?

   b. What type of radiation does ^{131}I emit?

   c. What are the possible side effects of ^{131}I treatment?

18. What classes of hormones are corticotropin releasing hormone and adrenocorticotropic hormone?

19. Adiponectin levels are increased by treatment with thiazoladinediones. Correlate these two observations, and explain them.

20. Goiter results from insufficient iodine in the diet. What are the metabolic symptoms of this disorder?

12.4 Metabolic Disease

21. Diabetes insipidus is a disease caused by a mutation to a gene coding for the vasopressin receptor. Describe how this mutation would affect vasopressin signaling and the vasopressin signaling loop, and lead to the symptoms of the disease.

22. Often, menstruation ceases in women who are professional athletes or bodybuilders or who have anorexia. Propose a role for hormonal signaling to explain this observation.

23. The Pima Native Americans of Arizona and New Mexico have high rates of obesity and diabetes. In some cases, this severe obesity is associated with a mutation in PYY, where glutamine-62 is replaced by proline (Q62P).

   a. How might this mutation chemically alter the peptide?

   b. How might it affect the tertiary structure of the peptide?

   c. How might this lead to the disease phenotype observed? Why isn't the correlation of disease with this phenotype 1:1?

24. Would you hypothesize levels of PPY to be elevated or depressed in people with anorexia?

25. Would the phenotype of the MC4R knockout mouse be lean or obese? Would you anticipate any problems maintaining a colony of these mice?

26. Bremalanotide is a hexapeptide analog of α-MSH. It was developed as a tanning agent but is now marketed for the treatment of sexual dysfunction. What is the reason for this?

27. Why can insulin not be taken orally?

28. Steroid hormones can be applied topically or delivered by patch. Why can only some hormones be delivered in this way?

29. Lysine can spontaneously form adducts with acetaldehyde. Draw this structure. What type of functional group is it?

30. Would you anticipate that some proteins would have more acetaldehyde adducts than others? What factors would influence adduct formation?

31. Oxytocin is colloquially known as the "cuddle hormone." It has been reported to increase trust and bonding between people. Provided this is truly the case, what is the evolutionary advantage of this adaptation?

32. Both plasma and urinary creatinine are typically measured as part of a panel of clinical chemistry tests. What organ function is being measured in these tests?

33. Why is creatine kinase used as a marker for heart attacks? How does this test work?

34. Would it benefit a golfer, baseball player, or weightlifter to supplement with creatine? How about an American football player or soccer player?

Data Interpretation

35. Only 5% of people with diabetes currently have type 1 diabetes, whereas 15 years ago, 10% had it. Why is the number dropping?

36. In the literature, there are several cases of a disorder known as hamburger thyrotoxicosis. In this disorder, subjects suffer from sleeplessness, nervousness, weight loss, headache, and fatigue. These cases have been linked to eating hamburger contaminated with thyroid tissue. Examine the graphs shown below.

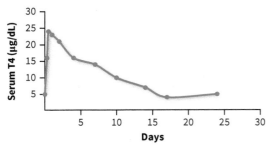

a. Do the data in these graphs substantiate or invalidate the hypothesis that an acute event caused the change in hormone levels?

b. What is an alternative hypothesis, and how might you test it (in either a human or animal model)?

c. Why does thyroid stimulating hormone drop?

d. Given what is known above, what would be an appropriate control for this study?

e. Is there an inherent weakness in the study?

Experimental Design

37. Engineered forms of insulin have point mutations that allow the molecule to form microcrystals that slowly dissolve, providing a "slow release" form of the hormone. How would you test to see whether an engineered protein was forming microscopic crystals? Design an assay to see how quickly these crystals would dissolve.

38. You identify a short (40 amino acid long) peptide that you hypothesize regulates appetite. How could you test to see which residues of the peptide are critical for function?

39. Following one week on a diet enriched in certain fats, mice have elevated plasma ketone bodies compared to control animals. How could you determine whether the effect on ketone bodies is due to increased gene expression, increased enzyme activity, or some other regulatory mechanism?

Ethics and Social Responsibility

40. In some countries, prisoners are punished by being fed a "starving ration" or by receiving no food for one in every three days. Is this ethical? Is it healthy? Is it punishment?

41. Political prisoners or those wishing to make a political statement sometimes undertake hunger strikes, in some instances literally starving themselves to death. Given that these people cannot resist medical intervention at some point, is it ethical to let them die? Why is starvation—a slow, degenerative and painful death—considered acceptable but other forms of suicide are not?

42. Numerous college students (both male and female) suffer from eating disorders. Seek out your campus student center and see what resources they have on eating disorders. Share this information with your friends and classmates.

43. Diabetes and obesity are diseases that carry with them a huge cost in terms of diminished quality of life; leading a healthier lifestyle can help to prevent or delay the onset of many of the problems associated with these diseases. These diseases are also expensive to manage and treat. Given this information, how would you develop a company policy to limit the liability associated with this risk?

44. It has been estimated that alcohol consumption increased during prohibition; nevertheless, higher taxes on some items, such as cigarettes, appear to decrease their consumption and younger people's access to them. Should "unhealthy" foods be taxed or outlawed?

Suggested Readings

Ehnholm, Christian, ed. *Cellular Lipid Metabolism*. New York, NY: Springer, 2009.

Fahy E., S. Subramaniam, R. C. Murphy, M. Nishijima, C. R. Raetz, T. Shimizu, F. Spener, G. van Meer, M. J. Wakelam, and E. A. Dennis. "Update of the LIPID MAPS Comprehensive Classification System for Lipids." *Journal of Lipid Research* 50 (April 2009): S9–14.

Hers, H. G., and L. Hue. "Gluconeogenesis and Related Aspects of Glycolysis." *Annual Review of Biochemistry* 52 (1983): 617–53.

Houten, S. M., and R. J. Wanders. "A General Introduction to the Biochemistry of Mitochondrial Fatty Acid β-oxidation." *Journal of Inherited Metabolic Diseases* 33, no. 5 (October 2010): 469–77.

Pilkis, S. J., and D. K. Granner. "Molecular Physiology of the Regulation of Hepatic Gluconeogenesis and Glycolysis." *Annual Review of Physiology* 54 (1992): 885–909.

Scrutton, M. C., and M. F. Utter. "Regulation of Glycolysis and Gluconeogenesis in Animal Tissues." *Annual Review of Biochemistry* 37 (1968): 249–58.

Wakil, S. J., and L. A. Abu-Elheiga. "Fatty Acid Metabolism: Target for Metabolic Syndrome." *Journal of Lipid Research* 50 (April 2009): S138–43.

Walsh, Patrick J., and Patricia A. Wright. "Nitrogen Metabolism and Excretion." Boca Raton, Florida: CRC Press, 1995.

Frayn, K. N. "Fat as a Fuel: Emerging Understanding of the Adipose Tissue-Skeletal Muscle Axis." *Acta Physiologica* 199, no. 4 (August 2010): 509–18.

Grundy, S. M., H. B. Brewer, Jr., J. I. Cleeman, S. C. Smith, Jr., and C. Lenfant. "Definition of Metabolic Syndrome: Report of the National Heart, Lung, and Blood Institute/American Heart Association Conference on Scientific Issues Related to Definition." *Circulation* 109, no. 3 (January 27, 2004): 433–8.

Gurr, M. I., J. L. Harwood, and K. N. Frayn. *Lipid Biochemistry: An Introduction.* Hoboken, New Jersey: Blackwell Science Ltd., 2002.

McIntosh, Brian, Phillip Gardiner, and Alan McComas. *Skeletal Muscle: Form and Function.* 2nd ed. Champagne, Illinois: Human Kinetics, 2005.

Symonds, Michael E. E., ed. *Adipose Tissue Biology.* Philadelphia, PA: Springer Science and Business Media, LLC, 2012.

Batterham, R. L., H. Heffron, S. Kapoor, J. Chivers, K. Chandarana, H. Herzog, C. W. Le Roux, E. L. Thomas, J. D. Bell, D. J. Withers. "Critical Role for Peptide YY in Protein-Mediated Satiation and Body-Weight Regulation." *Cell Metabolism* 4, no. 3 (2006): 223–33.

Batterham, R. L., M. A. Cowley, C. J. Small, H. Herzog, M. A. Cohen, C. L. Dakin, A. M. Wren, et al. "Gut Hormone PYY(3-36) Physiologically Inhibits Food Intake." *Nature* 418, no. 6898 (August 8, 2002): 650–4.

Boron, W. F. *Medical Physiology: A Cellular and Molecular Approach.* Philadelphia, PA: Elsevier-Saunders, 2003.

DeGroot, Leslie Jacob. *Endocrinology.* Edited by J. E. McGuigan. Philadelphia, PA: Saunders, 1989.

Gromada, J., I. Franklin, and C. B. Wollheim. "Alpha-Cells of the Endocrine Pancreas: 35 Years of Research but the Enigma Remains." *Endocrine Reviews* 28, no. 1 (February 2007): 84–116.

Guarente, L. "Sirtuins, Aging, and Medicine." *New England Journal of Medicine* 364, (2011): 2235–44.

Havel, P. J., J. O. Akpan, D. L. Curry, J. S. Stern, R. L. Gingerich, and B. Ahren. "Autonomic Control of Pancreatic Polypeptide and Glucagon Secretion During Neuroglucopenia and Hypoglycemia in Mice." *American Journal of Physiology* 265, no. 1 Pt 2 (July 1993): R246–54.

Holst, J. J. "Glucagon and Glucagon-Like Peptides 1 and 2." *Results and Problems in Cell Differentiation* 50, (2010): 121–35.

Lihn, A. S., S. B. Pedersen, and B. Richelsen. "Adiponectin: Action, Regulation and Association to Insulin Sensitivity." *Obesity Reviews* 6, no. 1 (February 2005): 13–21.

Lombard, David B., and Richard A. Miller. "Ageing: Sorting Out the Sirtuins." *Nature* 483 (2011): 166–7.

Minor, R. K., J. W. Chang, and R. de Cabo. "Hungry for Life: How the Arcuate Nucleus and Neuropeptide Y May Play a Critical Role in Mediating the Benefits of Calorie Restriction." *Molecular and Cellular Endocrinology* 299, no.1 (2009): 79–88.

Murphy, K. G., and S. R. Bloom. "Gut Hormones and the Regulation of Energy Homeostasis." *Nature* 444, no. 7121 (2006): 854–9.

Myers, M. G., M. A. Cowley, and H. Münzberg. "Mechanisms of Leptin Action and Leptin Resistance." *Annual Review of Physiology* 70 (2008): 537–56.

Wu, Y., and R. J. Koenig. "Gene Regulation by Thyroid Hormone." *Trends in Endocrinology and Metabolism* 11, no. 6 (August 2000): 207–11.

Yamauchi, T., J. Kamon, Y. Ito, A. Tsuchida, T. Yokomizo, S. Kita, T. Sugiyama, et al. "Cloning of Adiponectin Receptors That Mediate Antidiabetic Metabolic Effects." *Nature* 423, no. 6941 (2003): 762–9.

Zhang, J., and M. A. Lazar. "The Mechanism of Action of Thyroid Hormones." *Annual Review of Physiology* 62 (2000): 439–66.

Bray, G. A. "Pathophysiology of Obesity." *The American Journal of Clinical Nutrition* 55 (1992): 488S–94S.

Gatenby, R. A., and R. J. Gillies. "Why Do Cancers Have High Aerobic Glycolysis?" *Nature Reviews Cancer* 4, no. 11 (2004): 891–9.

Hansen, B. C., and G. A. Bray. "The Metabolic Syndrome: Epidemiology, Clinical Treatment, and Underlying Mechanisms." *Humana Press* 2010.

Lean, M. E. "Pathophysiology of Obesity." *The Proceedings of the Nutrition Society* 59, no. 3 (2000): 331–6.

Orth, Jeffrey D., Ines Thiele, and Bernhard Ø. Palsson. "What Is Flux Balance Analysis?" *Nature Biotechnology* 28, no. 3 (2010): 245–8.

Padwal, R. S., and S. R. Majumdar. "Drug Treatments for Obesity: Orlistat, Sibutramine, and Rimonabant." *The Lancet* 369, no. 9555 (2007): 6–12, 71–77.

Pi-Sunyer, F. Xavier. "The Obesity Epidemic: Pathophysiology and Consequences of Obesity." *Obesity Research* 10 (2002): 97S–104S.

Scacchi, M., A. I. Pincelli, and F. Cavagnini. "Growth Hormone in Obesity." *International Journal of Obesity and Related Metabolic Disorders* 23, no. 3 (1999): 260–71.

Regulation and Integration of Metabolism

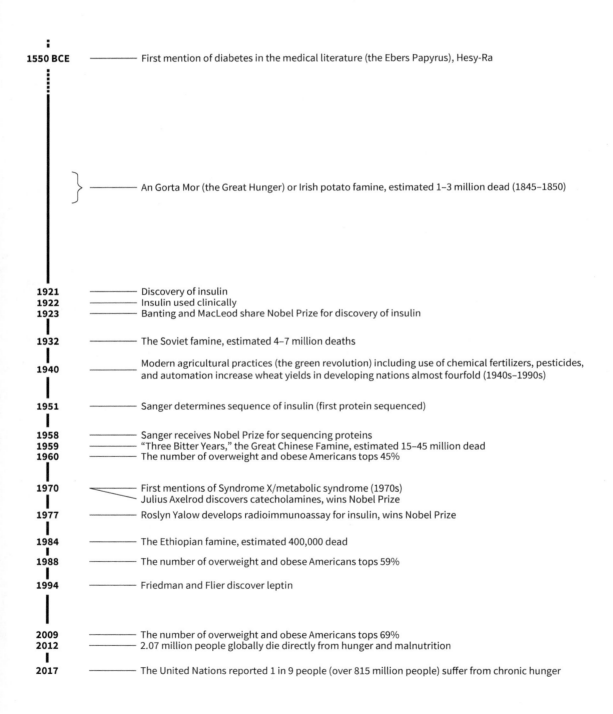

1550 BCE ——————— First mention of diabetes in the medical literature (the Ebers Papyrus), Hesy-Ra

An Gorta Mor (the Great Hunger) or Irish potato famine, estimated 1–3 million dead (1845–1850)

1921 ——————— Discovery of insulin
1922 ——————— Insulin used clinically
1923 ——————— Banting and MacLeod share Nobel Prize for discovery of insulin

1932 ——————— The Soviet famine, estimated 4–7 million deaths

1940 ——————— Modern agricultural practices (the green revolution) including use of chemical fertilizers, pesticides, and automation increase wheat yields in developing nations almost fourfold (1940s–1990s)

1951 ——————— Sanger determines sequence of insulin (first protein sequenced)

1958 ——————— Sanger receives Nobel Prize for sequencing proteins
1959 ——————— "Three Bitter Years," the Great Chinese Famine, estimated 15–45 million dead
1960 ——————— The number of overweight and obese Americans tops 45%

1970 ——————— First mentions of Syndrome X/metabolic syndrome (1970s)
Julius Axelrod discovers catecholamines, wins Nobel Prize

1977 ——————— Roslyn Yalow develops radioimmunoassay for insulin, wins Nobel Prize

1984 ——————— The Ethiopian famine, estimated 400,000 dead

1988 ——————— The number of overweight and obese Americans tops 59%

1994 ——————— Friedman and Flier discover leptin

2009 ——————— The number of overweight and obese Americans tops 69%
2012 ——————— 2.07 million people globally die directly from hunger and malnutrition

2017 ——————— The United Nations reported 1 in 9 people (over 815 million people) suffer from chronic hunger

Techniques

Affinity chromatography

When and why it is used: Affinity chromatography is one of the most common chromatography techniques, and it is used in nearly any biochemical isolation or purification.

How it works: In affinity chromatography, as in all chromatography, there is a mobile and a stationary phase. Molecules partition differentially between the two, leading to separation and enrichment of one molecule over another. In affinity chromatography, the solid phase can be more general such as a C8 or C18 matrix, meaning a matrix coated with hydrocarbon chains either 8 or 18 carbons long, or it can be more specific such as an antibody binding to a specific antigen or protein of interest. The mobile phase washes away molecules that have not bound as tightly, and the molecules of interest are eluted, or released from the solid phase, through a change in solvent polarity or pH, or outcompeted by addition of more ligand.

Strengths and weaknesses: There are many different types of affinity chromatography, and the technique can be easily scaled up to preparative levels or scaled down to run small analytical assays. While the matrix costs can vary across the different types of techniques, affinity chromatography is a common and flexible technique used in labs worldwide.

Analytical ultracentrifugation

When and why it is used: Analytical ultracentrifugation is a technique which measures the ability of a pure protein or macromolecular complex to sediment when subjected to a high centrifugal force. It is used to deduce the hydrodynamic properties of a particle or molecule, such as the number of subunits that are associated with one another in solution.

How it works: A sample is applied to the top of an analytical centrifuge tube and spun in the centrifuge. The optics of the centrifuge detect the progression of the band of protein as it migrates to the bottom of the tube as the tube is spun. Based on how quickly the sample sediments, the composition of the liquid in the tube, and several other factors, the sedimentation coefficient, S, can be determined. S for any protein or complex is dependent on several factors including the size and dimensions of the complex.

Strengths and weaknesses: Analytical ultracentrifugation requires a dedicated instrument; an ordinary ultracentrifuge will not work. The information it provides, for example, the stoichiometry of subunits in solution, is of interest but can also be derived from other techniques such as size exclusion chromatography or X-ray crystallography.

Chemical tests for carbohydrates

When and why it is used: Tests for carbohydrates are classic techniques in biochemistry. Although they have largely been replaced by enzymatic methods, the chemistry that underlies them is still the basis of several detection methods. These tests are often an excellent first step in the characterization of an unknown.

How it works: There are several assays for carbohydrates. Most take advantage of the observation that carbohydrates contain aldehyde and ketone groups and are subject to oxidation. Some common tests are:

Benedicts test consists of an alkaline solution of Cu^{2+} ions and citrate. The copper ions will react with free aldehydes generating brick-red copper I oxide (cuprous oxide, Cu_2O) from the blue Cu^{2+} ions and oxidizing the aldehyde to a carboxylic acid. Ketoses will isomerize to aldoses under the assay's alkaline conditions. This test is therefore a general test for almost any monosaccharide or disaccharide.

Barfoed's test uses similar chemistry to the Benedicts test with one important difference. The assay is run under mildly acidic conditions. Under these conditions, ketoses will not isomerize and disaccharides also fail to react. This test is more specific for aldoses.

Seliwanoff's test and *Bial's test* exploit different aspects of carbohydrate chemistry. In both of these tests, carbohydrates are dehydrated with acid to form a conjugated alkene, either furfural or hydroxymethyl furfural. *Seliwanoff's* reagent contains resorcinol, which undergoes a condensation reaction with hydroxymethylfurfural to give a red product. This test is used for ketohexoses or disaccharides containing a ketohexose. Bial's test contains orcinol instead of resorcinol and reacts with furfural to give a green product, indicative of pentoses.

The *Molisch test* uses somewhat similar chemistry to the Seliwanoff and Bial tests. A sample of carbohydrates is mixed with α-napthol. The mixture is overlaid on a sample of concentrated H_2SO_4; a purple color is indicative of monosaccharides that have formed a colored product (furfural or hydroxymethylfurfural) with the napthol.

The *iodine test for starches* takes advantage of the observation that iodine will bind to starches and turn blue. A solution of molecular iodine in water (I_2), often mixed with an iodine salt such as KI to help stabilize the iodine, is added to a sample. If the sample turns blue (the color can range from purple to green), it is a positive indication for starch. The blue color is thought to arise from I_3^- ions binding in the core of the starch helix.

Strengths and weaknesses: These tests are rapid, inexpensive, and easy to perform. The Benedicts test was the basis of home diabetes testing for over 80 years. The tests are usually qualitative, but some can be made quantitative with the use of standards. The tests are usually not specific; for example, they may reveal that a sample contains a reducing sugar but do not explicitly identify which sugar. They also require more material than modern analytical techniques.

Cell disruption

When and why it is used: Most biological samples are found inside the cell or tissue. It is often necessary to disrupt those cells to gain access to those molecules for purification or characterization. Following disruption, proteins can be studied or isolated, or the resulting cellular lysate can be fractionated using differential ultracentrifugation, a process termed cell fractionation. Cell fractionation is used to identify where in the cell a specific protein or process occurs, by colocalizing that protein or activity with known markers.

How it works: Numerous disruption techniques are available, but they require care because overambitious disruption can damage organelles, complexes, or proteins. Some cells can be lysed simply by incubating them in a hypotonic solution. Depending on the sample, detergents or enzymes may be added to assist in the lysis. Shearing a sample of cells by passing them through a narrow orifice, such as a narrow-gauge needle, is another way to gently disrupt the cell. These gentle techniques often leave many cellular complexes intact and are used to study larger organelles and complexes.

A more vigorous means of disrupting cells involves physically grinding them in a blender, homogenizer, or bead beater. Blenders and homogenizers shear or physically cut the cells open using mechanical force. Bead beaters use glass or ceramic beads sealed in a container with cells and buffer. The container is shaken vigorously, and the cells rupture. A French press homogenizer passes cells through a narrow orifice at high pressure, greater than 5000 psi. These techniques are used for cells that are more resistant to lysis or may have a cell wall or protective coating, as is the case with spores, for example.

In nitrogen cavitation, a sample is incubated with nitrogen or another inert gas at high pressure, greater than 20,000 psi, until the gas is dissolved in the cell. The pressure is rapidly released, and the gas boils out of the cell, rupturing cells and organelles.

Chemically, cells can be disrupted either using detergents to dissolve the plasma membrane or enzymes to degrade the cell wall or membrane. Here, care must be taken to choose detergents that will permeabilize the cell without denaturing the proteins of interest. Bacteria are often lysed open using lysozyme, an enzyme commonly isolated from hen eggs. This enzyme degrades the polysaccharides found in the bacterial cell wall. Without this wall the bacterium loses structural integrity and is more susceptible to hypotonic lysis.

Finally, ultrasonic disruption uses a titanium probe that vibrates at 20,000 Hz to disrupt cells. This is the most effective means of disrupting cells but is so strong that damage to macromolecules is a potential problem. Also, precautions must also be taken to avoid overheating of the sample.

Strengths and weaknesses: There are many techniques available to disrupt cells. Depending on the desired outcome, cells can be gently lysed or blown apart.

ChIP (chromatin immunoprecipitation) assay

When and why is it used: Chromatin immunoprecipitation assays are used to identify proteins, such as histones or transcription factors, that are bound to specific genes or DNA sequences.

How it works: Proteins and DNA are reversibly cross-linked using formaldehyde. The sample is sonicated to shear the DNA into smaller fragments. An immunoprecipitation is performed using an antibody directed against a protein of interest, for example, a specific transcription factor. This precipitation will pull down the protein-antibody complex, along with the DNA cross-linked to the protein. The cross-linking is reversed by heating, and the DNA fragments are amplified using PCR and sequenced. There are multiple variants of this assay, which vary with regard to cross-linking conditions and detection methods.

Strengths and weaknesses: The ChIP assay is relatively simple to perform and can be adapted for high-throughput analysis. However, the ChIP assay often suffers from low sensitivity and often cannot give a target sequence with high resolution. Finally, ChIP assays cannot give functional data; it is not possible to tell if the proteins bound to the DNA sequence are biologically significant.

Circular dichroism

When and why it is used: Circular dichroism is a technique used to analyze the ability of a sample to differentially absorb either left- or right-circularly polarized light. The absorbance of circularly polarized light is due to interactions with chiral structures. As such, it is used as a measure of α-helicity in proteins or the helical structures of nucleic acids.

How it works: The CD spectrophotometer measures the absorbance of polarized light. Basic units operate much like any other sort of absorbance spectrophotometer. There is a light source, typically in the UV range, the sample, and a detector. CD differs in that its filters circularly polarize the light before it reaches the sample. More advanced instruments enable investigators to alter experimental conditions, such as temperature, and measure changes in the spectra.

Strengths and weaknesses: CD spectroscopy is quick and simple to use and provides straightforward answers, but these answers are often limited. A CD experiment can tell you, for example, that a protein sample is 45% alpha helix, but it cannot tell you where that helix is found in the protein or what the rest of the structure looks like.

Click chemistry

When and why it is used: Click chemistry is a generic term used to describe small modular chemical reactions that proceed with high yield in a complex environment. These reactions do not occur in biochemical systems but can be effectively used to label or otherwise react biological molecules and do so under biological conditions.

How it works: There are several examples of click chemistry. One of the best studied examples of a click reaction is the copper catalyzed alkyne-azide cycloaddition (the Huisgen cycloaddition).

In this reaction an alkyne and an azide undergo a cycloaddition forming a five-membered ring, and Cu^+ serves as a catalyst. Because the reaction is specific and can occur at high yield in conditions typically found in a biological system, and neither the azo nor the alkyne functional moieties are typically found in nature, this reaction fits the description of a click reaction.

Either azo or alkyne functional groups are synthetically incorporated into a lipid, carbohydrate, nucleotide, or amino acid in the laboratory. These modified molecules (for example, an alkyne fatty acid) are then biosynthetically incorporated into a larger biological molecule, such as a phospholipid. This molecule can be labeled in a biological system using an azo click chemistry partner that is conjugated to a fluorescent dye or other molecule.

Strengths and weaknesses: The main advantage of click chemistry is the high yield of these reactions under what might normally be very difficult reaction conditions—generally biological conditions, relatively low temperature, numerous contaminants, and aqueous solvent. Click labels are very small compared to other labeling technologies. Numerous reagents are now commercially available for click labeling, and several assays, such as assays for cell proliferation and lipid peroxidation, are now commercially available. The weaknesses of this system are that the copper used can be mildly cytotoxic, and the click labeled reagents need to be generated in such a way that they are bioavailable to the cell; that is, the cells need to be able to incorporate these molecules as they normally would for other biological processes.

CRISPR-Cas9

When and why it is used: CRISPR is an acronym for Clustered Regularly Interspersed Short Palindromic Repeats. CRISPR describes short sequences identified in prokaryotes that act in conjunction with Cas9, a specific nuclease to serve as a primitive immune system in these organisms. CRISPR-Cas9 is a flexible and easy means of editing a genome.

How it works: There are two components to the CRISPR-Cas9 system. In prokaryotes, the Cas9 nuclease recognizes specific DNA sequences and cleaves them. In these organisms the DNA sequences that are recognized come from viruses that have previously infected the bacterium. Cas9 is directed to these sites through a guide RNA. It is relatively easy to transfect other cells using a cDNA that encodes the Cas9 nuclease and contains a guide RNA directed against the region of the genome that an investigator wishes to edit. This means that based on the design of the guide RNA, any gene can be altered using this technique, and it can be done in a live complex organism.

Strengths and weaknesses: CRISPR is a relatively new technology but one with incredible promise. CRISPR is a very simple and inexpensive technology to use, involving only transfection or infection of cells with a plasmid encoding Cas9 and the guide RNA. It effectively and efficiently edits the genome and can be altered to make several different types of changes, including deletions and insertions. People have raised ethical concerns that CRISPR could be used to edit human genomes, but these questions are often raised when novel technologies are developed.

Cryo-EM

When and why it is used: Cryo-EM is an imaging technique used to determine the structure of macromolecules, including proteins and nucleic acids. Often these are larger complexes of molecules.

How it works: Cryo-EM is a transmission electron microscopy technique. In this technique, there are several important differences between cryo-EM and traditional EM techniques. First, the experiment is conducted at very low temperature and using a weaker electron beam to keep from damaging the molecules. Second, the images of thousands of proteins are analyzed to generate a high-resolution image of the molecule in question.

Strengths and weaknesses: Structure determination of macromolecules is still in many instances the holy grail of biochemistry; however, these structures are still difficult to obtain. NMR is largely useful only for small molecules while X-ray diffraction is often limited by the ability to grow crystals of a protein. Cryo-EM does not require crystallization and therefore presents a much easier way to determine the structure of a protein or complex. In addition, complexes that will not crystalize due to complexity or other factors can still be imaged using cryo-EM.

Density gradient ultracentrifugation

When and why it is used: Ultracentrifugation is a classic technique used to separate the components found in cellular lysates or plasma lipoproteins. The technique is commonly employed in cell fractionation studies, where cells are lysed and the components separated based on density.

How it works: There are variations on this technique, but all use salts, sucrose, or colloidal solutions, such as Percoll (colloidal silica coated with polyvinyl pyrolidone) to adjust the density of the solution. Gradients are centrifuged until the molecular complexes pellet or band at their isopycnic density, the point where the density of the complex and the surrounding medium are equivalent. Typical centrifugation experiments span several hours to a day in length and employ

forces of 20,000–2,000,000× g to achieve separations. In differential centrifugation, the density of the centrifugation media is adjusted and the molecule, complex or organelle of interest, is floated or pelleted away from the other components of the lysate. In isopycnic centrifugation, samples are centrifuged until they float at the same density of the media in which they are suspended. Cellular lysates in buffer are overlaid, underlaid, or placed within a gradient of media of differing density. Samples are centrifuged until the complex of interest forms a band at the density of the complex. Complexes migrate through a density gradient based on the mass, shape, and partial specific volume of the complex. These techniques easily separate organelles, plasma lipoproteins, and macromolecular complexes, but they are not commonly used to purify or isolate soluble proteins.

Preparative ultracentrifugation differs from analytical ultracentrifugation experiments, which measures the sedimentation rate of a pure protein to give hydrodynamic information about the protein. Analytical ultracentrifugation is performed under very different conditions and with a different instrument.

Strengths and weaknesses: Ultracentrifugation is a simple and common technique for the isolation of organelles and macromolecular complexes. The technique used to disrupt the cell prior to centrifugation must be chosen carefully to avoid destroying the finer structure of organelles and complexes.

Dialysis and ultrafiltration

When and why it is used: Dialysis and ultrafiltration employ microporous membranes to achieve separation of molecules based on size or on concentration of larger molecules.

How it works: Dialysis uses a dialysis membrane—a bag with pores large enough to permit passage of small molecules but not larger ones. A range of different cutoff sizes is available, ranging from hundreds of Daltons to hundreds of thousands of Daltons. A sample is put into the dialysis bag and the bag is bathed in a beaker containing buffer or other solutions. Over time, generally several hours, molecules below the molecular weight cutoff, which correspond to the size of the pore, will diffuse between the bag and the buffer in the beaker, while the larger molecules will be retained. This technique is typically used to remove a small molecule, such as a salt, or in some cases larger molecules up to the size of large proteins.

Ultrafiltration is often used to concentrate a sample of macromolecules. This technique also employs a dialysis membrane but in a different configuration. Here, the membrane is found at the bottom of a chamber that is filled with the sample to be filtered. Pressure is applied using either a pressurized gas or a centrifuge to drive the solution through the dialysis membrane. In effect, this works like catching pasta in a colander, larger molecules are retained while the solvent and smaller molecules are lost. Newer versions of this apparatus are designed to prevent the loss of all solvent and thus prevent the filter from running dry.

Strengths and weaknesses: Dialysis has been employed for decades and is affordable and easy to do. Newer geometries of dialysis membranes minimize sample loss, but there is always a fear of losing sample due to a leaky membrane.

Differential scanning calorimetry (DSC)

When and why it is used: Differential scanning calorimetry (DSC) is a calorimetric technique that measures the absorbance of energy required to change the temperature of a sample. In the simplest case, DSC can detect phase transitions. Although it is frequently used to precisely detect how a protein and nucleic acid denature, DSC is used as a tool to measure protein stability and protein folding.

How it works: Highly pure samples are placed into the calorimeter. The device precisely measures the amount of energy input to the calorimetry chamber as well as the temperature. Based on these values, phase transitions or denaturation can be determined.

Strengths and weaknesses: DSC is a relatively common technique that is simple to perform. The experiment requires small but relatively pure samples for analysis but provides interesting and important thermodynamic data.

DNA (or RNA) footprinting assay

When and why is it used: Footprinting assays are used to determine which specific segments of a nucleic acid are protected from enzymatic degradation by nucleases. Classically, the footprint is thought of as being bound by proteins, such as histones or transcription factors, but can also be due to secondary structure, as in a riboswitch.

How it works: Typically, a fragment of nucleic acids, either DNA or RNA, are terminally labeled with radiolabeled nucleotides. These fragments are then partially digested by a nuclease such as DNAse I in the presence or absence of molecules thought to bind or otherwise protect the nucleic acid from degradation. The resulting fragments are separated by gel electrophoresis, usually acrylamide. In this instance, the fragments can be detected using autoradiography, but other techniques such as fluorescence, Southern, or northern blotting can also be used.

Strengths and weaknesses: Footprinting assays can be highly informative, revealing which DNA sequences are protected with base pair resolution, but finding the correct conditions for protein binding and digestion can be challenging.

DNA sequencing

When and why it is used: Classically, DNA sequencing is used to determine the nucleotide sequence in DNA. Newer techniques use parallel technologies to sequence entire genomes.

How it works: In first-generation DNA sequencing, there is a sequencing mixture that contains a DNA polymerase, a template to be sequenced, a primer, an oligonucleotide from which the polymerase can extend that will specifically bind the sequence to be sequenced, and radiolabeled deoxynucleotide triphosphates. This mixture is divided into four reactions; each reaction utilizes a small amount of a different dideoxynucleotide triphosphate. Because these dideoxynucleotides lack a hydroxyl group on C-3 of the deoxyribose ring, the polymerase is unable to extend from one of these nucleotides, blocking further elongation from that chain. Because a different dideoxynucleotide is in each reaction, the base found at the end of that chain can be identified. The products of the four reactions are resolved on a polyacrylamide electrophoresis gel that can resolve pieces of DNA that differ in length by a single base. A film exposed to this gel shows bands that give the order of the individual bases.

The next evolution of this technology employed terminator nucleotides tagged with fluorescent dye. Terminator or dideoxynucleotides lack a 3' hydroxyl group and prevent further elongation of the DNA chain. Because the different nucleotides could be labeled with different fluorophores, only one reaction was needed. In addition, the strands were separated with a capillary column rather than a gel. This enabled the entire system to be automated to run as many as 384 samples at once.

Using the latest techniques, it is possible to sequence an entire genome at once. These techniques use a combination of modern polymerase chain reaction (PCR), advances in microscopic techniques, and advanced data processing. Between hundreds of thousands and billions of individual sequencing reactions occur at once and are read on a microscope slide. Short sequences of 25–250 bases are gradually built up, analyzed for quality, and then assembled into a full genome.

Strengths and weaknesses: Knowing the nucleotide sequence of a piece of DNA is amazingly powerful. It can show which sequences code and which do not, what is coded for by the sequencing codes, and what control elements there are. The cost of sequencing has dropped by several orders of magnitude as the technology has developed and progressed. Perhaps the only weaknesses of the technology are the startup cost, the sheer volume of data that modern sequencing produces, and how to mine useful and meaningful information from that data.

Ectopic protein expression

When and why it is used: In many instances, it is desirable to study proteins in different cell types or to produce significant quantities of protein. In such cases, ectopic protein expression, or overexpression, is a useful technique.

How it works: The cDNA of the gene of interest is cloned into a vector (such as a plasmid) and transduced or infected into the cells of interest. The cells are often put under some type of selection, usually treatment with an antibiotic, to select for those that have acquired the vector. If the vector has been engineered with the proper promoter sequence for the cell type that has acquired the DNA, the gene will be expressed. The protein may accumulate within the cell or be secreted, depending on the nature of the protein and how it is processed in the cell. This too, will vary depending on the protein and the cell type.

Strengths and weaknesses: The ability of a cell to internalize a piece of DNA and produce protein is one of the most powerful tools of modern biochemistry. Overall, it is relatively easy to use DNA to get cells to produce a protein, but the process can be difficult when a specific protein needs to be expressed in a specific cell type or using a particular vector. Investigators must understand that not all cells process proteins in the same way or have the capacity to secrete these proteins. Likewise, when investigating proteins in cells that do not normally produce the protein in question, there can be complications, for example, other compensatory mechanisms or missing interaction partners.

Edman degradation

When and why it is used: The Edman degradation is a means of sequencing a protein by rounds of successive derivatization and cleavage of the amino terminus. Using this technique, it is possible to determine the sequence of an entire protein or identify a protein based on the sequence of the first few amino acids. The process was first described by Pehr Edman in 1950.

How it works: In an Edman degradation, the amino terminus of a protein is derivatized, usually with phenylisothiocyanate. This compound reacts with the free amino terminus to form a phenylthiocarbamoyl derivative, which is readily cleaved with acid to yield a thiazolinone. Subsequent treatment of the cleaved amino acid derivative with more acid gives a phenylthiohydantoin, which can be identified by high-performance liquid chromatography (HPLC) or mass spectrometry. The process is repeated until the protein is characterized.

Strengths and weaknesses: The Edman degradation was one of the first successful ways to determine the sequence of a protein. The process is simple and straightforward and has been used to develop automated sequencing devices. Unfortunately, in practice the characterization of a protein is complicated by incomplete reactions and usually only about 30 amino acids can be identified from a single amino terminus. Today, the amino acid sequence of a protein is more often determined from the mRNA sequence, while unknown proteins are identified by mass spectrometry.

Electron paramagnetic resonance

When and why it is used: Electron paramagnetic resonance (EPR), also known as electron spin resonance (ESR), is a technique that is used to probe the spin states of electrons and thus to detect unpaired electrons in a sample or reaction or to probe the redox states of a complex.

How it works: EPR is analogous to nuclear magnetic resonance (NMR). Samples are placed in a strong magnetic field. All electrons have a spin state associated with them known as the m quantum number. The electron either has a spin state of $+\frac{1}{2}$ or $-\frac{1}{2}$. Most electrons found in filled orbitals or in chemical bonds adhere to Hund's rule and must be spin-paired. However, unpaired electrons such as radicals and some redox states are not spin-paired. As a result, when probed with the correct wavelength of energy, typically microwaves in the EPR experiment, the system will absorb energy, giving a signal analogous to the NMR signal. The EPR signal is far simpler to interpret than an NMR signal because of the paucity of unpaired electrons in the sample.

Strengths and weaknesses: EPR can only be used when unpaired electrons are present; however, if they are, it is a relatively simple matter to obtain a spectrum. The normal complications in an NMR experiment such as complexity of signal, solvent effects, and overlap of peaks are not concerns in EPR.

Enzymatic assays

When and why it is used: Enzymatic assays are used to assay a sample for a specific molecule or metabolite. They do not typically require the isolation of the molecule to be tested, that is, they can be used on a crude mixture or biological sample, and they can be highly specific and sensitive.

How it works: An enzyme that catalyzes a reaction specific for the molecule of interest yields a product. For example, glucose oxidase reacts specifically with glucose to give glucuronic acid and hydrogen peroxide. One of these products is used in a secondary reaction to give a fluorescent, colored, or chemiluminescent product, which is detected spectrophotometrically. Hydrogen peroxide, for example, will react with dyes, fluorophores, or luminescent molecules to provide a signal. The assay is typically used with a standard curve to provide quantitative results.

Strengths and weaknesses: Enzymatic assays can be both highly specific and sensitive. For example, assays can detect glucose but not galactose or glucosamine and can detect this carbohydrate in the nanomolar range. With advances in molecular biology and protein expression, there are few enzymes that cannot be overexpressed; as a result, prices of enzymes have reduced dramatically, making these assays affordable, although not as inexpensive as chemical tests for functional groups, such as the tests used for carbohydrates. The tests are usually easy to perform, especially the commercial kits or clinical tests, and little to no specific equipment is needed other than a detection system. However, results must be validated in some way to ensure that the biological samples are not being complicated by other molecules in the mixture.

Enzyme-coupled assay

When and why it is used: Often in the laboratory or clinic, the concentration of a specific metabolite must be obtained. However, the concentration of the metabolite may be low submicromolar to nanomolar, and the metabolite may be in a complex mixture with other biomolecules. Also, the molecule in question may be similar to other molecules in the mix.

One method commonly used to assay molecules in such situations is to employ an enzyme-based assay. Enzymes often function perfectly well in complex mixtures and can be highly specific for a given substrate.

How it works: Enzyme-based assays consist of a sample, a reaction mixture that includes an enzyme specific for the molecule in question, and some means of detecting that the reaction has happened. Often these enzymes are oxidoreductases, which cause a change in the redox state of NAD^+, $NADP^+$, or FAD, or generate H_2O_2. Assays that cause a change in the redox state of an electron carrier can be detected spectrophotometrically. Assays that generate H_2O_2 include fluorophores or dyes that react with the H_2O_2 and are read spectrophotometrically. The values obtained are compared to a set of standards to determine the concentration in the sample. If a specific oxidoreductase is not available for the molecule in question, other enzymes may be included to transform the unknown molecule into one that can be used to produce a signal.

Strengths and weaknesses: Enzyme-coupled assays can be highly specific, rapid, and sensitive. With advances that have been made in recombinant enzyme expression and purification, the cost of these assays has dropped considerably. Likewise, advances in fluorescent dye chemistry have resulted in assays that can easily measure unknowns in microliter-sized samples. One weakness of these assays is the nature of the detection system. If the detection system is based on the amount of $FADH_2$ or H_2O_2 produced for a signal, any component in the sample producing those compounds could affect the result.

Enzyme-linked immunosorbent assay (ELISA) and radioimmunoassay (RIA)

When and why they are used: ELISA and RIA are techniques used to quantify the amount of a single biomolecule—often a protein—in a complex mixture.

How they work: ELISA and RIA take advantage of an antibody specific to the molecule of interest for detection. There are several different variations on the assay.

In a direct ELISA assay, a mixture of proteins is bound to an assay plate or dish. An antibody directed against the molecule of interest is added and binds specifically to the protein of interest; all other antibodies are washed away. The antibody can then be detected using a second antibody that will recognize the first. This second antibody has an enzyme conjugated to it that catalyzes a chemical reaction, resulting in the development of a colored product. In a sandwich ELISA assay, the dish is coated with an antibody that recognizes the protein of interest. All other proteins are washed away, and the protein is detected with a second enzyme-coupled antibody against the protein.

In an RIA, a small amount of pure target molecule is radiolabeled with iodine (^{125}I). The antibody is bound to the assay plate with the radiolabeled target molecule. An unknown sample is added and competes with the antibody for the radiolabeled target. If more sample is added, more radiolabeled protein will be released. This can be quantified in a gamma counter and the amount of protein in the unknown sample calculated.

Strengths and weaknesses: Both ELISA and RIA are able to quantify the amount of a molecule in a mixture; there is no need to purify the molecule of interest, and the assays are sensitive into the nanomolar range. Kits are currently available for many molecules that make the assay simple and quick to conduct, but kits can be expensive, ranging from several hundred to a thousand dollars for 100 assays. RIA assays use radioactivity, typically isotopes of iodine, and thus require special handling.

Fluorescence anisotropy

When and why it is used: Fluorescence anisotropy is used to determine how quickly a fluorescent molecule (fluorophore) rotates in a system. In effect, it is a measure of rotational freedom and can be used in conjunction with other parameters to calculate the general axial ratios of a molecule, referred to as the Stokes radius.

How it works: Polarized light is used to excite a fluorophore, which captures the photon. The fluorophore keeps this photon as the molecule freely rotates. At some later time, microseconds to milliseconds, the photon is emitted. Because the fluorophore can move, the degree of polarization of the emitted photon is lost, and the loss is dependent on the movement—with molecules exhibiting greater movement also exhibiting greater loss of polarization. Because the polarization can be easily measured, this is an excellent means of calculating the degree of rotation of the fluorophore.

Strengths and weaknesses: Fluorescence anisotropy is typically conducted using specialized fluorimeters, purified samples, and fluorescent tags or molecules. Once the initial setup is completed, anisotropy experiments often yield interesting biophysical data about a system.

Fluorescence *in situ* hybridization (FISH)

When and why it is used: FISH is used to quickly identify where in the genome a gene or fragment of a chromosome is located.

How it works: FISH is a fluorescence microscopy technique. A spread of metaphase chromosomes is obtained from a biological sample, such as a cheek swab or blood sample. The chromosomes are fixed and stained with fluorescent dyes to indicate where both the DNA and gene or sequence of interest is found. The samples are analyzed under a fluorescence microscope. Because of the availability of different colored dyes and advanced microscope optics, it is very common to compare multiple colors simultaneously, meaning that multiple sequences can be identified. FISH commonly uses three to five different dyes; however, as many as 23 different colors (a different color for each chromosome) can be compared, leading to the other name for this technique: chromosome painting.

Strengths and weaknesses: FISH is a relatively easy, rapid, straightforward technique. Better dyes and staining kits have improved the technique. The cost of the microscope is often the limiting factor, although simple FISH experiments can be done with any fluorescence microscope. FISH can provide quick answers to simple

questions, for instance, if there are multiple copies of a chromosome or whether or not a chromosomal rearrangement occurred. However, FISH is an optical technique and cannot provide information at the molecular level. For instance, it could be used to determine if a fragment of one chromosome has been fused to another, but it could not tell you exactly where in the sequence the fusion occurred.

Fluorescence microscopy or immunofluorescence

When and why it is used: Fluorescence microscopy or immunofluorescence is used to identify and localize proteins in the cell. It is also the foundation of several related techniques, including FRET (Forster's or fluorescence resonance energy transfer), FRAP (fluorescence recovery after photobleaching), FISH (fluorescence *in situ* hybridization), and a host of other techniques.

How it works: Cells are labeled with a fluorophore: a molecule that will fluoresce under certain wavelengths of light. The fluorophore can be a nonspecific dye, such as dyes for lipids and hydrophobic compartments, or nucleic acid dyes; dyes that target specific organelles, such as mitochondria or lysosomes; or chimeric proteins made by expressing the cDNA of a protein of interest fused to the cDNA from a naturally fluorescent protein such as Green Fluorescent Protein, Yellow Fluorescent Protein, or mCherry. Proteins may also be labeled with a fluorescent antibody. Often, two antibodies are used: the first one recognizes the protein of interest, while the second is fluorescently labeled and recognizes the first antibody. Using a combination of these techniques, multiple molecules can be detected at once.

Strengths and weaknesses: Fluorescence is a workhorse of modern experimental biology and has become one of the most common techniques of cell biology. It also provides invaluable information to the biochemist and offers additional means of localizing molecules in the cell, thus providing clues to the function of a molecule or complex. The technique requires a fluorescence microscope, the cost of which can be prohibitive, depending on the technique being employed; higher end confocal microscopes can cost upwards of half a million dollars. Specific antibodies or cDNA constructs are also required to visualize each molecule of interest.

Fluorescence recovery after photobleaching (FRAP)

When and why it is used: FRAP is used to measure the mobility of a molecule in a plasma membrane; that is, it measures whether a molecule is floating freely in the membrane or is tethered to other molecules or in other ways restrained.

How it works: FRAP is performed using a fluorescence microscope fitted with special optics. First, a cell is fluorescently labeled using a fluorescent tag or dye. A laser is used to photobleach a spot on the cell. If the labeled molecules are small and untethered, they will quickly diffuse back into the spot, and the fluorescent signal seen at the spot will recover. If, however, the labeled molecule is anchored to some immobile element, the fluorescent signal will not return after photobleaching. Based on the rate of return, the diffusional coefficient of the molecule in question can be determined. The diffusional coefficient can provide other information; for example, if the diffusional coefficient correlates with a much slower time, it indicates that the labeled molecule may be associated with a much larger complex.

Strengths and weaknesses: FRAP is a relatively simple and rapid way to determine the lateral diffusional coefficient of a molecule in a membrane, but it can be expensive. Usually, FRAP is part of a confocal microscope setup which costs several hundred thousand dollars.

Fluorescence spectroscopy

When and why it is used: Fluorescence spectroscopy is a common optical technique that is used to directly detect some biological molecules. It is now currently used in conjunction with synthetic dyes and techniques (such as anisotropy, FRET, or immunofluorescence microscopy) as a detection method.

How it works: Fluorescence is a physical property of some compounds; generally, organic compounds with highly conjugated pi bond systems or some inorganic compounds. When these molecules interact with light of a specific wavelength they absorb a photon, exciting an electron from the ground state to an excited energy state. That electron spends nanoseconds to milliseconds in the excited state before losing some energy as heat and dropping to a lower energy level. When the electron falls back to the ground state, it emits a photon of light; however, because this photon is at a lower energy level, it is at a longer wavelength and therefore a different color than the exciting photon.

Strengths and weaknesses: Fluorophores are typically on the order of a thousand times more sensitive than colorimetric molecules. Fluorescence is an environmentally dependent property and will vary based on the surroundings of the fluorophore. This property of fluorescence can also be used in experimental design.

Forster's or fluorescence resonance energy transfer (FRET)

When and why it is used: FRET is a technique used to identify two different fluorophores that are within close proximity (5Å) to one another. It is typically used to identify protein–protein interactions.

How it works: Molecules are tagged with two different fluorophores, often with two different fluorescent proteins such as GFP and mCherry. The FRET experiment is typically conducted using a fluorescence microscope with software that controls and analyzes the experiment. A fluorophore is excited with the correct wavelength of light; if a second fluorophore is within a specified distance and in the correct orientation, the energy of the excited state is transferred from the first fluorophore to the second, which will then emit a photon.

Strengths and weaknesses: Although FRET experiments require specialized equipment, there are few experiments that can detect protein–protein interactions. However, there are multiple reasons why a FRET pair of fluorophores may not interact, giving a false negative result.

Glucose tolerance test (GTT)

When and why it is used: The glucose tolerance test (GTT) is used to test for diabetes or insulin resistance in an organism.

How it works: In a GTT, a fasted test subject is given a dose of glucose. This may be taken orally, in which case it is an oral GTT or OGTT, or injected intraperitoneally, in which case it is an intraperitoneal GTT or IGTT. As the glucose is absorbed, the plasma glucose level increases. This is measured over a specific time interval, for example every 15 minutes for 3 hours, and the glucose concentration will increase rapidly over the first 15–30 minutes. In the healthy state, glucose concentrations will decrease as insulin is released and cells absorb the glucose. This should result in a decrease in plasma glucose. However, if the subject has diabetes or insulin resistance, the time for the glucose levels to return to normal is increased, if it occurs at all over the time course of the experiment. The time required for glucose levels to return to normal can be compared to normal values to determine the degree of insulin resistance.

Strengths and weaknesses: With the advent of microscale glucose monitoring, glucose tolerance tests have become more common, less expensive, and easier to perform in the laboratory setting. The GTT is a powerful tool but must be coupled with some other assay, such as plasma insulin concentrations or insulin clamp, to determine where a defect has occurred in metabolism.

High-pressure liquid chromatography (HPLC)

When and why it is used: HPLC is used to resolve closely related molecules, for example, different fatty acids or isomers of small organic molecules. Although an analytical technique, HPLC can be adapted for use on a preparative scale.

How it works: HPLC is a liquid chromatography technique. The stationary phase of the chromatography system consists of a column filled with fine beads coated with the molecule that gives the stationary phase its characteristic properties. Coatings can be polar, aromatic, ionic, or nonpolar. Nonpolar columns are often referred to as reverse-phase columns and are often used to separate nonpolar molecules. The mobile phase, which consists of a mixture of solvents, varies depending on the conditions of the experiment. Gradient HPLC employs more than one mobile phase. As the experiment is run, solvents are gradually mixed together, for example, to shift from one pH to another, or to make a mobile phase more or less polar. Analytes can be detected by various methods including ultraviolet or visible range spectrometry, MS, or refractive index.

Strengths and weaknesses: HPLC is a common and reliable technique, and autosamplers permit the analysis of tens to hundreds of samples with minimal labor. However, the technique can be time consuming; depending on conditions, a single analysis can take anywhere from several minutes to more than an hour. Identification of specific analytes often requires other techniques to positively confirm their identity.

Homologous recombination for gene deletion (knockout organisms)

When and why it is used: Knockout organisms are used to ascertain the function of a protein throughout the organism's development and life by deleting the gene coding for that protein. Knockout mice are one of the most often studied knockout organisms.

How it works: The creation of a knockout organism through homologous recombination uses numerous experimental techniques. In short, the gene to be deleted must be identified, mapped using restriction enzymes, and subcloned. Next, a DNA construct is created with two regions of homology flanking a selectable marker. Longer regions increase the likelihood of homologous recombination. The construct is electroporated into mouse stem cells. These cells are selected using the selectable marker and are assayed to see whether the construct has in fact recombined correctly in the genome and deleted the gene of interest. The cells with the proper deletion are then injected into a developing embryo and implanted into a female mouse. The mice that are born are heterozygotes; they are crossed with one another to give homozygous knockout mice.

Strengths and weaknesses: The surgical deletion of a single gene is quite a feat and can provide a wealth of information about that protein's functions in an organism. It may provide unexpected results in fields of science where one may not normally be focused. For example, deletion of the hormone-sensitive lipase gene also renders male mice infertile. However, recombination has several drawbacks. It can take more than a year to generate a knockout mouse. The process is highly involved and requires input from veterinarians, animal husbandry experts, cell biologists, and molecular biologists. These experiments are expensive and, depending on the laboratory, costs can easily range into hundreds of thousands of dollars. Finally, even if the deletion is achieved, it is possible that it will cause an embryonic lethality, in which case there is no mouse; a sterility, in which case there will be no more mice; or another protein or family of proteins that compensates for the gene that was deleted, in which case the mouse appears normal until it is tested or stressed in some way. Nevertheless, the opportunities to conduct science on basically a novel organism are almost limitless and exciting.

Ion selective electrodes (ISEs)

When and why it is used: Ion selective electrodes (ISEs) are electrochemical probes designed to detect specific solutes. Probes exist for many different molecules, but the most common example of an ISE is a pH probe.

How it works: ISEs consist of a glass tube with an ion-permeable window or membrane. This membrane is typically permeable only to the ion of interest. A wire (the electrode wire) is inserted into the glass tube. This wire is connected to one terminal of a galvanometer, while a reference wire is attached to the other terminal. The transmission of ions across the membrane is reflected and measured as current running across the membrane. This value can be converted to a chemical concentration.

Strengths and weaknesses: Newer ISEs are highly specific for solute and are robust compared to earlier generations but must still be handled with care. The main advantage of ISEs is that they are the only technique that can provide real-time monitoring of concentrations without further analysis. Electrodes exposed to conditions where living cells are present (for example, in bodies of water, tissue culture, or within organisms) can be subject to biofouling, or the growth of cells on the electrode. Although the price of ISEs continues to drop, they can be prohibitively expensive for certain applications.

Immunoblotting/western blotting

When and why it is used: Immunoblotting or western blotting is used to identify or quantitate amounts of a specific protein in a sample.

How it works: As the name implies, immunoblotting uses antibodies in the detection scheme. In this technique, a sample of proteins is separated using SDS-PAGE. The separated proteins are then transferred to a nylon or nitrocellulose membrane, typically performed using an electrophoretic technique. The blot is then coated with proteins that "block" the binding of any other proteins to the membrane, a step called blocking. Blocking ensures that antibodies used in the subsequent steps of the detection do not give high nonspecific backgrounds on the blot. Next, the blot is incubated in a sample of antibodies that bind to the protein of interest. The blot is washed, and a secondary antibody that recognizes the first antibody is added. This secondary antibody is coupled to an enzyme, protein, or fluorophore employed in the detection step. Finally, the blot is detected. Bands on the blot will vary in intensity depending on the amount of protein found.

Strengths and weaknesses: Immunoblotting is a standard technique used in many labs around the world. It has been optimized: it can be done relatively quickly and inexpensively and is the basis for several other techniques such as IP, pulldown assays, and ChIP. Drawbacks include the need for specific antibodies to detect each protein.

Immunoprecipitation/Co-immunoprecipitation/Pulldown assays (IP/CoIP/Pulldown)

When and why it is used: Immunoprecipitations or pulldown assays are used to help identify proteins that are either directly or indirectly interacting with one another.

How it works: Cells containing a protein of interest are lysed and centrifuged to remove insoluble material. An antibody directed against the protein of interest is added. This antibody binds to the protein of interest. The antibody complex is then precipitated using a bead coated with either a second antibody that recognizes the first or a bacterial protein that binds nonspecifically to antibodies; protein A or protein G is commonly used. If the protein of interest is bound to other proteins, these should also precipitate with the antibody-bead complex. The precipitated proteins are eluted from the bead and analyzed using western blotting. Variants of this experiment can be conducted using fusion proteins (proteins that are joined together and encoded by a single cDNA) that bind to other ligands, for example, an avidin fusion protein binding to a biotinylated bead.

Strengths and weaknesses: The IP experiment is useful for demonstrating that proteins are found in a complex with one another. In general, the experiment is easy and inexpensive and lends itself well to large-scale experimentation. Investigators need to be careful not to overinterpret results. The IP shows that proteins are found in the same complex but do not necessarily show direct protein-protein interactions. One drawback of the experiment is that the investigator must hypothesize which proteins interact with the protein of interest in order to identify them. As improvements are made in IP and mass spectrometry technology, it may become easier to identify unknown proteins using this technique.

In situ hybridization

When and why it is used: An *in situ* hybridization or *in situ* is a technique that is used to analyze which cells are expressing a specific gene. It differs from some related techniques in that it examines expression at the mRNA level and does it on a cell-by-cell basis.

How it works: In an *in situ*, a complimentary DNA or RNA probe is generated and binds to the RNA of interest. This probe may be fluorescent, radiolabeled, or detected with an antibody that generates a colored product. A section of tissue is fixed and permeabilized, and the probe is hybridized to the RNA of interest. If the probe is radiolabeled or generates a colored product, it must be developed by incubating the section with the appropriate chemicals. The sections are viewed under a microscope to determine which cells are expressing the gene of interest.

Strengths and weaknesses: *In situ* is one way of determining which cells of a sample express a gene of interest. It plays an important role in neuroscience, developmental biology, and some fields of microanatomy. The technique is relatively straightforward to complete, requires little specialized equipment, and yields specific results. Immunofluorescence microscopy asks similar questions at the protein level and can complement *in situ* studies.

Langmuir-Blodgett troughs (monolayer systems)

When and why it is used: A Langmuir-Blodgett trough is a device used to construct and study the physical properties of monolayers of amphiphiles including phospholipids and proteins that associate with them.

How it works: A Langmuir-Blodgett trough consists of a Teflon trough and moveable barrier, and a Wilhelmy plate or Langmuir balance (both devices are used to measure surface pressure). A buffer solution is placed in the trough and an amphiphile is floated on the surface of the buffer. The barrier is used to adjust the area available to the amphiphile and therefore the packing of those molecules on the surface of the monolayer or film. The Wilhelmy plate indicates the surface pressure, which will change as a function of the packing of the surface or any change made to the surface, such as the binding or loss of molecules, or any changes in molecular conformation or packing.

Strengths and weaknesses: Langmuir-Blodgett troughs are useful in determining the binding characteristics of proteins to a phospholipid monolayer as well as the packing of membrane lipids and can provide important and interesting biophysical data. Systems are typically a more specialized piece of equipment and are highly sensitive, often requiring some type of isolation from background vibration.

Lectin-based techniques

When and why it is used: Lectins are carbohydrate-binding proteins. These proteins can be labeled using a fluorescent tag and then used to detect carbohydrate sequences in microscopy or western blotting. Alternatively, lectins can be employed in a purification scheme.

How it works: Lectins bind to short specific carbohydrate sequences using the same types of interactions that are found between a receptor and a ligand or an enzyme and a substrate. When originally identified, they were used in a way that was similar to the way antibodies are commonly used today, for example, in fluorescence microscopy, western blotting, and affinity chromatography.

Strengths and weaknesses: Lectins have seen a resurgence in their popularity, with the advent of new fluorescent tags and further characterization of the specific carbohydrate each lectin recognizes. In some instances, lectins offer an alternative to antibodies. They are also still used in some clinical applications, such as blood typing.

Ligand binding assays

When and why it is used: A ligand binding assay is used to determine the affinity or binding constant (or dissociation constant) of two molecules, usually a ligand and a receptor. The ligand may be a small organic or inorganic compound or a larger molecule such as a protein.

How it works: Many different assays can be used to determine ligand binding. In most of these assays, the ligand is labeled either with a radiolabel or a fluorescent dye. In all of the assays, analytical techniques need to be used to identify which fraction of the ligand is bound to the receptor and which is unbound. Typically, this is performed by using a fixed concentration of the receptor, a fixed concentration of the labeled ligand, and a varying concentration of unlabeled ligand. In this format, the unlabeled ligand will compete with the labeled ligand for binding to the receptor. The higher the concentration of the more unlabeled ligand, the less the labeled ligand will bind to the receptor. The percentage of labeled ligand bound is graphed as a function of the log of the competing ligand and a sigmoidal curve is observed:

Strengths and weaknesses: Ligand binding assays require a labeled ligand, which either involves the use of radioactivity or a fluorescent tag. In the case of the latter, investigators must ensure that the modification to the ligand does not affect binding. Once developed, a ligand binding assay is a workhorse in many laboratories and is a common technique in receptor biology and pharmaceutical development.

Variants of ligand binding assays include enzyme-linked immunoassay (ELISA) and radioimmunoassay (RIA), both of which are used to measure the concentration of molecules.

Lipidomics

When and why it is used: Lipidomics is a relatively new field. Similar to other "-omics based" fields, such as genomics or proteomics, lipidomics seeks to identify and characterize all of the lipids in a sample.

How it works: Experimental lipid samples are often extracted away from cells, tissues, or media by an organic liquid–liquid extraction. The resulting lipids may be separated by thin layer chromatography or HPLC before characterization. The characterization is usually conducted using mass spectrometry with the samples being introduced via either ESI or MALDI; however, some samples are also identified using NMR. Depending on the separation and characterization scheme, the exact identity of lipids, including the percentages of individual phospholipid subclasses and their specific acyl chain composition, can be determined. Interestingly, several new lipids, in particular, signaling lipids found in low abundance, have been identified using this technique. The functions of these molecules remain unknown.

Strengths and weaknesses: A lipidomics experiment can generate massive amounts of data. Any given biological sample can contain many thousands of different lipid species, and the lipidomics experiment can enumerate each one. Even relatively pure samples, such as the lipoprotein subclasses, have significant diversity with regard to their lipid components. Lipids found in small quantities, while some of the more interesting molecules, are also often the hardest to isolate and characterize. Although the experiment can yield vast quantities of data, careful analysis and interpretation is needed. Another potential drawback is the cost incurred when trying to examine large numbers of samples by mass spectrometry.

Making solutions and buffers

When and why it is used: Buffers and solutions are central to most experimental biochemistry. All students of biochemistry must know how to calculate the correct concentrations in solutions and buffers and how to make these solutions properly.

How it works: Making solutions and buffers usually involves the dissolution of solids, liquids, or even gases in a solvent, typically water. Solutes are dissolved in a smaller amount of solvent and then diluted to the final volume. Similarly, when buffers are prepared, the salts and acids used in the buffer are dissolved in a small volume of liquid, the pH is adjusted to the proper value, and the solution is diluted to the final volume. This does not substantially affect the pH of the final product as long as the dilution factor is small compared to the buffering capacity of the solution.

Several measuring devices are commonly employed in the biochemistry laboratory. These include graduated cylinders and volumetric flasks for larger volumes, pipettes and burets for volumes of 1–50 mL, and micropipettes and syringes for smaller volumes (down to the nanoliter scale). Students should be reminded to use proper laboratory practice and accurately measure all liquids in the laboratory. The gradations on a beaker, capped test tube, or Erlenmeyer flask carry with them a generally large ($\pm 10\%$) error.

Strengths and weaknesses: There are really no strengths or weaknesses to making solutions and buffers because they are a basic part of laboratory life. However, some laboratories will purchase ready-made solutions; this may seem extravagant, but it can save time, a valuable commodity in a research endeavor. In addition, purchasing the solutions generally ensures that they are uniform, which in some cases, such as diagnostic or clinical chemistry, may be warranted.

Mass spectrometry (MS)

When and why it is used: Mass spectrometry (MS) is used to determine the mass of biological molecules. Historically, it has been used to identify and characterize small organic molecules, but advances in technology now permit analysis of macromolecules and complexes of macromolecules. Based on the mass, the user can positively identify a molecule or determine whether a modification has been made. Because MS can identify both the molecule in question and any modifications directly, it is rapidly gaining in popularity.

How it works: The mass spectrometer can be thought of as a modular instrument. Before mass determination, samples may be isolated by chromatography, depending on the experiment and the instrumental configuration. The instrument itself consists of a means of introducing and ionizing the sample (the ion source), a resolution chamber (the mass analyzer), and a detector. Common means of introducing and ionizing small organic molecules include fast atom bombardment (FAB) or chemical ionization (CI). Larger molecules, such as proteins, are ionized using matrix assisted laser desorption ionization (MALDI) or electrospray ionization (ESI). Resolution is accomplished by separating ions not solely by their mass but by their mass-to-charge ratio (m/z). Magnetic sector, time-of-flight, quadrupole, and ion traps are the main categories of instruments used to resolve ions. In an electron multiplier, ions are detected by the impact of the ion on the surface of a detector. In an Orbitrap (a type of ion trap) ions are detected by generation of a current in a nearby coil of wire.

Strengths and weaknesses: Mass spectroscopy identifies unknown molecules far more quickly and easily than any other technique, and often with unambiguous results. Likewise, it provides information about modifications of proteins that is difficult to obtain using other techniques. The primary drawback of MS is the cost. High-end instruments typically cost more than $300,000 and often require specialists to keep them running efficiently.

Microarrays

When and why it is used: Microarrays are used to obtain expression data for a large number of genes in a cell, tissue, organ, or organism at once.

How it works: To perform a microarray experiment, a microarray specific for the organism or tissue of interest and two RNA samples are needed for comparison. For example, these RNA samples could be one from a healthy tissue and one from a diseased tissue. A microarray is most often a glass microscope slide with anywhere from 3,000–20,000 microscopic spots of specific cDNAs arrayed on the slide; the location of each cDNA is known. These two RNA samples are labeled using two different colored fluorescent tags: red for the experimental sample and green for the control sample. Care must be taken to ensure that the degree of labeling is similar in both samples. Next, the labeled RNA samples are mixed in equal amounts and hybridized to the slide. The slides are washed and then detected. If the original RNA samples had more of one gene being expressed in the experimental sample than in the control, the correlating spot on the microarray will light up red. If a gene is more strongly expressed in the control sample, it will light up green. By comparing the intensity

differences of the two colors and knowing which genes are found at each spot, a complete map of how expression has been altered in the experimental sample can be determined.

Strengths and weaknesses: Microarrays provide data simultaneously on all of the transcripts of the cell. Expression of a transcript is measured relative to the other genes being compared. As a result, changes in gene expression levels with very low or high levels of expression may be harder to determine. While the strength of microarrays probably lies in the total amount of data obtained, this is in many ways also a liability. Microarrays provide clues regarding genes that warrant further investigation; however, microarrays do not usually provide critical information regarding a single gene. Likewise, the complexity, and in the past the cost, of the experiment usually kept experimental sample values low; $n = 3$ was not uncommon. The cost of microarrays has fallen dramatically since the technology was first developed.

Northern blotting

When and why it is used: Northern blotting is a technique that is used to identify and obtain the size of mRNAs. It is often used as a *de facto* measure of expression, although investigators should be cautioned that message levels do not always correlate with protein levels.

How it works: Total RNA or mRNA is isolated from a sample of interest. The RNA can be from an entire organism, organs, tissues, or cells. The RNA molecules are denatured and separated on an agarose gel similar to other nucleic acid separation techniques. The separated molecules are transferred to a membrane, typically nylon or PVDF, through osmosis; they are permanently affixed to the membrane by drying under vacuum or cross-linking with UV light. Next, unoccupied sites on the membrane are "blocked" by treating with a blocking agent, typically a solution of nucleic acids, proteins, or polymers that discourage the binding of other nucleic acids. The membrane is then probed with a radioactive cDNA generated against the gene or message of interest. Ideally the radioactive probe will bind only to its complementary mRNA on the blot. The unbound probe is washed away, and the blot is exposed to film or a detection system for imaging. Bands corresponding to the message or messages are seen and are proportional to the amount of RNA found in the sample.

Strengths and weaknesses: Northern blotting is a widely used and reliable technique. An experienced investigator can easily survey multiple genes or multiple samples for expression in a relatively short amount of time, usually over several days. While this technique is a workhorse for many labs, it is gradually being replaced by modern technologies such as RT-PCR, RNAseq, and microarrays. These newer technologies have advantages in throughput (number of samples analyzed over time) and flexibility. Another drawback of northern blotting is its reliance on radioisotopes for detection. Newer northern blot techniques employ fluorescent detection, decreasing the amount of regulation needed and general work load.

Nuclear magnetic resonance (NMR)

When and why it is used: Nuclear magnetic resonance (NMR) is a spectral technique used to determine the structure of molecules.

How it works: A sample is placed into an NMR spectrometer. This device consists of a strong magnet, a radio frequency generator, a detector, and a control panel used to run the experiment. In the magnetic field of the instrument, the sample absorbs energy in the radio wave frequency and reemits this energy as it returns to the ground state. Molecules differ in how they absorb and reemit this energy based on the nature and electronic environment of the nuclei. Based on these differences, the connectivity or structure of the molecule can be determined.

Strengths and weaknesses: NMR is a very popular technique in organic chemistry but less so in biochemistry, due partially to the size and complexity of the molecules involved. A common organic molecule may contain 20 protons that need to be assigned in an NMR spectrum, but a simple protein could easily have a thousand protons. To assist in resolving these peaks, NMR instruments needed for structure determination in biochemistry often employ high magnetic fields and are expensive instruments costing millions of dollars.

Polymerase chain reaction (PCR)

When and why it is used: PCR is used to amplify, that is, make multiple copies of, DNA sequences. PCR or variations on this technique are an integral part of many modern approaches to molecular biology, such as sequencing, site-directed mutagenesis, and genotyping.

How it works: The PCR reaction consists of four components: a DNA template to be replicated, short oligonucleotides that flank the region to be amplified, deoxynucleotide triphosphates, and a polymerase that does not denature at high temperatures. The components are mixed in a buffer solution and placed into a thermocycler—a programmable heating and cooling system that precisely cycles the temperature through multiple cycles. The thermocycler heats the sample to melt the template DNA, then cools it to a temperature where primers will anneal to the template strand, then warms it to enable the polymerase to copy the template strand. After 25–30 cycles, the target sequence may be amplified by as much as a million-fold.

Strengths and weaknesses: PCR is easy to conduct and is relatively inexpensive. Commercial availability of polymerases from thermophilic organisms has made PCR widely accessible to many; the limiting factor in many cases is access to a thermocycler, which can be purchased for less than $4000. The technique is rapid (less than three hours), easy to perform, and sensitive enough to detect a single molecule of DNA. However, the sensitivity means that even slight levels of contaminants will be amplified in the reaction, leading to false positives.

Protein assays

When and why they are used: Protein assays are used to determine the concentration of total protein in a sample. Many different methods can be used, depending on the purpose of the assay. In the clinic, protein assays are used to determine the presence or absence of protein in a sample such as urine. In the research laboratory, protein assays are a mainstay of many analytical and purification schemes. In those applications, knowing the concentration of proteins in a sample enables the investigator to make consistent comparisons between samples or track how well a purification scheme is going.

How they work: There are several different techniques available for protein determination:

UV spectrophotometry uses the absorbance of tyrosine and tryptophan residues at 280 nm to correlate to total protein in a sample.

The Bradford protein assay uses a blue dye (Coomassie Brilliant Blue G250) that non-specifically binds protein, causing a shift in the spectral characteristics of the dye. The assay is read using a visible range spectrophotometer.

The Lowry and BCA assays use similar chemistry. Both of these assays take advantage of the observation that peptide bonds and potentially some side chains will stoichiometrically reduce Cu^{2+} to Cu^+. The reduced Cu^+ will react with a mixture of phosphotungstic and phosphomolybdic acid in a Lowry assay, or with the dye bicinchoninic acid in a BCA. These complexes have characteristic absorbances and can be determined using a visible range spectrophotometer as with the Bradford assay.

Finally, protein can be assayed on a much larger scale using the *Kjeldahl assay*, which destroys proteins by digesting them with sulfuric acid to produce ammonium sulfate. The ammonia is titrated to give the total amount of nitrogen in the sample. Thus, the assay is actually measuring nitrogen rather than protein, but on the scale used (grams to kilograms) it is relatively accurate, provided several corrections are taken into consideration.

Strengths and weaknesses: UV is nondestructive but relatively insensitive. It also assumes a constant ratio of tyrosine and tryptophan to other amino acids in all proteins; a dangerous assumption when working with a purification scheme. In addition, other biological molecules (notably nucleosides and nucleic acids) also absorb in the UV.

The Bradford is a classic assay and is more sensitive than UV but is incompatible with several common laboratory reagents.

The Lowry is more time consuming than the Bradford but is used as a standard assay in many laboratories worldwide. The BCA—the newest of these assays—has the fewest interfering substances and takes less time than the Lowry. It is also the most sensitive of the methods discussed.

Interpretation of the Kjeldahl assay can be complicated by other nitrogen sources in the sample. It can be time consuming but is the standard method for measuring protein levels in many industrial applications such as food or dairy science.

Pulsed field gel electrophoresis (PFGE)

When and why it is used: PFGE is a variant on normal agarose gel electrophoresis. By varying the electric field, the resolution of very large (megabase) pieces of DNA is possible.

How it works: In a routine agarose gel electrophoresis, the electric field is applied in a single direction. This allows for the resolution of small pieces of DNA; when the pieces exceed approximately 20 kb, the ability to resolve them ceases, and larger pieces run as a single band. In PFGE, three different fields are used. The first one is oriented through the gel as in routine gel electrophoresis. Two other fields are oriented approximately 60 degrees to either side of the first field and are pulsed periodically, ranging from a few seconds every few minutes to an hour. When this happens, the very large molecules of DNA will react to the field at different rates, based on their size. This enables the resolution of these large molecules.

Strengths and weaknesses: PFGE is a common and relatively simple technique. A programmable power supply is needed. It is a central technique in genomic analysis, genotyping, or genetic fingerprinting of organisms. Due to the size of the fragments and the need to pulse the gel, PFGE experiments often have to run overnight (16 to 20 hours).

Quasi-elastic light scatter (QELS), Raleigh scattering, photon correlation spectroscopy, or dynamic light scattering (DLS)

When and why it is used: QELS is a technique that uses the ability of a particle, a protein, macromolecular complex, or organelle, to scatter light as a function of its shape and size. QELS can be used to determine the shape and size of a pure sample of particles or the distribution of a diverse population of particles.

How it works: The QELS experiment shines laser light on a sample and detects the scattered light 90° to the incident beam. When measured over short microsecond to millisecond time scales, the signal will vary over time due to the Brownian motion of particles in solution. The variation in the signal can be correlated with the size and crude shape of the particle and the distribution of particle sizes.

Strengths and weaknesses: QELS is a simple but elegant technique that provides data regarding size of particles. QELS is nondestructive and easy to perform quickly. It does require a dedicated instrument with sensitive optics.

Real-time PCR (RT-PCR) or q-PCR

When and why it is used: Real time or quantitative PCR is a technique that is used to measure the expression of a specific mRNA transcript.

How it works: RT-PCR is similar in many ways to PCR; RT-PCR employs a special thermocycler and relies on fluorescent detection methods. Like PCR there needs to be a template, generally a cDNA copy of the cell's mRNA, nucleotides, and a thermostable polymerase. RT-PCR differs in that it uses special primers. The primers contain a hairpin loop secondary structure in addition to the specific sequence that anneals to the template. At one end of the hairpin is a fluorophore; adjacent to it is a fluorescence quencher. Because the quencher is near the fluorophore, fluorescence is quenched and there is no signal; however, as the primer is incorporated into PCR product, the quencher and fluorophore become separated and the signal is no longer quenched. Therefore, accumulation of PCR product can be measured as an accumulation of fluorescent signal; the RT-PCR thermocycler has the capability to measure this fluorescence each cycle.

Newer generation RT-PCR employs normal PCR conditions and primers but includes dyes that intercalate into the PCR product as it accumulates. These are also quantitated by the thermocycler.

Strengths and weaknesses: The price of RT-PCR and specific primers has fallen dramatically as technology has improved. RT-PCR enables investigators to measure expression levels within a few hours as compared to several days when using northern blotting. In addition, the technology is PCR-based; it is simple to run hundreds of samples in a single day or automate the system. One drawback of RT-PCR is that, as a PCR-based technique, care must be taken to ensure that samples are not contaminated, leading to artifactual results.

Reporter gene assay

When and why is it used: Reporter gene assays are used to detect the segments of a promoter region involved in the regulation of a specific gene.

How it works: A region of DNA upstream of a gene of interest is selected. Typically, this region is anywhere from 2–5 kilobases upstream of the start site. This piece of DNA is cloned in a vector in front of a reporter gene, a gene encoding a protein that can be easily detected. Classical reporter genes include chloramphenicol acyl transferase (CAT) or luciferase, but often today green fluorescent protein (GFP) may be used. Different constructs using truncated segments of the promoter sequence are generated and tested to determine which regions are necessary for reporter gene expression.

Strengths and weaknesses: Reporter gene assays are relatively easy to conduct and can be informative but require the use of cultured cell systems, which may not accurately recreate the environment found in native tissue.

RNA silencing (shRNA, siRNA, RNAi)

When and why it is used: RNA silencing is a family of techniques, including shRNA, siRNA, and morpholino, that silence genes at the post transcriptional level using the RNAi or RNA interference pathway.

How it works: RNA silencing techniques introduce RNA or DNA constructs to the cell. These constructs code for specific sequences that form double-stranded RNA structures for processing by the cell's native RNAi enzymes. Ideally these constructs will silence a specific mRNA.

Strengths and weaknesses: RNA silencing techniques are rapidly evolving as more is known about the science underlying the technology. These are effective and easy experiments to conduct, and due to their nature—transfecting cells with nucleic acids—they are relatively straightforward and easy to scale up. Many constructs developed to silence RNAs only do so partially, resulting in an intermediate phenotype. While this in and of itself can be experimentally valuable, it also raises questions about the RNA of interest being completely silenced or if protein levels have been affected as predicted.

Salting in or salting out

When and why it is used: Salting in or salting out is simply precipitating (out) or increasing (in) the solubility of a macromolecule, usually a protein, through the addition of a salt.

How it works: Proteins are kept in solution through the interaction of water molecules with polar and hydrophilic parts of the protein surface. As increasing amounts of salt are added to a solution, the ions from the dissolved salt are hydrated and reorganize water molecules away from the protein. This causes the protein molecules to clump together and precipitate. Similarly, proteins are most soluble in weak salt solutions. Salting in occurs with weak salt solutions and happens partially due to ions neutralizing the charge on the surface of a protein, which in turn increases the activity of the solvent.

Strengths and weaknesses: Salting in or out is one of the simplest purification techniques and can quickly, easily, and inexpensively remove many contaminating molecules. The salt is typically used at a high concentration and must be removed in subsequent steps, which can be a consideration in some purification procedures. Conditions for salting in or out must be empirically determined.

Site-directed mutagenesis

When and why it is used: Site-directed mutagenesis is a means of surgically altering a DNA sequence often used to change a coding sequence.

How it works: There are several techniques available for generating site-directed mutants. The easiest and most straightforward technique involves the polymerase chain reaction (PCR) and mutagenic primers. In this reaction one of the primers is a normal complement to the template strand while the other primer contains the desired mutation. A stretch of nucleotides, which will base pair with the template, follows and provides a site for the polymerase to extend. Because the primer contains the mutation, the products generated from that template or amplified from that product will also contain the mutation. Modifications of this technique coupled with subcloning steps can be used to quickly generate a battery of specific mutants for any protein.

Strengths and weaknesses: Thanks to advances in primer synthesis and PCR, site-directed mutagenesis is now a very straightforward technique that can be accomplished in a very short time and on a very limited budget. Products generated using this technique should be sequenced to confirm that they have only the desired mutations.

Size exclusion or gel permeation chromatography

When and why it is used: Size exclusion chromatography is a technique used to separate molecules based on size. It is a common purification technique with many applications.

How it works: Size exclusion chromatography employs a size exclusion resin or medium. This resin consists of microscopic beads of a polymer; agarose and acrylamide are commonly used. The degree of polymerization is controlled to provide pores or channels in each bead that are on the order of the size of the molecules being separated. When a mixture of molecules is applied to the media, smaller molecules will fit into the pores while larger molecules will be excluded. This effectively gives the smaller molecules a larger volume to pass through and results in their retention, while larger molecules, being excluded, will elute from the media first. Variation in pore size means that depending on the type of media size, exclusion can be used for removing salt from larger molecules or single nucleotides from oligonucleotides. Larger molecules, such as proteins that differ in size or in some cases shape, can also be resolved from one another.

Strengths and weaknesses: Size exclusion chromatography is a well-studied and widely used technique. It is relatively inexpensive and easy to learn. It works best when separating molecules that vary greatly in size, for example, a salt and a protein. Coupling this media with a high-pressure chromatography system increases the resolving power.

Sodium dodecyl sulfate polyacrylamide gel electrophoresis (SDS-PAGE)

When and why it is used: Sodium dodecyl sulfate polyacrylamide gel electrophoresis (SDS-PAGE) is a nearly 50-year-old technique that is used to separate proteins from a mixture in a polymer gel matrix. This technique and several popular variants can be used on their own or as the basis for other techniques, including immunoblotting or western blotting.

How it works: A sample of proteins is denatured in the presence of SDS, a detergent. Often, disulfide reducing agents such as beta-mercaptoethanol or dithiothreitol are included. The detergent imparts a negative charge to the denatured proteins. An electric field is applied, and proteins are separated in a polyacrylamide gel matrix. The gel matrix has pores that are small enough to impede the movement of larger proteins; thus, proteins are separated largely by molecular weight. Modifications to this basic system, such as the use of a second "stacker" gel on top of the first with differing pH buffers in each, increases the resolution of the technique. There are numerous ways to detect proteins in the gel, including Coomassie blue, silver staining, or fluorescent dyes. Additionally, the proteins can be transferred to membranes for immunological detection, known as immunoblotting; individual bands can be isolated from a gel and characterized by mass spectrometry.

Strengths and weaknesses: SDS-PAGE is a workhorse of modern biochemistry; it is easy to learn and relatively inexpensive. Drawbacks of SDS-PAGE include difficulties resolving some proteins from each other, and post-translational modifications such as acylation, phosphorylation, or glycation can alter the behavior of proteins. Finally, although polymerized acrylamide is nontoxic and is used in numerous consumer products, the monomeric form of acrylamide used to make the gel is a neurotoxin. Care should be used in the handling of this compound.

Solid phase peptide synthesis (SPPS)

When and why it is used: Solid phase peptide synthesis (SPPS) is used to chemically synthesize peptides. The technique is often used to produce antigens for antibody production.

How it works: SPPS takes advantage of solid phase technology. The first amino acid in the synthesis, the carboxy terminal amino acid, is supplied bound to a plastic resin bead. Beads are incubated with a second amino acid that has a protective group on its amino terminus, and this amino acid couples to the bead. Unbound or unreacted amino acids are then washed off the bead. The newly formed dipeptide still bound to the bead is de-protected, and a third amino acid is added. The series is repeated until the desired peptide is complete. At that point, the peptide is released from the solid support using acid.

Strengths and weaknesses: SPPS is now commonly used in automated peptide synthesizers, and it is relatively inexpensive to order microgram quantities of peptides of up to 20 amino acids in length. For peptides of greater lengths, is it is generally more effective to use recombinant DNA techniques to overexpress a protein in bacteria or cultured eukaryotic cells.

Southern blotting

When and why it is used: Southern blotting is a means of identifying specific fragments of DNA. It has applications in genotyping some organisms and in cloning.

How it works: DNA, typically genomic DNA, is cleaved into smaller fragments using a restriction enzyme. These fragments are separated on an agarose gel. The DNA fragments are denatured and transferred to a nitrocellulose membrane. Next, a radiolabeled fragment of DNA that is complimentary to the fragment of interest, termed a probe, is incubated with the membrane. The probe should anneal or base-pair specifically to the fragment of interest. The unbound probe is washed away, and the membrane is exposed to film or a detection system. Final analysis should show specific bands corresponding to the size of the fragment of interest.

Strengths and weaknesses: Southern blotting is a very common and simple technique used to identify specific DNA fragments. It often employs radiolabeled DNA, although some fluorescent techniques have been developed. Southern blots are somewhat time-consuming, taking a full day to perform and up to two weeks before results can be analyzed. As a result, PCR-based techniques have often replaced them.

Thin layer chromatography (TLC)

When and why it is used: TLC is used to separate classes of small organic molecules. Generally these are lipids but occasionally other types of molecules based on their chemical properties. It is often coupled with subsequent detection or characterization steps to identify specific molecules of interest. Depending on the scale involved, TLC can be either an analytical or a preparative technique.

How it works: As the name implies, TLC is a chromatographic technique. The stationary phase is often a thin coating of silica gel bound to a glass plate, and the mobile phase is a solution of organic solvents, weak acids or bases, and water. A sample of the molecules is applied in a small spot to a TLC plate. Plates are developed in a TLC tank, a receptacle containing a small volume of the mobile phase at equilibrium with its vapor. As the mobile phase wicks up the TLC plate, it carries the analytes (the molecules in the sample) with it. Analytes that interact more strongly with the stationary than the mobile phase will not move up the plate as far as those that interact strongly with the mobile phase. By choosing appropriate mobile phases, a wide variety of separations can be conducted. Detection of samples can be accomplished by many different techniques including exposure to iodine vapor, charring, use of dyes or reagents specific to a functional group, radiometry, fluorescent detection, gas chromatography, or mass spectrometry.

Strengths and weaknesses: TLC has been in use for many years and is still employed in many laboratories. It is inexpensive, simple to perform, and versatile. Recent refinements of solid phase compositions have resulted in "high resolution TLC," which has higher resolving power than older techniques and allows the investigator to use smaller samples.

TLC lacks the resolving power of other analytical techniques, such as GC and HPLC; it is not commonly used to specifically identify molecules. For example, TLC cannot resolve two different fatty acids. It is also not typically thought of as a high throughput technique (testing many samples at once) and does not lend itself well to automation. Finally, although TLC seems benign, continued exposure to silica gel on TLC plates can lead to silicosis, or white lung, a potentially lethal pulmonary condition. Facemasks or other types of personal protective equipment are advised when working continually in an environment of silica dust.

Tissue-specific knockout organisms: the cre-lox system

When and why it is used: Many proteins are expressed in multiple tissues. Tissue specific knockout of a gene enables the investigator to determine the function of a gene in a specific tissue by deleting the gene only in the cells of that organ or tissue. These are similar to knockout mice discussed in the section "Homologous recombination for gene deletion (knockout organisms)."

How it works: Tissue specific knockouts using the cre-lox system involve the production of both a knockout mouse and a transgenic mouse. The DNA construct for the knockout mouse consists of the gene of interest flanked by loxP sites. These short sequences were originally found in bacteria. These sites are recognized by the enzyme cre. Cre is a recombinase that recombines and deletes DNA found between the lox p sites. Here, the deletion would remove all or a significant piece of the gene of interest, rendering it unable to transcribe. In wild type cells there is no cre recombinase and the cells—and mouse—will be normal. However, if the mouse in question were to be crossed with a mouse expressing the cre recombinase, the gene of interest would be deleted, creating a knockout. In order to produce a tissue-specific knockout, the expression of cre is driven by a tissue-specific promoter. Therefore, from one "floxed" (flanked lox) knockout mouse, a series of tissue-specific knockout mice can be created depending on the tissue-specific cre transgenic mouse used for breeding.

Strengths and weaknesses: The cre-lox system provides a very useful model system for asking big-picture questions, for example, what happens when liver or muscle can no longer respond to insulin? However, a tissue-specific knockout is a very complex experiment requiring numerous scientists and significant resources. Once a single floxed mouse is made, it can be crossed to transgenic mice expressing cre in a variety of tissues, providing multiple model organisms.

Transgenic organisms

When and why it is used: Transgenic organisms ectopically express a gene that has been added to an organism's genome. By doing this, the function of the protein encoded by that gene can be studied in a somewhat native environment.

How it works: A piece of DNA consisting of the cDNA coding for the protein of interest, a promotor, and a polyadenylation sequence is injected into a fertilized oocyte. The piece of DNA integrates somewhere in the genome of the organism. If done early enough in development, the DNA replicates with each cellular division and will be passed on in the progeny.

Strengths and weaknesses: Ectopic expression provides a way to study the function of a protein in an organism. It can be done relatively inexpensively, often for several thousand dollars. Care must be taken, however, to ensure that the effects observed in the organism are due to the gene of interest being expressed either at very high levels or in tissues where it is not normally found.

Transmission electron microscopy (TEM)

When and why it is used: While traditionally associated with cell biology, transmission electron microscopy (TEM) is also a technique involved with imaging macromolecular complexes. TEM cannot provide the resolution that diffraction techniques such as neutron or X-ray diffraction can, nor can it provide measurement of some of the smaller molecular distances afforded by spectral techniques such as NMR or FRET. Nonetheless, it is very useful for examining larger complexes of proteins and seeing how complexes may interface with one another.

How it works: TEM works much like a light microscope but takes advantage of the shorter wavelength of electrons. When using light to examine a structure, the resolution of the instrument is limited by the wavelength of light. Shorter wavelengths, and therefore higher energy particles, permit higher resolution and magnification. Whereas light microscopy is typically limited to approximately 400× magnification, the power and wavelength of electrons permit magnifications of over 1×10^6x with near-Angstrom resolution. At these magnifications, it becomes easy to visualize macromolecular complexes of proteins, lipoproteins, or ribosomes.

A source of electrons analogous to the light source in conventional microscopy is focused on the sample. Whereas lenses are used to focus light, magnets and magnetic fields are used to focus the electron beam. In TEM, heavy metals are used as contrast agents, rather than dyes, which are often used to stain molecules or increase contrast in light microscopy. Because of the high energy of the electrons, typically between 100 and 300 kEv, the entire system is held under high vacuum. Images are projected onto a fluorescent screen or captured using a digital camera.

Strengths and weaknesses: TEM samples are imaged under vacuum and must therefore be dry. A contrast agent is used to make the sample stand out from the background. The sample preparation process can introduce artifacts that need to be controlled, such as the aggregation of samples. As with any experimental technique, it behooves the investigator to validate the findings using a different technique, in this case, size-exclusion chromatography, laser light scatter, or non-denaturing gel electrophoresis when using TEM. TEM are expensive instruments (a standard TEM costs over $150,000) and require highly trained technical help to keep the instrument functional; however, they are relatively simple to use and data can be obtained quickly and easily.

Transposon mutagenesis

When and why it is used: Transposons are "jumping genes," segments of DNA that move from one chromosome to another. Transposon mutagenesis is a technique that is used either to disrupt genes, effectively knocking them out, or to insert a gene of interest into a genome. The technique is growing in popularity as commercially available kits enter the market and familiarity with the technique grows.

How it works: Transposon mutagenesis can be carried out in one of two different ways. In insertional activation, a transposon is randomly inserted across the genome. The insertion contains stop codons, often in all six reading frames. Should the transposon insert into a gene, that gene will be unable to properly code for mRNA and, ultimately, protein. These are considered loss-of-function experiments. Typically, a library of mutants is generated and used to screen for a particular phenotype. The sequence of the transposon can then be used as a primer to determine where in the genome the sequence has integrated. Purified transposonase makes it possible to use transposon mutagenesis *in vitro*. Alternately, the technique can be performed *in vivo* using a plasmid coding for transposonase.

The second type of mutagenesis involves insertion of a gene of interest into host cells. In this instance, the gene of interest (for example, a healthy copy of a defective gene in a patient) is cloned between the long terminal repeat sequences of the transposon. This piece of DNA can be delivered to cells through any one of several different transfection techniques, dependent on whether the DNA is delivered to an organism or cultured cells. Once inside the cell, the transposon is processed and integrated into the chromosome, and presumably the genes found in the transposon are expressed.

Strengths and weaknesses: Transposon technology is inexpensive and growing in popularity. It overcomes problems associated with viral infection of cells including immune response, random insertion of DNA, cost of producing high-quality virus, and naked DNA transfection or electroporation methods such as failure to integrate or low expression levels. The techniques are flexible and versatile and promise to be increasingly used in research and in the clinic. Transposons have been used in gene therapy trials in several mouse models of human disease, including hemophilia, sickle-cell anemia, and lymphoma. Clinical trials with humans have already begun.

Visible range spectroscopy

When and why it is used: Visible range spectroscopy is one of the oldest and most common forms of spectroscopy. It is used to detect changes in the concentration of a light-absorbing compound known as a chromophore. While you may be familiar with visible-range spectroscopy as a technique used to quantitatively measure dyes, it can also be used to monitor chemical changes in naturally occurring chromophores in a biochemical reaction.

How it works: In visible-range spectroscopy, a sample is placed in a clear chamber called a cuvette, and visible light is shined on the sample. Based on the molecular structure, the photons of light may interact with the compounds in the sample absorbing the light. The remaining light passes to a detector, either a photomultiplier tube or an array of light-sensitive diodes, where it is translated into an electronic signal. Biochemical samples that contain brightly colored or pigmented groups such as flavins and heme groups provide natural chromophores to be used in spectroscopy. As reactions occur and changes are made to the redox state of these molecules, there is an accompanying change in absorbance. Therefore, a change in the state of these molecules as a reaction progresses can be tracked spectrophotometrically.

Strengths and weaknesses: Visible-range spectroscopy is a classic technique and is the basis of many assays. It is hard to think of a laboratory that does not use it in some way. While it is the perfect tool for many situations, it is not as sensitive as fluorescence spectroscopy or the use of radiolabeled molecules.

X-ray diffraction/X-ray crystallography

When and why it is used: X-ray diffraction is a technique used to determine the structure of molecules.

How it works: Crystals of the molecule of interest are placed into a diffractometer, an instrument that generates X-rays, shines these X-rays on the crystal, and detects the angle and intensity of the diffracted spots. Mathematical analysis of the diffracted spots enables the identification of electron density in the original sample. Based on this, the structure of the molecule can be determined.

Strengths and weaknesses: X-ray structure analysis has arguably been one of the most transformative techniques of the last century. It provides detailed, high-resolution information on the structure of molecules that can yield important data related to molecular interactions, and mechanism of action. The drawbacks of X-ray crystallography are the time and investment needed to yield these results. Proteins must be highly purified, and crystallization conditions are experimentally determined. Advances in diffractometer design and X-ray sources have improved the acquisition of data, and advances in computing have no doubt made the analysis of the data easier (if not possible in some instances). Determination of a structure using X-ray diffraction has become much more accessible, but it is still one of the most difficult of biochemical experiments.

Yeast 2-hybrid system

When and why it is used: The yeast 2-hybrid system is one of only a few techniques that can be used to directly measure protein-protein interactions.

How it works: The yeast 2-hybrid system is a complementation assay that takes advantage of a reporter gene as an output. Transcription factors usually have two domains: a DNA binding domain and an activation domain that is responsible for transcriptional activation. If these two domains are expressed separately, expression will not occur; however, if they are in proximity to one another due to the interactions of other proteins, there is expression. The yeast 2-hybrid system can be used as a screening technique for protein-protein interactions. Two different types of plasmids are generated in the system. One plasmid has the DNA binding domain of a transcription factor fused to a protein of interest. The other plasmid has the activation domain fused to a cDNA library coding for different proteins. Some of these may interact with the first fusion protein, termed the bait. Cells are transformed with both plasmids. Colonies are selected that will only grow if the gene regulated by the transcription factor is expressed. Therefore, colonies that grow indicate an interaction between the bait protein and some other protein. These colonies are isolated, and the genes coding for the second protein are sequenced and identified.

There are several variants of the original yeast 2-hybrid system that can be used to detect protein-DNA interactions. These employ different host systems such as *E. coli* or eukaryotic cells or employ different detection systems, including fluorescent detection.

Strengths and weaknesses: While the yeast 2-hybrid system can identify interaction partners for the bait protein, it is easy to over- or under-interpret the results. For example, the lack of an interaction in the 2-hybrid cannot necessarily be interpreted as the absence of an interaction *in vivo*.

Answers to Worked Problem Follow-Up Questions

Chapter 1

Worked Problem 1.1 Factors that influence ΔG include the concentration of reactants and products, temperature, pH, and partial pressure of gases. The most common way ΔG can be driven to the negative in the cell is to increase the concentration of reactants and decrease the concentration of products. Altering ΔG will not affect reaction rate, but altering concentrations of reactants will.

Worked Problem 1.2 The products would be an amine and a carboxylic acid.

Worked Problem 1.3 Basic conditions would favor deprotonation of the amino group, which would generate the nucleophile that would attack the carbonyl carbon. A protonated amine won't do that.

Worked Problem 1.4 Using the Henderson-Hasselbalch equation, the volumes needed would be 863 ml of sodium acetate and 137 ml of acetic acid.

Chapter 2

Worked Problem 2.1 Two techniques used to determine the structure of a macromolecule would be NMR and X-ray crystallography. Both techniques could determine the structure of the tRNA and could therefore be used to help determine function.

Worked Problem 2.2 Oxidatively damaged or alkylated bases can lead to improper base paring in the double helix. These modified bases are incorrectly copied during replication. These mutations could alter a coding sequence, a splice site, or a regulatory sequence leading to changes in transcription and translation.

Worked Problem 2.3 This process would in many ways be the same. Two differences would be the type of plasmid or DNA construct used. If a plasmid were used instead of a virus or other means, it would need to have mammalian promoters to be expressed in a mammalian cell. The other significant way these would differ would be how the DNA was introduced to the cell. Transfection of mammalian cells differs from transduction of bacteria.

Chapter 3

Worked Problem 3.1 The pK_a of the carboxyl group of alanine has a pK_a around 2.34. Because the pK_a is more than one pH unit away from the pH of the buffer, we would expect it to be outside the buffer range. At a lower pH it could serve as a buffer.

Worked Problem 3.2 Myoglobin has a molecular weight of 16.7 kDa. An average protein has a MW of about 50 kDa with a range of 30 to 80. Myoglobin is a relatively small protein.

Worked Problem 3.3 Isoleucine is a medium-sized hydrophobic amino acid. If it were substituted with another similar amino acid, such as leucine or valine, this would probably not affect protein function. If other hydrophobic amino acids were substituted, such as a tryptophan or glycine, the change in size might create a steric clash.

If a charged or polar amino acid were substituted, the polar or charged group might orient toward solvent instead of the nonpolar core and alter protein structure or stability.

Worked Problem 3.4 This protein is globular and mostly α helical. It has a heme functional group, which is important in oxygen binding. If we were to compare it to other proteins we have seen in this chapter, we might most closely relate it to the oxygen transport protein hemoglobin. Unlike hemoglobin this protein has only a single subunit. Therefore, while it could transport or bind oxygen, it could not do it in an allosteric fashion. This protein is the muscle oxygen binding protein myoglobin.

Chapter 4

Worked Problem 4.1 Three examples here would include: alpha-ketoglutarate dehydrogenase, an oxidoreductase; lipase, a hydrolase; and T4 DNA ligase, an example of a ligase.

Worked Problem 4.2 To calculate k_{cat}, you would need $[E]_T$ in addition to V_{max}.

Worked Problem 4.3 Both glutamate and aspartate have a carboxyl group. They differ by the additional methylene group found in glutamate. It is likely that the aspartyl group would compensate for the loss of the glutamate group and, therefore, not effect the proposed mechanism.

Worked Problem 4.4 Allosteric enzymes or proteins with homotropic allosteric regulators are multimeric. When a substrate or molecule that is being transported binds to one site, it influences the affinity of the other sites.

Chapter 5

Worked Problem 5.1 The change in diffusional constant reflects a change in the structure of the protein. If the ligand is small, we would not expect the addition of ligand to change the diffusional coefficient directly, but a change to the conformation of the protein or a change in interaction partners for that protein might lead to a change in the diffusional coefficient.

Worked Problem 5.2 Caffeine causes increased alertness, flushing, increased heart rate, increased respiration and increased sweating. Caffeine has multiple effects in the body, but it generally activates the sympathetic nervous system and acts as a stimulant. Many of these effects are due to caffeine blocking phosphodiesterases, leading to increased cAMP levels and increased PKA signaling.

Chapter 6

Worked Problem 6.1

Worked Problem 6.2 Two glucose monomers joined by an α−1,4 linkage is maltose. It is able to be digested by humans, whereas cellobiose cannot be digested.

Worked Problem 6.3 Acetylated pectins have alcohols (typically methanol) found in ester linkages to the carboxyl groups on the pectin. The acetylation derivatizes the carboxyl and prevents formation of a cross-link through a metal ion.

Worked Problem 6.4 The products of glycolysis wouldn't be any different than those derived from glucose. The product would be two molecules of pyruvate.

Worked Problem 6.5 PEPCK would be a potentially good target to inhibit. It is highly regulated; it is isoform specific, so we could potentially target only one isoform; and it is found at the beginning of gluconeogenesis.

Worked Problem 6.6 A chemical approach would involve measurement of lactate. This could be done by enzymatic assay, HPLC, or mass spectrometry. A genetic approach might include deleting genes, such as lactate dehydrogenase, using CRISPR or other techniques.

Chapter 7

Worked Problem 7.1 This would imply that the reactions of the citric acid cycle, and perhaps the proteins and genes, existed prior to the evolution of the cycle as a cycle. In other words, it suggests that this complex pathway did not evolve as a complete pathway but rather as a series of individual steps that over time evolved into the pathway we now know.

Worked Problem 7.2 In some cells glutamate is used as a neurotransmitter. It is produced by the transamination of α-ketoglutarate. Therefore, reactions that deplete glutamate could in turn lead to a depletion of α-ketoglutarate, which would slow the citric acid cycle.

Worked Problem 7.3 Some of the redox centers mentioned in the problem, most notably heme and Cu^{2+}, will change their absorbance or color if they are reduced or oxidized. This could be determined spectrophotometrically and used to detect which redox centers are being affected. Spectroscopy could provide a means of determining which centers are reduced and potentially the order in which they are reduced. This could be done by removing some of the centers or reconstituting the structure in the presence or absence of some of the other centers.

Worked Problem 7.4 To react and bind, cyanide has to be able to access the central iron atom. In some heme groups this iron is shielded by proteins and is inaccessible.

Worked Problem 7.5 In the solution to worked problem 7.5, we saw that it took 16.45 kJ/mol to generate the proton gradient. Therefore, it would take approximately three protons (45 kJ/mol; 16.45 kJ/mol = 2.7 protons) to synthesize 1 molecule of ATP.

Worked Problem 7.6 Copper II is a divalent metal ion with a +2 charge. Amino acids that frequently interact with divalent metals include histidine and cysteine.

Chapter 8

Worked Problem 8.1 Either the unit could be added as a disaccharide to the growing chain or the enzymes incorporating new monosaccharides could have substrate specificity, which necessitates that the alternating monosaccharides be added. This could either be due to the geometry of the enzyme's active sites or the geometry of the carbohydrates that are being added.

Worked Problem 8.2 If glycogen is unavailable to provide glucose for the individual, the glucose could be replaced in part through gluconeogenesis. In this instance, the glucose would come from the catabolism of amino acid skeletons, which then undergo gluconeogenesis.

Worked Problem 8.3 Sucrose is a disaccharide, which will enter the cell either as fructose or glucose. Both of these will presumably be metabolized into glucose-6-phosphate, then glucose-1-phosphate, then UDP-glucose before incorporation into glycogen. Caffeine is a phosphodiesterase inhibitor. It blocks the breakdown of cAMP and in turn increases the activity of PKA. PKA will phosphorylate several proteins, most notably GSK-3, glycogen phosphorylase, and glycogen synthase. In these instances, it will inhibit glycogen synthesis and stimulate glycogen breakdown. In short, the two compounds will work against each other.

Worked Problem 8.4 Ribose could proceed through the pentose phosphate pathway and enter glycolysis either as fructose-6-phosphate or glyceraldehyde-3-phosphate.

Worked Problem 8.5 On one level this is a very simple question. Cells could be grown in the presence or absence of fructose, and the expression of several genes assayed using northern blotting or RT-PCR to determine if the carbohydrate affected the expression of these genes. However, this presumes the effect was large enough to see and the genes assayed were sensitive to fructose. This also assumes that fructose itself was not inadvertently providing some other effect (for example, increased energy). Another way to do the study would be to use two groups of organisms, such as mice or people, and then ascertain gene expression on the whole genome, either by using a technique such as a microarray or RNA-Seq. These experiments would also have challenges, not the least of which would be obtaining RNA to assay and determining what constitutes a change in gene expression.

Worked Problem 8.6 Humans lack α-1,3 galactose linkages, whereas pigs do not. Because pigs have this modification, their tissues may cause an immune response in some recipients. However, pigs lacking this modification would not be as immunogenic and would be better sources for tissue donation.

Worked Problem 8.7 Matrix proteins can be solubilized using strong detergents, cross-links chemically cleaved if at all possible, and carbohydrate modifications removed using glycosylases to facilitate their study.

Chapter 9

Worked Problem 9.1 This is $16:1^{\Delta 9}$ palmitoleic or 9-dodecahexaenoic acid.

Worked Problem 9.2 Yes, due to its amphipathic nature, lecithin could be used as a detergent but would probably not be as good a detergent as a synthetic one.

Worked Problem 9.3 You would yield 108 molecules of ATP from one molecule of palmitate. Examine Table 9.2 for a breakdown of where these ATP molecules originate.

Worked Problem 9.4 A drug that activated AMPK would lead to phosphorylation and inactivation of ACC1. This in turn would block malonyl-CoA production and fatty acid biosynthesis.

Worked Problem 9.5 Acetoacetate breakdown may not be beneficial because the energy found in acetoacetate is not reaching its destination (tissues that need it). CO_2 may contribute to the acidification of the blood, and it is not clear that acetone in high concentrations is not damaging to proteins or organs, especially the kidney.

Worked Problem 9.6   The prenylation of proteins is not affected by this class of drugs. Therefore, we can assume that the enzymes involved are not completely inhibited as some molecules are made. This also indicates that protein prenylation occurs preferentially to cholesterol biosynthesis.

Worked Problem 9.7   Prostaglandin creams are used because they can deliver the drug directly to the tissues that need it. Oral or intravenous delivery of drugs would mean that the drug would need to be absorbed and not entirely metabolized to get to the tissues that need it. Likewise, these drugs could potentially have broader impacts on health if distributed throughout the body.

Chapter 10

Worked Problem 10.1   The phospholipases found in spider venom could lead to damage to the plasma membrane of cells, in turn leading to tissue damage. These enzymes would also cause the release of fatty acids, such as arachidonyl acid, which could contribute to uncontrolled eicosanoid production.

Worked Problem 10.2   Short- or medium-chain triglycerides are not hydrolyzed and metabolized in the intestine like other fats. Rather, they are left intact and enter the bloodstream where they travel directly to the liver for metabolism.

Worked Problem 10.3   One hypothesis would be that because the organism cannot take cholesterol up from the circulation via LDL, it would sense that it had low levels of cholesterol and therefore down-regulate the production of HDL. Whether or not this is the case would require testing the hypothesis.

Worked Problem 10.4   Because clathrin plays a central role in receptor-mediated endocytosis, we would expect that the organism could not properly undergo this process. However, because receptor-mediated endocytosis is probably involved in many cellular processes, we might not expect a complex organism like a mouse to be viable.

Worked Problem 10.5   It potentially would. Adipocytes lack glycerol kinase, so any glycerol that was liberated would be released as glycerol. Fatty acids on the other hand could be re-esterified to other lipids in the cell, giving an artificially low value of the lipid breakdown occurring.

Worked Problem 10.6   Two techniques which could be used to determine if two proteins are interacting would be FRET and co-immunoprecipitation. FRET is fluorescence or Forster's energy resonance transfer. In this technique both proteins are tagged with fluorophores with overlapping spectra. One fluorophore is excited, and if the proteins are in close proximity, the second fluorophore will emit a photon. In co-immunoprecipitation, an antibody is used to selectively precipitate a select protein. Any proteins associated with this protein will co-precipitate and can be detected using western blotting or mass spectrometry.

Worked Problem 10.7   Methyl-β-cyclodextrin could be used to deplete a membrane of cholesterol. The cell could then be examined to see what effect if any this would have on raft formation.

Chapter 11

Worked Problem 11.1   Because these drugs are irreversible inhibitors, they would act like a suicide substrate, effectively lowering the concentration of enzyme as the inhibitor reacts.

Worked Problem 11.2   Transamination of these α-keto acids would regenerate the amino acids they were originally. Transamination reactions typically have ΔG values near zero.

Worked Problem 11.3   The enzymes could be isolated and the reactions performed in the presence and absence of EDTA to bind divalent metal ions. If the enzyme is able to catalyze the reaction in the absence of zinc, it indicates that zinc is not important.

Worked Problem 11.4   Lysine is an essential amino acid and one that contributes to both ketone and glucose production.

Worked Problem 11.5   Desmethyl tamoxifen is missing a methyl group on the amine (N). This would involve class I metabolism in which the substrate is oxidized. This could be due to a demethylase or oxidase such as a cytochrome enzyme or monoamine oxidase.

Worked Problem 11.6   To do this you would need some means of assaying glucose and a source of the transporter, presumably in a membrane or cell. Glucose transport would need to be measured as a function of glucose concentration. This would be graphed and if it saturates, the curve would look like the rectangular parabola found in Michaelis-Menten kinetics.

Chapter 12

Worked Problem 12.1   Two means of detecting ^{15}N are mass spectrometry and NMR. Both of these techniques are described in the appendix.

Worked Problem 12.2   If you consume no food for the next 24 hours, levels of plasma triacylglycerols should drop, but levels of free fatty acids and glycerol from adipose tissue should increase. Glucose may drop slightly but should be balanced off by glycogenolysis and gluconeogenesis from the liver. Ketone bodies should increase.

Worked Problem 12.3   Insulin is taken several times daily by millions of diabetics worldwide. Other hormones are delivered this way when their levels are low or elevated levels of a hormone are needed to combat a disease. This does not always work due to a post receptor defect in some diseases, but if we put that observation aside, it might work.

Worked Problem 12.4   With reduced adipose tissue mass, hormones such as leptin would presumably be decreased; however, based on the food consumption and body mass data, we might anticipate that leptin levels would be normal or some other mechanism might compensate. Elevated insulin levels would indicate that glucagon would probably be low as well.

Answers to Odd Problems

Chapter 1

1. The three laws of thermodynamics are: (1) Energy is conserved (meaning energy can neither be created nor destroyed); (2) The entropy or disorder of the universe is always increasing; and (3) The entropy of a pure crystal at absolute zero is zero. The system is the sample we are studying, and the surroundings are everything else in the universe. Free energy is the amount of energy available in a reaction to do work.

3. Because the structures form spontaneously, ΔG must be favorable (negative). This is due to several factors, including the formation of multiple weak interactions between the different parts of a macromolecule with itself. This organization may seem to decrease the overall disorder of the system. However, one of the main factors that are important in the formation of complex structures is the advantage that is gained by liberating water molecules, termed the hydrophobic effect.

5. The polymerization of the monomer into the polymer would seemingly have a positive entropy (the system is becoming more ordered and has fewer microstates). However, in the synthesis of the polymer, if water molecules can be liberated from caging individual monomers, the overall entropy may be lower.

7. All amino acids have carboxyl and amino groups. Many other amino acids contain amide, hydroxyl, carboxamide, thiol, or hydrocarbon groups. All of these groups can participate in London dispersion interactions. Those with amino or hydroxyl groups can participate in hydrogen bonding, charged groups can also participate in coloumbic interactions.

9. least, middle, most

11. Hydrogen bonding would occur between hydroxyl, carboxyl, and amino groups and water. Hydrophobic regions of these molecules would generally not interact and would instead have cages of water molecules surrounding them.

13.

15. deoxyribonucleotides

17. Hydroxyl and amino groups will hydrogen bond with water and act as hydrogen bond donors or acceptors. Carbonyl groups can act as hydrogen bond donors but not hydrogen bond acceptors.

19. We could calculate this number based on the heat capacity and boiling point of water. If we know how much water we have, how much energy has to go into the vaporization of that amount of water, and what the strength is of a hydrogen bond, we should be able to calculate how many hydrogen bonds are present in the sample. Dividing by the number of water molecules we should arrive at the number of bonds per water molecule. Measurement of this value might be more problematic, but infrared or Raman spectroscopy might provide some insights that could help answer this question.

21. 13.3, 14.3, 13.3, 12

23. 10.8, 9.76, 10.49 and 10.45

25. pH 7; The protons found in water begin to contribute more strongly than the HCl.

27. 12.3 mL

29. 1 M MOPS; The higher concentration has the higher capacity to absorb or donate protons.

31. Ionize it to an amine salt by treating it with strong acid in the case of an amine or use strong base in the case of a carboxylic acid.

33. There are numerous ways to approach this question. Simple organic analysis often employs solubility, melting point or boiling point, and several different spectroscopic techniques (NMR and IR being some of the most common). Most biochemicals are complex and have multiple functional groups. Often they are large polymers with complex tertiary shapes found in low abundance in complex mixtures.

35. Dissolve 6.1 g TRIS base in a beaker with approximately 400 mL of deionized water, adjust pH to 7.4 with HCl (measure using pH meter), and bring volume to 500 mL with deionized water (measure using volumetric flask or grad cylinder).

The answers for these questions will vary from individual to individual.

37. People are often surprised that codes of conduct are as vague as they are and often permit research into topics the students themselves may find unethical.

39. The definition of a drug is a legal and not a scientific one. This definition has changed over time and will probably continue to change as new molecules become known or synthesized.

41. While the new drug is far easier to develop and test than the original, it is a different compound and may elicit different pharmacological properties than the original. This new pure compound has to be approved and regulated.

Chapter 2

1. Consult Figure 2.2 for the structures of the five bases.

3. Purine and pyrimidine are generally insoluble in water, but the modifications made to them (carbonyl, hydroxyl, and amino groups outside the ring structures) make the compounds more soluble.

5. Check Figure 2.3 for the enol forms of each base. If the bases were enols instead of carbonyl groups, they could act as both hydrogen bond donors and acceptors instead of simply acceptors.

7. Yes, most likely. In a nonpolar solvent, such as hexane, the hydrophobic bases of DNA would be more soluble, but the ionized sugar phosphate backbone would be far less soluble and potentially interact more strongly with other charged species.

9. Less stable. There would be nothing to counter the charges on the phosphate backbone, and the backbone charges would repel each other.

11. See Figure 2.15 for an illustration of a riboswitch. One expression that would describe the equilibrium would be:

$$K_{eq} = [RNAbond]/[RNAfree] \cdot [ligand]$$

13. Each strand of DNA serves as a template. In the final product there is one newly synthesized strand and one template strand.

15. If guanine were methylated on the carbonyl group, it would lose the ability to participate in hydrogen bonding. Additionally, the methyl group makes the overall structure more hydrophobic, and addition of this group could alter interactions through steric effects.

17. Draw out a cartoon or schematic structure of DNA. The shortest unit of DNA is the base pair. The average mRNA is approximately 1,500 to 2,000 bases in length (approximately 680 nm long). A gene in humans can range from around 5,000 base pairs on the short side to over 50,000 base pairs, although most genes are around 10,000 base pairs in length. Chromosomes are tens to hundreds of millions of base pairs in length (several centimeters long), but we often think of them folded in their iconic metaphase form (approximately 10 microns). A ribosome is approximately 30 nm in diameter. Proteins range in size but are usually between 3 and 15 nm in diameter.

19. The synthesis of DNA requires the formation of a phosphodiester linkage between deoxyribose sugars in the backbone. The hydrolysis of those esters is favorable in terms of enthalpy, meaning that energy is necessary for their synthesis. In terms of entropy, DNA is a large complex molecule that is highly organized compared to a random mixture of nucleotides. There is a large decrease in entropy in the synthesis of a DNA molecule, making the process less favorable. What drives this process forward (what makes ΔG for the entire process negative) is the use of deoxynucleotide triphosphates in the synthesis of DNA. The loss of pyrophosphate and subsequent hydrolysis provides a large negative enthalpy, which makes the synthesis possible.

21. There are several reasons that bacteria are not used in all aspects of biochemical research. First, even though bacteria may synthesize a human protein, that particular protein may have modifications found only in eukaryotic systems. Second, the function of a protein may be dependent on what other proteins it interacts with or where it is found in a eukaryotic cell. Third, while we often focus on human proteins or human health in questions of biomedical research, there are many other interesting biochemical systems, including plants, that are also worthy of study.

23. Proteins, including restriction enzymes, often recognize specific DNA sequences through binding in the major groove of DNA with an alpha helix. Given that both the double helix and the alpha helix are relatively inflexible over the lengths being described, there is limited contact between the two structures. Sequences are often palindromic to assist in binding because multiple binding sites are better than a single site, or to assist in cutting, where the enzyme recognizes and cuts two sites, one on each strand. Sequences with a disrupted palindrome, and therefore greater distance between the binding sites, may be due to a dimeric protein.

25. It indicates that neither enzyme cuts a random sequence; it is likely that both the target sequences that are recognized and the enzyme that cuts them coevolved to get to where they are today. As a pathogen (phage) evolved and changes accumulated that enabled it to evade the restriction enzymes of an early host, the restriction enzymes of the host also randomly changed. In instances where the changes that accumulated in the host gave it some sort of advantage over the pathogen, the changes were selected for and tended to accumulate over time.

27. Exposure to UV light can damage DNA, leading to the formation of thymine dimers. There are enzymes in the cell that can help reverse this process, but the same cannot be said of DNA in a gel.

29. Polymerases vary with regard to the quality of the product produced, the length of product produced, and whether the ends produced are blunt or sticky. Polymerases may also have an exonuclease function (a proofreading capability). Because of the origins of some of these polymerases, they react best in different buffers.

31. PCR could be performed using mutagenic primers that contain the mutation or mutations necessary to incorporate the site.

33. Genomic DNA would contain the entire genomic sequence, including introns and exons. Reverse transcribed RNA and cDNA are effectively equivalent. Both would contain the coding sequence of the gene (the spliced exons) along with some 5′ and 3′ untranslated sequences.

35. The sigmoidal shape of the curve tells us that the transition from double stranded to single stranded occurs over a narrow temperature range. This suggests that the transition is cooperative.

37. Addition of acid would drop the pH of the solution. If the pH were to be dropped low enough, the phosphate backbone would protonate, leading to loss of the charge on the phosphate backbone. We might anticipate that this would make the double helix more stable, but the concentrations of acid needed to do this would also lead to shifts in the tautomeric forms of the bases and decreases in the interactions of the base pairs. As a result, the melting point of the DNA would drop and the curve would shift to the left.

39. EDTA is a compound that binds to divalent metal ions such as Ca^{2+} and Mg^{2+}. When EDTA is added, it binds to these metals, which usually interact with the phosphate backbone of DNA. If these metal ions are absent, then there is nothing to balance out the charges of the phosphate backbones, leading to repulsive forces between the two strands and a lower melting point.

41. To do this one would need a piece of DNA (often a plasmid) that has the cDNA of the protein in question, flanked by sequences that the host cell would recognize to express the protein. Typically, these sequences involve a strong promoter and a poly adenylation sequence. These vectors also contain some sort of selectable marker, which allows for selection of cells that are expressing the plasmid over those that are not. DNA could be introduced into eukaryotic cells using lipofection, electroporation, or some other chemical means, like calcium phosphate precipitation. The cells would be selected using a selectable marker, for example, an antibiotic, to produce cells that express the protein.

43. You would need a means of measuring the melting or denaturation of DNA. This could be done with a technique such as differential scanning calorimetry or possibly by examining single- and double-stranded DNA on a gel. The melting of DNA would be studied in the presence and absence of the protein to see if the protein had an effect on the melting temperature.

45. There are numerous ways to clone a gene. One of the simpler ways is to use primers that anneal to a related gene or a homologous gene from another species. These primers can be used to amplify template DNA from the new species.

The answers for these questions will vary from individual to individual.

47. People tend to fear the unknown or the new. It may be that bacteria are microscopic and are therefore perceived as less of a threat than a macroscopic organism.

49. While it may be noble to try to eliminate a disease that causes human suffering, one quickly gets onto a slippery slope when discussing genetic engineering of healthy people. In the past, eugenics has been used to legitimize racism, ethnic cleansing, or other beliefs that are baseless and abhorrent.

Chapter 3

1. Threonine and isoleucine.

3. No and yes. No, because all organisms use the same amino acids and potentially have since the beginning of time. Therefore, the changes are not as pronounced as they are in a gene or protein. Yes, because there are ways to examine the structures of amino acids and

identify based on their chemical properties why the structures that exist have been selected. These are specific for each amino acid.

5. All amino acids are white crystalline solids that appear like salts when found in the pure state. Likewise, when pure and dry many proteins are white solids. When a protein is bound to a cofactor (for example, heme, a metal ion, or group such as FAD), it can be brightly colored.

7.

9. Tyrosine is also characterized as aromatic.

11. Tryptophan, tyrosine, and to a lesser extent phenylalanine absorb light in the ultraviolet range of the electromagnetic spectrum. This is due to their conjugated double bonds. Other amino acids lack these conjugated double bond systems.

13. Selenium is found beneath sulfur in the periodic table. As we go down a column of the periodic table, elements become larger and become "softer" nucleophiles and less electronegative. Therefore, selenocystine would behave like cysteine in the same way that cysteine behaves like serine. In other words, selenocystine would be more acidic and have a lower pK_a than cysteine.

15. If a protein were 450 amino acids long and there were 20 possibilities at each step, then that would be 20^{450} different combinations or approximately 3×10^{585}, an astronomically huge number. Given that there are on the order of 10,000 to 100,000 proteins in an organism and that these are conserved through evolution, it is unlikely that proteins are random but are rather specific and selected for throughout time.

17. The amino acid sequence of a protein provides information regarding localization. More specifically, if an amino acid needed to be modified in some way (acylated, for example) and that residue was changed to one that could not be acylated, it might change how the protein was distributed in the cell.

19. ATP is used instead of free phosphate, for example, because of the free energy of the reaction. ATP is said to have high transfer potential for phosphate. In other words, the free energy of the reaction in which ATP transfers a phosphate to a hydroxyl group in a protein is negative compared to the phosphorylation of that same protein by a free phosphate group (which is positive). ATP is frequently used as a source of phosphate in phosphorylation reactions but several other molecules can also be used. It is the gamma phosphate (the one most distal from the ribose ring) that is used in the reaction. In terms of equilibrium, there is a relatively high concentration of free phosphate in the cell which could drive a reaction forward if it were the reactant in the reaction. Glycogen phosphorylase uses the energy of glucose hydrolysis from the glycogen main chain to generate glucose-1-phosphate. This happens without ATP.

21. If a single gene encoding for a protein with a four-helix bundle were to undergo duplication and then over time mutations accumulated that altered the sequence of the protein, we could envision a time when there would be two different proteins, both with four-helix bundle motifs but with different sequences or functions. This would be an example of divergent evolution. In terms of convergent evolution, there could be two different unrelated genes that both coded for proteins with helical regions. As these proteins accumulated changes over time, there could be alterations in amino acid sequence that would favor the formation of a four-helix bundle, for example, mutations that led to the formation of a hydrophobic face of amino acids on a helix which could then interact with other similar helices. While this sort of origin seems less likely than divergent evolution, an examination of the number of structures and their evolutionary diversity reveals that this is more likely the case. The four-helix bundle is selected for through a combination of structure and function, and it is more likely to arise through convergent evolution.

23. Knowing the structure of a molecule and not simply the formula provides a wealth of information about the properties and functions of that molecule. This is as true in biochemistry as it is in organic or inorganic chemistry.

25. 585 amino acids $\times$ 110 Daltons/amino acid = 64,300 Da or 63.4 kDa. The actual molecular weight of human serum albumin is 66.5 kDa, relatively close to our approximation.

27. With the loss of water many proteins would denature. The strength of salt bridges would potentially increase, but there would be no solvent to hydrogen-bond with, and contributions from the hydrophobic effect would decrease significantly enough to allow proteins to denature. Secondary, tertiary, and quaternary structures would all be disrupted.

29. Due to the fibrous nature of collagen and how the individual molecules interact with one another, collagen and other matrix proteins can be difficult to study. An advantage of studying collagen is that is it one of the most prevalent molecules in the body and therefore can be easily obtained.

31. Porcine insulin is a better choice, because there is less variability between that and human and bovine and human.

33. The controlled hydrolysis of ATP results in conformational changes to myosin, in turn resulting in motion. Binding of ATP to the active site of myosin elicits a conformational change releasing actin from myosin. ATP is hydrolyzed, and the head of myosin is moved back, resulting in myosin binding elsewhere on the actin molecule. Release of phosphate from myosin causes a conformational change in myosin so that the head rocks, moving closer to the tail in a movement termed the power stroke. Finally, ADP dissociates from the active site.

35. The region of immunoglobulins that binds to antigen is found at the tip of their variable regions generated through a special recombination event in the cells that produce these proteins. The rest of the protein is conserved among all cells of the organism.

37. As an electric charge is applied to the protein, it migrates from where it started to a region of the gel that has a lower pH. It moves toward the cathode (the positive electrode) until the protein stops moving. The pH at which it stops moving will have negatively and positively charged groups equally protonated (there will be no net charge on the protein). This pH is called the isoelectric point (pI) of the protein. The protein is in the pH 4–5 range, indicating that the protein has more acidic groups (aspartate and glutamate) than basic amino acids.

39. A strength of this technique is that it combines several simple techniques to try to probe a protein–protein interaction. A weakness is that the conditions chosen may not reveal the interaction or the interaction may be non-specific. There are several controls for this experiment. The first lane shows that the protein we are studying is found in the sample and we can detect it. Lanes 1 to 3 have no Mg^{2+} while lanes 4 to 6 contain it. Therefore, lanes 1 to 3 are acting as

controls for lanes 4 to 6. Lanes 1 and 5 lack cross-linking and are also controls for the lanes that have it. Generally, this experiment shows cross-linking between the protein of interest and something else only when Mg^{2+} was added. Detergent reversed or blocked this effect. We could test to see if the enzyme was interacting with the ER protein by performing the same experiment but detecting the ER protein instead of the cytosolic one.

41. Some two-dimensional NMR techniques can be used to determine the conformation of complex molecules like peptides.

43. If you had a technique to measure the folding of a protein (such as circular dichroism of an α helical protein), you could measure the reversible folding and unfolding of a protein under different conditions.

45. Purified samples of both domains could be compared to see if they are folded into the same conformations as the proteins in the complex. This would involve either determining the structure of the domains using a technique such as X-ray crystallography or NMR or determining if the domain retained a known function (which would only happen if the domain were properly folded).

The answers for these questions will vary from individual to individual.

47. Perhaps this should draw into question what those beliefs are and why they were instated.

49. Laws have been written prohibiting or regulating other unhealthy behaviors. Perhaps the question is, Should people be informed as to the risks and take those risks themselves?

Chapter 4

1. Active sites are often found in clefts such as the deep cleft between the two globular domains. There is a second notch at the upper right and a broad cuplike feature in the lower left that could also be the active site.

3. Because enzymes are proteins, they will unfold and denature at high temperatures. This leads to a loss of catalytic activity when the tertiary structure is lost.

5. RNA molecules are single stranded and can form complex shapes with crevices containing the functional groups necessary for catalysis. DNA in contrast is double stranded, which places these same functional groups in a different geometry that potentially prevents catalysis from occurring.

7. The difference between the codons encoding lysine and asparagine differ by only one letter in the genetic code; therefore, a single point mutation could lead to the lysine to asparagine change.

9. An examination of the structure reveals a modified peptide backbone with what appears to be the side chains of glycine, phenylalanine, valine, and several five-membered rings that might be analogous in some way to histidine or proline.

11. The slope of this line is K_M and the y-intercept is V_{max}. The advantage of this plot is that it is linear and easy to read and compares values of V_{max} and K_M. This form of the equation is simply a rearrangement of the Michaelis-Menten equation. Lineweaver-Burke plots suffer in that the data points with the lowest precision (the lowest level of activity and highest level of noise) have the largest weight on the reciprocal graph. Eadie-Hofstee plots even out the spacing of the points reducing biases in the graph.

13. Look for inversion of stereochemistry of the product. Recall that S_N2 reactions undergo an inversion of stereochemistry in the product.

15. Examine the structures of both succinate and aspartate. ATCase normally binds aspartate. If it also binds succinate, it suggests that the binding site on ATCase will most likely recognize the carboxyl moieties of both aspartate and succinate.

17. If the enzyme has achieved catalytic perfection, then the only way to improve upon it would be for it to diffuse more quickly, that is, to make it smaller.

19. Potentially. Both of these residues have negatively charged carboxyl groups as side chains. Based on that reasoning the enzyme may still function, although the extra methylene group on glutamate may cause changes in how substrate sterically fits in to the active site.

21. Residues that are highly conserved are found in most or all related proteins in the same organism or in the same protein found in different organisms. It is likely that some residues are more highly conserved than others due to the role they play in the enzyme. Residues that are essential may be more strongly selected for than those that are not.

23. The mechanism of the transacylase would proceed as the mechanism for the protease did in the chapter. However, following the formation of the acyl enzyme intermediate and loss of the first product, the acyl group would be transferred to the hydroxyl group of a recipient molecule completing the transesterification reaction, rather than having a water molecule hydrolyze the acyl enzyme intermediate.

25. This mutation would insert a large bulky side chain (an indole group) in place of the hydrogen atom found in glycine. Based on this large change we might predict that the enzyme would be dramatically affected, and we would predict that k_{cat} (catalysis) was affected more significantly than K_M (substrate binding).

27. Possible answers include western blotting with phosphospecific antibodies (antibodies that specifically recognize phosphorylated sequences), mass spectrometry, and incorporation of radiolabeled phosphate.

29. Both allosterism and phosphorylation are reversible modifications whereas proteolysis is not. Allosterism takes place very rapidly (as fast as the enzyme can bind to the regulator), whereas phosphorylation and proteolysis can be slower (from milliseconds to minutes). The question of fine tuning of a reaction rate is often a confusing one. In terms of most of these control mechanisms, an enzyme is either active or is not—there is no middle state. However, in terms of a population of enzyme molecules, each mechanism allows some level of fine tuning of activity as more or fewer enzymes are activated.

31. Using this equation, we calculate that the relative strength of this interaction across the protein to be 34.6 kJ/mol. If this were happening in water, the strength would be 1.7 kJ/mol.

33. There are several current models of allosteric regulation. In each of these the protein exists in one of two states, an active state and an inactive state. These are supported by two pieces of data. First, a combination of these two states (high activity and low activity) results in the observed sigmoidal curve. Second, structurally allosteric enzymes are found in one of two different conformations, not a spectrum of different conformations. Therefore, the two-state model is generally accepted as the foundational assumption for more elaborate models.

35. Allosteric regulators are not competing at the active site. Thus, these compounds can alter the structure of the protein-shifting amino acids in the active site or alter the way the enzyme can bind to the substrate. Additionally, allosteric regulators can shift activity significantly over a small concentration range and in some cases can activate the enzyme.

37. This observation does not lead to clear conclusions; however we do have some basis for hypothesizing about the role of the serine. The conversion of the serine to an alanine results in loss of some activity. This indicates that the serine is not essential for catalysis, but rather it may play some role in the regulation of the protein. If the serine is phosphorylated, it may play a role in the regulation of activity. The mutation of the serine to a negatively charged aspartate is consistent with this finding. Here the aspartate will mimic the phosphorylated state of the enzyme.

39. One interpretation of this data is that the chymotrypsin holoenzyme has a mass of approximately 26 kDa but that it is comprised of three smaller subunits held together by disulfide bonds and weak forces. The individual subunits are observed using SDS-PAGE but not size exclusion chromatography.

41. There are several ways to test this hypothesis. First, the enzyme could be assayed in the presence of a compound that binds to metals, such as EDTA. Second, the mass of the holoenzyme could be measured using mass spectrometry. Third, the conserved histidines could be mutated and the enzyme tested for activity.

43. Perform kinetics experiments on the HIV protease in the presence and absence of the inhibitor and analyze the results using a Lineweaver–Burke plot.

The answers for these questions will vary from individual to individual.

45. Is the lack of antibiotics considered a threat to the public health of the nation? If so, how would you propose funding this research and who would conduct it?

47. Both catalase and the metal are catalysts and catalyze the same reaction. As a protein, catalase has to be purified from a biological source and has to be stabilized in some way. On the other hand, the metals used in catalysts are often heavy metals such as manganese. Both have their advantages and disadvantages.

49. One might anticipate antibiotics, basic pain relievers, and blood pressure medications, but the basic list is actually far more extensive.

Chapter 5

1. If we assume the mass of a phospholipid to be approximately 1,000 g/mol and the mass of an average protein to be 50 kDa (50,000 g/mol), the approximate ratio is 50:1 lipid to protein.

3. This answer will depend on the size of your campus. In any event, the plasma membrane will be approximately one ten-thousandth the diameter of campus. If your campus is a mile in diameter, this means that the plasma membrane would be approximately 6 inches thick.

5. The removal of an integral membrane protein from the plasma membrane is an unfavorable process and therefore has a positive value of ΔG. Interactions of an integral membrane protein with the plasma membrane are governed by the hydrophobic effect. The interactions of a membrane-spanning α helix with the acyl chains of phospholipids in the bilayer or with water when removed from the lipid bilayer are minimal, and therefore ΔH is probably close to 0. When the integral membrane protein is removed from the lipid bilayer, there will be a significant decrease in entropy as water molecules organize to shield the hydrophobic α helix from the bulk phase of solvent. This makes the entropic term of the free energy expression ($\Delta G = \Delta H - T\Delta S$) positive and makes ΔG for the entire process positive.

7. Based on this observation the perilipins must be some sort of integral membrane protein; that is, they associate via some sort of interaction with the hydrophobic part of the lipid bilayer. This could be a transmembrane helix if we were discussing a lipid bilayer, but in the instance of the lipid storage droplet, it is likely that amphipathic alpha helices are imbedded in the phospholipid monolayer surrounding the lipid storage droplet.

9. If there were exposed edges of membrane, water molecules would be required to reorganize to cage the exposed acyl chains of the bilayer. This would cause a significant drop in entropy (a greater overall degree of organization and less randomness). This change in entropy would lead to a more positive value of ΔG for the overall process. Any reaction that would liberate these water molecules (such as the reorganization of phospholipids to shield these acyl chains and begin to form micelles or vesicles) would liberate water and make the reaction more energetically favorable by increasing entropy.

11. Proteins in the membrane that are tethered to the cytoskeleton or other structural proteins have a much slower rate of diffusion than unbound proteins. This could result in fewer interactions between a receptor and a ligand; however, if multiple ligands and multiple receptors were concentrated together, this would increase the likelihood of an interaction.

13. There are several models that describe the fusion or fission of two membranes. In one, the two membranes come close enough to each other that one leaflet begins to fuse with the other. These leaflets zipper together, which brings the second membrane in close proximity to the other leaflet. Figure 5.7 illustrates this model. Both fission and fusion are regulated by proteins in the cell.

15. Metformin acts via AMPK. Metformin stimulates AMPK which in turn blocks the production of glucose by the liver, relieving some of the symptoms of diabetes.

17. Some of the targets of protein kinase A include acetyl-CoA carboxylase, pyruvate kinase, pyruvate dehydrogenase, and fructose-2,6-bisphosphatase.

19. There is cross talk between the insulin signaling pathway and the PKA pathway at the level of phosphodiesterase (the enzyme that breaks down cAMP). There is also cross talk between some of the targets of AMPK, PKA, and insulin signaling (more than one pathway can phosphorylate the same target protein).

21. Based on what we have discussed in this chapter, Akt acts to stimulate glucose breakdown (glycolysis) and fatty acid breakdown (β-oxidation), but please be aware that Akt has multiple functions in the cell, many of which remain to be identified.

23. a. Because the protein is affecting cognition, we may hypothesize that it is found in the brain. A western blot or northern blot would be simple ways to test for this. If it is found in the brain, it is unlikely that liver cells would be a good model for study. To determine the function of the protein and not simply where it is found, we would probably need a functional system to study and not a cadaver (dead tissue). This leaves the mouse as the best model in this question.

b. Based on this result, imstudyin is found in the second band from the top (the one which is associated with smooth endoplasmic reticulum). We could also perform immunofluorescent staining of cells for the protein or immunohistochemistry to see where in the cell the protein could be found and if it colocalized with markers for different organelles (such as smooth ER).

c. When treated with detergent, the protein migrated in a fraction with a different (lower) density than the controls or than samples treated with salt or low pH. While we often think of lipids as having low density compared to other molecules (and they do), membranes are 50% protein by mass. It is likely that the addition of detergent disrupted the membranes resulting in the change in the migration seen in the experiment. Other experiments would have to be conducted to confirm these results.

d. The results in this figure indicate that samples treated with protease were protected from cleavage under control conditions or when treated with salt or low pH. However, when treated with detergent, the sample was cleaved, indicating that protease cleavage sites on the protein were exposed to the protease following exposure to detergent. This data, in conjunction with the data from panel D and panel E, indicate that the protein is found imbedded in the smooth endoplasmic reticulum. Disruption of the smooth ER membrane leads to exposure of the protein to the protease and subsequent degradation.

e. The data indicate that the amount of protein in the organellar fraction increases in lanes 3 and 5. This seems to happen with a concomitant loss of protein in the cytosolic fraction. We can conclude from this that the protein is trafficking from the cytosol to the organelle upon exposure to caffeine, but further experimentation would be required to demonstrate this. Using this assay as described, we cannot tell the phosphorylation state of the proteins. To do that, we would either need to perform a western blot using phosphospecific antibodies or examine radiolabeled phosphate incorporation into the protein.

25. You could test the asymmetry of a membrane using compounds that react with a membrane component such as an antibody that would bind to a protein or a molecule that would react with a functional group found in phospholipids. If the membrane were symmetric, one would expect one-half of the groups to be labeled, presuming that the compound was not able to pass through the membrane. However, if the membrane were asymmetric, one would hypothesize that some other fraction (either more or less, depending on the component) would be labeled. As a control, you might disrupt the membrane either physically or using detergents and see if the compounds are still labeled equally.

27. Samples of membrane lipids can be isolated and characterized, and their physical properties (such as melting point) can be measured.

29. There are several ways to assay receptor-ligand interactions. One way would be to use a radiolabeled ligand (radiolabeled EGF). This ligand can be incubated with the receptor, then the receptor isolated away from the unbound ligand. This is often accomplished using size exclusion chromatography, dialysis, or filtration. If the radiolabeled ligand binds to the receptor, the isolated receptor sample should now contain the radiolabeled ligand. In the second experiment, we could add EGF to a sample of cells expressing the insulin receptor and measure some output of the insulin signaling cascade (such as phosphorylation of the insulin receptor or activation of downstream kinases) using western blotting with phosphospecific antibodies. For more on this technique, please check the technical appendix.

The answers for these questions will vary from individual to individual.

31. Students should examine the controlled substances act and the updates and amendments that have been made to that act for information on this topic.

33. This is a complex issue with legal, genetic, and ethical components to it.

Chapter 6

1.

Ia. aldose	**IIa.** ketose	**IIIa.** aldose	**IVa.** aldose
Ib. pentose	**IIb.** hexose	**IIIb.** hexose	**IVb.** hexose
Ic. β	**IIc.** β	**IIIc.** α	**IVc.** β
Id. furanose	**IId.** furanose	**IIId.** pyranose	**IVd.** pyranose

3.

5.

7.

9. No, humans and most animals lack chitinase, the enzymes needed to degrade chitin; however, some fish and amphibians have chitinase and therefore can digest this material.

11. We would assume that lactose would remain soluble and partition with the whey. In this instance, we would assume that those who are lactose intolerant could consume these curds. In many cases, those who are lactose intolerant can consume some dairy products such as cheese.

13. While refluxing a biological sample with solvent is done in some instances to increase extraction, increasing the temperature of an extraction of a biological sample will lead to denaturation of the higher order structures of most biological molecules, including nucleic acids, proteins, and some carbohydrates, rendering the molecule useless or inactive.

15. The roller coaster would vary with the metabolic state of the cell (as the cell switched between glycolysis and gluconeogenesis), but for the most part the rest of the "ride" would be rather flat because many of these reactions have ΔG values in the cell close to 0 kJ/mol. The end of the ride would also finish lower than the starting point because ΔG for the entire pathway is negative

17. F-2,6-bP is an important regulator of glycolysis, regulating phosphofructokinase, the key rate determining enzyme in this pathway. Therefore, molecules that regulate the synthesis or degradation of F-2,6-bP will in turn regulate glycolysis.

19. Without a lysine residue, bacterial aldolase cannot generate a Schiff base. Instead, a plausible mechanism would use a metal ion to polarize a water molecule to attack the carbon–carbon bond of the aldol, resulting in bond cleavage.

21. Glycerol can contribute to gluconeogenesis through dihydroxyacetone phosphate. It is phosphorylated to glycerol-3-phosphate and then oxidized to DHAP. Fatty acids cannot contribute to gluconeogenesis.

23. They would be found on any of the carbons of glucose; the label would be scrambled by triose phosphate isomerase.

25. While many of the reactions of gluconeogenesis are reversible and used in glycolysis, only the liver and kidneys are capable of producing glucose through gluconeogenesis. Only the liver releases glucose for other organs (typically the brain).

27. The mechanisms are substantiated by the thermodynamic data. In mutase, the ΔG of the reaction is close to zero. The mechanism of this reaction shows the breaking and making of bonds that are very similar to one another. Likewise, the reaction of pyruvate decarboxylase is negative in part because of the release of CO_2.

29. If a person were on a high-fat diet, the diet would have low levels of carbohydrates. As a result, the liver would be producing more glucose through gluconeogenesis. This would potentially deplete levels of pyruvate from the liver. One source of these carbons would be the glycerol backbone of fats.

31. Pyruvate dehydrogenase is the committed step in the synthesis of acetyl-CoA from pyruvate. The molecules that regulate pyruvate dehydrogenase are all molecules that reflect the energetic state of the cell and therefore regulate flow of metabolites into the citric acid cycle.

33. This could be any molecule that can serve as a proton acceptor. Typically, these would be deprotonated carboxyl groups in aspartate and glutamate or deprotonated histidine or tyrosine residues.

35. These data would suggest that the molecule in question is a polysaccharide with a molecular weight of at least 10 kDa. The hydrolysis data suggest that the polysaccharide is a combination of glucose and glucosamine residues in a 1:1 ratio. It is likely that the acetate is found as a modification of the glucosamine residues (*N*-acetyl glucosamine), but further experimentation would need to be conducted to test this hypothesis.

37. The shells could easily be composed of a carbohydratelike chitin. I would advise her to test the samples for carbohydrate or perform mass spectrometry on the sample to help determine the composition.

39. The Molisch test is a test for all carbohydrates. In it a strong acid dehydrates an alcohol to an aldehyde, which reacts with napthol to give a purple-colored product. The positive Molisch test indicates that the sample is a carbohydrate. Other carbohydrate tests, such as the starch–iodine test, Benedict's test, or Bial's test, can be used to determine what types of carbohydrates are found in the sample.

41. This experiment would require two groups of mice—one treated with the drug and a control group. Both groups would need to be fasted to induce gluconeogenesis. A simple blood test to measure glucose would give an indication of glucose levels, but not the origin. To measure gluconeogenesis, mice could be administered radiolabeled alanine or pyruvate, and as the label accumulated in glucose or in the steps of gluconeogenesis, it could be used to measure gluconeogenesis. A similar approach could be used in cultured cells. This would be made somewhat easier by the lack of different tissues and ease of administering different metabolites to the dish of cells. A different approach would be needed in humans. Gluconeogenesis would largely be determined by measuring plasma glucose without radiolabels.

The answers for these questions will vary from individual to individual.

43. Have taxes worked before as a means to modify behavior? Is it the right of individuals to eat what they wish?

45. Sugarcane is a food source, and therefore using some of it for production of ethanol could raise the cost of food. Sugarcane is renewable (it must be grown every year), but the harvest is highly polluting (the fields are burned before the cane is harvested).

47. Why are some molecules that act as drugs illegal and some legal? What are the biological and societal implications of these regulations?

Chapter 7

1. **I.** It was lost as CO_2 in the first round.

    II. Half of the label would be lost as CO_2 in the oxidation of isocitrate; the other half would be in one of the two carboxyl groups of α-ketoglutarate.

    III. It was lost as CO_2 in the first round (half in the oxidation of isocitrate, half in the oxidation of α-ketoglutarate).

3. We might expect the reactions in which CO_2 is lost or in reactions in which there is a transfer of a group from CoA would drive reactions to negative ΔG values. Other reactions, such as isomerizations or hydrations, would quite likely have ΔG values near zero.

5. Regulation of the citric acid cycle is depicted in Figure 7.4. The citric acid cycle is positively regulated by Ca^{2+} and negatively regulated by NADH, succinyl-CoA, ATP, and citrate. The key points of control are at citrate synthase (the entry point to the pathway), isocitrate dehydrogenase, and α-ketoglutarate dehydrogenase.

7. Most of the reactions of the citric acid cycle could theoretically run in the reverse direction. There would be some need for different steps to fix CO_2 and overcome energetic barriers, but we have seen other pathways that are capable of doing this. Some have speculated that pieces of the citric acid cycle evolved from primitive biosynthetic pathways.

9. We often think of devices humans have engineered as having redundancies built into them as a failsafe to keep a device working in the event of an emergency. In a metabolic pathway, such as the citric acid cycle, this would mean that there would need to be redundant genes coding for proteins, all of which would need to have similar but not necessarily identical control mechanisms. It would radically complicate the pathway and is not typically observed in biological systems. This is true of most biochemical pathways.

11. While over 100,000 structures have been solved and deposited in the PDB, not all proteins have had their structures solved yet. Some reasons that proteins have not been solved include the perceived importance of the protein, how easy it is to crystallize, and how complicated the structure may be to solve.

13. The species that are found vary from *E. coli* to humans and *Bos taurus* (cow). Some species like cows have been chosen because they are a rich source of protein for purification. Others, such as microbes, are easy to work with in the lab.

15. We might imagine that if we could block electron flow through complex II with some sort of poison, electrons could still flow from complex I to complex III and we might still be able to generate ATP. The problem with this line of reasoning is that we would rapidly deplete the supply of FAD and be unable to generate NADH through the citric acid cycle. Anaerobic organisms can operate without the citric acid cycle, but aerobes cannot.

17. No, there is currently no way to identify a single electron in an experiment and trace it, for example, through a reaction or mechanism.

19. One means by which we could identify the location of the electron transport complex would be to fix and section cells and stain them with an antibody directed against one of the proteins of the electron transport chain. This could be detected using immunogold and electron microscopy to show the location. A second technique would involve isolating intact mitochondria and treating them with a protease. Proteins on the cytosolic side of the mitochondria would be exposed to the protease and degraded. Proteins in the mitochondrial matrix would be protected. This could be visualized using SDS-PAGE and Western blotting using antibodies that would detect proteins of the electron transport chain. A third means would be to chemically derivatize the proteins that are on the cytosolic side of the mitochondria using a dye or fluorophore and show that the proteins of the electron transport chain are not stained.

21. Organisms that fix CO_2 often employ biotin to bind and polarize the molecule. Reactions with oxygen most often use heme groups again to bind and polarize the molecule for subsequent chemical reactions.

23. The mechanism has electrons flowing from a partially positively charged carboxyl carbon to the negatively charged enolate, while it should be the other way around.

25. Due to the electron withdrawing nitro groups and resonance, the pK_a of picric acid is much lower (0.4) than that of 2,4-DNP (4.1). Therefore, it would be harder for picric acid to protonate and deprotonate and pass through the membrane, making DNP the better uncoupler.

27. Each of these ATPases and synthases can synthesize or hydrolyze ATP, and most are coupled to some sort of chemical gradient. Some, such as F, A, and V, have similar architecture, but others vary. E-type lacks a transmembrane domain while P has a single subunit unlike the others.

Questions 29, 31, and 33 are concerned with ATPases that acidify vesicular structures in the cell.

29. The volume of the lysosome would be 4.2×10^{-18} liters. The change in the hydrogen ion concentration (from the pH) is 3.2×10^{-5} M. This is 1.3×10^{-22} moles of H^+ or 1.4×10^{-23} moles of ATP.

31. 2.6×10^{-21} mol/min

33. The turnover number would not change; the turnover number is the number of reactions per unit time and depends on the enzyme, not the concentration. The lysosome would acidify ten times faster, but turnover would be unchanged.

35. No. While the reaction in which succinyl-CoA is cleaved to give succinate does generate GTP, that reaction is coupled to the hydrolysis of succinyl-CoA. None of the mass of succinyl-CoA, radiolabeled or not, will end up in GTP.

37. Based on the images, it appears that the complex has two heavier subunits, three identical medium subunits, and one smaller subunit. If we assume it has one copy of complex I, one of complex II, three of complex III, and one of complex IV, we arrive at 1900 kDa (1.9 MDa), which is close to the 1.8 value observed using the other technique. This can be predicted from the arrangement of the subunits, but the error in doing so would be relatively large.

39. Samples could be heated to denature the enzymes of the cycle to show that they are necessary for catalysis.

41. Radiolabeled FAD could be incubated with the succinate dehydrogenase complex to see if it exchanges from bulk solution to the enzyme. If radiolabeled FAD was found to associate with the enzyme, it would be evidence that it exchanged with the protein.

The answers for these questions will vary from individual to individual.

43. What is the data that indicate neonicotinoids may be responsible or not, and is it coming from a reputable source?

45. How do these fish get to market? Who are the players in this process?

47. What are the rules surrounding informed consent of patients and their data?

Chapter 8

1. Building up any molecule requires an input of energy. In the instance of polymers of monosaccharides, the energy is supplied in one way or another from a nucleotide triphosphate. When these bonds are hydrolyzed, more stable products are formed, and energy is released in the formation of those new molecules.

3. The term reducing sugar refers to a carbohydrate that will reduce a metal such as copper. It does this largely because it has a reactive aldehyde moiety, which becomes oxidized to a carboxylic acid. Because all of the reactive aldehyde groups in glycogen are polymerized into the molecule, it is not considered a reducing sugar.

5. Muscle lacks the phosphatase required to liberate free glucose from glucose-1-phosphate (the product of glycogen breakdown); as a result, glucose is unavailable to diffuse out of the myocyte as it does in the liver. Muscle keeps its carbohydrates and uses them for glycolysis instead of fueling the brain like the liver does.

7. If muscle expressed the glucagon receptor, it would become responsive to glucagon because the rest of the PKA signaling pathway is already in place. This would mean that a glucagon signal would elicit a response that is similar to those seen in other tissues. Glycogen would be catabolized, but muscle does not express glucose-1-phosphatase or glucose-6-phosphatase and would be unable to release the liberated glucose. Instead there would be an increased usage of glucose, futile cycling, or some pathophysiology resulting from increased glucose levels in the cell.

9. All of the substrates for the pathway are found in the cytosol. Likewise, this provides NADPH for biosynthetic pathways that are also found in cytosol.

11. Fructose-6-phosphate can react with either glyceraldehyde-3-phosphate or erythulose-4-phosphate to form xylulose-5-phosphate and erythulose-4-phosphate or sedoheptulose-7-phosphate and glyceraldehyde-3-phosphate, respectively. This could shift concentrations of those monosaccharides altering flux through pathways like glycolysis or gene expression via xylulose-5-phosphate. To determine flux through the pathway, you would need to know the concentrations of the different intermediates and the rates of catalysis.

13. Each of the cells or tissues noted have specific requirements for products of the pentose phosphate pathway; however, they do not all require the products all of the time. It is likely in each of these tissues that the pathway is inducible due to the environmental or developmental needs of the organism at the time. For example, macrophages require high levels of NADPH to provide the oxidative burst required to kill pathogens, but they may not require these levels until activated.

15. Selenium is just below sulfur in the periodic table and to some extent acts as sulfur or oxygen would. Sulfur is less electronegative and less of a nucleophile than oxygen, and selenium is even less so than sulfur.

17. Because a protein is covalently linked to the GPI anchor, it would need to be cleaved by a protease or the anchor degraded by a phospholipase (often phospholipase C in the cell) to separate the two.

19. These polysaccharides could be synthesized by the addition of activated monosaccharides (analogous to CDP-glucose), or they could be added as disaccharide units using a transferase to join the disaccharide unit to the growing polysaccharide chain.

21. The ABO blood type works by looking for sugars that are attached to the surface of red blood cells. Two different enzymes may be present, one that makes the A modification and one that makes the B modification. If both are present, then the cells have both modifications and are AB. If neither enzyme is present, then the cells just have the core sugar and are type O.

23. Penicillin blocks the cross-linking of the cell wall by irreversibly derivatizing the enzyme responsible for catalyzing the cross-linking. The sensitivity of bacteria to penicillin depends on the strain of bacteria and the presence or absence of a cross-linked cell wall (gram-positive versus gram-negative bacteria).

25. Cobalt would be more likely found in the active site of prolyl hydroxylase due to its ability to form multiple redox states.

27. No, the microbes in kombucha and kefir are different and secrete different matrix polysaccharides.

29. When using electron microscopy, we do not need to crystalize a protein. Elimination of that step can streamline the structure determination process.

31. The ring carbons in desmosine and isodesmosine come from the contributing lysine side chains. It is unlikely that other amino acids could participate, due to their lack of an amino group and their length. Desmosine is stabilized in part through resonance and aromaticity.

33. Multiple questions can be answered using a micrograph.

  a. Heavy atoms such as lead and uranium scatter electrons and are used as stains in electron microscopy.

  b. The image contains what appears to be the endoplasmic reticulum, Golgi apparatus, vesicles, and mitochondria. These may look different than how they are commonly drawn in biology books.

  c. Different organelles have absorbed the dyes (contrast agents).

  d. The darkest images in the micrograph are vesicles filled with glycogen.

  e. The image contains numerous large, darkly staining vesicles.

  f. This image contains more vesicles and endoplasmic reticulum and fewer mitochondria.

  g. The darker vesicles are much larger.

  h. Amylase is a salivary enzyme that cleaves starches.

  i. The hydrolysis of glucose from starch.

  j. It should cleave the glycogen into glucose.

  k. The dark staining has been replaced by very bright staining, indicating a loss of the material that was stained.

  l. The data indicate that the dark regions were glycogen, which was degraded by the amylase, leading to a loss of staining.

  m. Treatment with castanospermine promotes glycogen deposition in the liver. It is a toxic alkaloid that inhibits glycosidases, including glycogen phosphorylase.

35. The protein could be analyzed using mass spectroscopy before and after being treated with glycosylases (enzymes that would remove carbohydrate modifications). Differences in the mass observed could provide information about the carbohydrate modifications.

37. To conduct this experiment, we would need a sample of cells or tissue expressing the protein bound to the plasma membrane. We would need some technique, such as centrifugation, dialysis, or ultrafiltration, for isolating the protein away from the membrane and some means of dissociating the protein from the membrane, like a detergent. We would also need some way of identifying the protein, such as a western blot. To determine if the protein were bound via a GPI anchor, we could treat the membrane with an endoglycosylase, that is, an enzyme that recognizes and cleaves the glycosidic bond. If the protein were bound by a GPI anchor, this should dissociate the protein from the membrane, and we would find it free in solution using the western blot.

The answers for these questions will vary from individual to individual.

39. Some people have religious or personal objections to becoming an organ donor.

41. This partially has to do with the culture of sports and what is considered ethical or within the rules in each sport.

43. Individuals might have potential partners screened for similar mutations prior to having children together. Insurance companies might want to know that information to either plan ahead or potentially deny coverage to someone.

Chapter 9

1. a. In order, these molecules are: triacylglycerol, wax, steroid, fatty acid, terpenoid (vitamin A).

  b. The names of several of these molecules are found in section 9.1.

  c. The steroid, fatty acid, and terpenoid are amphipathic. The polar functional groups on these molecules (the hydroxyl and carboxyl groups) are the water soluble parts.

  d. Each of these is built up from acetyl-CoA.

  e. the triacylglycerol and wax

3. a. The fatty acid in this problem is 16:0.

  b. This fatty acid has no double bonds, so it has no omega nomenclature.

  c. hexadecanoic acid

5. Because lyso-PC is more cone-shaped, it would more likely form some sort of micelle or sphere than a bilayer.

7.

I. Lyso-phosphatidylethanolamine II. Cholesterol III. Cholesteryl ester IV. Palmitoyl linolyl phosphatidylcholine

9. Beta oxidation and fatty acid biosynthesis are compartmentalized in the cell. Beta oxidation occurs in the mitochondria, whereas fatty acid biosynthesis occurs in the cytosol. This is similar to the compartmentalization that is found in the reactions specific to glycolysis and gluconeogenesis. Other differences include the use of NAD^+ versus NADPH and the stereochemistry of different intermediates.

11. Oral contraceptives are synthetic hormones that mimic the hormones found in pregnancy. These block the release of signals that cause the body to ovulate, and therefore block ovulation. Steroid hormones cause the body to change which proteins it is making and how much protein is being made. In the case of anabolic steroids, these hormones help build more muscle protein.

13. Two sources are glycolysis and through catabolism of amino acids

15. AMPK acts on ACC1. Phosphorylation by AMPK inhibits ACC1 and would slow fatty acid synthesis by limiting the production of malonyl-CoA.

17. There are several reasons for this. First of all, the two enzyme complexes clearly play a fundamental role in lipid metabolism and therefore are germane to many diseases which have lipid metabolism as a central feature. Second, there are several important differences between eukaryotic and prokaryotic fatty acid metabolism, and therefore molecules that would target these enzymes would be potentially good drugs for the treatment of infections.

19. Because urine and blood have different compositions, the assay for these compounds is different. Testing ketones (or any compound) in the urine is affected by when the sample is obtained (early in the morning after waking versus in the middle of the day) and can also be affected by how much urine the patient is producing. Depending on the fluid being tested, there may be interference due to pH, electrolytes, and proteins.

21. Because D-β-hydroxybutyrate is converted to acetoacetate in heart and muscle tissue, we know that the reaction has to proceed with a negative ΔG value at these concentrations. Heart and muscle tissue cannot synthesize ketone bodies because of this energetic barrier and the lack of the enzymes required to synthesize them in these tissues.

23. The synthesis of ketone bodies is necessitated by the inability of the brain to catabolize fatty acids. If the brain could catabolize fatty acids, ketone body biosynthesis would be unnecessary. Because plants and prokaryotes lack barriers, such as the blood–brain barrier, it is unlikely that they use ketone body biosynthesis.

25. Rather than using cholesterol, cold water fish have high levels of polyunsaturated fatty acids. These fatty acids lower the melting point of the lipids and the entire membrane.

27. Pyrophosphomevalonate has both phosphates joined to one another and to C-5. The sequential addition of the phosphates is energetically favorable, while the transfer of both at once is not, potentially due to charge-charge repulsion between the carboxyl group and the pyrophosphate.

29. NSAIDs, such as ibuprofen, are inhibitors of the COX enzymes. These enzymes produce several important eicosanoids that play key roles in labor and delivery. Therefore, it is strongly suggested that women who are nearing delivery avoid these drugs.

31. K_d is the dissociation constant. If the molecule was binding with higher affinity, the dissociation constant would be proportionally lower.

33. Aspirin is a COX inhibitor. Several of the eicosanoids produced downstream of the COX enzymes mediate inflammation and blood clotting. Consumption of aspirin may help decrease levels of these signaling molecules and therefore help put people at a lower risk for heart attack and stroke.

35. You would obtain better results using a nonpolar mobile phase. Silica gel is quite polar. If you used a nonpolar solvent, cholesteryl ester would partition into the mobile phase and away from the stationary, moving up the plate with the solvent front. Lysophosphatidate would be left behind.

37. a. The percent of acetic acid decreases in proportion to the amount of drug used. Different concentrations were used to show the concentration dependence on the drug. Adding other time points may show similar data, but adds the additional variable of time.

  b. The drug is activating CPT I.

  c. Treatment with the drug is increasing palmitate oxidation over time. This is consistent with the other data observed; CPT activity is one of the rate-determining steps of β-oxidation.

39. Cobra venom contains phospholipases. These phospholipases could release arachidonate, which would be used for eicosanoid production, but could also damage the plasma membrane of cells to the point of causing cell lysis.

41. Incubate cells with radiolabeled carnitine. Fractionate cells at different time points and analyze for carnitine and acyl carnitine. Radiolabeled fatty acyl carnitines should appear in the cytosol before appearing in the mitochondrial matrix.

43. Incubate fatty acids, coenzyme A, and fatty acyl-CoA synthetase in the presence and absence of ATP and see if a product forms.

45. One way to test this would be to isolate the enzymatic activity responsible for each reaction. Use size exclusion chromatography to see if they are running together as a single complex.

The answers for these questions will vary from individual to individual.

47. Empirically examine the case for and against medical marijuana. Outside historical and cultural biases, does this make medical and scientific sense?

49. In all cases, side effects need to be balanced with the risk and benefit of the drug. If a drug is lifesaving, an intolerable side effect is more likely to be tolerated than for a drug that is used for a lifestyle.

51. What happens to these hormones from natural sources? What are the concentrations of these hormones, and are they high enough to cause an impact?

Chapter 10

1. The term *de novo* refers to synthesis from simple building blocks compared to transformation of one phospholipid to another.

3. If we consider the synthesis of any molecule, there are steps, such as the formation of an ester, which seem energetically unfavorable if the substrates were simply an alcohol and fatty acid (ΔG would be positive). In the synthesis of biological molecules, nature generates activated donors, often through coupling one molecule to another. An example of this in phospholipid metabolism is the addition of fatty acids to a lyso lipid. Fatty acyl-CoAs are used as the donor to form this ester bond. This overall reaction has a negative ΔG value.

5. Vitamin K is a fat-soluble vitamin. A concern is that fat-soluble vitamins would partition into olestra leading to vitamin deficiencies, hence the supplementation.

7. At a basic level, the enzymes responsible for the metabolism of these molecules are secreted into different compartments. Digestion of dietary carbohydrates begins with amylases in the saliva. Proteins require acidic conditions and the proteases found in the stomach, but these reactions need to be contained both physically by mucus and chemically by pH changes to prevent damage to tissues. Degradation of proteins in the stomach also ideally prevents some toxins or signaling molecules from entering the organism. Lipids are digested in the small intestine in part because the surfactant bile is secreted from the gallbladder and pancreatic lipase gains access to the lipid components of the diet.

9. a. A lactam is an amide group found in a ring, while a lactone is a cyclic ester. A β-lactam is a four-membered ring containing an amide.

  b. No. Other aspects of the structure direct binding in the active site.

  c. β-lactam or lactone drugs irreversibly derivatize the enzyme. The active site nucleophile attacks the β-lactam resulting in the formation of an adduct of the drug to the enzyme that cannot be removed.

11. MTBE is a hydrophobic solvent. It is used to dissolve the gallstones and flush the solubilized bile from the gallbladder.

13. These data indicate that the transport of cholesterol is not necessarily dependent on hydrolysis and that these enzymes may also in some way act as receptors for these lipoproteins.

15. Numerous factors are involved in the evolution of such a complex system. Several factors that should be considered are changes in diet and lifestyle in modern times compared to several hundred or several thousand years ago, and the observation that most people who develop cardiovascular disease do so after they have passed on their genes to their offspring.

17. a. LDL would accumulate in the plasma.

  b. LDL could bind to the LDL receptors, but the receptors would not form patches.

  c. LDL could bind to the LDL receptors, and receptors would patch but not undergo coated pit formation.

  d. All of the prior steps would happen, but the coated pits would not pinch off from the plasma membrane.

19. If we know the length and angles of a clathrin trimer and the size of the endosome, we could reconstruct how many trimers are needed to cover the surface.

21. This is somewhat true. Adipose tissue synthesizes the triacylglycerol it stores from fatty acids obtained from chylomicra and VLDL and esterifies these to glycerol phosphate, which is typically obtained as a side reaction of glycolysis.

23. Phosphatidate is at a crossroads between neutral lipid metabolism and phospholipid metabolism. Removal of the phosphate group yields diacylglycerol, which is esterified to triacylglycerol.

25. Beta-oxidation occurs in nearly all tissues except the brain, but predominantly in the heart and in muscle tissue. Gluconeogenesis occurs largely in the liver, which ensures that the liver can provide glucose for the brain. The other organs can use β-oxidation.

27. Perilipins are thought to associate with lipid storage droplets through amphipathic hydrophobic helices similar to apolipoproteins binding to a lipoprotein.

29. Lipid rafts are short-lived loose bundles of tens to hundreds of molecules of phospholipids and cholesterol held together by weak forces in the plasma membrane.

31. Lipid rafts are largely composed of sphingolipids and cholesterol. There are hydrophobic interactions between the ring systems of cholesterol and the fatty acyl chains of the sphingolipids. The head groups of the sphingolipids and the hydroxyl group of cholesterol can interact through hydrogen bonding.

33. a. Based on both the micrograph and the centrifugation gradient, the protein of interest appears to be in the endoplasmic reticulum.

 b. Multiple independent, redundant methods provide an added level of verification in any experiment.

 c. These proteins are commonly found in these organelles and are often used as indicators of protein localization.

35. a. The venom appears to break phosphatidylcholine into lysophosphatidylcholine.

 b. Lysophosphatidylcholine and free fatty acids

 c. EGTA seems to prevent the reaction from occurring. EGTA acts by binding divalent metal ions, such as Ca^{2+}, indicating that this ion may play a role in enzyme activity.

37. An investigator could ask if the other levels of lipoproteins are normal. She or he could also ask if the enzymes, receptors, and apolipoproteins had normal activity or were in anyway altered.

39. The hormone receptor could be labeled using an antibody labeled with gold beads. Electron microscopy images could be analyzed to note where in the cell the gold beads accumulated to determine if they used receptor-mediated endocytosis to enter the cell.

The answers for these questions will vary from individual to individual.

41. Current controversial topics in the media include genetic modification of crops or humans, effectiveness of alternative treatments, and what should or should not be in the diet.

43. On one hand olestra is not digested and offers people a zero-calorie alternative to fats in the diet; on the other, it could deplete the body of fat-soluble vitamins.

45. Would a molecule like orlistat help someone who is trying to lose weight? Is the problem of those who do not have enough to eat related to those who eat too much?

Chapter 11

1. Aminopeptidases cut from the amino terminus of a protein while carboxypeptidases cut from the carboxy terminus. While they are both proteases which catalyze a hydrolytic cleavage of the peptide bond, the difference is where each enzyme binds and cuts its protein target. Both proteases and peptidases cleave amide bonds, but proteases cleave protein substrates, whereas peptidases cleave smaller peptides.

3. a. Loss of function. Loss of the hydroxyl group on serine prevents formation of a nucleophile to attack the peptide. The enzyme may still be able to bind substrate but will not be catalytically active.

 b. Probable loss of function. The aspartate is a much weaker nucleophile than the hydroxyl of serine and therefore will probably not be able to attack the peptide bond. Substrate binding may be unchanged, but catalysis (k_{cat}) will be much lower.

 c. Probable loss of function. While the threonine contains a hydroxyl group, it is a secondary, not a primary, alcohol. This means that there are potentially steric concerns when attacking the peptide bond.

5. Cleaving a protein results in fragments that denature or denature more readily at a lower temperature. These denatured proteins form the curds of cheese. Any monomeric amino acids or short peptides that would be released are soluble.

7. No, the ionized amino and carboxyl groups on the free amino acid backbone ensure that this amino acid is quite soluble in the blood.

9. Transamination reactions swap an amino group for a carboxyl group generating a new amino acid and a new α-keto acid. The organism might not be able to metabolize several amino acids and may have difficulty replenishing intermediates for the citric acid cycle. Depending on the organism, this could be toxic.

11. Alanine can be transaminated to pyruvate, which can readily contribute to gluconeogenesis.

13. Decarboxylation of ornithine would yield 1,4-diaminobutane, also known as putrescene. Decarboxylation of amino acids, or any reaction involving the α carbon is often accomplished using a pyridoxal phosphate-dependent mechanism. Because CO_2 is being released in a decarboxylation, it probably contributes favorably to increasing entropy and therefore drives ΔG lower.

15. The animals themselves cannot use the urea; however, symbiotic bacteria in the gut of the animal can and would use the urea to help synthesize amino acids the animal can then use.

17. If ornithine forms a lactam in a protein, the formation of the amide bond in the lactam cleaves the peptide backbone.

Theoretically, lysine could form a lactam, but the greater size of lysine makes a seven-membered ring, which is unfavorable.

19. They could be generally categorized as glucogenic or ketogenic or arranged base on the products that are formed.

21. While it is likely that diet or genetics causes people to alter gene expression, humans cannot alter their gene expression to the extent that other organisms have evolved specified means of metabolizing nitrogen. In other words, humans cannot excrete nitrogenous waste as uric acid instead of urea.

23. If the components in grapefruit juice were being metabolized by an MAO or CYP, they might not metabolize the drug at the same rate.

This could effectively lead to changes to how the drug is metabolized and higher than normal concentrations of the drug in the blood.

25. The remaining MAOIs in the system react or are excreted, and the body synthesizes new enzymes to replace the ones that have been derivatized.

27. The molecule is probably being excreted in the filtrate and not reabsorbed.

29. 1.5 kg of salt is 25.7 mol of salt or moles of sodium ions. To separate 1 mol of ions requires 0.33 mol of ATP. If we consider that hydrolysis of a mole of ATP liberates 7.3 kcal, it means that the overall energy required to pump this many sodium ions is approximately 62.5 kcal.

31. In crush syndrome, damaged tissues release proteins (often myoglobin) that denature in the circulation or kidney and precipitate, damaging kidney function.

33. Based on where these reagents cleave, the order would be N-terminus SerMetIleTyrTrpTrpAlaLys C-terminus.

35. The disease is caused by a deficiency in one of the enzymes of valine degradation. Valine is being deaminated and potentially coupled to coenzyme-A but is unable to be desaturated to methylacrylyl-CoA. Instead, it accumulates and the acylcarnitine is made as a side product. Short-chain fatty acids are often odiferous. The odor likely comes from isovalerate in urine. As isovaleryl carnitine accumulates in the circulation, it is detoxified in the liver to isovaleryl glycine, which is then eliminated in the urine where it breaks down.

37. Isolate mitochondria and cytosol. Attempt to regenerate some of the reactions of these pathways in the presence of only cytosol or mitochondria as a source of enzymes.

39. Give the drug to an animal model like a rat or pig and see how and when it is secreted in the animal's urine. Characterization of the derivatives found in the urine would provide keys as to how the drug was metabolized.

The answers for these questions will vary from individual to individual.

41. How are the rights of an individual compared to the rights of a government to guarantee the health of their citizens?

43. Do we ever or always eat solely for economic reasons?

45. There are numerous factors in play when people are waiting for organ transplants.

Chapter 12

1. Muscle has relatively large reserves of glycogen it can mobilize into glucose. Muscle is able to use fatty acids from triacylglycerols via beta oxidation. Finally, muscle also has stores of proteins it can catabolize, if absolutely necessary.

3. The urea cycle detoxifies ammonia into urea. It happens predominantly in the liver. Other examples of organ specialization include gluconeogenesis and ketone body biosynthesis, both of which also occur in liver.

5. One isoform of HMG-CoA synthase is found in the cytosol, and the other is in the mitochondria. The cytosolic form is responsible for the synthesis of mevalonate for isoprenoids and for cholesterol biosynthesis and is SREBP dependent. The other is mitochondrial and is responsible for the ketone body biosynthesis and is PPRE dependent.

7. The double bond would be conjugated to the aromatic ring and would therefore be less likely to undergo hydration.

9. This would be a symporter. The sodium concentration is higher outside the cell than inside. Iodide and sodium ions are transported together down the sodium gradient.

11. This would look much like other proteolytic mechanisms. Here we show an aspartyl protease, but a serine or metalloprotease could be involved as well.

13. Many hormones are present in very low concentrations and exert effects that are not always apparent. Likewise, more sensitive essays and characterization of previously unidentified "orphan receptors" has led to the identification of novel hormones.

15. This is an advantage to organisms that eat meat because the organism eating the meat does not want to be affected by the hormonal state of what it is eating. It is another defense mechanism for the organism consuming these foods.

17. a. The radioactive iodine accumulates in the thyroid tissue, killing some of it.

b. ^{131}I emits high-energy beta and gamma particles.

c. ^{131}I could increase the recipient's risk for thyroid cancer.

19. Thiazoladinediones are oral antidiabetic drugs that act on PPAR-γ to increase expression of genes under the control of that transcription factor. If adiponectin levels were increasing, this would indicate that expression of this gene was under the control of PPAR-γ.

21. Lack of a functional vasopressin receptor means that vasopressin signaling would fail to occur, but there would still be a signal telling the pituitary to produce more vasopressin. Therefore, there would be high levels of the hormone, but also high levels of urinary output as the signal would not be received.

23. a. The substitution of a glutamine (a polar amino acid) by proline (a nonpolar amino acid) could affect many aspects of protein function including folding or interaction with a receptor.

b. Prolines are helix breakers. If the mutation were in an α helix, it would lead to a kink or break in the helix, changing the tertiary structure.

c. If the structure of the hormone were disrupted, it could affect PYY signaling, ultimately resulting in increased appetite and decreased metabolic rate. The correlation with disease isn't 1:1 because many other factors can also lead to obesity.

25. The melanocortin-4 receptor (MC4R) binds to melanocortins, especially α-MSH and POMC. Mutations to this receptor have been associated with obesity in humans. Based on that data we would anticipate that a knockout mouse for MC4R would also be obese. Because this receptor also plays a role in sexual function, we might also anticipate that eliminating this receptor could lead to a lower reproductive rate in these mice.

27. Insulin is a protein and would be degraded in the stomach by both the acidic environment of the stomach and proteases. Most peptide hormones that are eaten are degraded in the stomach and have little to no effect on human physiology.

29. Lys−N=CHCH$_3$
Schiff base

31. Increasing interactions between two individuals (such as members of a group, a couple, or a mother and her young) could help the survivability of that group through members of the group looking out for each other.

33. Creatine kinase is typically found in heart and muscle tissue. If heart tissue were damaged in a heart attack, the enzymes would leak out and instead be found in the circulation. An identification of the isoforms (muscle versus heart) would tell the source of the enzyme.

35. The data need to be examined on the whole. The overall number of people with diabetes is increasing and type 2 is increasing more quickly than type 1, making the numbers look as if type 1 were decreasing.

37. There are several biochemical techniques available to see how a protein is behaving in solution. An example of these techniques is size exclusion chromatography. Insulin is a small protein, and so deviations from that size indicate aggregates of insulin. Another technique is dynamic laser light scatter. This too would tell you the size is variable and the size of the complex. If you wanted to actually see the crystals of insulin, you would probably need a technique like electron microscopy, depending on the size of the aggregate.

39. Levels of gene expression could be tested through several different mechanisms. A simple means of doing this would be northern blotting of a tissue of interest or conducting RT-PCR on those same samples. A more complex bioinformatics technique would be something like RNAseq or using a microarray to identify changes in gene expression. Enzyme activity could be measured using an assay of ketone body biosynthesis, or the flux of ketone bodies through the mouse could be studied metabolically using radiolabeled tracers to see if the mouse made and consumed the ketones at the same rate in the presence or absence of drug.

The answers for these questions will vary from individual to individual.

41. Who is responsible for the behavior of the individual?

43. Company policies that promote healthy lifestyles are targeted in part to help promote employee health and decrease costs of healthcare.

Glossary

3_{10} **helix** a less common example of secondary structure. It is like an α helix but the coils are tighter than an α helix with hydrogen bonding occurring in an i+3 pattern compared to the α helical i+4.

Absorptive state the metabolic state in which someone is absorbing metabolites from the diet, typically up to six hours after eating.

Acetyl-CoA carboxylase (ACC) the enzyme that synthesizes malonyl-CoA from acetyl-CoA and CO_2.

Acidosis decreased plasma pH.

Activation energy, E_a the energy required to overcome the energetic barrier between reactants (substrates) and products.

Active site the place on an enzyme where catalysis occurs.

Active transport transport across a membrane which is driven via the expenditure of some form of energy. Two forms of active transport exist: primary active transport, which is driven by the breakdown of ATP, and secondary active transport, which is when the transport of a molecule is coupled to gradients of other molecules.

Adenine a purine base found in both DNA and RNA.

Adenylate cyclase the enzyme that produces cAMP from ATP.

Adipocyte triacylglycerol-storing cells found in adipose or fat tissue.

Adiponectin a peptide hormone produced in adipose tissue that acts in the brain to increase appetite.

Adipose tissue the tissues of the body that primarily store triacylglycerols.

Aestivation similar to hibernation, aestivation is a dormant metabolic state organisms enter as a result of dry or hot conditions.

Aldol organic molecules containing a carbonyl group such as an aldehyde with a hydroxyl moiety β to the carbonyl.

Aldose monosaccharide containing aldehyde groups.

Alginate an anionic polysaccharide comprised of polymers of glucuronic acid.

Allosteric regulation a regulatory mechanism where a molecule binds somewhere on a protein or enzyme other than the active site and affects enzyme activity.

Allosteric regulators molecules that regulate the function of a protein by binding at some site distant to the one where the protein's primary function is occurring. An example

is an enzyme that has a small molecule bind somewhere other than the active site of the enzyme to alter activity. Allosteric proteins are often multisubunit proteins.

Allosteric regulators regulators that act on an enzyme by binding elsewhere than the active site of the enzyme.

Alpha (α) helix the first element of secondary structure predicted, α helices consist of a right-handed twist of the peptide backbone. Side chains of the amino acids radiate outward from the central region.

Amino acid a family of biological molecules that contain an amino group and a carboxy group. Amino acids are the building blocks of proteins.

Amino sugar sugar in which an amino group has been substituted for a hydroxyl group.

Amino terminus the free amino end of the polypeptide also called the N terminus. This is the "beginning" of a protein; proteins are synthesized from the amino to the carboxy terminus.

Ammonotelic organisms that secrete waste as ammonia.

AMP-activated protein kinase (AMPK) a kinase that helps regulate metabolism.

Amphipathic a molecule containing functional groups with both polar and nonpolar moieties.

Amphipathic a term used to describe a molecule with several properties, for example, hydrophobic and hydrophilic.

Amphipathic literally having "more than one feeling"; a molecule with both hydrophobic and hydrophilic groups in it.

AMPK a kinase regulated by levels of AMP that coordinates metabolic processes in the cell.

Amylopectin one of the polysaccharides in starch, amylopectin is a branched polymer of glucose that plants use to store energy.

Amylose one of the polysaccharides in starch, amylopectin is a linear polymer of glucose that plants use to store energy.

Anabolic reaction a reaction that builds up or synthesizes biological molecules. Anabolic reactions typically require an input of energy.

Anaplerosis processes that elevate levels of a citric acid cycle intermediate.

Anaplerotic reaction a reaction that replenishes citric acid cycle intermediates.

Anomer the stereoisomer of the hemiacetal forms of a carbohydrate. Two anomers, α and β, are related to one another by the position of the hydroxyl group on the anomeric carbon (α on the bottom face, β on the top face).

Anomeric carbon the hemiacetal or hemiketal carbon in a carbohydrate; the new chiral center formed from the former carbonyl carbon.

Anorexigenic hormones or neurotransmitters that blunt appetite.

Antibody a protein produced by the immune system that recognizes and binds molecules foreign to the host organism. Antibodies are used in many modern biochemical techniques.

Antiparallel a structure in which the direction of strands are running in opposite directions. DNA is an antiparallel structure.

Antiparallel two strands of a molecule (DNA or protein) that run in opposite directions (e.g., the double helix of DNA or antiparallel strands of protein in a beta sheet).

Antiporter a transport protein that traffics two or more molecules across the lipid bilayer in opposite directions.

Apolipoproteins the protein component of a lipoprotein.

Apoprotein a protein lacking its cofactor or prosthetic group.

Apoptosis programmed cell death. In apoptosis cells undergo a systematic disassembly of cellular components culminating in the fragmentation of DNA.

Arcuate nucleus the region of the hypothalamus that integrates neuronal and hormonal signals that regulate metabolism and appetite.

ATP synthase (F_0/F_1ATPase) the mitochondrial complex that uses the energy of the proton gradient to synthesize ATP from ADP and P_i.

Base stacking the collective term for forces that stabilize the double helix of DNA. These weak forces include the hydrophobic effect, London-dispersion, Van der Waals, dipole–dipole and π–π stacking.

Beta (β) sheet or beta pleated sheet the second element of secondary structure formed. β sheets consist of elongated planks of amino acids that hydrogen-bond to each other, generating a sheetlike structure.

Beta (β)-oxidation the process through which fatty acids are catabolized into acetyl-CoA.

Bile salts steroid-based detergents made by the liver and stored in the bile duct until needed.

Binding site the site on a protein where binding of a small molecule occurs. This can be the active site of an enzyme, the ligand binding site of a receptor, or an allosteric regulatory site on an enzyme.

Body mass index (BMI) a measure of adiposity (obesity). BMI is calculated by dividing a person's body mass in kilograms by their height in meters squared.

Bowman's capsule the compartment that surrounds the glomerulus and collects the filtrate.

Branching enzyme the enzyme responsible for forming branches in the glycogen molecule.

Brønsted–Lowry acids Brønsted–Lowry acids are proton donors, while Brønsted–Lowry bases are proton acceptors.

Brumation the hibernation-like state that reptiles enter in cold weather.

Buffer a combination of a weak acid or base with its conjugate salt. Buffers are resistant to changes in pH near the pK_a value.

Buffer capacity the ability of a buffer to resist changes in pH. A more highly concentrated buffer has a higher buffer capacity than a dilute one.

Cachexia the wasting associated with cancer and some other diseases.

Cafeteria diet a diet enriched in fats and carbohydrates.

cAMP cyclic AMP, one of several cyclic nucleotides that act as second messengers.

Carbohydrate a molecule with the basic formula $C_x(H_2O)_x$

Carbohydrate response element binding protein (ChREBP) a transcription factor that binds to carbohydrates and regulates transcription of genes involved in carbohydrate and lipid metabolism.

Carboxy terminus the free carboxy end of the polypeptide also called the C terminus. This is the "end" of a protein; proteins are synthesized from the amino to the carboxy terminus.

Catabolic reaction a reaction that breaks down or degrades biological molecules. Catabolism typically results in the production of ATP.

Catalyst a participant in a chemical reaction that increases rate but is not consumed in the reaction.

Catalytic subunit a subunit of an enzyme where catalysis occurs.

Catecholamines hormones derived from tyrosine.

Cation-π interactions any interaction between a positively charged amino acid and one containing an aromatic π bond network.

Caveolae flask-shaped invaginations of the plasma membrane coated with the caveolins.

Cellulose a structural polymer of glucose made by plants and some microbes.

Channels gated transmembrane proteins that permit regulated passage of molecules across the membrane.

Chimeras organisms consisting of cells derived from multiple organisms.

Chiral and achiral chiral molecules have a chiral center, typically a carbon atom joined to four different groups. Achiral molecules lack chiral centers. Most biochemicals are chiral, including 19 of the 20 amino acids.

Chitin a structural polymer of glucosamine.

Cholesterol a membrane lipid and the most common steroid. Cholesterol regulates the fluidity of membranes.

Cholesterol the simplest of the steroid class of lipids, cholesterol is a major component of the plasma membrane.

Cholesteryl esters a storage form of cholesteryl, cholesteryl ester consists of a molecule of cholesterol joined to a fatty acid through an ester.

Chondroitin sulfate a linear polysaccharide composed of repeating glucuronic acid and N-Acetylgalactosamine disaccharides.

Chylomicra lipoprotein particles that form in the intestine and deliver dietary triacylglycerols to muscle and adipose tissue.

Chylomicron remnant the lipoprotein that remains after chylomicra are stripped of dietary triacylglycerols.

Citric acid cycle part of the central catabolic pathway, the citric acid cycle describes how carbons derived from acetyl-CoA are gradually oxidized to carbon dioxide. Electrons are harvested in this process on the carriers NADH and $FADH_2$. The citric acid cycle also serves as a central hub for the metabolism of many other molecules. It is also known as the tricarboxylic acid cycle or the Krebs cycle.

Clathrin a cytosolic protein that forms a coating around membranous pits, aiding in endocytosis.

Cloning the production of an exact copy of a piece of DNA or an organism.

Coated pits an intermediate step in receptor-mediated endocytosis, coated pits form when patched receptors are being pinched off the plasma membrane.

Coated vesicle a vesicle of plasma membrane coated with the protein clathrin and adapter proteins.

Cofactor or prosthetic group a part of an active holoprotein that is not comprised of amino acids. Metal ions, heme groups, and iron sulfur centers are all examples of cofactors.

Coil or loop lengthy sections of amino acid sequences that link elements of secondary structure.

Collagen triple helix the tertiary structure of the matrix protein collagen. The triple helix is a left-handed helical twist of three collagen strands.

Competitive inhibitors an inhibitor that competes with substrate for binding to the enzyme.

Complex I (NADH oxidase) complex I transfers electrons from NADH to ubiquinone and pumps four protons out of the mitochondrial matrix.

Complex II (succinate dehydrogenase) complex II takes electrons from $FADH_2$ from the citric acid cycle and transfers them to ubiquinone.

Complex III (ubiquinone/cytochrome c reductase) complex III transfers electrons from reduced ubiquinones to cytochrome c and in doing so electrons pass from two electron carriers to a one electron carrier.

Complex IV (cytochrome oxidase) complex IV transfers electrons from cytochrome c to oxygen to make water. Each oxidized cytochrome c results in one proton being consumed in the production of water and an additional proton being pumped out of the mitochondrial matrix.

Consensus recognition sequence a binding site found in one protein and recognized by another. The consensus recognition sequence of protein kinase A is –R-R-X-(S or T)-Y-Y–, and in this example, protein kinase A recognizes any protein with this sequence and phosphorylates the serine or threonine residue.

Conservative substitution a change to a protein which results in one amino acid being substituted for a similar amino acid. In evolution, we consider the substitution of a leucine for isoleucine to be a conservative substitution.

Copolymer a polymer in which the monomeric subunits alternate in the pattern [ABA-BAB]. Biological copolymers are typically built using dimeric building blocks.

Cortisol a glucocorticoid steroid hormone involved in regulation of metabolism.

Covalent catalysis catalysis in which at least one step of the mechanism involves a covalent linkage of the enzyme to the substrate.

Covalent modification a modification made to a protein through a covalent bond. Phosphorylation is a common covalent modification.

CRISPR a genome editing technique in which a guide RNA directs an enzyme to make specific changes (insertions or deletions) to a DNA strand.

Critical micellar concentration (CMC) the concentration of an amphipathic molecule at which micelles form. Below the CMC, amphiphiles are found as monomers.

Cyclooxygenase the enzyme that converts arachidonic acid into prostaglandins.

Cytidine diphosphate (CDP) a nucleotide that acts as an active carrier in the synthesis of lipids.

Cytochrome c a small, heme-containing redox active protein that transports electrons from complex III to complex IV in the electron transport chain.

Cytochrome P450 mixed function oxidases a broad family of oxidases that use heme to catalyze oxidation reactions. These enzymes function prominently in both xenobiotic and drug metabolism.

Cytosine a pyrimidine base found in both DNA and RNA.

Debranching enzyme the enzyme responsible for removing branches in glycogen breakdown.

Deoxy sugar a sugar lacking at least one hydroxyl group; 2-deoxy ribose found in DNA is the best known deoxy sugar.

Dextrose a commonly used term for glucose in a clinical setting.

Diabetes mellitus an endocrine disease of glucose metabolism in which insulin signaling is deficient either due to an autoimmune attack on the pancreas or due to a post-insulin receptor signaling defect.

Diacylglycerol (diglyceride) a glycerol molecule with two fatty acids esterified to it.

Dielectric constant a means of quantifying the polarity of a solvent or media.

Diffusion controlled limit the limit at which some enzymes operate. These enzymes are so effective as catalysts that they are limited by how fast substrate can diffuse into the active site.

Dipole-dipole interaction the weak force that describes the interaction of at least two dipoles in a molecule.

Disaccharide a carbohydrate comprised of two monosaccharide units.

Disulfide bond the S–S linkage created by the oxidation of two cysteine side chains.

Ditopic a protein or other molecule spanning both leaflets of the lipid bilayer, that is, transmembrane proteins.

DNA ligases enzymes that join two ends of DNA together. These enzymes are frequently employed in the laboratory in DNA manipulations.

Domain discretely folding structures that retain their shape in the absence of the rest of the protein.

EC numbers a serial number for an enzyme that describes its activity.

Eicosanoids signaling molecules that are derivatives of the 20-carbon unsaturated fatty acid arachidonate.

Electron transport chain the system by which electrons are used to drive the production of a proton gradient. In the process, electron carriers are oxidized, and water is made.

Electroporation a technique that uses pulses of electricity to introduce DNA into a cell.

Endocannabinoids naturally occurring ligands of the cannabinoid receptor. Arachidonylethanolamine is an endocannabinoid.

Endocrinology the study of hormones and their functions in the body.

Enthalpy the thermodynamic term associated with the energetics of a reaction or system. In biochemistry, enthalpy is typically associated with the energy needed to break a bond.

Entropy the thermodynamic term associated with the amount of disorder or microstates of a system.

Enzyme a protein catalyst; most reactions in the cell are catalyzed by enzymes.

Enzyme a protein catalyst; tens of thousands of enzymes exist. These catalyze most reactions in an organism.

Enzyme inhibitors molecules (generally small ones) which lower the rate of an enzymatically catalyzed reaction.

Enzyme kinetics the study of enzymatically catalyzed reactions and their rates.

Epimer a stereoisomer that differs at a single chiral center.

Epinephrine a type of catecholamine, epinephrine (also known as adrenalin) stimulates the fight or flight response.

Equilibrium the chemical state where the rates of the forward and reverse reactions are equal. Note that this does not mean that the concentrations of reactants and products are equal.

Equilibrium constant, K_{eq} the ratio of products to reactants at equilibrium.

Exons regions of nascent eukaryotic mRNA that are spliced together into a mature mRNA.

Fasted state the metabolic state in which someone has not eaten for 12 to 24 hours.

Fatty acid synthase (FAS) the multifunctional enzyme that synthesizes the fatty acid palmitate from malonyl-CoA.

Fed state the metabolic state from the time one has eaten until 12 hours after.

Feed forward activation a regulatory process in which the product of a reaction regulates that reaction and makes the reaction go at a faster rate.

Fischer projection a two-dimensional depiction of molecular structure in which crossed lines are used to represent chiral centers.

Free energy of the standard state (standard free energy state, $\Delta G^{\circ\prime}$) the free energy of the standard state gives the free energy of a reaction in the standard state as opposed to the one in which the reaction occurs in the cell.

Free energy of the transition state (free energy of activation, $\Delta G^{\ddagger}$) the free energy of the transition state describes the energy needed to form the transition state. It can be used to calculate the kinetics of a reaction.

Free fatty acid a fatty acid that is not esterified to any other group.

Functional group pieces of molecules (for example, carbonyl, hydroxyl, or carboxyl groups) with common known functions, properties, and reactivity. In both organic and biochemistry an understanding of functional groups and how they behave enables scientists to make and test predictions regarding chemistry of a molecule.

Furanose a monosaccharide in a five-membered ring (four carbons and one oxygen).

General acid-base catalysis an enzyme mechanism in which an amino acid side chain is acting as a proton donor or acceptor.

Genes sequences of DNA that code for protein.

Gene silencing any one of several different techniques used to reduce or prevent genes from being expressed.

Ghrelin a peptide hormone from the gut that regulates appetite. Ghrelin sends orexigenic signals to the brain to stimulate appetite.

Gibbs free energy (ΔG) or free energy the free energy equation combines enthalpy, entropy, and temperature to give the free energy, ΔG of a reaction. ΔG is generally used to predict the favorability of a reaction or the direction in which it will proceed spontaneously.

Glomerulus a network of porous capillaries that filter the blood, retaining things larger than proteins.

Glucagon a pancreatic peptide hormone that is released in the fasted or starved state.

Glucogenic amino acids that can contribute to gluconeogenesis.

Gluconeogenesis the metabolic pathway through which organisms generate glucose from simple building blocks.

Glucosamine a common amino sugar, glucosamine consists of glucose in which one hydroxyl group (at the number 2 position) has been replaced by an amino group.

Glucose–alanine cycle the metabolic pathway in which alanine from muscle is used to shuttle amino groups to the liver. In the liver, the amino groups are detoxified via the urea cycle, and the carbon skeletons are used in gluconeogenesis.

Glucose-alanine shuttle the name of the metabolic process through which nitrogenous wastes generated in muscle are transferred to pyruvate, generating alanine. The alanine in turn is transported to the liver where it is deaminated and the pyruvate presumably is used in gluconeogenesis.

Glucose tolerance test (GTT) a test used to determine if an individual is diabetic or insulin resistant.

Glucuronic acid an acidic carbohydrate that is covalently bound to molecules to increase their solubility and make them more prone to be excreted by the kidney.

Glutamate dehydrogenase the enzyme that catalyzes the oxidation of glutamate. This results in the formation of α-ketoglutarate.

Glutaminase the enzyme responsible for removal of the side chain amino group from glutamine, generating glutamate.

Glutamine synthetase the liver enzyme responsible for synthesizing glutamine from glutamate and free ammonia and ATP.

Glutathione a small peptide comprised of glycine, cysteine, and aspartate, this compound maintains a reducing atmosphere in the cell.

Glutathione (GSH) a tripeptide of glutamate, cysteine, and glycine in which glutamate is joined to cysteine via a peptide linkage through the side-chain carboxyl group.

Glutathione-*S*-transferases (GST) a family of enzymes that couple the tripeptide glutathione to molecules.

Glycerophosphate shuttle the process through which the electrons from NADH are shuttled into the mitochondria via glycerophosphate.

Glycerophospholipids a class of phospholipids that use glycerol as the base alcohol.

Glycogen a highly branched polymer of glucose found in animals and used as a source of stored energy.

Glycogenesis creation of new glycogen.

Glycogenin the protein found at the core of glycogen. Glycogenin synthesizes the initial steps of glycogen synthesis.

Glycogenolysis breaking down and mobilization of glycogen stores.

Glycogen phosphorylase the enzyme that catabolizes glycogen liberating glucose-1-phosphate.

Glycogen synthase the enzyme responsible for adding new molecules of glucose to glycogen. UDP-glucose is the donor molecule.

Glycolipid a phospholipid with a carbohydrate modification to it.

Glycolysis the metabolic pathway through which glucose is broken down into pyruvate.

Glycoprotein a protein with a carbohydrate modification to it.

Glycosidic bond (linkage) the acetal or ketal bond or linkage found between carbohydrates.

GPI anchor (glycosylphosphatidylinositol) a glycolipid that anchors some proteins to the cell membrane, often to a lipid raft.

G protein any one of several classes of signaling proteins that bind GTP. While GTP is bound, these proteins are in the active state.

Guanine a purine base found in both DNA and RNA.

Haworth projection a molecular representation of cyclic monosaccharides that depicts their three-dimensional structure.

HDL high density lipoproteins. HDL transport cholesterol back to the liver from the circulation.

Henderson–Hasselbach equation the equation that relates pH, pK_a, and the ratio of conjugate acid to conjugate base.

Heparan sulfate a linear polysaccharide comprised of repeating disaccharides, usually glucuronic acid and *N*-Acetylglucosamine.

Hepatocyte a liver cell.

Hexose a six-carbon monosaccharide.

Hibernation the dormant metabolic state mammals enter in winter.

HMG-CoA reductase the committed and rate-determining step in cholesterol biosynthesis.

Holoprotein a complete protein (i.e., one with its complementary cofactors).

Homeostasis living within your metabolic means; neither gaining nor losing weight over time.

Homeostasis the concept that a living system has control systems in place to maintain conditions necessary for life. Among these are a means to regulate pH, store and mobilize energy, and maintain temperature.

Hormone a chemical signal that is secreted in one part of the organism but works elsewhere.

Hydrogenated fats fats or oils in which double bonds have been removed by chemically treating them with hydrogen gas and a catalyst.

Hydrogen bonding the weak interaction that occurs between the lone pair of electrons on a very electronegative atom (oxygen, nitrogen, or fluorine) and a hydrogen bound to an electronegative atom.

Hydrophobic effect the name of the phenomenon in which hydrophobic groups cluster together in aqueous systems.

Hydrophobic effect the phenomenon by which hydrophobic groups in a molecule aggregate together. This liberates water molecules and increases the overall entropy of the structure.

Hyperglycemia high blood sugar.

Hypothalamus the region of the brain that integrates neuronal and hormonal signals.

IDL intermediate density lipoproteins. IDL are an intermediate that forms when VLDL are converted to LDL.

Induced fit a description of enzymatic catalysis in which a substrate helps form the shape of the active site as it binds the enzyme.

Initial rate or initial velocity, v_0 the instantaneous rate of an enzymatically catalyzed reaction at $t = 0$.

Insulin a peptide hormone from the pancreas that signals the fed state.

Insulin a peptide hormone made by the pancreas that has effects on both metabolism and transcription. Insulin functions using a receptor tyrosine kinase.

Insulin resistance a prediabetic state in which cells become refractory to the effect of insulin.

Integral membrane protein a membrane protein that cannot be removed from the lipid bilayer without the use of detergents.

Introns regions of a nascent eukaryotic mRNA that are spliced out to form a mature mRNA.

Iron-sulfur center a redox active cluster of iron and sulfur atoms. Fe2-S2, Fe3-S3, and Fe4-S4 are commonly seen. These clusters are found in electron transport.

Irreversible inhibitor *see* suicide substrate.

Isoform proteins with highly related structures that serve an identical function and are encoded by different genes

Keratan sulfate linear polysaccharide is a polymer of galactose and *N*-Acetylglucosamine.

Ketoacidosis acidification of the blood via the accumulation of ketone bodies.

Ketogenic amino acids that are broken down into ketone bodies.

Ketone bodies (acetone, acetoacetate and β-hydroxybutyrate) ketone bodies are small soluble molecules that are made in the liver in times of energetic scarcity. They can provide energy to tissues such as the brain when glucose isn't available.

Ketose monosaccharide containing a keto group.

Ketosis excessive ketone bodies in the blood.

Kinase an enzyme that adds a phosphate group to a molecule, typically the phosphate is donated from a molecule with a high transfer potential (such as ATP) and is added to a hydroxyl group.

K_M 1. The dissociation constant of the Michaelis complex. 2. The ratio of rate constants found which form the Michaelis complex over those that break it down. 3. The concentration of substrate required for an enzyme to operate at $V_{max}/2$.

Knockout an organism in which a gene (or multiple genes) have been removed or mutated to prevent their expression.

Lactose milk sugar; a disaccharide composed of a molecule of glucose and galactose.

Lagging strand the strand of DNA that is discontinuously copied.

LDL low density lipoproteins. LDL can deliver cholesterol from the liver to tissues that need it, but can also become oxidized and accumulate in the linings of arteries causing atherosclerosis.

Leading strand the strand of DNA that is continuously copied in the 5′ to 3′ direction.

Le Châtelier's principle systems tend to move toward equilibrium.

Leptin a peptide hormone produced by fat tissue that regulates satiety (feelings of fullness).

Leukotrienes a subclass of eicosanoid, a family of signaling molecules made from arachidonic acid by the enzyme lipoxygenase.

Lineweaver-Burke plot a double-reciprocal plot, that is, one in which $1/[S]$ versus $1/v$ is plotted to determine the values of V_{max} and K_M.

Lipid bilayer a structure comprised of two monomolecular films of phospholipids arrayed to form a hydrophobic barrier. Lipid bilayers form most of the membranous structure in cells and organelles.

Lipid raft a transient structure of weakly associated lipids, such as sphingolipids and cholesterol, found in the plasma membrane.

Lipid rafts transient, loosely bound, bundles of cholesterol and sphingolipids thought to be involved in signaling.

Lipid storage droplet the organelle that stores neutral lipids in the cell.

Lipopolysaccharide (LPS) a glycolipid found in the cell wall of some bacteria. LPS, also known as endotoxin, is inflammatory in a cell or organism.

Lipoproteins spherical micelles of phospholipids and apolipoproteins surrounding a neutral lipid core. Lipoproteins transport lipids in the circulation.

Lipoxygenase the enzyme that converts arachidonic acid into leukotrienes.

Lock and key one description of enzymatic catalysis in which a substrate fits an enzyme like a key in a lock.

London-dispersion a class of weak intermolecular forces that all molecules exhibit.

Loop of Henle the continuation of the convoluted tubule. Partial permeability and sodium pumps in this structure set up a concentration gradient between the lumen of the tube and the extracellular fluid.

Lysophospholipid a glycerophospholipid that is missing a single acyl chain.

Lysyl oxidase the enzyme that cross-links lysine residues in the extracellular matrix.

Malate-aspartate shuttle the process through which the electrons from NADH are shuttled into the mitochondria via malate and aspartate. Glutamate and α-ketoglutarate also play important roles.

Maltose malt sugar; a disaccharide composed of two glucose molecules.

Metabolic syndrome a group of ten related pathophysiologies related to obesity and diabetes.

Metabolite an intermediate in a metabolic pathway.

Metabolon a metabolic process in which a group of enzymes function in concert to synthesize a product.

Metal ion catalysis an enzyme mechanism in which a metal ion is participating in redox chemistry or acting as a Lewis acid or Lewis base.

Mevalonate an intermediate in cholesterol metabolism.

Micelle the structure formed from the aggregation of amphipathic molecules such as fatty acids or detergents. Micelles have a hydrophobic core and a hydrophilic coating.

Michaelis complex the complex formed between enzyme and substrate.

Michaelis-Menten equation $v_0 = V_{max}[S]/K_M + [S]$.

Michaelis-Menten kinetics the best-known model of enzyme kinetics which relates rate (velocity) to substrate concentration.

Mixed inhibitors an inhibitor that can bind to either free enzyme or *ES* complex.

Mixed meal a meal in which fats, proteins, and carbohydrates are consumed in proportion to each other.

Monoacylglycerol (monoglyceride) a glycerol molecule with a single fatty acid esterified to it.

Monoamine oxidases (MAO) a family of oxidases that oxidatively deaminate amines to carbonyl groups.

Monomer the building block of a polymer. Common building blocks include amino acids, nucleotides and carbohydrates.

Monomer the subunit or building block used to make a polymer or oligomer.

Monosaccharide the simplest carbohydrate.

Monotopic a protein or other molecule inserted into only one leaflet of the lipid bilayer.

Monounsaturated a fatty acid with one double bond.

Motif combinations of secondary structure in proteins, for example, a four-helix bundle or Greek key motif.

Multimer a molecule made of several monomers.

Mutation a change in the sequence of a nucleic acid.

Mutorotation the process through which one anomer can interconvert to another by ring opening and closing.

Myocyte a muscle cell.

Nephron the basic filtration unit of the kidney.

Neuropeptide Y (NPY) a peptide neurotransmitter that regulates and stimulates appetite.

Neutral lipids lipids without a charged group, typically triacylglycerol and cholesteryl ester.

***N*-linked carbohydrate** a carbohydrate moiety connected to a protein through an asparagine residue.

Norepinephrine a catecholamine hormone.

Nucleic acid a polymer of nucleotides (RNA) or deoxynucleotides (DNA).

Nucleoside/deoxynucleoside nucleosides and deoxynucleosides consist of a nitrogenous base joined to a sugar (either ribose or deoxyribose) through a glycosidic linkage. There is no phosphate in a nucleoside.

Nucleotide/deoxynucleotides nucleotides and deoxynucleotides consist of a nitrogenous base joined to a sugar (either ribose or 2-deoxyribose) phosphate via a glycosidic linkage.

Oligopeptide a molecule consisting of more than a few amino acids. Oligopeptides typically have between 8 and 20 amino acids.

Oligosaccharides short polymers of monosaccharides between four and twenty monosaccharides in length.

***O*-linked carbohydrate** a carbohydrate moiety connected to a protein through a serine or threonine residue.

Operons assemblies of multiple genes arrayed together with common control elements.

Orexigenic neurons, hormones, or drugs that promote appetite.

Osmosis the diffusion of water from areas of lower concentrations of molecules to higher concentrations of molecules.

Oxidative deamination the oxidative removal of an amino group as ammonia generating an α-keto acid. NADH is generated in this process.

Oxidative phosphorylation the process through which metabolites are oxidized and the energy of these processes is used to generate a proton gradient, which is then used to generate ATP.

Parallel a structure in which the direction strands are all running in the same direction.

Passive transport the transport of molecules across a membrane down a concentration gradient via diffusion.

Patches clusters of receptors on the cell surface. This is one of the initial steps in receptor-mediated endocytosis.

Pentose a five-carbon monosaccharide.

Pentose phosphate pathway the pathway through which the cell generates ribose, produces NADPH, and transforms monosaccharides.

Penultimate carbon the chiral center farthest from the anomeric carbon.

Peptide bond the amide bond that links amino acids together in a protein.

Peptide hormones hormones that are made from short chains of amino acids.

Peptide/polypeptide peptides and polypeptides are somewhat larger than oligopeptides and less than a protein. There is no strict guideline but generally between 20 and 100 amino acids in length.

Peptidoglycan a molecule composed of peptides and carbohydrates found in the bacterial cell wall.

Peripheral membrane protein a membrane protein that can be dissociated from the lipid bilayer through the use of salts or changes in pH.

Peroxisome proliferator-activated receptor (PPAR) a transcription factor important in expression of many genes involved in lipid metabolism.

Phosphatase an enzyme that removes a phosphate.

Phosphoglucomutase the enzyme that isomerizes glucose-6-phosphate and glucose-1-phosphate.

Phospholipid bilayer (a.k.a. lipid bilayer) a structure of phospholipids in which the hydrophobic acyl chains of phospholipids are oriented toward the core of the bilayer and the hydrophilic head groups are oriented to either face of the bilayer. Phospholipid bilayers are found in the plasma membrane and many organelles.

Phospholipids a class of polar lipids that have glycerol at their core.

Phosphorylation the addition of a phosphate to a hydroxyl group, typically of a protein.

pH the scale used to measure the concentration of H^+ in solution.

PKA protein kinase A, the cyclic AMP-dependent protein kinase.

pK_a the negative log of the acid ionization constant. This value can be used generically to discuss how acidic a proton is (how tightly a proton is bound to another atom).

Polar lipids lipid molecules containing polar groups such as phosphates. Polar lipids are typically found in lipid bilayers.

Polar lipids the other main division of lipids (*see* neutral lipids). Polar lipids include polar group.

Polymer a molecule made up of multiple subunits joined together. Many biochemicals including proteins and nucleic acids are polymers.

Polymerase chain reaction (PCR) a laboratory technique in which short stretches of RNA can be amplified many times over. PCR is the basis of numerous other techniques.

Polysaccharides polymers of monosaccharides.

Polyunsaturated having multiple double bonds.

Posterior pituitary the rear section of the pituitary gland that secretes two hormones, oxytocin and vasopressin.

Postprandial state the metabolic state found up to two hours after eating.

Primary protein structure the amino acid sequence of the protein.

Product the substance made in an enzymatic reaction.

Prostaglandins a subclass of eicosanoid, prostaglandins are a family of signaling molecules made from arachidonate by the enzyme cyclooxygenase.

Protein one of the basic molecules of biochemistry, proteins are polymers of amino acids that serve functions ranging from structural to catalytic.

Protein kinase an enzyme that adds a phosphate to a protein.

Protein kinase A the first protein kinase discovered, protein kinase A catalyzes the phosphorylation of many proteins altering their activity.

Proteinuria a condition in which protein is found in the urine. This is typically due to kidney damage.

Proteoglycans part of the extracellular matrix, composed of a protein core with significant carbohydrate modifications.

Proteolytic cleavage a break in the peptide backbone of a protein.

Proton motive force (pmf) the combined total of the proton chemical gradient and the electrical gradient across the inner mitochondrial membrane.

Proximal convoluted tubule the structure in the kidney that reabsorbs fluid and metabolites after filtration.

Purines the class of nitrogenous bases synthesized from a purine ring. Purines have both five- and six-membered rings in their structure.

Pyranose a monosaccharide in a six-membered ring (five carbons and one oxygen).

Pyridoxal phosphate (PLP) a cofactor found in several reactions involving the α carbon of amino acids.

Pyrimidines the class of nitrogenous bases that are derivatives of pyrimidine. Pyrimidines have a single ring.

Pyruvate a three carbon alpha keto acid which is found at the convergence of several metabolic pathways.

PYY(3-36) a peptide neurotransmitter that is involved in regulation of metabolism and appetite.

Q cycle the mechanism by which electrons are transferred in complex III from a two-electron carrier (ubiquinone) to a one-electron carrier (cytochrome *c*).

Quaternary protein structure how different subunits interact with one another to form a multisubunit complex.

Rate constant, *k* rate constants are used in rate laws, mathematical expressions which relate chemical rate or velocity to the concentration of reactants in the reaction.

Rate law a mathematical expression that describes how chemical reactions occur.

Receptor tyrosine kinase one class of signaling receptors. RTKs are receptors that upon binding of ligand (hormones such as insulin) will dimerize. The subunits of the receptor are themselves kinases and will phosphorylate the other subunit of the receptor as well as other proteins in the receptor complex.

Regulatory subunit a subunit of an enzyme that regulates binding of substrate or catalysis.

Replication the process through which DNA is replicated.

Replication licensing the process by which a sequence of DNA is activated to be copied.

Respirasome the name of the combination of multiple electron transport complexes working in unison.

Restriction enzymes bacterial enzymes that recognize and cleave specific DNA sequences. Restriction enzymes are employed in the laboratory in DNA manipulations.

Retroviruses viruses that use an RNA genome.

Reverse cholesterol transport the process through which cholesterol is removed from the circulation and returned to the liver.

Ribose a five-carbon (a pentose) sugar that forms a five-membered ring (a furanose). Ribose is used in the synthesis of ribonucleotides.

Ribosome the macromolecular complex responsible for the synthesis of proteins in the cell.

RNA interference (RNAi) a technique in which short RNA molecules interfere with the stability or translation of mRNA molecules, resulting in diminished expression levels. RNAi is commonly used to decrease or silence gene expression.

S-Adenosylmethionine a donor of activated methyl groups.

Salt bridging columbic interactions between positive and negatively charged amino acids in a protein.

Saturated having no double bonds.

Scaffolding protein protein that acts to bind and organize other proteins like a scaffold.

Scaffolding proteins proteins that act as to organize other proteins in the cell to coordinate a process such as signal transduction.

Schiff base the product resulting from the reaction of the nitrogen side chain of lysine with a carbonyl group.

Secondary active transport a cellular transport method that uses an electrochemical gradient to drive transport of a small molecule across a membrane.

Secondary protein structure basic common units of structure including α helix, parallel and antiparallel β sheets, and turns or coils.

Second messenger a chemical message made or released inside the cell which amplifies and propagates the message relayed by a hormonal signal. Ca^{2+}, cAMP, and IP_3 are all examples of second messengers.

Semiconservative replication the copying of one DNA strand using the other strand as a template; each of the final copies contains one copy of the original.

Serine protease an enzyme that uses an active site serine in the hydrolysis of proteins.

Side chain (residue) the unique part of each amino acid; amino acids are comprised of a region that is common to all amino acids (the amino group, α carbon, and carboxyl) and the side chain.

Signaling cascade a pathway through which signals in the cell are relayed and amplified. This often employs kinases.

Sphingolipids a class of phospholipids that use sphingosine as the base alcohol.

Standard state a defined state for comparison with others. The chemical standard state, $\Delta G°$, defines temperature at 25°C (298 K), a pressure of 1 atmosphere and solutes with an activity of 1 (roughly corresponding to their molar concentrations). The biochemical standard state is $\Delta G°'$; it includes the activity of water as 1, the pH as 7.0, and the concentration of any ionized molecules as that of all of the ionized forms as pH 7.0.

Starved state the metabolic state achieved when one has not eaten for more than 24 hours.

Steady state assumption the assumption that the enzyme is operating at a fixed rate, that is $d[ES]/dt = 0$.

Steroid hormones lipid hormones that are derived from cholesterol.

Steroids a group of steroid hormones that work by altering gene expression.

Substrate channeling the direct diversion of the product of one reaction into a subsequent reaction.

Substrate the reactant in an enzymatic reaction.

Substrate-level phosphorylation a reaction that directly results in the transfer of a phosphate in an enzymatic reaction. Substrate level phosphorylation is one means by which ATP can be produced; oxidative phosphorylation is the other.

Sucrose table sugar; a disaccharide comprised of glucose and fructose.

Sugar acid a monosaccharide in which one of the carbons has been oxidized to a carboxylic acid.

Sugar alcohols a monosaccharide in which the carbonyl carbon has been reduced to a hydroxyl group.

Suicide substrate or **irreversible inhibitor** an inhibitor of an enzymatic reaction that becomes irreversibly coupled to the enzyme preventing further catalytic events from occurring.

Sulfonylureas a class of oral antidiabetic drugs that act by promoting insulin secretion.

Symporter a transport protein that transports a molecule in conjunction with another molecule.

Tertiary protein structure how units of secondary structure assemble to form the shape of the protein.

Tetrahydrobiopterin a cofactor used in aromatic amino acid metabolism.

Tetrahydrofolate a donor of activated carbon groups.

Thiamine pyrophosphate (TPP) an organic cofactor in some enzymes that figures prominently in transaldolase.

Thiazoladinediones (TZDs) a class of oral antidiabetic drugs that generally act by activating genes involved in fat metabolism.

Thymine a pyrimidine base found exclusively in DNA.

Thyroid hormones iodinated hormones derived from tyrosine and made in the thyroid gland.

Transamination the transfer of an amino group from an α-keto acid to generate a new amino acid and new α-keto acid.

Transcription the copying of DNA into RNA.

trans **fats** fatty acids with a *trans* double bond. *Trans* double bonds result from the isomerization of *cis* double bonds during partial hydrogenation.

Transfection a technique that uses recombinant virus to introduce DNA into a eukaryotic cell.

Transformation a technique that uses chemical methods to introduce DNA into a bacterium.

Transgenic organism an organism that has been manipulated to express genes found in other organisms.

Transglutaminase the enzyme that crosslinks glutamine and lysine residues in the extracellular matrix.

Translation the synthesis of proteins from an mRNA template.

Transmembrane protein protein that spans the plasma membrane.

Transporter proteins or transporters proteins that are involved in the passage of small molecules across the plasma membrane.

Triacyclglycerol (triglyceride) a glycerol molecule with all three hydroxyl groups esterified to fatty acids.

Trisaccharides a short carbohydrate comprised of three monosaccharides.

Tunneling a quantum mechanics explanation of how small particles such as electrons are able to move from one place to another.

Turnover number the number of reactions that an enzyme can catalyze per second. In Michaelis-Menten kinetics, the turnover number is k_{cat} or k_2.

Turns short stretches of amino acids in a protein that link elements of secondary structure.

Two′-deoxyribose (Deoxyribose) a ribose sugar that is lacking the hydroxyl group on the 2 position. 2-deoxyribose is the sugar found in DNA.

Type 1 diabetes mellitus an autoimmune disease in which the immune system attacks the insulin producing β cells of the pancreas.

Type 2 diabetes mellitus the more common form of diabetes in which the organism gradually becomes refractory to the effects of insulin. Often related to obesity.

Ubiquinone (CoEnzyme Q or CoQ$_{10}$ or UQ) ubiquinone consists of a redox active quinoid group attached to a lengthy isoprenoid tail. It

shuttles electrons between complexes I and III and complex II.

Uncompetitive inhibitor an inhibitor that can only bind to the *ES* complex.

Uniporter a transport protein that moves a single molecule across a membrane. The flow across the membrane may be uni- or bidirectional.

Uracil a pyrimidine base found exclusively in RNA.

Urea the metabolic waste product formed through the urea cycle. It consists of two amino groups joined by a central carbonyl carbon. It is not ionized at neutral pH.

Urea cycle the metabolic pathway that generates urea from carbamoyl phosphate.

Uricotelic organisms that synthesize uric acid as a nitrogenous waste product.

Uridine diphosphate glucose (UDP-glucose) the source of glucose used in the synthesis of glycogen.

van der Waals forces a class of weak intermolecular forces that all molecules exhibit.

Vasa recta a network of capillaries that reabsorb electrolytes and water.

Viruses simple intracellular pathogens that require a host for replication.

VLDL very low density lipoproteins. VLDL are secreted by the liver to deliver triacylglycerols made in the liver to peripheral tissues.

V_{max} the theoretical maximal velocity at which an enzymatically catalyzed reaction can proceed.

Waxes a naturally hydrophobic coating, waxes consist of a fatty acid esterified to a fatty alcohol.

Xenobiotics molecules the body recognizes as foreign.

Xenobiotic metabolism how the body metabolizes foreign molecules prior to excretion.

Zwitterions molecules that bear both a positive and negative charge at the same time. Amino acids are zwitterions, as are some phospholipids and many metabolites.

Zymogen an inactive enzyme that requires proteolytic activation.

Zymogen (proenzymes) enzymes that are synthesized in an inactive state and require proteolytic cleavage for activation.

π helix a less common example of secondary structure. It is like an α helix but the coils are looser than an α helix with hydrogen bonding occurring in an i+5 pattern compared to the α helical i+4 pattern.

β-hydroxy-β-methylglutaryl-CoA (HMG-CoA) a metabolic intermediate at the crossroads of ketone body and cholesterol metabolism.

ω-3, or ω-6 fatty acids fatty acids with double bonds either three or six carbons from the carbon at the end of the acyl chain.

Index

Numbers and Greek letters are alphabetized as if they were spelled out. Page numbers in **bold** refer to a major discussion of the entry. F after a page number refers to a figure. Positional and configuration designations in chemical names are ignored in alphabetizing.

A

ABO blood group antigens, 275, 275F
Absorption
  amino acids, 401–403
  dietary lipids, 363–365
Absorptive state, 452
ACC. *See* Acetyl-CoA carboxylase (ACC)
Acetaldehyde, 201–202
Acetoacetate
  amino acid production, 418–421
  as ketone body, 329
Acetone, 329
Acetyl-CoA
  amino acid production of, 418–421
  in citric acid cycle, 211
  de novo synthesis, 380
  fatty acid generation from, 443
  fatty acid oxidation to, 312–315
  in fatty acid synthase (FAS), 320
  formation, 312
  ketone bodies and, 329–330, 443
  pyruvate conversion to, 197–199
Acetyl-CoA carboxylase (ACC)
  allosteric regulators, 327–328
  domains, 318–319, 319F
  isoforms, 318, 328
  malonyl-CoA and, 318–319, 327–328
  regulation, 327–328, 327F
  structure, 319F
Acetyl-CoA oxidation, 212
N-Acetylneuraminic acid (Neu5Ac), 277, 278
Achiral amino acids, 69
Acid-base catalysis, 118–121
Acid-base properties of fatty acids, 303–304
Acidic lipases, 363
Acid ionization constant, 18–19
Acids. *See also* Amino acids; Fatty acids; Nucleic acids
  Brønsted-Lowry definition, 18
  glucuronic, 427
  hyaluronic, 281
  N-Acetylneuraminic (Neu5Ac), 277, 278
  oleic, 302–303
  stomach, 399–401
  strength of, 18–19
  sugar, 167
  water ionization to, 18–20
ACP. *See* Acyl Carrier Protein (ACP)
Activation energy, 106–107, 106F
Active site
  ATCase, 131
  substrate-enzyme interactios, 103–104
Active transport, 144

Acyl Carrier Protein (ACP), 324, 324F
Acyl-enzyme intermediate, 125
Addison's disease, 458
Adenine (A), 28
Adenosine triphosphate (ATP)
  absence of a catalyst and, 5
  ADP ratios, 39
  biosynthesis, **241–248**
  in citric acid cycle, 218–219
  hydrolysis of, 5–6
  myosins and, 95
  in organelles, 245
  oxidation producing, 317
  structure, 3F
  transport by translocase, 245
Adenosine triphosphate (ATP) synthase
  driving ATP assembly, 243
  inhibitors, 246–248
  reactions, 242
  rotation, 243
  structure and function, 241F
Adenylate cyclase, 150
Adipocytes, 449
Adipocyte triacylglycerol lipase (ATGL), 385
Adiponectin, 456
Adipose tissue, 444, 449
A DNA, 31
ADP: ATP ratios, 39
Aestivation, 470
Affinity labels, 125
Alanine
  at crossroads, 444, 445
  function, 445
  pyruvate transamination to, 201
  transamination, 416
Albumin, 374–375, 375F
Alcohol dehydration, to an α-β double bond, 323
Alcohol overconsumption, 468–469
Aldehydes, 168
Aldolase, 183, 183F
Aldolases
  mechanism of, 183F
Aldols, 178–179
Aldoses, 163–164
  first fifteen D-, 164F
  ketoses and, 164F, 165F
Alginate, 176–177, 176F
Allosteric enzymes, 129F
Allosteric regulation, 129F, 131F. *See also* Enzyme regulation
  acetyl-CoA carboxylase (ACC), 327–328
  aspartate transcarbamoylase, 129–131
  covalent modification balance, 261–262
  defined, 129

effects on ATCase, 131
  mechanism, 129
  sigmoidal kinetics and, 129
Allosteric regulators, 92
Amides, 7, 303–304
Amine metabolism, 72, 397, 439
Amines, detoxification of, **423–429**
Amino (N) terminus, 74
Amino acid carbon skeletons
  in citric acid cycle, 415, 415F
  five-carbon skeletons, 418, 419
  four-carbon skeletons, 417–418
  metabolism, 416–417, 416F, 417F, 418F, 419F
  pathways of scavenging, **414–423**
  three-carbon skeletons, 416–417
  types of reactions, 416
Amino acid catabolism, 415, 417
Amino acid metabolism
  challenges of, 397
  inborn errors of, 403
  timeline, 439
Amino acids, **69–74**
  abbreviations, 72
  absorption, 401–403, 402F
  achiral, 69
  amino group, 69
  ammonia removal, 405
  biological roles, 403
  carboxyl group, 69
  chemical properties, 69–70
  chemistry, **69–74**
  chiral, 69
  deamination, 443
  defined, 68
  differentiation of, 70
  functions, 72–73
  glucogenic, 415
  hydrophobic, 71F
  hydroxylated, 78
  ketogenic, 415
  modification within proteins, 77–78
  names and grouping of, 71
  negatively charged side chains, 70, 71, 71F
  not commonly found in proteins, 72
  polar, 71F
  positively charged side chains, 70–72, 71F
  prior to being catabolized, 398
  proteins as polymers of, **74–79**
  salt bridging, 87
  secretion, 402
  side chains, 70–72
  structure, 69–70, 69F
  substituents, 69
  transamination, 443